CEDAR POST SET IN 1817 AND CAST-IRON MONUMENT ERECTED IN 1843 TO MARK THE BOUNDARY AT
THE SOURCE OF THE ST. CROIX RIVER

(Photograph taken in 1908)

INTERNATIONAL BOUNDARY COMMISSION

JOINT REPORT

UPON THE

SURVEY AND DEMARCATION OF THE BOUNDARY

BETWEEN THE

UNITED STATES AND CANADA

FROM THE SOURCE OF THE ST. CROIX RIVER TO THE ST. LAWRENCE RIVER

IN ACCORDANCE WITH THE PROVISIONS OF
ARTICLE III OF THE TREATY SIGNED
AT WASHINGTON, APRIL 11, 1908

HIS BRITANNIC MAJESTY'S COMMISSIONER
W. F. KING, 1908–1916
J. J. McARTHUR, 1917–

UNITED STATES COMMISSIONER
O. H. TITTMANN, 1908–1915
E. C. BARNARD, 1915–1921
E. LESTER JONES, 1921–

WASHINGTON
GOVERNMENT PRINTING OFFICE
1925

PUBLISHED UNDER THE AUTHORITY OF
THE INTERNATIONAL BOUNDARY
COMMISSIONERS

LETTER OF TRANSMITTAL

WASHINGTON, D. C., *October 30, 1924.*

The Honorable, the SECRETARY OF STATE.

SIR: I have the honor to submit herewith the printed joint report of the survey and demarcation of the international boundary between the United States and Canada from the source of the St. Croix River to the St. Lawrence River, together with duplicate sets of 61 signed joint maps, in accordance with the provisions of Article III of the treaty between the United States and Great Britain, signed at Washington, April 11, 1908.

The report is the third of seven reports which will cover the survey and demarcation of the international boundary between Alaska and Canada and between the United States and Canada from the Atlantic Ocean to the Pacific Ocean, excepting that part of the boundary through the Great Lakes and the St. Lawrence River, which was surveyed and reported upon by the International Waterways Commission in accordance with Article IV of the treaty of April 11, 1908.

The field work, office computations, and preparation of the maps of the section of the international boundary covered by this report were carried on simultaneously with similar operations on other portions of the boundary, under the direction of the original commissioners appointed under the treaty of 1908, for the United States Mr. O. H. Tittmann, who resigned April 15, 1915, and for His Britannic Majesty, Dr. W. F. King, who died April 23, 1916, and their successors, for the United States Mr. E. C. Barnard, appointed commissioner April 30, 1915, who died February 6, 1921, and Mr. E. Lester Jones, appointed commissioner February 28, 1921, and for His Majesty, Mr. J. J. McArthur, appointed commissioner February 26, 1917. The work was completed and the joint report was prepared under the direction of the present commissioners, Mr. J. J. McArthur and Mr. E. Lester Jones.

The report and accompanying 61 signed joint maps herewith submitted are identical with those transmitted by His Britannic Majesty's commissioner to his Government, the report having been printed from the same plates, and the signed original maps, as well as the copies thereof for both countries, having been printed from the same stones.

It is most gratifying to record that the location of the boundary line and the preparation of the maps and report have been accomplished in a spirit of hearty cooperation, and to state that the cordial relations which existed between the former commissioners have been continued by their successors.

I have the honor to be, Sir, very respectfully, your obedient servant,

E. Lester Jones

United States Commissioner.

CONTENTS

Sketches of the triangulation and precise traverse accompany this report under a
separate cover.

ILLUSTRATIONS

MAPS AND DRAWINGS

INTRODUCTION

The international boundary line between the United States and Canada from the source of the St. Croix River to the St. Lawrence River as surveyed and marked by the International Boundary Commission acting under Article III of the treaty of April 11, 1908, between the United States and Great Britain, is a reestablishment of the boundary as described in Article I of the treaty of August 9, 1842 (commonly called the Webster-Ashburton treaty) and as laid down under Article VI of that treaty by Commissioners Albert Smith and J. B. B. Estcourt, whose final report bears the date of June 28, 1847.

This portion of the international boundary is 670 miles in length, and, lying between the Provinces of New Brunswick and Quebec, on one side, and the States of Maine, New Hampshire, Vermont, and New York, on the other, forms a part of the boundaries of those Provinces and States. The lengths of these Provincial or State boundaries thus formed are: New Brunswick, 164.1 miles; Quebec, 506.2 miles; Maine, 456.6 miles; New Hampshire, 58.8 miles; Vermont, 90.3 miles; and New York, 64.6 miles. For convenience in describing the line, it was divided by the commissioners acting under the treaty of 1842 into nine parts, each of which includes a portion of the boundary topographically distinct from the adjoining subdivisions. To each of these subdivisions an appropriate name was given, and these names appear on the official boundary maps of 1843–1845, and have been used in treatises on the boundary. For this reason they have been retained in this report. The name and extent of each of these subdivisions is shown in the following list:

SUBDIVISIONS OF THE BOUNDARY

1. The North Line (77.6 miles).—The approximately straight line nearly due north from the source of the St. Croix River to the St. John River.

2. The St. John River (72.0 miles).—From its intersection with the North Line to the mouth of the St. Francis River.

3. The St. Francis River (42.6 miles).—From its mouth to the outlet of Lake Pohenagamook.

4. The Southwest Line (64.2 miles).—The straight line from Lake Pohenagamook to the Northwest Branch of the St. John River, near English Lake.

5. The South Line (19.5 miles).—The straight line from the Northwest Branch of the St. John River near English Lake to the Southwest Branch of the St. John River.

6. The Southwest Branch of the St. John River (38.4 miles).—From the end of the South Line to and through Little St. John Lake.

7. The Highlands[1] (174.6 miles).—From monument 314 on the shore of Little St. John Lake to monument 318 and thence along the crest of the watershed that separates the waters flowing into tributaries of the St. Lawrence River from those flowing into the Penobscot, Kennebec, Androscoggin, and Connecticut Rivers, to monument 507, at the source of Halls Stream.

8. Halls Stream (26.6 miles).—From its source to the intersection of the "Valentine and Collins" or West Line.

9. The West Line (154.9 miles).—The approximate forty-fifth parallel of latitude from Halls Stream to the St. Lawrence River, including the Vermont-Quebec and New York-Quebec lines.

The entire boundary, including its courses through the waterways as well as on land, had been charted by the commissioners under the provisions of Article VI of the Webster-Ashburton treaty above referred to. The land portions of the line had been monumented but, with the exception of monuments to indicate the nationality of the several islands in the St. John River and a series of monuments placed along the edges of certain watercourses to fix the general direction of the boundary, the line along the waterways had never been marked before the survey under the treaty of 1908 was undertaken. In the course of time many of these monuments had deteriorated and the vista along the boundary had become practically obliterated by new growth.

In 1902 the New York-Quebec line was remonumented, and a joint resurvey thereof was made by the State of New York and the Dominion of Canada, "without a formal treaty but by the joint and concurrent action of the Governments of the United States and Great Britain."[2]

In 1906, by concurrent action of the two Governments, the work of reopening the line and repairing and renewing the monuments between Halls Stream and the Richelieu River was undertaken. These events contributed to the conclusion of the treaty of 1908.

The operations of the commission in carrying out the provisions of Article III of the treaty of 1908 consisted of a careful retracement of the line in the field; the cutting of a vista along the land portion of the boundary; the remonumenting of the land portion of the boundary by the restoration of the original monuments and the establishment of additional monuments where needed; the establishment of reference monuments along the shores of the waterways through which the boundary runs; the determination of the geographic positions of these marks and the azimuths and distances between them by means of accurate triangulation and traverse; the execution of topographic surveys for the "accurate modern charts" required by the treaty; the preparation of these maps and the laying down thereon of the boundary in conformity with its true position as ascertained by the retracement; the preparation of the joint report required by the treaty; and the transmission of duplicate signed copies of the maps and report to each Government.

---

[1] In this report the Highlands are considered as beginning at monument 314, on the shore of Little St. John Lake, while the commissioners of 1842 considered the first point on the Highlands to be monument 318, very near the source of a small brook, which the boundary follows from near monument 318 to the lake at monument 314.

[2] See Appendix II, p. 314; also, Article III, treaty of 1908, p. 4.

While field work was being done on this portion of the boundary, there was a very great demand for work on other portions, such as between Alaska and Canada, and along the forty-ninth parallel, and the energies of much the larger part of the staffs of the commission were applied to those sections where the demand for work was most urgent.

The detailed description and definition of the course of the boundary, as marked by the commissioners and as certified by them, is presented in tabular form. It consists of the latitudes and longitudes on North American datum of all turning points or angle points in the line, together with the distances and azimuths between adjacent points.

Appendices containing information of historical interest pertaining to the boundary and supplemental geodetic data have been added. These data consist of elevations and descriptions of bench marks, and of geographic positions and descriptions of triangulation stations. They have been, and will continue to be, of much value to surveyors and engineers for quite other than boundary purposes.

Sketches of the triangulation and precise traverse have been prepared and published on 15 sheets, which accompany the report under a separate cover.

The official boundary maps prepared by the Commission as a part of their report consist of sixty-one (61) sheets and an index sheet, engraved on copper plates and printed from stone on heavy chart paper, size 26 by 38 inches. They show the topography of the country along the boundary, the course of the boundary line, and the locations of the boundary monuments and the boundary reference monuments as certified by the commissioners. The four original sets of these maps, specified by the treaty, are bound in atlas form, two for each Government, and a limited number of copies of each map have been published in sheet form for distribution to depository libraries and to anyone interested in the location of the boundary line at any place.

104709—25†——2

TREATY OF 1908, APPOINTMENTS OF THE COMMISSIONERS, PROCLAMATIONS, AND ORDERS IN COUNCIL

TREATY BETWEEN THE UNITED STATES OF AMERICA AND THE UNITED KINGDOM CONCERNING THE BOUNDARY BETWEEN THE UNITED STATES AND THE DOMINION OF CANADA FROM THE ATLANTIC OCEAN TO THE PACIFIC OCEAN

Signed at Washington, April 11, 1908

(Ratifications exchanged at Washington, June 4, 1908)

The United States of America and His Majesty Edward the Seventh, of the United Kingdom of Great Britain and Ireland, and of the British Dominions beyond the Seas, King, and Emperor of India, being desirous of providing for the more complete definition and demarcation of the international boundary between the United States and the Dominion of Canada, have for that purpose resolved to conclude a treaty, and to that end have appointed as their Plenipotentiaries:

The President of the United States of America, Elihu Root, Secretary of State of the United States; and

His Britannic Majesty, Right Honorable James Bryce, O. M., his Ambassador Extraordinary and Plenipotentiary at Washington;

Who, after having communicated to each other their respective full powers, which were found to be in due and proper form, have agreed to and concluded the following articles:

ARTICLE I

THE BOUNDARY THROUGH PASSAMAQUODDY BAY

The High Contracting Parties agree that each shall appoint, without delay, an expert geographer or surveyor to serve as Commissioners for the purpose of more accurately defining and marking the international boundary line between the United States and the Dominion of Canada in the waters of Passamaquoddy Bay from the mouth of the St. Croix River to the Bay of Fundy, and that in defining and marking said boundary line the Commissioners shall adopt and follow, as closely as may be, the line surveyed and laid down by the Commissioners appointed under Article II of the Treaty of July 22, 1892, between the United States and Great Britain, so far as said Commissioners agreed upon the location of said line, namely:

(1) From a point at the mouth of the St. Croix River defined by the ranges established by them, by a connected series of six straight lines defined by ranges and cross ranges, to a point between Treat Island and Friar Head, likewise defined by ranges and cross ranges established by them; and also

(2) From a point in Quoddy Roads, defined by the intersection of the range passing through the position of the Beacon of 1886 and Lubec Channel Light, with a range established by them on the west shore of Quoddy Roads along the course of this latter range, which is about 80° 35′ east of true south, into the Bay of Fundy.

In ascertaining the location of the above-described line, the Commissioners shall be controlled by the indications of the range marks and monuments established along its course by said former Commissioners and by the charts upon which the said Commissioners marked the line as tentatively agreed upon by them.

1

The remaining portion of the line, lying between the two above-described sections, and upon the location of which said former Commissioners did not agree, shall pass through the center of the Lubec Narrows Channel between Campo Bello Island and the mainland, and, subject to the provisions hereinafter stated, it shall follow on either side of the said Narrows such courses as will connect with the parts of the line agreed upon as aforesaid, and such boundary shall consist of a series of straight lines defined by distances and courses; but inasmuch as differences have arisen in the past as to the location of the line with respect to Pope's Folly Island above Lubec Narrows and with respect to certain fishing grounds east of the dredged channel below Lubec Narrows, it is agreed that each of the High Contracting Parties shall present to the other within six months after the ratification of this Treaty a full printed statement of the evidence, with certified copies of original documents referred to therein which are in its possession, and the arguments upon which it bases its contentions, with a view to arriving at an adjustment of the location of this portion of the line in accordance with the true intent and meaning of the provisions relating thereto of the treaties of 1783 and 1814 between the United States and Great Britain, and the award of the Commissioners appointed in that behalf under the treaty of 1814; it being understood that any action by either or both Governments or their representatives authorized in that behalf or by the local governments on either side of the line, whether prior or subsequent to such treaties and award, tending to aid in the interpretation thereof, shall be taken into consideration in determining their true intent and meaning. Such agreement, if reached, shall be reduced to writing in the form of a protocol and shall be communicated to the said Commissioners, who shall lay down and mark this portion of the boundary in accordance therewith and as herein provided.

In the event of a failure to agree within six months after the date of exchanging the printed statements aforesaid, the question of which Government is entitled to jurisdiction over such island and fishing grounds under treaty provisions, and proceedings thereunder, interpreted in accordance with their true intent and meaning as above provided, and by reason of any rights arising under the recognized principles of international law, shall be referred forthwith for decision upon the evidence and arguments submitted as aforesaid, with such additional statement of facts as may be appropriate, and an argument in reply on each side, to an arbitrator to be agreed upon by the two Governments, or, in case of a failure to agree, to be appointed by a third Power selected by the two Governments by common accord, or, if no agreement is thus arrived at, each Government shall select a different Power and the choice of the arbitrator shall be made in concert by the Powers thus selected. The decision of such arbitrator shall be final, and the line shall be laid down and marked by the said Commissioners in accordance therewith and as herein provided.

The arbitrator shall be requested to deliver, together with his award, a statement of all the costs and expenses incurred by him in connection with the arbitration, which shall forthwith be repaid by the two Governments in equal moieties.

It is further agreed that if, under the foregoing provisions, the boundary be located through the channel to the east of the dredged channel above mentioned, the latter shall be equally free and open for the passage of ships, vessels, and boats of both parties.

The entire boundary shall be marked by permanent range marks established on land and, if desirable in the opinion of Commissioners, by buoys in the water, so far as practicable, and by such other boundary marks and monuments and at such points as the Commissioners may determine to be necessary; but the said Commissioners shall proceed to define and mark and chart the portion of the line agreed upon by the former Commissioners under the Treaty of 1892 aforesaid without waiting for the final determination of the location of the remaining portion of the line.

The course of the said boundary line as defined and marked as aforesaid shall be laid down by said Commissioners on quadruplicate sets of accurate modern charts prepared or adopted by them for that purpose, which charts shall be certified and signed by the Commissioners, and two duplicate originals thereof shall be filed by them with each Government; and they shall also prepare in duplicate and file with each Government a joint report or reports under their hands and seals describing in detail the course and location of the boundary line and the range marks and monuments and buoys marking it.

The line so defined and laid down shall be taken and deemed to be the international boundary from the Bay of Fundy to the mouth of the St. Croix River, as established by treaty provisions and the proceedings thereunder.

ARTICLE II

THE BOUNDARY FROM THE MOUTH TO THE SOURCE OF THE ST. CROIX RIVER

Whereas Article II of the Treaty of 1783 between the United States and Great Britain provides that a line drawn along the middle of the River St. Croix from its mouth in the Bay of Fundy to its source shall be, between those points, the international boundary between the United States and the British possessions in North America, and the identity of the River St. Croix has been determined by the Commissioners appointed for that purpose under Article V of the Treaty of 1794 between the United States and Great Britain, and the location of the mouth and the source of said river has been duly established, and the course of said river has been described, surveyed, and charted by said Commissioners, as appears from their joint report dated the 25th day of October, 1798, and from the chart or plan of said river prepared and filed by them with said report, but said line of boundary along the middle of said river was not laid down by them on said chart or plan, and was not marked or monumented by them along the course of said river; and whereas, pursuant to an additional article, dated March 15, 1798, supplementing the provisions of the Treaty of 1794 above referred to, a monument was erected by joint action of the two Governments marking the source of the River St. Croix, but said line of boundary through the River St. Croix has not otherwise been monumented and has never been laid down on charts or by joint action of the two Governments: therefore, in order to complete and render thoroughly effective the demarcation of the boundary described and established as aforesaid,

It is agreed that each of the High Contracting Parties shall appoint, without delay, an expert geographer or surveyor as a Commissioner, and the Commissioners so appointed shall jointly lay down upon accurate modern charts, to be prepared or adopted by them for that purpose, the line of boundary along the middle of the River St. Croix from its mouth to its source as defined and established by the existing treaty provisions and the proceedings thereunder, above referred to, with the agreed understanding, however, that the line of boundary through said river shall be a water line throughout and shall follow the center of the main channel or thalweg as naturally existing, except where such course would change, or disturb, or conflict with the national character of an island as already established by mutual recognition and acquiescence, in which case the line shall pass on the other side of any such island, following the middle of the channel nearest thereto, or, if the Commissioners find that the national character of any island is in dispute, the question of its nationality shall be submitted by them to their respective Governments, with a chart or map certified jointly by said Commissioners, showing the depth and volume of the water at its high and low stages between such island and the river banks on each side and indicating the course of the main channel of the river as it passes such island, together with a descriptive statement by said Commissioners showing the reasons for selecting such channel as the main channel; and in all such cases the High Contracting Parties agree that the location of the boundary with respect to each island in dispute shall be determined and settled in accordance with the following rules:

(1) The nationality of each island in dispute shall be determined by the predominance of the claims established on either side to such island, arising from the exercise of jurisdiction and sovereignty over it, including such exercise of jurisdiction by the local governments on either side of the line.

(2) The burden of proving the nationality of any such island shall be upon the party seeking to change the general course of the boundary as above prescribed so as to include such island on its own side of the boundary.

(3) The selection by the Commissioners of the main channel passing such island shall not be conclusive upon the parties hereto and is subject to review, but the burden of proving the main channel to be other than the one selected shall be upon the party proposing the change.

The Government proposing such change in the prescribed course of the boundary shall, upon the submission of the question of the nationality of any island or islands by the Commissioners as aforesaid, promptly present to the other Government a printed statement, with certified copies of any original documents in its possession referred to therein, showing the grounds and arguments upon which its claim of jurisdiction and ownership with respect to such island rests. Unless an agreement is reached upon the presentation of such statement, the Government to which such statement is presented shall within six months after its receipt present in reply a similar statement showing the grounds and arguments upon which the claims of the other Government are contested. If an agreement is reached between the two Governments, it shall be reduced to writing in the form of a protocol and shall be communicated to the said Commissioners, who shall proceed to lay down and mark the boundary so as to leave such island on the side of the boundary to which it is shown it belongs, in accordance with the determination of its nationality arrived at as aforesaid.

In the event of a failure by the two Governments to come to an agreement within six months after the presentation of the printed statements in reply herein above provided for, then the question of the nationality of the islands in dispute shall be referred forthwith for decision under the rules herein above set forth for the determination of that question, and under the recognized principles of international law not inconsistent therewith, and upon the evidence and arguments submitted as aforesaid, with such additional statement of facts as may be appropriate, and such further printed argument on each side as may be desired, to an arbitrator to be agreed upon by the two Governments, or, in case of a failure to agree, to be appointed by a third Power selected by the two Governments by common accord, or, if no agreement is thus arrived at, each Government shall select a different Power and the choice of the arbitrator shall be made in concert by the Powers thus selected. The decision of such arbitrator shall be final, and the line shall be laid down and marked by the said Commissioners in accordance therewith and as herein provided.

The arbitrator shall be requested to deliver, together with his award, a statement of all the costs and expenses incurred by him in connection with the arbitration, which shall forthwith be repaid by the two Governments in equal moieties.

It is further agreed that so far as practicable the said Commissioners shall establish boundary monuments and ranges and buoys marking the course and location of the said line, and showing on which side of the boundary the several islands lying in said river belong, wherever in their judgment it is desirable that the boundary be so marked.

The charts upon which the boundary is marked as aforesaid shall be in quadruplicate, and shall be certified and signed by said Commissioners, and two duplicate originals thereof shall be filed by them with each Government, and it shall also be the duty of said Commissioners to prepare in duplicate, and file with each Government, a joint report under their hands and seals describing the line so marked by them and the monuments and range marks and buoys marking it.

The line so defined and laid down shall be taken and deemed to be the international boundary from the mouth to the source of the St. Croix River as established by treaty provisions and the proceedings thereunder as aforesaid.

Article III

The Boundary from the Source of the St. Croix River to the St. Lawrence River

Whereas the remonumenting of the course of the boundary defined and laid down under the provisions of Articles I and VI of the Treaty of August 9, 1842, between the United States and Great Britain has already been undertaken without a formal treaty agreement, but by the joint and concurrent action of the Governments of the United States and Great Britain, certain monuments between Vermont and Canada having been relocated in 1849, and the portion of said boundary extending between Hall's Stream and the St. Lawrence River in part having been remonumented in recent years and in part is now being remonumented under such action on both sides; and whereas the Commissioners appointed under Article VI of the Treaty of 1842 aforesaid were required to and did mark by monuments the land portion only of said line, and were not required to and did not mark by monuments the portions of the boundary extending along water courses, with the exception that the nationality of the several islands in the St. John River was indicated by monuments erected thereon and a series of monuments was placed by them along the edge of certain of the water courses to fix the general direction of the boundary, most of which monuments have since disappeared, but the entire boundary, including its course through the waterways as well as on land, was charted and marked on maps by said Commissioners under the provisions of Article VI above referred to, and the nationality of the respective islands in the St. John River was determined by them, as appears from the joint report filed by said Commissioners dated June 28, 1847, and the series of maps signed by said Commissioners and filed with their joint report; and whereas the portion of the line through said waterways has not since been monumented or marked along its course by joint action of the two Governments, and the monuments placed by said Commissioners along the land portion of said boundary require repairing and renewing where such work has not already been done in recent years, and additional or supplementary intermediate monuments at convenient points are required under modern conditions: therefore, in order to carry on and complete the work already undertaken as aforesaid, and to reestablish the location of said boundary and render thoroughly effective the demarcation of the said boundary as existent and established,

It is agreed that each of the High Contracting Parties shall appoint, without delay, an expert geographer or surveyor as a Commissioner, and under the joint direction of such Commissioners the lost or damaged boundary monuments shall be relocated and repaired, and additional monuments and boundary marks shall be established wherever necessary in the judgment of the Commissioners to meet the requirements of modern conditions along the course of the land portion of said boundary, and where the said boundary runs through waterways it shall be marked along its course, so far as practicable, by buoys and monuments in the water and by permanent ranges established on the land, and in such other way and at such points as in the judgment of the Commissioners it is desirable that the boundary be so marked; and it is further agreed that the course of the entire boundary, as described in Article I of the Treaty of 1842 and as laid down as aforesaid under Article VI of that Treaty, shall be marked by said Commissioners upon quadruplicate sets of accurate modern charts prepared or adopted by them for that purpose, and that said charts so marked shall be certified and signed by them and two duplicate originals thereof shall be filed with each Government, and said Commissioners shall also prepare in duplicate and file with each Government a joint report or reports describing in detail the course of the boundary so marked by them, and the character and location of the several monuments and boundary marks and ranges marking it.

The line so defined and laid down shall be taken and deemed to be the international boundary as defined and laid down under Articles I and VI of the said Treaty of 1842.

ARTICLE IV

THE BOUNDARY FROM ITS INTERSECTION WITH THE ST. LAWRENCE RIVER TO THE MOUTH OF PIGEON RIVER

The High Contracting Parties agree that the existing International Waterways Commission, constituted by concurrent action of the United States and the Dominion of Canada and composed of three Commissioners on the part of the United States and three Commissioners on the part of the Dominion of Canada, is hereby authorized and empowered to ascertain and reestablish accurately the location of the international boundary line beginning at the point of its intersection with the St. Lawrence River near the forty-fifth parallel of north latitude, as determined under Articles I and VI of the Treaty of August 9, 1842, between the United States and

Great Britain, and thence through the Great Lakes and communicating waterways to the mouth of Pigeon River, at the western shore of Lake Superior, in accordance with the description of such line in Article II of the Treaty of Peace between the United States and Great Britain, dated September 3, 1783, and of a portion of such line in Article II of the Treaty of August 9, 1842, aforesaid, and as described in the joint report dated June 18, 1822, of the Commissioners appointed under Article VI of the Treaty of December 24, 1814, between the United States and Great Britain, with respect to a portion of said line and as marked on charts prepared by them and filed with said report, and with respect to the remaining portion of said line as marked on the charts adopted as treaty charts of the boundary under the provisions of Article II of the Treaty of 1842, above mentioned, with such deviation from said line, however, as may be required on account of the cession by Great Britain to the United States of the portion of Horse Shoe Reef in the Niagara River necessary for the light-house erected there by the United States in accordance with the terms of the protocol of a conference held at the British Foreign Office December 9, 1850, between the representatives of the two Governments and signed by them agreeing upon such cession; and it is agreed that wherever the boundary is shown on said charts by a curved line along the water the Commissioners are authorized in their discretion to adopt, in place of such curved line, a series of connecting straight lines defined by distances and courses and following generally the course of such curved line, but conforming strictly to the description of the boundary in the existing treaty provisions, and the geographical coordinates of the turning points of such line shall be stated by said Commissioners so as to conform to the system of latitudes and longitudes of the charts mentioned below, and the said Commissioners shall so far as practicable mark the course of the entire boundary line located and defined as aforesaid, by buoys and monuments in the waterways and by permanent range marks established on the adjacent shores or islands, and by such other boundary marks and at such points as in the judgment of the Commissioners it is desirable that the boundary should be so marked; and the line of the boundary defined and located as aforesaid shall be laid down by said Commissioners on accurate modern charts prepared or adopted by them for that purpose, in quadruplicate sets, certified and signed by the Commissioners, two duplicate originals of which shall be filed by them with each Government; and the Commissioners shall also prepare in duplicate and file with each Government a joint report or reports describing in detail the course of said line and the range marks and buoys marking it, and the character and location of each boundary mark. The majority of the Commissioners shall have power to render a decision.

The line so defined and laid down shall be taken and deemed to be the international boundary as defined and established by treaty provisions and the proceedings thereunder as aforesaid from its intersection with the St. Lawrence River to the mouth of Pigeon River.

Article V

The Boundary from the Mouth of Pigeon River to the Northwesternmost Point of the Lake of the Woods

In order to complete and perfect the demarcation of the international boundary line between the United States and the Dominion of Canada from the mouth of Pigeon River, at the western shore of Lake Superior, to the northwesternmost point of the Lake of the Woods, which boundary is defined in Article II of the Treaty of Peace between the United States and Great Britain dated September 3, 1783, and in Article II of the Treaty of August 9, 1842, between the United States and Great Britain, wherein is defined also the location of the said northwesternmost point of the Lake of the Woods, and the greater part of the said boundary is marked on charts covering that section of the boundary adopted as treaty charts of the boundary under the provisions of Article II of the Treaty of 1842 aforesaid, but has never been actually located or monumented along its course by joint action of the two Governments, and no joint survey of its course has been made since the survey under the direction of the Commissioners appointed under Article VII of the Treaty of December 24, 1814, between the United States and Great Britain, under whose direction the charts above mentioned were prepared,

It is agreed that each of the High Contracting Parties shall appoint, without delay, an expert geographer or surveyor as Commissioners, who shall reestablish and fix the actual location of said entire boundary described and charted as aforesaid, and designate the side of the boundary upon which each island adjacent to the boundary belongs, it being mutually understood that the boundary, so far as practicable, shall be a water line and shall not intersect islands lying along its course, and the Commissioners shall so far as practicable mark such boundary along its course by monuments and buoys and range marks, and such other boundary marks as the Commissioners may determine, and at such points as in their judgment it is desirable that the boundary shall be so marked; and it is further agreed that the course of the entire boundary as described and laid down as aforesaid and as monumented by said Commissioners shall be marked by them upon quadruplicate sets of accurate modern charts prepared or adopted by them for that purpose, and that said charts so marked shall be certified and signed by them and two duplicate originals thereof shall be filed with each Government, and said Commissioners shall also prepare in duplicate and file with each Government a joint report or reports describing in detail the course of the boundary so marked by them and the character and location of the several monuments and boundary marks and ranges marking it.

The line so defined and laid down shall be taken and deemed to be the international boundary as defined and established under the aforesaid treaties from the mouth of Pigeon River to the northwesternmost point of the Lake of the Woods.

Article VI

The Boundary from the Northwesternmost Point of the Lake of the Woods to the Summit of the Rocky Mountains

In order to complete and render thoroughly effective the demarcation of the international boundary between the United States and the Dominion of Canada from the northwesternmost point of the Lake of the Woods to the summit of the Rocky Mountains, which boundary, according to existing treaties, runs due south from said northwesternmost point to the forty-ninth parallel of north latitude and thence along that parallel to the summit of the Rocky Mountains, and has been surveyed and charted and monumented as appears from the series of twenty-four sectional maps covering this portion of the boundary prepared and filed by the Joint Commission appointed for that purpose by joint action of the two Governments in 1872,

It is agreed that each of the High Contracting Parties shall appoint, without delay, an expert geographer or surveyor as a Commissioner, and under the joint direction of such Commissioners lost or damaged monuments along the course of said boundary shall be relocated and repaired and additional monuments and boundary marks shall be established wherever necessary, in the judgment of the Commissioners, to meet the requirements of modern conditions and to render more effective the demarcation of the existent boundary established under the treaty provisions and proceedings thereunder as aforesaid; and it is further agreed that in carrying out these provisions the said Commissioners shall observe the agreement stated in the protocol of the final meeting, dated May 29, 1876, of the Joint Commission aforesaid, which is as follows:

"2. In the intervals between the monuments along the parallel of latitude, it is agreed that the line has the curvature of a parallel of 49° north latitude; and that such characteristic shall determine all questions that may hereafter arise with reference to the position of the boundary at any point between neighboring monuments.

"3. It is further agreed that, in the event of any of the said three hundred and eighty-eight monuments or marks being obliterated beyond the power of recognition, the lost site or sites shall be recovered by their recorded position relatively to the next neighboring unobliterated mark or marks."

It is further agreed that the said Commissioners shall mark upon quadruplicate sets of accurate modern charts prepared or adopted by them for that purpose the entire course of said boundary and the location of the boundary monuments and marks established along the course of said boundary, and two duplicate originals thereof shall be filed with each Government, and said Commissioners shall also prepare in duplicate and file with each Government a joint report describing in detail the work done by them in replacing and repairing lost or damaged monuments and the character and location of the several monuments and boundary marks placed by them along said boundary.

The line so laid down and defined shall be taken and deemed to be the international boundary as defined and established by treaty provisions and the proceedings thereunder as aforesaid from the northwesternmost point of the Lake of the Woods to the summit of the Rocky Mountains.

ARTICLE VII

THE BOUNDARY FROM THE SUMMIT OF THE ROCKY MOUNTAINS TO THE GULF OF GEORGIA

Whereas, by concurrent action of the Government of the United States and the Government of Great Britain in 1902 and 1903, Commissioners were designated to act jointly for the purpose of renewing lost or damaged monuments and placing additional monuments where such were needed throughout the course of the boundary along the forty-ninth parallel of north latitude, from the summit of the Rocky Mountains westward to the eastern shore of the Gulf of Georgia, as defined in Article I of the Treaty of June 15, 1846, between the United States and Great Britain and as marked by monuments along its course and laid down on a series of charts, seven in number, by a Joint Commission organized in 1858 for that purpose and composed of two Commissioners appointed one by each Government, which charts, duly certified and authenticated in duplicate by said Commissioners, were approved and adopted by the two Governments, as appears from the declaration in writing to that effect signed on February 24, 1870, at Washington by duly authorized Plenipotentiaries of the respective Governments, and it appearing that the remonumenting of this line by the Commissioners first above referred to is now approaching completion;

It is hereby agreed by the High Contracting Parties that when such work is completed the entire course of said boundary, showing the location of the boundary monuments and marks established along the course of the boundary, shall be marked upon quadruplicate sets of accurate modern charts prepared or adopted for that purpose, and the said Commissioners, or their successors, are hereby authorized and required to so mark the line and designate the monuments on such charts, two duplicate originals of which shall be filed with each Government, and the said Commissioners, or their successors, shall also prepare in duplicate and file with each Government a joint report describing in detail the work done by them in replacing and repairing lost or damaged monuments and the character and location of the several monuments and boundary marks placed by them along said boundary.

The line so laid down and defined shall be taken and deemed to be the international boundary as defined and established by treaty provisions and the proceedings thereunder as aforesaid, from the summit of the Rocky Mountains to the eastern shore of the Gulf of Georgia.

ARTICLE VIII

THE BOUNDARY FROM THE FORTY-NINTH PARALLEL TO THE PACIFIC OCEAN

The High Contracting Parties agree that each shall appoint, without delay, an expert geographer or surveyor to serve as Commissioners for the purpose of delineating upon accurate modern charts, prepared or adopted by them for that purpose, the international boundary line between the United States and the Dominion of Canada from the forty-ninth parallel of north latitude along the middle of the channel which separates Vancouver's Island from the mainland and the middle of the Haro Channel and of Fuca's Straits to the Pacific Ocean, as defined in Article I of the Treaty of June 15, 1846, between the United States and Great Britain, and as determined by the award made on October 21, 1872, by the Emperor of Germany as arbitrator pursuant to the provisions of Articles XXXIV–XLII of the Treaty of May 8, 1871, between the United States and Great Britain, and as traced out and marked on a quadruplicate set of charts prepared for that purpose and agreed upon and signed by the duly authorized representatives of the respective Governments, as appears from the protocol of a conference at Washington on March 10, 1873, between such representatives which was signed by them on that date, and as defined by them in a written definition of said boundary signed by them and referred to in and attached to said protocol, and it is agreed that the said Commissioners shall adopt in place of the curved line passing between Saturna Island and Patos Island as shown on said charts a straight line running approximately north and south through a point midway between the eastern point of Saturna Island and the western point of Patos Island and intersecting the prolongations of the two straight lines of the boundary now joined by a curved line. The entire line thus laid down shall consist of a series of connecting straight lines defined by distances and courses; and the Commissioners are authorized to select and establish such reference marks on shore as they may deem necessary for the proper definition and location on the water of the boundary aforesaid. A quadruplicate set of such charts, showing the lines so laid down and marked by them and the location of the several marks or monuments selected or established by them along its course, shall be signed by them and two duplicate originals thereof shall be filed by them with each Government, and the Commissioners shall also prepare in duplicate and file with each Government a joint report, or reports, describing in detail the course of said line and the boundary marks and their location along its course.

The line so defined and laid down shall be taken and deemed to be the international boundary, as defined and established by treaty provisions and the proceedings thereunder as aforesaid, from the forty-ninth parallel of north latitude along the middle of the channel which separates Vancouver's Island from the mainland and the middle of Haro Channel and of Fuca's Straits to the Pacific Ocean.

Article IX

General Provisions

The Commissioners appointed under the provisions of this Treaty shall proceed without delay to perform the duties assigned to them, but each Commissioner shall, before entering upon his duties, make oath in writing that he will impartially and faithfully perform his duties as such Commissioner.

In case a vacancy occurs in any of the Commissions constituted by this Treaty, by reason of the death, resignation, or other disability of a Commissioner, before the work of such Commission is completed, the vacancy so caused shall be filled forthwith by the appointment of another Commissioner by the party on whose side the vacancy occurs, and the Commissioner so appointed shall have the same powers and be subject to the same duties and obligations as the Commissioner originally appointed.

If a dispute or difference should arise about the location or demarcation of any portion of the boundary covered by the provisions of this Treaty and an agreement with respect thereto is not reached by the Commissioners charged herein with locating and marking such portion of the line, they shall make a report in writing jointly to both Governments, or severally each to his own Government, setting out fully the questions in dispute and the differences between them, but such Commissioners shall, nevertheless, proceed to carry on and complete as far as possible the work herein assigned to them with respect to the remaining portions of the line.

In case of such a disagreement between the Commissioners, the two Governments shall endeavor to agree upon an adjustment of the questions in dispute, and if an agreement is reached between the two Governments it shall be reduced to writing in the form of a protocol, and shall be communicated to the said Commissioners, who shall proceed to lay down and mark the boundary in accordance therewith, and as herein provided, but without prejudice to the special provisions contained in Articles I and II regarding arbitration.

It is understood that under the foregoing articles the same persons will be appointed to carry out the delimitation of boundaries in the several sections aforesaid, other than the section covered by Article IV, unless either of the Contracting Powers finds it expedient for some reason which it may think sufficient to appoint some other person to be Commissioner for any one of the above-mentioned sections.

Each Government shall pay the expenses of its own Commissioners and their assistants, and the cost of marking and monumenting the boundary shall be paid in equal moieties by the two Governments.

Article X

This Treaty shall be ratified by the President of the United States, by and with the advice and consent of the Senate thereof, and by His Britannic Majesty; and the ratifications shall be exchanged in Washington as soon as practicable.

In faith whereof the respective Plenipotentiaries have signed this Treaty in duplicate and have hereunto affixed their seals.

Done at Washington the 11th day of April in the year of our Lord one thousand nine hundred and eight.

Elihu Root [SEAL.]
James Bryce [SEAL.]

APPOINTMENTS OF THE COMMISSIONERS, UNDER THE INFORMAL AGREEMENT OF 1906

Mr. O. H. Tittmann for the United States

Department of State, *Washington, July 10, 1906.*

Mr. O. H. Tittmann,
 Superintendent of the Coast and Geodetic Survey, Washington, D. C.

Sir: You are hereby designated as Commissioner to represent the United States in the more perfect mapping and demarcation of the Boundary between the United States and the Dominion of Canada from the Richelieu River eastward to the waters of the St. Croix.

The immediate duty assigned to you is to supervise the demarcation under the terms of the appropriation act approved June 16, 1906, which authorizes the work between the Richelieu River and Hall's Stream, and you are hereby authorized to arrange the details and to carry out the work and to sign the full report and maps as Commissioner for the United States jointly with the British Commissioner.

It has been arranged with respect to this work that each Government shall bear the expenses of its own Commissioner, his surveyor and assistants, and that the cost of the monuments, their transportation and erection shall be shared equally by the two Governments.

All vouchers for expenditures incurred under these instructions should be approved by you, or in your absence by the Acting Superintendent of the Coast and Geodetic Survey.

I am, Sir, Your obedient servant,

Robert Bacon,
Acting Secretary.

Dr. W. F. King for His Britannic Majesty

British Embassy, *Lenox, Mass., August 15, 1906.*

Sir: I have the honor to inform you that I have received from the Governor General of Canada a copy of an approved minute of the Privy Council for Canada nominating Mr. W. F. King, Chief Astronomer of the Department of the Interior, to be His Majesty's Commissioner for the re-survey and re-marking of the International Boundary line between the Richelieu and St. Croix Rivers.

With a view to the early commencement of field work the terms of the minute authorise Mr. King to communicate directly with the United States Commissioner, who, as you informed me in your note No. 480 of July 11th is Mr. O. H. Tittmann, of the United States Coast and Geodetic Survey.

I have, etc.

H. M. Durand.

The Honourable,
 Robert Bacon,
  Acting Secretary of State.

APPOINTMENTS OF THE COMMISSIONERS UNDER THE TREATY OF 1908

Mr. O. H. Tittmann for the United States

THEODORE ROOSEVELT, PRESIDENT OF THE UNITED STATES OF AMERICA

To all to whom these Presents shall come, Greeting:

Know ye, that reposing special trust and confidence in the integrity and ability of Otto H. Tittmann, of Missouri, Superintendent of the United States Coast and Geodetic Survey, I do appoint him the expert Commissioner on the part of the United States for the purpose of more accurately defining and marking the international boundary line between the United States and the Dominion of Canada, under the provisions of Articles I, II, III, V, VI, VII, and VIII of the treaty between the United States and Great Britain, signed at Washington on April 11, 1908, and do authorize and empower him to execute and fulfill the duties of this commission with all the powers, privileges, and emoluments thereunto of right appertaining, during the pleasure of the President of the United States.

In testimony whereof, I have caused the Seal of the United States to be hereunto affixed.

Given under my hand at the City of Washington this fifth day of June, in the year of our Lord one thousand nine hundred and eight, and of the Independence of the United States of America the one hundred and thirty-second.

[SEAL OF THE UNITED STATES OF AMERICA.]   THEODORE ROOSEVELT.

By the President:

ELIHU ROOT, *Secretary of State.*

AMERICAN EMBASSY, *London, June 24, 1908.*

SIR: I have the honour to inform you that Mr. Otto H. Tittmann, Superintendent of the United States Coast and Geodetic Survey, has been appointed the expert Commissioner on the part of the United States for the delimitation of the boundary line between the United States and Canada, under Articles I, II, III, V, VI, VII, and VIII of the Treaty of April 11th, 1908, between Great Britain and the United States.

I have, etc.,

WHITELAW REID.

Sir EDWARD GREY, Bart.

Dr. W. F. King for His Britannic Majesty

P. C. 2303–M

DOWNING STREET, *15th July, 1908.*

My Lord: I have the honour to transmit to you for the information of your Ministers, with reference to my telegram of the 13th of July, the papers noted in the subjoined schedule, on the subject of the appointment of Mr. W. F. King as British Commissioner under the Boundary Delimitation Treaty with the United States.

I have, etc.,

CREWE.

The OFFICER ADMINISTERING THE GOVERNMENT OF CANADA.

13th July, Foreign Office.

FOREIGN OFFICE, *13th July, 1908.*

Sir: In reply to your letter of the 11th instant, I am directed by Secretary Sir E. Grey to state that he concurs in the appointment of Mr. W. F. King as British Commissioner, under the Treaty of April 11th last with the United States Government for the delimitation of all the Sections of the Boundary between the United States and Canada mentioned in the above treaty, except the fourth, which includes the line through the St. Lawrence River and the Great Lakes.

His Majesty's Charge d'Affaires at Washington has been instructed by telegraph (copy enclosed) to inform the United States Government of Mr. King's appointment.

I am, etc.,

F. A. CAMPBELL.

The UNDER SECRETARY OF STATE, *Colonial Office.*

TELEGRAM TO MR. HOWARD, WASHINGTON, FROM FOREIGN OFFICE, NO. 87, DATED JULY 11, 1908

"Your despatch No. 213. (June 17th. Boundary Delimitation Treaty.)

"Inform United States Government that Mr. William Frederick King, C. M. G., Dominion Topographical Surveyor and Chief Astronomer of the Dominion, Department of the Interior, has been appointed British Commissioner for all sections of the boundary except the fourth, which includes the St. Lawrence River and Great Lakes."

P. C. 2288–M

FROM CHARGE D'AFFAIRES TO U. S. TO LORD GREY

BRITISH EMBASSY, *Manchester, Mass., 13th July, 1908.*

My Lord: I have the honour to inform your Excellency that upon receipt of telegraphic instructions to that effect from His Majesty's Principal Secretary of State for Foreign Affairs, I have communicated to the United States Government the appointment of Dr. William Frederick King, C. M. G., British Commissioner for the delimitation of such sections of the Boundary between Canada and the United States as are not otherwise provided for in the Treaty recently signed.

I have, etc.,

ESME HOWARD.

MR. E. C. BARNARD FOR THE UNITED STATES

WOODROW WILSON, PRESIDENT OF THE UNITED STATES OF AMERICA

To all to whom these Presents shall come, Greeting:

Know Ye, that reposing special trust and confidence in the integrity and ability of Edward C. Barnard, of New York, I do appoint him the expert Commissioner on the part of the United States for the purpose of more accurately defining and marking the international boundary line between the United States and the Dominion of Canada, under the provisions of Articles I, II, III, V, VI, VII, and VIII of the treaty between the United States and Great Britain, signed at Washington on April 11, 1908, and do authorize and empower him to execute and fulfill the duties of this commission with all the powers, privileges and emoluments thereunto of right appertaining, during the pleasure of the President of the United States.

In testimony whereof, I have caused the Seal of the United States to be hereunto affixed. Given under my hand at the City of Washington this thirtieth day of April, in the year of our Lord one thousand nine hundred and fifteen, and of the Independence of the United States of America the one hundred and thirty-ninth.

WOODROW WILSON.

[SEAL]

By the President,

W. J. BRYAN, *Secretary of State.*

Mr. J. J. McArthur for His Britannic Majesty

George by the Grace of God, of the United Kingdom of Great Britain and Ireland and of the British Dominions beyond the Seas, King, Defender of the Faith, Emperor of India, &c, &c.

To All and Singular to whom these Presents shall come, Greeting:

Whereas by a Treaty concluded at Washington on the 11th day of April, 1908, between our Royal Predecessor His Majesty King Edward VII and our Good Friends the United States of America, respecting the Demarcation of the International Boundary between the United States and the Dominion of Canada, it was in effect provided that Commissioners should be appointed on Our part and on that of Our said Good Friends, and that the Commissioners so appointed should define and mark the Boundary Line, with the exception of that portion of it extending from the 45th Parallel of north latitude through the St. Lawrence River, the Great Lakes and connecting waterways to the mouth of the Pigeon River;

Now Know Ye that We, reposing especial trust and confidence in the approved learning, wisdom and fidelity of Our Trusty and Well-Beloved James Joseph McArthur, Esquire, Dominion Land Surveyor, have named and appointed, as We do by these Presents name and appoint him to be Our Commissioner for the purposes aforesaid and pursuant to the said Treaty, to meet the other Commissioner appointed or to be appointed in like manner by Our Good Friends the United States of America, to do and determine all such matters as are provided to be done by him under the said Treaty, in the manner therein provided.

In witness whereof We have signed these presents with Our Royal Hand.

Given at Our Court of Saint James the Twenty-sixth day of February One thousand Nine Hundred and Seventeen in the Seventh year of Our Reign.

By His Majesty's Command:

Arthur James Balfour.

Mr. E. Lester Jones for the United States

WOODROW WILSON, PRESIDENT OF THE UNITED STATES OF AMERICA

To all to whom these Presents shall come, Greeting:

Know Ye, that reposing special trust and confidence in the integrity and ability of E. Lester Jones, of Virginia, I do appoint him the expert Commissioner on the part of the United States for the purpose of more accurately defining and marking the international boundary line between the United States and the Dominion of Canada, under the provisions of Articles I, II, III, V, VI, VII, and VIII of the treaty between the United States and Great Britain, signed at Washington on April 11, 1908, and do authorize and empower him to execute and fulfil the duties of this commission with all the powers, privileges and emoluments thereunto of right appertaining, during the pleasure of the President of the United States.

In testimony whereof, I have caused the Seal of the United States to be hereunto affixed.

Given under my hand, in the District of Columbia, this twenty-eighth day of February, in the year of our Lord one thousand nine hundred and twenty-one, and of the Independence of the United States of America the one hundred and forty-fifth.

[SEAL]

Woodrow Wilson.

By the President:

Bainbridge Colby, *Secretary of State.*

PROCLAMATIONS BY THE PRESIDENT OF THE UNITED STATES OF AMERICA (RESERVATION OF LANDS ON CANADIAN BOUNDARY)

Whereas, the customs and immigration laws of the United States can be better enforced and the public welfare thereby better advanced when the Federal Government has complete control of the use and occupation of lands abutting on international boundary lines;

Now, therefore, I, Theodore Roosevelt, President of the United States, do hereby proclaim and make known that all unpatented public lands of the United States, lying within sixty feet of the boundary line between the United States and the Dominion of Canada, are hereby declared to be, and are set apart as a public reservation, and shall hereafter be subject only to such rights as have been heretofore legally acquired under settlements, entries, reservations, or other forms of appropriation, and are now existing, but shall not be subject at any time to any other claim, use, or occupation, except for public highways; and any patent issued for any legal subdivision affected by this reservation under any claim hereafter initiated, shall contain a recital that it is issued subject to this proclamation.

In witness whereof, I have hereunto set my hand and caused the Seal of the United States to be affixed.

Done at the City of Washington this 15th day of June, in the year of our Lord one thousand nine hundred and eight, and of the Independence of the United States the one hundred and thirty-second.

[SEAL.]   THEODORE ROOSEVELT.

By the President:
ELIHU ROOT,
    Secretary of State.

(No. 810)

Whereas, the customs and immigration laws of the United States can be better enforced and the public welfare thereby advanced by the retention in the Federal Government of complete control of the use and occupation of lands abutting on International Boundary Lines;

Now, therefore, I, William Howard Taft, President of the United States, do hereby declare, proclaim, and make known that there are hereby reserved from entry, settlement, or other form of appropriation and disposition under the public-land laws, and set apart as a public reservation, all public lands lying within sixty feet of the Boundary Line between the United States and the Dominion of Canada.

Excepting from the force and effect of this proclamation all lands which were prior to June fifteenth, nineteen hundred and eight, embraced in any legal entry or covered by any lawful filing, selection, or right of way duly of record in the proper United States land office or upon which any valid settlement had been made pursuant to law, the statutory period within which to make or complete entry or filing of record had not expired, and which has been or may be perfected as required by law. Any claims lawfully initiated between June fifteenth, nineteen hundred and eight, and the date hereof, lawfully maintained and perfected, may be patented subject to the reservation prescribed in proclamation of the President dated June fifteenth, nineteen hundred and eight.

In witness whereof, I have hereunto set my hand and caused the seal of the United States to be affixed.

Done at the city of Washington, this third day of May, in the year of our Lord one thousand nine hundred and twelve, and of the Independence of the United States the one hundred and thirty-sixth.

[SEAL]   WM. H. TAFT

By the President:
HUNTINGTON WILSON
    Acting Secretary of State.

(No. 1196)

ORDERS IN COUNCIL CREATING A RESERVED STRIP ALONG THE BOUNDARY ON THE CANADIAN SIDE IN THE PROVINCE OF NEW BRUNSWICK

The Honourable the Minister of Lands and Mines reports for the information of the committee of the Executive Council:—

That the International Boundary Commission, Department of Interior, Ottawa, desires that a strip, sixty feet (60) in width, through the Crown Lands of the Province of New Brunswick, be reserved on the eastern side of the International Boundary between the Province of New Brunswick and State of Maine.

The Honourable the Minister of Lands and Mines now recommends that all ungranted crown lands bordering on the eastern side of the Internationl Boundary Line between the Province of New Brunswick and the State of Maine to the extent of sixty (60) feet, from said line be reserved for government purposes.

And His Honour the Lieutenant-Governor and Committee of Council concurring in said report and recommendation

IT IS ACCORDINGLY SO ORDERED.

Certified passed.

August 7th, 1923.

M. B. DIXON,
Clerk Executive Council.

16

AGREEMENTS OF THE COMMISSIONERS AS TO THE MANNER IN WHICH THE PROVISIONS OF ARTICLE III OF THE TREATY OF 1908 SHOULD BE CARRIED OUT

At a meeting of the commissioners held in Ottawa on December 28, 1908, the appointments of the commissioners under the treaty of April 11, 1908, were presented and found to be in due and proper form. At this and subsequent conferences of the commissioners it was agreed that the provisions of Article III of the treaty of 1908 should be carried out in the following manner:

I. That the work of retracement and remonumenting of the New York-Quebec boundary, which had already been done in 1902 jointly by the Dominion Government and the State of New York, and the similar work, which had been done in 1906 and 1907 on the line between Vermont and Quebec subsequent to joint and concurrent action of the Governments of the United States and Great Britain, should be accepted and the results incorporated in the commissioners' report.

II. That the boundary from the source of the St. Croix River to the St. Lawrence River, when reestablished, should consist throughout of a series of connecting straight courses, marked by permanent boundary monuments or where the boundary lies in a watercourse, referred to permanent monuments on the shores.

III. That in carrying out the provisions of the second paragraph of Article III of the treaty of 1908, relative to boundary monuments and marks, all original cast-iron boundary monuments set under the treaty of 1842, where found intact, should be filled with concrete and reset in concrete bases of uniform design, each 3 feet square and of sufficient depth to extend below the frost

General method of resetting the original cast-iron monuments

17

line; and that additional or supplementary intermediate monuments necessary to mark other points on the boundary, such as sites of original monuments which had been destroyed, important road crossings of the boundary and at "line houses," should be of cast-iron, concrete, or granite, set in concrete bases.

IV. That each monument should bear a suitable number, cut in the metal or stamped on its base, to identify it on the ground and in the final reports and maps.

V. That each deflection point of the reestablished boundary along the Highlands, other than those marked by the cast-iron monuments referred to in Paragraph III above, should be marked by a monument consisting of a 3-inch bronze disk set either in solid outcropping ledge of rock or in a concrete-filled section of 4-inch vitrified pipe set bell-end down with top flush with the ground, and that in addition to the number of the deflection point the disk should bear on the appropriate sides of a center line across its face the words "UNITED STATES" and "CANADA."

VI. That the boundary through timbered areas should be further marked by a vista along the line of sufficient width to give a cleared 20-foot sky line.

VII. That for the purpose of accurately defining, locating, and describing the boundary as laid down by the commissioners all boundary monuments and boundary reference marks should be located geodetically on North American datum by triangulation or by accurate traverses controlled by triangulation, and their positions should be certified by the commissioners in their joint report as being a true descrip-

tion and definition of the international boundary as reestablished, surveyed, and marked in accordance with Article III of the treaty of 1908.

VIII. That the charts of the boundary, specified in Article III of the treaty, should consist of a series of 61 topographic maps, to be prepared from surveys made by the commissioners, showing the boundary monuments and the course of the boundary and the topography for a minimum distance of one-half mile on each side of the line. That the scales of these maps should be as follows: the maps of Halls Stream and the Southwest Branch of the St. John River, 1:6,000; of the St. John River and the St. Francis River, 1:12,000; and of all the land portion of the boundary, 1:24,000. That the contour interval for all the maps should be 20 feet.

IX. That the maps of the boundary should be engraved on copper plates and printed from stone, using the conventional colors and symbols, and that after the completion of the print-

Intermediate boundary monument and cleared vista

ing, and the signing of the official maps by the commissioners, the engraved copper plates should be deposited in fireproof vaults for safe-keeping.

X. That the field work of retracing, locating, mapping, and monumenting the boundary should be divided, in approximately equal amounts, between the two sections of the commission, as follows:

All the work, except the main scheme triangulation, from the St. Croix River to the St. John River and along the St. John River to the St. Francis River to be allotted in general to joint parties of United States and Canadian surveyors, and similar work along the lower half of the St. Francis River to United States surveyors, and along the upper half of the river to Canadian surveyors; and the main scheme triangulation, furnishing the major control for the above work from the source of the St. Croix River to Lake Pohenagamook, to Canadian surveyors.

All the field work, except the monumenting, from Lake Pohenagamook along the Southwest Line to monument 187, and from monument 222 to English Lake, and thence along the South Line to the Southwest Branch of the St. John River, to surveyors of the United States section of the commission; and all the monumenting along the Southwest Line and the South Line, from Lake Pohenagamook to the Southwest Branch of the St. John River, and all the other field work from monument 187 to monument 222 on the Southwest Line, to surveyors of the Canadian section.

All the field work on the boundary along the Southwest Branch of the St. John River and on the boundary along the Highlands from the Southwest Branch of the St. John River southwestward to monument 402, the point where the Canadian Pacific Railway crosses the boundary, to be surveyed by Canadian parties; and all the work on the boundary along the Highlands westward from monument 402 to the head of Halls Stream and along Halls Stream to the "Valentine and Collins" line to be allotted to United States surveyors.

The main scheme triangulation along the Vermont-Quebec line westward from Halls Stream to the Richelieu River, to control the retracement, monumenting, and mapping of the boundary done jointly by the United States and Canadian surveyors under the joint and concurrent action of the two Governments in 1906 and 1907, to be done by Canadian surveyors.

The work of making a topographic map of the country adjacent to the boundary from the Richelieu River to the St. Lawrence River to be done by surveyors of the United States section, and the field work of tying the traverse of this line to the primary triangulation of the Geodetic Survey of Canada to be done by Canadian surveyors.

XI. That, along Halls Stream, the Southwest Branch of the St. John River, and the St. Francis River where the beds of the streams have been changed in certain places by avulsion since the boundary line was laid down in 1845, in order to "reestablish the location of the said boundary" in accordance with the provision of Article III of the treaty of 1908, specifying that the course of the entire boundary should be marked by said commissioners as described in Article I of the treaty of 1842 and as laid down as aforesaid under Article VI of that treaty, the line should be relocated along the old bed of the stream as shown on the maps prepared under the treaty of 1842, and not along the new channels which have been formed since then.

RETRACEMENT OF THE BOUNDARY LINE

Before the work of locating, remonumenting, and mapping any section of the boundary could be undertaken, it was necessary to identify on the ground the line as laid down under the provisions of the treaty of August 9, 1842.[3]

The character of this work varied according to conditions. Along the Highlands, the work consisted of running out the line between monuments in accordance with the old notes, or, where the notes were obviously in error, by following the crest of the watershed or traces of the old vista. On straight-line sections of the boundary, dependence was placed chiefly upon the location of important monuments, the operations consisting of searching for and finding the monuments and determining whether any of them had been moved from their original sites. Where the boundary followed watercourses, and no old notes were available and but few monuments had originally been set, the course of the line was taken entirely from the original boundary maps, the chief problem being to determine in each case whether the channel of the stream had been changed by avulsion since the treaty of 1842, as, for example, on parts of Halls Stream, and in such case to find the bed of the original channel, which, as agreed by the commissioners, was to determine the final location of the line.

---

[3] The details of the work of retracement are given in the chapters on "Field operations," "Description of field methods," and "Description of office methods."

Triangulation signal erected over boundary monument on North Line

THE NORTH LINE

The retracement of this portion of the boundary, from the source of the St. Croix River northward 78 miles to the St. John River, was made from the survey notes of 1843, accepting as fixed points on the boundary those monuments which were found not to have been moved. A vista was cleared between monuments where necessary, and the line run out and measured. The distances between monuments, and the 25 deflections in the line, averaging about 12 minutes of arc, were found to agree closely with the measurements made during the survey of 1843. One hundred and six of the old boundary monuments were found on their original sites, and eleven monuments were found to have been displaced and were later restored to the line by the monumenting party, only one, however, being placed in its original position.[4]

THE BOUNDARY ALONG THE ST. JOHN RIVER

The records of the original survey of the boundary through the St. John River, made under the treaty of 1842, consist of a set of general maps showing the islands and shore line of the river, the boundary, the mouths of tributary streams, and a few roads and buildings, on a scale of 4 inches to the mile, and a set of detail maps showing the soundings between the islands and the mainland, on a scale of 12 inches to the mile. The maps showed that 60 cast-iron monuments had been placed on the islands in the river to indicate their nationality, but no records or notes of the old survey could be found to show the exact relation of the monuments to the boundary or to the shore lines of the river. The original location of the boundary had to be determined, therefore, solely by its position as shown on the maps in relation to the topography of the adjacent islands and streams.

The work, therefore, of retracing the line along the river included making an accurate topographic map and comparing this map with the old maps to determine

Special type of cast-iron monument, as reset at source of St. Croix River

[4] See chapter "Monuments and monumenting," p. 107.

what changes had occurred in the shore lines of the river and islands since 1843, and then drawing on the new map a series of straight-line courses conforming as nearly as practicable to the course of the curved boundary shown on the original maps. It was agreed by the commissioners that this series of connecting straight lines should be tied to reference monuments set on the river banks and islands, and should constitute the final location of the boundary.

THE BOUNDARY ALONG THE ST. FRANCIS RIVER

The retracement of the boundary along the St. Francis River presented the same problem as that on the St. John River. No notes of the original survey were available, but the old commission maps of 1843 showed this part of the boundary as a curved line following the channel of the stream.

A new topographic map was made and the course of the stream was compared with that shown on the old maps. It was quite evident from this comparison that at some places there had been a gradual shifting of the channel, due to the swift current cutting away the banks at sharp bends and building up sand bars, and that at two places the stream had been changed by avulsion.

At the places where the change in the river had been gradual and due to erosion and accretion, the boundary was placed as near the center of the present channel as practicable, and at the two places where the stream had abruptly left the old channel the line was laid down along the course of the old channel, which was well defined and easily identified. Throughout its entire course, the new boundary consists of a series of connecting straight lines conforming as closely as practicable to the curved line shown on the old maps.

THE SOUTHWEST AND SOUTH LINES

The Southwest and South Lines, comprising the section of boundary from Lake Pohenagamook to the Southwest Branch of the St. John River, as surveyed under the treaty of 1842, consisted of two lines, intersecting near the southern end of English Lake and having a combined length of 84 miles, along which there had been set 131 cast-iron monuments, fairly uniformly distributed. The records of the original survey consisted of the old commission maps and survey notes which gave the distances between monuments and the results of astronomical observations, determining the azimuths of the lines.

The boundary was retraced by clearing a vista between monuments and running a precise traverse with theodolite and invar tape in accordance with the original notes. The direction of the line was verified by observing an astronomical azimuth at a station on the boundary at Lake Pohenagamook. The results of this observation differed from the azimuth of the line as observed in 1843–44 by only 4 seconds of arc. The precise traverse of the Southwest Line and the South Line developed the fact that sections of the monumented line running between prominent intervisible points deviated slightly from the two major straight lines indicated by the old notes. These deflections had a mean value of 14 seconds and were not cumulative. All the old monuments except four were found in place and were reset in concrete bases to make the line conform as closely as possible to the original straight-line locations indicated by the precise traverse.

THE BOUNDARY ALONG THE SOUTHWEST BRANCH OF THE ST. JOHN RIVER

The original records consist of a set of maps made during the survey under the treaty of 1842, upon which are shown the river with the boundary midway between its banks, also the tributary brooks and the five monuments set in 1845.

The retracement of this part of the line was accomplished by making an accurate topographic map of the stream and comparing its course with that shown on the maps made in 1844–45. This comparison indicated that, with one exception, only a few minor changes in the position of the stream had taken place due to erosion and accretion. Accordingly, the boundary was laid down as a series of straight lines following the center of the present channel as closely as practicable, except at the one place where the stream had abruptly left the old channel, where it was laid down along the course of the old channel, which was well defined and easily identified. The boundary throughout was made to conform as nearly as practicable to the curved boundary shown on the old maps. Because of the narrowness of the stream this was done in the field instead of by scaling from the map as was done in the case of the St. John River. The position of the line was fixed by permanent reference monuments established along the banks.

THE BOUNDARY ALONG THE HIGHLANDS

The Highlands boundary, which extends from a point near Little St. John Lake at the source of the Southwest Branch of the St. John River to the head of Halls Stream, a distance of 175 miles, follows the crest of the watershed which separates the headwaters of the Penobscot, Kennebec, Androscoggin, and Connecticut Rivers from the waters which flow into the St. Lawrence River. The course of this part of the boundary is very tortuous. As established under the treaty of 1842, it was marked by a vista and by 192 cast-iron monuments and 2 wooden monuments fairly uniformly distributed along the boundary. The records of the original survey include maps of the boundary and notes of two independent traverses run along the crest of the divide by British and United States parties, respectively, in 1844–45. The deflection points of neither of these traverses were permanently

Stump of old vista cuttings of 1845 on Highlands boundary

104709—25†——4

marked in any way between the iron monuments. Each traverse was tied to the iron monuments and each independent survey was controlled by a system of guide lines with offsets at frequent intervals to the boundary traverses.

The work of retracing the line was begun by searching for the iron monuments set in 1844–45. All of these were recovered, and in addition the sites of the two wooden monuments, identified by mounds of stone which had been piled around the posts, were found. In general the line between adjacent original monuments was laid down by determining the relative positions of the monuments by triangulation or precise traverse, and then reproducing on the ground the original traverse, which was first adjusted to make the distances along the boundary between monuments consistent with the newly determined positions of the monuments. By agreement the

Remains of survey post set in old vista on the Highlands about 1870

parties used the British notes of the old survey from the source of the Southwest Branch of the St. John River to monument 418 and the United States notes from that point to the head of Halls Stream. This resulted in a satisfactory retracement

Commissioner Barnard and timber cruiser tracing course of old vista on Highlands near Arnold Pond, 1916

of the boundary throughout the greater part of its course, but in several places the line, as thus redetermined, departed from the old vista or from the sharp crest of the watershed. In such instances, parts of the old survey notes had to be disregarded and the line reestablished by following the old vista or the crest of the divide.

THE BOUNDARY ALONG HALLS STREAM

The Halls Stream boundary retracement was based on the boundary maps of 1845, using the same method as along the Southwest Branch of the St. John River. No notes of the old survey were available.

The new topographic map of Halls Stream Valley furnished the means of comparing the present position of the stream with that shown on the old maps

Granite post originally set to mark point on Vermont-Quebec boundary in 1849; reset in concrete base

of 1845. The comparison showed that a considerable number of abrupt changes had occurred in the channel of the stream since the original survey, and in such cases the old abandoned channels, which in 1845 were a part of the main or boundary channel of Halls Stream, were still well defined on the ground. By means of a transit and tape traverse, the line was reestablished throughout its length as a series of straight lines tied to permanent reference monuments set along the shores and conforming as closely as practicable to the location of the course of the channel as it existed in 1845.

VERMONT-QUEBEC BOUNDARY

Along the section of the boundary from Halls Stream to the Richelieu River, surveyed originally by Valentine and Collins in 1771–72, the line was retraced by running straight lines between adjacent original boundary monuments found in place on the ground. A comparison was made of this traverse with the records of a similar traverse of 1845 to determine which monuments were in their original positions and could be accepted as fixed points on the boundary. One hundred and eleven of the one hundred and thirty monuments set by the boundary commission in 1845 and by Graham and Ord in 1849 were accepted as marking original boundary points, and as many as could be found of the other monuments, which had been moved or partially destroyed, were restored to their original positions. Many of the

Original granite monument (No. 646) set by the Commissioners in 1845 near Richelieu River on New York-Quebec line
(See descriptive note, page 27)

Instrument piers of old astronomic station used in 1845; near Rouses Point, N. Y.

monuments were leaning or were loose in the ground, and later, when being reset in concrete bases, were moved slightly to positions on straight lines between the deflection points shown by the records of 1845.

The new values obtained for the angles at the 69 deflection points and the distances along the line between original monuments showed a close agreement with the results of the survey of 1845.

THE NEW YORK-QUEBEC BOUNDARY

The retracement of this part of the boundary was made in 1902 by surveyors of the State of New York and surveyors of the Dominion of Canada acting under concurrent agreement of the two Governments. The retracement was governed solely by the positions of the cast-iron monuments which had been set to mark the line in 1845, rejecting only a few of the monuments which, by reference to the records of the survey of 1845, were found to have been moved from their original positions. Of the original 130 monuments, 118 were found in place.

A transit and tape traverse was run along or near the line, and offsets were measured to each monument. The distances and deflection angles between monuments were then computed from the traverse notes. It was found that they agreed closely with the corresponding distances and angles of the survey of 1845.

The resultant line as computed from the traverse was accepted as the final boundary line. The monuments were replaced with granite posts set at the sites of the original cast-iron monuments.

DESCRIPTION OF MONUMENT ON OPPOSITE PAGE

Original monument No. 646, illustrated on page 26, is a stone or granite shaft 6 feet 8 inches high, 1 foot square at the top and 1 foot 10 inches at the base. The monument is surrounded by an iron fence 5 feet 10 inches high, set in stone coping 1 foot above the ground. On the south side of the monument, beginning at the top, are inscribed the following lines: "Latitude 45–00–42.8," "J. D. Graham, Major Corps of Top. Engineers, U. S. Astronomer," "A. W. Whipple, Lieut. Corps of Top. Engineers, Assistant," "1845," "Boundary," "Treaty of Washington of Aug. 9th 1842." On the west side, on appropriate sides of a vertical center line consisting of a rope carved on the surface of the stone, appear the words "Canada" and "New York." On the north side, reading from the top, are the lines "Longitude west of Greenwich 73–21–27 or 4^h–53–25.8," "J. D. Graham, Major Top. Engineer, U. S. Astronomer" "1845." On the east side, reading vertically, is the word "Boundary," and on the appropriate sides of the carved rope which continues over the top of the monument from the west side, are inscribed "Albert Smith, U. S. Commissioner," and "J. B. B. Estcourt, L. T. Co., H. B. M. Commissioner."

FIELD OPERATIONS

The field work of retracing, remonumenting, locating, and mapping the boundary from the source of the St. Croix River to the St. Lawrence River was begun in the summer of 1902, when a joint resurvey was made of that portion of the boundary between the Province of Quebec and the State of New York by the State of New York and the Dominion of Canada "without a formal treaty agreement but by the joint and concurrent action of the Governments of the United States and Great Britain."[5]

Work was also carried on previous to the treaty of 1908 along the portion of the boundary between Quebec and Vermont, in 1906 and 1907. These latter field operations were under the direction of the commissioners who were supervising the work in connection with the demarcation of the boundary between Alaska and Canada. Later, these commissioners were also appointed to carry out the provisions of the treaty of 1908, and field operations were continued by them to completion in 1922, without any break in progress or material changes in methods.

[5] See Appendix II, p. 314; also Article III, treaty of 1908, p. 4.

Cross Lake Rapids, St. Francis River

Operations on the boundary were conducted by joint parties until the fall of 1910, by which time, in addition to the work along the New York-Quebec and Vermont-Quebec lines, the survey had been extended from the source of the St. Croix River to the St. Francis River. It was then decided, owing to the natural difficulties of transportation in the country to be traversed, that the work could be carried on more efficiently by dividing the remainder of the line into sections, to be allotted to independent Canadian and United States parties, respectively, apportioning the total amount of field work as equally as possible.

Pack train on Highlands boundary

Accordingly, in 1911 a Canadian party worked southward from Lake Pohenagamook along the St. Francis River, and a United States party worked north from Cross Lake. In 1912 a Canadian party worked along the line from monument 187 to monument 222, and a United States party operated from Lake Pohenagamook to monument 187 and from monument 222 to the vicinity of St. Pamphile. Similarly, in 1913, a Canadian party began work on the Southwest Branch of the St. John River, while a United States party completed the work on the Southwest and South Lines from the point where they had left off in 1912 to the Southwest Branch of the St. John River. In 1914 the Canadians finished the work on the Southwest Branch of the St. John River, and the United States parties began work on the boundary along Halls Stream, working northward from Beecher Falls, Vt.

In 1915 each section of the commission put two parties in the field. One Canadian party did the major control triangulation on the St. Francis and St. John Rivers, while that Canadian party which had been operating on the Southwest Branch of the St. John River in 1914 began work along the eastern portion of the Highlands

Transportation in Arnold River Valley; Highlands boundary, 1916

boundary. The United States party which, during the previous season, had been on Halls Stream, completed that work to the source of the stream, and a second party of the United States section began at monument 402 on the Highlands boundary and worked westward to monument 431. In 1916 a Canadian party completed the triangulation from the St. John River to the St. Croix River, and the party on the Highlands boundary continued westward to monument 347, and two United States parties completed the surveys along the Highlands from monument 431 to the head of Halls Stream.

Between 1917 and 1922 the Canadian parties completed the work along the Highlands westward to monument 402 and triangulated the Vermont-Quebec and New York-Quebec lines from Halls Stream to the St. Lawrence River. United States parties made a topographic map of the New York-Quebec line, relocated and marked the boundary in the old channels along Halls Stream, and reset the old monuments on the islands of the St. John River, and a joint party of Canadian and United States surveyors completed the control of the Southwest Branch of the St. John River and made a final field location of the boundary in the stream.

Along much of the boundary, the work of the field parties was materially delayed by difficulties due to transportation. For nearly half the length of the land portion of the boundary from the source of the St. Croix River to the St. Lawrence River, the line traverses a heavily wooded country of rolling hills and mountains. Particularly is this true of the entire 297 miles from Lake Pohenagamook to the head of Halls Stream. This country had been seldom entered except by logging companies operating in the winter over frozen snow roads, which were practically impassable during the field seasons of the surveying parties, generally from the middle of May to the middle of October. The surveying camps on or near the boundary were, therefore, almost inaccessible except by the use of pack trains and teams, operating over trails and tote roads which had to be cut through the underbrush. Also, as a considerable part of the line follows the crest of the watershed, the work of getting materials to the monument sites often involved long hikes and considerable back packing beyond points reached by the horses.

The more important of these and other problems incidental to the work of carrying on the survey are set forth in other chapters of the report, or are included in the accounts of the several seasons' field work which follow.

SEASON OF 1902—THE NEW YORK-QUEBEC BOUNDARY

An act passed by the Legislature of the State of New York in 1887 required the State engineer and surveyor to make an examination of the boundary lines of the State that year and every third year thereafter. In 1890, the examination of the international portion of the New York boundary was participated in by an officer appointed by the Canadian Government. It was discovered then, and in subsequent examinations, that very serious deterioration of the monuments had occurred, showing a progressive falling off in their condition and the necessity for repairs and renewals.

On October 29, 1900, at the request of the New York State engineer and surveyor, the Secretary of State wrote to the British ambassador, calling attention to the condition of the New York-Quebec boundary monuments, and inquiring whether the Government of Canada would be "willing to join in having these monuments replaced and put in proper and first-class condition."

A concurrence of views concerning the matter was reached in August, 1901, and it was arranged that the restoration of defective monuments marking the New York-Quebec boundary should be proceeded with under the joint direction of the State engineer of New York and a representative of the Canadian Department of the Interior.

Pursuant to this arrangement, the re-marking of the boundary was undertaken by Edward A. Bond, State engineer and surveyor, as commissioner for the State of New York, and William F. King, chief astronomer of the Department of the Interior, commissioner for Canada.

Type of new granite post monument set on New York-Quebec line in 1902

The commissioners decided, before proceeding with the replacing of the monuments, to have a careful examination of existing monuments made; and for that purpose, and for such further field operations as might be found necessary, appointed representatives, the State engineer of New York appointing Mr. H. P. Willis, of Schenectady, and the Canadian commissioner appointing Mr. C. A. Bigger, of Ottawa, in October, 1901. These gentlemen personally inspected the line in October and November, 1901. Beginning at monument 645, near the west bank of the Richelieu River, they proceeded westward along the boundary to the St. Lawrence River, inspecting each monument and making careful note of its condition. Their report showed that only 10 of the 130 monuments were in perfect condition; that is, intact, plumb, and solidly set.

After consideration of their report, it was thought advisable to replace all the old monuments with new ones, using for this purpose granite posts of uniform design set in 3-foot concrete bases. It was also decided to make a precise survey of the line for the purpose of determining accurately the positions of the monuments.

A contract for furnishing the granite monuments was awarded, during the winter of 1901–2, to a firm at Hardwick, Vt., and after the monuments had been inspected at the granite works they were delivered early that year to convenient railway stations along the line. In May the representatives met at Three Rivers, Quebec, and made out a statement of the number of men required, the tools necessary for remonumenting the line, and the surveying instruments to be furnished, which they submitted to the commissioners, who approved of the arrangements and directed them to commence the work as soon as possible.

On June 3 the commissioner for Canada and his representative, and the representative of the commissioner for the State of New York, met at Rouses Point, N. Y., and concluded the necessary arrangements, such as collecting the materials and hiring the teams and laborers, for executing the work westward from that point.

It was supposed that the monument building would not progress as rapidly as the surveying; consequently, at the beginning, the energies of the party were centered on that branch of the work. The first monument (No. 647) was built on June 9. The organization of the monumenting party was as follows: One foreman (expert concrete worker), two teamsters, and five laborers. In addition to the above, other laborers and teams were hired when necessary. A detailed description of the monuments and the work of the monumenting party, taken from the report of the representatives of the commissioners,[6] will be found elsewhere in this report under the chapter "Monuments and monumenting."

The surveying party, which included one assistant surveyor, four chainmen, and five axmen, ran a traverse consisting of a succession of straight lines, run with transit and steel tape, near the boundary and so placed as to make each course of the traverse as long as possible, keeping near the boundary line and yet avoiding, wherever necessary, orchards, buildings, and natural obstructions. The direction of each course of the traverse was determined by azimuth observations. The positions of the monuments were determined by measuring offsets from points on this traverse to the monuments. Observations for latitude were made at several important stations, and subsequently, in 1917 and 1923, the geodetic positions of the monuments were determined on the North American datum by tying this traverse at several points to the Canadian primary scheme of triangulation adjacent to the boundary on the north.

The new monuments were set and located on the sites of the original cast-iron monuments, which in every case were broken up and used in the concrete bases of the new ones. Besides replacing the old monuments, 16 additional new monuments were set to mark important road crossings and other intermediate points on the line. These intermediate monuments were appropriately numbered by stamping on the concrete base of each the number of the preceding original monument and the letter A.

The work ran through the field season of 1902 and was completed on June 6, 1903.

Since then the new monuments set in 1902 have been inspected twice by representatives of the International Boundary Commission and the State engineer and surveyor of New York. The first of these joint inspections—in addition to the regular three-year inspections of the line made by the State of New York—was made in 1910 by Mr. M. F. Cochrane, D. L. S., representing the Canadian section of the International Boundary Commission, and Mr. H. J. Stabile, of the New York

---

[6] See Report of the Chief Astronomer and Boundary Commissioner, Department of the Interior, Dominion of Canada, 1904, pp. 20, 21, and 32–34; and Annual Report of the New York State Engineer and Surveyor, 1902, pp. 71, 72, and 99–102.

State engineer's office. The second inspection was made in September, 1916, by Mr. J. D. Craig, D. L. S., engineer to the Canadian section of the commission; Mr. James H. Van Wagenen, engineer to the United States section of the commission; and Mr. H. F. Eagan, representing the State engineer and surveyor of New York.

On each of these inspection trips it was noticed that a marked and progressive depreciation had taken place in the condition of the monuments; a number of them had been heaved by frost and were leaning; one was found to have been broken by heat from the burning of a building close by; others were hidden by dense underbrush which filled the vista in many places.

The results of these inspection trips were

Granite monument 721 broken by heat from burning building

that in 1917 the boundary commissioners, cooperating with the State engineer of New York, reset and repaired 18 monuments,[7] erected one additional monument, No. 726–A, to mark a road crossing of the boundary between monuments 726 and 727, and reopened several miles of vista along the line.

The personnel of the field parties operating along the New York-Quebec boundary during the season of 1902 was as follows:

For His Britannic Majesty: Chief of party, C. A. Bigger, D. L. S.; assistants, C. A. Bourget, D. L. S., F. W. O. Werry.

For the State of New York: Chief of party, H. P. Willis.

View looking east along New York-Quebec line, near monument 653

[7] See "Field operations," 1917, p. 77, and "Monuments and monumenting," p. 111.

SEASON OF 1906—THE VER-
MONT-QUEBEC BOUND-
ARY

The correspondence between the United States Government and the Canadian Government which resulted in the agreement to remonument and resurvey the New York-Quebec Boundary in 1902 also resulted in the import-ance of re-marking and mapping the entire line from the Richelieu River eastward to the waters of the St. Croix River being recog-nized by both Governments; and it was agreed, where the work to be done involved no disputed question as to the course or loca-tion of the line, but required only the restoration of original monu-ments and the erection of new ones in order to render more effective the boundary as already surveyed and marked,

Typical condition of monuments at time of joint examination, 1905

that it was not necessary to enter into a formal con-vention for that purpose, and that an informal agree-ment making provision on both sides for the joint performance of the work was all that was required.

This led to the first step being taken toward the resurvey and more complete demarcation of the Ver-mont-Quebec line. On February 9, 1905, the Secre-tary of the Treasury of the United States addressed a letter to the Secretary of State setting forth the need of a better demarcation of the Vermont-Quebec por-tion of the international boundary and suggesting that the work should be undertaken by a joint commission representing the United States and Canada. The matter was referred to the Superintendent of the Coast and Geodetic Survey for an expression of his views of the best method of meeting the necessity of the case, and on February 21, 1905, he transmitted a letter to the Secretary of State suggesting that an ex-amination be made of the monuments along this por-tion of the boundary.

Monument 519, Vermont-Quebec line, before it was reset

The Canadian Government assented to a proposition that a joint examination should be made, and Mr. J. B. Baylor, assistant, United States Coast and Geodetic Survey, was appointed to represent the United States, and Mr. G. C. Rainboth, D. L. S., to represent Canada. These representatives were later directed to extend their examination to include the entire portion of the boundary from the Richelieu River to the source of the St. Croix River.

This examination was carried out during the summer of 1905, and the representatives made a report to their Governments under date of February 22, 1906, giving a general review of the condition of the boundary from the Richelieu River to the source of the St. Croix River, with recommendations as to what should be done.

Monument 519 after it was reset

Monument 505, at time of joint examination of the boundary prior to treaty of 1908. In this photograph is Frederick W. King, son of British Commissioner King. He was killed in action near Arras, France, August 26, 1918

The report strongly urged that this entire line be resurveyed and remonumented.

Pursuant to these recommendations, under an informal agreement between the two Governments, Mr. O. H. Tittmann was appointed commissioner for the United States and Dr. W. F. King, His Britannic Majesty's commissioner. At a meeting of the commissioners, held in Ottawa in July, 1906, which was also attended by the engineers who had made the inspection, it was decided to resurvey that part of the line forming the boundary between Vermont and Quebec, and the work of making the resurvey was placed in charge of the inspecting engineers, who were directed to commence operations at as early a date as possible. The engineers and their assistants reached the field on August 1 and made camp at Beecher Falls, Vt., where a joint party was organized. After considerable difficulty in obtaining the necessary laborers, work was begun at that point about August 10.

Like the New York-Quebec boundary, the portion of the boundary from Beecher Falls to the Richelieu River was a part of the line originally surveyed by Valentine and Collins in 1771–74, which was accepted at that time as being the forty-fifth parallel of latitude. However, it diverged considerably from the true parallel, and, as resurveyed in 1845, consisted of a series of straight lines which were marked at deflection points by monuments set diagonally, and at intermediate points by monuments set square with the line.

The old cast-iron monuments were filled with concrete and set in concrete bases on their old sites, except in a few cases where this was found to be impossible or inadvisable. Additional new monuments were placed along the line to mark important points, such as at the so-called "line houses" and at railroad crossings. These new monuments were blocks of granite, each 10 inches square, projecting about 1 foot above the concrete base in which it was set. All monuments were set square with the line.

The survey operations consisted of opening a vista 20 feet wide where the line passed through woods, measuring the distances along the line between monuments with stadia and steel tapes, observing the angles at the monuments marking deflection points, running levels along the line from a bench mark on the Maine Central Railroad at Beecher Falls, and making a topographic map on a field scale of 1:15,840 with plane table and stadia of a strip of country one-half mile wide on each side of the boundary.

The party discontinued work and disbanded for the season at a point near Derby Line, Vt., on November 15.

Survey camp near Lyster Lake, late in fall of 1906

The personnel of the field parties for the season of 1906 was as follows:

For His Britannic Majesty: Chief of party, G. C. Rainboth, D. L. S.; assistants, F. H. Mackie, D. L. S., G. L. Rainboth, A. J. Rainboth, O. Sills, B. Foley.

For the United States: Chief of party, J. B. Baylor; assistants, O. B. French, R. H. Blain, J. P. Locke.

SEASON OF 1907—THE VERMONT-QUEBEC BOUNDARY

The joint party resumed operations in 1907 where work had been discontinued the previous fall, near Derby Line, Vt.

The topographic surveying in 1906 had not proceeded as fast as the monumenting and line cutting. For this reason, the strength of this part of the party was doubled in 1907 to complete the mapping left unfinished the previous year and to

Monument 621, Vermont-Quebec line, before it was reset

Monument 621, after it was reset

have it keep pace with the other work of the party.

In general, operations were carried on in accordance with the plan followed during the previous year.

The party, when fully organized, consisted of two monumenting crews, each of which included a foreman and three or four hands with a team and wagon or drag, two topographers with the necessary rodmen and axmen, one surveyor in charge of a line location party of several chainmen and rodmen, a leveling party, and a vista-cutting gang.

Besides resetting all the old monuments along the Vermont-Quebec line, the monumenting parties built three large monuments of reinforced concrete to replace the monuments on the shore of Missisquoi Bay, Lake

Champlain. Also, near the end of the season, it was found that monument 645 on the west bank of the Richelieu River, which had been reset in 1902, had been destroyed by floating ice. This monument was not rebuilt; but an intermediate monument, No. 645–A (a large concrete structure of the same type as the three monuments set on Missisquoi Bay) was built on the line about 200 feet west of the river.

The line location, vista cutting, leveling, and topographic mapping were completed as far west as the Richelieu River.

The party lived in camp, which was moved along the boundary as the work progressed. Transportation was comparatively easy. The country, though quite hilly—in fact, in some places, even mountainous—

Type of intermediate monument used on Vermont-Quebec line

was easily accessible, as there are a number of prosperous farming and dairy communities and several flourishing manufacturing centers on both sides of the boundary.

The field work of surveying and marking the Vermont-Quebec boundary was completed early in November, and the party was disbanded.

The personnel of the party operating during the season of 1907 was as follows:

For the United States: Chief of party, J. B. Baylor; assistants, R. H. Blain, C. H. Van Orden, J. P. Locke.

For His Britannic Majesty: Chief of party, G. C. Rainboth, D. L. S.; assistants, G. L. Rainboth, A. J. Rainboth, A. M. Phillips, W. J. Sharpe, B. Foley.

SEASON OF 1908—THE NORTH LINE, NEW BRUNSWICK-MAINE

The work on the boundary between Vermont and Quebec having been completed in 1907, it was decided that operations should begin, in 1908, on the resurvey of the North Line, the old exploratory line of 1817–18, which runs northward from the source of the St. Croix River to the St. John River and which, by the treaty of 1842, became a part of the international boundary between the Province of New Brunswick and the State of Maine.

This portion of the boundary consists of a series of straight line courses of various lengths, all running approximately due north. Naturally, therefore, the system of survey adopted by the joint party in 1908 was practically the same as that used along the Vermont-Quebec line during the previous season. The old vista was reopened to a width of 20 feet, the several courses of the line were measured both with stadia and steel tape, and the angles at the deflection points were carefully measured. A topographic map of a strip of country one-half mile wide on each side of the line was made with plane table and stadia on a field scale of 1:10,000, and a line of levels was also carried along. The old monuments were reset, square with the line, in concrete bases, and new monuments, consisting of granite blocks 10 inches square and about 12 inches high, were set in concrete bases to replace original monuments which were broken or lost and to mark the line on each side of all the "line houses." Intermediate monuments of this type were also placed so that each monument is intervisible with the monument immediately north and south of it.

As during the previous season, the party lived in camp, which was moved often enough to provide the men with living quarters close to the work as it progressed. The country was well settled, and transportation, which was by teams and wagons, could be easily obtained whenever necessary.

Favorable weather throughout the season enabled good progress to be made, and by the end of October the vista along the line was opened throughout the entire distance to the St. John River. The stadia and steel tape measurement of the line was also completed, but smoke from forest fires and the burning of potato stalks seriously interfered with the more precise part of the work, so that it was impossible to complete the

Boundary monument and vista, on North Line

lining-in of all the monuments, and this work, together with some of the topographic mapping, was left until the following season.

The party withdrew from the field on November 20.

The personnel engaged on the work during the season of 1908 was as follows:

For His Britannic Majesty: Chief of party, G. C. Rainboth, D. L. S.; assistants, M. F. Cochrane, D. L. S., A. J. Rainboth, G. L. Rainboth, I. R. Pounder, C. R. Westland, W. J. Sharpe, B. Foley.

For the United States: Chief of party, J. B. Baylor; assistants, R. H. Blain, J. P. Locke.

SEASON OF 1909—THE BOUNDARY ALONG THE ST. JOHN RIVER

Field operations were resumed early in May, 1909, the first work being the completion of the northerly portion of the North Line which the party was unable to finish during the season of 1908. The first camp was established near the point where the North Line intersects the St. John River, about 3 miles above Grand Falls, New Brunswick.

When the survey along the St. John River was undertaken, the joint organization was divided into two parties, a Canadian party operating on the Canadian side of the river and a party of United States surveyors on the United States side. Reconnaissance, signal building, and triangulation were done by each party on its own side of the river. All the leveling was done by the Canadian party, and the monumenting on both sides of the river was done by the Canadian concrete fore-

"Line house" on North Line at monument 49

Grand Falls of St. John River, New Brunswick, 2¼ miles east of boundary

man. The rest of the work, which included principally the making of a topographic survey of the river and the adjacent country, was done in sections, each including about 3½ miles of the river. Each party did all the topographic work of each alternate section on both sides of the river.

A railroad on each side of the river and good highways provided ample and convenient transportation, so that the camps could be moved often and kept close to the general vicinity of the work, which proceeded westward along the river valley toward the mouth of the St. Francis River.

The triangulation which located the boundary reference monuments and furnished the control for the topographic map was of minor grade, the figures of which straddled the river, the stations being located at suitable points on each side of the

Boundary survey camp on St. John River at Ste. Anne de Madawaska, 1909

river valley. The triangulation was started about 6 miles west of Grand Falls from a measured base, which formed the side of one of the quadrilaterals. The lengths derived from this base were checked during the season by two other similar bases, one near Ste. Anne de Madawaska, New Brunswick, and the other about 3 miles above Edmundston, New Brunswick. The three bases were measured along tangents on the newly established grade of the Canadian National Railway. Near the end of the season, the triangulation was tied for azimuth and position to a Canadian astronomic station at Edmundston, New Brunswick. In 1915 and 1916, this triangulation was tied to the major triangulation connected with primary stations of the Geodetic Survey of Canada and the United States Coast and Geodetic Survey, and, when adjusted to that work, furnished the final control of the boundary along the St. John River.

The topographic survey was made with plane table and stadia on a field scale of 1:5,000. The maps covered an area which extended one-half mile on each side of the river and showed the highways, railroads, reference monuments, houses, and fence lines. Elevations for the topographic work were furnished by a line of levels run along the Canadian Pacific Railway, which closely follows the river on the Canadian side. At that time no precise bench marks of the geodetic surveys of either country had been established along the river, hence the datum used for the line of levels was that of the Canadian National Railway, which was then under construction. This datum has since been found to have a fairly uniform error of about 5 feet below the true mean sea-level datum, and this fact is noted on the boundary maps of this portion of the line.

Boundary reference monuments of concrete were constructed at suitable points along the shores, and, in general, were located at triangulation stations.

The season's operations, which included some 40 miles of triangulation, topography, and monumenting along the river, were greatly hampered by an unusual amount of rainy weather. During July and a part of August scarcely a day passed without rain, which was frequently continuous for two or three days at a time.

The parties withdrew from the field during the first week of November, and the outfits were stored for the winter at Fort Kent and Edmundston.

The personnel of the two parties was as follows:

For His Britannic Majesty: Chief of party, G. C. Rainboth, D. L. S.; assistants, G. L. Rainboth, I. R. Pounder, J. A. Pounder, W. M. Dennis, B. Foley.

For the United States: Chief of party, J. B. Baylor; assistants, R. H. Blain, F. H. Brundage, W. B. Gilmore, J. P. Locke.

SEASON OF 1910—THE BOUNDARY ALONG THE ST. JOHN AND ST. FRANCIS RIVERS

The survey of the remainder of the boundary along the St. John River in 1910 was simply a continuation of the procedure followed during the previous season.

The parties went into camp early in May, the Canadian surveyors near Edmundston, New Brunswick, and the United States party on the south side of the river near Frenchville, Me. The work progressed satisfactorily and the mouth of the St. Francis River was reached early in September.

Boundary survey camp at mouth of St. Francis River, 1910

At this point the character of the work had to be modified in order to meet the new conditions encountered in the narrow, heavily wooded valley of the St. Francis.   For the first 8 miles, the main scheme triangulation stations were established on the tops of the ridges bordering the river valley, and from these stations the boundary reference monuments along the stream were located by subsidiary figures, but when the head of Glazier Lake was reached, the main scheme was narrowed to the limits of the river banks.

The lengths of the triangulation lines were checked by the measurement of two base lines, one at Clair, New Brunswick, and one at St. Francis, Me.

Ferry between Canada and United States on St. John River

The leveling, as in the previous season, was done by the Canadian party and was based on the bench marks of the Canadian National Railway. From Caron Brook, New Brunswick, where this railway leaves the valley of the St. John, the levels were continued along the Temiscouata Railway to its terminus at Connors, New Brunswick, and from that point, along the highway to the foot of Glazier Lake. From there, the levels were carried to the head of the lake, and thence up the dead water to the foot of Cross Lake Rapids, by simultaneous readings of the water level at each end of the several lakes or ponds. These bodies of water are separated by falls of varying height, and around these the leveling was done with an instrument as usual.

The method of mapping the river, lakes, roads, and small clearings in the valley of the St. Francis was the same as had been used in the open country along the St. John, but the contouring in this densely wooded region could not efficiently be done by means of the stadia. Instead, the positions and elevations of conspicuous trees on the hillsides were determined by plane table intersections from stations along the shores of the river and lakes, and the contours were sketched to conform to these determinations. When the season's work terminated at the end of October at Cross Lake, the Canadians sent their outfit down river to be stored at St. Francis, Me., while the United States party moved to the head of Beau Lake by water and stored their equipment with the owner of a small farm there.

The personnel of the field parties for the season of 1910 was as follows:

For His Britannic Majesty: Chief of party, G. C. Rainboth, D. L. S.; assistants, G. L. Rainboth, D. L. S., I. R. Pounder, J. A. Pounder, B. Foley.

For the United States: Chief of party, J. B. Baylor; assistants, R. H. Blain, F. H. Brundage, L. J. Young, J. P. Locke.

SEASON OF 1911—THE BOUNDARY ALONG THE ST. FRANCIS RIVER AND THE SOUTHWEST LINE

By agreement between the chiefs of the two parties, the United States party took up the work at Cross Lake where it had been discontinued the previous season, and the Canadian party worked downstream toward that point from Lake Pohenagamook.

The triangulation consisted of small quadrilaterals carried along the banks of the river, expanding to larger figures only along Beau Lake. This part of the work proved to be extremely slow and laborious, particularly along the upper portion of the river, the banks of which for the most part were low and flat and covered with a dense growth of fir and alders which made it necessary to chop out almost the entire lengths of the lines.

This flat, wooded country also made it necessary to adopt special methods of mapping the topography. In the woods and underbrush the elevations were determined by hand levels and aneroid barometers and the contours located by compass and tape traverses, which were tied to the triangulation or to plane table and stadia traverses which were run along the roads, streams, and railroads.

The water levels which had been observed as far as Cross Lake during the previous season were continued to the head of Beau Lake and there checked by a

Boundary survey camp near Lake Pohenagamook, 1911

line of Y levels between that point and a bench mark of the Canadian National Railway at Blue River, Quebec. The vertical control for the work of the Canadian party along the upper part of the river was furnished by bench marks of the Canadian National Railway, which closely parallels the boundary.

The construction of the boundary reference monuments along the river was done by a Canadian subparty working in conjunction with the two main parties. These monuments were of concrete and of a design similar to those used on the St. John River.

The United States side of the St. Francis River is entirely uninhabited, and there are no roads other than lumber roads; while on the Canadian side there are scattered farms between the mouth of the river and the outlet of Glazier Lake, to which a fairly good road leads from Connors, New Brunswick. Farther up, the Canadian National Railway follows the river closely between Blue River and Lake Pohenagamook, along which section there is also a highway connecting scattered settlements. The principal settlement at Lake Pohenagamook is along the boundary west of the

Plane-table party on St. Francis River, 1911

lake and is mostly in Canada. Practically all of the settlers of the region are French Canadians.

While the survey of the St. Francis River was being made, a subparty of nine men under a foreman was engaged in opening that portion of the boundary known as the Southwest Line, which extends from the outlet of Lake Pohenagamook to the Northwest Branch of the St. John, at the village of Lac Frontiere, Quebec. This straight line was marked in 1845 by iron monuments set at intervals of a mile or less, so that the axmen did not require a surveyor to enable them to follow the line. The chief difficulty was the problem of transportation. Since no settlements approach this line until St. Pamphile is reached, 40 miles from Lake Pohenagamook, it was necessary for this vista-cutting party to handle all supplies on jumpers over the newly cut line. By the end of October the line was cleared for a distance of nearly 40 miles, reaching a point near St. Pamphile, where the subparty was paid off and disbanded.

In the meantime the surveys on the St. Francis were being completed, the United States and Canadian parties reaching a point of junction near the foot of Kelly Rapids, about 2 miles above the village of Blue River. The parties disbanded on November 10, and the camp equipment was stored at Lake Pohenagamook.

The personnel of the field parties for the season of 1911 was as follows:

For His Britannic Majesty: Chief of party, Thos. Fawcett, D. T. S.; assistants, G. L. Rainboth, D. L. S., I. R. Pounder, J. A. Pounder, B. Foley.

For the United States: Chief of party, J. B. Baylor; assistants, R. H. Blain, F. H. Brundage, J. P. Locke, J. Mercier.

SEASON OF 1912—THE SOUTHWEST LINE

The United States and Canadian parties went to the field between May 15 and May 20 and camped at Lake Pohenagamook. Unfavorable weather resulted in little being accomplished before the 1st of June.

The chiefs of parties, Messrs. J. B. Baylor and Thomas Fawcett, agreed that it was again advisable to allot to each party a portion of the line sufficiently large to provide continuous work for the season so as to avoid the necessity of either party making long moves to other parts of the line. The commissioners approved this recommendation, and accordingly, the United States party, after completing their share of the work near Lake Pohenagamook, moved by wagon and rail to St. Pamphile, Quebec, from which point they worked eastward, while the Canadians continued westward to meet them.

The Southwest Line was originally monumented in 1845, with cast-iron monuments projecting 3 feet above the ground, set at intervals of 1 mile or less. The line as surveyed in 1844 was found to be practically a straight line. The monuments, therefore, before being reset in concrete bases, were lined-in between intervisible monuments on the crests of distant hills. The distances between monuments were then determined by the two parties by invar tape measurements, and such angles as were found to exist between the courses of the line from ridge to ridge were carefully measured with theodolites.

Boundary survey camp on Southwest Line, 1912

The monumenting consisted of resetting the old cast-iron monuments in 3-foot concrete bases and in addition setting a few new intermediate monuments of concrete. This work, in 1912, was done by a subparty of the Canadian section of the commission, working in conjunction with the two main parties.

Lunch time, Southwest Line, 1912

Levels for controlling the topography and determining the elevations necessary for the invar taping were carried along the line from two bench marks of the Canadian National Railway, one near Lake Pohenagamook and the other near St. Pamphile. The level lines were checked on each other when the two parties joined work at the end of the season.

The topography of a strip of country extending one-half mile on each side of the boundary was mapped on a field scale of 1:10,000 by running traverses with prismatic compass, hand level, and stadia along streams and old logging roads and through lines cut at right angles to the boundary about 1,000 feet apart. This information was supplemented by sketches made in the field and transferred immediately to the field sheets. Plane tables were not used by either party during the season of 1912.

The control for the season's work was based upon the invar tape traverse of the boundary and a geodetic position and azimuth determined at monument 189 (Canadian primary triangulation station "Frontier") during the season by the Geodetic Survey of Canada.

A United States subparty continued the vista cutting westward along the line from the point reached the previous season near St. Pamphile.

The chief problem of each party in 1912 was that of transportation. Supplies were brought to the work on jumpers, which were dragged along old logging roads or over trails cut through the timber. The country, especially on the eastern part of the line, was rough and hilly, and in many places a team could handle loads of only a few hundred pounds. A particularly wet season made the trails and roads almost impassable for horses, and took out several of the log bridges which had been rudely constructed over some of the larger streams.

About the end of October, the United States and Canadian parties made a junction of the work at a point about 4 miles west of East Lake. The parties then withdrew from the field, the United States party returning to St. Pamphile, where they stored their camp equipment, and the Canadian party going back to East Lake, to the head of which they took their equipment by scows and thence by wagons to storage quarters at St. Philippe de Neri.

The personnel of the field parties for the season of 1912 was as follows:

For His Britannic Majesty: Chief of party, Thos. Fawcett, D. T. S.; assistants, G. L. Rainboth, D. L. S., I. R. Pounder, J. A. Pounder, B. Foley.

For the United States: Chief of party, J. B. Baylor; assistants, R. H. Blain, F. H. Brundage, J. P. Locke, J. Mercier.

SEASON OF 1913—THE SOUTHWEST AND SOUTH LINES AND THE BOUNDARY ALONG THE SOUTHWEST BRANCH OF THE ST. JOHN RIVER

The season of 1913 saw the completion of the two straight-line boundaries between northwestern Maine and the Province of Quebec, and a considerable part of the line along the Southwest Branch of the St. John River. To the United States party was assigned the portion of the boundary from the vicinity of St. Pamphile to the intersection of the South Line with the Southwest Branch of the

St. John River, while the Canadian party was to begin work upon a portion of the boundary which included the Southwest Branch of the St. John River and the Highlands as far west as Boundary Siding, the point where the boundary is crossed by the Canadian Pacific Railway.

The two parties went to the field about the middle of May, the United States party making their first camp near the Big Black River, a few miles west of St. Pamphile, Quebec, and the Canadian party, after shipping their outfit from St. Philippe de Neri, Quebec, where it had been stored for the winter, moving into camp on the Southwest Branch of the St. John River, about 10 miles from the village of St. Camille, Quebec.

The work of the United States party on the Southwest Line and the South Line was similar in most respects to that of the previous season, except that the topographic mapping was done by use of small plane tables, alidades, paraffined tapes, and aneroid barometers instead of compasses, hand levels, and stadia, which had been used in 1912. The tapes and aneroid barometers saved considerable line cutting, and the small plane tables enabled the topographers to sketch the contours in the field directly on the field maps. Elevations for this work were furnished by a line of levels which was continued westward along the boundary from bench marks established in 1912.

All the monumenting for both parties was done by a Canadian subparty.

The work of the Canadian party along the Southwest Branch of the St. John River was similar in most respects to the survey of the St. Francis River in 1910 and 1911. The river is narrow and winding, with flat banks covered with dense thickets of alders. Much line cutting was necessary in order to carry forward the small scheme of triangulation which determined the positions of the boundary

Boundary survey camp near Southwest Branch of the St. John River, 1913

reference monuments and furnished the control for a transit and stadia traverse of the river.

The triangulation was started from a base measured near the junction of the South Line and the Southwest Branch of the St. John River. As the work progressed, the triangulation was checked from time to time by two other bases and an azimuth determination. Later, in 1922, the survey of this portion of the boundary was tied to the primary triangulation stations of the Geodetic Survey of Canada and adjusted to the North American datum.

A line of levels was run to the boundary from a bench mark of the Quebec Central Railway, near St. Camille, Quebec. A bench mark was established at the junction of the South Line and the Southwest Branch of the St. John River, and the levels were carried westward along the river to determine the elevations of triangulation stations and boundary reference monuments and to furnish vertical control for the topography.

The mapping was done on a field scale of 1:5,000. The data for mapping the shore line of the river were obtained by transit and stadia traverses; the rest of the topography was taken with prismatic compasses, hand levels, and stadia, by traverses covering an area which extended about one-half mile on each side of the river. These compass and stadia lines were supplemented by notebook sketches, and the information was immediately transferred to field sheets on which the general map was compiled.

Transportation for both parties was a serious problem. The few bush roads which lead to the Southwest Branch of the St. John River were almost impassable, and the party on the river experienced considerable difficulty in bringing in supplies. The outfit was moved along the river with canoes and a flat-bottomed boat, built

Survey camp near Southwest Branch of the St. John River, 1913

by the party for that purpose at the first camp.   On the Southwest Line the United States party was able to use wagons along the boundary vista until English Lake was reached.   From this point to the Southwest Branch of the St. John River so many bogs and swamps were encountered that the wagons were abandoned in favor of mud sleds or jumpers.   Many of the swamps had to be corduroyed before the horses and sleds could pass.

Everywhere the country through which this part of the boundary runs is difficult of access.   From Lake Pohenagamook to a few miles west of East Lake the terrain is hilly to mountainous, and westward to Lac Frontiere it is slightly rolling, with intervening swamps.   From Lac Frontiere to the Southwest Branch of the St. John River it is almost flat and is interspersed throughout with small swamps and bogs.   Throughout the entire region the country is covered with a dense growth of timber and brush.

The only settlements along this stretch of the boundary are on the Canadian side.   They touch the line at the villages of Estcourt, St. Pamphile, and Lac Frontiere, Quebec.   Many lumbermen operating in northwestern Maine enter the country only through these points of access.   Since the surveys were made in 1912 and 1913, the Quebec Central Railway, the terminus of which was at that time Ste. Sabine, Quebec, has been extended to Lac Frontiere, near the intersection of the Southwest and South Lines, and this portion of the boundary can now be reached by rail.

The United States party completed their assignment, the remaining work on the Southwest and South Lines, about September 25 and made a junction with the triangulation, topography, and leveling done by the Canadian party earlier in the season at the Southwest Branch of the St. John River.   The party then moved their equipment by wagons and teams to Ste. Sabine, and thence by rail to Beecher Falls, Vt., anticipating work the following season along Halls Stream.   The Canadian party continued work along the Southwest Branch of the St. John River until about November 7, when cold weather brought operations to a close.   A log cache was built in the woods, the camp equipment was stored in it, and the party withdrew from the field.

The personnel of the field parties for the season of 1913 was as follows:

For His Britannic Majesty: Chief of party, Thos. Fawcett, D. T. S.; assistants, G. L. Rainboth, D. L. S., J. A. Pounder, D. L. S., D. F. Chisholm, B. Foley.

For the United States: Chief of party, J. B. Baylor; assistants, W. C. Guerin, R. H. Blain, F. H. Brundage, J. R. Sinclair, J. Mercier.

SEASON OF 1914—THE BOUNDARY ALONG THE SOUTHWEST BRANCH OF THE ST. JOHN RIVER, THE HIGHLANDS, AND HALLS STREAM

In 1914 the work of the two sections of the commission on the boundary from the St. Croix River to the St. Lawrence was in widely separated localities.   The Canadian party continued westward along the Southwest Branch of the St. John River, while the United States party started along Halls Stream.   Between the parties was the long stretch of the boundary along the Highlands, toward which each was working.

Canadian Party on the Southwest Branch of the St. John River and on the Highlands

About May 20, a small advance party of the Canadian surveyors made their way in to the cache built the preceding fall and moved the equipment by canoes and boat about 5 miles upstream to a point where a tote road from Ravignan, Quebec, crosses the river. Here the first camp of the season was pitched, and in the course of a few days the other members of the organization arrived with instruments and supplies and work was begun.

The control triangulation which was found so difficult to run through the flat forest-covered country along the river in 1913 was discontinued in 1914 in favor of a precise invar tape traverse. This furnished the control for the topographic mapping and a transit and stadia traverse of the river, and was the means of locating geodetically the boundary reference monuments.

This change in method proved to be most satisfactory. Long lines were cut through the woods in the general direction of the course of the river; and at intervisible points where the traverse line changed direction, signals were erected and the deflection angles carefully measured with the same degree of accuracy as in triangulation. The courses were measured with invar tapes under uniform tension, supported at the ends by well-braced posts bearing strips of metal on which the tape lengths were marked. The elevations of the tops of the posts were determined by running the lines of levels of the survey along the traverse line, using the tops of the posts as turning points. The azimuth of the traverse was checked during the season by two astronomic observations.

Boundary reference monuments of design similar to those used on the St. Francis River were set along the Southwest Branch of the St. John River. The

On the Southwest Branch of the St. John River, 1914

monuments on one side of the river were set at points on the precise traverse line, while those on the opposite side were located by offsets measured from the precise line with the same degree of accuracy of distance and direction as was used on the line itself. The monuments consist of concrete blocks, each about 10 inches square, and 1 foot high, set in a 3-foot concrete base extending 3 feet or more below the surface of the ground. Each reference monument was designated by a number stamped on the concrete surface of the base.

The levels were checked during the season by a line run out about 12 miles to a bench mark on the Quebec Central Railway at the village of Ste. Rose, Quebec.

The topographic mapping was done by the same methods employed by the Canadians in 1913. A series of traverses was made with hand levels and stadia, supplemented by notebook sketches, covering an area one-half mile wide on each side of the boundary.

The survey of the Southwest Branch of the St. John River was completed about the middle of September, and work was immediately begun by the Canadian party on the eastern end of the boundary along the Highlands, which joins the river portion of the boundary at Little St. John Lake.

The boundary along the Highlands had been originally marked by a vista through the timber and by cast-iron monuments of the type used elsewhere on the line. The monuments had been located by independent traverses run along the crest of the watershed by the British and United States officers, respectively, of the survey of 1844–45.

As this part of the Highlands boundary traverses a heavily wooded country of insufficient relief for the economical execution of triangulation, it was decided that the most feasible means of carrying forward the control would be by precise traverse. Accordingly, the precise line along the Southwest Branch of the St. John River was continued westward in long courses laid to fit as closely as possible the general direction of the boundary along the crest of the watershed, and the positions of the cast-iron monuments were determined on North American datum by offsets from the precise traverse line. The boundary line between monuments was then run with transit and tape, using the distances and deflection angles given in the notes of the original survey of 1845, corrected to make the boundary traverse fit the positions of the monuments as determined by the precise control.

The work of locating the monuments was kept well in advance of the other work, in order to furnish without delay the data for adjusting the old survey notes of the boundary line between monuments. It was frequently found that angles and distances in the old notes were inaccurate and that the line when run between a pair of monuments would not fall within the marks of the old vista or on the crest of the watershed, and that corrections were necessary. For this reason, all the line location was kept well ahead of the monumenting, vista cutting, and topographic mapping, in order that when discrepancies were encountered the time required for making the relocation would not delay the work.

The old cast-iron monuments were filled with concrete and reset in 3-foot concrete bases, and the turning points of the boundary between iron monuments were marked by placing at each point a monument consisting of a 3-inch bronze disk, set in a concrete-filled section of 4-inch vitrified sewer pipe, which was planted in the ground bell end down so that the top end bearing the disk was flush with the surface. Where the turning points came on outcropping ledges, the disks were set with cement in solid rock. On each disk was stamped the number of the turning point, numbering consecutively westward along the line from the nearest cast-iron monument on the east. On the concrete base of each cast-iron monument were stamped "Treaty 1842," the date the monument was reset, the number of the monument, and, on the appropriate sides, "U. S." and "Canada." This method of monumenting

Typical cast-iron monument as reset along the Highlands

was used throughout the Highlands in subsequent years by all parties.

The Canadian party discontinued work late in October and stored their camp equipment at St. Zacharie, Quebec. The personnel of the party was as follows: Chief of party, Thos. Fawcett, D. T. S.; assistants, G. L. Rainboth, D. L. S., J. A. Pounder, D. L. S., D. F. Chisholm, B. Foley.

UNITED STATES PARTY ON HALLS STREAM

The United States party began work northward along Halls Stream from a point near Beecher Falls, Vt., using methods for the survey in that locality similar to those used on the St. John and St. Francis Rivers. The positions of monuments and topographic control points were determined by triangulation, which was carried up the valley of the stream from a

Special type of cast-iron monument, No. 318, on Highlands, near source of Southwest Branch of St. John River

base line and azimuth measured near Beecher Falls. A topographic map was made, with plane table and stadia, on a scale of 1: 5,000 and contour interval of 20 feet. It included Halls Stream and most of the valley on each side. It showed all houses, highways, railroads, fence lines, and the boundary reference monuments. A line of levels for vertical control of the topography was run along the Maine Central Railroad from a railroad bench mark at Beecher Falls.

The boundary through Halls Stream was referenced by resetting, in concrete bases, the old cast-iron monuments placed in 1845, and by 2-inch bronze disks set in outcropping ledges or in concrete bases 12 inches square extending 3 feet or more below the surface of the ground. Four of the cast-iron monuments originally placed along the lower part of the stream had been lost by erosion of the banks and could not be found. Small reference monuments were set near the former sites to take the place of these lost monuments.

The valley of the lower part of Halls Stream is well settled. Throughout a distance of about 10 miles from Beecher Falls, as far as the village of Paquetteville, Quebec, most of the valley has been cleared of timber, and the survey for this distance was carried forward with comparatively little cutting. Beyond

Camp of United States party on Halls Stream, 1914

this point, the valley becomes quite narrow and is densely wooded, and the stream, which is narrow and crooked, is lined on either side with spruce, hardwood, and alders. There is a fairly good highway along the valley from Beecher Falls to Paquetteville, and the Maine Central Railroad runs along the west side of the stream and leaves the valley near the village of Malvina, Quebec.

Encountering bad weather, the party on Halls Stream withdrew from the field on November 12, and stored the camp outfit at Beecher Falls, Vt.

The personnel of the United States party for the season of 1914 was as follows: Chief of party, J. E. McGrath; assistants, R. H. Blain, F. H. Brundage, J. R. Sinclair.

SEASON OF 1915—THE HIGHLANDS BOUNDARY, THE BOUNDARY ALONG HALLS STREAM, AND MAJOR TRIANGULATION CONTROL OF THE SURVEYS OF THE ST. FRANCIS AND ST. JOHN RIVERS

In 1915 activities on the survey of the boundary from the source of the St. Croix River to the St. Lawrence River were considerably increased. There were four parties in the field: A United States party along the upper half of Halls Stream; a United States party on the Highlands boundary west of Boundary Siding at the

Canadian Pacific Railway crossing; a Canadian party on the extreme eastern end of the Highlands; and a Canadian triangulation party doing the major control necessary to establish the surveys of the St. Francis and St. John Rivers on North American datum. The aggregate number of engineers, surveyors, and hands employed in the four parties was about 85 men.

The Highlands boundary, which is the name usually given the portion of the line which follows the crest of the divide from the Southwest Branch of the St. John River to the head of Halls Stream, is the roughest and most inaccessible part of the international boundary east of the Rocky Mountains. Throughout most of its length of 175 miles, this part of the boundary follows a range of high hills or

Monument 402 at boundary crossing of Canadian Pacific Railway

mountains, densely wooded with fir, hardwood, and underbrush. In many places it has been burned over and is deeply covered with fallen timber. The whole section is a vast wilderness, which is seldom entered except by logging parties operating only in the winter time over snow roads. As these roads were practically impassable in the summer, it was necessary for the surveying parties to construct roads and trails for their own use over which their supplies and monumenting materials could be transported.

The work of surveying this part of the boundary was divided between the two sections of the commission as

United States survey camp at Boundary Siding, Quebec

follows: From the eastern end of the Highlands to monument 402, at the crossing of the Canadian Pacific Railway (74 miles) to the Canadian section, and from monument 402 to the head of Halls Stream (101 miles) to the United States section. In addition to the usual work of surveying, locating, mapping, and monumenting the line, each section of the commission was also to do the major control necessary to place its part of the work on North American datum by tying the survey to primary triangulation stations of the Geodetic Survey of Canada.

UNITED STATES PARTIES ON THE HIGHLANDS

A United States party began work on June 3 on the Highlands westward from Boundary Siding. The first camp was established on the Canadian Pacific Railway at the boundary line, with Lowelltown, Me., the nearest regular station on the Canadian Pacific Railway, about 3½ miles southeast of Boundary Siding, as the base of supplies. Around this point, on a radius of about 4 miles, the boundary line circles westward and southward, and was accessible by the railroad at Boundary Siding and by two abandoned logging roads leading westward into the hills. From this base, the survey of about 11 miles of the line west from Boundary Siding was completed before it was necessary to move the base of supplies to the other side of the mountain.

As soon as the officers of the party reached the field a general reconnaissance was made of the country, and it was decided that the most feasible means of transportation for moving the camp equipment, keeping the parties supplied, and transporting monumenting materials to the boundary line along the crest of the mountain range would be by pack trains. Accordingly, 20 horses were purchased and equipped with western pack outfits, most of which it was necessary to make at Lowelltown under the supervision of the officers of the party who had had experience in pack-train work in Alaska and in the Rocky Mountains, as no one could be found in the East who could supply the kind of outfit required, and there was not sufficient time to have it shipped from the West. By the time the party had completed the work from the camp at the railroad at Boundary Siding and were ready to move westward, the pack train was fully equipped and began taking supplies and equipment to the next camp, which was located at an old logging camp known as

Pack train leaving Lowelltown, Me., for Highlands boundary, 1915

Smyth's camp, near the boundary about one-half mile west of monument 404.

In addition to the matter of transportation, there were several other problems which had to be solved when the work began. One of these was the method of control which should be used for determining the positions of the old cast-iron monuments which had been set along the line in 1845. It was decided that the best

Canadian Pacific Railway along which triangulation base was measured near boundary crossing, 1916

method of doing this, as well as controlling the entire survey on North American datum, would be by triangulation, which at the start would be developed from a measured base along the railroad and later in the season connected to the primary triangulation stations "Megantic" and "Liniere" of the Geodetic Survey of Canada.

After the work was well started it was found advisable, in order to permit the men to live as near as possible to the localities of their work, to divide the organization into two camps. One of these was comyosed of the units doing triangulation and line location; and the other, the topographic mapping, vista cutting, monumenting, and leveling. This arrangement, however, was modified from time to time, depending upon the progress of the various parts of the work and the proximity of the camps to the several activities.

The topographic mapping of the strip of country along the boundary and of the comparatively large areas within the big loops of the line was done with plane table and stadia on a field scale of 1:20,000 and a contour interval of 20 feet. Each sheet was controlled by plotted geographic positions of the monuments and triangulation stations and the turning points of the transit and tape traverses

Camp of topographic party, near Moose Mountain, in Highlands, 1915

of the boundary between monuments. In those sections where the boundary forms loops some plane table triangulation was done, locations being made by three-point intersections. For filling in the topography between stadia traverses, each of which was tied to other traverses or started at the boundary line and was run around small areas about one-half mile square, aneroid barometers and paraffined string tapes were used, the topography at all times being sketched in the field directly on the plane table sheets.

Survey pack train on Spider River, Maine-Quebec Highlands, 1915

For the purpose of establishing a primary level bench mark on the base of each of the large boundary monuments, and for furnishing vertical control for the topographic mapping, a line of primary levels was run in closed circuits from a precise level bench mark which had been established by the Geodetic Survey of Canada on the Canadian Pacific Railway at Boundary Siding. At the end of the season this series of circuits of boundary levels was connected to a water gauge at the southern end of Lake Megantic, the elevation of which was determined from a Canadian precise level bench mark at the northern end of the lake at Megantic,

Fire lookout tower used as triangulation station, Snow Mountain, Me., 1915

Quebec, by a series of simultaneous readings of the water surface elevations at each end of the lake. The boundary was monumented as elsewhere on the Highlands.

By August 1, the work had reached the vicinity of monument 411, which is about 12 miles along the boundary from the railroad and about 9 miles by trail from Lowelltown. Beyond this point the line was more accessible from the other side of the mountain range. The base of supplies was therefore transferred from Lowelltown, Me., to Megantic, Quebec, from which point the supplies and materials were hauled 20 miles by teams and wagons to a supply camp at the terminus of the road in the Louise Valley. From here they were distributed by pack trains to the survey camps along the boundary.

When Louise Mountain was reached and the work was begun on the other large loop in the boundary around the Arnold River Valley, provisions, boundary marks, cement, and horse feed were transported from Megantic by boat on Lake Megantic to the wharf at Three Lakes, or to Woburn Wharf, near the south end of the lake, and from there taken by teams and wagons to the ends of roads leading toward the boundary, and thence by pack trains to the various camps and points on the boundary line.

On October 8, the topographic camp was moved to the site of an old "line house," where a fairly good road crosses the boundary, running east from the village of Woburn, Quebec, to a hunting and fishing camp on Arnold Pond. Since it was the most accessible point for beginning work on the boundary the following spring, it was selected as the general objective point for closing the operations of 1915. By October 20 the vicinity of this point was reached by the various units of the work as follows: The triangulation, monumenting, and vista cutting to monument 427; the leveling to monument 431; and the topographic mapping to monument 433.

There remained the tying in of the boundary triangulation to the Canadian primary stations "Liniere" and "Megantic." As it was desirable that this should be done before the close of the season's work, in order to furnish data for computation work in the office during the winter and to facilitate the start of the triangulation the following season, the topographic party discontinued work on October 27, so that the engineers and surveyors employed on that work would be available for assisting the triangulation party with the work of observing the long lines of the major triangulation necessary to connect the survey to triangulation stations of the Geodetic Survey of Canada.

On October 28 the topographic outfit was moved to Megantic and stored; and on the 29th, observers and light tenders went to stations "Megantic," "Liniere," "Snow," "Bald," "Kibby," and "Ste. Cecile." These stations are quite widely separated, the longest line being about 49 miles. They were all on mountain tops, and clear nights were necessary for making the observations. In the late fall, such nights seldom occur in that country, and the five cloudless ones necessary to complete the observations were scattered over a period of 19 days, during which time the men on the mountains experienced everything from fog and rain to heavy snows and zero weather. The low temperature caused the gas producers of the acetylene lights to freeze, and it was with great difficulty that the lamps were kept burning during the periods of observation.

Until the purpose of this night work was understood by the people living near some of the stations, the lights on the mountain tops excited much suspicion, which almost resulted in raids upon the parties. The Great War was on at that time, and it was suspected that the lights were part of a German spy system in operation. As soon as the facts became known, however, this uneasiness ceased and the work was finished without any unfortunate occurrences.

The night work was completed on November 18, and the observers and light tenders returned to Megantic.

In the meantime, the line location, vista cutting, and monumenting party had broken camp, the last load arriving at Megantic at 11.30 p. m. on November 4 in a blinding snowstorm. The outfit was dried and stored at Megantic and the horses shipped to Cookshire, Quebec, to be cared for during the winter.

The work of the United States parties on the Highlands was inspected during the season by the commissioners, Dr. W. F. King, for His Britannic Majesty, and Mr. E. C. Barnard, for the United States. This inspection trip was made during the second week in September, the commissioners visiting the camps of the triangulation and topographic parties and inspecting the boundary in the vicinity of Pisgah Mountain at the southern end of the Louise Valley. Also, on September 26 and 27, the

Boundary vista on Moose Mountain, Maine-Quebec Highlands, 1915

work was visited by Mr. J. E. McGrath, who was in charge of the United States party operating that year on Halls Stream.

The personnel of the United States organization on the Highlands boundary in 1915 was as follows: Engineer in charge of the work, James H. Van Wagenen; chiefs of parties, Jesse Hill, H. C. O. Clarke; assistants, E. V. Perkinson, Lee Morrison, R. K. Lynt, W. F. Lehfelt, George Brown, J. A. Stewart, Alex McDiarmid, J. E. Bump.

CANADIAN PARTIES ON THE HIGHLANDS

The Canadian section of the commission continued work in 1915 on the eastern end of the Highlands, and did the major control necessary to establish the surveys of the St. Francis and St. John Rivers on North American datum. The work of these two parties was in charge of Mr. Thomas Fawcett, D. T. S.

About the middle of May a small advance party went into the woods from St. Zacharie, Quebec, and cut a road through the woods to Metgermette Lake from the nearest farm, a distance of about 3 miles. A week later the entire party was in camp at the lake, ready for the season's work.

The methods of doing the work were similar in every way to those used by this party the previous season.

The precise traverse which had been so satisfactory in 1914 was again adopted as the best means of locating the monuments and furnishing the control for the topographic mapping. It was found that this method of control was more economical than triangulation because this part of the Highlands boundary is heavily timbered and not of sufficient relief to admit of triangulation control that would locate all the monuments without considerable tower building and much line cutting.

In locating the line between monuments, it was found, as in 1914, that there were many inaccuracies in the old survey notes which, after being adjusted to fit the positions of the monuments as determined by the precise traverse, were used to determine the positions of the intermediate boundary turning points. Occasionally the line as laid down from the old notes would depart from the crest of the ridge or, at times, fall entirely out of the old vista, which could still be traced by an experienced woodsman. In such cases, the old notes were discarded and the crest of the ridge and the line of the old cuttings were taken as conclusive evidence of the correct location of the boundary. By careful inspection, it was obvious in most of these cases of disagreement that the old notes were usually in error by an even number of degrees at some angle point or an even number of chains in distance. When such points of error could be identified and corrected, it was usually found that the notes fitted very closely to the line relocated in accordance with the old vista or the crest of the watershed.

The same scheme of monumenting was followed that had been used the year before on the Highlands.

As usual, a vista was cut along the boundary line. Levels were run in closed circuits along the precise traverse line and the boundary, and a topographic map was made of the strip of territory extending one-half mile on each side of the boundary line. The topography was taken by compass and stadia traverses supplemented by notebook sketches, which were transferred immediately to the field sheets. During the season three azimuths were observed to check directions on the precise traverse lines.

The first camp was on Metgermette Lake, the second near a small lake called Frost Pond, and the third at the outlet of Portage Lake. The two latter camps were supplied by teams and wagons operated over roads leading in from Armstrong, Quebec. Transportation of monumenting material along the boundary was also by teams and wagons over fairly passable roads cut along the boundary vista by the surveying party.

Camp of Canadian party on Portage Lake, 1915

About the middle of September, while the party was camped at Portage Lake, the work was inspected by the commissioners, Mr. E. C. Barnard and Dr. W. F. King. A short time later the party was also visited by Mr. J. E. McGrath and Mr. James H. Van Wagenen, engineers in charge, respectively, of United States parties on Halls Stream and on the Highlands south of Megantic, Quebec, for the purpose of inspecting the work and consulting with Mr. Fawcett.

The party on the eastern end of the Highlands discontinued work about the end of October and stored the camp equipment at a summer camp on Portage Lake. As soon as the party was disbanded, some of the personnel went to Van Buren, Me., and joined the triangulation party engaged on the major control of the surveys of the St. Francis and St. John Rivers.

The personnel of the Canadian party engaged on the survey of the Highlands during the season was as follows: Chief of party, Thos. Fawcett, D. T. S.; assistants, G. L. Rainboth, D. L. S., J. A. Pounder, D. L. S., D. F. Chisholm, B. Foley.

Canadian Triangulation Party on the St. Francis and St. John Rivers

A Canadian party began work in May, 1915, on a scheme of triangulation to furnish the major control of the surveys of the St. Francis and St. John Rivers and of the North Line. It was planned that this scheme should be connected to various stations of the minor triangulation schemes along those rivers and to frequent monuments along the North Line, and that it was to extend from the primary stations "Frontier" and "Parke" (the latter a Laplace station), of the Geodetic Survey of Canada, near the outlet of Lake Pohenagamook, to precise triangulation stations of the United States Coast and Geodetic Survey in the vicinity of the source of the St. Croix River. When completed, this work would tie the positions of boundary monuments and turning points, and the topographic surveys of the boundary, to the North American datum.

The triangulation stations were located principally on ridges and isolated hills, which are characteristic features of the topography of that part of the country. In most cases these high points were heavily timbered, and considerable clearing and some tower building were required to obtain the necessary lines of sight. At intervals of about 6 miles along the boundary, monuments or other control points of the survey made in 1909 and 1910 were connected to the major triangulation, usually by means of a single closed triangle. Occasionally such subsidiary work had to be carried through additional figures in order to reach the desired point.

The triangulation was strengthened by connecting it to an astronomical longitude station of the Geodetic Survey of Canada at Edmundston, New Brunswick, where an azimuth was observed, making this point a Laplace station, and by a $3\frac{1}{2}$-mile base which was measured in November along the St. John River a few miles above Van Buren, Me. The base line and the scheme of triangulation were connected at four different points to precise level bench marks of the Geodetic Survey of Canada. The triangulation party was assisted late in the season in measuring the base and running levels by members of the Canadian Highlands party who joined the triangulation party at the close of the season's work on the Highlands.

In September the work of the triangulation party was inspected by the commissioners.

The entire party withdrew from the field about the middle of November.

The personnel of the Canadian party engaged on the control triangulation along the St. Francis and St. John Rivers during the season of 1915 was as follows: Engineer in charge of the work, Thos. Fawcett, D. T. S.; chief of party, J. L. Rannie, D. T. S.; assistant, V. R. Davies.

UNITED STATES PARTY ON HALLS STREAM

Early in June, 1915, the United States party which had begun the survey of the boundary along Halls Stream the previous year resumed operations on the upper part of the stream, establishing the first camp of the season at Malvina, Quebec.

The work of this party was similar in most respects to that done the previous season on the lower part of the stream, except that when the dense timber and

Tree used as signal and instrument stand, triangulation on St. Francis River

brush were encountered in the upper part of the valley a considerable part of the topography was taken by using a plane table with paraffined string tapes and aneroid barometers, in order to avoid as much line cutting as possible. The topography of the strip of country immediately adjacent to the stream was surveyed very accurately, however, with plane table, alidade, and stadia. It was only on the more distant hillsides that the less accurate methods were used. The topographic map was made on a field scale of 1:5,000 with contour interval of 20 feet.

The level line which had been started the previous season at Beecher Falls, Vt., was continued up the valley and connected to a precise level bench mark of the Geodetic Survey of Canada on the Maine Central Railroad, at Malvina. From this point, a line of levels was run to the head of the stream and continued some distance along the western end of the Highlands boundary. When work was undertaken the following year, this line of levels, as well as the general system of levels of the survey along the Highlands, was closed on a Canadian precise bench mark on the Maine Central Railroad at St. Malo, Quebec.

During the first part of the season work was considerably retarded by dense smoke from forest fires and by the large amount of line cutting which had to be done in order to extend the small scheme of triangulation along the narrow wooded valley of the upper part of the stream.

Camp supplies were brought to Malvina station by rail. The only other form of transportation was teams and wagons, which were hired locally when camp was moved.

On September 11 the commissioners, Dr. W. F. King and Mr. E. C. Barnard, visited the camp and inspected the boundary and the work near the head of Halls Stream. The commissioners were accompanied on this inspection trip by the chief of party, Mr. J. E. Mc-Grath, and by Mr. James H. Van Wagenen, who was in charge of the United States parties working on the Highlands near Megantic, Quebec.

By November 1 the survey of Halls Stream had been completed, and, in addition, considerable topography and leveling had been done on the western end of the Highlands.

Mountain Lake, New Hampshire, looking east from monument 477

The party disbanded during the first week in November, and the outfit was taken to Beecher Falls, where it was stored for the winter.

The personnel of the party on Halls Stream was as follows: Chief of party, J. E. McGrath; assistants, R. H. Blain, F. H. Brundage, J. R. Sinclair, Jesse Young.

SEASON OF 1916—THE HIGHLANDS BOUNDARY AND THE COMPLETION OF THE MAJOR CONTROL OF THE ST. JOHN RIVER AND THE NORTH LINE

The season of 1916 marked the completion of the western portion of the Highlands boundary, which had been assigned to the United States section of the commission, and the major control of the boundary from Lake Pohenagamook to the source of the St. Croix River, which had been undertaken the previous season by the Canadian section. Also, on the eastern Highlands the Canadian party completed the work westward to the vicinity of the "line house" at the boundary crossing of the Kennebec Road.

United States Parties on the Highlands

The United States section of the commission began field work on the Highlands about May 15. The organization consisted of four parties under the direction of the engineer to the United States section of the commission. Two of these parties, one a line-locating, topographic, vista-cutting, monumenting, and leveling party, and the other a reconnaissance and triangulation party, conducted operations westward along the line from the vicinity of the village of Woburn, Quebec, the place where work was discontinued by these parties the previous season. Similarly, the other two units, a line-locating, topographic, vista-cutting, monumenting, and leveling party, and a triangulation and reconnaissance party, began at the head of Halls Stream and worked eastward. The four parties consisted, in all, of about 100 men. The size of each party was dependent upon the amount of work necessary in 1916 to complete, during that season, the portion of the Highlands boundary assigned to United States surveyors.

Triangulation party moving camp in Arnold River Valley, Maine-Quebec Highlands, 1916

The major triangulation, which had been tied to the Canadian primary stations "Liniere" and "Megantic" late in the fall of 1915, was continued westward from the line "Snow-Monument 425" through a series of quadrilaterals with lines of an average length of about 8 miles. This was joined at the end of the season by a similar scheme developed from a measured base and observed eastward from the head of Halls Stream. Subsidiary to this main scheme of control, there were also observed about 150 small figures to determine the positions of all the boundary monuments along the line from monument 426 to monument 505. During the last few weeks of the season, after a junction had been made by the two triangulation parties, the extreme western end of the triangulation, near the head of Halls Stream, was tied to the Canadian primary station "Hereford" and an azimuth obtained from the Canadian primary line "Hereford-Megantic." With "Hereford" as a common point, the major control was then extended down Halls Stream to Beecher Falls, Vt. This was done by three large figures, which at frequent intervals were tied to the small scheme which had been extended along Halls Stream in 1914 and 1915. This, together with the work of 1915, completed all the major triangulation necessary to place the survey of the boundary from the Canadian Pacific Railway crossing of the Highlands to the mouth of Halls Stream on the North American datum.

In addition to carrying forward the major scheme of control, it was necessary to obtain many subsidiary lines of sight from each station to locate boundary monuments. On the more mountainous part of the Highlands this was done by clearing the summits on which the stations were located. On the western portion, however, where the relief is not so great and the stations had to be located on low, flat-topped hills, 12 observing towers were built, of sufficient height (25 to 70 feet) to enable the triangulators to see over the surrounding timber. In all cases these towers were built of native timber cut near the station by the reconnaissance party.

United States party which worked eastward from head of Halls Stream, Highlands boundary, 1916

The boundary traverse was run with transit and tape. Along the steeper parts of the line the tape was held parallel to the slope and vertical angles were read at the end of each tape length and the distances were later reduced to the horizontal. In general, the vertical angle method of measuring along slopes was found to be more accurate than measuring directly the horizontal distance by "breaking tape."

Following the line location, a vista was cut through the timber, this line of cutting being of sufficient width to give a clear 10-foot sky line on each side of the boundary.

In some places considerable difficulty was experienced in locating the boundary from the old notes. A case of this kind occurred in locating the line from monument 430 to monument 431, which crosses the low divide in the vicinity of the site of the old line house east of Woburn, near Arnold Pond.

The dividing ridge at this point is not sharp and well defined; and in locating the line, dependence was placed at first entirely upon the angles and distances given in the old notes. It was not until the line had been run out and marked and the vista cut that the attention of the chief of party was called by an expert woodsman to the fact that by careful inspection of the timber it could be seen that the new line and vista did not follow the old line of cuttings. By plotting the old notes of the line between these monuments and comparing them with the course of the old cuttings, it appeared that there was an error of 10° in one of the angles. When modified to this extent and the line rerun, it fitted very closely to the traces of the old vista, which was further identified by a careful inspection of the age of the timber and by old stumps, evidences of which could be detected when pointed out by an experienced woodsman.

In this particular case the discrepancy of location was inspected and the relocation approved by Mr. E. C. Barnard, United States commissioner. and Mr. J. D. Craig, representing the Canadian Government, and it was agreed that in all other places where similar discrepancies had occurred the line should be relocated and the vista recut.

The boundary was monumented as elsewhere on the Highlands.

Some interesting facts were developed in running out and monumenting the line. For instance, monument 440 was not known to exist; there was no record of it in the old notes; it was found by accident by the

Triangulation station on Gosford Mountain, Maine-Quebec Highlands

chief of one of the triangulation parties while on his way along the boundary ridge to look for monument 441. Also two of the monuments, Nos. 483 and 484 in the old United States notes, were found to have been set only 18 inches apart. They marked an astronomic station of the survey of 1845. As this "double monument" was regarded as a landmark in that locality, the two monuments were reset in a single concrete base and numbered as one monument, No. 484. Monuments 481 and 482 were originally wooden posts. The rotted remains of these were found, with rocks piled around them, and they were replaced by two new cast-iron monuments of design similar to the other monuments. Monument 505 is a large iron monument cast in three sections. It marks the boundary near the head of Halls Stream and is one of several similar large monuments originally used to mark important

United States Commissioner E. C. Barnard (right) and J. D. Craig, D. L. S., at monument 492

boundary points from the source of the St. Croix River to the St. Lawrence River.

The topography of the country inside the loop around the Arnold River Valley (sheet No. 17 of the boundary maps) and, in every case, of the country within a distance of at least one-half mile on each side of the boundary was mapped with plane table, alidade, and stadia, supplemented by string tapes and aneroid barometers. In general, the method of taking the topography was the same as that adopted by the United States parties on the survey of the Highlands in 1915. The field scale of the map was 1:20,000 and the contour interval 20 feet.

The vertical control for the topography was furnished by two lines of levels, one run westward along the boundary from a bench mark established at the close of the season's work in 1915 at monument 431, and the other eastward from a Canadian precise

The "double monument" before it was reset, Highlands boundary, near source of Connecticut River

level bench mark (555–B) on the Maine Central Railroad, near St. Malo, Quebec.

During the first part of the season, the parties on the eastern end of the work were supplied, as in 1915, from Megantic, Quebec. Mess supplies, horse feed, and monumenting materials were transported by steamer on Lake Megantic to Woburn

The "double monument" after it was set

Third Lake, source of Connecticut River, looking south from the "double monument"

Wharf and thence by teams to logging camps in the Arnold River Valley. From these caches the supplies and materials were taken to the various camps and to the boundary line by pack trains operating over trails cut through the timber and brush by the surveying parties.

On the western end of the work, during the first few weeks, materials and supplies for the parties were shipped by rail to Malvina, Quebec, and from there taken to the camps by teams and wagons, and the materials were then distributed along the boundary by pack trains. After the work had progressed eastward about 7 miles, the camps became more accessible by way of a fairly good road from Sawyerville, Quebec, which place was thereafter used as the base of supplies until monument 489 was reached.

Pack-train supply base, Arnold River Valley, 1916

On August 22, a central base of supplies for all the parties was established on the Canadian Pacific Railway at Scotstown, Quebec. By this time the two parties which had started westward from Woburn, Quebec, had completed the loop in the boundary around the Arnold River Valley and were within reach of a good highway running through the settled valley south of Megantic Mountain. The parties on the west were also within reach of the

Triangulation camp on Halls Stream, 1916

Tower at triangulation station "Bien" near monument 489 on the Highlands

same road a few miles west of the village of Chartierville, Quebec. This made it possible to haul supplies by teams and wagons from Scotstown to La Patrie, Quebec, and thence in either direction directly to the several boundary camps. Pack trains operating in the mountains distributed the monumenting materials from the camps to points along the boundary.

Throughout the season the work required the continuous use of 6 teams and wagons and about 35 pack animals. Twenty-three of the animals were owned by the Government, and the others were hired for the season at settlements on the Canadian side of the boundary. In order that the pack-train transportation might be handled as efficiently as possible, two western packers were hired who had had considerable experience on the survey of the boundary along the one hundred and forty-first meridian between Alaska and Canada, with the result that the field transportation was considerably improved over that of 1915.

The most difficult part of the transportation was the delivery of monumenting materials to the boundary line.

A considerable portion of the line follows a high, sharp ridge, the crest of which in many places could not be reached by pack animals, and in such cases the materials, consisting of sand, cement, vitrified pipe, and water, had to be packed for considerable distances on men's backs.

During the season the parties camped at 25 different places, the outfits, consisting of light equipment, being moved frequently with the object of keeping the men close to their jobs, so as to avoid, as much as possible, long trips each day to and from work.

As soon as the two triangulation parties effected a junction near monument 478, they moved to Halls Stream and, during the first two weeks of October, completed the major control triangulation from the head of Halls Stream to Beecher Falls, Vt., and the entire scheme was tied, in position and azimuth, to the Canadian primary line " Hereford-Megantic."

By October 10, the other parties, working east and west, had met at monument 475, which is located at the point where the international boundary is intersected by the Maine-New Hampshire boundary, and a line-locating party, which had been sent to the head of Halls Stream, had completed a transit and tape traverse of the boundary along the upper end of the stream as far south as reference monument 508. This traverse had been found necessary in order to define accurately the course of the boundary along the narrow upper portion of the stream, which is there only a small intermittent brook, almost hidden in dense growths of alder brush.

The parties, which by this time had been greatly reduced in numbers, were disbanded, and the outfits and instruments were moved to Scotstown, Quebec, where they were inventoried and stored for the winter. A wagon and 11 horses were sold at public auction, and the remaining 12 horses were taken to Beecher Falls to be wintered.

An inspection of the work of the four parties was made during the last week of July by Mr. E. C. Barnard, United States boundary commissioner, and Mr. J. D. Craig, D. L. S., representing the Canadian Government.

The personnel of the United States organization on the Highlands boundary in 1916 was as follows: Engineer in charge of the work, James H. Van Wagenen; chiefs of parties, H. C. O. Clarke, W. C. Guerin, Jesse Hill, F. H. Brundage; assistants, Nelson W. Smith, E. V. Perkinson, Lee Morrison, M. E. Lutz, E. C. Guerin, W. F. Lehfelt, C. E. Carl, George Brown, Walter McCrea, J. A. Buchanan, R. C. Snyder, S. O. White, J. A. Stewart, J. E. Bump, Jesse Young, Joseph Mercier, Hollis Young.

CANADIAN PARTIES ON THE HIGHLANDS

The two Canadian parties which were engaged on the survey of the eastern end of the Highlands boundary and on the major control of the surveys of the St. John and St. Francis Rivers in 1915 continued these same activities in 1916.

Operations of the Highlands party were begun near Portage Lake about May 20. By methods similar in every respect to those employed by that party in 1915, the survey was carried westward into the more mountainous portion of the line, which begins a few miles east of the crossing of the Kennebec Road.

In many ways this change in the character of the country increased the difficulties of the work, but, on the other hand, it reduced considerably the amount of cutting necessary on the precise traverse line, as the lines of sight passed above much of the timber between the hills on which the ends of the courses were located.

The first camp of the season was on Portage Lake and was easily accessible by a good road from Armstrong, Quebec, to the outlet of the lake. The work about the lake was much facilitated by the use of canoes and boats, which enabled the men to work longer from this camp than would have been possible had it been necessary to walk the entire distance each day.

After moving camp from Portage Lake, the transportation problem was more difficult. The supplies and materials were hauled from Armstrong, Quebec, to the foot of the lake, and were then transported by canoes and boats to the head of the lake, from which point they were hauled by horses and jumpers over a road which the surveyors cut along the boundary to the next camp. As the work progressed, this haul by way of Portage Lake became longer and more difficult, but attempts to find a shorter route were unsuccessful, as a more direct road would necessarily have led through swamps which were impassable throughout practically the entire season on account of the heavy and frequent rains. The supply route by way of Portage Lake had to be used until the end of August, when a road was opened along the boundary eastward from the Kennebec Road to camp. The total amount of road cut during the season was about 15 miles.

The season was notable for unfavorable weather. Records kept in camp show that there were 45 days of rain during the 150 days the party was in the field.

Notwithstanding the difficult transportation and the unfavorable weather, the party made good progress, and by the end of the season the work had progressed to the vicinity of the "line house" at the Kennebec Road.

The party discontinued work about the middle of October and came out by the Kennebec Road, storing the equipment at Armstrong, Quebec.

The personnel of the field party operating in the Highlands in 1916 was as follows: Chief of party, Thos. Fawcett, D. T. S.; assistants, G. L. Rainboth, D. L. S., C. R. Westland, D. L. S., L. C. Nesham, B. Foley.

CANADIAN TRIANGULATION PARTY ON THE ST. JOHN RIVER AND NORTH LINE

While the above described activities were under way on the Highlands boundary, the Canadian triangulation party, which, by the end of the previous season, had completed the major control of the work along the St. Francis and most of the St. John River, began work about the middle of May from a camp near Van Buren, Me., and continued southward along the North Line to the source of the St. Croix.

When the vicinity of the source of the St. Croix River was reached, the scheme of control was tied to precise triangulation stations "Spring Hill," "Pole Hill," and "Kennedy," of the United States Coast and Geodetic Survey.

In addition to the triangulation, the party determined azimuths of the boundary and geographic positions of the monuments at intervals of about 5 miles along the North Line, and also made connections with two precise level bench marks.

The personnel of the Canadian triangulation party during the season of 1916 was as follows: Engineer in charge of the work, Thos. Fawcett, D. T. S.; chief of party, J. L. Rannie, D. T. S.; assistant, James Bowie.

SEASON OF 1917—THE BOUNDARY ALONG THE HIGHLANDS, THE VERMONT-QUEBEC BOUNDARY, THE NEW YORK-QUEBEC BOUNDARY, AND THE BOUNDARY ALONG THE ST. JOHN RIVER

In 1917, the work of the two sections of the commission on the line between the source of the St. Croix River and the St. Lawrence River was carried on by five parties, located as follows: On the boundary along the Highlands, a Canadian party continued westward on the part of that line which had been assigned to their section of the commission; and a small United States party put the finishing touches on the portion of the Highlands which had been allotted to them. On the line from Beecher Falls to the St. Lawrence River, a Canadian party did the triangulation for major control from Halls Stream to the Richelieu River, and tied the survey of the New York-Quebec line to primary triangulation stations of the Geodetic Survey of Canada. At the same time, a United States party mapped the topography and ran the levels of the New York-Quebec line. On the St. John River, a United States party set additional reference monuments and located them by triangulation.

CANADIAN PARTY ON THE HIGHLANDS

The Canadian party resumed operations on the Highlands about the middle of May, at a point near the crossing of the Kennebec Road, establishing their first camp at the "line house."

The methods of surveying were the same as used by the Canadians in 1914, 1915, and 1916, namely, horizontal control by invar tape traverse; vertical control by spirit levels run along the traverse line; and topography of the area one-half mile wide on each side of the line, taken with prismatic compass, hand level, and stadia. The old cast-iron monuments were reset in concrete bases, and a vista was opened along the boundary.

When camp was moved into the mountains west of the Kennebec Road, the only supply route for some distance was a road cut through the woods by the surveyors, which was extended as the work progressed. Everything taken over this

"Line house" at boundary crossing of Kennebec Road, 1917

road had to be hauled on jumpers. When Lake Emily was reached, a shorter and more passable supply route was furnished by an old road leading north from the boundary line about 10 miles to the farm of a Canadian settler, which was on a fairly good road about 3 miles south of the main highway between the villages of St. Gedeon and St. Theophile. Transportation of supplies and monumenting materials through the woods required the continuous use of two teams.

The work was retarded somewhat by the frequent rains which occurred in the mountains, records kept in camp showing that, on an average, it rained one day out of three throughout the season.

Another problem with which the party had to contend was that of securing labor, for, on account of the war, men were scarce and wages were high, and it was difficult to find good men who were willing to work on the boundary under the necessarily uncomfortable conditions that prevailed in the survey camps.

On September 20 and 21, the work of the Canadian party on the Highlands was inspected by Mr. James H. Van Wagenen, engineer to the United States section of the commission.

The party disbanded at the end of October and part of the outfit was cached at Lake Emily, the rest being taken out by way of Boutin's farm to Armstrong, where it was stored for the winter.

The organization of this party on the Highlands in 1917 was as follows: Chief of party, Thos. Fawcett, D. T. S.; assistants, G. L. Rainboth, D. L. S., C. R. Westland, D. L. S., J. N. Ingersoll, W. Smith, B. Foley.

UNITED STATES PARTY ON THE HIGHLANDS

When field operations of the United States parties engaged in surveying the Highlands were discontinued in October, 1916, there still remained uncompleted the setting of seven monuments (Nos. 403 to 409, inclusive), and the relocation and vista cutting on certain portions of the boundary where careful inspection showed that the first location made was erroneous and fell outside of the original vista. A small United States party undertook this unfinished work in 1917, going in from Lowelltown, Me., on May 15 with six pack animals and a light camp outfit.

The seven monuments referred to, west of the Canadian Pacific Railway, which had not been set in 1915, were set in concrete bases in the usual manner. A new cast-iron monument was dragged in to replace monument 403, which was the only monument not found intact in 1915 and 1916. The concrete bases of monuments 410 to 423, which had been left uncompleted in 1915, were finished and stamped.

Monument 418, set by United States monumenting party, 1917

The line was relocated for short distances in several places to make it conform more closely to the ridge or to the old vista, and in such places the bronze disk monuments were moved, a new vista opened, and the new angles and distances measured.

After completing the work as far as monument 423, the camp was moved to Woburn, Quebec, and thence to Arnold Bog, where a short time was spent tying in the boundary to the triangulation stations and checking deflection angles.

After a final inspection had been made of the line by Mr. H. C. O. Clarke to make certain that the boundary as relocated was everywhere within the old vista, the party withdrew from the woods on July 17. The horses were sold at auction the next day, and the men joined the United States parties which had begun work early in 1917 on Grand and Spednik Lakes and the St. Croix River.

The personnel of the United States party on the Highlands from May to July was as follows: Engineer in charge, James H. Van Wagenen; chief of party, Guy A. Perry; assistant, J. A. Stewart.

CANADIAN TRIANGULATION PARTY, HALLS STREAM TO THE ST. LAWRENCE

A Canadian party commenced operations near Beecher Falls, Vt., in the latter part of May, 1917. They began the triangulation from the line "Hereford-Beecher Tablet," which had been established by the party of the United States section of the commission working on Halls Stream in 1916, and the scheme was expanded westward along the boundary, locating monuments at intervals of about 3 or 4 miles. It was connected with the stations "Owl's Head" and "St. Armand," of the Canadian Geodetic Survey, with certain township and lot corners, and with four precise level bench marks.

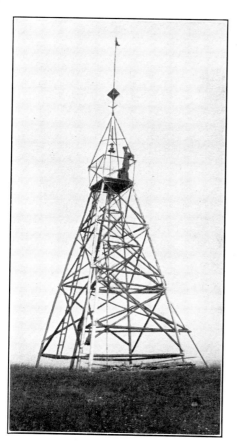

Transportation was comparatively simple, as there were good roads throughout the area covered and motor transportation was available for moving camp and going to and from the triangulation stations. A Ford truck belonging to the party was kept in constant use supplying camp and moving the observers. Occasionally, when required, teams and wagons and another automobile were hired locally. This was the first Canadian boundary party that had used motor transport throughout an entire season, and its use resulted in such a considerable saving of time that the party was able to complete in 1917 work which would have required part of a second season if the truck had not been used.

Observing tower, triangulation, Vermont-Quebec line

By the middle of October the work had progressed as far as Lake Champlain, beyond which point the triangulation was extended only far enough to make a connection with the eastern end of the Quebec-New York line. A few weeks were then spent in the neighborhood of the Canadian Geodetic Survey stations "Covey Hill" and "Huntingdon," where several monuments were tied to each of these stations by a combination of triangulation and traverse. The work was completed and the party withdrew from the field on November 10.

The personnel of this party was as follows: Chief of party, J. D. Craig, D. L. S.; assistants, F. Lambert, D. L. S., G. T. Prinsep, D. L. S., J. Sheppard, Jas. Bowie, T. P. Reilly.

United States Parties, New York-Quebec Line

When the New York-Quebec portion of the international boundary was surveyed in 1902, jointly by the Dominion Government and the State of New York, a transit and tape traverse was run to locate the line, and the cast-iron monuments were replaced by granite posts set in concrete bases, but no topographic map was made. The work, therefore, of mapping the line and the topography of the country adjacent thereto, from the Richelieu River to the St. Lawrence River, a distance of about 65 miles, was assigned to a small United States party in 1917.

In 1916 a joint inspection had been made of this part of the boundary by the engineers to the two sections of the commission to ascertain the number of monuments which had deteriorated since 1902 and the amount of vista cutting which would be necessary to reopen the line. The result of this inspection was that in 1917 a small party in charge of an engineer from the New York State engineer and surveyor's office worked in conjunction with the topographic party and reset a number of monuments which had been heaved by frost, replaced one which had been broken, set an additional monument to mark an important road crossing, and opened several miles of vista where it was found necessary.

The parties began operations at Lake Champlain on May 16. The topographic party lived in tents and boarded at hotels or farmhouses in the vicinity of their work, the necessary transportation for moving camp and going to and from work being hired locally as needed.

The topography was mapped on a field scale of 1:20,000, contour interval 20 feet, using plane table and stadia. The horizontal control was furnished by the transit and tape traverse run in 1902, and was later adjusted to take care of such corrections as were found necessary after the line had been tied to primary stations of the Geodetic Survey of Canada, by the Canadian triangulation party in 1917.

In order to furnish vertical control for the topography and to establish a series of permanent bench marks at the boundary monuments, a line of primary levels was run in closed circuits along the boundary from a United States Coast and Geodetic Survey precise level bench mark at Rouses Point, N. Y., to the Chateaugay River, where the line was tied to a bench mark of the United States Geological Survey. A single line of levels was then continued westward and tied to United States Geological Survey bench marks at Trout River, N. Y., and at Fort Covington, N. Y., and to a bench mark of the Board of Engineers on Deep Waterways at Hogansburg, N. Y. The party established 41 permanent bench marks, marked with bronze disks set in the concrete bases of the monuments.

Monument repair work, New York-Quebec line, 1917.   Resetting monument 736 which had been heaved by frost

The work of the parties was inspected by the United States boundary commissioner late in June, while the topographic party was camped at Mooers Forks.

The New York-Quebec line was completed on September 16.

The personnel engaged on the work was as follows: Engineer in charge of work, James H. Van Wagenen; chief of topographic party, Lee Morrison; chief of monumenting and vista-cutting party, H. F. Eagan; assistants, C. E. Carl, J. A. Buchanan.

UNITED STATES PARTY ON THE ST. JOHN RIVER

Subsequent to the resurvey of the boundary along the St. John River, which had been done during the field seasons of 1909 and 1910, the Bangor & Aroostook Railroad had extended its line along the south bank of the river from Grand Isle, Me., to Fort Kent, Me., and, in addition, a railroad bridge had been constructed across the river at Keegan, Me., and a highway bridge between Van Buren, Me., and St. Leonard, New Brunswick. The commissioners considered these features of sufficient importance to have them added to the boundary maps; and they also decided that the 33 islands of the river, which had originally been marked in 1844 with 60 monuments, most of which had been moved or destroyed, should each be remonumented with at least one cast-iron monument.

A United States party began this additional work on May 14 at St. Francis, Me., an inspection being first made to ascertain the number of iron monuments which still remained in place. Only 10 were found and, accordingly, the commissioners had cast, at Ottawa, 24 new monuments similar in design to the old ones, and had them shipped to the party and distributed along the river. Later in the season, 11 more of the old original monuments were found at near-by villages and farms, where they had been taken and used as hitching posts, and these were all restored to the islands and reset.

Islands in St. John River, near Connors, New Brunswick

104709—25†——7

The type of monument placed on the islands in 1844 was the same as that used to mark the boundary from the source of the St. Croix River to the St. Lawrence

Log jam in St. John River, near Keegan, Me.

River, with the exception of the inscription on one side. Instead of the words "Boundary Aug. 9, 1842," the inscription designates the nationality of the island by the words "Aug. 9, 1842, U. S. Island," or "Aug. 9, 1842, H. B. M. Island." The 21 old monuments and the 24 new ones were set in 3-foot square concrete bases. The base of each monument was stamped on one side with the number of the monument and the nationality of the island; and on the opposite side with the inscription "Renewed 1917." The two remaining sides of the base were left blank.

In addition to remonumenting the 33 islands which had been marked during the survey of 1843–44, five small islands were marked by 8-inch bronze post reference monuments set in rock or in concrete bases. Also 42 boundary reference monuments, consisting of 2-inch bronze disks in concrete bases 12 inches square, were set along the banks of the river at or near unmarked points of the triangulation of 1909 and 1910. The geographic positions of these boundary reference monuments and the monuments set on the islands were determined by triangulation, which was tied to the triangulation control of 1909 and 1910.

Boom piers in St. John River, near Lille, Me.

The topographic work of the season included the mapping of the bridges, the railroad, any features which had been changed or added during the construction of the railroad, and the revision of the shore line at the heads of some of the islands where an appreciable amount of erosion had occurred since 1909 and 1910.

The work was inspected by Mr. E. C. Barnard, United States boundary commissioner, and by Mr. James H. Van Wagenen, engineer to the United States section of the commission, on August 31 and September 1.

Reference monument S-54, St. John River

The party completed work on the St. John River about November 1, and on November 3 the part of the outfit which was no longer needed was sold at public auction at Fort Kent, Me. The rest of the outfit was shipped to Vanceboro, Me., for future use on the survey of the St. Croix River.

The personnel of the party was as follows: Engineer in charge of work, James H. Van Wagenen; chief of party, Frank H. Brundage; assistant, H. B. Sullivan.

SEASON OF 1918—THE CANADIAN PARTIES ON THE HIGHLANDS

The only parties operating on the portion of the boundary from the source of the St. Croix River to the St. Lawrence River in 1918 were two Canadian parties engaged on the Highlands boundary between the Southwest Branch of the St. John River and the crossing of the Canadian Pacific Railway.

Camp near Daigle's Island, St. John River, 1917

The Canadian parties worked on the Highlands from each end of the uncompleted section of the line. The eastern party went in to Lake Emily on June 1, and began operations at the point where work had been discontinued the previous season.

As usual, transportation was difficult and long hauls had to be made over poor roads, most of which were constructed by the parties. Two teams were employed, one bringing supplies from the outside, the other distributing the materials and supplies along the boundary line; and when camp was moved, extra teams were hired and brought in for a few days, and the equipment hauled to the next camp site on jumpers. After 8 miles of road had been constructed westward by the party, a connection was made with a road from the village of Ste. Rufine, Quebec, and the base of supplies was then moved from Armstrong to the village of St. Ludger.

The party was considerably hampered by inefficient labor, and toward the latter part of the season the situation became very acute. The Canadian Government would not permit the hiring of men who were subject to call for military service or who had failed to register; wages on farms and in factories were high, and living conditions much more pleasant than in the survey camps in the woods. Scarcely any laborers other than old men or boys could be hired, and many of these were practically useless. On account of this scarcity of labor, it was found necessary by the middle of the summer to abandon the topographic work of the party for that season.

The party left the woods at the end of October, after cacheing most of the camp equipment at a camp in the woods near Du Loup Pond. The more valuable part of the equipment, however, was hauled out on jumpers and stored at Ste. Rufine.

The organization of this party was as follows: Chief of party, Thos. Fawcett, D. T. S.; assistants, G. L. Rainboth, D. L. S., C. R. Westland, D. L. S., J. N. Ingersoll, B. Foley.

The other Canadian party began work on June 1, eastward from monument 402, at the Canadian Pacific Railway crossing, the point from which the United States parties started westward in 1915.

In general, the method of survey adopted by this party was similar to that which had been used for several years by the Canadian parties on the Highlands, namely, the location of monuments by means of precise traverse, the running of a line of levels along the traverse line and the boundary, and mapping the strip of country along the line by plane table supplemented by traverses with prismatic compass, hand level, and stadia. The topography immediately adjacent to the boundary line was done by plane table on a field scale of 1:10,000, the roads, ponds, and small streams were also traversed by plane table, and the map was filled in by transferring the other field notes directly to the plane table sheet. The boundary line was traversed between monuments in the usual way, and a 20-foot vista was cut, but no monumenting was done by this party in 1918.

The first camp of the season was at Boundary Siding, Quebec, and was supplied by rail from Megantic, Quebec. After camp was moved eastward from the railroad, supplies were hauled from Megantic by teams to the end of a road running toward the boundary from the village of Spalding, from which point they were taken to camp on jumpers over logging roads or roads cut through the timber by the party.

The survey had reached a point near Leech Lake early in October, when operations were interrupted by the epidemic of influenza which was prevalent throughout the country. At this time half of the personnel of the party were stricken, and until the close of the season, the time of those who escaped the "flu" was fully occupied in taking care of those who were ill.

The condition of the sick men was such that it was impossible to take them out over the bad roads, and a doctor from Megantic, Quebec, who visited the camp on October 23, at once sent for a trained nurse. On account of the large number of cases throughout the country, great difficulty was experienced in getting a doctor to take charge of the patients in camp, and it was not until October 28 that the continuous services of one could be secured. He remained in camp until November 9, by which time most of the men had recovered, and the one who had been most dangerously ill had recovered sufficiently to be able to be carried out of the woods on a stretcher and then taken to a hospital in Montreal. Altogether, there were 14 cases of the disease in the party, only 3 of the personnel entirely escaping it.

As soon as all were sufficiently well to move out, the party disbanded for the season and the outfit was stored at Megantic.

The personnel of the party was as follows: Chief of party, J. D. Craig, D. L. S.; assistants, T. C. Dennis, D. L. S., G. T. Prinsep, D. L. S., T. P. Reilly.

SEASON OF 1919—THE CANADIAN PARTIES ON THE HIGHLANDS

During the season of 1919, the eastern portion of the Highlands boundary which had been assigned to the Canadian section of the commission was completed, while the activities of the United States parties that year were centered on work on the boundary through Passamaquoddy Bay.

The Canadian party, which had discontinued operations near Du Loup Pond in 1918, resumed operations about June 1. On May 30, a small advance party went into the woods to the camp site near the pond, where they overhauled the equipment and repaired the roads. The other members of the party arrived on June 4, and the next day the party was organized in two divisions; one went back along the line to continue mapping the topography from the point at which it had been interrupted the year before, and the other remained at the camp at Du Loup Pond and continued westward with the boundary location and vista cutting. The parties used the same survey methods that had proved effectual during previous seasons.

From Du Loup Pond, a road was cut about 4 miles, to monument 392, at which point a junction with the western party was to be made. Camp was moved to this point, and, by the end of July, the precise traverse, boundary location, and monumenting were completed to monument 392.

A monumenting party then set the cast-iron monuments and bronze disks from monument 392 to monument 402 at the railway, the part of the line along which no monumenting had been done by the Canadian party in 1918. This work was completed and the party withdrew from the field on September 15. In the meantime, the topographic and leveling party finished work to monument 390 and withdrew from the field on September 4.

The eastern parties were supplied over two roads, one from Ste. Rufine to Du Loup Pond; the other from Spalding to a "line house" near monument 394. Transportation was considerably expedited by the dry weather.

The personnel of this party was as follows: Chief of party, Thos. Fawcett, D. T. S.; assistants, C. R. Westland, D. L. S., J. A. Pounder, D. L. S., J. N. Ingersoll, B. Foley.

The western party also began operations about June 1. They established two camps, a small one near Leech Lake which was occupied by the topographers, and a main camp at a "line house" near monument 394.

The precise traverse was continued eastward and a junction made with the precise traverse of the eastern party near monument 392. In order to strengthen the horizontal control, a point on the precise traverse, near the junction of the work of the two parties, was tied to the triangulation done by the United States parties in 1915, lines being cleared at this point to stations "Kibby," "Ste. Cecile," and "Ken," and the observations were completed by September 8.

In the meantime, all the other work of the party except the monumenting had been completed and the boundary location, vista cutting, and topographic mapping had been joined to similar work of the other party. The monumenting as far west as the Canadian Pacific Railway crossing was completed by the monumenting crew of the eastern party, which continued this work westward from monument 392.

The camps of the party were supplied from Megantic, Quebec, by means of a Ford motor truck owned by the Canadian Government and by teams operating over the road leading to the "line house" near monument 394.

The work was inspected by His Britannic Majesty's Commissioner, J. J. McArthur, D. L. S., during the month of August, and the party was also visited during the season by Mr. James H. Van Wagenen, engineer to the United States section of the commission.

The personnel of this party was as follows: Chief of party, J. D. Craig, D. L. S.; assistants, T. C. Dennis, D. L. S., G. T. Prinsep, D. L. S., T. P. Reilly, L. La Ferme, R. Tuite.

COMPLETION OF FIELD OPERATIONS, 1920 TO 1923

After the two sections of the commission had finished the surveys of the different portions of the boundary from the source of the St. Croix River to the St. Lawrence River, the last stretch of which was closed by the Canadian parties on the Highlands in 1919, the final computations showed that a small additional amount of field work should be done before the results would be complete. This included work made necessary by some modifications which the commissioners had decided to make in the method of laying down the boundary through the narrower streams and the work of correcting a few inaccuracies which were discovered on certain parts of the line.

It had been the original intention of the commissioners to locate the portions of the boundary which follow the several streams by laying down the line on the topographic maps and determining the geographic positions of the turning points of the boundary by scaling the distances and directions of the turning points from the boundary reference monuments. This method worked out very satisfactorily along the wider streams—the St. Francis and the St. John Rivers—but on Halls Stream and the Southwest Branch of the St. John River it was found that in many places the streams were so narrow that unless the maps were on a very large scale and absolutely free from errors, an accurate location of the line in the stream could not be made in this way. It was therefore necessary that the positions of the turning points of the line laid down by the commissioners should be verified by actually running out the line in the field to make sure that it properly divided the waters of the stream.

During the course of the office computations, which involved the determination of approximately 7,000 geographic positions of points on the boundary line, it was found that several of the traverses which were run along the Highlands boundary over particularly rough ground were below the standard of accuracy which the commissioners had fixed for that work. It was decided that, where such inaccuracies occurred, the line between those particular monuments should be rerun. Also, in determining the geographic position of the line in terms of North American datum, the final computations showed that the work would be considerably strengthened by a small additional amount of control to tie the line at a few more places to triangulation stations of the Geodetic Survey of Canada. This the commissioners decided to do.

These minor operations and the setting of a few monuments constituted the final field work which was done from time to time by small parties of the two sections of the commission during the field seasons 1920 to 1923.

In 1920 a Canadian party reset and relocated monuments 277, 278, 279, 280, 281, and 281–A near Lac Frontiere, Quebec, where, due to a misunderstanding, these monuments had been placed off the line. In restoring the monuments to the line, it was necessary to move them only short distances, varying from a few inches to about 3 feet. At the same time the party marked the intersection of the Southwest and the South Lines at Lac Frontiere with a concrete post set flush with the ground.

The work of running out in the field the boundary line in Halls Stream was done in 1921 by a United States party of seven men. Work was begun on July 5, and each turning point of the boundary, as agreed upon by the commissioners and indicated upon the map, was temporarily marked with a stake driven into the bed of the stream. These points were then tied to a transit and tape traverse which was run between the permanent reference monuments along the shore, beginning at monument 518 near the mouth of the stream and ending at monument 507 at the head of the stream. This work was completed on October 22.

Similarly, in 1922, the boundary in the Southwest Branch of the St. John River was run out by a Canadian party assisted by a representative of the United States commissioner. The turning points of the boundary were temporarily located in the stream and tied to a traverse between the permanent reference monuments on the banks, the procedure being similar in all respects to the work done on Halls Stream. The party began work near Little St. John Lake on June 5 and finished on September 10, at the intersection of the Southwest Branch of the St. John River and the South Line.

In 1922 a United States party remeasured the traverse of the boundary line between a number of monuments on the portion of the Highlands boundary from the head of Halls Stream to the Canadian Pacific Railway crossing. This work was begun on May 15 and completed on June 30.

The chief of this party then acted as United States representative on the Canadian party on the Southwest Branch of the St. John River, and while with this party did additional triangulation control to tie the survey of the boundary at monuments S-73 and S-74 on the Southwest Branch of the St. John River, monuments 303 and 307 on the South Line, and monuments 269 and 273 on the Southwest Line, to triangulation stations of the Geodetic Survey of Canada.

After the completion of the work on the Southwest Branch of the St. John River, he ran a line of levels along the Kennebec Road northward from a United States Geological Survey bench mark near Jackman, Me., to boundary survey bench marks at monuments 351, 351-A, 351-B, and 352. This was for the purpose of checking the long line of boundary levels from St. Pamphile, Quebec, to the Canadian Pacific Railway at Boundary Siding.

In 1923 a Canadian party went to the field on June 18 and did additional control triangulation necessary to tie the western end of the traverse along the New York-Quebec boundary to triangulation stations of the Geodetic Survey of Canada. They also connected that part of the survey to two stations of the United States Lake Survey and to three stations of the International Waterways Commission. This work was completed on July 31.

On September 13 a Canadian party, assisted by a United States representative, went to the section of the Highlands boundary which had been surveyed by the Canadian section of the commission, and remeasured some of the boundary traverses. This checking by the Canadians was similar to that done during the previous year by the United States party on the Highlands. Besides rerunning certain parts of the line, the party added to the topographic maps of the boundary the railroad at Lac Frontiere, Quebec, and two highways which had recently been constructed across the line. The party finished work on November 1.

This work in 1923 completed the field work on the boundary from the source of the St. Croix River to the St. Lawrence River.

During the fall of 1923, the commissioners, Mr. E. Lester Jones, for the United States, and Mr. J. J. McArthur, for His Britannic Majesty, made a final inspection of the line.

The personnel connected with the several field parties during the seasons 1920 to 1923, inclusive, was as follows:

For His Britannic Majesty: Engineer in charge of the work, J. D. Craig, D. L. S.; chiefs of party, Thos. Fawcett, D. T. S., J. A. Pounder, D. L. S.; assistants, G. T. Prinsep, D. L. S., D. F. Chisholm.

For the Unites States: Engineer in charge of the work, James H. Van Wagenen; chiefs of party, Jesse Hill, F. H. Brundage; assistants, E. R. Martin, George Scott.

104709—25†——8

SUMMARY OF PERSONNEL ENGAGED

Year	Location of work	Section of commission	Personnel engaged	Work in charge of—	Chiefs of parties and		
					Triangulation	Precise traverse	Boundary traverse
1902	New York - Quebec (West Line).	Canada	11	C. A. Bigger, D. L. S.		C. A. Bigger, D. L. S. C. A. Bourget, D. L. S. F. W. O. Werry	
		United States	9	H. P. Willis			
1906	Vermont-Quebec (West Line).	Canada	12	G. C. Rainboth, D. L. S.			G. L. Rainboth
		United States	11	J. B. Baylor			R. H. Blain J. P. Locke
1907	Vermont-Quebec (West Line).	Canada	13	G. C. Rainboth, D. L. S.			W. J. Sharpe
		United States	14	J. B. Baylor			R. H. Blain J. P. Locke
1908	Maine-New Brunswick (North Line).	Canada	18	G. C. Rainboth, D. L. S.			W. J. Sharpe
		United States	15	J. B. Baylor			R. H. Blain J. P. Locke
1909	Maine-New Brunswick (St. John River).	Canada	17	G. C. Rainboth, D. L. S.	G. L. Rainboth		
		United States	10	J. B. Baylor	R. H. Blain W. B. Gilmore		
1910	Maine-New Brunswick (St. John and St. Francis Rivers).	Canada	16	G. C. Rainboth, D. L. S.	G. L. Rainboth, D. L. S.		
		United States	14	J. B. Baylor	R. H. Blain L. J. Young		
1911	Maine-New Brunswick and Quebec (St. Francis River and Southwest Line).	Canada	19	Thos. Fawcett, D. T. S.	G. L. Rainboth, D. L. S. I. R. Pounder J. A. Pounder		
		United States	24	J. B. Baylor	R. H. Blain F. H. Brundage		
1912	Maine-Quebec (Southwest Line).	Canada	20	Thos. Fawcett, D. T. S.		I. R. Pounder J. A. Pounder	
		United States	21	J. B. Baylor	R. H. Blain	R. H. Blain	
1913	Maine-Quebec (Southwest and South Lines and Southwest Branch of St. John River).	Canada	23	Thos. Fawcett, D. T. S.	G. L. Rainboth, D. L. S. J. A. Pounder, D. L. S.		
		United States	29	J. B. Baylor		R. H. Blain	
1914	Maine-Quebec (Highlands and Southwest Branch of St. John River).	Canada	26	Thos. Fawcett, D. T. S.		G. L. Rainboth, D. L. S. J. A. Pounder, D. L. S.	G. L. Rainboth, D. L. S.
		United States					
	New Hampshire-Quebec (Halls Stream).	United States	17	J. E. McGrath	J. E. McGrath R. H. Blain		

ON THE FIELD WORK, 1902–1923

assistants engaged on—					Section of commission	Location of work	Year
Leveling	Topography	Vista cutting	Monumenting	Inspection			
				C. A. Bigger, D. L. S.	Canada	New York - Quebec (West Line).	1902
			H. P. Willis	H. P. Willis	United States		
O. Sills	F. H. Mackie, D. L. S.	A. J. Rainboth	B. Foley	G. C. Rainboth, D. L. S.	Canada	Vermont - Quebec (West Line).	1906
	O. B. French			J. B. Baylor	United States		
A. M. Phillips	G. L. Rainboth	A. J. Rainboth	B. Foley	G. C. Rainboth, D. L. S.	Canada	Vermont - Quebec (West Line).	1907
	C. H. Van Orden			J. B Baylor	United States		
M. F. Cochrane, D. L. S.	G. L. Rainboth I. R. Pounder C. R. Westland	A. J. Rainboth	B. Foley	G. C. Rainboth, D. L. S.	Canada	Maine - New Brunswick (North Line).	1908
				J. B. Baylor	United States		
W. M. Dennis	I. R. Pounder J. A. Pounder		B. Foley	G. C. Rainboth, D. L. S.	Canada	Maine - New Brunswick (St. John River).	1909
	F. H. Brundage J. P. Locke			J. B. Baylor	United States		
G. L. Rainboth, D. L. S.	I. R. Pounder J. A. Pounder		B. Foley	G. C. Rainboth, D. L. S.	Canada	Maine - New Brunswick (St. John and St. Francis Rivers).	1910
	F. H. Brundage J. P. Locke			J. B. Baylor	United States		
G. L. Rainboth, D. L. S.	I. R. Pounder J. A. Pounder		B. Foley	Thos. Fawcett, D. T. S.	Canada	Maine - New Brunswick and Quebec (St. Francis River and Southwest Line).	1911
J. P. Locke	F. H. Brundage J. P. Locke	Joseph Mercier		J. B. Baylor	United States		
G. L. Rainboth, D. L. S.	I. R. Pounder J. A. Pounder		B. Foley	Thos. Fawcett, D. T. S.	Canada	Maine-Quebec (Southwest Line).	1912
J. P. Locke	F. H. Brundage J. P. Locke	Joseph Mercier		J. B. Baylor	United States		
G. L. Rainboth, D. L. S.	J. A. Pounder, D. L. S. D. F. Chisholm		B. Foley	Thos. Fawcett, D. T. S.	Canada	Maine-Quebec (Southwest and South Lines and Southwest Branch of St. John River).	1913
J. R. Sinclair	W. C. Guerin F. H. Brundage	Joseph Mercier		J. B. Baylor	United States		
D. F. Chisholm	J. A. Pounder, D. L. S. D. F. Chisholm	G. L. Rainboth, D. L. S.	B. Foley	Thos. Fawcett, D. T. S.	Canada	Maine-Quebec Highlands and Sou hwest Branch of St. John River).	1914
				Jas. H. Van Wagenen (1915).	United States		
J. R. Sinclair	F. H. Brundage		J. R. Sinclair	J. E. McGrath	United States	New Hampshire-Quebec (Halls Stream).	

SUMMARY OF PERSONNEL ENGAGED

Year	Location of work	Section of commission	Personnel engaged	Work in charge of—	Chiefs of parties and		
					Triangulation	Precise traverse	Boundary traverse
1915	Maine - Quebec and New Brunswick (St. Francis and St. John Rivers).	Canada	9	Thos. Fawcett, D. T. S.	J. L. Rannie, D. T. S. V. R. Davies		
	Maine-Quebec (Highlands).	Canada	26	Thos. Fawcett, D. T. S.		J. A. Pounder, D. L. S. D. F. Chisholm	G. L. Rainboth, D. L. S.
		United States	51	Jas. H. Van Wagenen	Jesse Hill H. C. O. Clarke		Jesse Hill W. F. Lehfelt
	New Hampshire-Quebec (Halls Stream).	United States	22	J. E. McGrath	R. H. Blain Jesse Young		
1916	Maine-New Brunswick (St. John River and North Line).	Canada	8	Thos. Fawcett, D. T. S.	J. L. Rannie, D. T. S. J. Bowie		
	Maine and New Hampshire-Quebec (Highlands).	Canada	25	Thos. Fawcett, D. T. S.		C. R. Westland, D. L. S.	G. L. Rainboth, D. L. S.
		United States	106	Jas. H. Van Wagenen	Jesse Hill F. H. Brundage N. W. Smith M. E. Lutz S. O. White R. C. Snyder Hollis Young G. A. Perry		W. F. Lehfelt George Brown G. A. Perry M. E. Lutz
1917	Maine-Quebec (Highlands).	Canada	22	Thos. Fawcett, D. T. S.		C. R. Westland, D. L. S.	G. L. Rainboth, D. L. S.
		United States	9	Jas. H. Van Wagenen			G. A. Perry
	Vermont-Quebec (West Line).	Canada	10	J. D. Craig, D. L. S.	F. Lambert, D. L. S. G. T. Prinsep, D. L. S. J. Sheppard J. Bowie T. P. Reilly		
		United States					
	New York-Quebec (West Line).	Canada	10	J. D. Craig, D. L. S.	F. Lambert, D. L. S. G. T. Prinsep, D. L. S. J. Sheppard T. P. Reilly		
		United States	11	Jas. H. Van Wagenen			
	Maine-New Brunswick (St. John River).	United States	9	Jas. H. Van Wagenen	F. H. Brundage		
1918	Maine-Quebec (Highlands).	Canada	20	Thos. Fawcett, D. T. S.		C. R. Westland, D. L. S.	G. L. Rainboth, D. L. S.
			15	J. D. Craig, D. L. S.		T. C. Dennis, D. L. S. G. T. Prinsep, D. L. S.	T. C. Dennis, D. L. S.
		United States					

ON THE FIELD WORK, 1902–1923—Continued

assistants engaged on—					Section of commission	Location of work	Year
Leveling	Topography	Vista cutting	Monumenting	Inspection			
					Canada	Maine-Quebec and New Brunswick (St. Francis and St. John Rivers).	1915
D. F. Chisholm	J. A. Pounder, D. L. S. D. F. Chisholm	G. L. Rainboth, D. L. S. J. A. Pounder, D. L. S.	B. Foley	Thos. Fawcett, D. T. S.	Canada	Maine-Quebec (Highlands).	
R. K. Lynt George Brown	H. C. O. Clarke Lee Morrison R. K. Lynt E. V. Perkinson	Alex McDiarmid	J. A. Stewart	Jas. H. Van Wagenen.	United States		
J. R. Sinclair F. H. Brundage	F. H. Brundage		J. R. Sinclair		United States	New Hampshire-Quebec (Halls Stream).	
					Canada	Maine-New Brunswick (St. John River and North Line).	1916
L. C. Nesham	C. R. Westland, D. L. S. L. C. Nesham	G. L. Rainboth, D. L. S. C. R. Westland, D. L. S.	B. Foley	Thos. Fawcett, D. T. S.	Canada	Maine and New Hampshire-Quebec (Highlands).	
Walter McCrea J. A. Buchanan	H. C. O. Clarke W. C. Guerin Lee Morrison E. V. Perkinson E. C. Guerin C. E. Carl	J. E. Bump Joseph Mercier	J. A. Stewart Jesse Young	Jas. H. Van Wagenen.	United States		
W. Smith	C. R. Westland, D. L. S.	G. L. Rainboth, D. L. S. C. R. Westland, D. L. S.	B. Foley	J. D. Craig, D. L. S. (1918).	Canada	Maine-Quebec (Highlands).	1917
		G. A. Perry	J. A. Stewart	Jas. H. Van Wagenen.	United States		
					Canada	Vermont-Quebec (West Line).	
				Jas. H. Van Wagenen.	United States		
				J. D. Craig, D. L. S.	Canada	New York-Quebec (West Line).	
J. A. Buchanan	Lee Morrison C. E. Carl		H. F. Eagan	Jas. H. Van Wagenen.	United States		
	F. H. Brundage		H. B. Sullivan		United States	Maine-New Brunswick (St. John River).	
J. N. Ingersoll R. Polleys	C. R. Westland, D. L. S. G. T. Prinsep, D. L. S.	G. L. Rainboth, D. L. S. C. R. Westland, D. L. S. T. P. Reilly	B. Foley B. Foley		Canada	Maine-Quebec (Highlands).	1918
				Jas. H. Van Wagenen (1919).	United States		

SUMMARY OF PERSONNEL ENGAGED

Year	Location of work	Section of commission	Personnel engaged	Work in charge of—	Chiefs of parties and		
					Triangulation	Precise traverse	Boundary traverse
1919	Maine-Quebec (Highlands).	Canada	25	Thos. Fawcett, D. T. S.	T. C. Dennis, D. L. S. G. T. Prinsep, D. L. S.	J. A. Pounder, D. L. S. T. C. Dennis, D. L. S	J. A. Pounder, D. L. S. L. La Ferme
			22	J. D. Craig, D. L. S.			
		United States					
1920	Maine-Quebec (South Line).	Canada	6	Thos. Fawcett, D. T. S.			
		United States					
1921	New Hampshire-Quebec (Halls Stream).	United States	8	F. H. Brundage			F. H. Brundage
1922	Maine and New Hampshire-Quebec (Southwest Branch of St. John River, South Line, Southwest Line, and the Highlands).	Canada	7	J. A. Pounder, D. L. S.			J. A. Pounder, D. L. S. D. F. Chisholm
		United States	4	Jesse Hill	Jesse Hill		Jesse Hill E. R. Martin
	New Hampshire-Quebec (Halls Stream).	United States	4	F. H. Brundage			
1923	New York-Quebec (West Line).	Canada	4	J. A. Pounder, D. L. S.	J. A. Pounder, D. L. S. G. T. Prinsep, D. L. S.		
	Maine-Quebec (Highlands).	Canada	6	J. A. Pounder, D. L. S.			J. A. Pounder, D. L. S.
		United States					Jesse Hill

ON THE FIELD WORK, 1902–1923—Continued

assistants engaged on—

Leveling	Topography	Vista cutting	Monumenting	Inspection	Section of commission	Location of work	Year
J. N. Ingersoll R. Tuite	C. R. Westland, D. L. S. J. N. Ingersoll G. T. Prinsep, D. L. S.	J. A. Pounder, D. L. S. T. P. Reilly	B. Foley		Canada	Maine-Quebec (Highlands).	1919
				Jas. H. Van Wagenen.	United States		
			Thos. Fawcett, D. T. S.		Canada	Maine-Quebec (South Line).	1920
				F. H. Brundage (1922).	United States		
					United States	New Hampshire-Quebec (Halls Stream).	1921
				J. A. Pounder, D. L. S.	Canada	Maine and New Hampshire-Quebec (Southwest Branch of St. John River, South Line, Southwest Line, and the Highlands).	1922
Jesse Hill				Jesse Hill	United States		
			F. H. Brundage George Scott		United States	New Hampshire-Quebec (Halls Stream).	
					Canada	New York-Quebec (West Line).	1923
					Canada	Maine-Quebec (Highlands).	
				Jesse Hill	United States		

DESCRIPTION OF FIELD AND OFFICE METHODS AND RESULTS

HORIZONTAL CONTROL

The horizontal control for the topographic surveys and for the determination of the geographic positions of the monuments and turning points of the boundary from the source of the St. Croix River to the St. Lawrence River consists of schemes of major and minor triangulation, and precise, secondary,[8] and tertiary[9] grades of traverse, which are connected with the triangulation schemes of the Geodetic Survey of Canada and the United States Coast and Geodetic Survey. The general plan of the control is shown on 14 triangulation and precise traverse sketches, together with an index sketch, which accompany the report under separate cover. The geographic positions and descriptions of the triangulation stations, and of the stations of the precise traverses not run directly on the boundary line are listed in Appendix V, pages 345 to 483. The control stations which are marked by boundary monuments or reference monuments are listed on pages 139 to 266.

GENERAL DESCRIPTION

The North Line, the St. John River, and the St. Francis River are covered by a scheme of major triangulation, about 180 miles in length, which is connected with three triangulation stations ("Kennedy," "Pole Hill," and "Spring Hill") of the United States Coast and Geodetic Survey near the southern end of the North Line, and with two stations ("Frontier" and "Parke") of the Geodetic Survey of Canada near Lake Pohenagamook. In addition to the ties to precise triangulation at both ends, there is included in this scheme, midway between the ends, a Laplace station and a $3\frac{1}{2}$-mile base.

The discrepancy developed by the closure of the circuit formed by the above triangulation and the triangulation of the United States Coast and Geodetic Survey and the Geodetic Survey of Canada, was $0''.423$ of latitude and $0''.213$ of longitude, equivalent to 13.81 meters. As the circuit has a total length of about 1,000 miles, this discrepancy represents a proportional error of slightly less than 1 part in 100,000. This, however, was distributed only in the boundary triangulation.

Along the North Line the geographic positions of 13 monuments, averaging about 6 miles apart, were determined by the major triangulation. Secondary traverse lines were run along the boundary, and these traverses were adjusted[10]

---

[8] Carefully run transit and steel-tape traverse which checked with the triangulation control points within 1 part in 5,000; used on the North Line and the Vermont-Quebec line.

[9] Transit and steel-tape traverse which checked with the triangulation within 1 part in 1,000; includes the boundary traverse of the Southwest Branch of the St. John River, the Highlands, and Halls Stream.

[10] For methods of adjustment of traverses see pp.104 to 106.

94

to agree with the positions of the monuments determined by triangulation. The angles at the deflection points of this traverse were measured with a 6¼-inch Berger repeating theodolite, and the distances were measured in one direction with steel tape and in both directions with stadia.

Along the St. John River, a scheme of minor triangulation, which consisted of quadrilaterals, was extended from the North Line to the mouth of the St. Francis River and was connected with the major triangulation at 15 points, averaging about 5 miles apart. The signals were, in general, 8-foot braced poles 2 by 2 inches in cross section. Angles measured with the 6¼-inch or 7-inch Berger theodolites used by the United States parties were repeated six times with telescope direct and six times reversed. Those measured with the direction theodolites used by the Canadian parties were read on three positions of the circle, a direct and reverse pointing being made in each position. Five bases were measured with a high degree of accuracy with steel and invar tapes. The sites for triangulation stations were so chosen that they would be suitable locations for monuments to reference the turning points of the boundary line, which was laid down by the commissioners on the copper plates of the engraved maps as a series of straight-line courses in the river to conform with the course of the curved boundary shown on the maps of the survey of 1843. The reference monu-

Triangulation, St. John River, 1910

ments were generally placed so that each would be on line with a boundary turning point and another reference monument, and the geographic positions of the turning points of the boundary were determined by scaling from the copper plates the distances from the turning points to their respective reference monuments, the positions of which had been determined by triangulation.

The immediate control of the boundary along the St. Francis River was by a scheme of minor triangulation extended northward from the minor triangulation along the St. John River, using similar methods but reducing the size of the quadrilaterals to keep the stations near the banks of the river. Eight bases were measured and two azimuth determinations were made, and the scheme was connected with the major triangulation at five points, averaging about 6 miles apart. This triangulation determined the positions of the boundary reference monuments, which, in nearly all cases, were set at triangulation stations. It also furnished the control for making the map of the river upon which the commissioners marked the course of the boundary line. The geographic positions of the boundary turning points were then determined by scaling their latitudes and longitudes from the copper plates of the engraved maps, and from these positions the relation of the turning points to the boundary reference monuments was computed.

From Lake Pohenagamook to the Canadian Pacific Railway crossing of the boundary at monument 402, a distance of about 200 miles, the control consists of precise traverse except for about 13 miles along the Southwest Branch of the St. John River, where minor triangulation was used. This combined scheme of precise traverse and minor triangulation is connected with triangulation stations of the Geodetic Survey of Canada at eight points, averaging about 28 miles apart. The discrepancies at these tie points between the distances determined by the primary

Type of signal and instrument used for minor triangulation of St. Francis River

triangulation and those determined by the boundary control varied from 1 part in 21,000 in the rougher section of the country to 1 part in 145,000 in the more level portion, the average discrepancy being about 1 part in 50,000. The discrepancies were distributed by least square adjustment to make the boundary control agree with the primary triangulation.

From monument 402, on the Highlands, to monument 650–A, near the east end of the New York-Quebec line, the boundary is controlled by a scheme of major triangulation which is connected with the primary triangulation of the Geodetic Survey of Canada at five stations, averaging about 35 miles apart. The positions of all the cast-iron monuments from No. 402 to the source of Halls Stream were determined directly from this major scheme.

The angles of the main scheme of this triangulation were observed with $6\frac{1}{4}$-inch

Fire lookout tower, Hardwood Mountain, Me., used as triangulation station

or 7-inch Berger theodolites, repeating each angle at least six times with the telescope direct and six times reversed. Angles for determining the positions of subsidiary points, such as boundary monuments not included in the main scheme, were repeated three times with the telescope direct and three times reversed. The longest line over which observations were made was 49 miles in length. This and several other long lines were observed at night, using lights at the points observed upon.

Due to the fact that many of the monuments along the Highlands are in saddles of the boundary ridge, it was frequently impossible to observe upon them directly from a sufficient number of stations. In such cases, the positions of the monuments were determined by observing on eccentric signals, consisting of flags placed in the tops of tall

Triangulation station "Talon"; major control near English Lake

trees on the nearest high ground. In each location of this kind, the distance between the
monument and a point directly under its eccentric signal was measured, a line of sight was
opened from the monument to a triangulation
station, and the angle at the monument between
the flag and the triangulation station was measured. Such line was necessary not only for locating the monument but for obtaining a back sight
for running the boundary traverse to the next
monument ahead, as will be described later.

The signals at the triangulation stations
where observations on other stations could be
made from the ground were tall, braced poles.
But where considerable line cutting was necessary,
such as on the New Hampshire-Quebec line, where
the hills along the Highlands are flat-topped and
wooded, it was found more economical to build
towers. There were 12 such towers constructed,
with an average height of 45 feet. Each of these
consisted of a tripod for the instrument, surrounded by an independent structure for the sup-

Native timber triangulation tower, western end of Highlands boundary

port of the observer. They were
built of green timber cut in the vicinity of the triangulation stations.

Along Halls Stream the positions of the boundary reference
monuments were determined directly from a scheme of minor
triangulation, which included at
intervals six bases measured along
the sides of quadrilaterals. This
scheme of small quadrilaterals
with stations close to the stream
was connected with the major
triangulation at four points, averaging 5 miles apart. The angles
on all this work were measured
with a $6\frac{1}{4}$-inch Berger theodolite,
repeating each angle six times
with telescope direct and six
times reversed.

Along the Vermont-Quebec
line the positions of 27 of the
monuments, averaging about

Ideal triangulation station on a bare-topped mountain.

4 miles apart, were determined from a major scheme of triangulation which was tied to stations "Hereford," "Owl's Head," and "St. Armand," of the primary triangulation of the Geodetic Survey of Canada. The positions of the other boundary monuments were obtained by traverses run along the line between the monuments fixed by the triangulation.

The New York-Quebec line traverse, which was run in 1902 under the direction of the State engineer of New York and the Canadian boundary commissioner,[11] was at that time controlled by astronomic observations for azimuth and latitude made at nine stations distributed along the boundary from Rouses Point to the St. Lawrence River. These included eight determinations of azimuth and three determinations of latitude. The precision of the azimuth observations is shown by the computed probable errors of the results, which range from 0″.14 to 1″.08. The probable errors of the latitude determinations range from 0″.12 to 0″.40.

Type of low tripod and scaffold used on some of the mountain tops

The stations were located as follows:

Station No. 1: Latitude, on boundary line, 477 feet west of monument 648.

Station No. 2: Azimuth, on traverse, opposite monument 650–A.

Station No. 3: Azimuth, on traverse, 239 feet west of monument 657.

Station No. 4: Azimuth, on traverse, 27 feet west of monument 661.

Station No. 5: Latitude and azimuth, on traverse, 22 feet east of monument 678.

Station No. 6: Azimuth, on traverse, 9 feet east of monument 699.

Station No. 7: Azimuth, on traverse, 824 feet west of monument 731.

Station No. 8: Azimuth, on traverse, 1,344 feet west of monument 740.

Station No. 9: Latitude and azimuth, on traverse, 786 feet east of monument 760.

In 1917 and 1923 this traverse was connected with the triangulation of the Geodetic Survey of Canada at four points, averaging about 20 miles apart, and the traverse lengths were adjusted to agree with the triangulation and placed on the North American datum.

Triangulation reconnaissance party at station "Dennison," Maine-Quebec Highlands, 1916

[11] Chief Astronomer and (Canadian) Boundary Comm'r, Ann. Rept., 1904, pp. 22–30; New York State Engineer and Surveyor, Ann. Rept., 1902, pp. 67–102. Ibid., 1904, pp. 350–363.

Methods Used on Precise Traverse

This form of control was first used on the boundary in 1912 along the Southwest Line westward from Lake Pohenagamook. It was selected in preference to triangulation, for the reason that the country was heavily wooded and not of sufficient relief for doing triangulation without erecting high towers and cutting considerable timber to open lines of sight between triangulation stations and to the boundary monuments. Owing to the fact that many of the monuments on this part of the line are in valleys, on the banks of streams, difficult to see from distant stations, it was thought that a direct form of control run in the boundary vista from monument to monument would be the economical one to use. Furthermore, a precise traverse on the boundary through this wooded country would furnish more available control for mapping the topography than would triangulation stations outside the area to be mapped.

The method of running the precise traverse was similar to that used in measuring base lines for major triangulation. The measuring was done with 100-foot and 50-meter invar tapes. During the season of 1912 it was found that on the rough ground encountered, the 100-foot tapes were preferable to the 50-meter tapes, and this experience led to the adoption of the 100-foot tapes exclusively for this purpose during the seasons which followed.

The 100-foot tapes were supported at the ends and were drawn to a tension of 15 kilograms, using spring balances which were corrected frequently to agree with a standard balance kept in camp. Two mercury thermometers were fastened to the tape by clips a few feet from each end and were read for each tape length. The line was measured forward and backward, one measurement generally being made in the forenoon and the other in the afternoon. The tapes were frequently compared in length with a tape kept in camp for this purpose, using, when the comparisons were made, balances and thermometers that were employed in the field.

The procedure of staking out and measuring the line was as follows: A small transit was set over one monument, sighted on the other, and used to line in hubs, which were stout stakes from 3 to 6 feet long driven into the ground and solidly braced so that the center of each hub was one tape length from the center of the preceding hub. The preliminary taping necessary to set the hubs so that they would be exactly one invar tape length apart was done with 100-foot steel tapes and spring balances which had been compared with the standardized tapes and

Precise traverse line showing hub and vista

balances used on the precise measurement. A strip of thin copper about 3 inches long and one-half inch wide, upon which to mark the invar tape lengths, was then nailed on the top of each hub. Before attaching these strips, the tops of the hubs were sawed off and beveled, so as to permit the marked end of the tape under tension to lie in the same plane, parallel to and against the edge of the copper strip.

The precise measurement was made by a party of five men. The man in charge and an assistant were at the forward end of the tape, two men were stationed at the rear end, and the fifth was at the middle to support the tape when it was being moved forward along the line and to clear it from brush before the measurements were made. The measuring was done by the rear observer and his assistant holding the rear end of the tape while the assistant in front pulled steadily until the spring balance recorded the proper tension. As soon as the rear observer had the end of the tape beside the rear mark he called "Stick" or "Good." The forward observer watched both the spring balance and the front end of the tape, and when both were steady and the balance indicated the proper tension he made a mark on the copper strip opposite the mark on the front end of the tape with an awl or knife and called "Stuck" or "Good." Both thermometers were then read and the temperatures recorded. If the forward end of the tape fell ahead or behind the copper strip, as it occasionally did, a mark was made on the strip and the "set forward" or "set back" was measured with a scale and dividers.

The monuments were located by measuring the distance from each monument to the nearest hub with a steel tape. This location was checked by also measuring the distance from the monument to the next hub on the other side.

The elevation of the top of every hub was determined by levels which were run along the precise traverse line to furnish data for reducing the measured length to sea level, applying grade corrections, and for supplying elevations for the vertical control of the topographic mapping.

The above methods were used along the Southwest and South Lines traversed by the United States and Canadian parties in 1912 and 1913, and on the upper part of the Southwest Branch of the St. John River and along the portion of the Highlands traversed by the Canadian parties in 1914 to 1919, inclusive.

The precise traverse along the river and along the Highlands was run as a series of long straight-line courses paralleling the general course of the boundary. On the river portion of the traverse where the ground was flat it was easy to get lines of reasonable length; in fact, reconnaissance for this work was done almost entirely by use of the original boundary maps. When the Highlands were reached, however, this was no longer possible, and the reconnaissance had to be made on the ground in order that deflection points could be so chosen that they would be intervisible and that the courses would be fairly long and reasonably close to the boundary line. It was frequently possible by locating the deflection points upon the tops of hills to see over much of the intervening timber and thus to dispense with considerable line cutting, it being necessary in such cases to open only a narrow line in which to do the taping.

The angles of the precise traverse along the Southwest Branch of the St. John River and on the Highlands were measured with a $6\frac{1}{4}$-inch repeating theodolite or with a direction theodolite with the same degree of accuracy used on major triangulation. At intervals of about one-half mile on the river portion, offset lines were run to hubs across the river. At each offset a hub was carefully lined in on the traverse, and at this hub the angle between the main line and the hub at the end of the offset line across the river was carefully measured. The length of the offset was then measured by the same methods used on the main line. The hubs at each end of the offset line were later replaced by monuments, which were used as permanent monuments to reference the boundary line through the stream.

On the Highlands portion of the line, similar offsets were run to all boundary monuments. These offsets were comparatively short and averaged less than 1 mile apart.

Methods of Boundary Location by Tertiary Traverse

The geographic positions of the boundary turning points in the Southwest Branch of the St. John River and in Halls Stream, and the positions of the small intermediate monuments on the Highlands, were determined by a tertiary grade of transit and tape traverse run between fixed points about 1 mile apart, the positions of which had been determined by triangulation or precise traverse.

These short traverses along the Southwest Branch of the St. John River and along Halls Stream were run as follows: On the Southwest Branch of the St. John, where the reference monuments are, as a rule, in pairs, one on each side of the river, the transit was set over one of the monuments, sighted on the other monument of the pair, and a hub driven at the river bank on a line between the monuments. The distance from one of the monuments to the hub was then chained, the transit was set over the hub and, using one of the monuments as a back sight, the traverse was run along the stream to an intersection with the line joining the next pair of monuments where a hub was similarly located to mark the last station of this traverse and the first station of the next. On Halls Stream, where the reference monuments are not in pairs, the method was the same except that the back sights for starting the traverses had to be obtained by sighting on other stations of the control scheme from which the reference monuments had been located.

Due to the fact that there was much dry weather in those localities during the seasons of 1921 and 1922 and that the water in the streams was low, many of the traverse stations were placed in the beds of the streams, thus materially reducing the amount of line cutting. The traverse stations were marked with wooden hubs about 3 feet long driven solidly in the ground and in the top of each was placed a thin peg or a nail to set the transit over and to sight on.

The angles of the traverses on the Southwest Branch were measured with a $6\frac{1}{4}$-inch Berger theodolite graduated to 10 seconds, using one pointing direct and one reversed, and the distances were chained with a 500-foot steel tape. The angles on Halls Stream were measured with a 4-inch Berger theodolite graduated to minutes, using two pointings direct and two reversed, and the courses were measured forward and backward with a 100-foot or 200-foot steel tape. All chaining was done with an accuracy of 1 part in 1,000. Before moving camp the traverses in each locality were checked to make certain that the closing errors were within the allowable limit.

If the error of a closure was greater than 1 part in 1,000, the angles were re-observed and the courses rechained.[12]

The turning points of the boundary were located from the above traverses in the following manner: The chief of party or his assistant selected the turning points in the stream so that the right-line courses of the boundary between successive points would conform as near-ly as practicable to the original curved-line boundary shown on the old maps of the survey of 1843–1845. Each point was then temporarily marked by driving a blazed stake into the bed of the stream. From the nearest traverse sta-tion a line was cleared to this stake, the angle observed, and the distance meas-ured by stadia or chaining. There was also noted in the record book the dis-tances from the turning point to both banks of the stream.

Measuring boundary deflection angles, Highlands, 1917

In laying down the boundary from one cast-iron monument to the next along the Highlands, the right-line distance between the original monuments was calculated by latitudes and departures, using in this computation the angles and courses given in the old traverse notes. This distance was then compared with the true right-line distance, obtained by triangulation or precise traverse, and the discrepancy found was distributed into the several courses of the old traverse in proportion to their lengths, except on that portion of the boundary between monuments 314 and 392, where the discrepancy was distributed partly in the distances and partly in the angles.

The old notes corrected in the above manner were then used for running out the boundary traverse between monuments. The angles and back sights used in turning off the first courses of these traverses were obtained in each case as follows: First, there was computed from the triangulation or precise traverse notes the angle between a distant triangulation or precise traverse station and a right line to the monument ahead; there was then added to this angle, or subtracted, as the case might be, the angle between the first course of the traverse and the right line to the next monument, as determined from the adjusted latitude and departure computation made from the old notes.

Using the distant station as a back sight, the computed angle was then turned off at the monument and the traverse run out. The closure of the traverse on the monument ahead depended entirely upon the accuracy of the field work and not upon the correctness of the old notes.

---

[12] For method of final adjustment of the traverses see "Adjustment of special forms of traverse," p. 104.

In case this traverse failed to place the boundary line on the crest of the water-shed or along the site of the original vista, which could be traced across the low places by following the line of old stumps or by noting the character of the second-growth timber, a large error in one of the angles or in one of the courses given in the old notes was looked for. Such errors were generally multiples of 10°, or of chain lengths, and were found by searching for the change that should be made in an angle or course that would modify the location of the traversed line to make it agree closely with the original vista or the crest of the watershed. Many times, however, such corrections could not be found, in which cases the relocation of the line had to depend entirely on the course of the ridge or traces of the original vista.

On the part of the Highlands surveyed by the Canadian parties the lengths of the courses of the boundary traverse were measured with a 66-foot steel tape gradu-ated in links. The angles were turned off with a 4-inch theodolite graduated to minutes. On the portion surveyed by the United States parties, distances were measured with a 100-foot steel tape. The angles were laid off with a 4-inch Berger theodolite graduated to minutes. If a traverse did not close on the monument ahead within an error of less than 1 part in 1,000, it was rerun. Where the closing error was too large, it was generally due to "breaking chain" on steep slopes, and for this reason a considerable part of the taping was done along the slope, using a 300-foot steel tape and measuring the slope angle with a theodolite or a clinometer.

After the deflection points of the traverses between original monuments on the Highlands had been permanently marked with 3-inch bronze disks set in concrete or in solid rock, a considerable number of the angles which had been turned off at these points with the 4-inch theodolites when the traverses were run were remeasured by repetition with a $6\frac{1}{4}$-inch Berger theodolite, using one pointing direct and one re-versed. The traverses were then adjusted in the office by least squares to conform with the fixed positions of the cast-iron monuments.

ADJUSTMENT OF SPECIAL FORM OF TRAVERSE IN WHICH THE ACCURACY OF ANGLE MEASUREMENT IS GREATER THAN THAT OF CHAINING

In many of the tertiary traverses (those between boundary monuments on the Highlands and between boundary reference monuments along the Southwest Branch of the St. John River and Halls Stream) the accuracy of the measurement of the angles was considerably greater than that of chaining, and in this class of traverse lines the following method of adjustment was used:

The angles were adjusted to close the figure by distributing the angular error equally among the angles. The angles were then assumed to be correct and the traverse was adjusted assuming that all the remaining discrepancy was due to in-accuracy in chaining.

Let $l_1, l_2, l_3, \cdots l_n$, be the corrected lengths of the courses.

Let ϕ_1 and ϕ_n be the fixed latitudes of the initial and final points.

Let λ_1 and λ_n be the fixed longitudes of the initial and final points.

Let $V_1, V_2, \cdots V_n$ be small corrections to the logarithms of the measured lengths, $m_1, m_2, \cdots m_n$ such that $\log m + V = \log l$.

Let $\Delta\phi_1, \Delta\phi_2, \cdots \Delta\phi_n$ and $\Delta\lambda_1, \Delta\lambda_2, \cdots \Delta\lambda_n$ be the difference in latitude and longitude between the consecutive traverse stations.

Let $d\phi_1, d\phi_2, \cdots d\phi_n$ and $d\lambda_1, d\lambda_2, \cdots d\lambda_n$ be the small changes in latitude and longitude caused by the change in the lengths.

Then

$$d\phi_1 + d\phi_2 + \cdots d\phi_n = p \tag{1}$$

where p is the amount by which the measured latitude fails to equal the difference in latitude between the fixed points.

Let $y = \log_{10}\Delta\phi$.

Then

$$dy = M\frac{d\phi}{\Delta\phi},$$

where M is the modulus of common logarithms.

Since the length is the only factor in the computation of the latitude that changes, the change in the logarithms of the latitude will equal the change in the logarithm of the length, or $dy = V$.

Hence

$$d\phi = \frac{V\Delta\phi}{M}$$

Substituting this in equation (1) gives

$$\frac{V_1\Delta\phi_1}{M} + \frac{V_2\Delta\phi_2}{M} + \cdots \cdot \frac{V_n\Delta\phi_n}{M} = p$$

or

$$V_1\Delta\phi_1 + V_2\Delta\phi_2 + \cdots \cdot V_n\Delta\phi_n = pM$$

By a similar development the longitude equation becomes

$$V_1\Delta\lambda_1 + V_2\Delta\lambda_2 + \cdots \cdot V_n\Delta\lambda_n = qM$$

where q is the amount by which the measured longitude fails to equal the difference in longitude between the fixed points.

Since it is convenient in solving the equations to represent the fifth decimal place of logarithms as units, the roots of the equations should be multiplied by 10^5. The equations to be solved thus become:

$$V_1\Delta\phi_1 + V_2\Delta\phi_2 + \cdots \cdot V_n\Delta\phi_n = pM10^5$$

$$V_1\Delta\lambda_1 + V_2\Delta\lambda_2 + \cdots \cdot V_n\Delta\lambda_n = qM10^5$$

In order to obtain the most probable value of the V's, the equations should be solved subject to the condition that the sum of the squares of the V's shall be a minimum.

ADJUSTMENT OF SPECIAL FORM OF TRAVERSE IN WHICH THE TRAVERSE IS APPROXIMATELY A STRAIGHT LINE

Along the North Line, the Southwest Line, the South Line, and the West Line, the deflection angles of the traverse lines average less than 1°, and the deflection angles balance each other in such a way that the azimuth of any of the courses differs but little from the azimuth of the initial line.

The total error in surveying any traverse line is made up of the error in measuring the distances and the error in measuring the angles. When the traverse is of the kind described above, the total error can be divided into the component parts due to the error in measuring the distances and the error in measuring the angles, as will be seen from the following:

Let A and B be two fixed points; and let P_1, P_2, and P_3 be points nearly on the line AB whose positions are to be determined. The angles at A, P_1, P_2, P_3, and B and the distances AP_1, P_1P_2, P_2P_3, P_3B are measured.

Computing from A, the position of the final point falls on some point B_1, which, due to errors in the angles and errors in the distances, does not fall upon the point B. No reasonable change could be made in the measured lengths that would cause the position of the computed point B_1 to come much closer to the line AB nor could any change in the measured angles cause B_1 to fall much closer to B. Hence, changes in the angles must be made that would close the figure and that would cause the computed point B_1 to fall upon the point B_2, which is on the line passing through A and B. Then if all the measured lengths are increased or decreased in the same proportion, the point B_2 will move along the line AB and a proportional change in all the lengths should be made so that the point B_2 will fall exactly upon the point B.

For the adjustment of traverse lines of this special form, the following simple method was developed and used, wherever applicable, in adjusting the traverses of the boundary line.

Let P_0 and P_n be the two fixed points between which the traverse is run.

Let P_1, P_2, ... P_{n-1} be the remaining stations at which angles were observed.

Let l_1, l_2, ... l_n equal the measured lengths of the first, second, ... nth courses.

Let B_1, B_2, ... B_n equal the measured azimuths of the first, second, ... nth courses, assuming the azimuth of the line P_0P_n to be zero.

Let V_0, V_1, V_2 .... V_n be corrections to the angles at P_0, P_1, ... P_n such that the azimuth of the line P_nP_{n-1} plus the angle at P_n will equal the azimuth of the line P_nP_0, and the sum of the departures will equal zero.

Then

$$V_0 + V_1 + V_2 + \ldots . V_n = p$$

where p is the difference between the fixed azimuth of the line P_nP_0 and the azimuth as carried through the traverse.

Since the measured lines are nearly parallel to the line $P_0 P_n$ the latitude or the product of the length and the cosine of the azimuth differs but little from the length and for the purpose of this adjustment the lengths may be used in place of the latitudes.

A change of V_0 seconds in the angle at P_0 will produce a change in the departure of $V_0 (l_1 + l_2 + \ldots l_n)$ arc $1''$, a change of V_1 seconds at P_1 will produce a change in the departure of $V_1 (l_2 + l_3 \ldots l_n)$ arc $1''$, etc.

Then the V's must satisfy the condition

$V_0 (l_1 + l_2 + \ldots l_n)$ arc $1'' + V_1 (l_2 + l_3 \ldots l_n)$ arc $1'' + \ldots V_{n-1} (l_n)$ arc $1'' = q$

where $q = -$ (the sum of the computed departures or the error in departure), or

$$V_0 (l_1 + l_2 \ldots l_n) + V_1 (l_2 + l_3 \ldots l_n) \ldots V_{n-1} (l_n) = \frac{q}{\text{arc } 1''}$$

Hence the two equations that must be satisfied in order that there will be no azimuth error and in order that the sum of the departures will be zero are:

$$V_0 + V_1 + V_2 \ldots + V_n = p$$

$$V_0 (l_1 + l_2 \ldots l_n) + V_1 (l_2 + l_3 \ldots l_n) + \ldots V_{n-1} (l_n) = \frac{q}{\text{arc } 1''}$$

To obtain the most probable value of the V's, these equations should be solved subject to the condition that the sum of the squares of the V's shall be a minimum.

There remains to be satisfied the condition that the sum of the latitudes of the courses must equal the fixed distance between P_0 and P_n, and this may be satisfied by multiplying each course of the traverse by the ratio obtained by dividing the fixed distance by the sum of the measured latitudes.

MONUMENTS AND MONUMENTING

The international boundary from the source of the St. Croix River to the St. Lawrence River is marked by 4,204 monuments set on the land portions of the line and by 548 reference monuments along the banks of the boundary streams. The monuments have been placed so as to make the demarcation of the line as complete as possible. A monument has been set at every important road crossing and at every "line house," and a line mark is shown on each of the international bridges on the St. John River. Moreover, on all the straight-line sections of the boundary the monuments have been set at such intervals that it is possible in most cases to see from one monument to the next. The object has been to make it easy for anyone interested to determine the exact location of the boundary line at any point.

TYPES OF MONUMENTS

The monuments which mark the land portions of the line include the following six types:

1. General type of cast-iron monument made in 1843–1845 (fig. 1).
2. Special type of cast-iron monument made in 1843–1845 (fig. 2).
3. Granite monument (fig. 3).
4. Special type of concrete monument (fig. 4).
5. Small concrete or granite monument (fig. 5).
6. Bronze disk boundary monument (fig. 8).

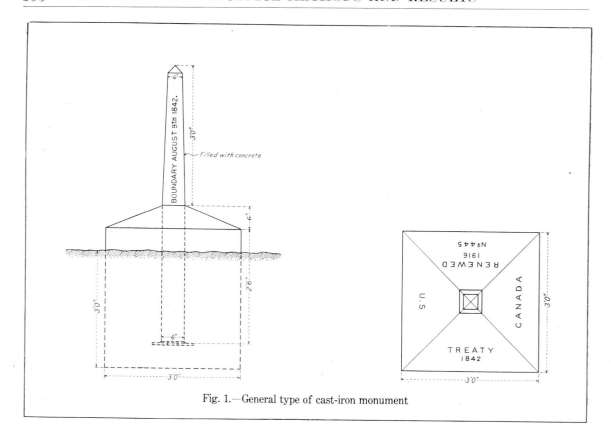

Fig. 1.—General type of cast-iron monument

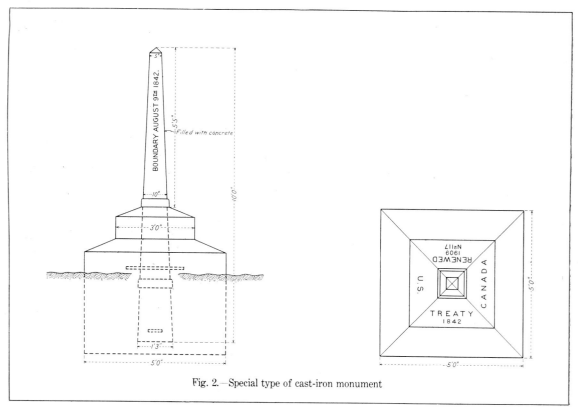

Fig. 2.—Special type of cast-iron monument

The monuments which reference the boundary through the waterways include four different types:

1. General type of cast-iron monument made in 1843–1845 (fig. 1).
2. Small concrete or granite monument (fig. 5).
3. Bronze disk reference monument (fig. 6).
4. Bronze post reference monument (fig. 7).

The general type of cast-iron monument is shown in Figure 1. These are the cast-iron posts which were set in 1843–1845 to mark the line on the land portions of the boundary and the line along some of the small streams, and to show the nationality of the islands of the St. John River. The monuments are 6 feet long and are now set in concrete bases 3 feet square with the top of the cast-iron post rising 3 feet above the surface of the base. All of the cast-iron monuments except those which are used to show the nationality of the islands in the St. John River bear the following inscriptions cast in raised letters on the sides of the posts: On the side facing the United States, "ALBERT SMITH U. S. COMssr."; on the side facing Canada, "LT. COL. I. B. B. ESTCOURT H. B. M. COMssr."; and on the other sides "TREATY OF WASHINGTON" and "BOUNDARY AUGst 9th, 1842." On the concrete bases are inscribed in sunken letters on the side facing each country the appropriate words "CANADA" or "U. S."; on the third side, the number of the monument and the words "RENEWED (date)"; and on the fourth side, "TREATY 1842." The inscriptions on the monuments which show

the nationality of the islands in the St. John River are the same as the above except that the words "BOUNDARY AUGst 9th, 1842," are replaced by "AUGst 9th, 1842, U. S. ISLAND" or "AUGst 9th, 1842, H. B. M. ISLAND," depending upon the nationality of the island monumented. On one side of the base of these island monuments is stamped in the concrete the name of the country, "U. S." or "CANADA," and the number of the monument, and on the opposite side, "RENEWED 1917."

The special cast-iron monuments of the type shown in Figure 2 were set in 1843–1845 to mark certain boundary points which were considered of more than usual importance. These monuments were cast in three sections, whose combined length is 10 feet, and are now

General type of cast-iron monument, on Daigle's Island, St. John River

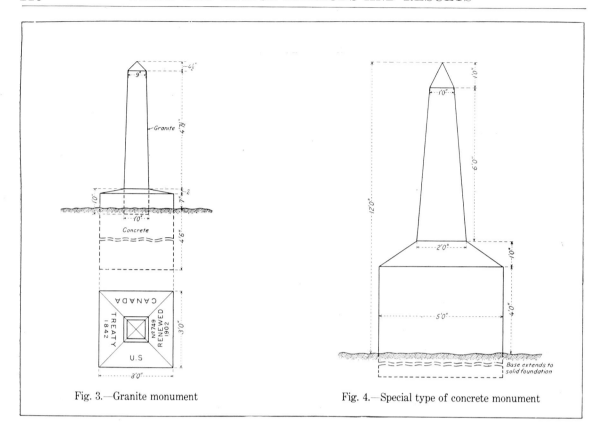

Fig. 3.—Granite monument

Fig. 4.—Special type of concrete monument

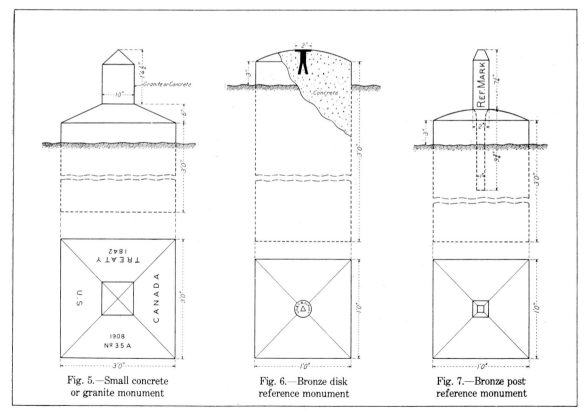

Fig. 5.—Small concrete
or granite monument

Fig. 6.—Bronze disk
reference monument

Fig. 7.—Bronze post
reference monument

set in concrete so that 5 feet 5 inches of each post extends above a base 5 feet square built on a solid foundation below the frost line. The locations of these special monuments are shown in the following list: [13]

Monument No.	Location
1	Source of St. Croix River.
117	Right bank of St. John River at its intersection with the North Line.
178	Outlet of Lake Pohenagamook.
[1] 276	Boundary point at Northwest Branch of St. John River (near junction of Southwest and South Lines).
304	On left bank of Southwest Branch of St. John River at its first intersection with the South Line.
[1] 309	Reference monument on left bank of Southwest Branch at its intersection with parallel 46° 25′ and also with the South Line produced.
318	The Highlands near source of Southwest Branch.
351	The Highlands at the Kennebec Road.
505	Near head of Halls Stream.
518	Right bank of Halls Stream at its intersection with the West Line.
644	East bank of Richelieu River.

[1] Top of cast-iron obelisk has been broken off.

The granite monuments shown in Figure 3 were set in 1902 on the New York-Quebec line to replace the original cast-iron posts. The monuments are described in the reports of the State engineer and surveyor of New York and the chief astronomer of Canada, under whose joint supervision the remonumenting was done. This description is as follows:

" The monuments are 6 feet in length, the lower portion of the stone having an ashlar face, 12 inches square, for 1 foot of its length. From this point for a distance of 4 feet $7\frac{1}{2}$ inches, the stone tapers from 12 inches to 9 inches on each side, with each corner having a beveled face one-half inch wide. The remaining $4\frac{1}{2}$ inches at the top is dressed in the form of a pyramid.

" It was decided that they should be set in concrete bases, 3 feet square, and averaging 4 feet 6

Special type of cast-iron monument, as shown in Figure 2, before being reset

[13] Monument 645 on the west bank of the Richelieu River and monument 775 which marked the line at the east bank of the St. Lawrence River were destroyed by caving banks and ice and could not be recovered and reset.

inches in the ground and 9 inches above the surface. One foot of the granite stone was embedded in the concrete. The upper surface of the concrete was given a slope to turn rain, and on it was imprinted the lettering, as follows:

"On the south side, 'U. S.'"

"On the north side, 'Canada.'"

"On the west side, 'Treaty 1842.'"

"On the east side, the number of the monument, with 'Renewed 1902.'"

"In the case of the new monuments, the word 'renewed' was omitted, and the letter 'A' followed the number."

The large concrete monuments of the special type shown in Figure 4 were built to mark the boundary at Lake Champlain and the Richelieu River. These consist of a base 5 feet square and 5 feet high, surmounted by a 7-foot shaft.

Large concrete monument of type shown in Figure 4, set on Province Point, Lake Champlain, in 1907

Only 4 monuments of this type were constructed, 3 on the shores of Lake Champlain and 1 at the west bank of the Richelieu River.

The small concrete or granite monuments shown in Figure 5 are used in many places along the boundary to mark the line at intermediate points between original monuments, to replace original monuments that could not be recovered, and to reference the boundary line along streams. These monuments consist of granite or concrete blocks, 10 inches square, projecting 8 to 18 inches above concrete bases of the same type as those of the cast-iron monuments. The inscriptions on the bases of those monuments which mark the intermediate points on the boundary line are the same as on the bases of the cast-iron monuments except that the word "RENEWED" is omitted. On the bases of those which are used as reference monuments there is shown the name of the country in which the monument is set, the number of the monument, and the year it was built. Monuments of this type were used on the North Line, the Southwest and South Lines, the Vermont-Quebec boundary, the Highlands at the Kennebec Road crossing, and as reference monu-

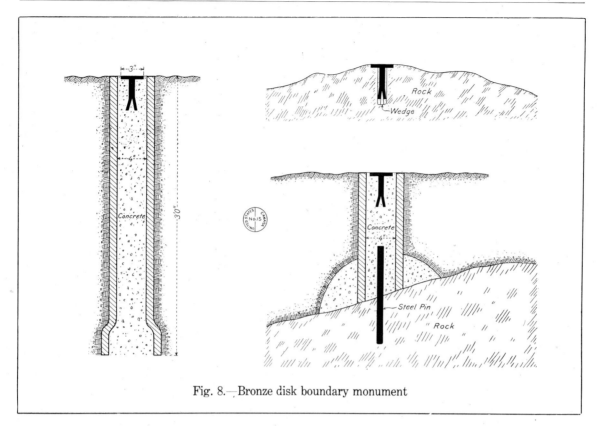

Fig. 8.—Bronze disk boundary monument

ments on the St. John River, the St. Francis River, and the Southwest Branch of the St. John River.

The bronze disk boundary monuments (fig. 8) were set at boundary angle points between the cast-iron monuments on the Highlands. They are 3-inch disks made of bronze which contains 88 per cent copper, 10 per cent tin, and 2 per cent zinc. They are set with wedges in solid rock or in concrete-filled sections of 4-inch drain tile, 24 inches to 36 inches in length, set flange ends down with their upper ends flush with the surface of the ground. The number of the mark is stamped on the disk, and on appropriate sides of a center line are cast the words " CANADA " and " U. S."

Bronze disk reference monuments (fig. 6) are used on the St. John River and on Halls Stream. These consist of 2-inch bronze disks with 3-inch shanks and are set either in concrete bases 12 inches square and 3 feet or more in depth, or in solid rock.

The bronze post reference monuments (fig. 7) are 8 inches high, with a shank 10 inches long. The posts are made of manganese bronze containing 59 per cent copper, 38 per cent zinc, 2 per cent iron, and 1 per cent manganese. The number of the mark is outlined in drill holes about one-fourth inch apart on the smooth side of the post, and the words " REF. MARK," " INT. BDRY.," and either "CANADA" or "U. S." are cast in raised letters on the other three sides. These small posts are set in solid rock or in concrete bases 12 inches square. They are used along the upper part of Halls Stream and at a few places on the St. Francis and St. John Rivers.

Bronze disks used as intermediate boundary monuments on the Highlands

Bronze disks used as reference monuments, triangulation station marks, and bench marks

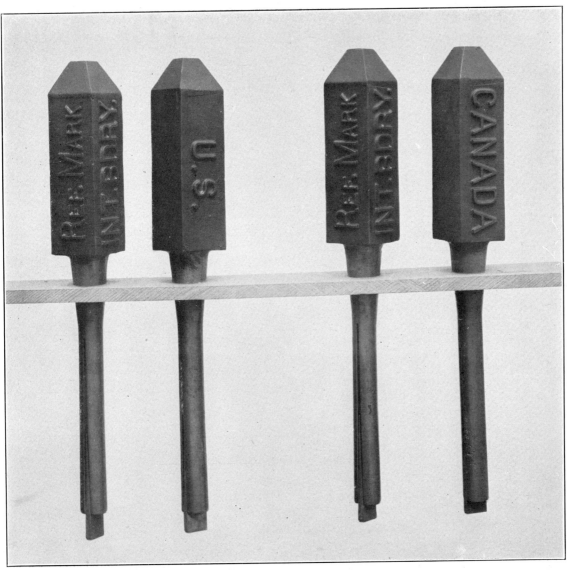

Bronze posts used as reference monuments along some of the boundary streams

Transfer of Original Monuments to More Desirable Sites

Most of the cast-iron monuments set in 1843–1845 have been reset, or replaced by new monuments, on their original sites. Some of the old monuments, however, were found in positions which were threatened by stream erosion or by caving

Monument and "line house" near Canaan, Vt.

banks of steep slopes; while others were found at inconspicuous places or on low ground which did not permit of good foundations except at a considerable cost. These were moved to other points on the boundary line, on near-by ridges or on firm ground. A list of these transferred monuments, with the distances between their original and present positions, follows:

MONUMENTS MOVED ALONG THE NORTH LINE IN 1908

Monument No.	Distance	Direction moved	Monument No.	Distance	Direction moved
	Feet			*Feet*	
2	581	North.	65	366	South.
3	564	Do.	66	840	North.
6	1,018	Do.	67	853	South.
7	544	Do.	69	27	Do.
8	1,281	South.	71	672	Do.
12	536	North.	72	1,396	North.
14	506	Do.	74	1,164	Do.
15	344	South.	75	732	South.
17	1,250	North.	77	646	North.
18	78	Do.	79	112	Do.
21	602	South.	80	386	South.
22	1	Do.	81	462	Do.
24	1	North.	85	357	Do.
26	87	Do.	87	1,334	North.
28	36	Do.	88	769	South.
31	545	South.	89	1,176	Do.
32	645	North.	92	417	Do.
33	969	Do.	93	681	Do.
35	201	South.	94	135	North.
36	983	North.	95	404	South.
37	652	Do.	97	252	North.
38	271	South.	99	436	Do.
40	698	North.	100	109	Do.
41	192	Do.	101	437	South.
43	62	South.	102	125	North.
45	362	North.	103	44	South.
46	223	Do.	104	140	Do.
47	5	South.	105	584	Do.
48	10	North.	106	629	Do.
49	466	South.	108	1,329	North.
51	418	Do.	110	536	Do.
52	681	North.	113	864	Do.
54	76	Do.	115	743	South.
55	647	South.	116	202	Do.
56	43	North.	117	4	Do.
57	244	South.			
58	473	North.			
59	222	South.			
61	1,136	North.			
63	464	South.			

MONUMENTS MOVED ALONG THE VERMONT-QUEBEC BOUNDARY IN 1906–1907

Monument No.	Distance	Direction moved	Monument No.	Distance	Direction moved
	Feet			*Feet*	
522	31	West.	596	6	West.
525	41	East.	601	1,145	East.
537	5,684	West.	602	1,740	Do.
544	3,149	East.	603	672	West.
553	9	West.	608	2,422	Do.
554	18	Do.	612	2,130	Do.
557	362	East.	623	148	Do.
560 ¹	15	West.	627	1,340	Do.
563	2,672	Do.	630	8	Do.
566	618	East.	632	320	Do.
567	597	Do.	633	40	East.
568	72	West.	639	2,723	Do.
572	38	Do.	642	6	West.
583	234	East.			
587	1,763	West.			

¹ Change in position made by Graham and Ord in 1849.

MONUMENTS MOVED ALONG THE NEW YORK-QUEBEC BOUNDARY IN 1902

The changes made in the positions of original monuments on the New York-Quebec boundary, when they were replaced by new ones in 1902, are shown by the following quotation from the report of the State engineer and surveyor of New

One of the monuments that had to be moved; No. 554, at Derby Line, Vermont

York and the report of the chief astronomer and boundary commissioner of Canada, under whom the monumenting was done.[14]

"It was a matter of current report that certain monuments, namely, Nos. 659, 719, 721, and 743, had been moved from their original positions by unauthorized persons. Our survey showed, however, that the first of these was only $4\frac{1}{4}$ inches from the true line, and No. 719 was exactly on line. Nos. 721 and 743 proved to be 3.39 feet and 4.41 feet, respectively, off line. No. 743 was also found to have been moved easterly a distance of 53.81 feet, and, as will be seen from the notes we have given of our examination of the monuments, was completely loose in the hole, and turned partly around. The dis-

Monument 554, after it had been moved and reset

crepancies in the positions of these two monuments were much greater than any others found, and far beyond the range of accidental error of line running or monument setting in the original survey. Our survey shows the probable error of the placing of an original monument to be not more than 2 or 3 inches. This was considered by us to be corroborative of the rumored displacement, and we set the new monuments on the true line: No. 721, 3.39 feet, and No. 743, 4.41 feet, south of where we found the old posts. No. 743 was also moved westerly 53.81 feet.

"Monument No. 734, previously referred to, was not rebuilt. No. 754, which originally stood in the center of the main street of Dundee, was erected 11.48 feet west of the bottom of the old monument, which was left in place. No. 770, formerly on the east bank of St. Regis River, was placed about 10 feet east of the highway, which runs nearly parallel to the river, a short distance back from the east bank.

---

[14] See footnote, p. 99.

"Monument 774, which formerly stood on the bank of the St. Lawrence River, has been carried away by erosion. The new monument was erected about 100 feet east of the present bank.

"In those cases where, as previously explained, two monuments had been set on line, to indicate an astronomical station, we did not consider it necessary to place more than one new granite monument.

"Monument No. 645, in the Richelieu River, was rebuilt in October at the close of our season's work. We measured easterly from No. 646, the distance given in the original notes, and found the stone foundation referred to in the report of the survey of 1845.

"Owing to the fact that water covered the site to a depth of 2 feet, we constructed a cofferdam 6 feet square. A hole 3 feet square was excavated 9 feet below the surface of the water before we obtained a solid foundation."

CONSTRUCTION OF MONUMENTS

In resetting the original cast-iron monuments in concrete bases, the iron post was first straightened up and its center referenced by two pairs of hubs or by a plumb bob suspended from a high frame erected over the monument site. The monument was then taken out and the cedar post, which had been placed in the hollow monument when originally set, was removed and the iron post filled with concrete. The excavation for the base was made 3 feet square and carried to a depth of at least 3 feet to firm ground or to rock ledge. If a solid foundation could not be found at reasonable depth, wooden piles were driven into the bottom of the excavation.

The construction of the base was begun by covering the bottom of the pit with a thick layer of wet concrete, consisting of 1 part Portland cement, 2 parts sand, and 5 parts gravel or broken stone, into which were placed clean stones 6 to 10 inches in diameter. Another layer of concrete was puddled into place and more stones added until the excavation was filled to the proper level. The iron post, filled with concrete which had been allowed to set, was then put in place and securely braced and the concreting continued around the monument until the excavation was nearly filled. A wooden form for the upper part of the base was then built around the top of the hole and filled with a somewhat drier and richer mixture in order that the surface of the base could be made to stand at a slope of about 1 vertical to 2½ horizontal. The surface was carefully troweled and metal plates bearing the proper inscriptions cast in beveled, raised letters

Old cast-iron monument in position to be filled with concrete

and numbers were pressed against the surface of the base on the four sides of the monument. When the concrete had become firm enough to retain the impressions, the plates were removed and the base was covered with wet cement sacks to prevent the formation of surface cracks while the cement was setting.

The methods employed in setting the granite monuments of the New York-Quebec boundary, which was done under the direction of the State engineer and surveyor of New York and the chief astronomer and boundary commissioner of Canada, are shown by the following quotation from their report:

"The new monuments were located and constructed as follows: Where there was no doubt as to the old monument being in its true position, it was first referenced by intersection hubs, east, west, north, and south. These hubs projected 12 inches, and were so placed that cords

Special type of cast-iron monument, No. 505, reconstructed at head of Halls Stream

stretched between nails on their tops passed exactly 6 inches east and north of the center of the old monument. The old monument was then removed, a hole 3 feet square (properly placed) was excavated to a depth of about 4 feet 6 inches. Where soft, marshy ground was encountered, the hole was excavated to a sufficient depth to secure a solid foundation; where ledge rock occurred, all loose material was removed and the site washed and roughened in order to secure a proper bond. Concrete mixture, 1 part Portland cement, 2 parts clean, sharp sand, and 5 parts broken stone, properly rammed, was used to fill the excavation to within 3 inches of the surface of the ground. The cords were placed in position, and the monument adjusted thereto, and kept in place by guys attached to an iron collar which fitted over the pyramidal top. A form 3 feet square inside and 12 inches high was then carefully placed at right angles to the line and the concrete carried up to its top.

Mixing concrete; resetting monument on the Highlands boundary

"This portion of the base was finished with a mixture of 1 part cement and 1 part sand, the top having an outward slope of about 1 in 10. While 'setting' was in progress, brass plates with inscriptions of beveled, projecting letters were placed in position on top and kept there until a perfect impression was obtained. Twenty-four hours after, the form was removed and the exposed surfaces given a brush coat of Portland cement grout."

Transporting monumenting materials, Highlands boundary, 1915

The materials for the construction work on the several parts of the boundary were transported to the monument sites by teams and wagons, pack horses, rowboats, or on the backs of the monumenting crew, depending upon local conditions. For convenience in handling and measuring, the sand and gravel were usually brought to the sites in cement sacks. The water was transported in galvanized tanks made especially for this purpose. The mixing of the concrete was done by

Monument construction, Vermont-Quebec line

hand, using a mixing platform or a mortar box at the easily accessible sites and a sheet of heavy canvas at the places which could not be reached with wagons.

System of Numbering the Monuments

The boundary line from the source of the St. Croix River to the St. Lawrence River is now marked and referenced by 4,752 monuments. Each monument bears the number by which it is designated and these numbers,

Numbering a bronze post reference monument

with the exception of those given to the small intermediate monuments interpolated between the original cast-iron monuments on the Highlands, are shown on the boundary maps.

The system of numbering the monuments begins with monument 1, at the source of the St. Croix River, and ends with monument 774, at the St. Lawrence River. This system was retained so that the original cast-iron monuments set in 1843–1845, when recovered and reset or replaced by new monuments, would bear the numbers by which they were designated in the United States notes of the old survey.

Bronze post reference monument on Halls Stream

However, as there are now about six times as many monuments as were set in 1843–1845, it has been necessary to supplement the original numbering with intermediate systems. On the land portion of the boundary, each new monument interpolated between the original cast-iron monuments has been given the number of the preceding original monument, together with a distinguishing letter or number, as, for example, 73–A, 73–B, 73–C, on the straight-line sections of the boundary, and 422–1, 422–2, 422–3 on the Highlands. Along most of the boundary streams, the reference monuments are in an independent series of numbers; as, for example, on the St. John and St. Francis Rivers, beginning at the intersection of the St. John River with the North Line, the reference monuments on the Canadian side start with No. 1 and end with No. 176 at Lake Pohenagamook; similarly, on the United States side they start with No. 1 and end with No. 167, these monuments being designated on the maps as C–1, C–2, and S–1, S–2, etc. On the islands of St. John River all of the old cast-iron reference monuments set in 1844 which had not been destroyed or lost have been reset and given their original numbers. New reference monuments set on the islands have been given the number of the next preceding original monument together with a distinguishing letter, as, for example, 159–A, 159–B. On the Southwest Branch of the St. John River the four old cast-iron monuments of 1844 at the two forks of the stream have been reset and given their original numbers; on the lower part of the stream the new monuments have been given the numbers of the triangulation stations at which they were set, but since monuments were not set at all triangulation stations, these numbers are not consecutive; on the upper part of the river, between the end of the triangulation and Little St. John Lake, the monuments are numbered consecutively on each side of the stream. Along Halls Stream all of the old cast-iron monuments of 1845 which could be recovered were reset and these retain their original numbers. The bronze post and bronze disk reference monuments set along the stream between the old monuments are numbered consecutively from each preceding cast-iron monument, as, for example, 511–1, 511–2, etc.

THE BOUNDARY VISTA

An important adjunct to the monuments, in the demarcation of the line through the wooded areas, is the boundary vista. This was recognized by the commissioners of the survey of 1843–1845, who cleared a strip along all the land portions of the line. This vista has been reopened and cleared to such width that there is now an open sky line at least 20 feet wide, 10 feet on each side of the boundary. The aggregate length of this clearing is approximately 389 miles.

Boundary vista looking northeast from point near East Lake, Southwest Line, 1912

The vista cutting was done by a crew of axmen organized for that purpose. It was generally one of the first operations in connection with the survey and was kept well in advance of the other work. The felled trees were trimmed of branches and in many places the logs were removed to the sides of the vista and the clearing used for a roadway over which materials and supplies for the survey were transported.

Besides the clearing along the boundary, considerable line cutting had to be done for other purposes. Along the Southwest Branch of the St. John River and on the eastern section of the Highlands, lines had to be opened for the precise traverse measurements, and on other parts of the line, particularly on the western portion of the Highlands, heavy cutting was frequently necessary for triangulation. Considerable cutting of a lighter character was required by the topographers in running stadia lines; and another item in the work of the ax crews was the opening of lines for roads and pack trails.

On most parts of the boundary, brush and second-growth timber appear very rapidly, and it will be necessary from time to time to reopen the vista if the demarcation of the line is to be maintained in its present state of effectiveness. An inspection made of some of the boundary vistas in 1922 showed varying rates of growth of trees and brush. In the wet bogs of the Southwest and South Lines only stunted brush 3 to 4 feet high had developed since the line was cleared in 1912 and 1913, but on the ridges dense thickets of maple, birch, and poplar, 15 to 20 feet high, had grown up. Unless the line is periodically cleared, the vista in these latter

Monument 543; tree grown since 1845

places will soon be entirely obliterated and the monuments difficult to find.

TOPOGRAPHY

The region traversed by the part of the international boundary described in this report is mostly wooded, and varies in relief from the flat spruce bogs along the South Line to the rugged highlands between the Province of Quebec and the States of Maine and New Hampshire, where peaks of the boundary ridge have an average elevation of approximately 1,700 feet above the neighboring valleys. In this last-named region, Gosford Mountain rises to an elevation of 3,887 feet above sea level and is, with the exception of the Sweetgrass Hills in Montana, the highest peak in the belt of boundary topography east of the Rocky Mountains. Throughout most of its course, however, the boundary from the source of the St. Croix to the St. Lawrence River traverses low, wooded hills, with few bold or rugged features, or follows natural watercourses.

As there were no maps of the country which satisfied the requirements of Article III of the treaty of 1908, which stipulates that "the course of the entire boundary * * * shall be marked by said commissioners upon accurate modern charts prepared or adopted by them for that purpose," the execution of an accurate topographic survey to provide such maps became part of the duties of the commissioners. The area surveyed by the field force of the commission for this purpose has a minimum width of one-half mile on each side of the boundary, though in several places, particularly along the Highlands, a much wider strip was covered.

All of the topography was mapped in the field, mostly with plane table and stadia, using a 20-foot contour interval, on field scales of 1:5,000, 1:10,000, 1:15,840, and 1:20,000, the size of the scales depending upon the detail necessary properly to show the relation of the boundary line and monuments to the natural topographic features. The field

Monument 480, showing growth of trees since original vista was opened in 1844

mapping was always done on a larger scale than that upon which the finished maps were to be published.

The horizontal control for the topographic survey was furnished by the boundary triangulation and the various grades of traverse, which determined the geographic positions of the boundary monuments and reference monuments. The vertical control was obtained from the lines of spirit levels which were run along or near the boundary.

Topographic Methods

Two different methods were used for mapping the topography on different parts of the line. The first and general method was with plane table and stadia, supplemented in the more densely wooded country by plane table and string tape traverses and aneroid barometers. The second method (used by the Canadian parties) was by a series of hand-level traverses and notebook sketches, which were immediately transferred to field sheets kept in camp.

For much of the plane-table work a telescopic alidade equipped either with the Beaman or with the ordinary vertical arc was used, together with a standard United States Geological Survey, 18 by 24 inch or 15 by 15 inch, plane table mounted on a Johnson head tripod. Along the North Line, the St. John River, and on the New York-Quebec line, where the country is more open, and also on the St. Francis River, the larger 24 by 30 inch plane table of the United States Coast and Geodetic Survey type was used. With this latter instrument the mapping was done on 30 by 52 inch sheets of muslin-backed cold-pressed antiquarian paper; and with the

Vista-cutting gang, United States party, Highlands boundary, 1916

smaller plane tables the field work was done on sheets of white celluloid or double-mounted Paragon paper of the same size as the plane-table boards.

With either of the plane-table outfits the first step was the preparation of the field sheet by plotting the positions of the triangulation or traverse points and the monuments. Closed stadia traverses were then run between these control points, and the topographic features were located by means of numerous stadia readings taken from the traverse stations, using for this purpose one to three rodmen, depending upon the character of the country being mapped. The topographer, as soon as he read the distance and vertical angle to a point, plotted it on his sheet and computed its elevation. After he had thus determined as many points as were needed, and while in the field with the topographic features

Taking topography with the plane table

before him, he drew the contour lines on his plane-table sheet. He also located and drew on the sheet the roads, buildings, streams, and other features. The stadia was supplemented where convenient by intersection work, particularly in sketching the wooded hills along the North Line, the St. Francis River, and the Vermont-Quebec line.

In the more densely wooded areas the above stadia methods were supplemented by the use of open-sight alidades, paraffined linen tapes, and aneroid barom-

United States topographic camp at Arnold Bog, 1916

eters, which were used after the method developed by the United States Geological Survey for filling in the topography of small, wooded areas around which stadia traverses had been run. The procedure with this method of mapping was as follows:

A plane-table-and-stadia traverse was first run along the boundary and the contours crossing the line were sketched. This very narrow belt of topography was then traced on thin tracing paper and transferred to the plane-table sheets of the topographers who were working on either side of the line. These topographers then blocked out small areas of approximately one-half square mile and ran stadia traverses around them through narrow lines cut through the timber and brush. Each of these traverses was usually started at a control point on the boundary and was run at right angles to the boundary for a distance of one-half mile, then parallel to the line for approximately 1 mile, and thence back to close on a boundary control point. Along this stadia traverse there were left marked stations of known elevation.

Low pass on Highlands boundary at head of Arnold Bog; elevation, 2,481 feet

After being adjusted, this traverse and the traverse along the boundary formed the skeleton control which was to be filled in by the paraffined tape traverses. In this filling-in process any marked station was taken as a starting point, and the man at the head end of the tape, aided by a prismatic or pocket compass, started dragging the tape across the unmapped area toward another marked point. When the 500-foot tape was extended, the plane-table man pointed the open-sight alidade in the general direction taken by the tape man, and a more exact pointing was made by observing the direction from which certain vocal signals of the tape man seemed to come. The traverse man then went forward along the tape, took aneroid readings at abrupt changes of elevation, explored the country on either side of the traverse, and sketched the contours. At the forward end of the tape the plane table was then set up and oriented, the aneroid was read, and the operation repeated. This procedure was continued until a closure was made on the marked point of the stadia traverse, toward which the line was being run.

This method proved most satisfactory when the string-tape traverse lines were not more than 1 mile in length and the differences in elevations were at least several contour intervals. Its immense advantage lay in eliminating the slow and costly cutting of lines through the brush and timber. It was used on the Highlands from the Canadian Pacific Railway crossing to the head of Halls Stream, on the South Line, the southern end of the Southwest Line, and along the northern end of Halls Stream.

The hand-level method used by the Canadian parties for taking the topography in heavily wooded areas was as follows: At intervals of 1,000 feet or less along the boundary, and usually at right angles to it, a narrow line was cut through the small forest growth, avoiding the large trees. The bearings of the courses of this line were determined with a prismatic compass. At the same time, with a Locke level mounted on a Jacob's staff and equipped with stadia wires, levels were run over the line and distances measured from station to station by stadia readings on the level rod. In the book in which the notes of this work were recorded, sketches were made of the contours and the other features for some distance on each side of the stadia line. The notes and sketches were then plotted and adjusted on a field sheet, and on this sheet were sketched all the contours of the areas mapped before leaving that locality. Ample opportunity was thus afforded for correcting errors and filling in areas which had not been thoroughly covered by the several level traverse parties.

The parts of the boundary mapped by this method include the Southwest Line from Lake Pohenagamook to monument 265, the Southwest Branch of the St. John River, and the Highlands eastward from the crossing of the Canadian Pacific Railway.

LEVELING

The vertical control for the topographic maps consists of lines of spirit levels run along the boundary just ahead of the mapping, most of which was done before precise-level bench marks of the two countries had been established near the boundary. The most accurately determined elevations available to the parties working along the boundary during the first few years of the survey were those of railroad bench marks, and this datum was used with the realization that the corrections to reduce the elevations to mean sea-level could be determined later. In later years, when these lines of levels were connected to precise-level bench marks of the United States Coast and Geodetic Survey and the Geodetic Survey of Canada, it was found that these corrections never exceeded 10 feet. The amount of each correction is shown in a note on the published map to which it is applicable. When the western part of the Highlands and the New York-Quebec boundary were mapped, precise-level bench marks were available, and the elevations along the line were determined directly on mean sea-level datum.

The elevations along the North Line were determined by a double-rodded line of levels run in one direction only and based on the Canadian Pacific Railway's elevation of rail at the boundary crossing near monument 14–A. During the course of the survey this line was checked by vertical angles and stadia distances measured with a small theodolite. Several years after the survey of the North Line was completed precise-level bench marks were established in that vicinity by the United States Coast and Geodetic Survey and the Geodetic Survey of Canada. Connections were made between the levels along the North Line and these bench marks at the following points: A line was run from a Coast and Geodetic Survey precise bench mark at Danforth, Me., to monument 1, and ties were made with precise bench marks of the Geodetic Survey of Canada at monument 14–A at the boundary crossing of the Houlton-Debec branch and at monument 82 at the boundary crossing of the Presque Isle-Andover branch of the Canadian Pacific Railway. These three connections provided the corrections necessary to reduce the North Line elevations to mean sea-level datum.

Elevations for the control of the topography along the St. John and St. Francis Rivers were obtained by running levels from numerous bench marks of the Canadian National Railway, which was then under construction. A continuous line of levels was run along the Canadian side of the St. John River, following one of the railroads, and, subsequently, when precise-level bench marks were available, this line was connected at six points to the Canadian Geodetic Survey levels, and the elevations determined along the St. Francis River were connected to a precise-level bench mark at Lake Pohenagamook.

From the Canadian National Railway bench mark at Lake Pohenagamook, levels were run independently in forward and backward directions along the Southwest and South Lines to the Southwest Branch of the St. John River, and elevations were determined at 100-foot intervals at the stakes set for tape measurement along the boundary. At St. Pamphile a closure was made with a line from a Canadian National Railway bench mark at Lafontaine, Quebec; and at monument 309 a connection was made with a circuit which had been run from the Quebec Central Railway bench mark at Ste. Sabine, thence along the Southwest Branch of the St. John, and back to the railroad at Ste. Rose. Levels on the Quebec Central Railway datum were continued along the Southwest Branch of the St. John River and thence along the Highlands to monument 392, at which point a junction was made with the levels carried along the Highlands boundary from the Canadian Geodetic Survey precise bench mark on the Canadian Pacific Railway at Boundary Siding, Quebec. In 1922, a line was run from a United States Coast and Geodetic Survey precise-level bench mark at Jackman, Me., to monuments 351 and 352; and from these two connections with precise levels, and from the connection made at Lake Pohenagamook with the Canadian Geodetic Survey levels, corrections were determined to reduce the intervening elevations to mean sea-level.

For the vertical control of the survey of the portion of the boundary along the Highlands from the crossing of the Canadian Pacific Railway to the head of Halls Stream, level lines were run in a series of closed circuits westward from a Canadian precise-level bench mark on the Canadian Pacific Railway at Boundary Siding, and eastward along the Highlands from a similar precise-level bench mark at St. Malo, Quebec. A junction was made between these lines at monument 475. At a point on the boundary near Woburn, Quebec, the levels were also connected with a line running north to Lake Megantic, the elevation of which was determined from a precise-level bench mark at Megantic, Quebec. A permanent bench mark, consisting of a bronze disk set in the concrete foundation of the monument, was established at each of the 106 monuments from the Canadian Pacific Railway crossing to the head of Halls Stream. The bench-mark elevations and the topographic maps of this portion of the line are on mean sea-level datum.

Levels for the vertical control of the topographic maps along Halls Stream were run from a bench mark of the Maine Central Railroad at Beecher Falls, Vt., and later, after precise leveling had been done in this vicinity, were tied to a precise bench mark at St. Malo, Quebec, and to a similar bench mark near the mouth of the stream.

The Vermont-Quebec boundary elevations depend upon a line of levels run along the boundary in one direction only, together with a double line of elevations determined from vertical angles and stadia distances measured with a theodolite. When this work was done in 1906 and 1907 the most reliable elevations available were those of the several railroads crossing the boundary. Accordingly these were used, and in 1919, when precise bench marks were available, the Vermont-Quebec boundary levels were connected with Canadian Geodetic Survey bench marks at five points—Beecher Falls, Vt., Norton Mills, Vt. (Stanhope, Quebec), Rock Island, Quebec (Derby Line, Vt.), Richford, Vt. (Abercorn, Quebec), and St. Armand, Quebec. The corrections to the boundary levels at these points averaged less than 2 feet. The levels were adjusted to mean sea-level datum, and the elevation of the ground at each monument is shown on this datum on the boundary maps.

The levels along the New York-Quebec boundary were started at a United States Coast and Geodetic Survey precise-level bench mark at Rouses Point, N. Y.,

Bench mark, Canadian Department of Public Works, established on boundary line at Rouses Point, 1844

and were run westward along the line
in small circuits to a closure on a
United States Geological Survey bench
mark at the Chateaugay River. From
that point to the St. Lawrence River
a line was run in one direction only,
touching on three United States Geological Survey bench marks and closing
on a bench mark established at Hogansburg, N. Y., by the Board of Engineers
on Deep Waterways. Permanent
bench marks, consisting of bronze disks
set in the bases of monuments, were
established at 41 of the New York-
Quebec boundary monuments.

Special type of leveling-rod target used on the Highlands boundary

The levels along the boundary
from the source of the St. Croix River
to the St. Lawrence may be divided
roughly into three classes, according to
their relative accuracy. Those along
the Vermont-Quebec line and along
the North Line were run only for the
purpose of furnishing vertical control
for the topographic maps of these re-
gions before any precise-level bench
marks had been established near the
work and before any limits of accuracy
for leveling and topography had been
adopted by the boundary surveyors. Levels of a higher degree of accuracy were
run along the St. John and St. Francis Rivers, the Southwest and South Lines, the
Southwest Branch of the St. John River, the eastern part of the Highlands, and
along Halls Stream. These levels were carefully run, but the accuracy attempted
was only of that degree necessary to determine the inclination of the tapes on the
precise traverse measurements and to afford a more accurate control for the topography than that first used, without attempting to establish a line of permanent
bench marks based on mean sea-level datum. The most accurate leveling was
done along the New York-Quebec boundary and along the Highlands from the
Canadian Pacific Railway to the head of Halls Stream. These levels are based on
precise-level bench marks. They were carefully run in closed circuits, permanent
bench marks were established along the line, and the results compare favorably
with the primary grade of leveling done by the United States Geological Survey.
The requirement for closure of circuits on these lines was that the discrepancy in
closure in feet should not exceed $0.04\sqrt{M}$, in which M is the length of the circuit
in miles.

To obtain this accuracy, it was necessary in the rough country along the Highlands to keep the lengths of the fore sights and back sights carefully balanced. As it was difficult to pace these distances with any degree of accuracy in the vista filled with fallen timber along the boundary, the lengths of the back sights and fore sights were read by stadia, using for this purpose a special form of stadia target designed by the engi-

A supply storehouse in the Highlands, 1916

neer to the United States section of the commission. This consisted simply of a small scale attached to the regular target, on which the stadia distance was read by the upper stadia wire after the target was set at the correct elevation. To prevent the possible error of setting the target on one of the stadia wires instead of on the center wire, the lower stadia wire was removed from the instrument, thereby making it impossible to read the stadia distance if the target was improperly set. The target is shown in the illustration on page 131.

Moving camp with boats and scow on Glazier Lake, 1910

FIELD TRANSPORTATION

The transportation of equipment, provisions, forage, and monumenting materials from the railway stations to camps of the surveying parties along the boundary and the movement of camp outfits from point to point was a problem with which the parties were always confronted. In some of the settled localities where there were good roads, it required little consideration; but in the rough, densely wooded areas it was perhaps the most difficult job of all in conducting the survey operations.

The work along the line northward from the source of the St. Croix River to the St. John River and thence along that river to the St. Francis River was through a settled country, a region of farms and small villages, where good roads were numerous, and the outfits and materials incidental to the survey were easily handled with teams and wagons.

Along the St. Francis River the parties used a road as far north as Glazier Lake, an expansion of that river 5 miles above its mouth. From the foot of Glazier Lake north to the head of Beau Lake there were no roads and dependence was placed entirely upon water transportation, the parties using a motor boat, a scow, and canoes on the river and lakes. From the head of Beau Lake to Lake Pohenagamook the stream is paralleled by a highway and throughout part of this distance by the Canadian National Railway, and here water transportation was supplemented by the use of the railway and the highway.

From Lake Pohenagamook to the source of the Southwest Branch of the St. John River the boundary traverses a forest-covered area of hills interspersed with streams and swamps. Where possible in this region wagons were used on the few tote roads and winter logging roads leading from the

Transportation difficulties in the Highlands, 1915 and 1916

settlements to the boundary. Where wagons could not be used they were replaced by sleds or jumpers, which were better suited to the roads across the bogs and marshes and to the narrow trails cut by the survey parties.

On the Highlands boundary, which extends from the source of the Southwest Branch of the St. John River to the head of Halls Stream, the line traverses some of the most mountainous country east of the Rocky Mountains. Throughout this region, which is densely wooded, equipment and supplies were hauled by teams and wagons from the railroads to supply camps at the ends of logging roads, and were distributed from there to

Supplies en route to one of the boundary camps, 1916

points on the boundary by jumpers or by pack trains operating over cut trails, although in many places animals could not be used at all and the packing was done by men.

The transportation difficulties in the Highlands can best be appreciated by following an average daily shipment of freight from one of the Canadian towns to survey camps near the boundary. Starting at Megantic, Quebec, which was the headquarters for the United States parties for parts of two seasons, 1915 and 1916, the daily shipment of mess supplies, monumenting materials, and forage, approximately 1 ton, was loaded on a steamboat at Lake Megantic and taken south 10 miles to Woburn Wharf, where it was transferred to heavy wagons and hauled 11 miles to a supply camp. From there it was taken in light loads over an 8-mile stretch of rough road ending at a pack-train base at Arnold Bog. Over this road 1,200 pounds was a good load for a 4-horse team. From the camp at Arnold Bog the supplies were relayed to the survey camps by pack trains operating over trails cut through the timber and thick underbrush.

Temporary substitute for broken wagon wheel

On the higher parts of the boundary ridge it was necessary to pack to the mountain tops not only the cement and boundary marks but also the water, sand, and gravel required for the concrete. This was done over trails cut into the mountain sides or built by felling trees against which rocks, brush, and earth were placed to afford footing for the pack animals.   Some of the points were inaccessible to the animals, and the materials were taken over the final distances by men.

The magnitude of this part of the work of the survey can perhaps be most easily grasped by considering just the single item of transportation for the monumenting. For example, in 1916 there were put in place on the western half of the Highlands boundary 878 vitrified tiles filled with concrete to mark the intermediate boundary points, and there were set 84 large boundary monuments, each in a base containing, approximately, 1 cubic yard of concrete.   The hollow cast-iron shafts of the monuments were also filled with concrete.   This construction work alone for that season required the transporting to the boundary line of over 190 tons of materials.

The rest of the boundary, from the head of Halls Stream to the forty-fifth parallel and westward along the old Valentine and Collins line to the St. Lawrence River, is through a region of farms and good roads, and on this portion of the line the parties used teams and wagons and motor trucks.

MAPS

Article III of the treaty of 1908 stipulates that " the course of the entire boundary, as described in Article I of the treaty of 1842 and as laid down as aforesaid under Article VI of that treaty, shall be marked by said commissioners upon quadruplicate sets of accurate modern charts prepared or adopted by them for that purpose, and that said charts so marked shall be certified and signed by them and two duplicate originals thereof shall be filed with each Government."

The charts upon which the commissioners have marked the boundary line from the source of the St. Croix to the St. Lawrence River, in accordance with the above, are topographic maps prepared from the surveys made by the field force of the commission.   They consist of a series of 61 sheets arranged and numbered as shown on the accompanying map.   They have been engraved on copper plates and printed from stone, and the engraved plates will be preserved by the two Governments as permanent records of the work.   The four official sets of maps, two for each Government, which bear the commissioners' signatures, are transmitted in portfolios and form a part of this report.   The copies of the maps for public distribution are identical with the originals, except that there appear on each map the word " Copy" and the date of publication, and the commissioners' signatures are in facsimile.

The size of each sheet is 23 by 35 inches inside the border.   The belt of topography shown has an average width of $1\frac{1}{4}$ miles.   The conventional signs used to represent the various topographic features are those adopted by the United States Board of Surveys and Maps.   The boundary line, monuments, culture, and lettering appear in black; relief (20-foot contour lines) in brown; drainage in blue; and timber in green.   The maps are constructed on the polyconic projection on scales of 1:6,000, 1:12,000 and 1:24,000, depending on the detail required to show clearly the location of the boundary line.   At the top of each map are the title, the number of the sheet, the names of the commissioners, and copies of the seals of the two countries; and in the lower right-hand corner is the commissioners' certificate, which reads as follows:

We certify that this map is one of the quadruplicate set of sixty-one (61) maps adopted under Article III of the Treaty between Great Britain and the United States, signed at Washington April 11, 1908, and that we have marked thereon the Boundary Line as re-established by the Commissioners designated above, in accordance with the provisions of the said Article. Signed (date of signature).

(Signed)   J. J. McArthur,   (Signed)   E. Lester Jones,
His Britannic Majesty's Commissioner.   *United States Commissioner.*

In addition to the above, each sheet bears the necessary scales and explanatory notes, and the names of the chiefs of parties and their assistants who were responsible for the field work shown thereon.

Preparation of the Maps

The first step in the preparation of the maps, after the completion of the surveys in the field, was the inking of the penciled plane-table sheets. This was done in the office at the close of the field seasons, usually by the topographers who had done the mapping. After inking the field drawings, the work on the 15 by 15 inch plane-table sheets was photographed on transparent celluloid sheets which were treated with graphite. The celluloid sheets were then adjusted to projections drawn on 24 by 36 inch office sheets and the field work transferred to these by rubbing the celluloid with an oiled burnisher. The graphite lines thus transferred were then inked in the various colors and the sheets delivered to the engraver. For the field work which had been done on the large plane-table sheets, size 30 by 50 inches, the above transfer process was unnecessary, and, after being inked, these were furnished to the engraver without any further preparation. The geographic positions of the control points, boundary monuments, reference monuments, and turning points to be shown on the maps were also given to the engraver.

For each map the engraver first engraved on a copper plate the lines of the polyconic projection carefully laid out to the publication scale of the map. From these projected parallels of latitude and meridians of longitude he then plotted the geographic positions of the control points, boundary monuments, reference monuments, and turning points. This operation was done under the supervision of the cartographer of the United States section of the commission, who verified the projection and checked the positions of the plotted points. By use of a wax transfer process the projection and control points were then transferred from this plate to two other copper plates, one for the brown lines of the map and one for the blue. The topographic drawings which had been furnished the engraver were photographed to the scale of the projection and wax impressions made of the negatives. These were transferred to the plates, which were then engraved, the part to be shown in brown on one plate and the part to be shown in blue on the other.

The three engraved copper plates were delivered to the printer, together with a timber sheet for the map showing the outlines of the wooded areas, the character of the forest growth, and sufficient control points for fitting this outline to the map projection. The printer "pulled" an impression from each of these three plates and transferred each impression to a lithographic stone. Likewise from standard

symbol patterns he transferred to a fourth stone the proper symbols for the areas outlined on the timber sheet. From these four stones the finished map was then printed.

A limited edition of the maps has been printed for each Government for distribution, either in the form of complete sets or individual maps. In the United States, copies of the report and maps are on file in the Library of Congress and in all other libraries designated by the Government as "depository libraries"; that is, those which receive all United States Government publications. In Canada they are on file in the Dominion archives, in the libraries of the Dominion Parliament and of the Provincial Legislative Assemblies, and in university and reference libraries throughout the country.

DESCRIPTION AND DEFINITION OF THE INTERNATIONAL BOUNDARY LINE FROM THE SOURCE OF THE ST. CROIX RIVER TO THE ST. LAWRENCE RIVER

The international boundary line from the source of the St. Croix River to the St. Lawrence River as now reestablished consists of a series of straight-line courses joining consecutively numbered monuments along the land boundary and consecutively numbered "turning points" along the water boundary. The line has a length of 670.31 miles, 490.79 miles on land and 179.52 miles along the streams. It is marked on the land by 4,204 boundary monuments and 389 miles of cleared vista, and is referenced on the waterways by 548 reference monuments.

The description of the course of the line as surveyed and monumented by the commissioners, and as marked by them on the 61 boundary maps which accompany this report, is set forth in tabular form. The tables give the geographic positions of all the boundary monuments and boundary turning points, together with the lengths and azimuths of the boundary courses. They also give the geographic positions of the boundary reference monuments and the lengths and azimuths of the lines to the boundary turning points which they reference. The latitudes and longitudes are given on the North American datum, the lengths of the courses are given in meters, and the azimuths are reckoned clockwise, south being 0°, west 90°, north 180°, and east 270°.

The North American datum is the standard geodetic datum used by both countries. It has been adopted by the Geodetic Survey of Canada, the United States Coast and Geodetic Survey, and the Comisión Geodésica Mexicana. It may be defined, in terms of the position of the United States Coast and Geodetic Survey station "Meades Ranch" and the azimuth from that station to "Waldo," as follows:

	°	′	″
Latitude	39	13	26. 686
Longitude	98	32	30. 506
Azimuth to station "Waldo"	75	28	14. 52

Points are said to be upon the North American datum when they are connected with the station "Meades Ranch" by continuous triangulation or traverse through which the latitudes, longitudes, and azimuths have been computed on the Clarke Spheroid of 1866, as expressed in meters, starting with the above position and azimuth.

The distances given in the tables are reduced to sea level. If the actual horizontal distances are desired, the distances given in the tables should be increased by an amount equal to 0.00000004785 $L E$ in which L is the length of the course in meters and E is the mean elevation of the two ends of the course in feet. The maximum value of this increase, for any course on this part of the international boundary, is less than $\frac{1}{5000}$ of the distance.

138

GEOGRAPHIC POSITIONS OF MONUMENTS MARKING THE INTERNATIONAL BOUNDARY FROM THE SOURCE OF THE ST. CROIX RIVER TO THE ST. JOHN RIVER

Station	Latitude and longitude	Azimuth	To station	Distance (meters)
Mon. 1 (initial monument).	45 56 37.00 / 67 46 54.71	180 05 53	Mon. 1-A	612.41
Mon. 1-A	45 56 56.84 / 67 46 54.66	0 05 53 / 180 05 53	Mon. 1 / Mon. 1-B	612.41 / 795.12
Mon. 1-B	45 57 22.59 / 67 46 54.60	0 05 53 / 180 06 13	Mon. 1-A / Mon. 2	795.12 / 381.18
Mon. 2	45 57 34.94 / 67 46 54.57	0 06 13 / 180 06 13	Mon. 1-B / Mon. 2-A	381.18 / 448.71
Mon. 2-A	45 57 49.47 / 67 46 54.53	0 06 13 / 180 06 13	Mon. 2 / Mon. 3	448.71 / 1,156.62
Mon. 3	45 58 26.93 / 67 46 54.43	0 06 13 / 180 06 13	Mon. 2-A / Mon. 3-A	1,156.62 / 816.10
Mon. 3-A	45 58 53.36 / 67 46 54.36	0 06 13 / 180 06 13	Mon. 3 / Mon. 4	816.10 / 624.67
Mon. 4	45 59 13.59 / 67 46 54.31	0 06 13 / 180 06 13	Mon. 3-A / Mon. 5	624.67 / 572.89
Mon. 5	45 59 32.15 / 67 46 54.26	0 06 13 / 180 08 39	Mon. 4 / Mon. 5-A	572.89 / 446.18
Mon. 5-A	45 59 46.60 / 67 46 54.21	0 08 39 / 180 08 39	Mon. 5 / Mon. 6	446.18 / 906.97
Mon. 6	46 00 15.97 / 67 46 54.11	0 08 39 / 180 08 39	Mon. 5-A / Mon. 6-A	906.97 / 757.09
Mon. 6-A	46 00 40.50 / 67 46 54.02	0 08 39 / 180 08 39	Mon. 6 / Mon. 7	757.09 / 712.80
Mon. 7	46 01 03.58 / 67 46 53.94	0 08 39 / 180 08 39	Mon. 6-A / Mon. 8	712.80 / 1,057.49
Mon. 8	46 01 37.83 / 67 46 53.81	0 08 40 / 180 08 33	Mon. 7 / Mon. 8-A	1,057.49 / 757.48
Mon. 8-A	46 02 02.37 / 67 46 53.72	0 08 33 / 180 08 33	Mon. 8 / Mon. 9	757.48 / 446.06
Mon. 9	46 02 16.81 / 67 46 53.67	0 08 33 / 179 48 55	Mon. 8-A / Mon. 10	446.06 / 801.04
Mon. 10	46 02 42.76 / 67 46 53.79	179 48 55 / 179 48 55	Mon. 9 / Mon. 10-A	801.04 / 566.57
Mon. 10-A	46 03 01.11 / 67 46 53.88	359 48 55 / 179 48 55	Mon. 10 / Mon. 10-B	566.57 / 120.54
Mon. 10-B	46 03 05.01 / 67 46 53.90	359 48 55 / 179 48 35	Mon. 10-A / Mon. 10-C	120.54 / 305.08
Mon. 10-C	46 03 14.89 / 67 46 53.94	359 48 35 / 179 48 30	Mon. 10-B / Mon. 10-D	305.08 / 326.16
Mon. 10-D	46 03 25.46 / 67 46 53.99	359 48 30 / 179 48 14	Mon. 10-C / Mon. 10-E	326.16 / 113.37
Mon. 10-E	46 03 29.13 / 67 46 54.01	359 48 14 / 179 48 15	Mon. 10-D / Mon. 11	113.37 / 170.26
Mon. 11	46 03 34.64 / 67 46 54.04	359 48 15 / 179 42 41	Mon. 10-E / Mon. 11-A	170.26 / 134.24
Mon. 11-A	46 03 38.99 / 67 46 54.07	359 42 40 / 179 42 40	Mon. 11 / Mon. 11-B	134.24 / 936.57
Mon. 11-B	46 04 09.33 / 67 46 54.29	359 42 40 / 179 42 40	Mon. 11-A / Mon. 12	936.57 / 719.45
Mon. 12	46 04 32.63 / 67 46 54.46	359 42 40 / 179 42 34	Mon. 11-B / Mon. 13	719.45 / 211.83
Mon. 13	46 04 39.49 / 67 46 54.51	359 42 34 / 179 55 59	Mon. 12 / Mon. 13-A	211.83 / 816.54
Mon. 13-A	46 05 05.93 / 67 46 54.55	359 55 59 / 179 55 59	Mon. 13 / Mon. 13-B	816.54 / 102.06
Mon. 13-B	46 05 09.24 / 67 46 54.56	359 55 59 / 179 55 59	Mon. 13-A / Mon. 14	102.06 / 474.49
Mon. 14	46 05 24.61 / 67 46 54.58	359 55 59 / 179 55 59	Mon. 13-B / Mon. 14-A	474.49 / 559.28
Mon. 14-A	46 05 42.72 / 67 46 54.61	359 55 59 / 179 55 59	Mon. 14 / Mon. 15	559.28 / 796.51
Mon. 15	46 06 08.52 / 67 46 54.66	359 55 59 / 179 55 59	Mon. 14-A / Mon. 15-A	796.51 / 490.16
Mon. 15-A	46 06 24.39 / 67 46 54.68	359 55 59 / 179 55 59	Mon. 15 / Mon. 15-B	490.16 / 448.90
Mon. 15-B	46 06 38.93 / 67 46 54.71	359 55 59 / 179 55 59	Mon. 15-A / Mon. 16	448.90 / 215.11
Mon. 16	46 06 45.90 / 67 46 54.72	359 55 59 / 179 59 48	Mon. 15-B / Mon. 16-A	215.11 / 87.79
Mon. 16-A	46 06 48.74 / 67 46 54.72	359 59 48 / 179 59 48	Mon. 16 / Mon. 17	87.79 / 859.99
Mon. 17	46 07 16.60 / 67 46 54.72	359 59 48 / 179 59 48	Mon. 16-A / Mon. 17-A	859.99 / 971.62
Mon. 17-A	46 07 48.06 / 67 46 54.72	359 59 48 / 179 59 48	Mon. 17 / Mon. 18	971.62 / 283.37
Mon. 18	46 07 57.24 / 67 46 54.72	359 59 48 / 179 59 48	Mon. 17-A / Mon. 18-A	283.37 / 88.19
Mon. 18-A	46 08 00.10 / 67 46 54.72	359 59 48 / 179 59 48	Mon. 18 / Mon. 19	88.19 / 19.95
Mon. 19	46 08 00.74 / 67 46 54.72	359 59 48 / 179 59 48	Mon. 18-A / Mon. 19-A	19.95 / 97.68
Mon. 19-A	46 08 03.91 / 67 46 54.72	359 59 48 / 179 59 48	Mon. 19 / Mon. 19-B	97.68 / 370.21
Mon. 19-B	46 08 15.90 / 67 46 54.73	359 59 48 / 179 59 48	Mon. 19-A / Mon. 19-C	370.21 / 665.63
Mon. 19-C	46 08 37.46 / 67 46 54.73	359 59 48 / 179 59 48	Mon. 19-B / Mon. 20	665.63 / 347.23
Mon. 20	46 08 48.70 / 67 46 54.73	359 59 48 / 179 48 30	Mon. 19-C / Mon. 20-A	347.23 / 598.84
Mon. 20-A	46 09 08.10 / 67 46 54.82	359 48 30 / 179 48 30	Mon. 20 / Mon. 21	598.84 / 830.38
Mon. 21	46 09 34.99 / 67 46 54.95	359 48 30 / 179 48 30	Mon. 20-A / Mon. 21-A	830.38 / 1,097.70
Mon. 21-A	46 10 10.54 / 67 46 55.12	359 48 30 / 179 48 30	Mon. 21 / Mon. 21-B	1,097.70 / 221.03
Mon. 21-B	46 10 17.70 / 67 46 55.16	359 48 30 / 179 48 30	Mon. 21-A / Mon. 21-C	221.03 / 128.14
Mon. 21-C	46 10 21.85 / 67 46 55.18	359 48 30 / 179 48 34	Mon. 21-B / Mon. 21-D	128.14 / 59.35
Mon. 21-D	46 10 23.77 / 67 46 55.19	359 48 33 / 179 48 33	Mon. 21-C / Mon. 22	59.35 / 289.66
Mon. 22	46 10 33.15 / 67 46 55.23	359 48 33 / 179 48 33	Mon. 21-D / Mon. 22-A	289.66 / 1,059.01
Mon. 22-A	46 11 07.45 / 67 46 55.40	359 48 33 / 179 48 33	Mon. 22 / Mon. 23	1,059.01 / 553.40
Mon. 23	46 11 25.38 / 67 46 55.48	359 48 33 / 179 42 58	Mon. 22-A / Mon. 23-A	553.40 / 799.45
Mon. 23-A	46 11 51.27 / 67 46 55.67	359 42 58 / 179 42 58	Mon. 23 / Mon. 24	799.45 / 815.44
Mon. 24	46 12 17.68 / 67 46 55.86	359 42 58 / 179 42 58	Mon. 23-A / Mon. 24-A	815.44 / 945.31
Mon. 24-A	46 12 48.29 / 67 46 56.07	359 42 58 / 179 42 58	Mon. 24 / Mon. 24-B	945.31 / 393.71
Mon. 24-B	46 13 01.05 / 67 46 56.16	359 42 58 / 179 42 58	Mon. 24-A / Mon. 25	393.71 / 48.87

BOUNDARY MONUMENTS—SOURCE OF ST. CROIX RIVER TO ST. JOHN RIVER—Continued

Station	Latitude and longitude	Azimuth	To station	Distance (meters)	Station	Latitude and longitude	Azimuth	To station	Distance (meters)
	° ′ ″	° ′ ″				° ′ ″	° ′ ″		
Mon. 25	46 13 02.63 / 67 46 56.18	359 42 58 / 179 35 20	Mon. 24–B / Mon. 25–A	48.87 / 38.23	Mon. 37	46 20 14.13 / 67 47 00.69	359 28 17 / 179 28 17	Mon. 36–A / Mon. 37–A	651.49 / 809.83
Mon. 25–A	46 13 03.87 / 67 46 56.19	359 35 20 / 179 35 20	Mon. 25 / Mon. 25–B	38.23 / 29.81	Mon. 37–A	46 20 40.36 / 67 47 01.04	359 28 17 / 179 28 17	Mon. 37 / Mon. 38	809.83 / 520.51
Mon. 25–B	46 13 04.83 / 67 46 56.20	359 35 20 / 179 35 20	Mon. 25–A / Mon. 26	29.81 / 183.45	Mon. 38	46 20 57.22 / 67 47 01.26	359 28 17 / 179 28 17	Mon. 37–A / Mon. 39	520.51 / 497.90
Mon. 26	46 13 10.77 / 67 46 56.26	359 35 20 / 179 37 45	Mon. 25–B / Mon. 26–A	183.45 / 706.77	Mon. 39	46 21 13.34 / 67 47 01.48	359 28 17 / 179 20 42	Mon. 38 / Mon. 39–A	497.90 / 342.74
Mon. 26–A	46 13 33.66 / 67 46 56.47	359 37 45 / 179 37 45	Mon. 26 / Mon. 27	706.77 / 108.59	Mon. 39–A	46 21 24.44 / 67 47 01.66	359 20 42 / 179 20 42	Mon. 39 / Mon. 39–B	342.74 / 437.66
Mon. 27	46 13 37.18 / 67 46 56.51	359 37 45 / 179 37 45	Mon. 26–A / Mon. 27–A	108.59 / 560.26	Mon. 39–B	46 21 38.62 / 67 47 01.90	359 20 42 / 179 20 42	Mon. 39–A / Mon. 40	437.66 / 630.99
Mon. 27–A	46 13 55.33 / 67 46 56.68	359 37 45 / 179 37 45	Mon. 27 / Mon. 28	560.26 / 225.49	Mon. 40	46 21 59.05 / 67 47 02.23	359 20 42 / 179 20 42	Mon. 39–B / Mon. 40–A	630.99 / 162.30
Mon. 28	46 14 02.63 / 67 46 56.74	359 37 45 / 179 37 45	Mon. 27–A / Mon. 28–A	225.49 / 212.94	Mon. 40–A	46 22 04.31 / 67 47 02.32	359 20 42 / 179 20 42	Mon. 40 / Mon. 40–B	162.30 / 978.88
Mon. 28–A	46 14 09.53 / 67 46 56.81	359 37 45 / 179 37 45	Mon. 28 / Mon. 28–B	212.94 / 662.42	Mon. 40–B	46 22 36.01 / 67 47 02.84	359 20 41 / 179 20 41	Mon. 40–A / Mon. 41	978.88 / 318.60
Mon. 28–B	46 14 30.98 / 67 46 57.01	359 37 44 / 179 37 44	Mon. 28–A / Mon. 28–C	662.42 / 489.73	Mon. 41	46 22 46.33 / 67 47 03.01	359 20 41 / 179 20 41	Mon. 40–B / Mon. 41–A	318.60 / 121.67
Mon. 28–C	46 14 46.84 / 67 46 57.16	359 37 44 / 179 37 44	Mon. 28–B / Mon. 29	489.73 / 229.27	Mon. 41–A	46 22 50.27 / 67 47 03.08	359 20 41 / 179 20 41	Mon. 41 / Mon. 41–B	121.67 / 353.76
Mon. 29	46 14 54.27 / 67 46 57.22	359 37 44 / 179 55 02	Mon. 28–C / Mon. 29–A	229.27 / 260.71	Mon. 41–B	46 23 01.73 / 67 47 03.27	359 20 41 / 179 20 41	Mon. 41–A / Mon. 42	353.76 / 1,082.71
Mon. 29–A	46 15 02.71 / 67 46 57.24	359 55 02 / 179 55 02	Mon. 29 / Mon. 29–B	260.71 / 1,106.49	Mon. 42	46 23 36.79 / 67 47 03.85	359 20 41 / 179 20 41	Mon. 41–B / Mon. 42–A	1,082.71 / 781.27
Mon. 29–B	46 15 38.55 / 67 46 57.32	359 55 02 / 179 55 02	Mon. 29–A / Mon. 30	1,106.49 / 245.39	Mon. 42–A	46 24 02.10 / 67 47 04.27	359 20 40 / 179 20 40	Mon. 42 / Mon. 43	781.27 / 817.90
Mon. 30	46 15 46.49 / 67 46 57.33	359 55 02 / 179 32 03	Mon. 29–B / Mon. 30–A	245.39 / 188.56	Mon. 43	46 24 28.58 / 67 47 04.70	359 20 40 / 179 20 40	Mon. 42–A / Mon. 43–A	817.90 / 528.35
Mon. 30–A	46 15 52.60 / 67 46 57.40	359 32 03 / 179 32 03	Mon. 30 / Mon. 30–B	188.56 / 679.66	Mon. 43–A	46 24 45.70 / 67 47 04.99	359 20 40 / 179 20 40	Mon. 43 / Mon. 43–B	528.35 / 212.59
Mon. 30–B	46 16 14.61 / 67 46 57.66	359 32 03 / 179 32 03	Mon. 30–A / Mon. 31	679.66 / 356.66	Mon. 43–B	46 24 52.58 / 67 47 05.10	359 20 40 / 179 20 40	Mon. 43–A / Mon. 44	212.59 / 390.73
Mon. 31	46 16 26.16 / 67 46 57.80	359 32 03 / 179 32 03	Mon. 30–B / Mon. 32	356.66 / 590.78	Mon. 44	46 25 05.24 / 67 47 05.31	359 20 39 / 179 15 42	Mon. 43–B / Mon. 44–A	390.73 / 185.95
Mon. 32	46 16 45.30 / 67 46 58.02	359 32 03 / 179 32 03	Mon. 31 / Mon. 32–A	590.78 / 534.26	Mon. 44–A	46 25 11.26 / 67 47 05.42	359 15 42 / 179 15 42	Mon. 44 / Mon. 45	185.95 / 430.42
Mon. 32–A	46 17 02.60 / 67 46 58.23	359 32 03 / 179 32 03	Mon. 32 / Mon. 32–B	534.26 / 278.16	Mon. 45	46 25 25.20 / 67 47 05.68	359 15 42 / 179 15 42	Mon. 44–A / Mon. 45–A	430.42 / 558.62
Mon. 32–B	46 17 11.61 / 67 46 58.33	359 32 03 / 179 32 03	Mon. 32–A / Mon. 33	278.16 / 893.89	Mon. 45–A	46 25 43.29 / 67 47 06.02	359 15 42 / 179 15 42	Mon. 45 / Mon. 45–B	558.62 / 713.64
Mon. 33	46 17 40.56 / 67 46 58.67	359 32 02 / 179 32 02	Mon. 32–B / Mon. 33–A	893.89 / 366.92	Mon. 45–B	46 26 06.40 / 67 47 06.45	359 15 41 / 179 15 41	Mon. 45–A / Mon. 46	713.64 / 301.18
Mon. 33–A	46 17 52.44 / 67 46 58.81	359 32 02 / 179 32 02	Mon. 33 / Mon. 34	366.92 / 190.54	Mon. 46	46 26 16.15 / 67 47 06.63	359 15 41 / 179 15 41	Mon. 45–B / Mon. 46–A	301.18 / 522.17
Mon. 34	46 17 58.61 / 67 46 58.88	359 32 02 / 179 28 05	Mon. 33–A / Mon. 35	190.54 / 697.88	Mon. 46–A	46 26 33.06 / 67 47 06.95	359 15 41 / 179 15 41	Mon. 46 / Mon. 47	522.17 / 381.62
Mon. 35	46 18 21.22 / 67 46 59.19	359 28 05 / 179 28 05	Mon. 34 / Mon. 35–A	697.88 / 375.50	Mon. 47	46 26 45.42 / 67 47 07.18	359 15 41 / 179 15 38	Mon. 46–A / Mon. 47–A	381.62 / 130.77
Mon. 35–A	46 18 33.38 / 67 46 59.35	359 28 05 / 179 28 18	Mon. 35 / Mon. 35–B	375.50 / 713.49	Mon. 47–A	46 26 49.66 / 67 47 07.26	359 15 38 / 179 15 38	Mon. 47 / Mon. 48	130.77 / 278.73
Mon. 35–B	46 18 56.48 / 67 46 59.66	359 28 18 / 179 28 18	Mon. 35–A / Mon. 35–C	713.49 / 197.76	Mon. 48	46 26 58.69 / 67 47 07.43	359 15 38 / 179 15 38	Mon. 47–A / Mon. 48–A	278.73 / 64.70
Mon. 35–C	46 19 02.89 / 67 46 59.74	359 28 18 / 179 28 18	Mon. 35–B / Mon. 35–D	197.76 / 36.27	Mon. 48–A	46 27 00.78 / 67 47 07.46	359 15 38 / 179 15 38	Mon. 48 / Mon. 49	64.70 / 26.29
Mon. 35–D	46 19 04.06 / 67 46 59.76	359 28 18 / 179 28 18	Mon. 35–C / Mon. 35–E	36.27 / 59.53	Mon. 49	46 27 01.63 / 67 47 07.48	359 15 38 / 179 15 38	Mon. 48–A / Mon. 49–A	26.29 / 312.59
Mon. 35–E	46 19 05.99 / 67 46 59.78	359 28 18 / 179 28 18	Mon. 35–D / Mon. 36	59.53 / 592.79	Mon. 49–A	46 27 11.76 / 67 47 07.67	359 15 38 / 179 15 38	Mon. 49 / Mon. 49–B	312.59 / 163.58
Mon. 36	46 19 25.19 / 67 47 00.04	359 28 18 / 179 28 18	Mon. 35–E / Mon. 36–A	592.79 / 859.78	Mon. 49–B	46 27 17.05 / 67 47 07.77	359 15 38 / 179 15 38	Mon. 49–A / Mon. 49–C	163.58 / 245.09
Mon. 36–A	46 19 53.03 / 67 47 00.41	359 28 17 / 179 28 17	Mon. 36 / Mon. 37	859.78 / 651.49	Mon. 49–C	46 27 24.99 / 67 47 07.92	359 15 38 / 179 15 38	Mon. 49–B / Mon. 49–D	245.09 / 752.44

BOUNDARY MONUMENTS—SOURCE OF ST. CROIX RIVER TO ST. JOHN RIVER—Continued

Station	Latitude and longitude	Azimuth	To station	Distance (meters)
Mon. 49–D	46 27 49.36 / 67 47 08.37	359 15 37 / 179 15 37	Mon. 49–C / Mon. 50	752.44 / 284.31
Mon. 50	46 27 58.57 / 67 47 08.54	359 15 37 / 179 10 58	Mon. 49–D / Mon. 50–A	284.31 / 262.65
Mon. 50–A	46 28 07.07 / 67 47 08.72	359 10 58 / 179 10 58	Mon. 50 / Mon. 50–B	262.65 / 647.08
Mon. 50–B	46 28 28.03 / 67 47 09.15	359 10 58 / 179 10 58	Mon. 50–A / Mon. 50–C	647.08 / 334.40
Mon. 50–C	46 28 38.86 / 67 47 09.38	359 10 58 / 179 10 58	Mon. 50–B / Mon. 51	334.40 / 244.63
Mon. 51	46 28 46.78 / 67 47 09.54	359 10 58 / 179 10 58	Mon. 50–C / Mon. 51–A	244.63 / 245.54
Mon. 51–A	46 28 54.73 / 67 47 09.70	359 10 58 / 179 10 58	Mon. 51 / Mon. 51–B	245.54 / 695.94
Mon. 51–B	46 29 17.27 / 67 47 10.17	359 10 57 / 179 10 57	Mon. 51–A / Mon. 51–C	695.94 / 392.54
Mon. 51–C	46 29 29.98 / 67 47 10.43	359 10 57 / 179 10 57	Mon. 51–B / Mon. 52	392.54 / 619.60
Mon. 52	46 29 50.05 / 67 47 10.85	359 10 57 / 179 10 57	Mon. 51–C / Mon. 52–A	619.60 / 637.20
Mon. 52–A	46 30 10.69 / 67 47 11.27	359 10 56 / 179 10 56	Mon. 52 / Mon. 53	637.20 / 286.78
Mon. 53	46 30 19.98 / 67 47 11.46	359 10 56 / 179 00 15	Mon. 52–A / Mon. 54	286.78 / 507.11
Mon. 54	46 30 36.40 / 67 47 11.88	359 00 15 / 179 00 15	Mon. 53 / Mon. 54–A	507.11 / 682.57
Mon. 54–A	46 30 58.50 / 67 47 12.44	359 00 15 / 179 00 15	Mon. 54 / Mon. 55	682.57 / 710.89
Mon. 55	46 31 21.53 / 67 47 13.02	359 00 14 / 179 00 14	Mon. 54–A / Mon. 55–A	710.89 / 542.57
Mon. 55–A	46 31 39.10 / 67 47 13.46	359 00 14 / 179 00 20	Mon. 55 / Mon. 55–B	542.57 / 321.93
Mon. 55–B	46 31 49.52 / 67 47 13.72	359 00 20 / 179 00 20	Mon. 55–A / Mon. 55–C	321.93 / 508.21
Mon. 55–C	46 32 05.98 / 67 47 14.13	359 00 20 / 179 00 20	Mon. 55–B / Mon. 56	508.21 / 450.62
Mon. 56	46 32 20.58 / 67 47 14.50	359 00 20 / 179 00 20	Mon. 55–C / Mon. 56–A	450.62 / 495.58
Mon. 56–A	46 32 36.62 / 67 47 14.90	359 00 19 / 179 00 19	Mon. 56 / Mon. 57	495.58 / 1,029.96
Mon. 57	46 33 09.98 / 67 47 15.74	359 00 18 / 179 00 18	Mon. 56–A / Mon. 57–A	1,029.96 / 595.98
Mon. 57–A	46 33 29.28 / 67 47 16.23	359 00 18 / 179 00 18	Mon. 57 / Mon. 57–B	595.98 / 464.65
Mon. 57–B	46 33 44.33 / 67 47 16.61	359 00 18 / 179 00 18	Mon. 57–A / Mon. 58	464.65 / 770.20
Mon. 58	46 34 09.27 / 67 47 17.24	359 00 17 / 179 00 17	Mon. 57–B / Mon. 58–A	770.20 / 728.19
Mon. 58–A	46 34 32.86 / 67 47 17.83	359 00 17 / 179 00 17	Mon. 58 / Mon. 58–B	728.19 / 511.44
Mon. 58–B	46 34 49.42 / 67 47 18.25	359 00 16 / 179 00 16	Mon. 58–A / Mon. 59	511.44 / 162.80
Mon. 59	46 34 54.69 / 67 47 18.38	359 00 16 / 179 00 11	Mon. 58–B / Mon. 59–A	162.80 / 354.92
Mon. 59–A	46 35 06.18 / 67 47 18.67	359 00 11 / 179 00 11	Mon. 59 / Mon. 60	354.92 / 527.41
Mon. 60	46 35 23.26 / 67 47 19.09	359 00 11 / 179 01 01	Mon. 59–A / Mon. 60–A	527.41 / 375.19
Mon. 60–A	46 35 35.42 / 67 47 19.40	359 01 01 / 179 01 01	Mon. 60 / Mon. 61	375.19 / 765.72
Mon. 61	46 36 00.21 / 67 47 20.01	359 01 00 / 179 01 00	Mon. 60–A / Mon. 61–A	765.72 / 51.22
Mon. 61–A	46 36 01.87 / 67 47 20.05	359 01 00 / 179 01 00	Mon. 61 / Mon. 62	51.22 / 102.78
Mon. 62	46 36 05.20 / 67 47 20.14	359 01 00 / 179 54 19	Mon. 61–A / Mon. 62–A	102.78 / 339.08
Mon. 62–A	46 36 16.18 / 67 47 20.16	359 54 19 / 179 54 19	Mon. 62 / Mon. 63	339.08 / 630.50
Mon. 63	46 36 36.60 / 67 47 20.21	359 54 19 / 179 54 19	Mon. 62–A / Mon. 63–A	630.50 / 388.78
Mon. 63–A	46 36 49.19 / 67 47 20.24	359 54 19 / 179 54 32	Mon. 63 / Mon. 64	388.78 / 235.85
Mon. 64	46 36 56.83 / 67 47 20.26	359 54 32 / 179 43 23	Mon. 63–A / Mon. 65	235.85 / 1,020.11
Mon. 65	46 37 29.86 / 67 47 20.49	359 43 23 / 179 43 23	Mon. 64 / Mon. 66	1,020.11 / 738.31
Mon. 66	46 37 53.78 / 67 47 20.66	359 43 23 / 179 43 39	Mon. 65 / Mon. 66–A	738.31 / 154.71
Mon. 66–A	46 37 58.78 / 67 47 20.70	359 43 39 / 179 43 39	Mon. 66 / Mon. 66–B	154.71 / 226.32
Mon. 66–B	46 38 06.11 / 67 47 20.75	359 43 39 / 179 43 39	Mon. 66–A / Mon. 66–C	226.32 / 55.86
Mon. 66–C	46 38 07.92 / 67 47 20.76	359 43 39 / 179 43 39	Mon. 66–B / Mon. 67	55.86 / 284.07
Mon. 67	46 38 17.12 / 67 47 20.82	359 43 39 / 179 43 39	Mon. 66–C / Mon. 67–A	284.07 / 521.81
Mon. 67–A	46 38 34.02 / 67 47 20.94	359 43 39 / 179 43 39	Mon. 67 / Mon. 67–B	521.81 / 345.78
Mon. 67–B	46 38 45.22 / 67 47 21.02	359 43 39 / 179 43 39	Mon. 67–A / Mon. 67–C	345.78 / 717.98
Mon. 67–C	46 39 08.47 / 67 47 21.18	359 43 38 / 179 43 38	Mon. 67–B / Mon. 67–D	717.98 / 126.14
Mon. 67–D	46 39 12.56 / 67 47 21.20	359 43 38 / 179 43 38	Mon. 67–C / Mon. 68	126.14 / 160.68
Mon. 68	46 39 17.76 / 67 47 21.24	359 43 38 / 179 44 18	Mon. 67–D / Mon. 68–A	160.68 / 409.21
Mon. 68–A	46 39 31.01 / 67 47 21.33	359 44 18 / 179 44 18	Mon. 68 / Mon. 68–B	409.21 / 526.83
Mon. 68–B	46 39 48.07 / 67 47 21.44	359 44 18 / 179 44 18	Mon. 68–A / Mon. 69	526.83 / 668.71
Mon. 69	46 40 09.73 / 67 47 21.59	359 44 18 / 179 44 18	Mon. 68–B / Mon. 69–A	668.71 / 406.22
Mon. 69–A	46 40 22.88 / 67 47 21.67	359 44 18 / 179 44 18	Mon. 69 / Mon. 69–B	406.22 / 232.40
Mon. 69–B	46 40 30.41 / 67 47 21.72	359 44 18 / 179 44 18	Mon. 69–A / Mon. 70	232.40 / 75.82
Mon. 70	46 40 32.87 / 67 47 21.74	359 44 18 / 179 44 18	Mon. 69–B / Mon. 71	75.82 / 699.69
Mon. 71	46 40 55.52 / 67 47 21.89	359 44 17 / 179 44 17	Mon. 70 / Mon. 71–A	699.69 / 562.00
Mon. 71–A	46 41 13.72 / 67 47 22.01	359 44 17 / 179 44 12	Mon. 71 / Mon. 71–B	562.00 / 248.58
Mon. 71–B	46 41 21.78 / 67 47 22.06	359 44 12 / 179 44 12	Mon. 71–A / Mon. 71–C	248.58 / 686.37
Mon. 71–C	46 41 44.00 / 67 47 22.21	359 44 12 / 179 44 12	Mon. 71–B / Mon. 72	686.37 / 745.09
Mon. 72	46 42 08.13 / 67 47 22.38	359 44 12 / 179 44 12	Mon. 71–C / Mon. 72–A	745.09 / 425.64
Mon. 72–A	46 42 21.92 / 67 47 22.47	359 44 12 / 179 45 40	Mon. 72 / Mon. 72–B	425.64 / 201.44
Mon. 72–B	46 42 28.44 / 67 47 22.51	359 45 40 / 179 45 40	Mon. 72–A / Mon. 73	201.44 / 558.50
Mon. 73	46 42 46.53 / 67 47 22.62	359 45 40 / 179 40 31	Mon. 72–B / Mon. 73–A	558.50 / 177.91
Mon. 73–A	46 42 52.29 / 67 47 22.66	359 40 31 / 179 40 31	Mon. 73 / Mon. 73–B	177.91 / 943.26
Mon. 73–B	46 43 22.84 / 67 47 22.92	359 40 31 / 179 40 31	Mon. 73–A / Mon. 73–C	943.26 / 199.74

BOUNDARY MONUMENTS—SOURCE OF ST. CROIX RIVER TO ST. JOHN RIVER—Continued

Station	Latitude and longitude	Azimuth	To station	Distance (meters)
Mon. 73-C	46 43 29.30 / 67 47 22.97	359 40 31 / 179 40 31	Mon. 73-B / Mon. 74	199.74 / 645.49
Mon. 74	46 43 50.21 / 67 47 23.14	359 40 31 / 179 40 31	Mon. 73-C / Mon. 74-A	645.49 / 612.23
Mon. 74-A	46 44 10.03 / 67 47 23.31	359 40 31 / 179 40 31	Mon. 74 / Mon. 75	612.23 / 420.51
Mon. 75	46 44 23.65 / 67 47 23.42	359 40 31 / 179 40 31	Mon. 74-A / Mon. 75-A	420.51 / 673.53
Mon. 75-A	46 44 45.46 / 67 47 23.60	359 40 30 / 179 40 30	Mon. 75 / Mon. 75-B	673.53 / 178.22
Mon. 75-B	46 44 51.23 / 67 47 23.65	359 40 30 / 179 40 30	Mon. 75-A / Mon. 75-C	178.22 / 507.44
Mon. 75-C	46 45 07.67 / 67 47 23.78	359 40 30 / 179 40 30	Mon. 75-B / Mon. 76	507.44 / 331.15
Mon. 76	46 45 18.39 / 67 47 23.87	359 40 30 / 179 40 30	Mon. 75-C / Mon. 77	331.15 / 340.62
Mon. 77	46 45 29.42 / 67 47 23.96	359 40 30 / 179 40 30	Mon. 76 / Mon. 77-A	340.62 / 419.78
Mon. 77-A	46 45 43.02 / 67 47 24.07	359 40 30 / 179 40 30	Mon. 77 / Mon. 77-B	419.78 / 233.49
Mon. 77-B	46 45 50.58 / 67 47 24.14	359 40 30 / 179 40 30	Mon. 77-A / Mon. 78	233.49 / 165.20
Mon. 78	46 45 55.93 / 67 47 24.18	359 40 30 / 179 40 30	Mon. 77-B / Mon. 78-A	165.20 / 80.86
Mon. 78-A	46 45 58.55 / 67 47 24.20	359 40 30 / 179 40 30	Mon. 78 / Mon. 79	80.86 / 549.72
Mon. 79	46 46 16.35 / 67 47 24.35	359 40 30 / 179 40 30	Mon. 78-A / Mon. 79-A	549.72 / 529.48
Mon. 79-A	46 46 33.50 / 67 47 24.49	359 40 30 / 179 40 30	Mon. 79 / Mon. 80	529.48 / 472.33
Mon. 80	46 46 48.79 / 67 47 24.62	359 40 30 / 179 40 30	Mon. 79-A / Mon. 81	472.33 / 435.33
Mon. 81	46 47 02.89 / 67 47 24.73	359 40 30 / 179 40 30	Mon. 80 / Mon. 81-A	435.33 / 640.34
Mon. 81-A	46 47 23.63 / 67 47 24.90	359 40 29 / 179 40 29	Mon. 81 / Mon. 81-B	640.34 / 300.73
Mon. 81-B	46 47 33.36 / 67 47 24.98	359 40 29 / 179 40 27	Mon. 81-A / Mon. 82	300.73 / 126.93
Mon. 82	46 47 37.48 / 67 47 25.02	359 40 27 / 179 40 27	Mon. 81-B / Mon. 83	126.93 / 135.19
Mon. 83	46 47 41.85 / 67 47 25.05	359 40 27 / 179 40 27	Mon. 82 / Mon. 84	135.19 / 124.00
Mon. 84	46 47 45.87 / 67 47 25.09	359 40 27 / 179 40 27	Mon. 83 / Mon. 84-A	124.00 / 145.06
Mon. 84-A	46 47 50.57 / 67 47 25.12	359 40 27 / 179 40 27	Mon. 84 / Mon. 85	145.06 / 168.57
Mon. 85	46 47 56.02 / 67 47 25.17	359 40 27 / 179 40 27	Mon. 84-A / Mon. 85-A	168.57 / 370.46
Mon. 85-A	46 48 08.02 / 67 47 25.27	359 40 27 / 179 40 27	Mon. 85 / Mon. 86	370.46 / 428.27
Mon. 86	46 48 21.89 / 67 47 25.38	359 40 27 / 180 12 29	Mon. 85-A / Mon. 86-A	428.27 / 306.80
Mon. 86-A	46 48 31.83 / 67 47 25.33	0 12 29 / 180 12 29	Mon. 86 / Mon. 87	306.80 / 1,019.32
Mon. 87	46 49 04.84 / 67 47 25.16	0 12 29 / 180 12 29	Mon. 86-A / Mon. 87-A	1,019.32 / 625.44
Mon. 87-A	46 49 25.09 / 67 47 25.05	0 12 29 / 180 12 29	Mon. 87 / Mon. 87-B	625.44 / 172.41
Mon. 87-B	46 49 30.67 / 67 47 25.02	0 12 29 / 180 12 42	Mon. 87-A / Mon. 88	172.41 / 173.82
Mon. 88	46 49 36.30 / 67 47 24.99	0 12 42 / 180 12 42	Mon. 87-B / Mon. 88-A	173.82 / 425.62
Mon. 88-A	46 49 50.08 / 67 47 24.92	0 12 42 / 180 12 42	Mon. 88 / Mon. 89	425.62 / 1,063.59

Station	Latitude and longitude	Azimuth	To station	Distance (meters)
Mon. 89	46 50 24.53 / 67 47 24.73	0 12 42 / 180 12 42	Mon. 88-A / Mon. 89-A	1,063.59 / 763.31
Mon. 89-A	46 50 49.25 / 67 47 24.60	0 12 42 / 180 12 42	Mon. 89 / Mon. 89-B	763.31 / 399.43
Mon. 89-B	46 51 02.18 / 67 47 24.53	0 12 42 / 180 12 42	Mon. 89-A / Mon. 90	399.43 / 292.51
Mon. 90	46 51 11.65 / 67 47 24.48	0 12 42 / 180 12 42	Mon. 89-B / Mon. 91	292.51 / 515.92
Mon. 91	46 51 28.36 / 67 47 24.39	0 12 42 / 179 58 39	Mon. 90 / Mon. 91-A	515.92 / 89.39
Mon. 91-A	46 51 31.26 / 67 47 24.39	359 58 39 / 179 59 14	Mon. 91 / Mon. 91-B	89.39 / 226.31
Mon. 91-B	46 51 38.58 / 67 47 24.39	359 59 14 / 179 59 14	Mon. 91-A / Mon. 91-C	226.31 / 523.54
Mon. 91-C	46 51 55.54 / 67 47 24.40	359 59 14 / 179 59 14	Mon. 91-B / Mon. 92	523.54 / 644.53
Mon. 92	46 52 16.41 / 67 47 24.40	359 59 14 / 179 59 30	Mon. 91-C / Mon. 92-A	644.53 / 630.64
Mon. 92-A	46 52 36.83 / 67 47 24.41	359 59 30 / 179 59 30	Mon. 92 / Mon. 93	630.64 / 94.76
Mon. 93	46 52 39.90 / 67 47 24.41	359 59 30 / 179 59 30	Mon. 92-A / Mon. 93-A	94.76 / 567.13
Mon. 93-A	46 52 58.27 / 67 47 24.41	359 59 30 / 179 59 30	Mon. 93 / Mon. 94	567.13 / 487.62
Mon. 94	46 53 14.06 / 67 47 24.42	359 59 30 / 179 59 30	Mon. 93-A / Mon. 94-A	487.62 / 757.72
Mon. 94-A	46 53 38.60 / 67 47 24.42	359 59 30 / 179 59 30	Mon. 94 / Mon. 95	757.72 / 690.80
Mon. 95	46 54 00.97 / 67 47 24.42	359 59 30 / 179 59 30	Mon. 94-A / Mon. 95-A	690.80 / 348.19
Mon. 95-A	46 54 12.24 / 67 47 24.43	359 59 30 / 179 59 30	Mon. 95 / Mon. 95-B	348.19 / 514.36
Mon. 95-B	46 54 28.90 / 67 47 24.43	359 59 30 / 179 59 30	Mon. 95-A / Mon. 96	514.36 / 484.51
Mon. 96	46 54 44.59 / 67 47 24.44	359 59 30 / 179 40 45	Mon. 95-B / Mon. 97	484.51 / 463.47
Mon. 97	46 54 59.60 / 67 47 24.56	359 40 45 / 179 40 45	Mon. 96 / Mon. 97-A	463.47 / 330.63
Mon. 97-A	46 55 10.30 / 67 47 24.64	359 40 45 / 179 40 45	Mon. 97 / Mon. 97-B	330.63 / 588.08
Mon. 97-B	46 55 29.35 / 67 47 24.80	359 40 45 / 179 40 45	Mon. 97-A / Mon. 98	588.08 / 219.16
Mon. 98	46 55 36.44 / 67 47 24.86	359 40 45 / 179 53 28	Mon. 97-B / Mon. 99	219.16 / 530.60
Mon. 99	46 55 53.63 / 67 47 24.91	359 53 28 / 179 53 28	Mon. 98 / Mon. 99-A	530.60 / 630.82
Mon. 99-A	46 56 14.06 / 67 47 24.96	359 53 28 / 179 53 28	Mon. 99 / Mon. 99-B	630.82 / 657.78
Mon. 99-B	46 56 35.36 / 67 47 25.02	359 53 28 / 179 53 28	Mon. 99-A / Mon. 100	657.78 / 223.55
Mon. 100	46 56 42.60 / 67 47 25.04	359 53 28 / 179 53 28	Mon. 99-B / Mon. 100-A	223.55 / 449.62
Mon. 100-A	46 56 57.16 / 67 47 25.08	359 53 28 / 179 53 28	Mon. 100 / Mon. 100-B	449.62 / 257.36
Mon. 100-B	46 57 05.49 / 67 47 25.11	359 53 28 / 179 53 28	Mon. 100-A / Mon. 100-C	257.36 / 225.38
Mon. 100-C	46 57 12.79 / 67 47 25.13	359 53 28 / 179 53 28	Mon. 100-B / Mon. 101	225.38 / 513.44
Mon. 101	46 57 29.42 / 67 47 25.17	359 53 28 / 179 53 28	Mon. 100-C / Mon. 101-A	513.44 / 515.49
Mon. 101-A	46 57 46.11 / 67 47 25.22	359 53 28 / 179 53 28	Mon. 101 / Mon. 101-B	515.49 / 836.82
Mon. 101-B	46 58 13.21 / 67 47 25.29	359 53 27 / 179 53 27	Mon. 101-A / Mon. 102	836.82 / 432.09

BOUNDARY MONUMENTS—SOURCE OF ST. CROIX RIVER TO ST. JOHN RIVER—Continued

Station	Latitude and longitude	Azimuth	To station	Distance (meters)	Station	Latitude and longitude	Azimuth	To station	Distance (meters)
	° ′ ″	° ′ ″				° ′ ″	° ′ ″		
Mon. 102	46 58 27.20 67 47 25.33	359 53 27 179 53 20	Mon. 101–B Mon. 103	432.09 703.46	Mon. 110–A	47 02 16.21 67 47 26.37	359 42 42 179 42 42	Mon. 110 Mon. 110–B	500.03 491.96
Mon. 103	46 58 49.98 67 47 25.40	359 53 20 179 53 37	Mon. 102 Mon. 104	703.46 124.72	Mon. 110–B	47 02 32.14 67 47 26.48	359 42 42 179 42 42	Mon. 110–A Mon. 111	491.96 119.68
Mon. 104	46 58 54.02 67 47 25.41	359 53 37 179 53 37	Mon. 103 Mon. 104–A	124.72 422.66	Mon. 111	47 02 36.02 67 47 26.51	359 42 42 179 42 42	Mon. 110–B Mon. 111–A	119.68 179.66
Mon. 104–A	46 59 07.71 67 47 25.45	359 53 37 179 53 37	Mon. 104 Mon. 105	422.66 144.32	Mon. 111–A	47 02 41.84 67 47 26.56	359 42 42 179 42 36	Mon. 111 Mon. 112	179.66 158.16
Mon. 105	46 59 12.38 67 47 25.46	359 53 37 179 53 37	Mon. 104–A Mon. 105–A	144.32 815.87	Mon. 112	47 02 46.96 67 47 26.59	359 42 36 179 42 36	Mon. 111–A Mon. 113	158.16 656.06
Mon. 105–A	46 59 38.80 67 47 25.53	359 53 37 179 53 37	Mon. 105 Mon. 106	815.87 782.21	Mon. 113	47 03 08.21 67 47 26.75	359 42 36 179 42 27	Mon. 112 Mon. 113–A	656.06 738.46
Mon. 106	47 00 04.13 67 47 25.60	359 53 37 179 53 37	Mon. 105–A Mon. 106–A	782.21 779.95	Mon. 113–A	47 03 32.12 67 47 26.93	359 42 27 179 42 27	Mon. 113 Mon. 114	738.46 218.10
Mon. 106–A	47 00 29.39 67 47 25.67	359 53 37 179 53 37	Mon. 106 Mon. 107	779.95 595.91	Mon. 114	47 03 39.18 67 47 26.98	359 42 27 179 42 27	Mon. 113–A Mon. 114–A	218.10 42.16
Mon. 107	47 00 48.68 67 47 25.72	359 53 37 179 42 37	Mon. 106–A Mon. 108	595.91 831.84	Mon. 114–A	47 03 40.55 67 47 26.99	359 42 27 179 42 27	Mon. 114 Mon. 115	42.16 166.43
Mon. 108	47 01 15.62 67 47 25.92	359 42 36 179 42 36	Mon. 107 Mon. 109	831.84 570.79	Mon. 115	47 03 45.94 67 47 27.03	359 42 27 179 42 27	Mon. 114–A Mon. 116	166.43 226.46
Mon. 109	47 01 34.10 67 47 26.06	359 42 36 179 42 36	Mon. 108 Mon. 109–A	570.79 156.15	Mon. 116	47 03 53.27 67 47 27.09	359 42 27 179 42 27	Mon. 115 Mon. 117	226.46 145.46
Mon. 109–A	47 01 39.16 67 47 26.09	359 42 36 179 42 42	Mon. 109 Mon. 110	156.15 644.23	Mon. 117	47 03 57.98 67 47 27.12	359 42 27 179 42 27	Mon. 116 T. P. 1	145.46 139.2
Mon. 110	47 02 00.02 67 47 26.25	359 42 42 179 42 42	Mon. 109–A Mon. 110–A	644.23 500.03					

104709—25†——11

GEOGRAPHIC POSITIONS OF BOUNDARY TURNING POINTS DEFINING THE INTERNATIONAL BOUNDARY THROUGH THE ST. JOHN RIVER

Station	Latitude and longitude	Azimuth	To station	Distance (meters)	Station	Latitude and longitude	Azimuth	To station	Distance (meters)
	° ′ ″	° ′ ″				° ′ ″	° ′ ″		
T. P. 1	47 04 02.49	56 04 30	Ref. Mon. S–1	123.6	T. P. 18	47 07 10.83	2 40 00	T. P. 17	602.9
	67 47 27.16	127 12 00	T. P. 2	419.4		67 53 23.51	19 18 20	Ref. Mon. S–16	425.3
		236 04 30	Ref. Mon. C–1	171.0			163 49 50	T. P. 19	324.9
		359 42 30	Mon. 117	139.2			199 18 20	Ref. Mon. C–16	371.4
T. P. 2	47 04 10.70	116 27 50	T. P. 3	783.9	T. P. 19	47 07 20.94	79 47 00	Ref. Mon. S–17	272.5
	67 47 42.99	139 33 30	Ref. Mon. C–2	303.9		67 53 27.81	189 17 30	T. P. 20	221.3
		307 11 50	T. P. 1	419.4			259 47 00	Ref. Mon. C–16	216.7
		319 33 30	Mon. 117	516.1			343 49 50	T. P. 18	324.9
T. P. 3	47 04 22.01	35 31 10	Ref. Mon. S–3	175.8	T. P. 20	47 07 28.01	9 17 30	T. P. 19	221.3
	67 48 16.25	123 58 20	T. P. 4	675.9		67 53 26.11	135 23 40	Ref. Mon. 120	170.1
		215 31 10	Ref. Mon. C–3	108.2			165 27 10	T. P. 21	248.8
		296 27 30	T. P. 2	783.9			315 23 40	Ref. Mon. C–16	252.8
T. P. 4	47 04 34.24	39 34 50	Ref. Mon. S–4	116.2	T. P. 21	47 07 35.81	25 26 10	Ref. Mon. S–17	562.0
	67 48 42.82	143 52 20	T. P. 5	736.0		67 53 29.08	25 26 10	Ref. Mon. 120	132.6
		219 34 50	Ref. Mon. C–4	154.6			144 44 10	T. P. 22	364.2
		303 58 00	T. P. 3	675.9			345 27 10	T. P. 20	248.8
T. P. 5	47 04 53.49	81 20 10	Ref. Mon. S–6	366.2	T. P. 22	47 07 45.44	159 49 00	T. P. 23	155.0
	67 49 03.39	125 18 20	T. P. 6	389.0		67 53 39.05	159 49 00	Ref. Mon. C–17	356.4
		261 20 10	Ref. Mon. C–5	172.5			324 44 00	T. P. 21	364.2
		323 52 10	T. P. 4	736.0			339 49 00	Ref. Mon. 120	444.4
T. P. 6	47 05 00.77	110 34 40	T. P. 7	397.7	T. P. 23	47 07 50.15	134 15 40	T. P. 24	198.6
	67 49 18.44	143 29 50	Ref. Mon. C–6	309.3		67 53 41.59	159 49 00	Ref. Mon. C–17	201.4
		305 18 10	T. P. 5	389.0			339 49 00	Ref. Mon. 120	599.4
		323 29 50	Ref. Mon. S–5	709.9			339 49 00	T. P. 22	155.0
T. P. 7	47 05 05.30	59 58 00	Ref. Mon. S–7	201.3	T. P. 24	47 07 54.63	55 14 50	Ref. Mon. S–18	234.2
	67 49 36.08	95 26 40	T. P. 8	345.4		67 53 48.34	126 09 40	T. P. 25	263.8
		239 58 00	Ref. Mon. C–6	217.5			235 14 50	Ref. Mon. C–17	88.5
		290 34 30	T. P. 6	397.7			314 15 30	T. P. 23	198.6
T. P. 8	47 05 06.36	116 59 00	T. P. 9	659.7	T. P. 25	47 07 59.67	137 04 10	T. P. 26	512.0
	67 49 52.38	128 13 00	Ref. Mon. C–7	618.3		67 53 58.45	175 55 40	Ref. Mon. C–18	472.9
		275 26 20	T. P. 7	345.4			306 09 30	T. P. 24	263.8
		308 13 00	Ref. Mon. S–7	215.8			355 55 40	Ref. Mon. S–18	289.9
T. P. 9	47 05 16.06	50 50 20	Ref. Mon. S–8	315.3	T. P. 26	47 08 11.81	1 18 30	Ref. Mon. S–19	214.4
	67 50 20.25	128 29 10	T. P. 10	1,007.4		67 54 15.00	159 59 00	T. P. 27	902.9
		230 50 20	Ref. Mon. C–7	131.7			181 18 30	Ref. Mon. C–19	607.2
		296 58 40	T. P. 8	659.7			317 04 00	T. P. 25	512.0
T. P. 10	47 05 36.36	71 24 40	Ref. Mon. 119	162.9	T. P. 27	47 08 39.28	126 46 00	Ref. Mon. S–21	636.0
	67 50 57.64	116 10 10	T. P. 11	894.3		67 54 29.67	153 28 50	T. P. 28	385.5
		251 24 40	Ref. Mon. C–8	258.0			306 46 00	Ref. Mon. C–19	403.1
		308 28 40	T. P. 9	1,007.4			339 58 50	T. P. 26	902.9
T. P. 11	47 05 49.13	120 40 20	T. P. 12	805.2	T. P. 28	47 08 50.45	131 48 30	T. P. 29	260.9
	67 51 35.70	151 58 20	Ref. Mon. C–9	448.1		67 54 37.84	167 34 40	Ref. Mon. C–20	305.6
		296 09 40	T. P. 10	894.3			333 28 40	T. P. 27	385.5
		331 58 20	Ref. Mon. S–9	883.3			347 34 40	Ref. Mon. S–20	598.3
T. P. 12	47 06 02.43	48 53 30	Ref. Mon. S–11	269.5	T. P. 29	47 08 56.09	45 57 00	Ref. Mon. S–21	198.8
	67 52 08.54	98 06 40	T. P. 13	494.9		67 54 47.07	115 26 10	T. P. 30	747.8
		228 53 30	Ref. Mon. C–10	128.3			225 57 00	Ref. Mon. C–20	179.1
		300 40 00	T. P. 11	805.2			311 48 20	T. P. 28	260.9
T. P. 13	47 06 04.69	114 10 30	T. P. 14	408.4	T. P. 30	47 09 06.49	103 44 10	Ref. Mon. S–22	405.0
	67 52 31.78	130 43 20	Ref. Mon. C–11	390.6		67 55 19.12	128 56 00	T. P. 31	582.1
		278 06 20	T. P. 12	494.9			283 44 10	Ref. Mon. C–20	827.7
		310 43 20	Ref. Mon. S–11	378.6			295 25 40	T. P. 29	747.8
T. P. 14	47 06 10.10	41 00 10	Ref. Mon. S–12	273.8	T. P. 31	47 09 18.33	142 54 10	T. P. 32	174.6
	67 52 49.45	128 26 00	T. P. 15	309.0		67 55 40.62	167 34 20	Ref. Mon. C–22	431.6
		221 00 10	Ref. Mon. C–11	116.3			308 55 40	T. P. 30	582.1
		294 10 20	T. P. 13	408.4			347 34 20	Ref. Mon. S–22	276.1
T. P. 15	47 06 16.32	48 08 20	Ref. Mon. S–13	291.6	T. P. 32	47 09 22.84	89 05 30	Ref. Mon. S–23	184.5
	67 53 00.93	146 28 50	T. P. 16	721.6		67 55 45.62	157 04 30	T. P. 33	636.1
		228 08 20	Ref. Mon. C–12	150.9			269 05 30	Ref. Mon. C–21	480.5
		308 25 50	T. P. 14	309.0			322 54 00	T. P. 31	174.6
T. P. 16	47 06 35.80	65 17 10	Ref. Mon. S–15	150.5	T. P. 33	47 09 41.81	136 15 10	T. P. 34	327.2
	67 53 19.83	167 34 40	T. P. 17	491.1		67 55 57.38	173 51 40	Ref. Mon. C–23	346.2
		245 17 10	Ref. Mon. C–14	142.8			337 04 20	T. P. 32	636.1
		326 28 30	T. P. 15	721.6			353 51 40	Ref. Mon. S–23	592.1
T. P. 17	47 06 51.33	150 43 40	Ref. Mon. S–16	230.2	T. P. 34	47 09 49.47	60 20 10	Ref. Mon. S–24	257.6
	67 53 24.84	182 40 00	T. P. 18	602.9		67 56 08.13	151 01 50	T. P. 35	311.1
		330 43 40	Ref. Mon. C–14	481.4			240 20 10	Ref. Mon. C–23	217.8
		347 34 30	T. P. 16	491.1			316 15 00	T. P. 33	327.2

BOUNDARY TURNING POINTS—ST. JOHN RIVER—Continued

Station	Latitude and longitude	Azimuth	To station	Distance (meters)	Station	Latitude and longitude	Azimuth	To station	Distance (meters)
	° ′ ″	° ′ ″				° ′ ″	° ′ ″		
T. P. 35	47 09 58.28	115 48 20	Ref. Mon. S–25	235.3	T. P. 54	47 14 36.43	62 59 10	Ref. Mon. S–39	250.2
	67 56 15.28	165 02 40	T. P. 36	560.7		68 02 02.50	129 03 00	T. P. 55	559.5
		295 48 20	Ref. Mon. C–23	377.6			242 59 10	Ref. Mon. C–37	460.9
		331 01 40	T. P. 34	311.1			301 32 50	T. P. 53	717.9
T. P. 36	47 10 15.82	69 07 00	Ref. Mon. S–26	225.3	T. P. 55	47 14 47.84	121 37 40	T. P. 56	1,157.8
	67 56 22.15	149 20 30	T. P. 37	662.0		68 02 23.16	155 34 50	Ref. Mon. C–38	608.7
		249 07 00	Ref. Mon. C–24	122.7			309 02 50	T. P. 54	559.5
		345 02 40	T. P. 35	560.7			335 34 50	Ref. Mon. S–39	511.9
T. P. 37	47 10 34.26	38 14 10	Ref. Mon. S–27	348.2	T. P. 56	47 15 07.50	123 51 20	T. P. 57	643.6
	67 56 38.19	144 21 10	T. P. 38	238.5		68 03 10.04	158 47 10	Ref. Mon. 128	242.8
		218 14 10	Ref. Mon. C–25	144.8			301 37 10	T. P. 55	1,157.8
		329 20 20	T. P. 36	662.0			338 47 10	Ref. Mon. S–40	398.8
T. P. 38	47 10 40.54	50 27 30	Ref. Mon. S–28	286.5	T. P. 57	47 15 19.11	32 49 50	Ref. Mon. S–41	172.7
	67 56 44.79	149 29 50	T. P. 39	495.7		68 03 35.46	118 11 30	T. P. 58	486.9
		230 27 30	Ref. Mon. C–26	147.7			212 49 50	Ref. Mon. C–39	309.4
		324 21 00	T. P. 37	238.5			303 51 00	T. P. 56	643.6
T. P. 39	47 10 54.37	67 25 10	Ref. Mon. S–29	276.9	T. P. 58	47 15 26.56	106 59 40	T. P. 59	724.0
	67 56 56.74	131 11 50	T. P. 40	307.0		68 03 55.87	138 11 20	Ref. Mon. C–40	1,282.2
		247 25 10	Ref. Mon. C–27	121.9			298 11 20	T. P. 57	486.9
		329 29 40	T. P. 38	495.7			318 11 20	Ref. Mon. S–41	503.3
T. P. 40	47 11 00.92	114 20 20	Ref. Mon. S–30	335.5	T. P. 59	47 15 33.41	77 07 20	Ref. Mon. S–42	943.2
	67 57 07.70	183 26 30	T. P. 41	739.7		68 04 28.80	137 25 50	Ref. Mon. 130	1,055.5
		294 20 20	Ref. Mon. C–27	377.1			151 54 50	T. P. 60	424.9
		311 11 40	T. P. 39	307.0			286 59 10	T. P. 58	724.0
T. P. 41	47 11 24.83	3 26 40	T. P. 40	739.7	T. P. 60	47 15 45.55	128 03 40	Ref. Mon. 130	652.8
	67 57 05.59	150 58 10	Ref. Mon. 121	624.8		68 04 38.31	171 41 20	T. P. 61	378.7
		170 39 20	T. P. 42	499.1			308 03 40	Ref. Mon. S–41	1,559.6
		330 58 10	Ref. Mon. C–28	342.6			331 54 40	T. P. 59	424.9
T. P. 42	47 11 40.78	103 37 40	Ref. Mon. S–31	699.3	T. P. 61	47 15 57.68	93 27 40	Ref. Mon. 130	460.1
	67 57 09.44	103 37 40	Ref. Mon. 121	228.6		68 04 40.91	148 28 50	T. P. 62	664.2
		154 57 00	T. P. 43	264.7			273 27 40	Ref. Mon. C–40	92.3
		350 39 20	T. P. 41	499.1			351 41 20	T. P. 60	378.7
T. P. 43	47 11 48.54	30 37 20	Ref. Mon. 121	216.1	T. P. 62	47 16 16.02	11 44 50	Ref. Mon. S–42	1,558.7
	67 57 14.76	138 31 30	T. P. 44	434.5		68 04 57.43	11 44 50	Ref. Mon. 130	550.0
		210 37 20	Ref. Mon. C–29	50.0			128 15 20	T. P. 63	998.1
		334 57 00	T. P. 42	264.7			328 28 40	T. P. 61	664.2
T. P. 44	47 11 59.08	34 56 50	Ref. Mon. S–31	488.5	T. P. 63	47 16 36.03	115 53 40	T. P. 64	418.6
	67 57 28.43	34 56 50	Ref. Mon. 122	189.4		68 05 34.72	134 12 10	Ref. Mon. C–41	668.5
		123 21 20	T. P. 45	1,449.8			308 14 50	T. P. 62	998.1
		318 31 20	T. P. 43	434.5			314 12 10	Ref. Mon. C–40	1,706.4
T. P. 45	47 12 24.89	105 55 50	T. P. 46	757.5	T. P. 64	47 16 41.95	117 19 10	T. P. 65	433.5
	67 58 25.97	113 30 10	Ref. Mon. C–32	866.0		68 05 52.64	160 04 50	Ref. Mon. C–41	301.3
		293 30 10	Ref. Mon. C–30	383.1			295 53 30	T. P. 63	418.6
		303 20 40	T. P. 44	1,449.8			340 04 50	Ref. Mon. S–42	2,474.9
T. P. 46	47 12 31.62	100 54 30	T. P. 47	349.0	T. P. 65	47 16 48.39	73 22 30	Ref. Mon. S–43	769.3
	67 59 00.58	154 25 20	Ref. Mon. C–32	152.4		68 06 10.96	128 50 20	T. P. 66	256.8
		285 55 20	T. P. 45	757.5			253 22 30	Ref. Mon. C–41	294.8
		334 25 20	Ref. Mon. S–33	721.7			297 18 50	T. P. 64	433.5
T. P. 47	47 12 33.76	75 32 10	Ref. Mon. S–35	397.7	T. P. 66	47 16 53.61	99 02 00	Ref. Mon. S–44	1,623.1
	67 59 16.87	115 33 30	T. P. 48	198.3		68 06 20.48	118 57 50	T. P. 67	1,376.6
		255 32 10	Ref. Mon. C–32	286.0			279 02 00	Ref. Mon. C–41	488.6
		280 54 20	T. P. 46	349.0			308 50 20	T. P. 65	256.8
T. P. 48	47 12 36.53	140 54 10	T. P. 49	1,016.3	T. P. 67	47 17 15.19	44 03 20	Ref. Mon. S–44	573.1
	67 59 25.37	160 09 30	Ref. Mon. C–33	354.2		68 07 17.80	148 59 50	T. P. 68	318.4
		295 33 20	T. P. 47	198.3			224 03 20	Ref. Mon. C–42	216.0
		340 09 30	Ref. Mon. S–34	441.3			298 57 10	T. P. 66	1,376.6
T. P. 49	47 13 02.07	31 54 10	Ref. Mon. 124	133.2	T. P. 68	47 17 24.02	110 31 50	Ref. Mon. 134	323.3
	67 59 55.83	149 28 30	T. P. 50	1,296.4		68 07 25.60	144 01 40	T. P. 69	565.6
		211 54 10	Ref. Mon. C–34	149.1			290 31 50	Ref. Mon. C–42	335.5
		320 53 50	T. P. 48	1,016.3			328 59 40	T. P. 67	318.4
T. P. 50	47 13 38.23	123 08 40	Ref. Mon. S–38	1,394.4	T. P. 69	47 17 38.84	106 05 10	T. P. 70	661.0
	68 00 27.13	139 22 30	T. P. 51	1,138.5		68 07 41.41	324 01 30	T. P. 68	565.6
		303 08 40	Ref. Mon. C–35	306.5			355 06 40	Ref. Mon. 134	345.6
		329 28 00	T. P. 49	1,296.4			355 06 40	Ref. Mon. S–44	1,146.4
T. P. 51	47 14 06.20	76 34 40	Ref. Mon. S–38	438.2	T. P. 70	47 17 44.77	136 58 30	T. P. 71	594.3
	68 01 02.37	149 59 30	T. P. 52	457.7		68 08 11.64	151 03 30	Ref. Mon. C–43	663.1
		256 34 40	Ref. Mon. C–36	160.4			286 04 50	T. P. 69	661.0
		319 22 00	T. P. 50	1,138.5			331 03 30	Ref. Mon. S–44	1,514.6
T. P. 52	47 14 19.04	21 36 50	Ref. Mon. S–38	535.7	T. P. 71	47 17 58.84	30 06 50	Ref. Mon. S–45	619.4
	68 01 13.25	110 50 50	T. P. 53	453.8		68 08 30.94	147 49 00	T. P. 72	801.6
		313 00 40	Ref. Mon. C–36	526.4			210 06 50	Ref. Mon. C–43	168.6
		329 59 20	T. P. 51	457.7			316 58 20	T. P. 70	594.3
T. P. 53	47 14 24.27	121 33 10	T. P. 54	717.9	T. P. 72	47 18 20.81	137 59 20	T. P. 73	600.2
	68 01 33.41	161 01 20	Ref. Mon. C–37	618.6		68 08 51.27	174 31 40	Ref. Mon. C–44	974.5
		290 50 30	T. P. 52	453.8			327 48 40	T. P. 71	801.6
		341 01 20	Ref. Mon. S–38	697.4			354 31 40	Ref. Mon. S–45	1,219.8

BOUNDARY TURNING POINTS—ST. JOHN RIVER—Continued

Station	Latitude and longitude	Azimuth	To station	Distance (meters)	Station	Latitude and longitude	Azimuth	To station	Distance (meters)
	° ′ ″	° ′ ″			T. P. 92	47 21 17.63	68 29 40	T. P. 93	807.8
T. P. 73	47 18 35.25	30 30 00	Ref. Mon. S-46	811.6		68 14 19.30	153 56 00	Ref. Mon. C-51	681.3
	68 09 10.39	164 01 50	T. P. 74	427.5			257 52 20	T. P. 91	274.6
		210 30 00	Ref. Mon. C-44	608.3			333 56 00	Ref. Mon. S-52	1,169.6
		317 59 10	T. P. 72	600.2	T. P. 93	47 21 08.04	26 27 50	Ref. Mon. S-53	196.5
T. P. 74	47 18 48.56	14 50 50	Ref. Mon. S-46	1,148.7		68 14 55.12	90 30 20	T. P. 94	1,279.3
	68 09 15.99	191 04 30	T. P. 75	195.7			206 27 50	Ref. Mon. C-51	1,014.5
		194 50 50	Ref. Mon. C-45	1,099.5			248 29 20	T. P. 92	807.8
		344 01 50	T. P. 73	427.5	T. P. 94	47 21 08.40	39 52 50	Ref. Mon. S-54	656.3
T. P. 75	47 18 54.78	11 04 30	T. P. 74	195.7		68 15 56.07	118 38 50	T. P. 95	532.7
	68 09 14.20	101 28 50	Ref. Mon. S-47	981.0			219 52 50	Ref. Mon. C-52	956.6
		185 14 00	T. P. 76	776.7			270 29 30	T. P. 93	1,279.3
		281 28 50	Ref. Mon. C-44	396.7	T. P. 95	47 21 16.67	66 06 20	Ref. Mon. S-55	1,470.4
T. P. 76	47 19 19.83	5 14 00	T. P. 75	776.7		68 16 18.35	128 25 00	T. P. 96	914.0
	68 09 10.83	60 44 50	Ref. Mon. S-47	1,183.1			246 06 20	Ref. Mon. C-52	1,182.1
		153 01 00	T. P. 77	390.9			298 38 40	T. P. 94	532.7
		240 44 50	Ref. Mon. C-45	198.7	T. P. 96	47 21 35.06	28 21 50	Ref. Mon. S-55	1,322.3
T. P. 77	47 19 31.10	42 41 50	Ref. Mon. S-47	1,260.6		68 16 52.47	103 01 30	T. P. 97	327.6
	68 09 19.27	118 50 50	T. P. 78	458.2			208 21 50	Ref. Mon. C-53	127.1
		305 36 40	Ref. Mon. C-45	431.4			308 24 40	T. P. 95	914.0
		333 01 00	T. P. 76	390.9	T. P. 97	47 21 37.45	84 16 50	Ref. Mon. C-54	1,225.2
T. P. 78	47 19 38.26	21 33 40	Ref. Mon. S-47	1,233.9		68 17 07.68	84 16 50	T. P. 98	421.0
	68 09 38.39	101 01 50	T. P. 79	764.2			264 16 50	Ref. Mon. C-53	381.5
		298 50 30	T. P. 77	458.2			283 01 20	T. P. 96	327.6
		302 07 30	Ref. Mon. C-45	888.0	T. P. 98	47 21 36.09	66 14 10	T. P. 99	259.5
T. P. 79	47 19 43.00	95 11 10	T. P. 80	465.8		68 17 27.65	84 16 40	Ref. Mon. C-54	804.2
	68 10 14.10	112 22 10	Ref. Mon. C-46	488.1			264 16 40	Ref. Mon. C-53	802.5
		281 01 30	T. P. 78	764.2			264 16 40	T. P. 97	421.0
		292 22 10	Ref. Mon. C-45	1,624.4	T. P. 99	47 21 32.71	53 55 40	T. P. 100	566.6
T. P. 80	47 19 44.36	4 58 20	Ref. Mon. S-48	507.4		68 17 38.96	79 53 40	Ref. Mon. 138	694.1
	68 10 36.19	117 59 50	T. P. 81	315.8			246 14 00	T. P. 98	259.5
		184 58 20	Ref. Mon. C-46	144.2			259 53 40	Ref. Mon. C-53	1,052.3
		275 11 00	T. P. 79	465.8	T. P. 100	47 21 21.90	73 51 30	T. P. 101	292.1
T. P. 81	47 19 49.16	20 24 40	Ref. Mon. S-49	337.7		68 18 00.78	133 13 40	Ref. Mon. 138	309.3
	68 10 49.47	120 56 00	T. P. 82	1,992.7			233 55 20	T. P. 99	566.6
		200 24 40	Ref. Mon. C-47	130.7			313 13 40	Ref. Mon. S-55	1,105.5
		297 59 40	T. P. 80	315.8	T. P. 101	47 21 19.27	21 48 10	Ref. Mon. S-56	463.0
T. P. 82	47 20 22.32	93 16 40	T. P. 83	375.7		68 18 14.15	90 50 10	T. P. 102	145.7
	68 12 10.89	163 52 50	Ref. Mon. C-49	419.9			201 48 10	Ref. Mon. C-54	472.9
		300 55 00	T. P. 81	1,992.7			253 51 20	T. P. 100	292.1
		343 52 50	Ref. Mon. S-50	525.8	T. P. 102	47 21 19.34	3 28 30	Ref. Mon. S-56	432.8
T. P. 83	47 20 23.02	34 05 30	Ref. Mon. S-51	180.5		68 18 21.09	103 48 10	T. P. 103	459.3
	68 12 28.76	74 24 20	T. P. 84	317.2			183 28 30	Ref. Mon. 136	144.5
		214 05 30	Ref. Mon. C-49	461.2			270 50 10	T. P. 101	145.7
		273 16 20	T. P. 82	375.7	T. P. 103	47 21 22.89	112 34 50	T. P. 104	922.1
T. P. 84	47 20 20.26	109 29 10	T. P. 85	254.5		68 18 42.34	142 13 00	Ref. Mon. C-55	821.5
	68 12 43.31	230 21 40	Ref. Mon. C-49	732.4			283 47 50	T. P. 102	459.3
		254 24 10	T. P. 83	317.2			322 13 00	Ref. Mon. S-56	685.2
		287 26 30	Ref. Mon. S-51	214.2	T. P. 104	47 21 34.35	49 41 50	Ref. Mon. S-58	1,016.4
T. P. 85	47 20 23.00	121 32 40	T. P. 86	425.8		68 19 22.92	100 05 50	T. P. 105	406.9
	68 12 54.74	244 33 40	Ref. Mon. C-49	890.0			229 41 50	Ref. Mon. C-55	456.4
		288 33 00	Ref. Mon. S-51	468.6			292 34 20	T. P. 103	922.1
		289 29 00	T. P. 84	254.5	T. P. 105	47 21 36.66	88 13 10	T. P. 106	342.2
T. P. 86	47 20 30.22	114 43 50	Ref. Mon. S-52	989.0		68 19 42.01	164 36 30	Ref. Mon. C-56	192.5
	68 13 12.03	136 04 50	T. P. 87	477.6			280 05 40	T. P. 104	406.9
		294 43 50	Ref. Mon. S-51	888.7			344 36 30	Ref. Mon. S-57	805.3
		301 32 30	T. P. 85	425.8	T. P. 106	47 21 36.32	55 59 40	Ref. Mon. S-59	1,186.8
T. P. 87	47 20 41.35	97 00 40	Ref. Mon. S-52	571.3		68 19 58.31	84 06 10	T. P. 107	258.3
	68 13 27.81	173 02 20	T. P. 88	621.0			235 59 40	Ref. Mon. C-56	350.9
		277 00 40	Ref. Mon. C-49	1,509.3			268 13 00	T. P. 105	342.2
		316 04 40	T. P. 86	477.6	T. P. 107	47 21 35.45	48 45 30	Ref. Mon. S-59	966.6
T. P. 88	47 21 01.31	41 58 30	Ref. Mon. S-52	735.3		68 20 10.56	73 38 50	T. P. 108	614.6
	68 13 31.39	149 32 10	T. P. 89	104.0			264 06 00	T. P. 106	258.3
		221 58 30	Ref. Mon. C-50	126.5			342 00 20	Ref. Mon. S-58	727.1
		353 02 20	T. P. 87	621.0	T. P. 108	47 21 29.85	85 24 30	T. P. 109	329.4
T. P. 89	47 21 04.22	88 10 00	Ref. Mon. S-53	1,793.1		68 20 38.65	122 28 40	Ref. Mon. C-57	558.1
	68 13 33.90	141 21 20	T. P. 90	327.7			253 38 30	T. P. 107	614.6
		268 10 00	Ref. Mon. C-50	137.4			302 28 40	Ref. Mon. S-58	965.4
		329 32 10	T. P. 88	104.0	T. P. 109	47 21 29.00	78 26 00	T. P. 110	316.4
T. P. 90	47 21 12.51	114 13 40	T. P. 91	526.1		68 20 54.30	156 23 40	Ref. Mon. C-57	355.8
	68 13 43.65	126 20 10	Ref. Mon. C-51	1,300.3			265 24 20	T. P. 108	329.4
		306 20 10	Ref. Mon. C-50	424.5			336 23 40	Ref. Mon. S-59	477.8
		321 21 20	T. P. 89	327.7	T. P. 110	47 21 26.94	70 32 40	T. P. 111	903.9
T. P. 91	47 21 19.50	64 26 40	Ref. Mon. S-53	1,227.8		68 21 09.08	126 44 50	Ref. Mon. C-58	165.1
	68 14 06.51	77 52 30	T. P. 92	274.6			258 25 50	T. P. 109	316.4
		294 13 20	T. P. 90	526.1			306 44 50	Ref. Mon. S-59	625.7
		347 31 00	Ref. Mon. S-52	1,135.2					

BOUNDARY TURNING POINTS—ST. JOHN RIVER—Continued

Station	Latitude and longitude	Azimuth	To station	Distance (meters)	Station	Latitude and longitude	Azimuth	To station	Distance (meters)
	° ′ ″	° ′ ″				° ′ ″	° ′ ″		
T. P. 111	47 21 17.19	51 52 50	T. P. 112	562.0	T. P. 130	47 17 10.98	87 09 20	T. P. 131	633.9
	68 21 49.69	100 34 00	Ref. Mon. C-59	646.2		68 22 56.17	130 40 50	Ref. Mon. C-66	1,672.8
		250 32 10	T. P. 110	903.9			246 27 20	T. P. 129	308.7
		280 34 00	Ref. Mon. S-60	837.3			310 40 50	Ref. Mon. 139	119.7
T. P. 112	47 21 05.95	42 05 20	T. P. 113	326.6	T. P. 131	47 17 09.96	68 03 00	Ref. Mon. 142	620.4
	68 22 10.76	157 27 30	Ref. Mon. C-59	503.9		68 23 26.30	68 03 00	Ref. Mon. 140	314.7
		231 52 30	T. P. 111	562.0			104 14 20	T. P. 132	360.1
		337 27 30	Ref. Mon. S-61	292.2			267 09 00	T. P. 130	633.9
T. P. 113	47 20 58.10	2 04 40	Ref. Mon. S-62	739.0	T. P. 132	47 17 12.83	92 01 20	T. P. 133	648.5
	68 22 21.18	34 22 20	T. P. 114	782.0		68 23 42.91	164 29 50	Ref. Mon. C-66	1,072.1
		182 04 40	Ref. Mon. C-59	708.2			284 14 10	T. P. 131	360.1
		222 05 10	T. P. 112	326.6			344 29 50	Ref. Mon. 140	214.0
T. P. 114	47 20 37.21	22 55 10	T. P. 115	471.5	T. P. 133	47 17 13.57	102 40 00	T. P. 134	519.4
	68 22 42.21	102 39 00	Ref. Mon. C-60	463.3		68 24 13.75	129 08 50	Ref. Mon. C-67	682.5
		214 22 10	T. P. 113	782.0			272 01 00	T. P. 132	648.5
		282 39 00	Ref. Mon. S-62	425.0			309 08 50	Ref. Mon. 142	543.9
T. P. 115	47 20 23.15	6 41 20	T. P. 116	883.3	T. P. 134	47 17 17.26	81 13 00	T. P. 135	401.8
	68 22 50.96	153 22 50	Ref. Mon. C-60	599.2		68 24 37.87	175 55 50	Ref. Mon. C-67	317.8
		202 55 00	T. P. 114	471.5			282 39 40	T. P. 133	519.4
		333 22 50	Ref. Mon. S-63	609.0			355 55 50	Ref. Mon. S-71	704.2
T. P. 116	47 19 54.74	20 38 00	T. P. 117	360.2	T. P. 135	47 17 15.27	53 20 10	T. P. 136	1,009.1
	68 22 55.87	48 27 40	Ref. Mon. C-62	370.2		68 24 56.77	224 42 30	Ref. Mon. C-67	532.4
		186 41 20	T. P. 115	883.3			261 12 50	T. P. 134	401.8
		228 27 40	Ref. Mon. S-63	502.0			325 06 10	Ref. Mon. S-71	781.6
T. P. 117	47 19 43.82	12 34 40	T. P. 118	528.4	T. P. 136	47 16 55.76	50 21 00	Ref. Mon. S-72	737.3
	68 23 01.91	121 22 10	Ref. Mon. C-62	175.9		68 25 35.28	74 07 00	T. P. 137	315.5
		200 38 00	T. P. 116	360.2			230 21 00	Ref. Mon. C-67	1,537.5
		301 22 10	Ref. Mon. S-64	313.7			233 19 40	T. P. 135	1,009.1
T. P. 118	47 19 27.12	104 09 30	Ref. Mon. C-63	229.1	T. P. 137	47 16 52.96	34 31 10	Ref. Mon. S-72	466.2
	68 23 07.39	192 34 40	T. P. 117	528.4		68 25 49.72	103 45 50	T. P. 138	355.1
		284 09 30	Ref. Mon. S-65	466.4			153 51 50	Ref. Mon. C-68	1,155.4
		357 22 10	T. P. 119	306.7			254 06 50	T. P. 136	315.5
T. P. 119	47 19 17.20	29 14 30	Ref. Mon. C-64	907.3	T. P. 138	47 16 55.69	109 17 10	T. P. 139	556.4
	68 23 06.72	177 22 10	T. P. 118	306.7		68 26 06.13	170 13 30	Ref. Mon. C-68	966.8
		209 14 30	Ref. Mon. S-64	755.1			283 45 40	T. P. 137	355.1
		338 22 30	T. P. 120	221.3			350 13 30	Ref. Mon. S-72	475.5
T. P. 120	47 19 10.54	41 51 00	Ref. Mon. C-64	786.6	T. P. 139	47 17 01.64	66 14 20	T. P. 140	409.5
	68 23 02.83	158 22 30	T. P. 119	221.3		68 26 31.12	137 06 40	Ref. Mon. C-69	1,862.2
		221 51 00	Ref. Mon. S-65	534.2			289 17 00	T. P. 138	556.4
		349 35 20	T. P. 121	1,040.3			317 06 40	Ref. Mon. S-72	890.3
T. P. 121	47 18 37.41	103 16 30	Ref. Mon. C-65	793.9	T. P. 140	47 16 56.30	84 03 20	T. P. 141	190.8
	68 22 53.88	169 35 30	T. P. 120	1,040.3		68 26 48.95	116 25 10	Ref. Mon. 144	1,019.7
		283 16 30	Ref. Mon. S-66	311.1			246 14 00	T. P. 139	409.5
		357 45 20	T. P. 122	228.0			296 25 10	Ref. Mon. S-72	1,095.1
T. P. 122	47 18 30.03	30 26 30	T. P. 123	588.6	T. P. 141	47 16 55.66	101 07 50	T. P. 142	301.5
	68 22 53.46	117 41 10	Ref. Mon. C-65	882.7		68 26 57.98	134 30 30	Ref. Mon. 143	536.6
		177 45 20	T. P. 121	228.0			224 08 10	Ref. Mon. C-68	1,328.9
		297 41 10	Ref. Mon. S-67	220.3			264 03 10	T. P. 140	190.8
T. P. 123	47 18 13.60	50 36 20	Ref. Mon. C-66	1,329.4	T. P. 142	47 16 57.54	114 55 10	T. P. 143	484.5
	68 23 07.65	210 26 20	T. P. 122	588.6		68 27 12.06	164 43 20	Ref. Mon. C-69	1,545.5
		230 36 20	Ref. Mon. S-67	638.3			164 43 20	Ref. Mon. 143	329.6
		346 19 20	T. P. 124	286.9			281 07 40	T. P. 141	301.5
T. P. 124	47 18 04.58	166 19 30	T. P. 123	286.9	T. P. 143	47 17 04.15	3 11 10	Ref. Mon. S-73	125.8
	68 23 04.42	211 53 10	Ref. Mon. S-67	805.4		68 27 32.97	155 56 50	T. P. 144	1,127.9
		281 11 00	Ref. Mon. S-68	736.6			183 11 10	Ref. Mon. 144	211.6
		315 55 10	T. P. 125	353.1			294 54 50	T. P. 142	484.5
T. P. 125	47 17 56.37	76 55 40	Ref. Mon. C-66	1,376.3	T. P. 144	47 17 37.50	62 25 10	Ref. Mon. S-74	645.4
	68 22 52.74	135 55 20	T. P. 124	353.1		68 27 54.85	143 43 20	T. P. 145	134.8
		256 55 40	Ref. Mon. S-68	489.7			242 25 10	Ref. Mon. C-69	554.9
		321 26 40	T. P. 126	524.5			335 56 30	T. P. 143	1,127.9
T. P. 126	47 17 43.08	16 04 50	Ref. Mon. 139	1,113.1	T. P. 145	47 17 41.02	75 27 30	Ref. Mon. S-75	1,623.0
	68 22 37.18	141 27 00	T. P. 125	524.5		68 27 58.64	122 38 10	T. P. 146	432.4
		196 04 50	Ref. Mon. S-68	542.1			255 27 30	Ref. Mon. C-69	590.5
		345 23 00	T. P. 127	478.9			323 43 20	T. P. 144	134.8
T. P. 127	47 17 28.08	16 36 50	T. P. 128	237.8	T. P. 146	47 17 48.57	11 19 20	Ref. Mon. S-74	653.3
	68 22 31.43	35 18 10	Ref. Mon. 139	742.7		68 28 15.97	97 56 00	T. P. 147	350.6
		107 27 20	Ref. Mon. C-66	1,874.8			191 19 20	Ref. Mon. C-70	396.9
		165 23 00	T. P. 126	478.9			302 37 50	T. P. 145	432.4
T. P. 128	47 17 20.70	43 40 40	T. P. 129	244.6	T. P. 147	47 17 50.13	51 17 10	Ref. Mon. S-75	1,101.7
	68 22 34.66	43 40 40	Ref. Mon. S-70	1,921.7		68 28 32.50	69 56 30	T. P. 148	723.7
		43 40 40	Ref. Mon. 139	523.0			231 17 10	Ref. Mon. C-70	544.9
		196 36 50	T. P. 127	237.8			277 55 50	T. P. 146	350.6
T. P. 129	47 17 14.97	43 40 40	Ref. Mon. S-70	1,677.1	T. P. 148	47 17 42.10	22 11 20	Ref. Mon. S-75	476.1
	68 22 42.70	43 40 40	Ref. Mon. 139	278.4		68 29 04.85	75 54 10	T. P. 149	479.4
		66 27 30	T. P. 130	308.7			202 11 20	Ref. Mon. 147	135.7
		223 40 40	T. P. 128	244.6			249 56 00	T. P. 147	723.7

BOUNDARY TURNING POINTS—ST. JOHN RIVER—Continued

Station	Latitude and longitude	Azimuth	To station	Distance (meters)	Station	Latitude and longitude	Azimuth	To station	Distance (meters)
	° ′ ″	° ′ ″				° ′ ″	° ′ ″		
T. P. 149	47 17 38.31 / 68 29 26.98	88 01 30 / 138 39 00 / 255 54 00 / 318 39 00	T. P. 150 / Ref. Mon. C–72 / T. P. 148 / Ref. Mon. S–75	324.5 / 1,474.0 / 479.4 / 431.7	T. P. 168	47 16 12.98 / 68 35 54.03	12 20 40 / 128 51 50 / 222 18 30 / 308 51 50	T. P. 169 / Ref. Mon. C–81 / T. P. 167 / Ref. Mon. S–87	186.5 / 806.7 / 597.9 / 483.4
T. P. 150	47 17 37.95 / 68 29 42.42	99 34 30 / 117 10 20 / 268 01 20 / 297 10 20	T. P. 151 / Ref. Mon. 151–A / T. P. 149 / Ref. Mon. S–75	169.0 / 896.1 / 324.5 / 685.1	T. P. 169	47 16 07.09 / 68 35 55.93	139 29 00 / 192 20 40 / 319 29 00 / 343 45 40	Ref. Mon. C–81 / T. P. 168 / Ref. Mon. S–88 / T. P. 170	905.5 / 186.5 / 1,237.3 / 190.7
T. P. 151	47 17 38.86 / 68 29 50.35	77 21 40 / 113 40 00 / 257 21 40 / 279 34 20	Ref. Mon. S–76 / T. P. 152 / Ref. Mon. 147 / T. P. 150	304.0 / 561.2 / 1,032.3 / 169.0	T. P. 170	47 16 01.16 / 68 35 53.39	143 38 20 / 163 45 40 / 260 18 10 / 333 48 20	Ref. Mon. C–81 / T. P. 169 / Ref. Mon. S–87 / T. P. 171	1,082.2 / 190.7 / 368.2 / 716.4
T. P. 152	47 17 46.15 / 68 30 14.82	97 40 40 / 143 18 30 / 293 39 40 / 323 18 30	T. P. 153 / Ref. Mon. 151–A / T. P. 151 / Ref. Mon. S–76	367.6 / 194.8 / 561.2 / 363.9	T. P. 171	47 15 40.34 / 68 35 38.34	3 47 40 / 153 48 30 / 183 47 40 / 284 46 20	T. P. 172 / T. P. 170 / Ref. Mon. S–87 / Ref. Mon. S–88	258.0 / 716.4 / 706.4 / 448.8
T. P. 153	47 17 47.74 / 68 30 32.16	86 09 30 / 179 34 20 / 277 40 30 / 359 34 20	T. P. 154 / Ref. Mon. 153 / T. P. 152 / Ref. Mon. S–77	644.6 / 131.7 / 367.6 / 245.9	T. P. 172	47 15 32.00 / 68 35 39.15	33 16 50 / 183 47 40 / 183 47 40 / 252 24 30	T. P. 173 / Ref. Mon. S–87 / T. P. 171 / Ref. Mon. S–88	346.6 / 964.4 / 258.0 / 473.2
T. P. 154	47 17 46.34 / 68 31 02.77	72 01 20 / 152 55 40 / 266 09 00 / 332 55 40	T. P. 155 / Ref. Mon. C–73 / T. P. 153 / Ref. Mon. S–78	571.2 / 477.9 / 644.6 / 237.8	T. P. 173	47 15 22.62 / 68 35 48.20	55 59 00 / 55 59 00 / 213 16 40 / 235 59 00	T. P. 174 / Ref. Mon. C–83 / T. P. 172 / Ref. Mon. S–88	333.4 / 1,340.6 / 346.6 / 773.6
T. P. 155	47 17 40.63 / 68 31 28.63	59 58 20 / 127 41 50 / 252 01 00 / 307 41 50	T. P. 156 / Ref. Mon. C–74 / T. P. 154 / Ref. Mon. S–79	549.3 / 319.9 / 571.2 / 263.6	T. P. 174	47 15 16.58 / 68 36 01.34	32 41 00 / 55 58 50 / 235 58 50 / 235 58 50	T. P. 175 / Ref. Mon. C–83 / Ref. Mon. S–88 / T. P. 173	685.8 / 1,007.2 / 1,107.0 / 333.4
T. P. 156	47 17 31.73 / 68 31 51.27	40 48 00 / 80 33 40 / 239 58 00 / 260 33 40	T. P. 157 / Ref. Mon. C–75 / T. P. 155 / Ref. Mon. S–79	990.2 / 745.1 / 549.3 / 693.5	T. P. 175	47 14 57.89 / 68 36 18.95	40 42 10 / 178 08 00 / 212 40 50 / 358 08 00	T. P. 176 / Ref. Mon. C–82 / T. P. 174 / Ref. Mon. S–90	339.0 / 543.7 / 685.8 / 521.7
T. P. 157	47 17 07.46 / 68 32 22.06	54 41 00 / 172 00 30 / 220 47 40 / 352 00 30	T. P. 158 / Ref. Mon. C–75 / T. P. 156 / Ref. Mon. S–81	187.7 / 633.5 / 990.2 / 329.5	T. P. 176	47 14 49.57 / 68 36 29.46	62 02 50 / 138 00 00 / 220 42 10 / 318 00 00	T. P. 177 / Ref. Mon. C–83 / T. P. 175 / Ref. Mon. S–90	856.4 / 363.9 / 339.0 / 355.8
T. P. 158	47 17 03.95 / 68 32 29.35	70 28 00 / 137 34 40 / 234 40 50 / 317 34 40	T. P. 159 / Ref. Mon. C–76 / T. P. 157 / Ref. Mon. S–81	721.0 / 611.3 / 187.7 / 295.0	T. P. 177	47 14 36.57 / 68 37 05.43	77 29 10 / 158 45 10 / 242 02 30 / 338 45 10	T. P. 178 / Ref. Mon. C–84 / T. P. 176 / Ref. Mon. S–91	616.8 / 625.3 / 856.4 / 526.4
T. P. 159	47 16 56.14 / 68 33 01.68	21 05 30 / 94 29 50 / 201 05 30 / 250 27 30	Ref. Mon. S–82 / T. P. 160 / Ref. Mon. C–76 / T. P. 158	323.9 / 299.7 / 742.1 / 721.0	T. P. 178	47 14 32.24 / 68 37 34.06	27 39 20 / 88 20 40 / 207 39 20 / 257 28 50	Ref. Mon. S–92 / T. P. 179 / Ref. Mon. C–84 / T. P. 177	514.3 / 245.9 / 808.9 / 616.8
T. P. 160	47 16 56.90 / 68 33 15.89	106 06 00 / 150 46 30 / 274 29 40 / 330 46 30	T. P. 161 / Ref. Mon. C–77 / T. P. 159 / Ref. Mon. S–82	328.5 / 754.9 / 299.7 / 373.2	T. P. 179	47 14 32.01 / 68 37 45.75	93 01 20 / 179 05 50 / 268 20 30 / 359 05 50	T. P. 180 / Ref. Mon. C–85 / T. P. 178 / Ref. Mon. S–92	485.2 / 297.2 / 245.9 / 448.5
T. P. 161	47 16 59.85 / 68 33 30.91	56 44 40 / 112 39 50 / 236 44 40 / 286 05 50	Ref. Mon. S–83 / T. P. 162 / Ref. Mon. C–76 / T. P. 160	493.7 / 1,148.0 / 1,053.9 / 328.5	T. P. 180	47 14 32.84 / 68 38 08.78	65 16 40 / 133 57 10 / 273 01 00 / 313 57 10	T. P. 181 / Ref. Mon. C–86 / T. P. 179 / Ref. Mon. S–92	429.8 / 289.3 / 485.2 / 682.9
T. P. 162	47 17 14.17 / 68 34 21.32	96 53 00 / 169 46 10 / 292 39 10 / 349 46 10	T. P. 163 / Ref. Mon. C–78 / T. P. 161 / Ref. Mon. S–84	433.8 / 321.3 / 1,148.0 / 717.3	T. P. 181	47 14 27.02 / 68 38 27.34	73 11 10 / 130 06 00 / 245 16 30 / 310 06 00	T. P. 182 / Ref. Mon. C–87 / T. P. 180 / Ref. Mon. S–93	475.5 / 756.1 / 429.8 / 503.4
T. P. 163	47 17 15.86 / 68 34 41.82	73 03 30 / 234 43 50 / 276 52 40 / 323 37 40	T. P. 164 / Ref. Mon. C–78 / T. P. 162 / Ref. Mon. S–84	192.5 / 457.6 / 433.8 / 941.2	T. P. 182	47 14 22.57 / 68 38 48.98	87 22 10 / 168 50 10 / 253 10 50 / 348 50 10	T. P. 183 / Ref. Mon. C–87 / T. P. 181 / Ref. Mon. S–94	516.8 / 636.6 / 475.5 / 157.6
T. P. 164	47 17 14.04 / 68 34 50.58	44 13 10 / 240 07 40 / 253 03 30 / 313 23 20	T. P. 165 / Ref. Mon. C–78 / T. P. 163 / Ref. Mon. S–84	1,019.5 / 643.2 / 192.5 / 1,021.5	T. P. 183	47 14 21.80 / 68 39 13.53	31 13 20 / 75 23 50 / 211 13 20 / 267 21 50	Ref. Mon. S–95 / T. P. 184 / Ref. Mon. C–87 / T. P. 182	395.0 / 181.3 / 758.1 / 516.8
T. P. 165	47 16 50.38 / 68 35 24.41	23 04 20 / 176 17 40 / 224 12 40 / 275 52 30	T. P. 166 / Ref. Mon. C–79 / T. P. 164 / Ref. Mon. S–85	209.2 / 564.3 / 1,019.5 / 800.4	T. P. 184	47 14 20.32 / 68 39 21.87	41 23 40 / 96 42 50 / 255 23 40 / 276 42 50	T. P. 185 / Ref. Mon. 155 / T. P 183 / Ref. Mon. S–94	277.1 / 807.5 / 181.3 / 727.3
T. P. 166	47 16 44.14 / 68 35 28.31	14 54 10 / 82 49 30 / 203 04 20 / 262 49 30	T. P. 167 / Ref. Mon. C–80 / T. P. 165 / Ref. Mon. S–85	537.8 / 701.9 / 209.2 / 885.1	T. P. 185	47 14 13.59 / 68 39 30.58	57 41 30 / 118 42 30 / 221 23 40 / 298 42 30	T. P. 186 / Ref. Mon. 154 / T. P. 184 / Ref Mon. S–95	180.1 / 182.5 / 277.1 / 175.6
T. P. 167	47 16 27.31 / 68 35 34.89	42 18 40 / 93 33 20 / 194 54 00 / 273 33 20	T. P. 168 / Ref. Mon. C–81 / T. P. 166 / Ref. Mon. S–86	597.9 / 1,032.6 / 537.8 / 557.0	T. P. 186	47 14 10.47 / 68 39 37.82	93 53 00 / 177 33 40 / 177 33 40 / 237 41 20	T. P. 187 / Ref. Mon. C–88 / Ref. Mon. 154 / T. P. 185	254.5 / 1,023.9 / 184.1 / 180.1

BOUNDARY TURNING POINTS—ST. JOHN RIVER—Continued

Station	Latitude and longitude	Azimuth	To station	Distance (meters)
	° ′ ″	° ′ ″		
T. P. 187	47 14 11.03 68 39 49.89	55 52 40 122 28 40 235 52 40 273 52 50	Ref. Mon. S–96 T. P. 188 Ref. Mon. 154 T. P. 186	1,024.7 388.1 297.2 254.5
T. P. 188	47 14 17.78 68 40 05.46	33 37 40 129 30 30 213 37 40 302 28 30	Ref. Mon. S–96 T. P. 189 Ref. Mon. 155 T. P. 187	940.6 729.2 207.2 388.1
T. P. 189	47 14 32.80 68 40 32.21	75 00 10 103 24 50 255 00 10 309 30 10	Ref. Mon. S–97 T. P. 190 Ref. Mon. C–89 T. P. 188	1,802.3 351.6 477.3 729.2
T. P. 190	47 14 35.44 68 40 48.48	87 00 20 125 23 30 267 00 20 283 24 30	T. P. 191 Ref. Mon. C–90 Ref. Mon. C–89 T. P. 189	369.8 1,106.0 804.2 351.6
T. P. 191	47 14 34.82 68 41 06.04	62 48 10 128 36 30 141 06 20 267 00 10	Ref. Mon. S–97 T. P. 192 Ref. Mon. C–90 T. P. 190	1,157.4 271.3 847.8 369.8
T. P. 192	47 14 40.30 68 41 16.12	79 33 10 146 51 20 308 36 20 326 51 20	T. P. 193 Ref. Mon. C–90 T. P. 191 Ref. Mon. S–96	350.7 585.9 271.3 1,766.0
T. P. 193	47 14 38.24 68 41 32.52	36 39 40 61 50 20 259 33 00 317 11 30	Ref. Mon. S–97 T. P. 194 T. P. 192 Ref. Mon. S–96	791.3 302.6 350.7 1,928.7
T. P. 194	47 14 33.62 68 41 45.20	22 41 00 48 24 30 202 41 00 241 50 10	Ref. Mon. S–97 T. P. 195 Ref. Mon. C–90 T. P. 193	533.2 712.0 755.4 302.6
T. P. 195	47 14 18.32 68 42 10.52	76 58 00 93 22 50 228 24 10 273 22 50	T. P. 196 Ref. Mon. S–98 T. P. 194 Ref. Mon. S–97	281.6 905.9 712.0 327.4
T. P. 196	47 14 16.26 68 42 23.56	113 03 30 192 27 30 256 57 50 265 47 40	T. P. 197 Ref. Mon. C–91 T. P. 195 Ref. Mon. S–97	236.3 1,175.0 281.6 602.8
T. P. 197	47 14 19.25 68 42 33.90	93 22 30 149 02 00 273 22 30 293 03 20	Ref. Mon. S–98 T. P. 198 Ref. Mon. S–97 T. P. 196	413.3 105.8 820.0 236.3
T. P. 198	47 14 22.20 68 42 36.49	99 02 50 114 49 50 279 02 50 329 02 00	Ref. Mon. 158 T. P. 199 Ref. Mon. S–97 T. P. 197	1,025.1 237.5 884.0 105.8
T. P. 199	47 14 25.43 68 42 46.74	40 36 10 105 10 10 220 36 10 294 49 40	Ref. Mon. S–98 T. P. 200 Ref. Mon. C–91 T. P. 198	219.0 235.2 1,138.3 237.5
T. P. 200	47 14 27.42 68 42 57.53	77 44 40 159 38 30 285 10 00 339 38 30	T. P. 201 Ref. Mon. 156 T. P. 199 Ref. Mon. S–98	131.2 163.5 235.2 243.0
T. P. 201	47 14 26.51 68 43 03.63	65 10 20 201 30 20 257 44 40 313 13 10	T. P. 202 Ref. Mon. 156 T. P. 200 Ref. Mon. S–98	663.3 194.7 131.2 292.0
T. P. 202	47 14 17.49 68 43 32.25	49 05 10 154 56 10 245 09 50 334 56 10	T. P. 203 Ref. Mon. 159–A T. P. 201 Ref. Mon. 159–B	294.2 50.5 663.3 28.9
T. P. 203	47 14 11.25 68 43 42.82	66 06 20 100 39 00 229 06 00 280 39 00	T. P. 204 Ref. Mon. 160 T. P. 202 Ref. Mon. S–99	190.4 510.3 294.2 420.5
T. P. 204	47 14 08.75 68 43 51.09	90 03 40 117 37 40 246 06 10 270 03 30	T. P. 205 Ref. Mon. 160 T. P. 203 Ref. Mon. S–99	309.6 369.6 190.4 587.3
T. P. 205	47 14 08.76 68 44 05.81	31 45 40 47 38 10 211 45 40 270 03 30	Ref. Mon. 162 T. P. 206 Ref. Mon. 159 T. P. 204	358.9 379.9 751.1 309.6
T. P. 206	47 14 00.47 68 44 19.15	57 46 10 118 11 20 227 38 00 298 11 20	T. P. 207 Ref. Mon. 161 T. P. 205 Ref. Mon. 162	471.3 292.8 379.9 104.1
T. P. 207	47 13 52.33 68 44 38.10	51 15 30 163 13 50 237 45 50 343 13 50	T. P. 208 Ref. Mon. C–94 T. P. 206 Ref. Mon. 163	849.7 1,271.0 471.3 220.4
T. P. 208	47 13 35.11 68 45 09.60	60 39 40 118 57 30 231 15 00 298 57 30	T. P. 209 Ref. Mon. C–95 T. P. 207 Ref. Mon. S–100	448.9 971.8 849.7 506.7
T. P. 209	47 13 27.98 68 45 28.20	65 20 40 146 22 50 240 39 20 326 22 50	T. P. 210 Ref. Mon. C–95 T. P. 208 Ref. Mon. S–101	605.5 829.1 448.9 295.7
T. P. 210	47 13 19.80 68 45 54.35	5 31 10 74 20 00 185 31 10 245 20 20	Ref. Mon. S–102 T. P. 211 Ref. Mon. C–95 T. P. 209	187.5 354.0 947.4 605.5
T. P. 211	47 13 16.71 68 46 10.56	89 06 10 105 44 40 254 19 50 285 44 40	T. P. 212 Ref. Mon. 163–A T. P. 210 Ref. Mon. S–102	937.6 773.8 354.0 335.4
T. P. 212	47 13 16.23 68 46 55.12	40 36 40 70 12 00 220 36 40 269 05 30	Ref. Mon. S–103 T. P. 213 Ref. Mon. 163–A T. P. 211	557.1 1,847.3 296.0 937.6
T. P. 213	47 12 55.96 68 48 17.72	1 03 40 87 02 50 181 03 40 250 11 00	Ref. Mon. 165 T. P. 214 Ref. Mon. C–98 T. P. 212	375.9 545.1 324.9 1,847.3
T. P. 214	47 12 55.05 68 48 43.59	16 51 50 56 20 50 267 02 30 296 24 30	Ref. Mon. 167 T. P. 215 T. P. 213 Ref. Mon. 166	174.3 337.5 545.1 255.6
T. P. 215	47 12 49.00 68 48 56.94	31 56 20 84 58 30 236 20 40 264 58 30	T. P. 216 Ref. Mon. C–99 T. P. 214 Ref. Mon. 167	300.0 759.0 337.5 231.3
T. P. 216	47 12 40.75 68 49 04.48	57 25 50 107 28 20 211 56 20 287 28 20	T. P. 217 Ref. Mon. C–99 T. P. 215 Ref. Mon. 168	822.0 626.3 300.0 460.9
T. P. 217	47 12 26.42 68 49 37.40	8 35 30 46 09 50 188 35 30 237 25 30	Ref. Mon. 169 T. P. 218 Ref. Mon. C–99 T. P. 216	296.1 530.2 637.7 822.0
T. P. 218	47 12 14.53 68 49 55.57	60 09 50 160 41 50 226 09 40 340 41 50	T. P. 219 Ref. Mon. C–100 T. P. 217 Ref. Mon. S–106	542.2 367.4 530.2 443.6
T. P. 219	47 12 05.79 68 50 17.91	63 28 40 103 33 50 240 09 30 283 33 50	T. P. 220 Ref. Mon. C–101 T. P. 218 Ref. Mon. S–106	442.6 604.7 542.2 634.7
T. P. 220	47 11 59.39 68 50 36.73	54 18 40 150 31 20 243 28 30 330 31 20	T. P. 221 Ref. Mon. C–101 T. P. 219 Ref. Mon. S–107	660.1 389.9 442.6 287.5
T. P. 221	47 11 46.92 68 51 02.20	22 55 00 78 44 30 234 18 20 258 44 30	T. P. 222 Ref. Mon. C–103 T. P. 220 Ref. Mon. S–107	192.5 920.7 660.1 690.9
T. P. 222	47 11 41.18 68 51 05.76	45 42 30 137 31 40 202 55 00 317 31 40	T. P. 223 Ref. Mon. C–102 T. P. 221 Ref. Mon. S–108	686.8 449.3 192.5 193.3
T. P. 223	47 11 25.65 68 51 29.11	65 52 00 144 49 00 225 42 20 324 49 00	T. P. 224 Ref. Mon. C–103 T. P. 222 Ref. Mon. S–109	343.0 584.1 686.8 140.1
T. P. 224	47 11 21.11 68 51 43.98	86 15 20 86 53 10 245 51 40 266 15 20	Ref. Mon. C–105 T. P. 225 T. P. 223 Ref. Mon. S–109	1390.7 346.6 343.0 394.6

BOUNDARY TURNING POINTS—ST. JOHN RIVER—Continued

Station	Latitude and longitude	Azimuth	To station	Dis-tance (meters)	Station	Latitude and longitude	Azimuth	To station	Dis-tance (meters)
	° ′ ″	° ′ ″				° ′ ″	° ′ ″		
T. P. 225	47 11 20.50	4 39 40	Ref. Mon. S-110	461.6	T. P. 228	47 10 58.83	79 53 50	Ref. Mon. 173	716.7
	68 52 00.42	92 44 20	T. P. 226	371.8		68 52 57.93	99 30 30	T. P. 229	177.6
		184 39 40	Ref. Mon. C-104	426.4			223 19 10	T. P. 227	667.1
		266 53 00	T. P. 224	346.6			259 53 50	Ref. Mon. S-110	1191.7
T. P. 226	47 11 21.07	62 10 20	T. P. 227	431.5	T. P. 229	47 10 59.78	46 33 10	Ref. Mon. 171	278.4
	68 52 18.05	82 22 10	Ref. Mon. C-105	676.5		68 53 06.25	70 18 30	T. P. 230	375.7
		272 44 10	T. P. 225	371.8			226 33 10	Ref. Mon. 170	398.8
		325 03 30	Ref. Mon. S-110	582.9			279 30 30	T. P. 228	177.6
T. P. 227	47 11 14.55	43 19 30	T. P. 228	667.1	T. P. 230	47 10 55.68	15 52 00	Ref. Mon. 172	380.6
	68 52 36.18	111 07 00	Ref. Mon. C-105	309.7		68 53 23.05	103 46	T. P. 231	361.6
		242 10 10	T. P. 226	431.5			195 52 00	Ref. Mon. C-106	127.9
		291 07 00	Ref. Mon. S-110	767.0			250 18 10	T. P. 229	375.7

GEOGRAPHIC POSITIONS OF MONUMENTS REFERENCING THE TURNING POINTS OF THE INTERNATIONAL BOUNDARY THROUGH THE ST. JOHN RIVER

Station	Latitude and longitude	Azimuth	To station	Distance (meters)
	° ′ ″	° ′ ″		
Ref. Mon. S-1___	47 04 00.26	236 04 20	T. P. 1	123.6
	67 47 32.02	236 04 20	Ref. Mon. C-1	294.6
		304 14 00	Mon. 117	124.9
Ref. Mon. C-1_	47 04 05.58	31 02 10	Mon. 117	273.9
	67 47 20.43	56 04 30	T. P. 1	171.0
		56 04 30	Ref. Mon. S-1	294.6
Mon. 117___	47 03 57.98	124 14 00	Ref. Mon. S-1	124.9
	67 47 27.12	139 33 40	T. P. 2	516.1
		139 33 40	Ref. Mon. C-2	820.0
		179 42 30	T. P. 1	139.2
		211 02 00	Ref. Mon. C-1	273.9
Ref. Mon. C-2_	47 04 18.19	19 02 50	Ref. Mon. S-2	270.0
	67 47 52.33	319 33 20	T. P. 2	303.9
		319 33 20	Mon. 117	820.0
Ref. Mon. S-2_	47 04 09.92	199 02 40	Ref. Mon. C-2	270.0
	67 47 56.51			
Ref. Mon. S-3_	47 04 17.38	215 31 00	T. P. 3	175.8
	67 48 21.09	215 31 00	Ref. Mon. C-3	284.0
Ref. Mon. C-3_	47 04 24.86	35 31 10	T. P. 3	108.2
	67 48 13.27	35 31 10	Ref. Mon. S-3	284.0
Ref. Mon. S-4_	47 04 31.34	219 34 40	T. P. 4	116.2
	67 48 46.33	219 34 40	Ref. Mon. C-4	270.8
Ref. Mon. C-4_	47 04 38.10	39 34 50	T. P. 4	154.6
	67 48 38.15	39 34 50	Ref. Mon. S-4	270.8
Ref. Mon. S-5_	47 04 42.29	143 30 10	T. P. 6	709.9
	67 48 58.42	143 30 10	Ref. Mon. C-6	1,019.2
Ref. Mon. C-5_	47 04 54.33	81 20 20	T. P. 5	172.5
	67 48 55.30	81 20 20	Ref. Mon. S-6	538.7
Ref. Mon. S-6_	47 04 51.70	261 20 00	T. P. 5	366.2
	67 49 20.55	261 20 00	Ref. Mon. C-5	538.7
Ref. Mon. C-6_	47 05 08.82	59 58 10	T. P. 7	217.5
	67 49 27.16	59 58 10	Ref. Mon. S-7	418.8
		323 29 40	T. P. 6	309.3
		323 29 40	Ref. Mon. S-5	1,019.2
Ref. Mon. S-7_	47 05 02.04	128 13 10	T. P. 8	215.8
	67 49 44.34	128 13 10	Ref. Mon. C-7	834.1
		239 57 50	T. P. 7	201.3
		239 57 50	Ref. Mon. C-6	418.8
Ref. Mon. C-7_	47 05 18.75	50 50 30	T. P. 9	131.7
	67 50 15.41	50 50 30	Ref. Mon. S-8	447.0
		308 12 50	T. P. 8	618.3
		308 12 50	Ref. Mon. S-7	834.1
Ref. Mon. S-8_	47 05 09.61	230 50 10	T. P. 9	315.3
	67 50 31.84	230 50 10	Ref. Mon. C-7	447.0
Ref. Mon. C-8_	47 05 39.03	71 24 50	T. P. 10	258.0
	67 50 46.05	71 24 50	Ref. Mon. 119	420.9
Ref. Mon. 119_	47 05 34.68	251 24 30	T. P. 10	162.9
	67 51 04.96	251 24 30	Ref. Mon. C-8	420.9
Ref. Mon. S-9_	47 05 23.88	151 58 40	T. P. 11	883.3
	67 51 16.02	151 58 40	Ref. Mon. C-9	1,331.4
Ref. Mon. C-9_	47 06 01.94	19 18 00	Ref. Mon. S-10	489.4
	67 51 45.68	331 58 20	T. P. 11	448.1
		331 58 20	Ref. Mon. S-9	1,331.4
Ref. Mon. S-10_	47 05 46.98	199 17 50	Ref. Mon. C-9	489.4
	67 51 53.35			
Ref. Mon. C-10_	47 06 05.16	48 53 30	T. P. 12	128.3
	67 52 03.96	48 53 30	Ref. Mon. S-11	397.8
Ref. Mon. S-11_	47 05 56.69	130 43 30	T. P. 13	378.6
	67 52 18.17	130 43 30	Ref. Mon. C-11	769.5
		228 53 20	T. P. 12	269.5
		228 53 20	Ref. Mon. C-10	397.8
Ref. Mon. C-11_	47 06 12.94	41 00 10	T. P. 14	116.3
	67 52 45.83	41 00 10	Ref. Mon. S-12	390.1
		310 43 10	T. P. 13	390.1
		310 43 10	Ref. Mon. S-11	769.5
Ref. Mon. S-12_	47 06 03.41	221 00 00	T. P. 14	273.8
	67 52 57.97	221 00 00	Ref. Mon. C-11	390.1
Ref. Mon. C-12_	47 06 19.58	48 08 30	T. P. 15	150.9
	67 52 55.60	48 08 30	Ref. Mon. S-13	442.5
Ref. Mon. S-13_	47 06 10.02	127 41 50	Ref. Mon. S-14	363.8
	67 53 11.23	228 08 20	T. P. 15	291.6
		228 08 20	Ref. Mon. C-12	442.5
Ref. Mon. S-14_	47 06 17.22	307 41 40	Ref. Mon. S-13	363.8
	67 53 24.88			
Ref. Mon. C-13_	47 06 30.62	103 04 00	Ref. Mon. S-15	429.2
	67 53 06.49			
Ref. Mon. C-14_	47 06 37.73	65 17 20	T. P. 16	142.8
	67 53 13.68	65 17 20	Ref. Mon. S-15	293.3
		150 43 50	T. P. 17	481.4
		150 43 50	Ref. Mon. S-16	711.6
Ref. Mon. S-15_	47 06 33.76	245 17 10	T. P. 16	150.5
	67 53 26.32	245 17 10	Ref. Mon. C-14	293.3
		283 03 40	Ref. Mon. C-13	429.2
Ref. Mon. S-16_	47 06 57.83	199 18 10	T. P. 18	425.3
	67 53 30.18	199 18 10	Ref. Mon. C-16	796.7
		287 11 40	Ref. Mon. C-15	320.0
		330 43 30	T. P. 17	230.2
		330 43 30	Ref. Mon. C-14	711.6
Ref. Mon. C-15_	47 06 54.77	107 11 50	Ref. Mon. S-16	320.0
	67 53 15.68			
Ref. Mon. C-16_	47 07 22.18	19 18 20	T. P. 18	371.4
	67 53 17.69	19 18 20	Ref. Mon. S-16	796.7
		79 47 10	T. P. 19	216.7
		79 47 10	Ref. Mon. S-17	489.2
		135 23 40	T. P. 20	252.8
		135 23 40	Ref. Mon. 120	422.9
Ref. Mon. S-17_	47 07 19.37	205 26 00	Ref. Mon. 120	429.4
	67 53 40.53	205 26 00	T. P. 21	562.0
		259 46 50	T. P. 19	272.5
		259 46 50	Ref. Mon. C-16	489.2
Ref. Mon. 120_	47 07 31.93	25 26 10	Ref. Mon. S-17	429.4
	67 53 31.78	159 49 00	T. P. 22	444.4
		159 49 00	T. P. 23	599.4
		159 49 00	Ref. Mon. C-17	800.8
		205 26 10	T. P. 21	132.6
		315 23 30	T. P 20	170.1
		315 23 30	Ref. Mon. C-16	422.9
Ref. Mon. C-17_	47 07 56.27	55 14 50	T. P. 24	88.5
	67 53 44.89	55 14 50	Ref. Mon. S-18	322.7
		339 48 50	T. P. 23	201.4
		339 48 50	T. P. 22	356.4
		339 48 50	Ref. Mon. 120	800.8
Ref. Mon. S-18_	47 07 50.31	175 55 40	T. P. 25	289.9
	67 53 57.47	175 55 40	Ref. Mon. C-18	762.8
		235 14 40	T. P. 24	234.2
		235 14 40	Ref. Mon. C-17	322.7
Ref. Mon. C-18_	47 08 14.95	355 55 40	T. P. 25	472.9
	67 54 00.04	355 55 40	Ref. Mon. S-18	762.8
Ref. Mon. S-19_	47 08 04.87	181 18 30	T. P. 26	214.4
	67 54 15.23	181 18 30	Ref. Mon. C-19	821.6
Ref. Mon. C-19_	47 08 31.47	1 18 30	T. P. 26	607.2
	67 54 14.34	1 18 30	Ref. Mon. S-19	821.6
		126 46 10	T. P. 27	403.1
		126 46 10	Ref. Mon. S-21	1,039.1
Ref. Mon. S-20_	47 08 31.53	167 34 50	T. P. 28	598.3
	67 54 31.73	167 34 50	Ref. Mon. C-20	903.9
Ref. Mon. C-20_	47 09 00.12	45 57 10	T. P. 29	179.1
	67 54 40.96	45 57 10	Ref. Mon. S-21	377.9
		103 44 40	T. P. 30	827.7
		103 44 40	Ref. Mon. S-22	1,232.7
		347 34 40	T. P. 28	305.6
		347 34 40	Ref. Mon. S-20	903.9
Ref. Mon. S-21_	47 08 51.61	225 57 00	T. P. 29	198.8
	67 54 53.85	225 57 00	Ref. Mon. C-20	377.9
		306 45 40	T. P. 27	636.0
		306 45 40	Ref. Mon. C-19	1,039.1

REFERENCE MONUMENTS—ST. JOHN RIVER—Continued

Station	Latitude and longitude	Azimuth	To station	Distance (meters)	Station	Latitude and longitude	Azimuth	To station	Distance (meters)
Ref. Mon. S-22	47 09 09.60	167 34 20	T. P. 31	276.1	Ref. Mon. 123	47 12 03.42	301 01 30	Ref. Mon. 122	561.2
	67 55 37.80	167 34 20	Ref. Mon. C-22	707.7		67 57 56.43			
		283 44 00	T. P. 30	405.0	Ref. Mon. C-30	47 12 19.94	28 46 30	Ref. Mon. S-32	782.9
		283 44 00	Ref. Mon. C-20	1,232.7		67 58 09.28	113 30 30	T. P. 45	383.1
Ref. Mon. C-21	47 09 23.09	89 05 40	T. P. 32	480.5			113 30 30	Ref. Mon. C-32	1,249.1
	67 55 22.82	89 05 40	Ref. Mon. S-23	665.0	Ref. Mon. S-32	47 11 57.72	208 46 10	Ref. Mon. C-30	782.9
Ref. Mon. C-22	47 09 31.98	347 34 20	T. P. 31	431.6		67 58 27.19			
	67 55 45.03	347 34 20	Ref. Mon. S-22	707.7	Ref. Mon. S-33	47 12 10.54	154 25 30	T. P. 46	721.7
Van Buren highway bridge boundary point.	47 09 35.37	3 04 10	Ref. Mon. S-23	390.2		67 58 45.78	154 25 30	Ref. Mon. C-32	874.1
	67 55 53.39	157 04 20	T. P. 33	216.2			190 37 00	Ref Mon. C-31	631.8
		337 04 20	T. P. 32	419.9	Ref. Mon. C-31	47 12 30.65	10 37 00	Ref. Mon. S-33	631.8
Ref. Mon. S-23	47 09 22.75	173 51 40	T. P. 33	592.1		67 58 40.26			
	67 55 54.38	173 51 40	Ref. Mon. C-23	938.3	Ref. Mon. C-32	47 12 36.07	75 32 20	T. P. 47	286.0
		183 04 10	Van Buren highway bridge boundary point.	390.2		67 59 03.71	75 32 20	Ref. Mon. S-35	683.7
		269 05 20	T. P. 32	184.5			293 29 50	T. P. 45	866.0
		269 05 20	Ref. Mon. C-21	665.0			293 29 50	Ref. Mon. C-30	1,249.1
Ref. Mon. S-24	47 09 45.34	240 20 00	T. P. 34	257.6			334 25 20	T. P. 46	152.4
	67 56 18.76	240 20 00	Ref. Mon. C-23	475.4			334 25 20	Ref. Mon. S-33	874.1
Ref. Mon. C-23	47 09 52.96	60 20 10	T. P. 34	217.8	Ref. Mon. S-34	47 12 23.09	160 09 30	T. P. 48	441.3
	67 55 59.14	60 20 10	Ref. Mon. S-24	475.4		67 59 18.25	160 09 30	Ref. Mon. C-33	795.5
		115 48 30	T. P. 35	377.6	Ref. Mon. S-35	47 12 30.54	255 32 00	T. P. 47	397.7
		115 48 30	Ref. Mon. S-25	612.9		67 59 35.17	255 32 00	Ref. Mon. C-32	683.7
		353 51 40	T. P. 33	346.2	Ref. Mon. C-33	47 12 47.32	340 09 30	T. P. 48	354.2
		353 51 40	Ref. Mon. S-23	938.3		67 59 31.08	340 09 30	Ref. Mon. S-34	795.5
Ref. Mon. S-25	47 10 01.60	295 48 10	T. P. 35	235.3	Ref. Mon. 124	47 12 58.41	43 56 10	Ref. Mon. S-36	243.3
	67 56 25.34	295 48 10	Ref. Mon. C-23	612.9		67 59 59.17	211 54 10	T. P. 49	133.2
Ref. Mon. S-26	47 10 13.22	249 06 50	T. P. 36	225.3			211 54 10	Ref. Mon. C-34	282.3
	67 56 32.15	249 06 50	Ref. Mon. C-24	348.0	Ref. Mon. S-36	47 12 52.74	223 56 10	Ref. Mon. 124	243.3
Ref. Mon. C-24	47 10 17.24	69 07 00	T. P. 36	122.7		68 00 07.19			
	67 56 16.71	69 07 00	Ref. Mon. S-26	348.0	Ref. Mon. C-34	47 13 06.17	31 54 20	T. P. 49	149.1
Ref. Mon. S-27	47 10 25.40	218 14 00	T. P. 37	348.2		67 59 52.08	31 54 20	Ref. Mon. 124	282.3
	67 56 48.42	218 14 00	Ref. Mon. C-25	493.0	Ref. Mon. C-35	47 13 32.80	83 44 40	Ref. Mon. 126	320.5
Keegan railroad bridge boundary point.	47 10 30.16	149 20 20	T. P. 37	147.1		68 00 14.93	123 08 50	T. P. 50	306.5
	67 56 34.63	183 28 50	Ref. Mon. C-25	240.7			123 08 50	Ref. Mon. S-38	1,700.9
		329 20 20	T. P. 36	514.9	Ref. Mon. 126	47 13 31.67	263 44 30	Ref. Mon. C-35	320.5
Ref. Mon. C-25	47 10 37.94	3 28 50	Keegan railroad bridge boundary point.	240.7		68 00 30.07			
	67 56 33.93				Ref. Mon. S-37	47 13 15.28	141 42 30	Ref. Mon. S-38	1,874.2
		38 14 10	T. P. 37	144.8		68 00 27.42			
		38 14 10	Ref. Mon. S-27	493.0	Ref. Mon. S-38	47 14 02.91	161 01 30	T. P. 53	697.4
Ref. Mon. S-28	47 10 34.63	230 27 30	T. P. 38	286.5		68 01 22.63	161 01 30	Ref. Mon. C-37	1,316.0
	67 56 55.28	230 27 30	Ref. Mon. C-26	434.2			201 36 40	T. P. 52	535.7
Ref. Mon. C-26	47 10 43.58	50 27 40	T. P. 38	147.7			256 34 30	T. P. 51	438.2
	67 56 39.38	50 27 40	Ref. Mon. S-28	434.2			256 34 30	Ref. Mon. C-36	598.6
Ref. Mon. S-29	47 10 50.93	247 25 00	T. P. 39	276.9			303 08 00	T. P. 50	1,394.4
	67 57 08.88	247 25 00	Ref. Mon. C-27	398.8			303 08 00	Ref. Mon. C-35	1,700.9
Ref. Mon. C-27	47 10 55.89	67 25 10	T. P. 39	121.9			321 41 50	Ref. Mon. S-37	1,874.2
	67 56 51.39	67 25 10	Ref. Mon. S-29	398.8	Ref. Mon. C-36	47 14 07.41	76 34 50	T. P. 51	160.4
		114 20 30	T. P. 40	377.1		68 00 54.95	76 34 50	Ref. Mon. S-38	598.6
		114 20 30	Ref. Mon. S-30	712.6			133 00 50	T. P. 52	526.4
Ref. Mon. S-30	47 11 05.40	294 20 00	T. P. 40	335.5	Ref. Mon. C-37	47 14 43.21	62 59 20	T. P. 54	460.9
	67 57 22.22	294 20 00	Ref. Mon. C-27	712.6		68 01 42.97	62 59 20	Ref. Mon. S-39	711.1
Ref. Mon. C-28	47 11 15.13	150 58 20	T. P. 41	342.6			341 01 20	T. P. 53	618.6
	67 56 57.69	150 58 20	Ref. Mon. 121	967.4			341 01 20	Ref. Mon. S-38	1,316.0
Ref. Mon. 121	47 11 42.52	103 37 40	Ref. Mon. S-31	470.7	Ref. Mon. S-39	47 14 32.75	155 35 00	T. P. 55	511.9
	67 57 19.99	210 37 20	T. P. 43	216.1		68 02 13.10	155 35 00	Ref. Mon. C-38	1,120.6
		210 37 20	Ref. Mon. C-29	266.1			242 59 00	T. P. 54	250.2
		283 37 40	T. P. 42	228.6			242 59 00	Ref. Mon. C-37	711.1
		330 58 00	T. P. 41	624.8	Ref. Mon. C-38	47 15 05.79	335 34 40	T. P. 55	608.7
		330 58 00	Ref. Mon. C-28	967.4		68 02 35.13	335 34 40	Ref. Mon. S-39	1,120.6
Ref. Mon. C-29	47 11 49.94	30 37 20	T. P. 43	50.0	Ref. Mon. S-40	47 14 55.46	158 47 20	T. P. 56	398.8
	67 57 13.55	30 37 20	Ref. Mon. 121	266.1		68 03 03.18	158 47 20	Ref. Mon. 128	641.6
Ref. Mon. S-31	47 11 46.11	214 56 40	Ref. Mon. 122	299.1	Ref. Mon. 128	47 15 14.83	338 47 10	T. P. 56	242.8
	67 57 41.72	214 56 40	T. P. 44	488.5		68 03 14.22	338 47 10	Ref. Mon. S-40	641.6
		283 37 20	Ref. Mon. 121	470.7	Ref. Mon. S-41	47 15 14.41	128 04 20	T. P. 60	1,559.6
		283 37 20	T. P. 42	699.3		68 03 39.91	128 04 20	Ref. Mon. 130	2,212.4
Ref. Mon. 122	47 11 54.05	34 56 50	Ref. Mon. S-31	299.1			138 11 30	T. P. 58	503.3
	67 57 33.58	121 01 40	Ref. Mon. 123	561.2			138 11 30	Ref. Mon. C-40	1,785.5
		214 56 50	T. P. 44	189.4			212 49 50	T. P. 57	172.7
							212 49 50	Ref. Mon. C-39	482.1
					Ref. Mon. C-39	47 15 27.52	32 50 00	T. P. 57	309.4
						68 03 27.48	32 50 00	Ref. Mon. S-41	482.1

REFERENCE MONUMENTS—ST. JOHN RIVER—Continued

Station	Latitude and longitude	Azimuth	To station	Distance (meters)
	° ′ ″	° ′ ″		
Ref. Mon. C-40	47 15 57.50	93 27 40	T. P. 61	92.3
	68 04 36.53	93 27 40	Ref. Mon. 130	552.4
		134 13 00	T. P. 63	1,706.4
		134 13 00	Ref. Mon. C-41	2,374.9
		318 10 50	T. P. 58	1,282.2
		318 10 50	Ref. Mon. S-41	1,785.5
Ref. Mon. S-42	47 15 26.60	160 05 10	T. P. 64	2,474.9
	68 05 12.53	160 05 10	Ref. Mon. C-41	2,776.2
		191 44 40	T. P. 62	1,558.7
		191 44 40	Ref. Mon. 130	1,008.7
		257 06 50	T. P. 59	943.2
Ref. Mon. 130	47 15 58.58	11 44 40	Ref. Mon. S-42	1,008.7
	68 05 02.76	191 44 40	T. P. 62	550.0
		273 27 20	T. P. 61	460.1
		273 27 20	Ref. Mon. C-40	552.4
		308 03 20	T. P. 60	652.8
		308 03 20	Ref. Mon. S-41	2,212.4
		317 25 30	T. P. 59	1,055.5
Ref. Mon. C-41	47 16 51.12	73 22 40	T. P. 65	294.8
	68 05 57.52	73 22 40	Ref. Mon. S-43	1,064.1
		99 02 20	T. P. 66	488.6
		99 02 20	Ref. Mon. S-44	2,111.7
		314 12 00	T. P. 63	668.5
		314 12 00	Ref. Mon. C-40	2,374.9
		340 04 40	T. P. 64	301.3
		340 04 40	Ref. Mon. S-42	2,776.2
Ref. Mon. S-43	47 16 41.26	253 22 00	T. P. 65	769.3
	68 06 46.03	253 22 00	Ref. Mon. C-41	1,064.1
Ref. Mon. S-44	47 17 01.85	151 04 00	T. P. 70	1,514.6
	68 07 36.76	151 04 00	Ref. Mon. C-43	2,177.7
		175 06 40	Ref. Mon. 134	800.8
		175 06 40	T. P. 69	1,146.4
		224 03 10	T. P. 67	573.1
		224 03 10	Ref. Mon. C-42	789.1
		279 01 00	T. P. 66	1,623.1
		279 01 00	Ref. Mon. C-41	2,111.7
Ref. Mon. C-42	47 17 20.21	44 03 30	T. P. 67	216.0
	68 07 10.65	44 03 30	Ref. Mon. S-44	789.1
		110 32 00	T. P. 68	335.5
		110 32 00	Ref. Mon. 134	658.8
Ref. Mon. 134	47 17 27.69	175 06 40	T. P. 69	345.6
	68 07 40.01	290 31 40	T. P. 68	323.8
		290 31 40	Ref. Mon. C-42	658.8
		355 06 40	Ref. Mon. S-44	800.8
Ref. Mon. C-43	47 18 03.56	30 06 50	T. P. 71	168.6
	68 08 26.91	30 06 50	Ref. Mon. S-45	788.0
		331 03 20	T. P. 70	663.1
		331 03 20	Ref. Mon. S-44	2,177.7
Ref. Mon. S-45	47 17 41.49	174 31 50	T. P. 72	1,219.8
	68 08 45.73	174 31 50	Ref. Mon. C-44	2,194.3
		210 06 40	T. P. 71	619.4
		210 06 40	Ref. Mon. C-43	788.0
Ref. Mon. S-46	47 18 12.60	194 50 40	T. P. 74	1,148.7
	68 09 30.00	194 50 40	Ref. Mon. C-45	2,248.2
		210 29 40	T. P. 73	811.6
		210 29 40	Ref. Mon. C-44	1,419.9
Ref. Mon. C-44	47 18 52.22	30 30 10	T. P. 73	608.3
	68 08 55.69	30 30 10	Ref. Mon. S-46	1,419.9
		101 29 10	T. P. 75	396.7
		101 29 10	Ref. Mon. S-47	1,377.7
		354 31 40	T. P. 72	974.5
		354 31 40	Ref. Mon. S-45	2,194.3
Ref. Mon. C-45	47 19 22.97	14 51 00	T. P. 74	1,099.5
	68 09 02.57	14 51 00	Ref. Mon. S-46	2,248.2
		60 44 50	T. P. 76	198.7
		60 44 50	Ref. Mon. S-47	1,381.8
		112 23 10	T. P. 79	1,624.4
		112 23 10	Ref. Mon. C-46	2,112.5
		122 07 50	T. P. 78	888.0
		125 37 00	T. P. 77	431.4
Ref. Mon. S-47	47 19 01.10	201 33 30	T. P. 78	1,233.9
	68 09 59.98	222 41 20	T. P. 77	1,260.6
		240 44 10	T. P. 76	1,183.1
		240 44 10	Ref. Mon. C-45	1,381.8
		281 28 20	T. P. 75	981.0
		281 28 20	Ref. Mon. C-44	1,377.7
Ref. Mon. S-48	47 19 27.99	184 58 20	T. P. 80	507.4
	68 10 38.29	184 58 20	Ref. Mon. C-46	651.6
Ref. Mon. C-46	47 19 49.01	4 58 20	T. P. 80	144.6
	68 10 35.60	4 58 20	Ref. Mon. S-48	651.1
		292 22 00	T. P. 79	488.5
		292 22 00	Ref. Mon. C-45	2,112.2
Ref. Mon. C-47	47 19 53.12	20 24 40	T. P. 81	130.7
	68 10 47.30	20 24 40	Ref. Mon. S-49	468.4
Ref. Mon. S-49	47 19 38.91	200 24 30	T. P. 81	337.7
	68 10 55.08	200 24 30	Ref. Mon. C-47	468.4
Ref. Mon. S-50	47 20 05.96	163 53 00	T. P. 82	525.8
	68 12 03.94	163 53 00	Ref. Mon. C-49	945.7
		241 49 00	Ref. Mon. C-48	517.3
Ref. Mon. C-48	47 20 13.87	61 49 20	Ref. Mon. S-50	517.3
	68 11 42.22			
Ref. Mon. C-49	47 20 35.38	34 05 40	T. P. 83	461.2
	68 12 16.44	34 05 40	Ref. Mon. S-51	641.7
		50 22 00	T. P. 84	732.4
		64 34 10	T. P. 85	890.2
		97 01 30	T. P. 87	1,509.3
		97 01 30	Ref. Mon. S-52	2,080.6
		343 52 50	T. P. 82	419.9
		343 52 50	Ref. Mon. S-50	945.7
Ref. Mon. S-51	47 20 18.18	107 26 40	T. P. 84	214.2
	68 12 33.58	108 33 10	T. P. 85	468.6
		114 44 20	T. P. 86	888.7
		114 44 20	Ref. Mon. S-52	1,877.7
		214 05 30	T. P. 83	180.5
		214 05 30	Ref. Mon. C-49	641.7
Ref. Mon. C-50	47 21 04.36	41 58 30	T. P. 88	126.5
	68 13 27.36	41 58 30	Ref. Mon. S-52	861.8
		88 10 00	T. P. 89	137.3
		88 10 00	Ref. Mon. S-53	1,930.3
		126 20 20	T. P. 90	424.5
		126 20 20	Ref. Mon. C-51	1,724.8
Ref. Mon. S-52	47 20 43.61	153 56 20	T. P. 92	1,169.6
	68 13 54.82	153 56 20	Ref. Mon. C-51	1,850.9
		167 31 10	T. P. 91	1,135.2
		221 58 10	T. P. 88	735.3
		221 58 10	Ref. Mon. C-50	861.8
		277 00 20	T. P. 87	571.3
		277 00 20	Ref. Mon. C-49	2,080.6
		294 43 20	T. P. 86	989.0
		294 43 20	Ref. Mon. S-51	1,877.7
Ref. Mon. C-51	47 21 37.45	26 28 10	T. P. 93	1,014.5
	68 14 33.57	26 28 10	Ref. Mon. S-53	1,211.0
		306 19 30	T. P. 90	1,300.3
		306 19 30	Ref. Mon. C-50	1,724.8
		333 55 50	T. P. 92	681.3
		333 55 50	Ref. Mon. S-52	1,850.9
Ref. Mon. S-53	47 21 02.35	206 27 50	T. P. 93	196.5
	68 14 59.29	206 27 50	Ref. Mon. C-51	1,211.0
		244 26 00	T. P. 91	1,227.8
		268 08 50	T. P. 89	1,793.0
		268 08 50	Ref. Mon. C-50	1,930.3
Ref. Mon. C-52	47 21 32.17	1 08 10	Ref. Mon. 134-A	632.3
	68 15 26.85	39 53 10	T. P. 94	956.6
		39 53 10	Ref. Mon. S-54	1,612.9
		66 07 00	T. P. 95	1,182.1
		66 07 00	Ref. Mon. S-55	2,652.5
Ref. Mon. 134-A	47 21 11.70	181 08 10	Ref. Mon. C-52	632.3
	68 15 27.44			
Ref. Mon. S-54	47 20 52.09	219 52 40	T. P. 94	656.3
	68 16 16.12	219 52 40	Ref. Mon. C-52	1,612.8
Ref. Mon. C-53	47 21 38.68	28 21 50	T. P. 96	127.1
	68 16 49.59	28 21 50	Ref. Mon. S-55	1,449.4
		79 54 20	T. P. 99	1,052.3
		79 54 20	Ref. Mon. 138	1,746.4
		84 17 10	T. P. 97	381.5
		84 17 10	T. P. 98	802.5
		84 17 10	Ref. Mon. C-54	1,606.7
Ref. Mon. S-55	47 20 57.38	133 14 10	T. P. 100	1,105.5
	68 17 22.40	133 14 10	Ref. Mon. 138	1,414.8
		208 21 30	T. P. 96	1,322.3
		208 21 30	Ref. Mon. C-53	1,449.4
		246 05 40	T. P. 95	1,470.4
		246 05 40	Ref. Mon. C-52	2,652.5

REFERENCE MONUMENTS—ST. JOHN RIVER—Continued

Station	Latitude and longitude	Azimuth	To station	Distance (meters)
	° ′ ″	° ′ ″		
Ref. Mon. C-54	47 21 33.49 / 68 18 05.78	21 48 10	T. P. 101	472.9
		21 48 10	Ref. Mon. S-56	935.9
		264 16 10	T. P. 98	804.2
		264 16 10	T. P. 97	1,225.2
		264 16 10	Ref. Mon. C-53	1,606.7
Ref. Mon. 136	47 21 24.01 / 68 18 20.67	3 28 30	T. P. 102	144.5
		3 23 30	Ref. Mon. S-56	577.3
Ref. Mon. 138	47 21 28.76 / 68 18 11.52	259 53 20	T. P. 99	694.1
		259 53 20	Ref. Mon. C-53	1,746.4
		313 13 40	T. P. 100	309.3
		313 13 40	Ref. Mon. S-55	1,414.8
Ref. Mon. S-56	47 21 05.35 / 68 18 22.34	142 13 10	T. P. 103	685.2
		142 13 10	Ref. Mon. C-55	1,506.7
		183 28 30	T. P. 102	432.8
		183 28 30	Ref. Mon. 136	577.3
		201 48 00	T. P. 101	463.0
		201 48 00	Ref. Mon. C-54	935.9
Ref. Mon. C-55	47 21 43.91 / 68 19 06.33	49 42 00	T. P. 104	456.4
		49 42 00	Ref. Mon. S-58	1,472.8
		322 12 40	T. P. 103	821.5
		322 12 40	Ref. Mon. S-56	1,506.7
Ref. Mon. S-57	47 21 11.52 / 68 19 31.83	164 36 30	T. P. 105	805.3
		164 36 30	Ref. Mon. C-56	997.8
Ref. Mon. C-56	47 21 42.67 / 68 19 44.45	55 59 50	T. P. 106	350.9
		55 59 50	Ref. Mon. S-59	1,537.7
		344 36 20	T. P. 105	192.5
		344 36 20	Ref. Mon. S-57	997.8
Ref. Mon. S-58	47 21 13.06 / 68 19 59.85	122 29 00	T. P. 108	965.4
		122 29 00	Ref. Mon. C-57	1,523.5
		162 00 30	T. P. 107	727.1
		229 41 20	T. P. 104	1,016.4
		229 41 20	Ref. Mon. C-55	1,472.8
Ref. Mon. C-57	47 21 39.55 / 68 21 01.09	302 28 20	T. P. 108	558.1
		302 28 20	Ref. Mon. S-58	1,523.5
		336 23 40	T. P. 109	355.8
		336 23 40	Ref. Mon. S-59	833.6
Ref. Mon. S-59	47 21 14.82 / 68 20 45.19	126 45 10	T. P. 110	625.7
		126 45 10	Ref. Mon. C-58	790.8
		156 23 50	T. P. 109	477.8
		156 23 50	Ref. Mon. C-57	833.6
		228 45 00	T. P. 107	966.6
		235 59 10	T. P. 106	1,186.8
		235 59 10	Ref. Mon. C-56	1,537.7
Ref. Mon. C-58	47 21 30.14 / 68 21 15.38	306 44 50	T. P. 110	165.1
		306 44 50	Ref. Mon. S-59	790.8
Ref. Mon. S-60	47 21 12.21 / 68 21 10.47	100 34 30	T. P. 111	837.3
		100 34 30	Ref. Mon. C-59	1,483.5
Ref. Mon. S-61	47 20 57.21 / 68 22 05.42	157 27 40	T. P. 112	292.2
		157 27 40	Ref. Mon. C-59	796.1
Ref. Mon. C-59	47 21 21.02 / 68 22 19.96	2 04 40	T. P. 113	708.2
		2 04 40	Ref. Mon. S-62	1,447.2
		280 33 40	T. P. 111	646.2
		280 33 40	Ref. Mon. S-60	1,483.5
		337 27 30	T. P. 112	503.9
		337 27 30	Ref. Mon. S-61	796.1
Ref. Mon. S-62	47 20 34.19 / 68 22 22.46	102 39 10	T. P. 114	425.0
		102 39 10	Ref. Mon. C-60	888.3
		182 04 40	T. P. 113	739.0
		182 04 40	Ref. Mon. C-59	1,447.2
Ref. Mon. C-60	47 20 40.49 / 68 23 03.75	282 38 40	T. P. 114	463.3
		282 38 40	Ref. Mon. S-62	888.3
		333 22 40	T. P. 115	599.2
		333 22 40	Ref. Mon. S-63	1,208.2
Ref. Mon. S-63	47 20 05.52 / 68 22 37.97	48 28 00	T. P. 116	502.0
		48 28 00	Ref. Mon. C-62	872.2
		153 23 00	T. P. 115	609.0
		153 23 00	Ref. Mon. C-60	1,208.2
Ref. Mon. C-61	47 20 03.56 / 68 23 05.01	9 19 40	Ref. Mon. C-62	525.0
Ref. Mon. C-62	47 19 46.79 / 68 23 09.06	189 19 40	Ref. Mon. C-61	525.0
		228 27 30	T. P. 116	370.2
		228 27 30	Ref. Mon. S-63	872.2
		301 22 10	T. P. 117	175.9
		301 22 10	Ref. Mon. S-64	489.6
Ref. Mon. S-64	47 19 38.53 / 68 22 49.15	29 14 50	T. P. 119	755.1
		29 14 50	Ref. Mon. C-64	1,662.4
		121 22 20	T. P. 117	313.7
		121 22 20	Ref. Mon. C-62	489.6

Station	Latitude and longitude	Azimuth	To station	Distance (meters)
	° ′ ″	° ′ ″		
Ref. Mon. C-63	47 19 28.93 / 68 23 17.97	284 09 30	T. P. 118	229.1
		284 09 30	Ref. Mon. S-65	695.5
Ref. Mon. S-65	47 19 23.42 / 68 22 45.86	41 51 10	T. P. 120	534.2
		41 51 10	Ref. Mon. C-64	1,320.8
		104 09 50	T. P. 118	466.4
		104 09 50	Ref. Mon. C-63	695.5
Ref. Mon. C-64	47 18 51.56 / 68 23 27.82	209 14 20	T. P. 119	907.3
		209 14 20	Ref. Mon. S-64	1,662.4
		221 50 40	T. P. 120	786.6
		221 50 40	Ref. Mon. S-65	1,320.8
Ref. Mon. S-66	47 18 35.10 / 68 22 39.47	103 16 40	T. P. 121	311.1
		103 16 40	Ref. Mon. C-65	1,105.0
Ref. Mon. C-65	47 18 43.31 / 68 23 30.67	283 16 00	T. P. 121	793.9
		283 16 00	Ref. Mon. S-66	1,105.0
		297 40 50	T. P. 122	882.7
		297 40 50	Ref. Mon. S-67	1,103.0
Ref. Mon. S-67	47 18 26.72 / 68 22 44.17	31 53 30	T. P. 124	805.4
		50 36 40	T. P. 123	638.3
		50 36 40	Ref. Mon. C-66	1,967.7
		117 41 20	T. P. 122	220.3
		117 41 20	Ref. Mon. C-65	1,103.0
Ref. Mon. S-68	47 17 59.95 / 68 22 30.03	16 05 00	T. P. 126	542.1
		16 05 00	Ref. Mon. 139	1,655.2
		76 56 00	T. P. 125	489.7
		76 56 00	Ref. Mon. C-66	1,866.0
		101 11 20	T. P. 124	736.6
Ref. Mon. C-66	47 17 46.28 / 68 23 56.55	230 35 40	T. P. 123	1,329.4
		230 35 40	Ref. Mon. S-67	1,967.7
		256 55 00	T. P. 125	1,376.3
		256 55 00	Ref. Mon. S-68	1,866.0
		287 26 20	T. P. 127	1,874.8
		310 40 00	T. P. 130	1,672.8
		310 40 00	Ref. Mon. 139	1,792.5
		344 29 40	T. P. 132	1,072.1
		344 29 40	Ref. Mon. 140	1,286.1
Ref. Mon. S-69	47 16 57.19 / 68 22 29.62	126 39 40	Ref. Mon. 139	582.5
Ref. Mon. 139	47 17 08.45 / 68 22 51.85	43 40 30	Ref. Mon. S-70	1,398.7
		130 40 50	T. P. 130	119.7
		130 40 50	Ref. Mon. C-66	1,792.5
		196 04 40	T. P. 126	1,113.1
		196 04 40	Ref. Mon. S-68	1,655.2
		215 17 50	T. P. 127	742.7
		223 40 30	T. P. 128	523.0
		223 40 30	T. P. 129	278.4
		306 39 30	Ref. Mon. S-69	582.5
Ref. Mon. S-70	47 16 35.69 / 68 23 37.81	223 40 00	Ref. Mon. 139	1,398.7
		223 40 00	T. P. 129	1,677.1
		223 40 00	T. P. 128	1,921.7
Ref. Mon. 140	47 17 06.15 / 68 23 40.19	68 02 50	Ref. Mon. 142	305.7
		164 30 00	T. P. 132	214.0
		164 30 00	Ref. Mon. C-66	1,286.1
		248 02 50	T. P. 131	314.7
Ref. Mon. 141	47 17 09.20 / 68 23 48.18	28 57 50	Ref. Mon. 142	238.3
Ref. Mon. 142	47 17 02.45 / 68 23 53.68	129 09 10	T. P. 133	543.9
		129 09 10	Ref. Mon. C-67	1,226.4
		208 57 50	Ref. Mon. 141	238.3
		248 02 40	Ref. Mon. 140	305.7
		248 02 40	T. P. 131	620.4
Ref. Mon. S-71	47 16 54.51 / 68 24 35.49	145 06 20	T. P. 135	781.6
		175 55 50	T. P. 134	704.2
		175 55 50	Ref. Mon. C-67	1,022.0
Ref. Mon. C-67	47 17 27.52 / 68 24 38.94	44 42 40	T. P. 135	532.4
		50 21 40	T. P. 136	1,537.5
		50 21 40	Ref. Mon. S-72	2,274.8
		309 08 40	T. P. 133	682.5
		309 08 40	Ref. Mon. 142	1,226.4
		355 55 40	T. P. 134	317.8
		355 55 40	Ref. Mon. S-71	1,022.0
Ref. Mon. S-72	47 16 40.52 / 68 26 02.29	116 25 50	T. P. 140	1,095.1
		116 25 50	Ref. Mon. 144	2,114.8
		137 07 00	T. P. 139	890.3
		137 07 00	Ref. Mon. C-69	2,752.5
		170 13 40	T. P. 138	475.5
		170 13 40	Ref. Mon. C-68	1,442.3
		214 31 00	T. P. 137	466.2
		230 20 40	T. P. 136	737.3
		230 20 40	Ref. Mon. C-67	2,274.8

REFERENCE MONUMENTS—ST. JOHN RIVER—Continued

Station	Latitude and longitude	Azimuth	To station	Distance (meters)	Station	Latitude and longitude	Azimuth	To station	Distance (meters)
	° ′ ″	° ′ ″				° ′ ″	° ′ ″		
Ref. Mon. C-68_	47 17 26.54	44 08 40	T. P. 141	1,328.9	Ref. Mon. S-79_	47 17 35.41	80 34 00	T. P. 156	693.5
	68 26 13.94	333 51 30	T. P. 137	1,155.4		68 31 18.71	80 34 00	Ref. Mon. C-75	1,438.6
		350 13 30	T. P. 138	966.8			127 42 00	T. P. 155	263.6
		350 13 30	Ref. Mon. S-72	1,442.3			127 42 00	Ref. Mon. C-74	583.5
Ref. Mon. 143___	47 17 07.84	164 43 20	Ref. Mon. C-69	1,215.9	Ref. Mon. C-74_	47 17 46.97	307 41 40	T. P. 155	319.9
	68 27 16.19	314 30 20	T. P. 141	536.6		68 31 40.68	307 41 40	Ref. Mon. S-79	583.5
		344 43 20	T. P. 142	329.6			357 25 20	Ref. Mon. S-80	762.9
Ref. Mon. S-73_	47 17 00.08	183 11 10	T. P. 143	125.8	Ref. Mon. S-80_	47 17 22.29	177 25 20	Ref. Mon. C-74	762.9
	68 27 33.30	183 11 10	Ref. Mon. 144	337.4		68 31 39.05			
Ref. Mon. 144___	47 17 10.99	3 11 10	T. P. 143	211.6	Ref. Mon. C-75_	47 17 27.77	260 33 10	T. P. 156	745.1
	68 27 32.41	3 11 10	Ref. Mon. S-73	337.4		68 32 26.25	260 33 10	Ref. Mon. S-79	1,438.6
		296 24 40	T. P. 140	1,019.7			352 00 30	T. P. 157	633.5
		296 24 40	Ref. Mon. S-72	2,114.8			352 00 30	Ref. Mon. S-81	963.0
Ref. Mon. C-69_	47 17 45.82	62 25 30	T. P. 144	554.9	Ref. Mon. S-81_	47 16 56.89	137 34 50	T. P. 158	295.0
	68 27 31.44	62 25 30	Ref. Mon. S-74	1,200.3		68 32 19.88	137 34 50	Ref. Mon. C-76	906.3
		75 27 50	T. P. 145	590.5			172 00 30	T. P. 157	329.5
		75 27 50	Ref. Mon. S-75	2,213.5			172 00 30	Ref. Mon. C-75	963.0
		317 06 00	T. P. 139	1,862.2	Ref. Mon. C-76_	47 17 18.56	21 05 40	T. P. 159	742.1
		317 06 00	Ref. Mon. S-72	2,752.5		68 32 48.97	21 05 40	Ref. Mon. S-82	1,066.0
		344 43 10	Ref. Mon. 143	1,215.9			56 45 10	T. P. 161	1,053.9
		344 43 10	T. P. 142	1,545.5			56 45 10	Ref. Mon. S-83	1,547.6
Ref. Mon. S-74_	47 17 27.82	191 19 10	T. P. 146	653.3			317 34 30	T. P. 158	611.3
	68 28 22.08	191 19 10	Ref. Mon. C-70	1,050.2			317 34 30	Ref. Mon. S-81	906.3
		242 24 50	T. P. 144	645.4	Ref. Mon. S-82_	47 16 46.35	150 46 40	T. P. 160	373.2
		242 24 50	Ref. Mon. C-69	1,200.3		68 33 07.22	150 46 40	Ref. Mon. C-77	1,128.1
Ref. Mon. C-70_	47 18 01.17	11 19 20	T. P. 146	396.9			201 05 30	T. P. 159	323.9
	68 28 12.26	11 19 20	Ref. Mon. S-74	1,050.2			201 05 30	Ref. Mon. C-76	1,066.0
		51 17 20	T. P. 147	544.9	Ref. Mon. C-77_	47 17 18.23	330 46 20	T. P. 160	754.9
		51 17 20	Ref. Mon. S-75	1,646.6		68 33 33.43	330 46 20	Ref. Mon. S-82	1,128.1
Ref. Mon. S-75_	47 17 27.82	117 10 40	T. P. 150	685.1	Ref. Mon. S-83_	47 16 51.08	236 44 20	T. P. 161	493.7
	68 29 13.41	117 10 40	Ref. Mon. 151-A	1,581.2		68 33 50.56	236 44 20	Ref. Mon. C-76	1,547.6
		138 39 10	T. P. 149	431.7	Ref. Mon. S-84_	47 16 51.32	133 23 50	T. P. 164	1,021.5
		138 39 10	Ref. Mon. C-72	1,905.7		68 34 15.26	143 38 00	T. P. 163	941.2
		167 21 00	Ref. Mon. 146	1,243.4			169 46 10	T. P. 162	717.3
		202 11 10	T. P. 148	476.1			169 46 10	Ref. Mon. C-78	1,038.6
		202 11 10	Ref. Mon. 147	611.8	Ref. Mon. C-78_	47 17 24.41	54 44 00	T. P. 163	457.6
		231 16 40	T. P. 147	1,101.7		68 34 24.04	60 08 00	T. P. 164	643.2
		231 16 40	Ref. Mon. C-70	1,646.6			349 46 10	T. P. 162	321.3
		255 26 30	T. P. 145	1,623.0			349 46 10	Ref. Mon. S-84	1,038.6
		255 26 30	Ref. Mon. C-69	2,213.5	Ref. Mon. S-85_	47 16 47.72	82 50 00	T. P. 166	885.1
Ref. Mon. 145___	47 17 53.33	71 27 10	Ref. Mon. S-76	1,613.6		68 34 46.53	82 50 00	Ref. Mon. C-80	1,587.0
	68 28 51.66						95 53 00	T. P. 165	800.4
Ref. Mon. 146___	47 18 07.11	347 20 50	Ref. Mon. S-75	1,243.4			127 46 20	Ref. Mon. C-79	1,053.3
	68 29 26.37				Ref. Mon. C-79_	47 17 08.61	307 45 50	Ref. Mon. S-85	1,053.3
Ref. Mon. 147___	47 17 46.17	22 11 20	T. P. 148	135.7		68 35 26.15	356 17 40	T. P. 165	564.3
	68 29 02.41	22 11 20	Ref. Mon. S-75	611.8	Ref. Mon. C-80_	47 16 41.30	262 49 10	T. P. 166	701.9
		77 22 10	T. P. 151	1,032.3		68 36 01.45	262 49 10	Ref. Mon. S-85	1,587.0
		77 22 10	Ref. Mon. S-76	1,336.3	Ref. Mon. S-86_	47 16 26.19	93 33 40	T. P. 167	557.0
Ref. Mon. S-76_	47 17 36.70	143 18 30	T. P. 152	363.9		68 35 08.44	93 33 40	Ref. Mon. C-81	1,589.6
	68 30 04.47	143 18 30	Ref. Mon. 151-A	558.7	Ref. Mon. C-81_	47 16 29.38	273 32 40	T. P. 167	1,032.6
		192 02 50	Ref. Mon. 149	482.3		68 36 23.92	273 32 40	Ref. Mon. S-86	1,589.6
		251 26 10	Ref. Mon. 145	1,613.6			308 51 20	T. P. 168	806.7
		257 21 30	T. P. 151	304.0			308 51 20	Ref. Mon. S-87	1,290.1
		257 21 30	Ref. Mon. 147	1,336.3			319 28 40	T. P. 169	905.5
Ref. Mon. 149___	47 17 51.98	12 02 50	Ref. Mon. S-76	482.3			319 28 40	Ref. Mon. S-88	2,142.8
	68 29 59.68						323 38 00	T. P. 170	1,082.2
Ref. Mon. C-71_	47 18 19.49	82 52 40	Ref. Mon. C-72	1,331.5	Ref. Mon. S-87_	47 16 03.16	3 47 40	T. P. 171	706.4
	68 29 10.45					68 35 36.12	3 47 40	T. P. 172	964.4
Ref. Mon. C-72_	47 18 14.14	262 52 00	Ref. Mon. C-71	1,331.5			80 18 20	T. P. 170	368.2
	68 30 13.34	318 38 20	T. P. 149	1,474.0			128 52 00	T. P. 168	483.4
		318 38 20	Ref. Mon. S-75	1,905.7			128 52 00	Ref. Mon. C-81	1,290.1
Ref. Mon. 151___	47 17 56.98	28 13 30	Ref. Mon. S-77	602.8	Ref. Mon. S-88_	47 15 36.63	55 59 30	T. P. 173	773.6
	68 30 18.50					68 35 17.70	55 59 30	T. P. 174	1,107.0
Ref. Mon. 151-A_	47 17 51.20	297 09 50	T. P. 150	896.1			55 59 30	Ref. Mon. C-83	2,114.2
	68 30 20.36	297 09 50	Ref. Mon. S-75	1,581.2			72 24 50	T. P. 169	473.2
		323 18 20	T. P. 152	194.8			139 29 30	T. P. 169	1,237.3
		323 18 20	Ref. Mon. S-76	558.7			139 29 30	Ref. Mon. C-81	2,142.8
Ref. Mon. S-77_	47 17 39.78	179 34 20	T. P. 153	245.9	Ref. Mon. C-82_	47 15 15.49	301 39 50	Ref. Mon. S-89	1,597.8
	68 30 32.07	179 34 20	Ref. Mon. 153	377.6		68 36 19.79	358 08 00	T. P. 175	543.7
		208 13 20	Ref. Mon. 151	602.8			358 08 00	Ref. Mon. S-90	1,065.4
Ref. Mon. 153___	47 17 52.01	359 34 20	T. P. 153	131.7	Ref. Mon. S-89_	47 14 48.33	121 40 40	Ref. Mon. C-82	1,597.8
	68 30 32.20	359 34 20	Ref. Mon. S-77	377.6		68 35 15.13			
Ref. Mon. S-78_	47 17 39.48	152 55 50	T. P. 154	237.8	Ref. Mon. S-90_	47 14 41.01	138 00 10	T. P. 176	355.8
	68 30 57.62	152 55 50	Ref. Mon. C-73	715.7		68 36 18.14	138 00 10	Ref. Mon. C-83	719.7
Ref. Mon. C-73_	47 18 00.12	332 55 40	T. P. 154	477.9			178 08 00	T. P. 175	521.7
	68 31 13.12	332 55 40	Ref. Mon. S-78	715.7			178 08 00	Ref. Mon. C-82	1,065.4

REFERENCE MONUMENTS—ST. JOHN RIVER—Continued

Station	Latitude and longitude	Azimuth	To station	Distance (meters)
	° ′ ″	° ′ ″		
Ref. Mon. C-83	47 14 58.33 / 68 36 41.04	235 58 30	T. P. 174	1,007.2
		235 58 30	T. P. 173	1,340.6
		235 58 30	Ref. Mon. S-88	2,114.2
		317 59 50	T. P. 176	363.9
		317 59 50	Ref. Mon. S-90	719.7
Ref. Mon. S-91	47 14 20.68 / 68 36 56.36	158 45 20	T. P. 177	526.4
		158 45 20	Ref. Mon. C-84	1,151.7
Ref. Mon. C-84	47 14 55.44 / 68 37 16.21	27 39 30	T. P. 178	808.9
		27 39 30	Ref. Mon. S-92	1,323.2
		338 45 00	T. P. 177	625.3
		338 45 00	Ref. Mon. S-91	1,151.7
Ref. Mon. S-92	47 14 17.49 / 68 37 45.41	133 57 30	T. P. 180	682.9
		133 57 30	Ref. Mon. C-86	972.2
		179 05 50	T. P. 179	448.5
		179 05 50	Ref. Mon. C-85	745.7
		207 39 10	T. P. 178	514.3
		207 39 10	Ref. Mon. C-84	1,323.2
Ref. Mon. C-85	47 14 41.63 / 68 37 45.97	359 05 50	T. P. 179	297.2
		359 05 50	Ref. Mon. S-92	745.7
Ref. Mon. C-86	47 14 39.34 / 68 38 18.69	313 57 00	T. P. 180	289.3
		313 57 00	Ref. Mon. S-92	972.2
Ref. Mon. S-93	47 14 16.52 / 68 38 09.03	130 06 10	T. P. 181	503.4
		130 06 10	Ref. Mon. C-87	1,259.5
Ref. Mon. S-94	47 14 17.56 / 68 38 47.53	96 43 20	T. P. 184	727.3
		96 43 20	Ref. Mon. 155	1,534.8
		168 50 10	T. P. 182	157.6
		168 50 10	Ref. Mon. C-87	794.2
Ref. Mon. C-87	47 14 42.79 / 68 38 54.84	31 13 30	T. P. 183	758.1
		31 13 30	Ref. Mon. S-95	1,153.1
		310 05 40	T. P. 181	756.1
		310 05 40	Ref. Mon. S-93	1,259.5
		348 50 00	T. P. 182	636.6
		348 50 00	Ref. Mon. S-94	794.2
Ref. Mon. S-95	47 14 10.86 / 68 39 23.26	118 42 30	T. P. 185	175.6
		118 42 30	Ref. Mon. 154	358.1
		211 13 10	T. P. 183	395.0
		211 13 10	Ref. Mon. C-87	1,153.1
Ref. Mon. 154	47 14 16.43 / 68 39 38.19	55 52 50	T. P. 187	297.2
		55 52 50	Ref. Mon. S-96	1,321.9
		177 33 40	Ref. Mon. C-88	839.8
		298 42 20	T. P. 185	182.5
		298 42 20	Ref. Mon. S-95	358.1
		357 33 40	T. P. 186	184.1
Ref. Mon. C-88	47 14 43.60 / 68 39 39.89	357 33 40	Ref. Mon. 154	839.8
		357 33 40	T. P. 186	1,023.9
Ref. Mon. 155	47 14 23.37 / 68 40 00.00	33 37 40	T. P. 188	207.2
		33 37 40	Ref. Mon. S-96	1,147.8
		276 42 20	T. P. 184	807.5
		276 42 20	Ref. Mon. S-94	1,534.8
Ref. Mon. C-89	47 14 36.80 / 68 40 10.29	75 00 20	T. P. 189	477.3
		75 00 20	Ref. Mon. S-97	2,279.6
		87 00 50	T. P. 190	804.2
		87 00 50	T. P. 191	1,174.0
Ref. Mon. S-96	47 13 52.42 / 68 40 30.22	137 12 20	T. P. 193	1,928.7
		146 51 50	T. P. 192	1,766.0
		146 51 50	Ref. Mon. C-90	2,351.9
		213 37 20	T. P. 188	940.6
		213 37 20	Ref. Mon. 155	1,147.8
		235 52 10	T. P. 187	1,024.7
		235 52 10	Ref. Mon. 154	1,321.9
Ref. Mon. C-90	47 14 56.18 / 68 41 31.35	22 41 10	T. P. 194	755.4
		22 41 10	Ref. Mon. S-97	1,288.6
		305 23 00	T. P. 190	1,106.0
		321 06 00	T. P. 191	847.8
		326 51 10	T. P. 192	585.9
		326 51 10	Ref. Mon. S-96	2,351.9
Ref. Mon. S-97	47 14 17.69 / 68 41 54.98	85 48 00	T. P. 196	602.8
		93 23 00	T. P. 195	327.4
		93 23 00	T. P. 197	820.0
		93 23 00	Ref. Mon. S-98	1,233.3
		99 03 20	T. P. 198	884.0
		99 03 20	Ref. Mon. 158	1,909.1
		202 41 00	T. P. 194	533.2
		202 41 00	Ref. Mon. C-90	1,288.6
		216 39 20	T. P. 193	791.3
		242 47 30	T. P. 191	1,157.4
		254 59 10	T. P. 189	1,802.3
		254 59 10	Ref. Mon. C-89	2,279.6

Station	Latitude and longitude	Azimuth	To station	Distance (meters)
	° ′ ″	° ′ ″		
Ref. Mon. C-91	47 14 53.41 / 68 42 11.51	12 27 40	T. P. 196	1,175.0
		40 36 30	T. P. 199	1,138.3
		40 36 30	Ref. Mon. S-98	1,357.3
Ref. Mon. S-98	47 14 20.04 / 68 42 53.51	132 29 40	Ref. Mon. C-93	1,446.5
		133 13 20	T. P. 201	292.0
		137 39 10	Ref. Mon. 157	928.9
		150 26 30	Ref. Mon. C-92	1,316.6
		159 38 40	T. P. 200	243.0
		159 38 40	Ref. Mon. 156	406.5
		220 36 00	T. P. 199	219.0
		220 36 00	Ref. Mon. C-91	1,357.3
		273 22 20	T. P. 197	413.3
		273 22 20	T. P. 195	905.9
		273 22 20	Ref. Mon. S-97	1,233.3
Ref. Mon. C-92	47 14 57.12 / 68 43 24.40	330 26 10	Ref. Mon. S-98	1,316.6
Ref. Mon. C-93	47 14 51.68 / 68 43 44.23	312 29 10	Ref. Mon. S-98	1,446.5
Ref. Mon. 156	47 14 32.38 / 68 43 00.23	21 30 20	T. P. 201	194.7
		339 38 30	T. P. 200	163.5
		339 38 30	Ref. Mon. S-98	406.5
Ref. Mon. 157	47 14 42.27 / 68 43 23.27	317 38 50	Ref. Mon. S-98	928.9
Ref. Mon. 158	47 14 27.41 / 68 43 24.62	279 02 10	T. P. 198	1,025.1
		279 02 10	Ref. Mon. S-97	1,909.1
Ref. Mon. S-99	47 14 08.73 / 68 43 23.17	90 03 50	T. P. 204	587.3
		90 03 50	T. P. 205	896.9
		100 39 20	T. P. 203	420.5
		100 39 20	Ref. Mon. 160	930.8
Ref. Mon. 159	47 14 29.44 / 68 43 47.01	31 46 00	T. P. 205	751.1
		31 46 00	Ref. Mon. 162	1,110.0
Ref. Mon. 159-A	47 14 18.97 / 68 43 33.27	334 56 10	T. P. 202	50.5
		334 56 10	Ref. Mon. 159-B	79.4
Ref. Mon. 159-B	47 14 16.64 / 68 43 31.67	154 56 10	T. P. 202	28.9
		154 56 10	Ref. Mon. 159-A	79.4
Ref. Mon. 160	47 14 14.30 / 68 44 06.66	280 38 50	T. P. 203	510.3
		280 38 50	Ref. Mon. S-99	930.8
Ref. Mon. 161	47 14 04.95 / 68 44 31.42	298 11 10	T. P. 206	292.8
		298 11 10	Ref. Mon. 162	396.9
Ref. Mon. 162	47 13 58.88 / 68 44 14.79	118 11 20	T. P. 206	104.1
		118 11 20	Ref. Mon. 161	396.9
		211 45 40	T. P. 205	358.9
		211 45 40	Ref. Mon. 159	1,110.0
Ref. Mon. 163	47 13 45.50 / 68 44 35.08	163 14 00	T. P. 207	220.4
		163 14 00	Ref. Mon. C-94	1,491.4
Ref. Mon. C-94	47 14 31.74 / 68 44 55.54	343 13 40	T. P. 207	1,271.0
		343 13 40	Ref. Mon. 163	1,491.4
Ref. Mon. S-100	47 13 27.16 / 68 44 48.53	118 57 40	T. P. 208	506.7
		118 57 40	Ref. Mon. C-95	1,478.5
Ref. Mon. S-101	47 13 20.01 / 68 45 20.42	146 22 50	T. P. 209	295.7
		146 22 50	Ref. Mon. C-95	1,124.8
Ref. Mon. C-95	47 13 50.34 / 68 45 50.02	5 31 10	T. P. 210	947.4
		5 31 10	Ref. Mon. S-102	1,134.9
		298 57 00	T. P. 208	971.8
		298 57 00	Ref. Mon. S-100	1,478.5
		326 22 30	T. P. 209	829.1
		326 22 30	Ref. Mon. S-101	1,124.8
Ref. Mon. S-102	47 13 13.76 / 68 45 55.21	105 44 50	T. P. 211	335.4
		105 44 50	Ref. Mon. 163-A	1,109.2
		133 56 50	Ref. Mon. C-96	1,462.0
		185 31 10	T. P. 210	187.5
		185 31 10	Ref. Mon. C-95	1,134.9
Ref. Mon. C-96	47 13 46.61 / 68 46 45.25	313 56 10	Ref. Mon. S-102	1,462.0
Ref. Mon. 163-A	47 13 23.51 / 68 46 45.96	40 36 50	T. P. 212	296.0
		40 36 50	Ref. Mon. S-103	853.1
		285 44 20	T. P. 211	773.8
		285 44 20	Ref. Mon. S-102	1,109.2
Ref. Mon. S-103	47 13 02.54 / 68 47 12.35	172 39 00	Ref. Mon. C-97	617.4
		220 36 30	T. P. 212	557.1
		220 36 30	Ref. Mon. 163-A	853.1
Ref. Mon. C-97	47 13 22.36 / 68 47 16.11	352 39 00	Ref. Mon. S-103	617.4

REFERENCE MONUMENTS—ST. JOHN RIVER—Continued

Station	Latitude and longitude	Azimuth	To station	Distance (meters)
	° ′ ″	° ′ ″		
Ref. Mon. 164	47 12 55.01 / 68 48 00.88	135 28 50	Ref. Mon. C-98	496.7
Ref. Mon. 165	47 12 43.79 / 68 48 18.05	181 03 40	T. P. 213	375.9
		181 03 40	Ref. Mon. C-98	700.8
		268 49 50	Ref. Mon. S-104	382.3
Ref. Mon. S-104	47 12 44.04 / 68 47 59.88	88 50 00	Ref. Mon. 165	382.3
Ref. Mon. C-98	47 13 06.48 / 68 48 17.43	1 03 40	T. P. 213	324.9
		1 03 40	Ref. Mon. 165	700.8
		315 28 40	Ref. Mon. 164	496.7
Ref. Mon. 166	47 12 51.37 / 68 48 32.71	79 14 20	Ref. Mon. 167	284.5
		116 24 30	T. P. 214	255.6
Ref. Mon. 167	47 12 49.65 / 68 48 45.99	84 58 40	T. P. 215	231.3
		84 58 40	Ref. Mon. C-99	990.3
		196 51 50	T. P. 214	174.3
		259 14 10	Ref. Mon. 166	284.5
Ref. Mon. 168	47 12 36.27 / 68 48 43.59	107 28 40	T. P. 216	460.9
		107 28 40	Ref. Mon. C-99	1,087.2
Ref. Mon. C-99	47 12 46.84 / 68 49 32.87	8 35 40	T. P. 217	637.7
		8 35 40	Ref. Mon. 169	933.8
		264 58 00	T. P. 215	759.0
		264 58 00	Ref. Mon. 167	990.3
		287 28 00	T. P. 216	626.3
		287 28 00	Ref. Mon. 168	1,087.2
		317 50 10	Ref. Mon. S-105	1,093.0
Ref. Mon. S-105	47 12 20.60 / 68 48 58.01	137 50 30	Ref. Mon. C-99	1,093.0
Ref. Mon. 169	47 12 16.94 / 68 49 39.50	188 35 30	T. P. 217	296.1
		188 35 30	Ref. Mon. C-99	933.8
Ref. Mon. S-106	47 12 00.97 / 68 49 48.60	103 34 10	T. P. 219	634.7
		103 34 10	Ref. Mon. C-101	1,239.4
		160 41 50	T. P. 218	443.6
		160 41 50	Ref. Mon. C-100	811.0
Ref. Mon. C-100	47 12 25.76 / 68 50 01.34	340 41 40	T. P. 218	367.4
		340 41 40	Ref. Mon. S-106	811.0
Ref. Mon. S-107	47 11 51.29 / 68 50 30.01	78 44 50	T. P. 221	690.9
		78 44 50	Ref. Mon. C-103	1,611.6
		150 31 20	T. P. 220	287.5
		150 31 20	Ref. Mon. C-101	677.4
Ref. Mon. C-101	47 12 10.38 / 68 50 45.84	283 33 20	T. P. 219	604.7
		283 33 20	Ref. Mon. S-106	1,239.4
		330 31 10	T. P. 220	389.9
		330 31 10	Ref. Mon. S-107	677.4
Ref. Mon. S-108	47 11 36.56 / 68 50 59.56	137 31 40	T. P. 222	193.3
		137 31 40	Ref. Mon. C-102	642.6
Ref. Mon. C-102	47 11 51.91 / 68 51 20.18	317 31 30	T. P. 222	449.3
		317 31 30	Ref. Mon. S-108	642.6
Ref. Mon. S-109	47 11 21.94 / 68 51 25.28	86 15 30	T. P. 224	394.6
		86 15 30	Ref. Mon. C-105	1,785.3
		144 49 10	T. P. 223	140.1
		144 49 10	Ref. Mon. C-103	724.2
Ref. Mon. C-103	47 11 41.10 / 68 51 45.10	258 44 00	T. P. 221	920.7
		258 44 00	Ref. Mon. S-107	1,611.6
		324 48 50	T. P. 223	584.1
		324 48 50	Ref. Mon. S-109	724.2
Ref. Mon. C-104	47 11 34.26 / 68 51 58.77	4 39 40	T. P. 225	426.4
		4 39 40	Ref. Mon. S-110	888.0
Ref. Mon. S-110	47 11 05.60 / 68 52 02.20	79 54 30	T. P. 228	1,191.7
		79 54 30	Ref. Mon. 173	1,908.4
		111 07 30	T. P. 227	767.0
		111 07 30	Ref. Mon. C-105	1,076.7
		145 03 40	T. P. 226	582.9
		184 39 40	T. P. 225	461.6
		184 39 40	Ref. Mon. C-104	888.0
Ref. Mon. 170	47 11 08.66 / 68 52 52.50	46 33 20	T. P. 229	398.8
		46 33 20	Ref. Mon. 171	677.2
Ref. Mon. C-105	47 11 18.16 / 68 52 49.90	262 21 40	T. P. 226	676.5
		266 14 30	T. P. 224	1,390.7
		266 14 30	Ref. Mon. S-109	1,785.3
		291 06 50	T. P. 227	309.7
		291 06 50	Ref. Mon. S-110	1,076.7
Ref. Mon. 171	47 10 53.58 / 68 53 15.85	226 33 00	T. P. 229	278.4
		226 33 00	Ref. Mon. 170	677.2
Ref. Mon. C-106	47 10 59.66 / 68 53 21.39	15 52 00	T. P. 230	127.9
		15 52 00	Ref. Mon. 172	508.5
		278 43 00	Ref. Mon. S-111	1,372.1
Ref. Mon. S-111	47 10 52.92 / 68 52 16.98	98 43 40	Ref. Mon. C-106	1,372.1
Ref. Mon. 172	47 10 43.82 / 68 53 27.99	7 50 20	Ref. Mon. S-113	1,254.7
		195 52 00	T. P. 230	380.6
		195 52 00	Ref. Mon. C-106	508.5
		288 32 00	Ref. Mon. S-112	896.3
Ref. Mon. S-112	47 10 34.59 / 68 52 47.64	108 32 30	Ref. Mon. 172	896.3
Ref. Mon. S-113	47 10 03.57 / 68 53 36.12	187 50 10	Ref. Mon. 172	1,254.7
Ref. Mon. 173	47 10 54.76 / 68 53 31.44	73 16 40	Ref. Mon. 175	647.2
		73 16 40	T. P. 234	583.6
		123 16	T. P. 231	208.7
		259 53 20	T. P. 228	716.7
		259 53 20	Ref. Mon. S-110	1,908.4

GEOGRAPHIC POSITIONS OF BOUNDARY TURNING POINTS AND REFERENCE MONUMENTS DEFINING THE INTERNATIONAL BOUNDARY THROUGH THE ST. FRANCIS RIVER

Station	Latitude and longitude	Azimuth	To station	Distance (meters)	Station	Latitude and longitude	Azimuth	To station	Distance (meters)
	° ′ ″	° ′ ″				° ′ ″	° ′ ″		
T. P. 231	47 10 58.47 68 53 39.73	73 45 283 46 303 16	T. P. 232 T. P. 230 Ref. Mon. 173	142.2 361.6 208.7	T. P. 251	47 11 24.16 68 55 13.54	175 26 310 37	T. P. 252 T. P. 250	176.2 79.6
T. P. 232	47 10 57.18 68 53 46.21	49 40 253 45	T. P. 233 T. P. 231	207.4 142.2	T. P. 252	47 11 29.85 68 55 14.20	181 43 355 26	T. P. 253 T. P. 251	250.1 176.2
T. P. 233	47 10 52.83 68 53 53.72	39 39 229 40	T. P. 234 T. P. 232	140.9 207.4	T. P. 253	47 11 37.94 68 55 13.85	1 43 176 53	T. P. 252 T. P. 254	250.1 119.5
T. P. 234	47 10 49.32 68 53 57.99	18 37 73 16 20 219 39 253 16 20	T. P. 235 Ref. Mon. 175 T. P. 233 Ref. Mon. 173	294.5 63.6 140.9 583.6	T. P. 254	47 11 41.81 68 55 14.16	144 35 356 53	T. P. 255 T. P. 253	78.5 119.5
Ref. Mon. 175	47 10 48.73 68 54 00.88	31 28 30 31 28 30 66 39 253 16 20 253 16 20	T. P. 236 Ref. Mon. S-114 Ref. Mon. S-115 T. P. 234 Ref. Mon. 173	252.4 538.4 299.1 63.6 647.2	T. P. 255	47 11 43.88 68 55 16.32	132 10 324 35	T. P. 256 T. P. 254	326.1 78.5
T. P. 235	47 10 40.28 68 54 02.45	114 46 198 37	T. P. 236 T. P. 234	108.8 294.5	T. P. 256	47 11 50.97 68 55 27.80	112 09 312 10	T. P. 257 T. P. 255	149.6 326.1
T. P. 236	47 10 41.76 68 54 07.14	31 28 132 35 211 28 294 46	Ref. Mon. S-114 T. P. 237 Ref. Mon. 175 T. P. 235	286.0 159.3 252.4 108.8	T. P. 257	47 11 52.79 68 55 34.39	32 35 255 22 292 09	T. P. 258 Ref. Mon. C-108 T. P. 256	142.4 82.6 149.6
Ref. Mon. S-114	47 10 33.86 68 54 14.23	211 28 20 211 28 20	T. P. 236 Ref. Mon. 175	286.0 538.4	Ref. Mon. C-108	47 11 53.47 68 55 30.59	39 40 75 22	Ref. Mon. S-117 T. P. 257	196.7 82.6
T. P. 237	47 10 45.25 68 54 12.71	66 38 159 22 246 38 312 35	Ref. Mon. S-115 T. P. 238 Ref. Mon. 175 T. P. 236	27.8 74.9 271.3 159.3	T. P. 258	47 11 48.91 68 55 38.03	73 06 212 35 288 40	T. P. 259 T. P. 257 Ref. Mon. S-117	109.0 142.4 32.7
Ref. Mon. S-115	47 10 44.89 68 54 13.92	246 38 246 38	T. P. 237 Ref. Mon. 175	27.8 299.1	Ref. Mon. S-117	47 11 48.57 68 55 36.56	108 40 219 40	T. P. 258 Ref. Mon. C-108	32.7 196.7
T. P. 238	47 10 47.52 68 54 13.96	122 49 339 22	T. P. 239 T. P. 237	148.1 74.9	T. P. 259	47 11 47.88 68 55 42.98	103 25 253 06	T. P. 260 T. P. 258	37.9 109.0
T. P. 239	47 10 50.12 68 54 19.88	162 25 302 49	T. P. 240 T. P. 238	135.7 148.1	T. P. 260	47 11 48.17 68 55 44.74	134 06 283 25	T. P. 261 T. P. 259	158.9 37.9
T. P. 240	47 10 54.31 68 54 21.82	136 00 342 25	T. P. 241 T. P. 239	85.4 135.7	T. P. 261	47 11 51.75 68 55 50.16	228 54 314 06	T. P. 262 T. P. 260	190.6 158.9
T. P. 241	47 10 56.30 68 54 24.64	158 22 316 00	T. P. 242 T. P. 240	240.5 85.4	T. P. 262	47 11 55.81 68 55 43.34	48 54 137 12	T. P. 261 T. P. 263	190.6 113.9
T. P. 242	47 11 03.54 68 54 28.85	179 04 338 22	T. P. 243 T. P. 241	135.3 240.5	T. P. 263	47 11 58.51 68 55 47.02	95 11 317 12	T. P. 264 T. P. 262	289.7 113.9
T. P. 243	47 11 07.92 68 54 28.96	142 19 359 04	T. P. 244 T. P. 242	129.9 135.3	T. P. 264	47 11 59.36 68 56 00.72	117 28 275 11	T. P. 265 T. P. 263	105.2 289.7
T. P. 244	47 11 11.25 68 54 32.73	73 56 322 19	T. P. 245 T. P. 243	146.6 129.9	T. P. 265	47 12 00.93 68 56 05.15	163 53 297 28	T. P. 266 T. P. 264	127.2 105.2
T. P. 245	47 11 09.93 68 54 39.42	113 20 253 56	T. P. 246 T. P. 244	136.3 146.6	T. P. 266	47 12 04.89 68 56 06.83	147 49 343 53	T. P. 267 T. P. 265	125.2 127.2
T. P. 246	47 11 11.68 68 54 45.37	141 24 293 20	T. P. 247 T. P. 245	169.4 136.3	T. P. 267	47 12 08.32 68 56 10.00	135 18 327 49	T. P. 268 T. P. 266	109.5 125.2
T. P. 247	47 11 15.97 68 54 50.39	84 07 128 35 264 07 321 24	Ref. Mon. S-116 T. P. 248 Ref. Mon. C-107 T. P. 246	59.6 164.5 37.1 169.4	T. P. 268	47 12 10.84 68 56 13.66	101 57 123 27 315 18	Ref. Mon. S-118 T. P. 269 T. P. 267	68.4 141.2 109.5
Ref. Mon. S-116	47 11 15.77 68 54 53.21	264 07 264 07	T. P. 247 Ref. Mon. C-107	59.6 96.7	Ref. Mon. S-118	47 12 11.30 68 56 16.84	209 22 281 57	Ref. Mon. C-109 T. P. 268	180.0 68.4
Ref. Mon. C-107	47 11 16.09 68 54 48.64	84 07 84 07	T. P. 247 Ref. Mon. S-116	37.1 96.7	T. P. 269	47 12 13.36 68 56 19.26	135 02 236 09 303 27	T. P. 270 Ref. Mon. C-109 T. P. 268	143.9 167.4 141.2
T. P. 248	47 11 19.29 68 54 56.50	119 02 308 35	T. P. 249 T. P. 247	236.1 164.5	Ref. Mon. C-109	47 12 16.38 68 56 12.65	29 22 56 09	Ref. Mon. S-118 T. P. 269	180.0 167.4
T. P. 249	47 11 23.00 68 55 06.31	80 07 299 02	T. P. 250 T. P. 248	93.2 236.1	T. P. 270	47 12 16.66 68 56 24.09	143 45 315 02	T. P. 271 T. P. 269	215.6 143.9
T. P. 250	47 11 22.49 68 55 10.67	130 37 260 07	T. P. 251 T. P. 249	79.6 93.2	T. P. 271	47 12 22.29 68 56 30.15	90 50 323 45	T. P. 272 T. P. 270	117.1 215.6
					T. P. 272	47 12 22.34 68 56 35.71	52 03 270 50	T. P. 273 T. P. 271	474.0 117.1
					T. P. 273	47 12 12.90 68 56 53.47	47 49 232 03	T. P. 274 T. P. 272	218.6 474.0

BOUNDARY TURNING POINTS AND REFERENCE MONUMENTS—ST. FRANCIS RIVER—Con.

Station	Latitude and longitude	Azimuth	To station	Distance (meters)
	° ′ ″	° ′ ″		
T. P. 274	47 12 08.15 / 68 57 01.16	79 05 / 227 49	T. P. 275 / T. P. 273	85.5 / 218.6
T. P. 275	47 12 07.63 / 68 57 05.16	130 22 / 259 05	T. P. 276 / T. P. 274	116.6 / 85.5
T. P. 276	47 12 10.07 / 68 57 09.37	102 32 / 169 46 / 310 22	Ref. Mon. S-119 / T. P. 277 / T. P. 275	75.4 / 150.4 / 116.6
Ref. Mon. S-119	47 12 10.60 / 68 57 12.87	218 03 / 282 32	Ref. Mon. C-110 / T. P. 276	372.6 / 75.4
T. P. 277	47 12 14.86 / 68 57 10.64	192 25 / 349 46	T. P. 278 / T. P. 276	116.3 / 150.4
T. P. 278	47 12 18.54 / 68 57 09.46	12 25 / 173 41 / 253 02	T. P. 277 / T. P. 279 / Ref. Mon. C-110	116.3 / 89.1 / 164.9
Ref. Mon. C-110	47 12 20.10 / 68 57 01.96	38 03 / 73 02	Ref. Mon. S-119 / T. P. 278	372.6 / 164.9
T. P. 279	47 12 21.41 / 68 57 09.92	154 20 / 353 41	T. P. 280 / T. P. 278	130.9 / 89.1
T. P. 280	47 12 25.23 / 68 57 12.62	80 19 / 334 20	T. P. 281 / T. P. 279	72.5 / 130.9
T. P. 281	47 12 24.84 / 68 57 16.01	70 11 / 260 19	T. P. 282 / T. P. 280	123.9 / 72.5
T. P. 282	47 12 23.48 / 68 57 21.55	60 48 / 250 11	T. P. 283 / T. P. 281	160.3 / 123.9
T. P. 283	47 12 20.94 / 68 57 28.20	76 53 / 240 48	T. P. 284 / T. P. 282	219.4 / 160.3
T. P. 284	47 12 19.33 / 68 57 38.35	118 03 / 256 53	T. P. 285 / T. P. 283	101.6 / 219.4
T. P. 285	47 12 20.88 / 68 57 42.62	149 15 / 298 03	T. P. 286 / T. P. 284	93.3 / 101.6
T. P. 286	47 12 23.48 / 68 57 44.88	161 03 / 329 15	T. P. 287 / T. P. 285	389.1 / 93.3
T. P. 287	47 12 35.39 / 68 57 50.89	117 25 / 341 03	T. P. 288 / T. P. 286	111.6 / 389.1
T. P. 288	47 12 37.06 / 68 57 55.60	160 59 / 297 25	T. P. 289 / T. P. 287	118.4 / 111.6
T. P. 289	47 12 40.68 / 68 57 57.43	180 53 / 340 59	T. P. 290 / T. P. 288	148.6 / 118.4
T. P. 290	47 12 45.50 / 68 57 57.32	0 53 / 123 47	T. P. 289 / T. P. 291	148.6 / 177.1
T. P. 291	47 12 48.68 / 68 58 04.32	111 10 / 218 53 / 303 47	T. P. 292 / Ref. Mon. C-111 / T. P. 290	383.0 / 56.1 / 177.1
Ref. Mon. C-111	47 12 50.10 / 68 58 02.65	38 53 / 60 28	T. P. 291 / Ref. Mon. S-120	56.1 / 436.8
T. P. 292	47 12 53.16 / 68 58 21.30	135 47 / 291 10 / 357 43	T. P. 293 / T. P. 291 / Ref. Mon. S-120	322.4 / 383.0 / 310.1
Ref. Mon. S-120	47 12 43.13 / 68 58 20.71	177 43 / 240 28	T. P. 292 / Ref. Mon. C-111	310.1 / 436.8
T. P. 293	47 13 00.65 / 68 58 31.98	111 00 / 315 47	T. P. 294 / T. P. 292	299.4 / 322.4
T. P. 294	47 13 04.12 / 68 58 45.27	152 58 / 226 30 / 291 00	T. P. 295 / Ref. Mon. C-112 / T. P. 293	301.2 / 392.4 / 299.4
Ref. Mon. C-112	47 13 12.87 / 68 58 31.74	46 30 / 110 26 50	T. P. 294 / Ref. Mon. S-121	392.4 / 2,529.5
T. P. 295	47 13 12.81 / 68 58 51.78	122 51 10 / 332 58	T. P. 296 / T. P. 294	711.0 / 301.2
T. P. 296	47 13 25.30 / 68 59 20.17	119 30 50 / 302 50 50	T. P. 297 / T. P. 295	1,660.7 / 711.0
T. P. 297	47 13 51.79 / 69 00 28.88	120 17 20 / 163 33 / 299 30 00 / 343 33	T. P. 298 / Ref. Mon. C-113 / T. P. 296 / Ref. Mon. S-121	1,276.9 / 416.2 / 1,660.7 / 332.2
Ref. Mon. C-113	47 14 04.72 / 69 00 34.48	343 33 10 / 343 33 10	T. P. 297 / Ref. Mon. S-121	416.2 / 748.4
Ref. Mon. S-121	47 13 41.47 / 69 00 24.41	163 33 20 / 163 33 20 / 290 25 30	T. P. 297 / Ref. Mon. C-113 / Ref. Mon. C-112	332.2 / 748.4 / 2,529.5
T. P. 298	47 14 12.64 / 69 01 21.30	126 39 / 300 16 40	T. P. 299 / T. P. 297	484.9 / 1,276.9
T. P. 299	47 14 22.02 / 69 01 39.80	106 35 / 306 39	T. P. 300 / T. P. 298	241.1 / 484.9
T. P. 300	47 14 24.25 / 69 01 50.78	100 06 / 286 35	T. P. 301 / T. P. 299	280.4 / 241.1
T. P. 301	47 14 25.84 / 69 02 03.91	132 39 / 138 23 / 280 06 / 312 39	Ref. Mon. S-123 / T. P. 302 / T. P. 300 / Ref. Mon. S-122	158.0 / 91.0 / 280.4 / 377.6
Ref. Mon. S-122	47 14 17.56 / 69 01 50.71	132 39 40 / 132 39 40	Ref. Mon. S-123 / T. P. 301	535.6 / 377.6
Ref. Mon. S-123	47 14 29.31 / 69 02 09.44	162 15 / 312 39 20 / 312 39 20	Ref. Mon. C-114 / T. P. 301 / Ref. Mon. S-122	271.5 / 158.0 / 535.6
T. P. 302	47 14 28.04 / 69 02 06.78	168 15 / 318 23	T. P. 303 / T. P. 301	101.1 / 91.0
T. P. 303	47 14 31.25 / 69 02 07.76	121 44 / 348 15	T. P. 304 / T. P. 302	78.0 / 101.1
T. P. 304	47 14 32.58 / 69 02 10.91	111 02 / 301 44	T. P. 305 / T. P. 303	137.1 / 78.0
T. P. 305	47 14 34.17 / 69 02 17.00	133 58 / 215 04 / 291 02	T. P. 306 / Ref. Mon. C-114 / T. P. 304	367.4 / 132.5 / 137.1
Ref. Mon. C-114	47 14 37.68 / 69 02 13.38	35 04 / 342 15	T. P. 305 / Ref. Mon. S-123	132.5 / 271.5
T. P. 306	47 14 42.43 / 69 02 29.58	147 20 / 313 58	T. P. 307 / T. P. 305	171.9 / 367.4
T. P. 307	47 14 47.11 / 69 02 33.99	152 46 00 / 327 20	T. P. 308 / T. P. 306	514.4 / 171.9
T. P. 308	47 15 01.93 / 69 02 45.19	147 25 / 332 45 50	T. P. 309 / T. P. 307	124.0 / 514.4
T. P. 309	47 15 05.31 / 69 02 48.36	59 53 / 148 22 20 / 327 25	Ref. Mon. S-124 / T. P. 310 / T. P. 308	34.5 / 667.4 / 124.0
Ref. Mon. S-124	47 15 04.75 / 69 02 49.78	161 22 50 / 239 53	Ref. Mon. C-115 / T. P. 309	694.1 / 34.5
T. P. 310	47 15 23.71 / 69 03 05.02	181 32 / 233 50 / 328 22 10	T. P. 311 / Ref. Mon. C-115 / T. P. 309	411.8 / 122.3 / 667.4
Ref. Mon. C-115	47 15 26.05 / 69 03 00.32	53 50 / 161 43	T. P. 310 / Ref. Mon. S-125	122.3 / 345.7
T. P. 311	47 15 37.04 / 69 03 04.49	1 32 / 61 30 / 195 38	T. P. 310 / Ref. Mon. S-125 / T. P. 312	411.8 / 23.6 / 102.8
Ref. Mon. S-125	47 15 36.68 / 69 03 05.48	241 30 / 341 43	T. P. 311 / Ref. Mon. C-115	23.6 / 345.7
T. P. 312	47 15 40.25 / 69 03 03.18	15 38 / 199 18	T. P. 311 / T. P. 313	102.8 / 73.5
T. P. 313	47 15 42.50 / 69 03 02.02	19 18 / 216 19	T. P. 312 / T. P. 314	73.5 / 108.7
T. P. 314	47 15 45.33 / 69 02 58.96	36 19 / 219 33 / 345 07	T. P. 313 / T. P. 315 / Ref. Mon. C-116	108.7 / 111.5 / 30.8
Ref. Mon. C-116	47 15 44.37 / 69 02 58.58	165 07 / 187 12 30	T. P. 314 / Ref. Mon. S-126	30.8 / 588.0
T. P. 315	47 15 48.12 / 69 02 55.58	39 33 / 161 17	T. P. 314 / T. P. 316	111.5 / 176.1
T. P. 316	47 15 53.52 / 69 02 58.27	205 13 / 341 17	T. P. 317 / T. P. 315	307.4 / 176.1

BOUNDARY TURNING POINTS AND REFERENCE MONUMENTS—ST. FRANCIS RIVER—Con.

Station	Latitude and longitude	Azimuth	To station	Distance (meters)	Station	Latitude and longitude	Azimuth	To station	Distance (meters)
	° ′ ″	° ′ ″				° ′ ″	° ′ ″		
T. P. 317	47 16 02.53 / 69 02 52.04	25 13 / 109 36 / 159 04	T. P. 316 / Ref. Mon. S-126 / T. P. 318	307.4 / 67.6 / 169.4	Ref. Mon. C-122	47 17 36.73 / 69 03 08.35	342 02 50 / 342 02 50 / 342 02 50	Ref. Mon. C-121 / T. P. 336 / T. P. 335	565.8 / 122.1 / 484.3
Ref. Mon. S-126	47 16 03.26 / 69 02 55.07	7 12 30 / 289 36	Ref. Mon. C-116 / T. P. 317	588.0 / 67.6	T. P. 336	47 17 32.97 / 69 03 06.56	95 33 / 162 03 / 342 03 / 342 03	T. P. 337 / Ref. Mon. C-122 / T. P. 335 / Ref. Mon. C-121	126.1 / 122.1 / 362.2 / 443.7
T. P. 318	47 16 07.65 / 69 02 54.92	156 28 / 339 04	T. P. 319 / T. P. 317	89.4 / 169.4					
T. P. 319	47 16 10.30 / 69 02 56.62	210 36 / 336 28	T. P. 320 / T. P. 318	120.6 / 89.4	T. P. 337	47 17 33.37 / 69 03 12.53	149 12 / 275 33	T. P. 338 / T. P. 336	41.2 / 126.1
T. P. 320	47 16 13.66 / 69 02 53.70	30 36 / 202 48 / 217 00	T. P. 319 / T. P. 321 / Ref. Mon. C-117	120.6 / 148.4 / 60.1	T. P. 338	47 17 34.51 / 69 03 13.54	179 29 / 329 12	T. P. 339 / T. P. 337	78.7 / 41.2
Ref. Mon. C-117	47 16 15.22 / 69 02 51.98	37 00 / 170 34	T. P. 320 / Ref. Mon. C-118	60.1 / 350.3	T. P. 339	47 17 37.06 / 69 03 13.57	196 14 / 359 29	T. P. 340 / T. P. 338	113.0 / 78.7
T. P. 321	47 16 18.09 / 69 02 50.97	22 48 / 151 52	T. P. 320 / T. P. 322	148.4 / 208.3	T. P. 340	47 17 40.57 / 69 03 12.06	16 14 / 175 59 / 263 59	T. P. 339 / T. P. 341 / Ref. Mon. C-123	113.0 / 111.4 / 46.0
T. P. 322	47 16 24.04 / 69 02 55.64	178 09 / 331 52	T. P. 323 / T. P. 321	111.8 / 208.3	Ref. Mon. C-123	47 17 40.73 / 69 03 09.89	83 59 / 173 58 / 345 21	T. P. 340 / Ref. Mon. C-124 / Ref. Mon. C-122	46.0 / 113.2 / 127.8
T. P. 323	47 16 27.66 / 69 02 55.81	149 14 / 184 48 / 329 14 / 358 09	Ref. Mon. S-127 / T. P. 324 / Ref. Mon. C-118 / T. P. 322	78.2 / 96.8 / 45.1 / 111.8	T. P. 341	47 17 44.17 / 69 03 12.44	169 17 / 261 14 / 355 59	T. P. 342 / Ref. Mon. C-124 / T. P. 340	107.0 / 42.2 / 111.4
Ref. Mon. S-127	47 16 29.84 / 69 02 57.71	177 25 / 329 14 / 329 14	Ref. Mon. C-119 / T. P. 323 / Ref. Mon. C-118	140.6 / 78.2 / 123.3	Ref. Mon. C-124	47 17 44.38 / 69 03 10.45	81 14 / 353 58	T. P. 341 / Ref. Mon. C-123	42.2 / 113.2
Ref. Mon. C-118	47 16 26.41 / 69 02 54.71	149 14 / 149 14	T. P. 323 / Ref. Mon. S-127	45.1 / 123.3	T. P. 342	47 17 47.57 / 69 03 13.38	159 52 / 349 17	T. P. 343 / T. P. 341	87.4 / 107.0
T. P. 324	47 16 30.78 / 69 02 55.43	4 48 / 158 47	T. P. 323 / T. P. 325	96.8 / 77.3	T. P. 343	47 17 50.23 / 69 03 14.82	184 36 / 339 52	T. P. 344 / T. P. 342	57.3 / 87.4
T. P. 325	47 16 33.12 / 69 02 56.76	92 01 / 146 13 / 338 47	T. P. 326 / Ref. Mon. C-119 / T. P. 324	62.3 / 47.2 / 77.3	T. P. 344	47 17 52.08 / 69 03 14.60	4 36 / 195 05	T. P. 343 / T. P. 345	57.3 / 95.3
Ref. Mon. C-119	47 16 34.39 / 69 02 58.01	326 13 / 357 25	T. P. 325 / Ref. Mon. S-127	47.2 / 140.6	T. P. 345	47 17 55.06 / 69 03 13.42	15 05 / 30 17 / 210 17 / 258 18	T. P. 344 / Ref. Mon. S-130 / Ref. Mon. S-131 / T. P. 346	95.3 / 105.5 / 79.7 / 120.4
T. P. 326	47 16 33.19 / 69 02 59.72	159 13 / 272 01	T. P. 327 / T. P. 325	320.5 / 62.3	Ref. Mon. S-130	47 17 52.11 / 69 03 15.95	210 17 / 210 17	T. P. 345 / Ref. Mon. S-131	105.5 / 185.2
T. P. 327	47 16 42.90 / 69 03 05.14	92 11 / 174 46 / 339 13	Ref. Mon. S-128 / T. P. 328 / T. P. 326	92.8 / 181.1 / 320.5	Ref. Mon. S-131	47 17 57.29 / 69 03 11.50	30 17 / 30 17 / 232 18	T. P. 345 / Ref. Mon. S-130 / Ref. Mon. C-125	79.7 / 185.2 / 229.4
Ref. Mon. S-128	47 16 43.01 / 69 03 09.55	206 33 / 272 11	Ref. Mon. C-120 / T. P. 327	248.0 / 92.8	T. P. 346	47 17 55.85 / 69 03 07.81	78 18 / 217 05	T. P. 345 / T. P. 347	120.4 / 110.8
T. P. 328	47 16 48.73 / 69 03 05.92	188 57 / 354 46	T. P. 329 / T. P. 327	61.0 / 181.1	T. P. 347	47 17 58.71 / 69 03 04.63	37 05 / 158 41	T. P. 346 / T. P. 348	110.8 / 132.3
T. P. 329	47 16 50.69 / 69 03 05.47	8 57 / 182 57 / 301 15	T. P. 328 / T. P. 330 / Ref. Mon. C-120	61.0 / 87.5 / 29.5	T. P. 348	47 18 02.71 / 69 03 06.92	191 30 / 287 41 / 338 41	T. P. 349 / Ref. Mon. C-125 / T. P. 347	217.1 / 89.2 / 132.3
Ref. Mon. C-120	47 16 50.19 / 69 03 04.27	26 33 / 121 15	Ref. Mon. S-128 / T. P. 329	248.0 / 29.5	Ref. Mon. C-125	47 18 01.83 / 69 03 02.87	52 18 / 107 41	Ref. Mon. S-131 / T. P. 348	229.4 / 89.2
T. P. 330	47 16 53.52 / 69 03 05.26	2 57 / 222 28	T. P. 329 / T. P. 331	87.5 / 109.1	T. P. 349	47 18 09.59 / 69 03 04.86	11 30 / 180 00	T. P. 348 / T. P. 350	217.1 / 155.3
T. P. 331	47 16 56.12 / 69 03 01.75	42 28 / 200 28	T. P. 330 / T. P. 332	109.1 / 139.5	T. P. 350	47 18 14.62 / 69 03 04.86	0 00 / 103 17 / 215 25	T. P. 349 / Ref. Mon. S-132 / T. P. 351	155.3 / 85.6 / 107.9
T. P. 332	47 17 00.36 / 69 02 59.43	20 28 / 111 52 / 162 46	T. P. 331 / Ref. Mon. S-129 / T. P. 333	139.5 / 65.0 / 152.9	Ref. Mon. S-132	47 18 15.26 / 69 03 08.82	140 27 / 283 17	Ref. Mon. S-133 / T. P. 350	255.1 / 85.6
Ref. Mon. S-129	47 17 01.14 / 69 03 02.30	184 48 20 / 291 52	Ref. Mon. C-121 / T. P. 332	563.0 / 65.0	T. P. 351	47 18 17.47 / 69 03 01.88	35 25 / 201 24	T. P. 350 / T. P. 352	107.9 / 131.6
T. P. 333	47 17 05.08 / 69 03 01.58	179 51 / 342 46	T. P. 334 / T. P. 332	380.6 / 152.9	T. P. 352	47 18 21.44 / 69 02 59.60	21 24 / 90 58 / 158 02 00	T. P. 351 / Ref. Mon. S-133 / T. P. 353	131.6 / 356.1 / 1,136.4
T. P. 334	47 17 17.41 / 69 03 01.63	183 22 / 359 51	T. P. 335 / T. P. 333	136.1 / 380.6	Ref. Mon. S-133	47 18 21.63 / 69 03 16.55	270 58 / 320 27	T. P. 352 / Ref. Mon. S-132	356.1 / 255.1
T. P. 335	47 17 21.81 / 69 03 01.25	3 22 / 162 03 / 162 03 / 342 03	T. P. 334 / T. P. 336 / Ref. Mon. C-122 / Ref. Mon. C-121	136.1 / 362.2 / 484.3 / 81.5	T. P. 353	47 18 55.56 / 69 03 19.85	183 12 20 / 266 18 / 338 01 50	T. P. 354 / Ref. Mon. C-126 / T. P. 352	1,287.8 / 409.5 / 1,136.4
Ref. Mon. C-121	47 17 19.30 / 69 03 00.05	162 02 50 / 162 02 50 / 162 02 50	Ref. Mon. C-122 / T. P. 335 / T. P. 336	565.8 / 81.5 / 443.7	Ref. Mon. C-126	47 18 56.42 / 69 03 00.40	17 31 00 / 86 18	Ref. Mon. S-133 / T. P. 353	1,126.8 / 409.5

BOUNDARY TURNING POINTS AND REFERENCE MONUMENTS—ST. FRANCIS RIVER—Con.

Station	Latitude and longitude	Azimuth	To station	Distance (meters)
T. P. 354	47 19 37.20 69 03 16.43	3 12 20 110 01 181 05 30 290 01	T. P. 353 Ref. Mon. S-134 T. P. 355 Ref. Mon. C-127	1,287.8 410.0 1,528.4 348.5
Ref. Mon. S-134	47 19 41.75 69 03 34.78	290 01 10 290 01 10	T. P. 354 Ref. Mon. C-127	410.0 758.5
Ref. Mon. C-127	47 19 33.34 69 03 00.84	110 01 40 110 01 40	Ref. Mon. S-134 T. P. 354	758.5 348.5
T. P. 355	47 20 26.68 69 03 15.05	1 05 30 119 44 50 179 33 00 299 44 50	T. P. 354 Ref. Mon. S-135 T. P. 356 Ref. Mon. C-128	1,528.4 606.6 2,783.4 504.4
Ref. Mon. S-135	47 20 36.42 69 03 40.14	299 44 30 299 44 30	T. P. 355 Ref. Mon. C-128	606.6 1,111.0
Ref. Mon. C-128	47 20 18.57 69 02 54.19	119 45 00 119 45 00	T. P. 355 Ref. Mon. S-135	504.4 1,111.0
T. P. 356	47 21 56.80 69 03 16.10	42 04 30 102 58 10 177 51 10 282 58 10 359 33 00	Ref. Mon. S-136 Ref. Mon. S-137 T. P. 357 Ref. Mon. C-129 T. P. 355	734.8 586.9 1,208.4 427.1 2,783.4
Ref. Mon. S-136	47 21 39.14 69 03 39.56	173 16 30 222 04 10	Ref. Mon. S-137 T. P. 356	681.8 734.8
Ref. Mon. S-137	47 22 01.06 69 03 43.36	282 57 50 282 57 50	T. P. 356 Ref. Mon. C-129	586.9 1,014.0
Ref. Mon. C-129	47 21 53.69 69 02 56.27	102 58 20 102 58 20	T. P. 356 Ref. Mon. S-137	427.1 1,014.0
T. P. 357	47 22 35.90 69 03 18.26	118 10 30 165 10 298 10 30 357 51 00	Ref. Mon. S-137-A T. P. 358 Ref. Mon. C-130 T. P. 356	39.1 135.2 551.6 1,208.4
Ref. Mon. S-137-A.	47 22 36.50 69 03 19.90	236 44 10 298 10 30 298 10 30	Ref. Mon. C-131 T. P. 357 Ref. Mon. C-130	537.5 39.1 590.7
Ref. Mon. C-130	47 22 27.47 69 02 55.08	118 10 50 118 10 50	T. P. 357 Ref. Mon. S-137-A	551.6 590.7
T. P. 358	47 22 40.13 69 03 19.91	230 10 345 10	T. P. 359 T. P. 357	159.5 135.2
T. P. 359	47 22 43.44 69 03 14.07	50 10 277 52	T. P. 358 T. P. 360	159.5 82.5
T. P. 360	47 22 43.08 69 03 10.18	97 52 295 05	T. P. 359 T. P. 361	82.5 81.2
T. P. 361	47 22 41.96 69 03 06.67	115 05 247 55	T. P. 360 T. P. 362	81.2 96.0
T. P. 362	47 22 43.13 69 03 02.43	67 55 204 44	T. P. 361 T. P. 363	96.0 90.8
T. P. 363	47 22 45.80 69 03 00.62	24 44 175 32 260 18	T. P. 362 T. P. 364 Ref. Mon C-131	90.8 76.9 45.5
Ref. Mon. C-131	47 22 46.05 69 02 58.48	80 18 208 00	T. P. 363 Ref. Mon. C-132	45.5 410.9
T. P. 364	47 22 48.29 69 03 00.91	138 37 355 32	T. P. 365 T. P. 363	147.2 76.9
T. P. 365	47 22 51.86 69 03 05.54	236 54 318 37	T. P. 366 T. P. 364	215.7 147.2
T. P. 366	47 22 55.67 69 02 56.93	56 54 206 21	T. P. 365 T. P. 367	215.7 172.5
T. P. 367	47 23 00.68 69 02 53.28	26 21 247 21 316 43	T. P. 366 T. P. 368 Ref. Mon. C-132	172.5 133.7 122.2
Ref. Mon. C-132	47 22 57.80 69 02 49.28	28 00 136 43 304 06	Ref. Mon. C-131 T. P. 367 Ref. Mon. C-133	410.9 122.2 280.1
T. P. 368	47 23 02.35 69 02 47.39	67 21 268 07	T. P. 367 T. P. 369	133.7 91.6
T. P. 369	47 23 02.44 69 02 43.03	88 07 343 58	T. P. 368 T. P. 370	91.6 136.5
T. P. 370	47 22 58.20 69 02 41.23	163 58 273 46 339 35	T. P. 369 T. P. 371 Ref. Mon. C-133	136.5 150.8 180.8
Ref. Mon. C-133	47 22 52.71 69 02 38.22	124 06 159 35 217 30 20	Ref. Mon. C-132 T. P. 370 Ref. Mon. C-134	280.1 180.8 586.9
T. P. 371	47 22 57.88 69 02 34.05	93 46 245 03	T. P. 370 T. P. 372	150.8 119.9
T. P. 372	47 22 59.51 69 02 28.87	65 03 213 02	T. P. 371 T. P. 373	119.9 147.0
T. P. 373	47 23 03.50 69 02 25.05	33 02 169 24	T. P. 372 T. P. 374	147.0 204.0
T. P. 374	47 23 10.00 69 02 26.84	123 12 299 53 349 24	T. P. 375 Ref. Mon. C-134 T. P. 373	313.7 136.7 204.0
Ref. Mon. C-134	47 23 07.79 69 02 21.19	37 30 30 119 53	Ref. Mon. C-133 T. P. 374	586.9 136.7
T. P. 375	47 23 15.56 69 02 39.36	141 54 303 12	T. P. 376 T. P. 374	155.4 313.7
T. P. 376	47 23 19.52 69 02 43.93	161 34 321 54	T. P. 377 T. P. 375	190.7 155.4
T. P. 377	47 23 25.38 69 02 46.81	182 36 341 34	T. P. 378 T. P. 376	192.1 190.7
T. P. 378	47 23 31.59 69 02 46.39	2 36 186 22 315 28	T. P. 377 T. P. 379 Ref. Mon. C-135	192.1 109.2 107.5
Ref. Mon. C-135	47 23 29.11 69 02 42.80	135 28 184 17	T. P. 378 Ref. Mon. C-136	107.5 272.4
T. P. 379	47 23 35.10 69 02 45.82	6 22 201 12	T. P. 378 T. P. 380	109.2 109.5
T. P. 380	47 23 38.41 69 02 43.93	21 12 210 42 289 19	T. P. 379 T. P. 381 Ref. Mon. C-136	109.5 203.7 46.7
Ref. Mon. C-136	47 23 37.91 69 02 41.83	4 17 109 19 229 58	Ref. Mon. C-135 T. P. 380 Ref. Mon. C-137	272.4 46.7 286.5
T. P. 381	47 23 44.08 69 02 38.97	30 42 170 45	T. P. 380 T. P. 382	203.7 80.2
T. P. 382	47 23 46.64 69 02 39.59	159 58 350 45	T. P. 383 T. P. 381	79.4 80.2
T. P. 383	47 23 49.06 69 02 40.89	197 50 339 58	T. P. 384 T. P. 382	66.6 79.4
T. P. 384	47 23 51.11 69 02 39.91	17 50 238 44	T. P. 383 T. P. 385	66.6 49.7
T. P. 385	47 23 51.95 69 02 37.89	58 44 298 26	T. P. 384 T. P. 386	49.7 210.7
T. P. 386	47 23 48.70 69 02 29.05	118 26 344 01	T. P. 385 T. P. 387	210.7 145.9
T. P. 387	47 23 44.16 69 02 27.13	84 30 164 01 278 29	Ref. Mon. C-137 T. P. 386 T. P. 388	89.3 145.9 77.3
Ref. Mon. C-137	47 23 43.88 69 02 31.37	49 58 246 44 264 30	Ref. Mon. C-136 Ref. Mon. S-138 T. P. 387	286.5 218.1 89.3
T. P. 388	47 23 43.79 69 02 23.48	98 29 201 29 217 40	T. P. 387 Ref. Mon. S-138 T. P. 389	77.3 95.3 202.9
Ref. Mon. S-138	47 23 46.66 69 02 21.82	21 29 66 44	T. P. 388 Ref. Mon. C-137	95.3 218.1
T. P. 389	47 23 48.99 69 02 17.57	37 40 152 47 264 21	T. P. 388 T. P. 390 Ref. Mon. C-138	202.9 66.7 145.0
Ref. Mon. C-138	47 23 49.45 69 02 10.69	84 21 175 09	T. P. 389 Ref. Mon. C-139	145.0 313.9
T. P. 390	47 23 50.91 69 02 19.03	102 26 332 47	T. P. 391 T. P. 389	81.7 66.7

BOUNDARY TURNING POINTS AND REFERENCE MONUMENTS—ST. FRANCIS RIVER—Con.

Station	Latitude and longitude	Azimuth	To station	Distance (meters)
	° ′ ″	° ′ ″		
T. P. 391	47 23 51.48	75 08	T. P. 392	101.4
	69 02 22.83	282 26	T. P. 390	81.7
T. P. 392	47 23 50.64	132 00	T. P. 393	155.1
	69 02 27.51	255 08	T. P. 391	101.4
T. P. 393	47 23 54.00	160 38	T. P. 394	199.7
	69 02 33.00	312 00	T. P. 392	155.1
T. P. 394	47 24 00.10	179 55	T. P. 395	227.0
	69 02 36.16	340 38	T. P. 393	199.7
T. P. 395	47 24 07.45	183 29	Ref. Mon. S-139	65.1
	69 02 36.18	277 31	T. P. 396	106.3
		359 55	T. P. 394	227.0
Ref. Mon. S-139	47 24 09.55	3 29	T. P. 395	65.1
	69 02 35.99	180 38	Ref. Mon. S-140	203.7
		254 35	Ref. Mon. C-140	284.8
T. P. 396	47 24 07.00	97 31	T. P. 395	106.3
	69 02 31.15	354 11	T. P. 397	74.1
T. P. 397	47 24 04.61	174 11	T. P. 396	74.1
	69 02 30.79	334 12	T. P. 398	77.9
T. P. 398	47 24 02.34	154 12	T. P. 397	77.9
	69 02 29.18	299 43	T. P. 399	66.0
T. P. 399	47 24 01.28	119 43	T. P. 398	66.0
	69 02 26.44	269 37	T. P. 400	89.5
T. P. 400	47 24 01.30	89 37	T. P. 399	89.5
	69 02 22.18	252 28	T. P. 401	261.6
T. P. 401	47 24 03.85	14 56	Ref. Mon. C-139	136.6
	69 02 10.28	72 28	T. P. 400	261.6
		216 42	T. P. 402	45.5
Ref. Mon. C-139	47 23 59.58	149 08	Ref. Mon. C-140	447.1
	69 02 11.96	194 56	T. P. 401	136.6
		355 09	Ref. Mon. C-138	313.9
T. P. 402	47 24 05.04	36 42	T. P. 401	45.5
	69 02 08.98	175 17	T. P. 403	55.9
T. P. 403	47 24 06.84	124 34	T. P. 404	39.8
	69 02 09.20	355 17	T. P. 402	55.9
T. P. 404	47 24 07.57	63 24	T. P. 405	122.4
	69 02 10.77	304 34	T. P. 403	39.8
T. P. 405	47 24 05.80	99 15	T. P. 406	94.6
	69 02 15.99	243 24	T. P. 404	122.4
T. P. 406	47 24 06.29	120 08	T. P. 407	131.7
	69 02 20.44	279 15	T. P. 405	94.6
T. P. 407	47 24 08.43	155 26	T. P. 408	101.7
	69 02 25.87	300 08	T. P. 406	131.7
T. P. 408	47 24 11.42	145 19	T. P. 409	120.7
	69 02 27.89	335 26	T. P. 407	101.7
T. P. 409	47 24 14.64	115 11	T. P. 410	71.8
	69 02 31.17	115 11	Ref. Mon. S-140	109.2
		295 11	Ref. Mon. C-140	191.7
		325 19	T. P. 408	120.7
Ref. Mon. S-140	47 24 16.15	0 38	Ref. Mon. S-139	203.7
	69 02 35.88	295 11	T. P. 410	37.4
		295 11	T. P. 409	109.2
		295 11	Ref. Mon. C-140	300.9
Ref. Mon. C-140	47 24 12.00	115 11	T. P. 409	191.7
	69 02 22.90	115 11	T. P. 410	263.5
		115 11	Ref. Mon. S-140	300.9
		150 14	T. P. 419	62.1
		289 02	Ref. Mon. C-141	394.9
		329 08	Ref. Mon. C-139	447.1
T. P. 410	47 24 15.63	115 11	Ref. Mon. S-140	37.4
	69 02 34.27	158 29	T. P. 411	60.0
		295 11	T. P. 409	71.8
		295 11	Ref. Mon. C-140	263.5
T. P. 411	47 24 17.44	196 38	T. P. 412	54.5
	69 02 35.32	338 29	T. P. 410	60.0
T. P. 412	47 24 19.13	16 38	T. P. 411	54.5
	69 02 34.57	217 04	T. P. 413	73.8
T. P. 413	47 24 21.03	37 04	T. P. 412	73.8
	69 02 32.45	257 18	T. P. 414	37.3
T. P. 414	47 24 21.30	77 18	T. P. 413	37.3
	69 02 30.71	277 53	T. P. 415	32.1
T. P. 415	47 24 21.16	97 53	T. P. 414	32.1
	69 02 29.20	286 01	T. P. 416	36.6
T. P. 416	47 24 20.83	106 01	T. P. 415	36.6
	69 02 27.52	315 06	T. P. 417	77.6
T. P. 417	47 24 19.05	14 09	T. P. 418	105.5
	69 02 24.91	135 06	T. P. 416	77.6
T. P. 418	47 24 15.74	194 09	T. P. 417	105.5
	69 02 26.14	328 58	T. P. 419	71.8
T. P. 419	47 24 13.75	148 58	T. P. 418	71.8
	69 02 24.37	270 42	T. P. 420	155.4
		330 14	Ref. Mon. C-140	62.1
T. P. 420	47 24 13.68	90 42	T. P. 419	155.4
	69 02 16.96	301 09	T. P. 421	131.8
T. P. 421	47 24 11.48	121 09	T. P. 420	131.8
	69 02 11.58	270 53	T. P. 422	124.2
T. P. 422	47 24 11.41	90 53	T. P. 421	124.2
	69 02 05.66	320 18	T. P. 423	124.6
T. P. 423	47 24 08.31	77 43	Ref. Mon. C-141	69.5
	69 02 01.86	140 18	T. P. 422	124.6
		268 54	T. P. 424	62.1
Ref. Mon. C-141	47 24 07.83	109 02	Ref. Mon. C-140	394.9
	69 02 05.10	228 34	Ref. Mon. S-141	187.5
		257 43	T. P. 423	69.5
T. P. 424	47 24 08.35	88 54	T. P. 423	62.1
	69 01 58.89	233 31	T. P. 425	88.3
T. P. 425	47 24 10.05	53 31	T. P. 424	88.3
	69 01 55.51	165 48	T. P. 426	50.5
T. P. 426	47 24 11.63	121 54	T. P. 427	81.7
	69 01 56.10	345 48	T. P. 425	50.5
T. P. 427	47 24 13.03	146 38	T. P. 428	122.4
	69 01 59.41	301 54	T. P. 426	81.7
		329 40	Ref. Mon. S-141	42.3
Ref. Mon. S-141	47 24 11.85	48 34	Ref. Mon. C-141	187.5
	69 01 58.39	149 40	T. P. 427	42.3
T. P. 428	47 24 16.34	196 07	T. P. 429	181.5
	69 02 02.62	326 38	T. P. 427	122.4
T. P. 429	47 24 21.99	16 07	T. P. 428	181.5
	69 02 00.22	164 12	Ref. Mon. S-142	52.2
		214 44	T. P. 430	95.1
		344 12	Ref. Mon. C-142	166.3
Ref. Mon. S-142	47 24 23.62	110 51	Ref. Mon. S-143	203.7
	69 02 00.90	344 12	T. P. 429	52.2
		344 12	Ref. Mon. C-142	218.5
Ref. Mon. C-142	47 24 16.81	164 12	T. P. 429	166.3
	69 01 58.06	164 12	Ref. Mon. S-142	218.5
T. P. 430	47 24 24.52	34 44	T. P. 429	95.1
	69 01 57.63	249 07	T. P. 431	82.7
T. P. 431	47 24 25.48	69 07	T. P. 430	82.7
	69 01 53.95	211 49	T. P. 432	57.7
T. P. 432	47 24 27.06	31 49	T. P. 431	57.7
	69 01 52.50	181 28	T. P. 433	136.7
T. P. 433	47 24 31.49	1 28	T. P. 432	136.7
	69 01 52.33	150 20	T. P. 434	48.7
T. P. 434	47 24 32.86	95 48	T. P. 435	31.7
	69 01 53.48	330 20	T. P. 433	48.7
T. P. 435	47 24 32.96	58 12	T. P. 436	59.8
	69 01 54.99	275 48	T. P. 434	31.7
T. P. 436	47 24 31.94	43 45	T. P. 437	119.7
	69 01 57.41	190 26	Ref. Mon. C-143	34.8
		238 12	T. P. 435	59.8
Ref. Mon. C-143	47 24 33.05	10 26	T. P. 436	34.8
	69 01 57.11	50 58	Ref. Mon. S-143	347.3
T. P. 437	47 24 29.14	65 51	T. P. 438	139.3
	69 02 01.36	223 45	T. P. 436	119.7

BOUNDARY TURNING POINTS AND REFERENCE MONUMENTS—ST. FRANCIS RIVER—Con·

Station	Latitude and longitude	Azimuth	To station	Distance (meters)	Station	Latitude and longitude	Azimuth	To station	Distance (meters)
	° ′ ″	° ′ ″				° ′ ″	° ′ ″		
T. P. 438	47 24 27.30 / 69 02 07.42	71 21 / 245 51	T. P. 439 / T. P. 437	77.6 / 139.3	T. P. 461	47 25 15.89 / 69 02 24.46	180 33 / 271 15 / 351 52	T. P. 462 / Ref. Mon. C-147 / T. P. 460	144.8 / 31.8 / 149.2
T. P. 439	47 24 26.49 / 69 02 10.93	124 54 / 251 21 / 309 23	T. P. 440 / T. P. 438 / Ref. Mon. S-143	80.6 / 77.6 / 26.0	Ref. Mon. C-147	47 25 15.87 / 69 02 22.94	91 15 / 170 43	T. P. 461 / Ref. Mon. C-148	31.8 / 189.6
Ref. Mon. S-143	47 24 25.96 / 69 02 09.97	129 23 / 230 58 / 290 51	T. P. 439 / Ref. Mon. C-143 / Ref. Mon. S-142	26.0 / 347.3 / 203.7	T. P. 462	47 25 20.58 / 69 02 24.39	0 33 / 135 42	T. P. 461 / T. P. 463	144.8 / 64.1
T. P. 440	47 24 27.99 / 69 02 14.08	160 09 / 304 54	T. P. 441 / T. P. 439	102.5 / 80.6	T. P. 463	47 25 22.07 / 69 02 26.53	98 50 / 275 26 / 315 42	T. P. 464 / Ref. Mon. C-148 / T. P. 462	81.5 / 44.8 / 64.1
T. P. 441	47 24 31.11 / 69 02 15.74	190 28 / 340 09	T. P. 442 / T. P. 440	177.3 / 102.5	Ref. Mon. C-148	47 25 21.93 / 69 02 24.40	95 26 / 350 43	T. P. 463 / Ref. Mon. C-147	44.8 / 189.6
T. P. 442	47 24 36.75 / 69 02 14.20	10 28 / 244 29	T. P. 441 / T. P. 443	177.3 / 105.8	T. P. 464	47 25 22.47 / 69 02 30.37	123 59 / 278 50	T. P. 465 / T. P. 463	58.1 / 81.5
T. P. 443	47 24 38.23 / 69 02 09.65	64 29 / 191 35 / 246 55	T. P. 442 / T. P. 444 / Ref. Mon. C-144	105.8 / 80.6 / 41.9	T. P. 465	47 25 23.52 / 69 02 32.67	144 54 / 303 59	T. P. 466 / T. P. 464	65.4 / 58.1
Ref. Mon. C-144	47 24 38.76 / 69 02 07.81	66 55 / 182 57	T. P. 443 / Ref. Mon. C-145	41.9 / 293.4	T. P. 466	47 25 25.26 / 69 02 34.46	175 37 / 198 05 / 324 54	T. P. 467 / Ref. Mon. C-149 / T. P. 465	172.8 / 68.3 / 65.4
T. P. 444	47 24 40.79 / 69 02 08.88	11 35 / 160 28	T. P. 443 / T. P. 445	80.6 / 67.3	Ref. Mon. C-149	47 25 27.36 / 69 02 33.45	18 05 / 173 21	T. P. 466 / Ref. Mon. C-150	68.3 / 360.7
T. P. 445	47 24 42.84 / 69 02 09.95	163 23 / 340 28	T. P. 446 / T. P. 444	95.1 / 67.3	T. P. 467	47 25 30.84 / 69 02 35.09	164 43 / 355 37	T. P. 468 / T. P. 466	122.2 / 172.8
T. P. 446	47 24 45.79 / 69 02 11.25	186 34 / 343 23	T. P. 447 / T. P. 445	74.4 / 95.1	T. P. 468	47 25 34.65 / 69 02 36.63	157 30 / 344 43	T. P. 469 / T. P. 467	70.6 / 122.2
T. P. 447	47 24 48.18 / 69 02 10.84	6 34 / 223 06 / 268 28	T. P. 446 / T. P. 448 / Ref. Mon. C-145	74.4 / 132.3 / 78.7	T. P. 469	47 25 36.76 / 69 02 37.92	141 54 / 217 28 / 337 30	T. P. 470 / Ref. Mon. C-150 / T. P. 468	105.3 / 85.4 / 70.6
Ref. Mon. C-145	47 24 48.25 / 69 02 07.09	88 28 / 135 36 / 175 03	T. P. 447 / Ref. Mon. S-144 / Ref. Mon. C-146	78.7 / 164.8 / 242.0	Ref. Mon. C-150	47 25 38.96 / 69 02 35.44	37 28 / 353 21	T. P. 469 / Ref. Mon. C-149	85.4 / 360.7
T. P. 448	47 24 51.31 / 69 02 06.53	43 06 / 178 00	T. P. 447 / T. P. 449	132.3 / 45.7	T. P. 470	47 25 39.45 / 69 02 41.02	96 33 / 321 54	T. P. 471 / T. P. 469	153.5 / 105.3
T. P. 449	47 24 52.79 / 69 02 06.61	135 07 / 358 00	T. P. 450 / T. P. 448	36.3 / 45.7	T. P. 471	47 25 40.02 / 69 02 48.30	93 31 / 186 11 / 276 33	T. P. 472 / Ref. Mon. C-151 / T. P. 470	101.0 / 34.3 / 153.5
T. P. 450	47 24 53.62 / 69 02 07.83	113 58 / 315 07	T. P. 451 / T. P. 449	51.4 / 36.3	Ref. Mon. C-151	47 25 41.12 / 69 02 48.12	6 11 / 284 04	T. P. 471 / Ref. Mon. C-150	34.3 / 273.9
T. P. 451	47 24 54.30 / 69 02 10.07	37 26 / 71 49 / 217 26 / 293 58	Ref. Mon. S-144 / T. P. 452 / Ref. Mon. C-146 / T. P. 450	86.8 / 116.3 / 68.5 / 51.4	T. P. 472	47 25 40.22 / 69 02 53.11	35 04 / 273 31	T. P. 473 / T. P. 471	69.6 / 101.0
Ref. Mon. S-144	47 24 52.06 / 69 02 12.59	217 26 / 217 26 / 315 36	T. P. 451 / Ref. Mon. C-146 / Ref. Mon. C-145	86.8 / 155.3 / 164.8	T. P. 473	47 25 38.37 / 69 02 55.01	0 00 / 215 04	T. P. 474 / T. P. 472	62.7 / 69.6
Ref. Mon. C-146	47 24 56.06 / 69 02 08.08	37 26 / 37 26 / 355 03	T. P. 451 / Ref. Mon. S-144 / Ref. Mon. C-145	68.5 / 155.3 / 242.0	T. P. 474	47 25 36.34 / 69 02 55.01	180 00 / 307 54	T. P. 473 / T. P. 475	62.7 / 66.4
T. P. 452	47 24 53.12 / 69 02 15.34	86 44 / 251 49	T. P. 453 / T. P. 451	94.6 / 116.3	T. P. 475	47 25 35.02 / 69 02 52.51	127 54 / 294 12	T. P. 474 / T. P. 476	66.4 / 58.5
T. P. 453	47 24 52.95 / 69 02 19.84	112 15 / 266 44	T. P. 454 / T. P. 452	177.7 / 94.6	T. P. 476	47 25 34.24 / 69 02 49.96	114 12 / 326 56	T. P. 475 / T. P. 477	58.5 / 48.6
T. P. 454	47 24 55.13 / 69 02 27.69	94 35 / 292 15	T. P. 455 / T. P. 453	90.0 / 177.7	T. P. 477	47 25 32.92 / 69 02 48.70	146 56 / 349 05	T. P. 476 / T. P. 478	48.6 / 77.6
T. P. 455	47 24 55.36 / 69 02 31.97	132 59 / 274 35	T. P. 456 / T. P. 454	70.5 / 90.0	T. P. 478	47 25 30.46 / 69 02 48.00	25 28 / 169 05	T. P. 479 / T. P. 477	93.3 / 77.6
T. P. 456	47 24 56.92 / 69 02 34.43	180 26 / 312 59	T. P. 457 / T. P. 455	66.9 / 70.5	T. P. 479	47 25 27.73 / 69 02 49.91	48 31 / 205 28	T. P. 480 / T. P. 478	204.4 / 93.3
T. P. 457	47 24 59.08 / 69 02 34.41	0 26 / 204 24	T. P. 456 / T. P. 458	66.9 / 74.6	T. P. 480	47 25 23.35 / 69 02 57.21	40 27 / 228 31	T. P. 481 / T. P. 479	49.9 / 204.4
T. P. 458	47 25 01.28 / 69 02 32.94	24 24 / 202 03 / 220 17	T. P. 457 / Ref. Mon. S-145 / T. P. 459	74.6 / 132.9 / 265.3	T. P. 481	47 25 22.12 / 69 02 58.76	66 27 / 220 27	T. P. 482 / T. P. 480	168.7 / 49.9
Ref. Mon. S-145	47 25 05.27 / 69 02 30.56	22 03 / 206 01	T. P. 458 / Ref. Mon. C-147	132.9 / 364.1	T. P. 482	47 25 19.93 / 69 03 06.14	92 42 / 246 27 / 264 34	T. P. 483 / T. P. 481 / Ref. Mon. S-146	82.6 / 168.7 / 73.9
T. P. 459	47 25 07.84 / 69 02 24.76	40 17 / 195 13	T. P. 458 / T. P. 460	265.3 / 104.8	Ref. Mon. S-146	47 25 20.16 / 69 03 02.63	84 34 / 153 56 / 153 56	T. P. 482 / T. P. 487 / Ref. Mon. S-147	73.9 / 184.4 / 227.3
T. P. 460	47 25 11.11 / 69 02 23.45	15 13 / 171 52	T. P. 459 / T. P. 461	104.8 / 149.2	T. P. 483	47 25 20.06 / 69 03 10.08	119 47 / 272 42	T. P. 484 / T. P. 482	49.3 / 82.6
					T. P. 484	47 25 20.85 / 69 03 12.12	170 21 / 299 47	T. P. 485 / T. P. 483	51.3 / 49.3

BOUNDARY TURNING POINTS AND REFERENCE MONUMENTS—ST. FRANCIS RIVER—Con.

Station	Latitude and longitude	Azimuth	To station	Distance (meters)	Station	Latitude and longitude	Azimuth	To station	Distance (meters)
	° ′ ″	° ′ ″				° ′ ″	° ′ ″		
T. P. 485	47 25 22.49 69 03 12.53	217 22 350 21	T. P. 486 T. P. 484	63.9 51.3	T. P. 510	47 25 47.56 69 03 21.32	93 54 322 12	T. P. 511 T. P. 509	61.7 96.9
T. P. 486	47 25 24.14 69 03 10.68	37 22 244 04	T. P. 485 T. P. 487	63.9 97.6	T. P. 511	47 25 47.69 69 03 24.26	107 25 196 44 273 54	T. P. 512 Ref. Mon. C-154 T. P. 510	58.8 37.0 61.7
T. P. 487	47 25 25.52 69 03 06.49	64 04 153 56 271 14 333 56	T. P. 486 Ref. Mon. S-147 T. P. 488 Ref. Mon. S-146	97.6 42.9 69.3 184.4	Ref. Mon. C-154	47 25 48.84 69 03 23.75	16 44 170 25 170 25 304 40	T. P. 511 T. P. 514 Ref. Mon. S-150 Ref. Mon. C-153	37.0 125.9 162.9 142.3
Ref. Mon. S-147	47 25 26.77 69 03 07.39	333 56 333 56	T. P. 487 Ref. Mon. S-146	42.9 227.3	T. P. 512	47 25 48.26 69 03 26.94	180 53 287 25	T. P. 513 T. P. 511	98.1 58.8
T. P. 488	47 25 25.47 69 03 03.18	91 14 278 29	T. P. 487 T. P. 489	69.3 47.4	T. P. 513	47 25 51.44 69 03 26.86	0 53 225 16	T. P. 512 T. P. 514	98.1 62.4
T. P. 489	47 25 25.24 69 03 00.94	98 29 251 34	T. P. 488 T. P. 490	47.4 40.2	T. P. 514	47 25 52.86 69 03 24.75	45 16 170 25 244 09 350 25	T. P. 513 Ref. Mon. S-150 T. P. 515 Ref. Mon. C-154	62.4 37.0 68.8 125.9
T. P. 490	47 25 25.65 69 02 59.13	71 34 217 14	T. P. 489 T. P. 491	40.2 69.6	Ref. Mon. S-150	47 25 54.04 69 03 25.04	132 19 132 19 350 25 350 25	T. P. 517 Ref. Mon. C-155 T. P. 514 Ref. Mon. C-154	63.8 117.0 37.0 162.9
T. P. 491	47 25 27.45 69 02 57.12	37 14 171 49	T. P. 490 T. P. 492	69.6 103.4	T. P. 515	47 25 53.83 69 03 21.80	64 09 166 19	T. P. 514 T. P. 516	68.8 74.8
T. P. 492	47 25 30.76 69 02 57.82	150 16 351 49	T. P. 493 T. P. 491	87.3 103.4	T. P. 516	47 25 56.19 69 03 22.64	76 29 346 19	T. P. 517 T. P. 515	100.2 74.8
T. P. 493	47 25 33.22 69 02 59.89	136 04 330 16	T. P. 494 T. P. 492	111.0 87.3	T. P. 517	47 25 55.43 69 03 27.29	100 07 132 18 256 29 312 18	T. P. 518 Ref. Mon. C-155 T. P. 516 Ref. Mon. S-150	58.1 53.2 100.2 63.8
T. P. 494	47 25 35.80 69 03 03.56	100 30 316 04	T. P. 495 T. P. 493	57.1 111.0	Ref. Mon. C-155	47 25 56.59 69 03 29.17	312 18 312 18	T. P. 517 Ref. Mon. S-150	53.2 117.0
T. P. 495	47 25 36.14 69 03 06.24	7 19 83 19 280 30	Ref. Mon. S-148 T. P. 496 T. P. 494	37.7 49.8 57.1	T. P. 518	47 25 55.76 69 03 30.02	149 01 280 07	T. P. 519 T. P. 517	55.2 58.1
Ref. Mon. S-148	47 25 34.93 69 03 06.47	140 32 187 19	Ref. Mon. S-149 T. P. 495	302.4 37.7	T. P. 519	47 25 57.29 69 03 31.38	122 25 329 01	T. P. 520 T. P. 518	37.7 55.2
T. P. 496	47 25 35.95 69 03 08.60	164 40 263 19	T. P. 497 T. P. 495	143.7 49.8	T. P. 520	47 25 57.94 69 03 32.89	56 55 302 25	T. P. 521 T. P. 519	90.1 37.7
T. P. 497	47 25 40.44 69 03 10.42	125 06 344 40	T. P. 498 T. P. 496	69.1 143.7	T. P. 521	47 25 56.35 69 03 36.50	90 00 236 55	T. P. 522 T. P. 520	47.3 90.1
T. P. 498	47 25 41.72 69 03 13.11	155 26 305 06	T. P. 499 T. P. 497	45.0 69.1	T. P. 522	47 25 56.35 69 03 38.75	164 46 270 00	T. P. 523 T. P. 521	78.0 47.3
T. P. 499	47 25 43.05 69 03 14.00	63 15 181 41 335 26	Ref. Mon. S-149 T. P. 500 T. P. 498	38.4 34.0 45.0	T. P. 523	47 25 58.79 69 03 39.73	111 06 111 06 291 06 344 46	T. P. 524 Ref. Mon. C-157 Ref. Mon. C-156 T. P. 522	32.6 84.3 74.0 78.0
Ref. Mon. S-149	47 25 42.49 69 03 15.64	243 15 320 32	T. P. 499 Ref. Mon. S-148	38.4 302.4	Ref. Mon. C-156	47 25 57.93 69 03 36.43	111 06 111 06 111 06	T. P 523 T. P. 524 Ref. Mon. C-157	74.0 106.6 158.3
T. P. 500	47 25 44.15 69 03 13.96	1 41 218 04	T. P. 499 T. P. 501	34.0 61.5	Ref. Mon. C-157	47 25 59.77 69 03 43.48	291 05 291 05 291 05	T. P. 524 T. P. 523 Ref. Mon. C-156	51.7 84.3 158.3
T. P. 501	47 25 45.72 69 03 12.15	38 04 233 51	T. P. 500 T. P. 502	61.5 64.4	T. P. 524	47 25 59.17 69 03 41.18	44 54 111 05 291 05 291 05	T. P. 525 Ref. Mon. C-157 T. P. 523 Ref. Mon. C-156	78.3 51.7 32.6 106.6
T. P. 502	47 25 46.95 69 03 09.67	53 51 171 45	T. P. 501 T. P. 503	64.4 44.6	T. P. 525	47 25 57.37 69 03 43.82	107 25 224 54	T. P. 526 T. P. 524	49.8 78.3
T. P. 503	47 25 48.38 69 03 09.97	119 06 351 45	T. P. 504 T. P. 502	91.1 44.6	T. P. 526	47 25 57.85 69 03 46.09	177 21 287 25	T. P. 527 T. P. 525	123.4 49.8
T. P. 504	47 25 49.81 69 03 13.77	87 08 299 06	T. P. 505 T. P. 503	48.1 91.1	T. P. 527	47 26 01.85 69 03 46.36	128 54 357 21	T. P. 528 T. P. 526	60.5 123.4
T. P. 505	47 25 49.73 69 03 16.06	57 26 146 05 267 08	T. P. 506 Ref. Mon. C-152 T. P. 504	38.4 34.1 48.1	T. P. 528	47 26 03.08 69 03 48.61	85 59 308 54	T. P. 529 T. P. 527	52.7 60.5
Ref. Mon. C-152	47 25 50.65 69 03 16.97	10 21 326 05	Ref. Mon. C-153 T. P. 505	139.0 34.1	T. P. 529	47 26 02.96 69 03 51.12	21 25 265 59	T. P. 530 T. P. 528	114.2 52.7
T. P. 506	47 25 49.06 69 03 17.61	237 26 336 03	T. P. 505 T. P. 507	38.4 96.1	T. P. 530	47 25 59.51 69 03 53.11	201 25 348 31	T. P. 529 T. P. 531	114.2 136.5
T. P. 507	47 25 46.22 69 03 15.75	17 50 156 03	T. P. 508 T. P. 506	45.1 96.1	T. P. 531	47 25 55.18 69 03 51.81	168 31 328 44	T. P. 530 T. P. 532	136.5 67.0
T. P. 508	47 25 44.83 69 03 16.40	99 53 197 50	T. P. 509 T. P. 507	44.3 45.1					
T. P. 509	47 25 45.08 69 03 18.49	142 12 190 54 279 53	T. P. 510 Ref. Mon. C-153 T. P. 508	96.9 36.0 44.3					
Ref. Mon. C-153	47 25 46.22 69 03 18.16	10 54 124 40	T. P. 509 Ref. Mon. C-154	36.0 142.3					

BOUNDARY TURNING POINTS AND REFERENCE MONUMENTS—ST. FRANCIS RIVER—Con.

Station	Latitude and longitude	Azimuth	To station	Distance (meters)
T. P. 532	47 25 53.33 / 69 03 50.15	148 44 / 296 51	T. P. 531 / T. P. 533	67.0 / 45.2
T. P. 533	47 25 52.67 / 69 03 48.22	116 51 / 291 52	T. P. 532 / T. P. 534	45.2 / 64.4
T. P. 534	47 25 51.89 / 69 03 45.37	111 52 / 355 21	T. P. 533 / T. P. 535	64.4 / 44.4
T. P. 535	47 25 50.45 / 69 03 45.20	61 31 / 175 21	T. P. 536 / T. P. 534	48.2 / 44.4
T. P. 536	47 25 49.71 / 69 03 47.22	122 48 / 241 31	T. P. 537 / T. P. 535	73.3 / 48.2
T. P. 537	47 25 51.00 / 69 03 50.16	112 04 / 235 46 / 302 48	T. P. 538 / Ref. Mon. C-158 / T. P. 536	99.8 / 37.0 / 73.3
Ref. Mon. C-158	47 25 51.67 / 69 03 48.70	55 46 / 203 36	T. P. 537 / Ref. Mon. C-157	37.0 / 273.2
T. P. 538	47 25 52.21 / 69 03 54.57	75 24 / 292 04	T. P. 539 / T. P. 537	90.4 / 99.8
T. P. 539	47 25 51.47 / 69 03 58.75	55 06 / 255 24	T. P. 540 / T. P. 538	154.0 / 90.4
T. P. 540	47 25 48.62 / 69 04 04.77	47 00 / 235 06 / 298 10	T. P. 541 / T. P. 539 / Ref. Mon. S-151	97.6 / 154.0 / 88.9
Ref. Mon. S-151	47 25 47.26 / 69 04 01.03	47 46 / 118 10	Ref. Mon. C-159 / T. P. 540	277.6 / 88.9
T. P. 541	47 25 46.46 / 69 04 08.18	1 55 / 227 00	T. P. 542 / T. P. 540	230.3 / 97.6
T. P. 542	47 25 39.01 / 69 04 08.55	72 56 / 144 51 / 181 55	T. P. 543 / Ref. Mon. C-159 / T. P. 541	219.7 / 83.2 / 230.3
Ref. Mon. C-159	47 25 41.21 / 69 04 10.83	34 37 / 227 46 / 324 51	Ref. Mon. S-152 / Ref. Mon. S-151 / T. P. 542	242.9 / 277.6 / 83.2
T. P. 543	47 25 36.92 / 69 04 18.57	111 51 / 252 56 / 340 23	T. P. 544 / T. P. 542 / Ref. Mon. S-152	189.9 / 219.7 / 71.5
Ref. Mon. S-152	47 25 34.74 / 69 04 17.42	78 37 / 160 23 / 214 37	Ref. Mon. S-153 / T. P. 543 / Ref. Mon. C-159	377.8 / 71.5 / 242.9
T. P. 544	47 25 39.21 / 69 04 26.98	79 10 / 291 51	T. P. 545 / T. P. 543	103.2 / 189.9
T. P. 545	47 25 38.58 / 69 04 31.82	40 47 / 259 10	T. P. 546 / T. P. 544	113.6 / 103.2
T. P. 546	47 25 35.80 / 69 04 35.36	79 32 / 220 47	T. P. 547 / T. P. 545	40.2 / 113.6
T. P. 547	47 25 35.56 / 69 04 37.24	64 59 / 155 41 / 259 32 / 335 41	T. P. 548 / Ref. Mon. C-160 / T. P. 546 / Ref. Mon. S-153	174.0 / 132.9 / 40.2 / 109.6
Ref. Mon. C-160	47 25 39.48 / 69 04 39.85	335 41 / 335 41	T. P. 547 / Ref. Mon. S-153	132.9 / 242.5
Ref. Mon. S-153	47 25 32.33 / 69 04 35.09	155 41 / 155 41 / 258 36	T. P. 547 / Ref. Mon. C-160 / Ref. Mon. S-152	109.6 / 242.5 / 377.8
T. P. 548	47 25 33.18 / 69 04 44.76	32 24 / 244 59	T. P. 549 / T. P. 547	189.8 / 174.0
T. P. 549	47 25 27.99 / 69 04 49.62	60 07 / 212 24	T. P. 550 / T. P. 548	135.9 / 189.8
T. P. 550	47 25 25.79 / 69 04 55.24	103 41 / 240 07	T. P. 551 / T. P. 549	229.9 / 135.9
T. P. 551	47 25 27.56 / 69 05 05.89	120 33 / 283 41	T. P. 552 / T. P. 550	248.6 / 229.9
T. P. 552	47 25 31.65 / 69 05 16.11	104 29 / 173 48 / 300 33 / 353 48	T. P. 553 / Ref. Mon. C-161 / T. P. 551 / Ref. Mon. S-154	76.3 / 44.6 / 248.6 / 100.8
Ref. Mon. C-161	47 25 33.09 / 69 05 16.34	353 48 / 353 48	T. P. 552 / Ref. Mon. S-154	44.6 / 145.4

Station	Latitude and longitude	Azimuth	To station	Distance (meters)
Ref. Mon. S-154	47 25 28.41 / 69 05 15.59	173 48 / 173 48	T. P. 552 / Ref. Mon. C-161	100.8 / 145.4
T. P. 553	47 25 32.27 / 69 05 19.63	57 28 / 284 29	T. P. 554 / T. P. 552	70.5 / 76.3
T. P. 554	47 25 31.04 / 69 05 22.47	37 45 / 237 28	T. P. 555 / T. P. 553	149.0 / 70.5
T. P. 555	47 25 27.23 / 69 05 26.82	105 48 / 217 45	T. P. 556 / T. P. 554	62.5 / 149.0
T. P. 556	47 25 27.78 / 69 05 29.69	185 00 / 285 48	T. P. 557 / T. P. 555	197.6 / 62.5
T. P. 557	47 25 34.15 / 69 05 28.87	5 00 / 153 45	T. P. 556 / T. P. 558	197.6 / 95.7
T. P. 558	47 25 36.93 / 69 05 30.89	114 03 / 333 45	T. P. 559 / T. P. 557	83.4 / 95.7
T. P. 559	47 25 38.03 / 69 05 34.52	84 42 / 294 03	T. P. 560 / T. P. 558	259.8 / 83.4
T. P. 560	47 25 37.25 / 69 05 46.86	69 34 / 264 42	T. P. 561 / T. P. 559	110.2 / 259.8
T. P. 561	47 25 36.00 / 69 05 51.79	120 54 / 249 34	T. P. 562 / T. P. 560	68.5 / 110.2
T. P. 562	47 25 37.14 / 69 05 54.60	14 07 / 200 54 / 300 54	Ref. Mon. S-155 / T. P. 563 / T. P. 561	34.5 / 132.8 / 68.5
Ref. Mon. S-155	47 25 36.06 / 69 05 55.00	184 05 20 / 194 07	Ref. Mon. C-162 / T. P. 562	558.6 / 34.5
T. P. 563	47 25 41.16 / 69 05 52.34	20 54 / 161 14	T. P. 562 / T. P. 564	132.8 / 84.0
T. P. 564	47 25 43.74 / 69 05 53.63	195 49 / 341 14	T. P. 565 / T. P. 563	117.8 / 84.0
T. P. 565	47 25 47.40 / 69 05 52.10	15 49 / 135 15	T. P. 564 / T. P. 566	117.8 / 112.5
T. P. 566	47 25 49.99 / 69 05 55.88	155 08 / 315 15	T. P. 567 / T. P. 565	121.2 / 112.5
T. P. 567	47 25 53.55 / 69 05 58.31	80 13 / 261 13 / 335 08	T. P. 568 / Ref. Mon. C-162 / T. P. 566	89.5 / 110.5 / 121.2
Ref. Mon. C-162	47 25 54.10 / 69 05 53.10	4 05 20 / 81 13	Ref. Mon. S-155 / T. P. 567	558.6 / 110.5
T. P. 568	47 25 53.06 / 69 06 02.52	260 13 / 340 04	T. P. 567 / T. P. 569	89.5 / 110.3
T. P. 569	47 25 49.70 / 69 06 00.73	75 09 / 160 04	T. P. 570 / T. P. 568	78.4 / 110.3
T. P. 570	47 25 49.05 / 69 06 04.34	162 29 / 255 09	T. P. 571 / T. P. 569	93.0 / 78.4
T. P. 571	47 25 51.92 / 69 06 05.68	77 37 / 342 29	T. P. 572 / T. P. 570	155.7 / 93.0
T. P. 572	47 25 50.84 / 69 06 12.94	101 21 / 257 37	T. P. 573 / T. P. 571	96.0 / 155.7
T. P. 573	47 25 51.46 / 69 06 17.43	18 41 / 281 21	T. P. 574 / T. P. 572	71.1 / 96.0
T. P. 574	47 25 49.27 / 69 06 18.51	198 41 / 342 34	T. P. 573 / T. P. 575	71.1 / 140.1
T. P. 575	47 25 44.94 / 69 06 16.51	33 24 / 162 34	T. P. 576 / T. P. 574	153.7 / 140.1
T. P. 576	47 25 40.79 / 69 06 20.55	67 17 / 213 24	T. P. 577 / T. P. 575	158.0 / 153.7
T. P. 577	47 25 38.81 / 69 06 27.50	123 00 / 247 17	T. P. 578 / T. P. 576	67.4 / 158.0
T. P. 578	47 25 40.00 / 69 06 30.19	34 56 / 193 01 / 303 00	Ref. Mon. S-156 / T. P. 579 / T. P. 577	43.0 / 82.6 / 67.4
Ref. Mon. S-156	47 25 38.86 / 69 06 31.37	204 38 / 214 56	Ref. Mon. C-163 / T. P. 578	289.8 / 43.0
T. P. 579	47 25 42.61 / 69 06 29.31	13 01 / 180 22	T. P. 578 / T. P. 580	82.6 / 140.6

BOUNDARY TURNING POINTS AND REFERENCE MONUMENTS—ST. FRANCIS RIVER—Con.

Station	Latitude and longitude	Azimuth	To station	Distance (meters)
	° ′ ″	° ′ ″		
T. P. 580	47 25 47.16 69 06 29.26	0 22 211 54 264 44	T. P. 579 T. P. 581 Ref. Mon. C-163	140.6 131.3 76.9
Ref. Mon. C-163	47 25 47.39 69 06 25.61	24 38 84 44	Ref. Mon. S-156 T. P. 580	289.8 76.9
T. P. 581	47 25 50.77 69 06 25.95	31 54 171 42	T. P. 580 T. P. 582	131.3 79.0
T. P. 582	47 25 53.30 69 06 26.50	140 32 351 42	T. P. 583 T. P. 581	105.6 79.0
T. P. 583	47 25 55.94 69 06 29.70	164 11 320 32	T. P. 584 T. P. 582	101.2 105.6
T. P. 584	47 25 59.10 69 06 31.02	197 30 344 11	T. P. 585 T. P. 583	160.3 101.2
T. P. 585	47 26 04.05 69 06 28.72	17 30 162 48	T. P. 584 T. P. 586	160.3 118.0
T. P. 586	47 26 07.70 69 06 30.38	136 11 342 48	T. P. 587 T. P. 585	137.1 118.0
T. P. 587	47 26 10.90 69 06 34.91	99 07 316 11	T. P. 588 T. P. 586	72.0 137.1
T. P. 588	47 26 11.27 69 06 38.31	65 47 279 07	T. P. 589 T. P. 587	158.7 72.0
T. P. 589	47 26 09.16 69 06 45.21	56 45 92 19 236 45 245 47	Ref. Mon. S-157 T. P. 590 Ref. Mon. C-164 T. P. 588	41.6 51.8 243.8 158.7
Ref. Mon. S-157	47 26 08.42 69 06 46.87	236 45 236 45	T. P. 589 Ref. Mon. C-164	41.6 285.4
Ref. Mon. C-164	47 26 13.49 69 06 35.48	56 46 56 46	T. P. 589 Ref. Mon. S-157	243.8 285.4
T. P. 590	47 26 09.23 69 06 47.68	147 12 272 19	T. P. 591 T. P. 589	46.5 51.8
T. P. 591	47 26 10.49 69 06 48.89	202 52 327 12	T. P. 592 T. P. 590	164.6 46.5
T. P. 592	47 26 15.41 69 06 45.83	22 52 135 09	T. P. 591 T. P. 593	164.6 128.2
T. P. 593	47 26 18.35 69 06 50.15	98 07 315 09	T. P. 594 T. P. 592	58.8 128.2
T. P. 594	47 26 18.62 69 06 52.93	78 59 278 07	T. P. 595 T. P. 593	86.3 58.8
T. P. 595	47 26 18.08 69 06 56.97	116 01 258 59	T. P. 596 T. P. 594	236.6 86.3
T. P. 596	47 26 21.45 69 07 07.11	141 00 296 01	T. P. 597 T. P. 595	109.0 236.6
T. P. 597	47 26 24.19 69 07 10.38	162 58 321 00	T. P. 598 T. P. 596	82.3 109.0
T. P. 598	47 26 26.74 69 07 11.54	128 50 342 58	T. P. 599 T. P. 597	104.1 82.3
T. P. 599	47 26 28.85 69 07 15.41	147 36 308 50	T. P. 600 T. P. 598	111.2 104.1
T. P. 600	47 26 31.89 69 07 18.25	59 22 133 52 239 22 327 36	Ref. Mon. S-158 T. P. 601 Ref. Mon. C-165 T. P. 599	316.8 96.5 46.8 111.2
Ref. Mon. S-158	47 26 26.66 69 07 31.26	229 07 239 22 239 22	T. P. 606 T. P. 600 Ref. Mon. C-165	47.6 316.8 363.6
Ref. Mon. C-165	47 26 32.66 69 07 16.33	59 22 59 22	T. P. 600 Ref. Mon. S-158	46.8 363.6
T. P. 601	47 26 34.06 69 07 21.57	104 35 313 52	T. P. 602 T. P. 600	61.2 96.5
T. P. 602	47 26 34.56 69 07 24.40	59 43 284 35	T. P. 603 T. P. 601	50.4 61.2
T. P. 603	47 26 33.73 69 07 26.47	239 43 354 38	T. P. 602 T. P. 604	50.4 178.6
T. P. 604	47 26 27.98 69 07 25.68	43 46 174 38	T. P. 605 T. P. 603	49.4 178.6
T. P. 605	47 26 26.82 69 07 27.31	119 14 223 46	T. P. 606 T. P. 604	53.6 49.4
T. P. 606	47 26 27.67 69 07 29.54	49 07 167 18 299 14	Ref. Mon. S-158 T. P. 607 T. P. 605	47.6 134.7 53.6
T. P. 607	47 26 31.92 69 07 30.96	134 33 347 18	T. P. 608 T. P. 606	231.4 134.7
T. P. 608	47 26 37.18 69 07 38.83	112 24 314 33	T. P. 609 T. P. 607	110.2 231.4
T. P. 609	47 26 38.54 69 07 43.69	95 21 292 24	T. P. 610 T. P. 608	98.5 110.2
T. P. 610	47 26 38.84 69 07 48.37	113 48 275 21	T. P. 611 T. P. 609	97.6 98.5
T. P. 611	47 26 40.11 69 07 52.64	100 15 189 47 293 48	T. P. 612 Ref. Mon. C-166 T. P. 610	50.6 40.0 97.6
Ref. Mon. C-166	47 26 41.39 69 07 52.31	9 47 113 17 00	T. P. 611 Ref. Mon. C-167	40.0 684.4
T. P. 612	47 26 40.40 69 07 55.01	79 36 280 15	T. P. 613 T. P. 611	164.4 50.6
T. P. 613	47 26 39.44 69 08 02.73	119 08 259 36	T. P. 614 T. P. 612	99.0 164.4
T. P. 614	47 26 41.00 69 08 06.86	149 17 299 08	T. P. 615 T. P. 613	69.1 99.0
T. P. 615	47 26 42.93 69 08 08.54	128 38 329 17	T. P. 616 T. P. 614	72.1 69.1
T. P. 616	47 26 44.38 69 08 11.23	103 13 308 38	T. P. 617 T. P. 615	151.7 72.1
T. P. 617	47 26 45.51 69 08 18.28	136 56 283 13	T. P. 618 T. P. 616	73.2 151.7
T. P. 618	47 26 47.24 69 08 20.67	115 11 316 56	T. P. 619 T. P. 617	72.4 73.2
T. P. 619	47 26 48.24 69 08 23.79	56 38 207 35 295 11	T. P. 620 Ref. Mon. C-167 T. P. 618	58.9 66.7 72.4
Ref. Mon. C-167	47 26 50.15 69 08 22.32	27 35 293 16 40	T. P. 619 Ref. Mon. C-166	66.7 684.4
T. P. 620	47 26 47.19 69 08 26.14	8 33 236 38	T. P. 621 T. P. 619	121.2 58.9
T. P. 621	47 26 43.31 69 08 27.00	188 33 324 26	T. P. 620 T. P. 622	121.2 85.4
T. P. 622	47 26 41.06 69 08 24.63	25 43 144 26	T. P. 623 T. P. 621	78.8 85.4
T. P. 623	47 26 38.76 69 08 26.26	89 47 205 43	T. P. 624 T. P. 622	80.8 78.8
T. P. 624	47 26 38.75 69 08 30.12	44 02 137 02 269 47	Ref. Mon. S-159 T. P. 625 T. P. 623	17.6 83.6 80.8
Ref. Mon. S-159	47 26 38.34 69 08 30.70	150 04 00 224 02	Ref. Mon. C-168 T. P. 624	627.2 17.6
T. P. 625	47 26 40.73 69 08 32.84	165 57 317 02	T. P. 626 T. P. 624	165.2 83.6
T. P. 626	47 26 45.92 69 08 34.75	142 03 345 57	T. P. 627 T. P. 625	177.9 165.2
T. P. 627	47 26 50.46 69 08 39.97	130 55 322 03	T. P. 628 T. P. 626	59.5 177.9
T. P. 628	47 26 51.73 69 08 42.12	139 50 310 55	T. P. 629 T. P. 627	142.6 59.5
T. P. 629	47 26 55.26 69 08 46.52	124 50 221 00 319 50	T. P. 630 Ref. Mon. C-168 T. P. 628	87.4 28.0 142.6
Ref. Mon. C-168	47 26 55.94 69 08 45.64	41 00 330 03 50	T. P. 629 Ref. Mon. S-159	28.0 627.2
T. P. 630	47 26 56.87 69 08 49.94	101 23 304 50	T. P. 631 T. P. 629	49.2 87.4

BOUNDARY TURNING POINTS AND REFERENCE MONUMENTS—ST. FRANCIS RIVER—Con.

Station	Latitude and longitude	Azimuth	To station	Distance (meters)
	° ′ ″	° ′ ″		
T. P. 631	47 26 57.19 / 69 08 52.24	58 17 / 281 23	T. P. 632 / T. P. 630	58.2 / 49.2
T. P. 632	47 26 56.20 / 69 08 54.60	74 43 / 238 17	T. P. 633 / T. P. 631	64.9 / 58.2
T. P. 633	47 26 55.64 / 69 08 57.59	91 37 / 254 43 / 359 14	T. P. 634 / T. P. 632 / Ref. Mon. S-160	127.1 / 64.9 / 31.9
Ref. Mon. S-160	47 26 54.61 / 69 08 57.57	179 14 / 260 38	T. P. 633 / Ref. Mon. C-168	31.9 / 253.4
T. P. 634	47 26 55.76 / 69 09 03.65	113 04 / 271 37	T. P. 635 / T. P. 633	71.2 / 127.1
T. P. 635	47 26 56.66 / 69 09 06.78	139 10 / 293 04	T. P. 636 / T. P. 634	182.8 / 71.2
T. P. 636	47 27 01.14 / 69 09 12.48	106 58 / 319 10	T. P. 637 / T. P. 635	158.7 / 182.8
T. P. 637	47 27 02.64 / 69 09 19.73	136 16 / 286 58	T. P. 638 / T. P. 636	115.3 / 158.7
T. P. 638	47 27 05.34 / 69 09 23.53	121 20 / 208 10 / 316 16	T. P. 639 / Ref. Mon. C-169 / T. P. 637	53.3 / 28.2 / 115.3
Ref. Mon. C-169	47 27 06.14 / 69 09 22.90	28 10 / 31 37	T. P. 638 / Ref. Mon. S-161	28.2 / 442.4
T. P. 639	47 27 06.23 / 69 09 25.71	89 37 / 301 20	T. P. 640 / T. P. 638	44.0 / 53.3
T. P. 640	47 27 06.22 / 69 09 27.81	40 35 / 269 37	T. P. 641 / T. P. 639	40.4 / 44.0
T. P. 641	47 27 05.23 / 69 09 29.06	6 28 / 220 35	T. P. 642 / T. P. 640	63.9 / 40.4
T. P. 642	47 27 03.17 / 69 09 29.40	14 16 / 186 28	T. P. 643 / T. P. 641	189.5 / 63.9
T. P. 643	47 26 57.23 / 69 09 31.63	39 42 / 194 16	T. P. 644 / T. P. 642	103.5 / 189.5
T. P. 644	47 26 54.65 / 69 09 34.79	53 30 / 219 42 / 321 55	T. P. 645 / T. P. 643 / Ref. Mon. S-161	168.1 / 103.5 / 27.8
Ref. Mon. S-161	47 26 53.94 / 69 09 33.97	141 55 / 211 37	T. P. 644 / Ref. Mon. C-169	27.8 / 442.4
T. P. 645	47 26 51.41 / 69 09 41.24	72 32 / 233 30	T. P. 646 / T. P. 644	54.3 / 168.1
T. P. 646	47 26 50.88 / 69 09 43.71	96 17 / 252 32	T. P. 647 / T. P. 645	57.5 / 54.3
T. P. 647	47 26 51.09 / 69 09 46.44	126 53 / 276 17	T. P. 648 / T. P. 646	222.9 / 57.5
T. P. 648	47 26 55.42 / 69 09 54.95	154 03 / 306 53	T. P. 649 / T. P. 647	74.7 / 222.9
T. P. 649	47 26 57.59 / 69 09 56.51	204 16 / 334 03	T. P. 650 / T. P. 648	53.5 / 74.7
T. P. 650	47 26 59.17 / 69 09 55.46	24 16 / 120 45 / 263 18	T. P. 649 / Ref. Mon. S-162 / T. P. 651	53.5 / 43.8 / 95.0
Ref. Mon. S-162	47 26 59.90 / 69 09 57.26	137 03 / 300 45	Ref. Mon. S-163 / T. P. 650	368.0 / 43.8
T. P. 651	47 26 59.53 / 69 09 50.96	83 18 / 207 38	T. P. 650 / T. P. 652	95.0 / 62.5
T. P. 652	47 27 01.33 / 69 09 49.57	27 38 / 135 25	T. P. 651 / T. P. 653	62.5 / 193.5
T. P. 653	47 27 05.79 / 69 09 56.06	107 32 / 315 25	T. P. 654 / T. P. 652	193.9 / 193.5
T. P. 654	47 27 07.68 / 69 10 04.88	129 52 / 287 32	T. P. 655 / T. P. 653	92.5 / 193.9
T. P. 655	47 27 09.60 / 69 10 08.27	33 30 / 142 17 / 213 30 / 309 52	Ref. Mon. S-163 / T. P. 656 / Ref. Mon. C-170 / T. P. 654	36.4 / 101.5 / 36.4 / 92.5
Ref. Mon. S-163	47 27 08.62 / 69 10 09.23	213 30 / 213 30	T. P. 655 / Ref. Mon. C-170	36.4 / 72.8
Ref. Mon. C-170	47 27 10.58 / 69 10 07.31	33 30 / 33 30	T. P. 655 / Ref. Mon. S-163	36.4 / 72.8
T. P. 656	47 27 12.20 / 69 10 11.23	96 06 / 322 17	T. P. 657 / T. P. 655	255.8 / 101.5
T. P. 657	47 27 13.08 / 69 10 23.37	196 37 / 276 06	T. P. 658 / T. P. 656	98.3 / 255.8
T. P. 658	47 27 16.13 / 69 10 22.03	16 37 / 96 50	T. P. 657 / T. P. 659	98.3 / 74.0
T. P. 659	47 27 16.42 / 69 10 25.54	192 27 / 276 50	T. P. 660 / T. P. 658	134.5 / 74.0
T. P. 660	47 27 20.67 / 69 10 24.16	12 27 / 110 31	T. P. 659 / T. P. 661	134.5 / 37.4
T. P. 661	47 27 21.09 / 69 10 25.83	74 06 / 290 31	T. P. 662 / T. P. 660	146.8 / 37.4
T. P. 662	47 27 19.79 / 69 10 32.57	114 45 / 254 06	T. P. 663 / T. P. 661	35.3 / 146.8
T. P. 663	47 27 20.27 / 69 10 34.10	197 39 / 294 45	T. P. 664 / T. P. 662	98.6 / 35.3
T. P. 664	47 27 23.31 / 69 10 32.67	17 39 / 122 53	T. P. 663 / T. P. 665	98.6 / 76.1
T. P. 665	47 27 24.65 / 69 10 35.72	65 38 / 302 53	T. P. 666 / T. P. 664	87.5 / 76.1
T. P. 666	47 27 23.48 / 69 10 39.53	81 40 / 245 38	T. P. 667 / T. P. 665	75.2 / 87.5
T. P. 667	47 27 23.13 / 69 10 43.08	150 57 / 261 40	T. P. 668 / T. P. 666	46.6 / 75.2
T. P. 668	47 27 24.45 / 69 10 44.16	191 23 / 330 57	T. P. 669 / T. P. 667	41.5 / 46.6
T. P. 669	47 27 25.76 / 69 10 43.77	11 23 / 123 03	T. P. 668 / T. P. 670	41.5 / 64.2
T. P. 670	47 27 26.90 / 69 10 46.34	35 07 / 184 16 / 303 03	T. P. 671 / Ref. Mon. C-171 / T. P. 669	138.0 / 123.3 / 64.2
Ref. Mon. C-171	47 27 30.88 / 69 10 45.90	4 16 / 38 40	T. P. 670 / Ref. Mon. S-164	123.3 / 396.7
T. P. 671	47 27 23.24 / 69 10 50.13	63 12 / 215 07	T. P. 672 / T. P. 670	65.2 / 138.0
T. P. 672	47 27 22.29 / 69 10 52.91	83 25 / 243 12	T. P. 673 / T. P. 671	180.4 / 65.2
T. P. 673	47 27 21.62 / 69 11 01.46	136 38 / 263 25	T. P. 674 / T. P. 672	76.8 / 180.4
T. P. 674	47 27 23.43 / 69 11 03.97	89 48 / 316 38	T. P. 675 / T. P. 673	56.5 / 76.8
T. P. 675	47 27 23.42 / 69 11 06.67	25 31 / 112 57 / 269 48 / 292 57	T. P. 676 / Ref. Mon. C-172 / T. P. 674 / Ref. Mon. S-164	126.1 / 49.6 / 56.5 / 203.7
Ref. Mon. C-172	47 27 24.04 / 69 11 08.84	292 57 / 292 57	T. P. 675 / Ref. Mon. S-164	49.6 / 253.3
Ref. Mon. S-164	47 27 20.85 / 69 10 57.73	112 57 / 112 57	T. P. 675 / Ref. Mon. C-172	203.7 / 253.3
T. P. 676	47 27 19.74 / 69 11 09.26	92 56 / 205 31	T. P. 677 / T. P. 675	123.4 / 126.1
T. P. 677	47 27 19.94 / 69 11 15.14	68 16 / 272 56	T. P. 678 / T. P. 676	111.5 / 123.4
T. P. 678	47 27 18.60 / 69 11 20.09	43 28 / 248 16	T. P. 679 / T. P. 677	87.5 / 111.5
T. P. 679	47 27 16.55 / 69 11 22.96	0 00 / 223 28	T. P. 680 / T. P. 678	66.5 / 87.5
T. P. 680	47 27 14.39 / 69 11 22.96	59 06 / 180 00	T. P. 681 / T. P. 679	74.0 / 66.5
T. P. 681	47 27 13.16 / 69 11 25.99	88 17 / 239 06 / 325 05	T. P. 682 / T. P. 680 / Ref. Mon. S-165	40.2 / 74.0 / 52.4

BOUNDARY TURNING POINTS AND REFERENCE MONUMENTS—ST. FRANCIS RIVER—Con.

Station	Latitude and longitude	Azimuth	To station	Distance (meters)	Station	Latitude and longitude	Azimuth	To station	Distance (meters)
	° ′ ″	° ′ ″				° ′ ″	° ′ ″		
Ref. Mon. S-165	47 27 11.77 69 11 24.56	123 45 10 145 05	Ref. Mon. C-173 T. P. 681	517.2 52.4	T. P. 699	47 27 10.94 69 12 22.53	231 05 357 31	T. P. 700 T. P. 698	82.8 85.7
T. P. 682	47 27 13.12 69 11 27.91	153 28 268 17	T. P. 683 T. P. 681	91.3 40.2	T. P. 700	47 27 12.62 69 12 19.46	51 05 126 35	T. P. 699 T. P. 701	82.8 128.5
T. P. 683	47 27 15.77 69 11 29.86	141 26 333 28	T. P. 684 T. P. 682	84.7 91.3	T. P. 701	47 27 15.10 69 12 24.38	100 40 306 35	T. P. 702 T. P. 700	213.9 128.5
T. P. 684	47 27 17.91 69 11 32.38	119 54 321 26	T. P. 685 T. P. 683	96.9 84.7	T. P. 702	47 27 16.38 69 12 34.42	139 39 280 40	T. P. 703 T. P. 701	68.0 213.9
T. P. 685	47 27 19.48 69 11 36.39	102 19 299 54	T. P. 686 T. P. 684	118.6 96.9	T. P. 703	47 27 18.06 69 12 36.52	122 54 319 39	T. P. 704 T. P. 702	72.2 68.0
T. P. 686	47 27 20.30 69 11 41.92	87 02 282 19	T. P. 687 T. P. 685	109.9 118.6	T. P. 704	47 27 19.33 69 12 39.41	75 30 302 54	T. P. 705 T. P. 703	88.6 72.2
T. P. 687	47 27 20.11 69 11 47.17	70 45 235 29 267 02	T. P. 688 Ref. Mon. C-173 T. P. 686	160.5 52.8 109.9	T. P. 705	47 27 18.61 69 12 43.51	113 06 255 30	T. P. 706 T. P. 704	54.8 88.6
Ref. Mon. C-173	47 27 21.08 69 11 45.09	55 29 303 44 50	T. P. 687 Ref. Mon. S-165	52.8 517.2	T. P. 706	47 27 19.31 69 12 45.92	107 04 198 20 293 06	T. P. 707 Ref. Mon. C-175 T. P. 705	67.2 195.6 54.8
T. P. 688	47 27 15.40 69 11 54.40	60 39 250 45	T. P. 689 T. P. 687	226.5 160.5	Ref. Mon. C-175	47 27 25.32 69 12 42.98	18 20 75 01	T. P. 706 Ref. Mon. S-167	195.6 444.0
T. P. 689	47 27 14.80 69 12 03.82	29 37 209 50 240 39	T. P. 690 Ref. Mon. C-174 T. P. 688	137.6 70.7 226.5	T. P. 707	47 27 19.95 69 12 48.98	147 43 287 04	T. P. 708 T. P. 706	108.2 67.2
Ref. Mon. C-174	47 27 16.79 69 12 02.14	29 50 48 44 48 44	T. P. 689 T. P. 694 Ref. Mon. S-166	70.7 361.1 486.0	T. P. 708	47 27 22.91 69 12 51.74	121 42 327 43	T. P. 709 T. P. 707	52.9 108.2
T. P. 690	47 27 10.93 69 12 07.07	43 56 209 37	T. P. 691 T. P. 689	110.7 137.6	T. P. 709	47 27 23.81 69 12 53.89	91 40 301 42	T. P. 710 T. P. 708	181.7 52.9
T. P. 691	47 27 08.35 69 12 10.73	67 33 223 56	T. P. 692 T. P. 690	34.3 110.7	T. P. 710	47 27 23.98 69 13 02.55	14 19 93 13 271 40	Ref. Mon. S-167 T. P. 711 T. P. 709	75.9 87.1 181.7
T. P. 692	47 27 07.93 69 12 12.24	85 21 247 33	T. P. 693 T. P. 691	40.6 34.3	Ref. Mon. S-167	47 27 21.60 69 13 03.45	194 19 255 01	T. P. 710 Ref. Mon. C-175	75.9 444.0
T. P. 693	47 27 07.82 69 12 14.18	153 37 265 21	T. P. 694 T. P. 692	43.4 40.6	T. P. 711	47 27 24.14 69 13 06.71	132 17 273 13	T. P. 712 T. P. 710	104.5 87.1
T. P. 694	47 27 09.08 69 12 15.10	48 44 76 06 228 44 333 37	Ref. Mon. S-166 T. P. 695 Ref. Mon. C-174 T. P. 693	124.9 32.5 361.1 43.4	T. P. 712	47 27 26.42 69 13 10.40	107 48 312 17	T. P. 713 T. P. 711	106.3 104.5
Ref. Mon. S-166	47 27 06.41 69 12 19.58	228 44 228 44	T. P. 694 Ref. Mon. C-174	124.9 486.0	T. P. 713	47 27 27.47 69 13 15.23	124 24 287 48	T. P. 714 T. P. 712	187.3 106.3
T. P. 695	47 27 08.83 69 12 16.60	28 41 256 06	T. P. 696 T. P. 694	40.0 32.5	T. P. 714	47 27 30.89 69 13 22.61	150 29 304 24	T. P. 715 T. P. 713	122.6 187.3
T. P. 696	47 27 07.69 69 12 17.52	82 13 208 41	T. P. 697 T. P. 695	73.9 40.0	T. P. 715	47 27 34.35 69 13 25.49	112 53 330 29	T. P. 716 T. P. 714	111.8 122.6
T. P. 697	47 27 07.37 69 12 21.01	131 19 262 13	T. P. 698 T. P. 696	37.4 73.9	T. P. 716	47 27 35.76 69 13 30.41	34 55 214 55 292 53	Monument 178 Ref. Mon. C-176 T. P. 715	36.0 423.7 111.8
T. P. 698	47 27 08.17 69 12 22.36	177 31 311 19	T. P. 699 T. P. 697	85.7 37.4	Ref. Mon. C-176	47 27 47.01 69 13 18.83	34 55 34 55	T. P. 716 Monument 178	423.7 459.7

GEOGRAPHIC POSITIONS OF MONUMENTS MARKING THE INTERNATIONAL BOUNDARY FROM LAKE POHENAGAMOOK TO THE SOUTHWEST BRANCH OF THE ST. JOHN RIVER

Station	Latitude and longitude	Azimuth	To station	Distance (meters)
	° ′ ″	° ′ ″		
Mon. 178	47 27 34.80	214 54 43	T. P. 716	36.0
	69 13 31.39	34 54 43	Mon. 179	91.36
Mon. 179	47 27 32.37	214 54 41	Mon. 178	91.36
	69 13 33.88	34 54 41	Mon. 180	91.91
Mon. 180	47 27 29.93	214 54 39	Mon. 179	91.91
	69 13 36.40	34 54 39	Mon. 180-A	141.71
Mon. 180-A	47 27 26.17	214 54 36	Mon. 180	141.71
	69 13 40.27	34 54 36	Mon. 181	466.76
Mon. 181	47 27 13.78	214 54 27.0	Mon. 180-A	466.76
	69 13 53.02	34 54 27.0	Mon. 181-A	685.24
Mon. 181-A	47 26 55.580	214 54 13.2	Mon. 181	685.24
	69 14 11.735	34 54 13.2	Mon. 182	925.79
Mon. 182	47 26 30.994	214 53 54.6	Mon. 181-A	925.79
	69 14 37.018	34 53 54.6	Mon. 183	1,610.03
Mon. 183	47 25 48.234	214 53 22.2	Mon. 182	1,610.03
	69 15 20.971	34 53 22.2	Mon. 184	1,610.59
Mon. 184	47 25 05.454	214 52 49.9	Mon. 183	1,610.59
	69 16 04.920	34 52 49.9	Mon. 185	1,612.00
Mon. 185	47 24 22.632	214 52 17.5	Mon. 184	1,612.00
	69 16 48.887	34 52 17.5	Mon. 186	1,607.60
Mon. 186	47 23 39.922	214 51 45.3	Mon. 185	1,607.60
	69 17 32.715	34 51 45.3	Mon. 187	449.59
Mon. 187	47 23 27.977	214 51 36.3	Mon. 186	449.59
	69 17 44.969	34 51 42.3	Mon. 188	1,160.09
Mon. 188	47 22 57.153	214 51 19.0	Mon. 187	1,160.09
	69 18 16.581	34 51 19.0	Mon. 189	628.34
Mon. 189	47 22 40.457	214 51 06.4	Mon. 188	628.34
	69 18 33.699	34 51 07.5	Mon. 190	979.50
Mon. 190	47 22 14.428	214 50 47.9	Mon. 189	979.50
	69 19 00.378	34 50 47.9	Mon. 191	1,610.52
Mon. 191	47 21 31.628	214 50 15.6	Mon. 190	1,610.52
	69 19 44.228	34 50 15.6	Mon. 192	693.75
Mon. 192	47 21 13.189	214 50 01.7	Mon. 191	693.75
	69 20 03.111	34 50 01.7	Mon. 193	914.17
Mon. 193	47 20 48.891	214 49 43.4	Mon. 192	914.17
	69 20 27.988	34 49 43.4	Mon. 194	1,131.19
Mon. 194	47 20 18.823	214 49 20.8	Mon. 193	1,131.19
	69 20 58.762	34 49 20.8	Mon. 195	475.94
Mon. 195	47 20 06.171	214 49 11.3	Mon. 194	475.94
	69 21 11.707	34 49 11.3	Mon. 195-A	302.09
Mon. 195-A	47 19 58.141	214 49 05.3	Mon. 195	302.09
	69 21 19.923	34 49 05.3	Mon. 196	1,306.08
Mon. 196	47 19 23.419	214 48 39.2	Mon. 195-A	1,306.08
	69 21 55.435	34 48 39.2	Mon. 197	704.83
Mon. 197	47 19 04.680	214 48 25.1	Mon. 196	704.83
	69 22 14.594	34 48 25.1	Mon. 198	907.61
Mon. 198	47 18 40.549	214 48 07.0	Mon. 197	907.61
	69 22 39.259	34 48 07.0	Mon. 198-A	489.21
Mon. 198-A	47 18 27.541	214 47 57.2	Mon. 198	489.21
	69 22 52.551	34 47 57.2	Mon. 199	1,097.06
Mon. 199	47 17 58.369	214 47 35.3	Mon. 198-A	1,097.06
	69 23 22.352	34 47 35.3	Mon. 200	350.80
Mon. 200	47 17 49.040	214 47 28.3	Mon. 199	350.80
	69 23 31.880	34 47 28.3	Mon. 201	1,282.10
Mon. 201	47 17 14.944	214 47 02.7	Mon. 200	1,282.10
	69 24 06.693	34 47 02.7	Mon. 202	1,608.54
Mon. 202	47 16 32.163	214 46 30.6	Mon. 201	1,608.54
	69 24 50.352	34 46 30.6	Mon. 202-A	1,082.06
Mon. 202-A	47 16 03.382	214 46 09.0	Mon. 202	1,082.06
	69 25 19.710	34 46 09.0	Mon. 203	519.86
Mon. 203	47 15 49.553	214 45 58.6	Mon. 202-A	519.86
	69 25 33.812	34 45 58.6	Mon. 204	1,610.87
Mon. 204	47 15 06.700	214 45 26.5	Mon. 203	1,610.87
	69 26 17.495	34 45 26.5	Mon. 205	995.45
Mon. 205	47 14 40.217	214 45 06.7	Mon. 204	995.45
	69 26 44.480	34 44 58.9	Mon. 206	616.91
Mon. 206	47 14 23.803	214 44 46.6	Mon. 205	616.91
	69 27 01.198	34 44 46.6	Mon. 207	1,608.16
Mon. 207	47 13 41.012	214 44 14.6	Mon. 206	1,608.16
	69 27 44.767	34 44 14.6	Mon. 208	1,609.16
Mon. 208	47 12 58.189	214 43 42.6	Mon. 207	1,609.16
	69 28 28.343	34 43 42.6	Mon. 209	1,611.50
Mon. 209	47 12 15.301	214 43 10.6	Mon. 208	1,611.50
	69 29 11.963	34 43 10.6	Mon. 210	570.85
Mon. 210	47 12 00.106	214 42 59.3	Mon. 209	570.85
	69 29 27.410	34 42 56.5	Mon. 211	1,039.20
Mon. 211	47 11 32.445	214 42 35.9	Mon. 210	1,039.20
	69 29 55.523	34 42 35.9	Mon. 212	1,609.70
Mon. 212	47 10 49.594	214 42 04.0	Mon. 211	1,609.70
	69 30 39.054	34 42 04.0	Mon. 213	1,603.33
Mon. 213	47 10 06.907	214 41 32.2	Mon. 212	1,603.33
	69 31 22.394	34 41 32.2	Mon. 214	100.25
Mon. 214	47 10 04.238	214 41 30.2	Mon. 213	100.25
	69 31 25.103	34 41 30.2	Mon. 215	843.07
Mon. 215	47 09 41.791	214 41 13.5	Mon. 214	843.07
	69 31 47.884	34 41 13.5	Mon. 216-217	959.30
Mon. 216-217	47 09 16.247	214 40 54.5	Mon. 215	959.30
	69 32 13.799	34 40 54.5	Mon. 218	1,314.60
Mon. 218	47 08 41.240	214 40 29.5	Mon. 216-217	1,314.60
	69 32 49.301	34 40 29.5	Mon. 219	1,612.97
Mon. 219	47 07 58.283	214 39 57.6	Mon. 218	1,612.97
	69 33 32.843	34 39 56.5	Mon. 220	1,613.77
Mon. 220	47 07 15.300	214 39 24.6	Mon. 219	1,613.77
	69 34 16.387	34 39 24.6	Mon. 221	656.10
Mon. 221	47 06 57.823	214 39 11.6	Mon. 220	656.10
	69 34 34.085	34 39 30.6	Mon. 222	954.16
Mon. 222	47 06 32.407	214 39 11.7	Mon. 221	954.16
	69 34 59.821	34 39 11.7	Mon. 223	1,611.82
Mon. 223	47 05 49.469	214 38 39.9	Mon. 222	1,611.82
	69 35 43.279	34 38 39.9	Mon. 224	501.67
Mon. 224	47 05 36.104	214 38 30.0	Mon. 223	501.67
	69 35 56.801	34 38 29.4	Mon. 225	1,124.29
Mon. 225	47 05 06.150	214 38 07.2	Mon. 224	1,124.29
	69 36 27.099	34 38 07.2	Mon. 226	1,597.58
Mon. 226	47 04 23.582	214 37 35.7	Mon. 225	1,597.58
	69 37 10.134	34 37 35.7	Mon. 227	1,634.88
Mon. 227	47 03 40.016	214 37 03.5	Mon. 226	1,634.88
	69 37 54.155	34 37 03.5	Mon. 228	1,591.28
Mon. 228	47 02 57.607	214 36 32.2	Mon. 227	1,591.28
	69 38 36.983	34 36 32.2	Mon. 229	681.41
Mon. 229	47 02 39.445	214 36 18.8	Mon. 228	681.41
	69 38 55.317	34 36 18.8	Mon. 230	933.22
Mon. 230	47 02 14.570	214 36 00.4	Mon. 229	933.22
	69 39 20.420	34 36 00.4	Mon. 231	1,615.37
Mon. 231	47 01 31.510	214 35 28.6	Mon. 230	1,615.37
	69 40 03.857	34 35 28.6	Mon. 232	245.97

BOUNDARY MONUMENTS—LAKE POHENAGAMOOK TO SOUTHWEST BRANCH OF ST. JOHN RIVER—Continued

Station	Latitude and longitude	Azimuth	To station	Distance (meters)	Station	Latitude and longitude	Azimuth	To station	Distance (meters)
	° ′ ″	° ′ ″				° ′ ″	° ′ ″		
Mon. 232	47 01 24.954 / 69 40 10.470	214 35 23.7 / 34 34 54.9	Mon. 231 / Mon. 233	245.97 / 1,392.75	Mon. 257	46 50 02.416 / 69 51 35.543	214 27 22.8 / 34 27 22.8	Mon. 256–A / Mon. 258	779.49 / 634.07
Mon. 233	47 00 47.820 / 69 40 47.895	214 34 27.5 / 34 34 27.5	Mon. 232 / Mon. 234	1,392.75 / 388.31	Mon. 258	46 49 45.485 / 69 51 52.469	214 27 10.4 / 34 27 10.4	Mon. 257 / Mon. 259	634.07 / 1,044.19
Mon. 234	47 00 37.466 / 69 40 58.327	214 34 19.9 / 34 34 19.9	Mon. 233 / Mon. 235	388.31 / 570.96	Mon. 259	46 49 17.601 / 69 52 20.337	214 26 50.1 / 34 26 50.1	Mon. 258 / Mon. 260	1,044.19 / 1,378.29
Mon. 235	47 00 22.241 / 69 41 13.664	214 34 08.7 / 34 34 08.7	Mon. 234 / Mon. 236	570.96 / 635.13	Mon. 260	46 48 40.792 / 69.52 57.109	214 26 23.3 / 34 26 23.3	Mon. 259 / Mon. 261	1,378.29 / 523.82
Mon. 236	47 00 05.305 / 69 41 30.722	214 33 56.2 / 34 33 56.2	Mon. 235 / Mon. 237	635.13 / 1,616.84	Mon. 261	46 48 26.802 / 69 53 11.081	214 26 13.1 / 34 26 13.1	Mon. 260 / Mon. 262	523.82 / 41.41
Mon. 237	46 59 22.187 / 69 42 14.132	214 33 24.5 / 34 33 24.5	Mon. 236 / Mon. 238	1,616.84 / 608.47	Mon. 262	46 48 25.696 / 69 53 12.185	214 26 12.3 / 34 26 12.3	Mon. 261 / Mon. 263	41.41 / 1,229.79
Mon. 238	46 59 05.959 / 69 42 30.464	214 33 12.6 / 34 33 12.6	Mon. 237 / Mon. 239	608.47 / 70.65	Mon. 263	46 47 52.848 / 69 53 44.978	214 25 48.4 / 34 25 48.4	Mon. 262 / Mon. 264	1,229.79 / 592.06
Mon. 239	46 59 04.075 / 69 42 32.360	214 33 11.2 / 34 33 11.2	Mon. 238 / Mon. 240	70.65 / 933.82	Mon. 264	46 47 37.033 / 69 54 00.762	214 25 36.9 / 34 24 36.5	Mon. 263 / Mon. 265	592.06 / 1,022.83
Mon. 240	46 58 39.169 / 69 42 57.418	214 32 52.9 / 34 32 52.9	Mon. 239 / Mon. 241	933.82 / 1,614.18	Mon. 265	46 47 09.705 / 69 54 28.012	214 24 16.6 / 34 24 16.6	Mon. 264 / Mon. 266	1,022.83 / 1,615.08
Mon. 241	46 57 56.113 / 69 43 40.718	214 32 21.2 / 34 32 21.2	Mon. 240 / Mon. 242	1,614.18 / 1,613.65	Mon. 266	46 46 26.550 / 69 55 11.025	214 23 45.3 / 34 23 45.3	Mon. 265 / Mon. 267	1,615.08 / 1,612.98
Mon. 242	46 57 13.066 / 69 44 23.984	214 31 49.5 / 34 31 49.5	Mon. 241 / Mon. 242–A	1,613.65 / 1,488.51	Mon. 267	46 45 43.446 / 69 55 53.963	214 23 14.0 / 34 23 14.0	Mon. 266 / Mon. 268	1,612.98 / 1,615.02
Mon. 242–A	46 56 33.354 / 69 45 03.878	214 31 20.4 / 34 31 20.4	Mon. 242 / Mon. 243	1,488.51 / 126.53	Mon. 268	46 45 00.283 / 69 56 36.936	214 22 42.7 / 34 22 42.7	Mon. 267 / Mon. 269	1,615.02 / 700.28
Mon. 243	46 56 29.978 / 69 45 07.268	214 31 17.9 / 34 31 17.9	Mon. 242–A / Mon. 243–A	126.53 / 946.84	Mon. 269	46 44 41.566 / 69 56 55.564	214 22 29.2 / 34 22 40.6	Mon. 268 / Mon. 270	700.28 / 912.87
Mon. 243–A	46 56 04.715 / 69 45 32.635	214 30 59.4 / 34 30 59.4	Mon. 243 / Mon. 244	946.84 / 667.95	Mon. 270	46 44 17.166 / 69 57 19.843	214 22 22.9 / 34 22 22.9	Mon. 269 / Mon. 271	912.87 / 1,620.18
Mon. 244	46 55 46.892 / 69 45 50.526	214 30 46.3 / 34 30 46.3	Mon. 243–A / Mon. 245	667.95 / 1,014.54	Mon 271	46 43 33.858 / 69 58 02.919	214 21 51.5 / 34 21 51.5	Mon. 270 / Mon. 272	1,620.18 / 1,609.81
Mon. 245	46 55 19.820 / 69 46 17.694	214 30 26.4 / 34 30 32.6	Mon. 244 / Mon. 246	1,014.54 / 599.24	Mon. 272	46 42 50.822 / 69 58 45.700	214 21 20.4 / 34 21 20.4	Mon. 271 / Mon. 273	1,609.81 / 1,615.90
Mon. 246	46 55 03.829 / 69 46 33.738	214 30 20.9 / 34 30 20.9	Mon. 245 / Mon. 247	599.24 / 1,613.30	Mon. 273	46 42 07.619 / 69 59 28.624	214 20 49.2 / 34 20 09.6	Mon. 272 / Mon. 274	1,615.90 / 507.86
Mon. 247	46 54 20.774 / 69 47 16.920	214 29 49.4 / 34 29 49.4	Mon. 246 / Mon. 247–A	1,613.30 / 369.42	Mon. 274	46 41 54.038 / 69 59 42.107	214 19 59.8 / 34 19 59.8	Mon. 273 / Mon. 275	507.86 / 183.49
Mon. 247–A	46 54 10.914 / 69 47 26.805	214 29 42.2 / 34 29 42.2	Mon. 247 / Mon. 248	369.42 / 399.66	Mon. 275	46 41 49.131 / 69 59 46.978	214 19 56.2 / 34 19 56.2	Mon. 274 / Mon. 276	183.49 / 180.46
Mon. 248	46 54 00.248 / 69 47 37.498	214 29 34.4 / 34 29 34.4	Mon. 247–A / Mon. 249	399.66 / 351.88	Mon. 276	46 41 44.305 / 69 59 51.768	214 19 52.7 / 34 19 52.7	Mon. 275 / Mon. 276–A	180.46 / 3.00
Mon. 249	46 53 50.856 / 69 47 46.912	214 29 27.5 / 34 29 27.5	Mon. 248 / Mon. 250	351.88 / 490.93	Mon. 276–A	46 41 44.225 / 69 59 51.848	214 19 52.6 / 8 23 13.2	Mon. 276 / Mon. 277	3.00 / 713.94
Mon. 250	46 53 37.752 / 69 48 00.044	214 29 17.9 / 34 29 17.9	Mon. 249 / Mon. 250–A	490.93 / 551.67	Mon. 277	46 41 21.351 / 69 59 56.749	188 23 09.6 / 8 23 09.6	Mon. 276–A / Mon. 278	713.94 / 91.80
Mon. 250–A	46 53 23.027 / 69 48 14.799	214 29 07.1 / 34 29 07.1	Mon. 250 / Mon. 251	551.67 / 81.22	Mon. 278	46 41 18.410 / 69 59 57.379	188 23 09.2 / 8 23 09.2	Mon. 277 / Mon. 279	91.80 / 91.93
Mon. 251	46 53 20.859 / 69 48 16.972	214 29 05.5 / 34 29 02.4	Mon. 250–A / Mon. 251–A	81.22 / 38.29	Mon. 279	46 41 15.464 / 69 59 58.010	188 23 08.7 / 8 23 08.7	Mon. 278 / Mon. 280	91.93 / 183.20
Mon. 251–A	46 53 19.837 / 69 48 17.996	214 29 01.6 / 34 29 01.6	Mon. 251 / Mon. 252	38.29 / 943.05	Mon. 280	46 41 09.595 / 69 59 59.267	188 23 08.0 / 8 23 08.0	Mon. 279 / Mon. 281	183.20 / 1,337.91
Mon. 252	46 52 54.663 / 69 48 43.212	214 28 43.2 / 34 28 43.2	Mon. 251–A / Mon. 253	943.05 / 1,615.53	Mon. 281	46 40 26.731 / 70 00 08.446	188 23 01.3 / 8 23 01.3	Mon. 280 / Mon. 281–A	1,337.91 / 147.86
Mon. 253	46 52 11.534 / 69 49 26.395	214 28 11.7 / 34 28 11.7	Mon. 252 / Mon. 254	1,615.53 / 1,614.02	Mon. 281–A	46 40 21.994 / 70 00 09.461	188 23 00.6 / 8 22 54.8	Mon. 281 / Mon. 282	147.86 / 1,465.08
Mon. 254	46 51 28.441 / 69 50 09.518	214 27 40.2 / 34 27 40.2	Mon. 253 / Mon. 255	1,614.02 / 1,028.74	Mon. 282	46 39 35.055 / 70 00 19.506	188 22 47.5 / 8 22 36.2	Mon. 281–A / Mon. 283	1,465.08 / 1,612.97
Mon. 255	46 51 00.972 / 69 50 36.994	214 27 20.2 / 34 27 20.2	Mon. 254 / Mon. 256	1,028.74 / 586.15	Mon. 283	46 38 43.377 / 70 00 30.555	188 22 28.2 / 8 22 28.2	Mon. 282 / Mon. 283–A	1,612.97 / 186.45
Mon. 256	46 50 45.320 / 69 50 52.646	214 27 08.8 / 34 27 08.8	Mon. 255 / Mon. 256–A	586.15 / 827.24	Mon. 283–A	46 38 37.402 / 70 00 31.831	188 22 27.2 / 8 22 29.7	Mon. 283 / Mon. 284	186.45 / 1,425.82
Mon. 256–A	46 50 23.230 / 69 51 14.731	214 26 52.7 / 34 27 38.0	Mon. 256 / Mon. 257	827.24 / 779.49	Mon. 284	46 37 51.719 / 70 00 41.594	188 22 22.6 / 8 22 22.6	Mon. 283–A / Mon. 285	1,425.82 / 940.93

BOUNDARY MONUMENTS—LAKE POHENAGAMOOK TO SOUTHWEST BRANCH OF ST. JOHN RIVER—Continued

Station	Latitude and longitude	Azimuth	To station	Distance (meters)	Station	Latitude and longitude	Azimuth	To station	Distance (meters)
	° ′ ″	° ′ ″				° ′ ″	° ′ ″		
Mon. 285	46 37 21.572 / 70 00 48.034	188 22 17.9 / 8 22 17.9	Mon. 284 / Mon. 286	940.93 / 52.37	Mon. 297	46 30 56.932 / 70 02 09.998	188 20 58.3 / 8 20 58.3	Mon. 296 / Mon. 297-A	1,653.05 / 1,062.42
Mon. 286	46 37 19.894 / 70 00 48.392	188 22 17.6 / 8 22 17.6	Mon. 285 / Mon. 287	52.37 / 620.52	Mon. 297-A	46 30 22.890 / 70 02 17.233	188 20 53.1 / 8 21 22.3	Mon. 297 / Mon. 298	1,062.42 / 510.44
Mon. 287	46 37 00.013 / 70 00 52.638	188 22 14.5 / 8 22 14.5	Mon. 286 / Mon. 287-A	620.52 / 311.94	Mon. 298	46 30 06.535 / 70 02 20.712	188 21 19.8 / 8 21 19.8	Mon. 297-A / Mon. 299	510.44 / 1,611.56
Mon. 287-A	46 36 50.018 / 70 00 54.772	188 22 13.1 / 8 22 07.8	Mon. 287 / Mon. 288	311.94 / 1,300.78	Mon. 299	46 29 14.897 / 70 02 31.692	188 21 11.8 / 8 21 11.8	Mon. 298 / Mon. 300	1,611.56 / 1,611.83
Mon. 288	46 36 08.341 / 70 01 03.667	188 22 01.3 / 8 22 01.3	Mon. 287-A / Mon. 289	1,300.78 / 806.56	Mon. 300	46 28 23.251 / 70 02 42.668	188 21 03.8 / 8 21 03.8	Mon. 299 / Mon. 301	1,611.83 / 1,612.60
Mon. 289	46 35 42.498 / 70 01 09.181	188 21 57.3 / 8 21 57.3	Mon. 288 / Mon. 290	806.56 / 342.71	Mon. 301	46 27 31.579 / 70 02 53.643	188 20 55.9 / 8 20 55.9	Mon. 300 / Mon. 301-A	1,612.60 / 426.68
Mon. 290	46 35 31.517 / 70 01 11.523	188 21 55.6 / 8 21 55.6	Mon. 289 / Mon. 291	342.71 / 80.94	Mon. 301-A	46 27 17.907 / 70 02 56.546	188 20 53.8 / 8 20 37.6	Mon. 301 / Mon. 302	426.68 / 1,185.39
Mon. 291	46 35 28.924 / 70 01 12.079	188 21 55.2 / 8 21 55.2	Mon. 290 / Mon. 292	80.94 / 382.98	Mon. 302	46 26 39.923 / 70 03 04.605	188 20 31.8 / 8 20 31.8	Mon. 301-A / Mon. 303	1,185.39 / 1,612.07
Mon. 292	46 35 16.653 / 70 01 14.696	188 21 53.3 / 8 21 53.3	Mon. 291 / Mon. 293	382.98 / 1,612.65	Mon. 303	46 25 48.267 / 70 03 15.559	188 20 23.8 / 8 20 36.7	Mon. 302 / Mon. 304	1,612.07 / 524.57
Mon. 293	46 34 24.983 / 70 01 25.713	188 21 45.3 / 8 21 45.3	Mon. 292 / Mon. 293-A	1,612.65 / 890.14	Mon. 304	46 25 31.458 / 70 03 19.124	188 20 34.1 / 8 20 34.1	Mon. 303 / Mon. 305	524.57 / 120.89
Mon. 293-A	46 33 56.462 / 70 01 31.789	188 21 40.9 / 8 21 38.7	Mon. 293 / Mon. 294	890.14 / 723.51	Mon. 305	46 25 27.584 / 70 03 19.946	188 20 33.5 / 8 20 33.5	Mon. 304 / Mon. 306	120.89 / 99.10
Mon. 294	46 33 33.280 / 70 01 36.728	188 21 35.1 / 8 21 35.1	Mon. 293-A / Mon. 294-A	723.51 / 1,189.39	Mon. 306	46 25 24.408 / 70 03 20.619	188 20 33.0 / 8 20 33.0	Mon. 305 / Mon. 307	99.10 / 361.30
Mon. 294-A	46 32 55.171 / 70 01 44.845	188 21 29.2 / 8 21 16.6	Mon. 294 / Mon. 295	1,189.39 / 423.76	Mon. 307	46 25 12.831 / 70 03 23.074	188 20 31.2 / 8 20 31.2	Mon. 306 / Mon. 308	361.30 / 322.76
Mon. 295	46 32 41.593 / 70 01 47.735	188 21 14.5 / 8 21 14.5	Mon. 294-A / Mon. 296	423.76 / 1,613.33	Mon. 308	46 25 02.489 / 70 03 25.267	188 20 29.6 / 8 20 29.6	Mon. 307 / T. P. 1	322.76 / 79.8
Mon. 296	46 31 49.899 / 70 01 58.734	188 21 06.5 / 8 21 06.5	Mon. 295 / Mon. 297	1,613.33 / 1,653.05					

GEOGRAPHIC POSITIONS OF BOUNDARY TURNING POINTS AND REFERENCE MONUMENTS DEFINING THE INTERNATIONAL BOUNDARY THROUGH THE SOUTHWEST BRANCH OF THE ST. JOHN RIVER

Station	Latitude and longitude	Azimuth	To station	Distance (meters)
T. P. 1	46 24 59.93 70 03 25.81	188 20 340 26 8 20	Mon. 308 T. P. 2 Ref. Mon. 309	79.8 51.6 42.4
Ref. Mon. 309	46 24 58.58 70 03 26.10	188 20 188 20	Mon. 308 T. P. 1	122.2 42.4
T. P. 2	46 24 58.36 70 03 25.00	160 26 12 23	T. P. 1 T. P. 3	51.6 60.7
T. P. 3	46 24 56.44 70 03 25.61	192 23 35 45	T. P. 2 T. P. 4	60.7 96.4
T. P. 4	46 24 53.90 70 03 28.25	215 45 78 01	T. P. 3 T. P. 5	96.4 179.9
T. P. 5	46 24 52.69 70 03 36.49	258 01 64 39	T P. 4 T. P. 6	179.9 198.2
T. P. 6	46 24 49.94 70 03 44.87	244 39 102 20	T. P. 5 T. P. 7	198.2 185.1
T. P. 7	46 24 51.22 70 03 53.34	282 20 63 53	T. P. 6 T. P. 8	185.1 68.7
T. P. 8	46 24 50.24 70 03 56.23	243 53 26 16	T. P. 7 T. P. 9	68.7 154.2
T. P. 9	46 24 45.77 70 03 59.43	206 16 51 29	T. P. 8 T. P. 10	154.2 101.0
T. P. 10	46 24 43.73 70 04 03.13	231 29 65 30 28 18 131 35	T. P. 9 T. P. 11 Ref. Mon. S-8 Ref. Mon. C-8	101.0 105.2 55.8 87.7
Ref. Mon. S-8	46 24 42.14 70 04 04.36	159 58 208 18	Ref. Mon. C-8 T. P. 10	114.2 55.8
Ref. Mon. C-8	46 24 45.62 70 04 06.20	311 35 339 58	T. P. 10 Ref. Mon. S-8	87.7 114.2
T. P. 11	46 24 42.32 70 04 07.61	245 30 79 39	T. P. 10 T. P. 12	105.2 301.5
T. P. 12	46 24 40.56 70 04 21.49	259 39 56 36	T. P. 11 T. P. 13	301.5 178.4
T. P. 13	46 24 37.38 70 04 28.46	236 36 66 30	T. P. 12 T. P. 14	178.4 208.3
T. P. 14	46 24 34.69 70 04 37.41	246 30 94 37 13 21 193 05	T. P. 13 T. P. 15 Ref. Mon. 311 Ref. Mon. 310	208.3 71.7 17.8 26.5
Ref. Mon. 310	46 24 35.53 70 04 37.13	13 05 13 12	T. P. 14 Ref. Mon. 311	26.5 44.3
Ref. Mon. 311	46 24 34.13 70 04 37.60	193 12 193 21	Ref. Mon. 310 T. P. 14	44.3 17.8
T. P. 15	46 24 34.88 70 04 40.76	274 37 109 52	T. P. 14 T. P. 16	71.7 53.8
T. P. 16	46 24 35.47 70 04 43.12	289 52 151 21	T. P. 15 T. P. 17	53.8 73.3
T. P. 17	46 24 37.55 70 04 44.77	331 21 121 19	T. P. 16 T. P. 18	73.3 41.0
T. P. 18	46 24 38.24 70 04 46.41	301 19 104 28	T. P. 17 T. P. 19	41.0 39.7
T. P. 19	46 24 38.56 70 04 48.21	284 28 92 23	T. P. 18 T. P. 20	39.7 138.4
T. P. 20	46 24 38.75 70 04 54.68	272 23 81 13	T. P. 19 T. P. 21	138.4 191.0
T. P. 21	46 24 37.81 70 05 03.52	261 13 63 27	T. P. 20 T. P. 22	191.0 154.4
T. P. 22	46 24 35.57 70 05 09.99	243 27 48 47	T. P. 21 T. P. 23	154.4 98.6
T. P. 23	46 24 33.47 70 05 13.46	228 47 97 06	T. P. 22 T. P. 24	98.6 43.8
T. P. 24	46 24 33.64 70 05 15.49	277 06 126 18	T. P. 23 T. P. 25	43.8 47.0
T. P. 25	46 24 34.55 70 05 17.27	306 18 161 58	T. P. 24 T. P. 26	47.0 81.2
T. P. 26	46 24 37.04 70 05 18.45	341 58 148 38	T. P. 25 T. P. 27	81.2 40.3
T. P. 27	46 24 38.16 70 05 19.43	328 38 129 31	T. P. 26 T. P. 28	40.3 52.8
T. P. 28	46 24 39.25 70 05 21.34	309 31 110 44	T. P. 27 T. P. 29	52.8 38.5
T. P. 29	46 24 39.69 70 05 23.02	290 44 74 09	T. P. 28 T. P. 30	38.5 56.4
T. P. 30	46 24 39.19 70 05 25.56	254 09 63 55	T. P. 29 T. P. 31	56.4 43.1
T. P. 31	46 24 38.58 70 05 27.38	243 55 51 17	T. P. 30 T. P. 32	43.1 85.2
T. P. 32	46 24 36.85 70 05 30.49	231 17 39 56	T. P. 31 T. P. 33	85.2 99.4
T. P. 33	46 24 34.38 70 05 33.48	219 56 89 37	T. P. 32 T. P. 34	99.4 70.5
T. P. 34	46 24 34.37 70 05 36.78	269 37 100 59 248 16 10	T. P. 33 T. P. 35 Ref. Mon. C-13	70.5 32.9 527.9
Ref. Mon. C-13	46 24 40.70 70 05 13.82	66 11 40 68 16 30	Ref. Mon. S-14 T. P. 34	530.2 527.9
T. P. 35	46 24 34.57 70 05 38.29	280 59 106 04	T. P. 34 T. P. 36	32.9 78.1
T. P. 36	46 24 35.27 70 05 41.80	286 04 109 39	T. P. 35 T. P. 37	78.1 65.4
T. P. 37	46 24 35.98 70 05 44.69	289 39 77 22	T. P. 36 T. P. 38	65.4 37.5
T. P. 38	46 24 35.72 70 05 46.40	257 22 64 06	T. P. 37 T. P. 39	37.5 41.5
T. P. 39	46 24 35.13 70 05 48.15	244 06 90 26	T. P. 38 T. P. 40	41.5 29.9
T. P. 40	46 24 35.14 70 05 49.55	270 26 59 52	T. P. 39 T. P. 41	29.9 40.8
T. P. 41	46 24 34.48 70 05 51.20	239 52 9 07 74 50 274 00	T. P. 40 T. P. 42 Ref. Mon. C-16 Ref. Mon. S-14	40.8 25.9 20.6 314.2
Ref. Mon. C-16	46 24 34.30 70 05 52.13	254 50 272 50	T. P. 41 Ref. Mon. S-14	20.6 333.7
Ref. Mon. S-14	46 24 33.77 70 05 36.53	92 50 94 00	Ref. Mon. C-16 T. P. 41	333.7 314.2
T. P. 42	46 24 33.65 70 05 51.39	189 07 318 24	T. P. 41 T. P. 43	25.9 71.3
T. P. 43	46 24 31.92 70 05 49.17	138 24 289 02	T. P. 42 T. P. 44	71.3 82.1
T. P. 44	46 24 31.05 70 05 45.54	109 02 276 00	T. P. 43 T. P. 45	82.1 51.6
T. P. 45	46 24 30.88 70 05 43.14	96 00 324 45	T. P. 44 T. P. 46	51.6 24.7
T. P. 46	46 24 30.22 70 05 42.47	144 45 5 21	T. P. 45 T. P. 47	24.7 35.0
T. P. 47	46 24 29.10 70 05 42.63	185 21 40 43	T. P. 46 T. P. 48	35.0 34.3

BOUNDARY TURNING POINTS AND REFERENCE MONUMENTS—SOUTHWEST BRANCH OF ST. JOHN RIVER—Continued

Station	Latitude and longitude	Azimuth	To station	Distance (meters)	Station	Latitude and longitude	Azimuth	To station	Distance (meters)
	° ′ ″	° ′ ″				° ′ ″	° ′ ″		
T. P. 48	46 24 28.25 / 70 05 43.67	220 43 / 67 18	T. P. 47 / T. P. 49	34.3 / 145.5	T. P. 80	46 24 09.49 / 70 06 01.53	246 16 / 35 46	T. P. 79 / T. P. 81	47.7 / 40.2
T. P. 49	46 24 26.44 / 70 05 49.96	247 18 / 33 50	T. P. 48 / T. P. 50	145.5 / 33.0	T. P. 81	46 24 08.43 / 70 06 02.64	215 46 / 313 53	T. P. 80 / T. P. 82	40.2 / 93.6
T. P. 50	46 24 25.55 / 70 05 50.82	213 50 / 346 18	T. P. 49 / T. P. 51	33.0 / 24.7	T. P. 82	46 24 06.33 / 70 05 59.48	133 53 / 331 20	T. P. 81 / T. P. 83	93.6 / 74.6
T. P. 51	46 24 24.77 / 70 05 50.55	166 18 / 288 24	T. P. 50 / T. P. 52	24.7 / 31.8	T. P. 83	46 24 04.21 / 70 05 57.80	151 20 / 26 50	T. P. 82 / T. P. 84	74.6 / 32.2
T. P. 52	46 24 24.44 / 70 05 49.13	108 24 / 244 04	T. P. 51 / T. P. 53	31.8 / 71.6	T. P. 84	46 24 03.28 / 70 05 58.48	206 50 / 116 06	T. P. 83 / T. P. 85	32.2 / 144.0
T. P. 53	46 24 25.46 / 70 05 46.12	64 04 / 299 16	T. P. 52 / T. P. 54	71.6 / 29.4	T. P. 85	46 24 05.33 / 70 06 04.54	296 06 / 59 12	T. P. 84 / T. P. 86	144.0 / 25.6
T. P. 54	46 24 24.99 / 70 05 44.92	119 16 / 337 38	T. P. 53 / T. P. 55	29.4 / 19.5	T. P. 86	46 24 04.90 / 70 06 05.57	239 12 / 355 04	T. P. 85 / T. P. 87	25.6 / 253.7
T. P. 55	46 24 24.41 / 70 05 44.57	157 38 / 10 35	T. P. 54 / T. P. 56	19.5 / 30.0	T. P. 87	46 23 56.72 / 70 06 04.55	175 04 / 8 26 / 123 14 / 284 40	T. P. 86 / T. P. 88 / Ref. Mon. C-18 / Ref. Mon. S-16	253.7 / 51.7 / 108.6 / 182.2
T. P. 56	46 24 23.46 / 70 05 44.83	190 35 / 36 00	T. P. 55 / T. P. 57	30.0 / 58.2					
T. P. 57	46 24 21.93 / 70 05 46.43	216 00 / 53 07	T. P. 56 / T. P. 58	58.2 / 126.2	Ref. Mon. C-18	46 23 58.65 / 70 06 08.80	291 35 / 303 14	Ref. Mon. S-16 / T. P. 87	287.2 / 108.6
T. P. 58	46 24 19.48 / 70 05 51.16	233 07 / 92 19	T. P. 57 / T. P. 59	126.2 / 281.7	Ref. Mon. S-16	46 23 55.22 / 70 05 56.30	104 40 / 111 35	T. P. 87 / Ref. Mon. C-18	182.2 / 287.2
T. P. 59	46 24 19.84 / 70 06 04.33	272 19 / 56 31	T. P. 58 / T. P. 60	281.7 / 31.5	T. P. 88	46 23 55.06 / 70 06 04.90	188 26 / 23 20	T. P. 87 / T. P. 89	51.7 / 175.9
T. P. 60	46 24 19.28 / 70 06 05.56	236 31 / 8 47	T. P. 59 / T. P. 61	31.5 / 30.7	T. P. 89	46 23 49.83 / 70 06 08.16	203 20 / 31 48	T. P. 88 / T. P. 90	175.9 / 190.2
T. P. 61	46 24 18.30 / 70 06 05.78	188 47 / 333 10	T. P. 60 / T. P. 62	30.7 / 33.2	T. P. 90	46 23 44.60 / 70 06 12.85	211 48 / 46 33	T. P. 89 / T. P. 91	190.2 / 125.0
T. P. 62	46 24 17.34 / 70 06 05.08	153 10 / 305 52	T. P. 61 / T. P. 63	33.2 / 73.7	T. P. 91	46 23 41.81 / 70 06 17.10	226 33 / 11 16	T. P. 90 / T. P. 92	125.0 / 97.0
T. P. 63	46 24 15.94 / 70 06 02.28	125 52 / 273 19	T. P. 62 / T. P. 64	73.7 / 37.6	T. P. 92	46 23 38.73 / 70 06 17.99	191 16 / 30 31	T. P. 91 / T. P. 93	97.0 / 35.0
T. P. 64	46 24 15.87 / 70 06 00.53	93 19 / 249 12	T. P. 63 / T. P. 65	37.6 / 66.1	T. P. 93	46 23 37.75 / 70 06 18.82	210 31 / 47 45	T. P. 92 / T. P. 94	35.0 / 43.8
T. P. 65	46 24 16.63 / 70 05 57.63	69 12 / 256 52	T. P. 64 / T. P. 66	66.1 / 39.5	T. P. 94	46 23 36.80 / 70 06 20.34	227 45 / 89 24	T. P. 93 / T. P. 95	43.8 / 70.6
T. P. 66	46 24 16.92 / 70 05 55.83	76 52 / 299 17	T. P. 65 / T. P. 67	39.5 / 26.0	T. P. 95	46 23 36.78 / 70 06 23.65	269 24 / 64 10	T. P. 94 / T. P. 96	70.6 / 51.2
T. P. 67	46 24 16.51 / 70 05 54.77	119 17 / 335 09	T. P. 66 / T. P. 68	26.0 / 29.8	T. P. 96	46 23 36.05 / 70 06 25.80	244 10 / 53 34	T. P. 95 / T. P. 97	51.2 / 62.5
T. P. 68	46 24 15.63 / 70 05 54.18	155 09 / 16 42	T. P. 67 / T. P. 69	29.8 / 28.4	T. P. 97	46 23 34.85 / 70 06 28.16	233 34 / 38 46	T. P. 96 / T. P. 98	62.5 / 38.9
T. P. 69	46 24 14.75 / 70 05 54.56	196 42 / 34 23	T. P. 68 / T. P. 70	28.4 / 41.6	T. P. 98	46 23 33.87 / 70 06 29.30	218 46 / 325 40	T. P. 97 / T. P. 99	38.9 / 91.0
T. P. 70	46 24 13.64 / 70 05 55.66	214 23 / 53 48	T. P. 69 / T. P. 71	41.6 / 55.3	T. P. 99	46 23 31.43 / 70 06 26.90	145 40 / 349 06	T. P. 98 / T. P. 100	91.0 / 68.1
T. P. 71	46 24 12.58 / 70 05 57.76	233 48 / 101 20	T. P. 70 / T. P. 72	55.3 / 91.9	T. P. 100	46 23 29.27 / 70 06 26.29	169 06 / 354 34	T. P. 99 / T. P. 101	68.1 / 62.4
T. P. 72	46 24 13.17 / 70 06 01.97	281 20 / 63 31	T. P. 71 / T. P. 73	91.9 / 17.3	T. P. 101	46 23 27.25 / 70 06 26.02	174 34 / 30 44	T. P. 100 / T. P. 102	62.4 / 35.4
T. P. 73	46 24 12.92 / 70 06 02.70	243 31 / 52 00	T. P. 72 / T. P. 74	17.3 / 19.8	T. P. 102	46 23 26.27 / 70 06 26.86	210 44 / 100 45	T. P. 101 / T. P. 103	35.4 / 33.3
T. P. 74	46 24 12.52 / 70 06 03.43	232 00 / 13 03	T. P. 73 / T. P. 75	19.8 / 26.2	T. P. 103	46 23 26.47 / 70 06 28.39	280 45 / 140 50	T. P. 102 / T. P. 104	33.3 / 85.0
T. P. 75	46 24 11.70 / 70 06 03.70	193 03 / 321 20	T. P. 74 / T. P. 76	26.2 / 30.8	T. P. 104	46 23 28.60 / 70 06 30.90	320 50 / 111 27	T. P. 103 / T. P. 105	85.0 / 59.8
T. P. 76	46 24 10.92 / 70 06 02.80	141 20 / 255 46	T. P. 75 / T. P. 77	30.8 / 46.3	T. P. 105	46 23 29.31 / 70 06 33.51	291 27 / 76 11	T. P. 104 / T. P. 106	59.8 / 29.5
T. P. 77	46 24 11.28 / 70 06 00.70	75 46 / 289 39	T. P. 76 / T. P. 78	46.3 / 25.0	T. P. 106	46 23 29.08 / 70 06 34.85	256 11 / 40 28	T. P. 105 / T. P. 107	29.5 / 48.1
T. P. 78	46 24 11.01 / 70 05 59.60	109 39 / 355 14	T. P. 77 / T. P. 79	25.0 / 28.0	T. P. 107	46 23 27.90 / 70 06 36.31	220 28 / 21 08	T. P. 106 / T. P. 108	48.1 / 85.0
T. P. 79	46 24 10.11 / 70 05 59.49	175 14 / 66 16	T. P. 78 / T. P. 80	28.0 / 47.7	T. P. 108	46 23 25.33 / 70 06 37.75	201 08 / 299 59	T. P. 107 / T. P. 109	85.0 / 125.4

BOUNDARY TURNING POINTS AND REFERENCE MONUMENTS—SOUTHWEST BRANCH OF ST. JOHN RIVER—Continued

Station	Latitude and longitude	Azimuth	To station	Distance (meters)
	° ′ ″	° ′ ″		
T. P. 109	46 23 23.30 / 70 06 32.66	119 59 / 321 44 / 149 16 / 303 56	T. P. 108 / T. P. 110 / Ref. Mon. C-20 / Ref. Mon. S-18	125.4 / 30.4 / 322.3 / 73.2
Ref. Mon. C-20	46 23 32.27 / 70 06 40.37	324 39 / 329 16	Ref. Mon. S-18 / T. P. 109	389.8 / 322.3
Ref. Mon. S-18	46 23 21.98 / 70 06 29.82	123 56 / 144 39	T. P. 109 / Ref. Mon. C-20	73.2 / 389.8
T. P. 110	46 23 22.53 / 70 06 31.78	141 44 / 327 18	T. P. 109 / T. P. 111	30.4 / 65.2
T. P. 111	46 23 20.75 / 70 06 30.13	147 18 / 0 39	T. P. 110 / T. P. 112	65.2 / 22.2
T. P. 112	46 23 20.03 / 70 06 30.14	180 39 / 350 08	T. P. 111 / T. P. 113	22.2 / 36.0
T. P. 113	46 23 18.88 / 70 06 29.85	170 08 / 339 32	T. P. 112 / T. P. 114	36.0 / 49.2
T. P. 114	46 23 17.39 / 70 06 29.05	159 32 / 31 08	T. P. 113 / T. P. 115	49.2 / 44.7
T. P. 115	46 23 16.15 / 70 06 30.13	211 08 / 74 09	T. P. 114 / T. P. 116	44.7 / 28.9
T. P. 116	46 23 15.90 / 70 06 31.43	254 09 / 130 51	T. P. 115 / T. P. 117	28.9 / 50.8
T. P. 117	46 23 16.97 / 70 06 33.23	310 51 / 160 24	T. P. 116 / T. P. 118	50.8 / 21.7
T. P. 118	46 23 17.64 / 70 06 33.57	340 24 / 223 57	T. P. 117 / T. P. 119	21.7 / 65.8
T. P. 119	46 23 19.17 / 70 06 31.43	43 57 / 175 39	T. P. 118 / T. P. 120	65.8 / 20.4
T. P. 120	46 23 19.83 / 70 06 31.51	355 39 / 97 26	T. P. 119 / T. P. 121	20.4 / 58.3
T. P. 121	46 23 20.07 / 70 06 34.21	277 26 / 100 54	T. P. 120 / T. P. 122	58.3 / 78.8
T. P. 122	46 23 20.55 / 70 06 37.83	280 54 / 80 32	T. P. 121 / T. P. 123	78.8 / 22.0
T. P. 123	46 23 20.44 / 70 06 38.85	260 32 / 6 27	T. P. 122 / T. P. 124	22.0 / 28.8
T. P. 124	46 23 19.51 / 70 06 39.00	186 27 / 328 45	T. P. 123 / T. P. 125	28.8 / 80.7
T. P. 125	46 23 17.28 / 70 06 37.04	148 45 / 8 33	T. P. 124 / T. P. 126	80.7 / 41.7
T. P. 126	46 23 15.94 / 70 06 37.33	188 33 / 52 27	T. P. 125 / T. P. 127	41.7 / 43.9
T. P. 127	46 23 15.07 / 70 06 38.96	232 27 / 101 13	T. P. 126 / T. P. 128	43.9 / 24.9
T. P. 128	46 23 15.23 / 70 06 40.10	281 13 / 129 26	T. P. 127 / T. P. 129	24.9 / 58.6
T. P. 129	46 23 16.44 / 70 06 42.22	309 26 / 157 15	T. P. 128 / T. P. 130	58.6 / 70.4
T. P. 130	46 23 18.54 / 70 06 43.50	337 15 / 63 38	T. P. 129 / T. P. 131	70.4 / 72.3
T. P. 131	46 23 17.50 / 70 06 46.53	243 38 / 47 09	T. P. 130 / T. P. 132	72.3 / 26.7
T. P. 132	46 23 16.91 / 70 06 47.45	227 09 / 14 00	T. P. 131 / T. P. 133	26.7 / 30.2
T. P. 133	46 23 15.96 / 70 06 47.79	194 00 / 296 34	T. P. 132 / T. P. 134	30.2 / 66.2
T. P. 134	46 23 15.01 / 70 06 45.02	116 34 / 322 58	T. P. 133 / T. P. 135	66.2 / 137.6
T. P. 135	46 23 11.45 / 70 06 41.14	142 58 / 352 54	T. P. 134 / T. P. 136	137.6 / 34.1
T. P. 136	46 23 10.35 / 70 06 40.94	172 54 / 56 12	T. P. 135 / T. P. 137	34.1 / 31.3
T. P. 137	46 23 09.79 / 70 06 42.16	236 12 / 86 42	T. P. 136 / T. P. 138	31.3 / 122.6
T. P. 138	46 23 09.56 / 70 06 47.89	266 42 / 64 17	T. P. 137 / T. P. 139	122.6 / 66.6
T. P. 139	46 23 08.62 / 70 06 50.70	244 17 / 35 12	T. P. 138 / T. P. 140	66.6 / 49.9
T. P. 140	46 23 07.30 / 70 06 52.04	215 12 / 76 32	T. P. 139 / T. P. 141	49.9 / 28.7
T. P. 141	46 23 07.08 / 70 06 53.35	256 32 / 117 43	T. P. 140 / T. P. 142	28.7 / 35.6
T. P. 142	46 23 07.62 / 70 06 54.82	297 43 / 144 23	T. P. 141 / T. P. 143	35.6 / 23.9
T. P. 143	46 23 08.25 / 70 06 55.48	324 23 / 196 17	T. P. 142 / T. P. 144	23.9 / 65.7
T. P. 144	46 23 10.29 / 70 06 54.61	16 17 / 156 05 / 153 22 / 308 36	T. P. 143 / T. P. 145 / Ref. Mon. C-22 / Ref. Mon. C-21	65.7 / 61.0 / 401.5 / 14.3
Ref. Mon. C-21	46 23 10.01 / 70 06 54.09	128 36 / 152 31	T. P. 144 / Ref. Mon. C-22	14.3 / 414.3
Ref. Mon. C-22	46 23 21.91 / 70 07 03.04	332 31 / 333 22	Ref. Mon. C-21 / T. P. 144	414.3 / 401.5
T. P. 145	46 23 12.10 / 70 06 55.77	336 05 / 177 30	T. P. 144 / T. P. 146	61.0 / 158.2
T. P. 146	46 23 17.22 / 70 06 56.09	357 30 / 140 14	T. P. 145 / T. P. 147	158.2 / 21.7
T. P. 147	46 23 17.76 / 70 06 56.74	320 14 / 99 30	T. P. 146 / T. P. 148	21.7 / 82.7
T. P. 148	46 23 18.20 / 70 07 00.56	279 30 / 76 32	T. P. 147 / T. P. 149	82.7 / 34.2
T. P. 149	46 23 17.94 / 70 07 02.12	256 32 / 39 48	T. P. 148 / T. P. 150	34.2 / 50.4
T. P. 150	46 23 16.69 / 70 07 03.63	219 48 / 355 18	T. P. 149 / T. P. 151	50.4 / 52.2
T. P. 151	46 23 15.00 / 70 07 03.43	175 18 / 298 25	T. P. 150 / T. P. 152	52.2 / 87.6
T. P. 152	46 23 13.65 / 70 06 59.82	118 25 / 347 11	T. P. 151 / T. P. 153	87.6 / 46.6
T. P. 153	46 23 12.18 / 70 06 59.34	167 11 / 18 02	T. P. 152 / T. P. 154	46.6 / 81.9
T. P. 154	46 23 09.66 / 70 07 00.52	198 02 / 45 14	T. P. 153 / T. P. 155	81.9 / 115.2
T. P. 155	46 23 07.03 / 70 07 04.35	225 14 / 54 25	T. P. 154 / T. P. 156	115.2 / 498.9
T. P. 156	46 22 57.63 / 70 07 23.34	234 24 / 61 45	T. P. 155 / T. P. 157	498.9 / 140.2
T. P. 157	46 22 55.48 / 70 07 29.12	241 45 / 69 11	T. P. 156 / T. P. 158	140.2 / 136.6
T. P. 158	46 22 53.91 / 70 07 35.10	249 11 / 46 10	T. P. 157 / T. P. 159	136.6 / 44.3
T. P. 159	46 22 52.91 / 70 07 36.59	226 10 / 32 43	T. P. 158 / T. P. 160	44.3 / 114.2
T. P. 160	46 22 49.80 / 70 07 39.48	212 43 / 27 05 / 130 09 / 289 45	T. P. 159 / T. P. 161 / Ref. Mon. C-24 / Ref. Mon. S-20	114.2 / 182.4 / 398.8 / 52.6
Ref. Mon. C-24	46 22 58.13 / 70 07 53.75	307 48 / 310 08	Ref. Mon. S-20 / T. P. 160	448.5 / 398.8
Ref. Mon. S-20	46 22 49.22 / 70 07 37.16	109 45 / 127 48	T. P. 160 / Ref. Mon. C-24	52.6 / 448.5
T. P. 161	46 22 44.54 / 70 07 43.37	207 05 / 354 21	T. P. 160 / T. P. 162	182.4 / 291.2
T. P. 162	46 22 35.16 / 70 07 42.03	174 21 / 355 47	T. P. 161 / T. P. 163	291.2 / 482.0
T. P. 163	46 22 19.59 / 70 07 40.37	175 47 / 332 00 / 109 42 / 220 28	T. P. 162 / T. P. 164 / Ref. Mon. C-26 / Ref. Mon. S-22	482.0 / 72.6 / 189.4 / 180.7

BOUNDARY TURNING POINTS AND REFERENCE MONUMENTS—SOUTHWEST BRANCH OF ST. JOHN RIVER—Continued

Station	Latitude and longitude	Azimuth	To station	Distance (meters)
	° ′ ″	° ′ ″		
Ref. Mon. C-26	46 22 21.66	256 01	Ref. Mon. S-22	304.6
	70 07 48.71	289 42	T. P. 163	189.4
Ref. Mon. S-22	46 22 24.04	40 28	T. P. 163	180.7
	70 07 34.88	76 01	Ref. Mon. C-26	304.6
T. P. 164	46 22 17.51	152 00	T. P. 163	72.6
	70 07 38.78	344 54	T. P. 165	33.5
T. P. 165	46 22 16.46	164 54	T. P. 164	33.5
	70 07 38.37	30 06	T. P. 166	42.3
T. P. 166	46 22 15.28	210 06	T. P. 165	42.3
	70 07 39.36	87 23	T. P. 167	110.4
T. P. 167	46 22 15.12	267 23	T. P. 166	110.4
	70 07 44.52	68 28	T. P. 168	31.4
T. P. 168	46 22 14.74	248 28	T. P. 167	31.4
	70 07 45.89	39 49	T. P. 169	42.2
T. P. 169	46 22 13.69	219 49	T. P. 168	42.2
	70 07 47.15	359 53	T. P. 170	86.6
T. P. 170	46 22 10.89	179 53	T. P. 169	86.6
	70 07 47.14	51 32	T. P. 171	31.2
T. P. 171	46 22 10.26	231 32	T. P. 170	31.2
	70 07 48.29	101 02	T. P. 172	178.6
T. P. 172	46 22 11.37	281 02	T. P. 171	178.6
	70 07 56.49	58 34	T. P. 173	178.7
T. P. 173	46 22 08.35	238 34	T. P. 172	178.7
	70 08 03.62	93 56	T. P. 174	59.8
T. P. 174	46 22 08.48	273 56	T. P. 173	59.8
	70 08 06.41	127 52	T. P. 175	81.2
		30 47	Ref. Mon. S-25	183.3
Ref. Mon. S-25	46 22 03.38	31 45 40	Ref. Mon. S-26	511.9
	70 08 10.80	210 47	T. P. 174	183.3
T. P. 175	46 22 10.09	307 52	T. P. 174	81.2
	70 08 09.41	169 02	T. P. 176	52.2
T. P. 176	46 22 11.75	349 02	T. P. 175	52.2
	70 08 09.88	127 32	T. P. 177	30.1
T. P. 177	46 22 12.35	307 32	T. P. 176	30.1
	70 08 10.99	74 54	T. P. 178	52.3
T. P. 178	46 22 11.91	254 54	T. P. 177	52.3
	70 08 13.36	49 53	T. P. 179	112.5
T. P. 179	46 22 09.56	229 53	T. P. 178	112.5
	70 08 17.38	29 57	T. P. 180	96.4
T. P. 180	46 22 06.85	209 57	T. P. 179	96.4
	70 08 19.63	3 01	T. P. 181	44.9
T. P. 181	46 22 05.40	183 01	T. P. 180	44.9
	70 08 19.74	350 00	T. P. 182	45.4
T. P. 182	46 22 03.96	170 00	T. P. 181	45.4
	70 08 19.37	1 12	T. P. 183	46.7
T. P. 183	46 22 02.44	181 12	T. P. 182	46.7
	70 08 19.42	19 03	T. P. 184	111.6
T. P. 184	46 21 59.03	199 03	T. P. 183	111.6
	70 08 21.12	38 30	T. P. 185	102.5
T. P. 185	46 21 56.43	218 30	T. P. 184	102.5
	70 08 24.11	66 54	T. P. 186	124.9
T. P. 186	46 21 54.84	246 54	T. P. 185	124.9
	70 08 29.48	44 12	T. P. 187	50.7
		118 37	Ref. Mon. C-28	190.4
		322 53	Ref. Mon. S-26	215.2
Ref. Mon. C-28	46 21 57.80	298 37	T. P. 186	190.4
	70 08 37.30	311 30	Ref. Mon. S-26	396.6
Ref. Mon. S-26	46 21 49.28	131 30	Ref. Mon. C-28	396.6
	70 08 23.41	142 53	T. P. 186	215.2
T. P. 187	46 21 53.66	224 12	T. P. 186	50.7
	70 08 31.14	5 11	T. P. 188	34.7
T. P. 188	46 21 52.54	185 11	T. P. 187	34.7
	70 08 31.28	317 36	T. P. 189	121.4

Station	Latitude and longitude	Azimuth	To station	Distance (meters)
	° ′ ″	° ′ ″		
T. P. 189	46 21 49.64	137 36	T. P. 188	121.4
	70 08 27.46	14 15	T. P. 190	79.6
T. P. 190	46 21 47.14	194 15	T. P. 189	79.6
	70 08 28.37	35 40	T. P. 191	64.2
T. P. 191	46 21 45.45	215 40	T. P. 190	64.2
	70 08 30.12	57 26	T. P. 192	72.1
T. P. 192	46 21 44.19	237 26	T. P. 191	72.1
	70 08 32.97	91 04	T. P. 193	116.8
T. P. 193	46 21 44.26	271 04	T. P. 192	116.8
	70 08 38.43	95 39	T. P. 194	88.4
T. P. 194	46 21 44.54	275 39	T. P. 193	88.4
	70 08 42.54	56 03	T. P. 195	33.1
T. P. 195	46 21 43.95	236 03	T. P. 194	33.1
	70 08 43.83	29 43	T. P. 196	162.4
T. P. 196	46 21 39.38	209 43	T. P. 195	162.4
	70 08 47.60	43 48	T. P. 197	119.5
T. P. 197	46 21 36.59	223 48	T. P. 196	119.5
	70 08 51.46	17 19	T. P. 198	73.1
T. P. 198	46 21 34.33	197 19	T. P. 197	73.1
	70 08 52.48	51 12	T. P. 199	77.7
T. P. 199	46 21 32.75	231 12	T. P. 198	77.7
	70 08 55.31	78 58	T. P. 200	59.8
T. P. 200	46 21 32.38	258 58	T. P. 199	59.8
	70 08 58.06	102 44	T. P. 201	210.8
T. P. 201	46 21 33.88	282 44	T. P. 200	210.8
	70 09 07.68	120 43	T. P. 202	119.0
		152 14	Ref. Mon. C-30	286.9
		329 34	Ref. Mon. S-29	201.6
Ref. Mon. C-30	46 2 42.10	332 14	T. P. 201	286.9
	70 09 13.93	331 08	Ref. Mon. S-29	488.4
Ref. Mon. S-29	46 21 28.25	149 34	T. P. 201	201.6
	70 09 02.90	151 08	Ref. Mon. C-30	488.4
T. P. 202	46 21 35.85	300 43	T. P. 201	119.0
	70 09 12.46	104 42	T. P. 203	111.3
T. P. 203	46 21 36.76	284 42	T. P. 202	111.3
	70 09 17.50	138 55	T. P. 204	175.3
T. P. 204	46 21 41.04	318 55	T. P. 203	175.3
	70 09 22.89	107 45	T. P. 205	55.0
T. P. 205	46 21 41.59	287 45	T. P. 204	55.0
	70 09 25.34	42 50	T. P. 206	81.3
T. P. 206	46 21 39.66	222 50	T. P. 205	81.3
	70 09 27.92	67 50	T. P. 207	49.6
T. P. 207	46 21 39.05	247 50	T. P. 206	49.6
	70 09 30.07	50 15	T. P. 208	32.3
T. P. 208	46 21 38.38	230 15	T. P. 207	32.3
	70 09 31.23	345 01	T. P. 209	79.3
T. P. 209	46 21 35.90	165 01	T. P. 208	79.3
	70 09 30.27	13 36	T. P. 210	43.4
T. P. 210	46 21 34.53	193 36	T. P. 209	43.4
	70 09 30.75	61 28	T. P. 211	58.5
T. P. 211	46 21 33.63	241 28	T. P. 210	58.5
	70 09 33.16	102 14	T. P. 212	77.3
T. P. 212	46 21 34.16	282 14	T. P. 211	77.3
	70 09 36.69	118 32	T. P. 213	41.4
T. P. 213	46 21 34.80	298 32	T. P. 212	41.4
	70 09 38.39	147 34	T. P. 214	39.6
T. P. 214	46 21 35.88	327 34	T. P. 213	39.6
	70 09 39.38	212 16	T. P. 215	81.9
T. P. 215	46 21 38.13	32 16	T. P. 214	81.9
	70 09 37.34	170 29	T. P. 216	33.0
T. P. 216	46 21 39.18	350 29	T. P. 215	33.0
	70 09 37.60	130 51	T. P. 217	32.1

BOUNDARY TURNING POINTS AND REFERENCE MONUMENTS—SOUTHWEST BRANCH OF ST. JOHN RIVER—Continued

Station	Latitude and longitude	Azimuth	To station	Distance (meters)
	° ′ ″	° ′ ″		
T. P. 217	46 21 39.86 / 70 09 38.73	310 51 / 105 37	T. P. 216 / T. P. 218	32.1 / 64.4
T. P. 218	46 21 40.42 / 70 09 41.63	285 37 / 82 35 / 173 50 / 345 56	T. P. 217 / T. P. 219 / Ref. Mon. C-31 / Ref. Mon. S-31	64.4 / 55.5 / 106.2 / 404.7
Ref. Mon. C-31	46 21 43.84 / 70 09 42.16	347 34 10 / 353 50	Ref. Mon. S-31 / T. P. 218	510.1 / 106.2
Ref. Mon. S-31	46 21 27.71 / 70 09 37.03	165 56 / 167 34 10	T. P. 218 / Ref. Mon. C-31	404.7 / 510.1
T. P. 219	46 21 40.19 / 70 09 44.21	262 35 / 50 28	T. P. 218 / T. P. 220	55.5 / 78.2
T. P. 220	46 21 38.58 / 70 09 47.03	230 28 / 2 28	T. P. 219 / T. P. 221	78.2 / 100.2
T. P. 221	46 21 35.33 / 70 09 47.23	182 28 / 34 50	T. P. 220 / T. P. 222	100.2 / 74.4
T. P. 222	46 21 33.36 / 70 09 49.22	214 50 / 84 47	T. P. 221 / T. P. 223	74.4 / 89.1
T. P. 223	46 21 33.09 / 70 09 53.37	264 47 / 48 23	T. P. 222 / T. P. 224	89.1 / 105.8
T. P. 224	46 21 30.82 / 70 09 57.07	228 23 / 348 46	T. P. 223 / T. P. 225	105.8 / 34.6
T. P. 225	46 21 29.72 / 70 09 56.75	168 46 / 39 57	T. P. 224 / T. P. 226	34.6 / 103.0
T. P. 226	46 21 27.17 / 70 09 59.84	219 57 / 77 54	T. P. 225 / T. P. 227	103.0 / 43.0
T. P. 227	46 21 26.87 / 70 10 01.81	257 54 / 136 41	T. P. 226 / T. P. 228	43.0 / 193.5
T. P. 228	46 21 31.43 / 70 10 08.02	316 41 / 113 52	T. P. 227 / T. P. 229	193.5 / 213.8
T. P. 229	46 21 34.24 / 70 10 17.17	293 52 / 87 48 / 268 36 / 328 04	T. P. 228 / T. P. 230 / Ref. Mon. C-32 / Ref. Mon. S-32	213.8 / 70.8 / 86.3 / 397.8
Ref. Mon. C-32	46 21 34.30 / 70 10 13.14	88 36 / 339 55	T. P. 229 / Ref. Mon. S-32	86.3 / 361.6
Ref. Mon. S-32	46 21 23.30 / 70 10 07.33	148 04 / 159 55	T. P. 229 / Ref. Mon. C-32	397.8 / 361.6
T. P. 230	46 21 34.15 / 70 10 20.48	267 48 / 75 59	T. P. 229 / T. P. 231	70.8 / 90.0
T. P. 231	46 21 33.44 / 70 10 24.57	255 59 / 59 12	T. P. 230 / T. P. 232	90.0 / 112.2
T. P. 232	46 21 31.58 / 70 10 29.07	239 12 / 55 29	T. P. 231 / T. P. 233	112.2 / 112.2
T. P. 233	46 21 29.52 / 70 10 33.40	235 29 / 20 32	T. P. 232 / T. P. 234	112.2 / 178.4
T. P. 234	46 21 24.11 / 70 10 36.32	200 32 / 36 42	T. P. 233 / T. P. 235	178.4 / 142.1
T. P. 235	46 21 20.42 / 70 10 40.30	216 42 / 67 06 / 138 54 / 293 43	T. P. 234 / T. P. 236 / Ref. Mon. C-33 / Ref. Mon. S-34	142.1 / 271.2 / 149.1 / 271.8
Ref. Mon. C-33	46 21 24.06 / 70 10 44.88	302 35 / 318 54	Ref. Mon. S-34 / T. P. 235	411.6 / 149.1
Ref. Mon. S-34	46 21 16.88 / 70 10 28.66	113 43 / 122 35	T. P. 235 / Ref. Mon. C-33	271.8 / 411.6
T. P. 236	46 21 17.00 / 70 10 51.98	247 06 / 42 22	T. P. 235 / T. P. 237	271.2 / 69.2
T. P. 237	46 21 15.35 / 70 10 54.16	222 22 / 8 25	T. P. 236 / T. P. 238	69.2 / 184.6
T. P. 238	46 21 09.43 / 70 10 55.42	188 25 / 25 43 / 131 18 / 326 39	T. P. 237 / T. P. 239 / Ref. Mon. C-34 / Ref. Mon. S-35	184.6 / 41.5 / 85.8 / 176.8
Ref. Mon. C-34	46 21 11.27 / 70 10 58.44	311 18 / 321 39	T. P. 238 / Ref. Mon. S-35	85.8 / 260.6
Ref. Mon. S-35	46 21 04.65 / 70 10 50.88	141 39 / 146 39	Ref. Mon. C-34 / T. P. 238	260.6 / 176.8
T. P. 239	46 21 08.22 / 70 10 56.26	205 43 / 56 57	T. P. 238 / T. P. 240	41.5 / 73.1
T. P. 240	46 21 06.93 / 70 10 59.13	236 57 / 72 29	T. P. 239 / T. P. 241	73.1 / 68.0
T. P. 241	46 21 06.27 / 70 11 02.16	252 29 / 115 35	T. P. 240 / T. P. 242	68.0 / 84.4
T. P. 242	46 21 07.45 / 70 11 05.72	295 35 / 45 35	T. P. 241 / T. P. 243	84.4 / 135.3
T. P. 243	46 21 04.38 / 70 11 10.24	225 35 / 56 19	T. P. 242 / T. P. 244	135.3 / 219.8
T. P. 244	46 21 00.43 / 70 11 18.80	236 19 / 80 17	T. P. 243 / T. P. 245	219.8 / 49.5
T. P. 245	46 21 00.16 / 70 11 21.08	260 17 / 126 04	T. P. 244 / T. P. 246	49.5 / 101.5
T. P. 246	46 21 02.10 / 70 11 24.91	306 04 / 76 09	T. P. 245 / T. P. 247	101.5 / 122.0
T. P. 247	46 21 01.15 / 70 11 30.45	256 09 / 34 52	T. P. 246 / T. P. 248	122.0 / 132.3
T. P. 248	46 20 57.64 / 70 11 33.99	214 52 / 6 18	T. P. 247 / T. P. 249	132.3 / 22.8
T. P. 249	46 20 56.90 / 70 11 34.11	186 18 / 281 46	T. P. 248 / T. P. 250	22.8 / 39.9
T. P. 250	46 20 56.64 / 70 11 32.28	101 46 / 340 29	T. P. 249 / T. P. 251	39.9 / 100.9
T. P. 251	46 20 53.56 / 70 11 30.70	160 29 / 0 24 / 98 06 / 305 26	T. P. 250 / T. P. 252 / Ref. Mon. C-36 / Ref. Mon. S-37	100.9 / 22.5 / 111.0 / 161.5
Ref. Mon. C-36	46 20 54.07 / 70 11 35.84	278 06 / 294 21	T. P. 251 / Ref. Mon. S-37	111.0 / 265.1
Ref. Mon. S-37	46 20 50.53 / 70 11 24.55	114 21 / 125 26	Ref. Mon. C-36 / T. P. 251	265.1 / 161.5
T. P. 252	46 20 52.83 / 70 11 30.71	180 24 / 24 20	T. P. 251 / T. P. 253	22.5 / 41.2
T. P. 253	46 20 51.62 / 70 11 31.50	204 20 / 71 17	T. P. 252 / T. P. 254	41.2 / 89.6
T. P. 254	46 20 50.69 / 70 11 35.47	251 17 / 42 06	T. P. 253 / T. P. 255	89.6 / 62.5
T. P. 255	46 20 49.18 / 70 11 37.43	222 06 / 12 27	T. P. 254 / T. P. 256	62.5 / 107.2
T. P. 256	46 20 45.79 / 70 11 38.51	192 27 / 34 12	T. P. 255 / T. P. 257	107.2 / 225.9
T. P. 257	46 20 39.74 / 70 11 44.45	214 12 / 26 12	T. P. 256 / T. P. 258	225.9 / 121.9
T. P. 258	46 20 36.20 / 70 11 46.97	206 12 / 339 49	T. P. 257 / T. P. 259	121.9 / 133.5
T. P. 259	46 20 32.14 / 70 11 44.82	159 49 / 20 01	T. P. 258 / T. P. 260	133.5 / 104.9
T. P. 260	46 20 28.95 / 70 11 46.49	200 01 / 4 54	T. P. 259 / T. P. 261	104.9 / 49.0
T. P. 261	46 20 27.37 / 70 11 46.69	184 54 / 36 10	T. P. 260 / T. P. 262	49.0 / 34.8
T. P. 262	46 20 26.46 / 70 11 47.65	216 10 / 59 53 / 131 31 / 255 39	T. P. 261 / T. P. 263 / Ref. Mon. C-38 / Ref. Mon. S-39	34.8 / 101.3 / 137.2 / 170.9
Ref. Mon. C-38	46 20 29.41 / 70 11 52.45	280 16 / 311 31	Ref. Mon. S-39 / T. P. 262	272.7 / 137.2
Ref. Mon. S-39	46 20 27.83 / 70 11 39.91	75 39 / 100 17	T. P. 262 / Ref. Mon. C-38	170.9 / 272.7
T. P. 263	46 20 24.82 / 70 11 51.74	239 53 / 33 38	T. P. 262 / T. P. 264	101.3 / 163.4

BOUNDARY TURNING POINTS AND REFERENCE MONUMENTS—SOUTHWEST BRANCH OF ST. JOHN RIVER—Continued

Station	Latitude and longitude	Azimuth	To station	Distance (meters)	Station	Latitude and longitude	Azimuth	To station	Distance (meters)
	° ′ ″	° ′ ″				° ′ ″	° ′ ″		
T P. 264	46 20 20.41	213 38	T. P. 263	163.4	T. P. 288	46 19 03.29	147 12	T. P. 287	151.0
	70 11 55.98	47 37	T. P. 265	146.6		70 12 22.40	307 22	T. P. 289	126.7
T. P. 265	46 20 17.21	227 37	T. P. 264	146.6	T. P. 289	46 19 00.80	127 22	T. P. 288	126.7
	70 12 01.04	24 56	T. P. 266	42.9		70 12 17.69	11 43	T. P. 290	67.3
T. P. 266	46 20 15.95	204 56	T. P. 265	42.9	T. P. 290	46 18 58.66	191 43	T. P. 289	67.3
	70 12 01.89	44 44	T. P. 267	107.9		70 12 18.33	336 17	T. P. 291	98.7
T. P. 267	46 20 13.47	224 44	T. P. 266	107.9	T. P. 291	46 18 55.74	156 17	T. P. 290	98.7
	70 12 05.44	23 29	T. P. 268	208.2		70 12 16.48	314 47	T. P. 292	86.3
T. P. 268	46 20 07.28	203 29	T. P. 267	208.2	T. P. 292	46 18 53.77	134 47	T. P. 291	86.3
	70 12 09.32	54 48	T. P. 269	209.5		70 12 13.61	344 20	T. P. 293	54.6
		128 28	Ref. Mon. C-40	143.6	T. P. 293	46 18 52.07	164 20	T. P. 292	54.6
		311 46	Ref. Mon. S-41	116.3		70 12 12.92	2 54	T. P. 294	55.9
Ref. Mon. C-40	46 20 10.18	308 28	T. P. 268	143.6	T. P. 294	46 18 50.26	182 54	T. P. 293	55.9
	70 12 14.58	309 56	Ref. Mon. S-41	259.9		70 12 13.06	16 28	T. P. 295	99.6
Ref. Mon. S-41	46 20 04.77	129 56	Ref. Mon. C-40	259.9	T. P. 295	46 18 47.16	196 28	T. P. 294	99.6
	70 12 05.26	131 46	T. P. 268	116.3		70 12 14.38	22 45	T. P. 296	56.9
T. P. 269	46 20 03.37	234 48	T. P. 268	209.5	T. P. 296	46 18 45.46	202 45	T. P. 295	56.9
	70 12 17.32	37 23	T. P. 270	116.5		70 12 15.41	30 32	T. P. 297	96.6
T. P. 270	46 20 00.37	217 23	T. P. 269	116.5	T. P. 297	46 18 42.77	210 32	T. P. 296	96.6
	70 12 20.63	8 08	T. P. 271	79.3		70 12 17.70	22 35	T. P. 298	135.8
T. P. 271	46 19 57.83	188 08	T. P. 270	79.3			89 41	Ref. Mon. C-48	56.1
	70 12 21.16	45 50	T. P. 272	130.2			276 10	Ref. Mon. S-49	200.2
T. P. 272	46 19 54.89	225 50	T. P. 271	130.2	Ref. Mon. C-48	46 18 42.76	269 41	T. P. 297	56.1
	70 12 25.52	64 44	T. P. 273	82.1		70 12 20.32	274 45	Ref. Mon. S-49	256.0
T. P. 273	46 19 53.76	244 44	T. P. 272	82.1	Ref. Mon. S-49	46 18 42.07	94 45	Ref. Mon. C-48	256.0
	70 12 29.00	29 36	T. P. 274	204.2		70 12 08.40	96 10	T. P. 297	200.2
T. P. 274	46 19 48.00	209 36	T. P. 273	204.2	T. P. 298	46 18 38.71	202 35	T. P. 297	135.8
	70 12 33.71	17 38	T. P. 275	47.2		70 12 20.14	44 06	T. P. 299	123.3
		78 38	Ref. Mon. C-42	65.5	T. P. 299	46 18 35.84	224 06	T. P. 298	123.3
		310 38	Ref. Mon. S-43	231.2		70 12 24.15	0 49	T. P. 300	267.4
Ref. Mon. C-42	46 19 47.59	258 38	T. P. 274	65.5	T. P. 300	46 18 27.18	180 49	T. P. 299	267.4
	70 12 36.72	299 52	Ref. Mon. S-43	276.4		70 12 24.32	13 15	T. P. 301	132.7
Ref. Mon. S-43	46 19 43.13	119 52	Ref. Mon. C-42	276.4			47 55	Ref. Mon. C-50	170.0
	70 12 25.51	130 38	T. P. 274	231.2			218 45	Ref. Mon. S-50	281.0
T. P. 275	46 19 46.55	197 38	T. P. 274	47.2	Ref. Mon. C-50	46 18 23.49	222 12	Ref. Mon. S-50	449.7
	70 12 34.38	327 27	T. P. 276	189.8		70 12 30.22	227 55	T. P. 300	170.0
T. P. 276	46 19 41.37	147 27	T. P. 275	189.8	Ref. Mon. S-50	46 18 34.28	38 45	T. P. 300	281.0
	70 12 29.61	345 34	T. P. 277	301.2		70 12 16.10	42 12	Ref. Mon. C-50	449.7
T. P. 277	46 19 31.92	165 34	T. P. 276	301.2	T. P. 301	46 18 23.00	193 15	T. P. 300	132.7
	70 12 26.10	336 33	T. P. 278	46.4		70 12 25.75	353 00	T. P. 302	90.4
T. P. 278	46 19 30.54	156 33	T. P. 277	46.4	T. P. 302	46 18 20.09	173 00	T. P. 301	90.4
	70 12 25.23	321 08	T. P. 279	43.6		70 12 25.23	334 15	T. P. 303	72.4
T. P. 279	46 19 29.44	141 08	T. P. 278	43.6	T. P. 303	46 18 17.98	154 15	T. P. 302	72.4
	70 12 23.96	355 31	T. P. 280	94.4		70 12 23.76	350 57	T. P. 304	128.1
T. P. 280	46 19 26.39	175 31	T. P. 279	94.4	T. P. 304	46 18 13.88	170 57	T. P. 303	128.1
	70 12 23.61	26 17	T. P. 281	213.3		70 12 22.82	333 32	T. P. 305	67.5
T. P. 281	46 19 20.20	206 17	T. P. 280	213.3	T. P. 305	46 18 11.92	153 32	T. P. 304	67.5
	70 12 28.02	350 43	T. P. 282	60.9		70 12 21.41	358 02	T. P. 306	43.2
T. P. 282	46 19 18.25	170 43	T. P. 281	60.9	T. P. 306	46 18 10.53	178 02	T. P. 305	43.2
	70 12 27.57	323 30	T. P. 283	45.7		70 12 21.34	21 39	T. P. 307	57.1
		91 55	Ref. Mon. C-44	194.7	T. P. 307	46 18 08.81	201 39	T. P. 306	57.1
		264 04	Ref. Mon. S-45	97.7		70 12 22.33	41 40	T. P. 308	121.0
Ref. Mon. C-44	46 19 18.46	269 17	Ref. Mon. S-45	291.9	T. P. 308	46 18 05.88	221 40	T. P. 307	121.0
	70 12 36.66	271 54	T. P. 282	194.7		70 12 26.09	11 41	T. P. 309	38.2
Ref. Mon. S-45	46 19 18.58	84 04	T. P. 282	97.7	T. P. 309	46 18 04.67	191 41	T. P. 308	38.2
	70 12 23.02	89 18	Ref. Mon. C-44	291.9		70 12 26.45	334 24	T. P. 310	39.7
T. P. 283	46 19 17.06	143 30	T. P. 282	45.7	T. P. 310	46 18 03.51	154 24	T. P. 309	39.7
	70 12 26.29	4 51	T. P. 284	109.0		70 12 25.65	298 20	T. P. 311	55.6
T. P. 284	46 19 13.55	184 51	T. P. 283	109.0	T. P. 311	46 18 02.66	118 20	T. P. 310	55.6
	70 12 26.72	30 59	T. P. 285	61.2		70 12 23.36	320 58	T. P. 312	29.5
T. P. 285	46 19 11.85	210 59	T. P. 284	61.2	T. P. 312	46 18 01.91	140 58	T. P. 311	29.5
	70 12 28.20	8 33	T. P. 285	34.0		70 12 22.49	354 00	T. P. 313	27.6
T. P. 286	46 19 10.76	188 33	T. P. 285	34.0	T. P. 313	46 18 01.02	174 00	T. P. 312	27.6
	70 12 28.44	335 28	T. P. 287	113.9		70 12 22.36	22 47	T. P. 314	55.0
T P. 287	46 19 07.40	155 28	T. P. 286	113.9					
	70 12 26.22	327 12	T. P. 288	151.0					

BOUNDARY TURNING POINTS AND REFERENCE MONUMENTS—SOUTHWEST BRANCH OF ST. JOHN RIVER—Continued

Station	Latitude and longitude	Azimuth	To station	Distance (meters)
	° ′ ″	° ′ ″		
T. P. 314	46 17 59.38 / 70 12 23.35	202 47 / 49 49 / 114 35 / 327 12	T. P. 313 / T. P. 315 / Ref. Mon. C-52 / Ref. Mon. S-53	55.0 / 91.6 / 202.8 / 67.6
Ref. Mon. C-52	46 18 02.11 / 70 12 31.97	294 35 / 302 34	T. P. 314 / Ref. Mon. S-53	202.8 / 262.3
Ref. Mon. S-53	46 17 57.54 / 70 12 21.64	122 34 / 147 12	Ref. Mon. C-52 / T. P. 314	262.3 / 67.6
T. P. 315	46 17 57.47 / 70 12 26.62	229 49 / 76 25	T. P. 314 / T. P. 316	91.6 / 182.4
T. P. 316	46 17 56.08 / 70 12 34.91	256 25 / 54 55	T. P. 315 / T. P. 317	182.4 / 119.4
T. P. 317	46 17 53.86 / 70 12 39.47	234 55 / 87 55	T. P. 316 / T. P. 318	119.4 / 65.3
T. P. 318	46 17 53.78 / 70 12 42.52	267 55 / 133 04	T. P. 317 / T. P. 319	65.3 / 70.3
T. P. 319	46 17 55.33 / 70 12 44.92	313 04 / 79 46	T. P. 318 / T. P. 320	70.3 / 39.2
T. P. 320	46 17 55.11 / 70 12 46.72	259 46 / 25 18	T. P. 319 / T. P. 321	39.2 / 62.1
T. P. 321	46 17 53.29 / 70 12 47.96	205 18 / 59 29 / 125 50	T. P. 320 / T. P. 322 / Ref. Mon. C-53	62.1 / 61.1 / 119.4
Ref. Mon. C-53	46 17 55.55 / 70 12 52.48	245 14 / 305 50	Ref. Mon. C-52 / T. P. 321	483.4 / 119.4
T. P. 322	46 17 52.29 / 70 12 50.42	239 29 / 40 14	T. P. 321 / T. P. 323	61.1 / 82.5
T. P. 323	46 17 50.25 / 70 12 52.91	220 14 / 16 02	T. P. 322 / T. P. 324	82.5 / 47.3
T. P. 324	46 17 48.78 / 70 12 53.52	196 02 / 291 27	T. P. 323 / T. P. 325	47.3 / 47.2
T. P. 325	46 17 48.22 / 70 12 51.46	111 27 / 333 10	T. P. 324 / T. P. 326	47.2 / 28.7
T. P. 326	46 17 47.39 / 70 12 50.86	153 10 / 56 19	T. P. 325 / T. P. 327	28.7 / 91.4
T. P. 327	46 17 45.75 / 70 12 54.41	236 19 / 351 29	T. P. 326 / T. P. 328	91.4 / 61.6
T. P. 328	46 17 43.77 / 70 12 53.99	171 29 / 96 23	T. P. 327 / T. P. 329	61.6 / 32.3
T. P. 329	46 17 43.89 / 70 12 55.49	276 23 / 79 32	T. P. 328 / T. P. 330	32.3 / 31.2
T. P. 330	46 17 43.71 / 70 12 56.92	259 32 / 350 10	T. P. 329 / T. P. 331	31.2 / 40.7
T. P. 331	46 17 42.41 / 70 12 56.60	170 10 / 21 14	T. P. 330 / T. P. 332	40.7 / 28.9
T. P. 332	46 17 41.53 / 70 12 57.09	201 14 / 102 59	T. P. 331 / T. P. 333	28.9 / 42.5
T. P. 333	46 17 41.84 / 70 12 59.02	282 59 / 152 00	T. P. 332 / T. P. 334	42.5 / 71.8
T. P. 334	46 17 43.90 / 70 13 00.60	332 00 / 92 18	T. P. 333 / T. P. 335	71.8 / 51.9
T. P. 335	46 17 43.96 / 70 13 03.02	272 18 / 56 41	T. P. 334 / T. P. 336	51.9 / 42.4
T. P. 336	46 17 43.21 / 70 13 04.67	236 41 / 322 57	T. P. 335 / T. P. 337	42.4 / 76.5
T. P. 337	46 17 41.23 / 70 13 02.52	142 57 / 337 25	T. P. 336 / T. P. 338	76.5 / 29.5
T. P. 338	46 17 40.35 / 70 13 01.99	157 25 / 48 30	T. P. 337 / T. P. 339	29.5 / 35.8
T. P. 339	46 17 39.58 / 70 13 03.24	228 30 / 87 32	T. P. 338 / T. P. 340	35.8 / 68.7
T. P. 340	46 17 39.49 / 70 13 06.45	267 32 / 67 13	T. P. 339 / T. P. 341	68.7 / 130.6
T. P. 341	46 17 37.85 / 70 13 12.08	247 13 / 58 20	T. P. 340 / T. P. 342	130.6 / 118.4

Station	Latitude and longitude	Azimuth	To station	Distance (meters)
	° ′ ″	° ′ ″		
T. P. 342	46 17 35.84 / 70 13 16.78	238 20 / 89 43 / 113 32 / 293 12	T. P. 341 / T. P. 343 / Ref. Mon. C-56 / Ref. Mon. S-56	118.4 / 159.3 / 196.3 / 265.8
Ref. Mon. C-56	46 17 38.38 / 70 13 25.19	120 11 40 / 293 21 / 293 32	Ref. Mon. C-57 / Ref. Mon. S-56 / T. P. 342	519.7 / 462.1 / 196.3
Ref. Mon. C-57	46 17 46.84 / 70 13 46.18	300 11 20	Ref. Mon. C-56	519.7
Ref. Mon. S-56	46 17 32.45 / 70 13 05.37	113 12 / 113 21	T. P. 342 / Ref. Mon. C-56	265.8 / 462.1
T. P. 343	46 17 35.81 / 70 13 24.23	269 43 / 47 43	T. P. 342 / T. P. 344	159.3 / 61.5
T. P. 344	46 17 34.47 / 70 13 26.35	227 43 / 74 30	T. P. 343 / T. P. 345	61.5 / 68.2
T. P. 345	46 17 33.88 / 70 13 29.42	254 30 / 97 05	T. P. 344 / T. P. 346	68.2 / 111.3
T. P. 346	46 17 34.33 / 70 13 34.58	277 05 / 73 14	T. P. 345 / T. P. 347	111.3 / 104.3
T. P. 347	46 17 33.35 / 70 13 39.25	253 14 / 45 14	T. P. 346 / T. P. 348	104.3 / 51.4
T. P. 348	46 17 32.18 / 70 13 40.95	225 14 / 66 24	T. P. 347 / T. P. 349	51.4 / 25.8
T. P. 349	46 17 31.84 / 70 13 42.06	246 24 / 107 06	T. P. 348 / T. P. 350	25.8 / 26.3
T. P. 350	46 17 32.10 / 70 13 43.23	287 06 / 135 03	T. P. 349 / T. P. 351	26.3 / 39.6
T. P. 351	46 17 33.00 / 70 13 44.54	315 03 / 73 12	T. P. 350 / T. P. 352	39.6 / 20.5
T. P. 352	46 17 32.81 / 70 13 45.46	253 12 / 40 51	T. P. 351 / T. P. 353	20.5 / 26.1
T. P. 353	46 17 32.17 / 70 13 46.25	220 51 / 351 04	T. P. 352 / T. P. 354	26.1 / 44.5
T. P. 354	46 17 30.75 / 70 13 45.93	171 04 / 23 33	T. P. 353 / T. P. 355	44.5 / 23.4
T. P. 355	46 17 30.05 / 70 13 46.37	203 33 / 73 25	T. P. 354 / T. P. 356	23.4 / 82.6
T. P. 356	46 17 29.29 / 70 13 50.07	253 25 / 84 35	T. P. 355 / T. P. 357	82.6 / 70.1
T. P. 357	46 17 29.08 / 70 13 53.33	264 35 / 62 08	T. P. 356 / T. P. 358	70.1 / 66.2
T. P. 358	46 17 28.07 / 70 13 56.06	242 08 / 0 45	T. P. 357 / T. P. 359	66.2 / 205.9
T. P. 359	46 17 21.40 / 70 13 56.19	180 45 / 17 00	T. P. 358 / T. P. 360	205.9 / 44.3
T. P. 360	46 17 20.03 / 70 13 56.79	197 00 / 349 36	T. P. 359 / T. P. 361	44.3 / 74.7
T. P. 361	46 17 17.65 / 70 13 56.16	169 36 / 12 56	T. P. 360 / T. P. 362	74.7 / 64.1
T. P. 362	46 17 15.63 / 70 13 56.84	192 56 / 2 42	T. P. 361 / T. P. 363	64.1 / 86.9
T. P. 363	46 17 12.82 / 70 13 57.03	182 42 / 20 33	T. P. 362 / T. P. 364	86.9 / 138.6
T. P. 364	46 17 08.62 / 70 13 59.30	200 33 / 359 55 / 111 24 / 311 59	T. P. 363 / T. P. 365 / Ref. Mon. C-58 / Ref. Mon. S-58	138.6 / 102.0 / 128.4 / 64.6
Ref. Mon. C-58	46 17 10.13 / 70 14 04.88	291 24 / 298 15	T. P. 364 / Ref. Mon. S-58	128.4 / 190.2
Ref. Mon. S-58	46 17 07.22 / 70 13 57.06	118 15 / 131 59	Ref. Mon. C-58 / T. P. 364	190.2 / 64.6
T. P. 365	46 17 05.31 / 70 13 59.29	179 55 / 36 12	T. P. 364 / T. P. 366	102.0 / 64.5
T. P. 366	46 17 03.63 / 70 14 01.07	216 12 / 49 23	T. P. 365 / T. P. 367	64.5 / 133.3

BOUNDARY TURNING POINTS AND REFERENCE MONUMENTS—SOUTHWEST BRANCH OF ST. JOHN RIVER—Continued

Station	Latitude and longitude	Azimuth	To station	Distance (meters)	Station	Latitude and longitude	Azimuth	To station	Distance (meters)
	° ′ ″	° ′ ″				° ′ ″	° ′ ″		
T. P. 367	46 17 00.82 / 70 14 05.80	229 23 / 20 45	T. P. 366 / T. P. 368	133.3 / 94.2	Ref. Mon. C-60	46 16 16.42 / 70 14 56.21	298 19 / 306 34	Ref. Mon. S-60 / T. P. 394	367.4 / 242.6
T. P. 368	46 16 57.96 / 70 14 07.36	200 45 / 29 57	T. P. 367 / T. P. 369	94.2 / 76.3	Ref. Mon. S-60	46 16 10.78 / 70 14 41.10	103 02 / 118 19	T. P. 394 / Ref. Mon. C-60	132.0 / 367.4
T. P. 369	46 16 55.82 / 70 14 09.14	209 57 / 13 23	T. P. 368 / T. P. 370	76.3 / 68.6	T. P. 395	46 16 07.89 / 70 14 49.99	207 24 / 44 21	T. P. 394 / T. P. 396	134.0 / 153.0
T. P. 370	46 16 53.66 / 70 14 09.88	193 23 / 54 31	T. P. 369 / T. P. 371	68.6 / 127.8	T. P. 396	46 16 04.35 / 70 14 54.98	224 21 / 33 39	T. P. 395 / T. P. 397	153.0 / 92.3
T. P. 371	46 16 51.26 / 70 14 14.74	234 31 / 88 17	T. P. 370 / T. P. 372	127.8 / 68.2	T. P. 397	46 16 01.86 / 70 14 57.37	213 39 / 356 40	T. P. 396 / T. P. 398	92.3 / 72.8
T. P 372	46 16 51.19 / 70 14 17.93	268 17 / 47 30	T. P. 371 / T. P. 373	68.2 / 98.5	T. P. 398	46 15 59.50 / 70 14 57.18	176 40 / 337 11	T. P. 397 / T. P. 399	72.8 / 57.6
T. P. 373	46 16 49.04 / 70 14 21.32	227 30 / 39 24	T. P. 372 / T. P. 374	98.5 / 149.2	T. P. 399	46 15 57.78 / 70 14 56.13	157 11 / 8 37	T. P. 398 / T. P. 400	57.6 / 86.8
T. P. 374	46 16 45.30 / 70 14 25.74	219 24 / 358 27	T. P. 373 / T. P. 375	149.2 / 155.5	T. P. 400	46 15 55.00 / 70 14 56.74	188 37 / 47 46	T. P. 399 / T. P. 401	86.8 / 107.7
T. P. 375	46 16 40.27 / 70 14 25.55	178 27 / 29 40	T. P. 374 / T. P. 376	155.5 / 56.8	T. P. 401	46 15 52.66 / 70 15 00.46	227 46 / 26 58	T. P. 400 / T. P. 402	107.7 / 24.7
T. P. 376	46 16 38.67 / 70 14 26.86	209 40 / 357 17	T. P. 375 / T. P. 377	56.8 / 36.6	T. P. 402	46 15 51.94 / 70 15 00.99	206 58 / 308 24	T. P. 401 / T. P. 403	24.7 / 45.2
T. P. 377	46 16 37.49 / 70 14 26.78	177 17 / 319 15	T. P. 376 / T. P. 378	36.6 / 79.0	T. P. 403	46 15 51.04 / 70 14 59.33	128 24 / 10 50	T. P. 402 / T. P. 404	45.2 / 22.3
T. P. 378	46 16 35.55 / 70 14 24.37	139 15 / 356 35	T. P. 377 / T. P. 379	79.0 / 76.1	T. P. 404	46 15 50.33 / 70 14 59.53	190 50 / 83 28	T. P. 403 / T. P. 405	22.3 / 35.0
T. P. 379	46 16 33.09 / 70 14 24.16	176 35 / 29 56 / 115 41 / 307 36	T. P. 378 / T. P. 380 / Ref. Mon. C-59 / Ref. Mon. S-59	76.1 / 42.0 / 361.5 / 95.6	T. P. 405	46 15 50.20 / 70 15 01.16	263 28 / 52 14	T. P. 404 / T. P. 406	35.0 / 35.7
Ref. Mon. C-59	46 16 38.16 / 70 14 39.38	295 40 / 298 09	T. P. 379 / Ref. Mon. S-59	361.5 / 455.5	T. P. 406	46 15 49.49 / 70 15 02.47	232 14 / 21 36	T. P. 405 / T. P. 407	35.7 / 67.9
Ref. Mon. S-59	46 16 31.20 / 70 14 20.62	118 10 / 127 36	Ref. Mon. C-59 / T. P. 379	455.5 / 95.6	T. P. 407	46 15 47.45 / 70 15 03.64	201 36 / 11 40	T. P. 406 / T. P. 408	67.9 / 36.2
T. P. 380	46 16 31.91 / 70 14 25.14	209 56 / 52 20	T. P. 379 / T. P. 381	42.0 / 95.8	T. P. 408	46 15 46.30 / 70 15 03.98	191 40 / 334 01	T. P. 407 / T. P. 409	36.2 / 30.1
T. P. 381	46 16 30.01 / 70 14 28.68	232 20 / 11 21	T. P. 380 / T. P. 382	95.8 / 84.8	T. P. 409	46 15 45.42 / 70 15 03.37	154 01 / 259 23	T. P. 408 / T. P. 410	30.1 / 45.1
T. P. 382	46 16 27.32 / 70 14 29.46	191 21 / 340 40	T. P. 381 / T. P. 383	84.8 / 85.9	T. P. 410	46 15 45.69 / 70 15 01.30	79 23 / 333 58	T. P. 409 / T. P. 411	45.1 / 23.0
T. P. 383	46 16 24.70 / 70 14 28.13	160 40 / 10 39	T. P. 382 / T. P. 384	85.9 / 53.6	T. P. 411	46 15 45.02 / 70 15 00.82	153 58 / 51 58	T. P. 410 / T. P. 412	23.0 / 62.6
T. P. 384	46 16 22.99 / 70 14 28.59	190 39 / 51 29	T. P. 383 / T. P. 385	53.6 / 48.1	T. P. 412	46 15 43.77 / 70 15 03.12	231 58 / 36 56	T. P. 411 / T. P. 413	62.6 / 18.6
T. P. 385	46 16 22.02 / 70 14 30.35	231 29 / 102 18	T. P. 384 / T. P. 386	48.1 / 37.4	T. P. 413	46 15 43.29 / 70 15 03.65	216 56 / 320 34	T. P. 412 / T. P. 414	18.6 / 35.4
T. P. 386	46 16 22.28 / 70 14 32.06	282 18 / 149 57	T. P. 385 / T. P. 387	37.4 / 81.4	T. P. 414	46 15 42.40 / 70 15 02.60	140 34 / 356 22	T. P. 413 / T. P. 415	35.4 / 27.5
T. P. 387	46 16 24.56 / 70 14 33.96	329 57 / 104 38	T. P. 386 / T. P. 388	81.4 / 27.2	T. P. 415	46 15 41.51 / 70 15 02.52	176 22 / 51 40	T. P. 414 / T. P. 416	27.5 / 51.6
T. P. 388	46 16 24.78 / 70 14 35.19	284 38 / 57 16	T. P. 387 / T. P. 389	27.2 / 78.1	T. P. 416	46 15 40.48 / 70 15 04.41	231 40 / 358 13	T. P. 415 / T. P. 417	51.6 / 43.2
T. P. 389	46 16 23.41 / 70 14 38.26	237 16 / 12 21	T. P. 388 / T. P. 390	78.1 / 46.6	T. P. 417	46 15 39.08 / 70 15 04.34	178 13 / 46 58	T. P. 416 / T. P. 418	43.2 / 24.2
T. P. 390	46 16 21.94 / 70 14 38.72	192 21 / 331 17	T. P. 389 / T. P. 391	46.6 / 71.6	T. P. 418	46 15 38.54 / 70 15 05.17	226 58 / 103 24	T. P. 417 / T. P. 419	24.2 / 39.2
T. P. 391	46 16 19.90 / 70 14 37.12	151 17 / 1 19	T. P. 390 / T. P. 392	71.6 / 31.4	T. P. 419	46 15 38.84 / 70 15 06.95	283 24 / 48 22 / 114 08 / 273 28	T. P. 418 / T. P. 420 / Ref. Mon. C-61 / Ref. Mon. S-61	39.2 / 121.7 / 347.1 / 68.2
T. P. 392	46 16 18.89 / 70 14 37.15	181 19 / 44 04	T. P. 391 / T. P. 393	31.4 / 218.8	Ref. Mon. C-61	46 15 43.43 / 70 15 21.74	294 08 / 303 12	T. P. 419 / Ref. Mon. S-61	347.1 / 383.5
T. P. 393	46 16 13.80 / 70 14 44.26	224 04 / 43 58	T. P. 392 / T. P. 394	218.8 / 88.0	Ref. Mon. S-61	46 15 36.63 / 70 15 06.76	93 28 / 123 12	T. P. 419 / Ref. Mon. C-61	68.2 / 383.5
T. P. 394	46 16 11.74 / 70 14 47.11	223 58 / 27 24 / 126 34 / 283 02	T. P. 393 / T. P. 395 / Ref. Mon. C-60 / Ref. Mon. S-60	88.0 / 134.0 / 242.6 / 132.0	T. P. 420	46 15 36.22 / 70 15 11.20	228 22 / 13 04	T. P. 419 / T. P. 421	121.7 / 70.6
					T. P. 421	46 15 33.99 / 70 15 11.94	193 04 / 26 00	T. P. 420 / T. P. 422	70 6 / 63.6

BOUNDARY TURNING POINTS AND REFERENCE MONUMENTS—SOUTHWEST BRANCH OF ST. JOHN RIVER—Continued

Station	Latitude and longitude	Azimuth	To station	Distance (meters)
	° ′ ″	° ′ ″		
T. P. 422	46 15 32.14 / 70 15 13.24	206 00 / 347 34	T. P. 421 / T. P. 423	63.6 / 77.6
T. P. 423	46 15 29.69 / 70 15 12.46	167 34 / 19 12	T. P. 422 / T. P. 424	77.6 / 157.5
T. P. 424	46 15 24.87 / 70 15 14.88	199 12 / 352 05	T. P. 423 / T. P. 425	157.5 / 76.1
T. P. 425	46 15 22.43 / 70 15 14.39	172 05 / 335 28	T. P. 424 / T. P. 426	76.1 / 68.0
T. P. 426	46 15 20.43 / 70 15 13.08	155 28 / 1 32 / 93 28 / 308 25	T. P. 425 / T. P. 427 / Ref. Mon. C-62 / Ref. Mon. S-62	68.0 / 45.2 / 286.4 / 54 6
Ref. Mon. C-62	46 15 20.99 / 70 15 26.42	273 28 / 278 52	T. P. 426 / Ref. Mon. S-62	286.4 / 332.6
Ref. Mon. S-62	46 15 19.33 / 70 15 11.08	98 52 / 128 25	Ref. Mon. C-62 / T. P. 426	332.6 / 54.6
T. P. 427	46 15 18.96 / 70 15 13.13	181 32 / 25 59	T. P. 426 / T. P. 428	45.2 / 49.1
T. P. 428	46 15 17.53 / 70 15 14.14	205 59 / 71 34	T. P. 427 / T. P. 429	49.1 / 84.0
T. P. 429	46 15 16.67 / 70 15 17.86	251 34 / 35 27	T. P. 428 / T. P. 430	84.0 / 43.1
T. P. 430	46 15 15.54 / 70 15 19.02	215 27 / 349 29	T. P. 429 / T. P. 431	43.1 / 46.6
T. P. 431	46 15 14.05 / 70 15 18.62	169 29 / 320 27	T. P. 430 / T. P. 432	46.6 / 130.4
T. P. 432	46 15 10.80 / 70 15 14.75	140 27 / 291 56	T. P. 431 / T. P. 433	130.4 / 120.7
T. P. 433	46 15 09.33 / 70 15 09.52	111 56 / 329 14 / 93 55 / 295 15	T. P. 432 / T. P. 434 / Ref. Mon. C-63 / Ref. Mon. S-63	120.7 / 80.4 / 410.9 / 72.4
Ref. Mon. C-63	46 15 10.24 / 70 15 28.66	273 55 / 277 04	T. P. 433 / Ref. Mon. S-63	410.9 / 479.1
Ref. Mon. S-63	46 15 08.34 / 70 15 06.46	97 04 / 115 15	Ref. Mon. C-63 / T. P. 433	479.1 / 72.4
T. P. 434	46 15 07.10 / 70 15 07.60	149 14 / 10 25	T. P. 433 / T. P. 435	80.4 / 96.6
T. P. 435	46 15 04.02 / 70 15 08.42	190 25 / 354 01	T. P. 434 / T. P. 436	96.6 / 41.5
T. P. 436	46 15 02.68 / 70 15 08.21	174 01 / 333 55	T. P. 435 / T. P. 437	41.5 / 131.1
T. P. 437	46 14 58.87 / 70 15 05.52	153 55 / 356 58	T. P. 436 / T. P. 438	131.1 / 53.0
T. P. 438	46 14 57.15 / 70 15 05.39	176 58 / 33 47	T. P. 437 / T. P. 439	53.0 / 57.1
T. P. 439	46 14 55.62 / 70 15 06.87	213 47 / 55 11	T. P. 438 / T. P. 440	57.1 / 108.3
T. P. 440	46 14 53.61 / 70 15 11.03	235 11 / 48 26	T. P. 439 / T. P. 441	108.3 / 112.8
T. P. 441	46 14 51.19 / 70 15 14.97	228 26 / 38 07 / 107 13 / 287 11	T. P. 440 / T. P. 442 / Ref. Mon. C-64 / Ref. Mon. S-64	112.8 / 117.5 / 379.1 / 290.6
Ref. Mon. C-64	46 14 54.82 / 70 15 31.87	17 15 / 287 11 40 / 287 13	Ref. Mon. C-65 / Ref. Mon. S-64 / T. P. 441	258.8 / 669.8 / 379.1
Ref. Mon. S-64	46 14 48.41 / 70 15 02.01	107 11 / 107 12 00	T. P. 441 / Ref. Mon. C-64	290.6 / 669.8
Ref. Mon. C-65	46 14 46.82 / 70 15 35.46	197 14	Ref. Mon. C-64	258.8
T. P. 442	46 14 48.20 / 70 15 18.35	218 07 / 59 20	T. P. 441 / T. P. 443	117.5 / 58.0
T. P. 443	46 14 47.24 / 70 15 20.68	239 20 / 37 45	T. P. 442 / T. P. 444	58.0 / 32.0
T. P. 444	46 14 46.42 / 70 15 21.60	217 45 / 3 03	T. P. 443 / T. P. 445	32.0 / 23.6
T. P. 445	46 14 45.66 / 70 15 21.65	183 03 / 258 22	T. P. 444 / T. P. 446	23.6 / 51.6
T. P. 446	46 14 45.99 / 70 15 19.30	78 22 / 282 40	T. P. 445 / T. P. 447	51.6 / 39.5
T. P. 447	46 14 45.71 / 70 15 17.50	102 40 / 328 41	T. P. 446 / T. P. 448	39.5 / 29.6
T. P. 448	46 14 44.89 / 70 15 16.78	148 41 / 25 16	T. P. 447 / T. P. 449	29.6 / 32.3
T. P. 449	46 14 43.95 / 70 15 17.42	205 16 / 68 18	T. P. 448 / T. P. 450	32.3 / 63.5
T. P. 450	46 14 43.19 / 70 15 20.18	248 18 / 56 52	T. P. 449 / T. P. 451	63.5 / 52.5
T. P. 451	46 14 42.26 / 70 15 22.23	236 52 / 27 25	T. P. 450 / T. P. 452	52.5 / 83.5
T. P. 452	46 14 39.86 / 70 15 24.03	207 25 / 359 05	T. P. 451 / T. P. 453	83.5 / 114.0
T. P. 453	46 14 36.16 / 70 15 23.94	179 05 / 33 15	T. P. 452 / T. P. 454	114.0 / 102.0
T. P. 454	46 14 33.40 / 70 15 26.55	213 15 / 22 04	T. P. 453 / T. P. 455	102.0 / 83.3
T. P. 455	46 14 30.90 / 70 15 28.01	202 04 / 342 29	T. P. 454 / T. P. 456	83.3 / 77.4
T. P. 456	46 14 28.51 / 70 15 26.93	162 29 / 1 11	T. P. 455 / T. P. 457	77.4 / 51.5
T. P. 457	46 14 26.84 / 70 15 26.98	181 11 / 21 46	T. P. 456 / T. P. 458	51.5 / 49.8
T. P. 458	46 14 25.34 / 70 15 27.84	201 46 / 52 43	T. P. 457 / T. P. 459	49.8 / 101.5
T. P. 459	46 14 23.35 / 70 15 31.61	232 43 / 41 38	T. P. 458 / T. P. 460	101.5 / 119.0
T. P. 460	46 14 20.47 / 70 15 35.30	221 38 / 18 26	T. P. 459 / T. P. 461	119.0 / 45.2
T. P. 461	46 14 19.08 / 70 15 35.96	198 26 / 297 34	T. P. 460 / T. P. 462	45.2 / 87.4
T. P. 462	46 14 17.77 / 70 15 32.35	117 34 / 310 39	T. P. 461 / T. P. 463	87.4 / 40.7
T. P. 463	46 14 16.91 / 70 15 30.90	130 39 / 5 44 / 90 11 / 347 08	T. P. 462 / T. P. 464 / Ref. Mon. C-66 / Ref. Mon. S-65	40.7 / 266.6 / 383.7 / 121.0
Ref. Mon. C-66	46 14 16.95 / 70 15 48.82	270 11 / 286 11	T. P. 463 / Ref. Mon. S-65	383.7 / 427.6
Ref. Mon. S-65	46 14 13.09 / 70 15 29.65	106 11 / 167 08	Ref. Mon. C-66 / T. P. 463	427.6 / 121.0
T. P. 464	46 14 08.32 / 70 15 32.15	185 44 / 32 52	T. P. 463 / T. P. 465	266.6 / 142.1
T. P. 465	46 14 04.46 / 70 15 35.75	212 52 / 16 27	T. P. 464 / T. P. 466	142.1 / 100.5
T. P. 466	46 14 01.34 / 70 15 37.08	196 27 / 1 52	T. P. 465 / T. P. 467	100.5 / 134.7
T. P. 467	46 13 56.98 / 70 15 37.28	181 52 / 13 55	T. P. 466 / T. P. 468	134.7 / 52.4
T. P. 468	46 13 55.33 / 70 15 37.87	193 55 / 44 58	T. P. 467 / T. P. 469	52.4 / 75.2
T. P. 469	46 13 53.61 / 70 15 40.35	224 58 / 31 24	T. P. 468 / T. P. 470	75.2 / 47.1
T. P. 470	46 13 52.31 / 70 15 41.49	211 24 / 277 21	T. P. 469 / T. P. 471	47.1 / 41.9
T. P. 471	46 13 52.13 / 70 15 39.55	97 21 / 294 25	T. P. 470 / T. P. 472	41.9 / 26.0
T. P. 472	46 13 51.78 / 70 15 38.45	114 25 / 15 48	T. P. 471 / T. P. 473	26.0 / 83.1

BOUNDARY TURNING POINTS AND REFERENCE MONUMENTS—SOUTHWEST BRANCH OF ST. JOHN RIVER—Continued

Station	Latitude and longitude	Azimuth	To station	Distance (meters)	Station	Latitude and longitude	Azimuth	To station	Distance (meters)
	° ′ ″	° ′ ″				° ′ ″	° ′ ″		
T. P. 473	46 13 49.19 70 15 39.50	195 48 39 53	T. P. 472 T. P. 474	83.1 71.1	T. P. 502	46 13 07.96 70 16 09.07	77 09 321 40	T. P. 501 T. P. 503	38.8 26.6
T. P. 474	46 13 47.43 70 15 41.63	219 53 54 44	T. P. 473 T. P. 475	71.1 114.4	T. P. 503	46 13 07.29 70 16 08.30	141 40 21 27	T. P. 502 T. P. 504	26.6 73.0
T. P. 475	46 13 45.29 70 15 45.99	234 44 83 00	T. P. 474 T. P. 476	114.4 107.1	T. P. 504	46 13 05.09 70 16 09.55	201 27 55 21	T. P. 503 T. P. 505	73.0 43.6
T. P. 476	46 13 44.86 70 15 50.95	263 00 40 00	T. P. 475 T. P. 477	107.1 37.4	T. P. 505	46 13 04.29 70 16 11.22	235 21 142 44	T. P. 504 T. P. 506	43.6 36.8
T. P. 477	46 13 43.94 70 15 52.07	220 00 18 07	T. P. 476 T. P. 478	37.4 71.1	T. P. 506	46 13 05.23 70 16 12.26	322 44 34 07	T. P. 505 T. P. 507	36.8 40.8
T. P. 478	46 13 41.75 70 15 53.10	198 07 328 30	T. P. 477 T. P. 479	71.1 44.7	T. P. 507	46 13 04.14 70 16 13.33	214 07 0 21	T. P. 506 T. P. 508	40.8 51.9
T. P. 479	46 13 40.52 70 15 52.01	148 30 357 32	T. P. 478 T. P. 480	44.7 20.9	T. P. 508	46 13 02.46 70 16 13.34	180 21 63 20	T. P. 507 T. P. 509	51.9 80.5
T. P. 480	46 13 39.84 70 15 51.97	177 32 44 37	T. P. 479 T. P. 481	20.9 52.0	T. P. 509	46 13 01.29 70 16 16.70	243 20 131 38	T. P. 508 T. P. 510	80.5 43.2
T. P. 481	46 13 38.64 70 15 53.67	224 37 39 06	T. P. 480 T. P. 482	52.0 149.1	T. P. 510	46 13 02.22 70 16 18.20	311 38 52 02	T. P. 509 T. P. 511	43.2 27.1
T. P. 482	46 13 34.89 70 15 58.06	219 06 9 16	T. P. 481 T. P. 483	149.1 61.7	T. P. 511	46 13 01.68 70 16 19.20	232 02 350 50	T. P. 510 T. P. 512	27.1 37.2
T. P. 483	46 13 32.92 70 15 58.52	189 16 64 58 126 04 301 01	T. P. 482 T. P. 484 Ref. Mon. C-67 Ref. Mon. S-66	61.7 128.5 467.0 200.0	T. P. 512	46 13 00.49 70 16 18.92	170 50 29 53	T. P. 511 T. P. 513	37.2 28.4
Ref. Mon. C-67	46 13 41.83 70 16 16.14	304 32 40 306 04	Ref. Mon. S-66 T. P. 483	666.5 467.0	T. P. 513	46 12 59.69 70 16 19.58	209 53 110 20	T. P. 512 T. P. 514	28.4 43.0
Ref. Mon. S-66	46 13 29.59 70 15 50.52	121 01 124 33 00	T. P. 483 Ref. Mon. C-67	200.0 666.5	T. P. 514	46 13 00.18 70 16 21.47	290 20 159 16	T. P. 513 T. P. 515	43.0 51.8
T. P. 484	46 13 31.16 70 16 03.96	244 58 31 18	T. P. 483 T. P. 485	128.5 26.6	T. P. 515	46 13 01.75 70 16 22.32	339 16 102 01	T. P. 514 T. P. 516	51.8 23.7
T. P. 485	46 13 30.43 70 16 04.60	211 18 318 21	T. P. 484 T. P. 486	26.6 176.5	T. P. 516	46 13 01.91 70 16 23.40	282 01 43 28	T. P. 515 T. P. 517	23.7 40.7
T. P. 486	46 13 26.16 70 15 59.13	138 21 350 37	T. P. 485 T. P. 487	176.5 24.5	T. P. 517	46 13 00.95 70 16 24.71	223 28 89 43	T. P. 516 T. P. 518	40.7 56.0
T. P. 487	46 13 25.37 70 15 58.94	170 37 19 16	T. P. 486 T. P. 488	24.5 101.3	T. P. 518	46 13 00.94 70 16 27.32	269 43 1 40	T. P. 517 T. P. 519	56.0 27.4
T. P. 488	46 13 22.28 70 16 00.50	199 16 32 40	T. P. 487 T. P. 489	101.3 150.6	T. P. 519	46 13 00.05 70 16 27.36	181 40 290 38	T. P. 518 T. P. 520	27.4 40.2
T. P. 489	46 13 18.17 70 16 04.30	212 40 39 02	T. P. 488 T. P. 490	150.6 65.7	T. P. 520	46 12 59.59 70 16 25.61	110 38 329 23	T. P. 519 T. P. 521	40.2 23.8
T. P. 490	46 13 16.52 70 16 06.23	219 02 18 14	T. P. 489 T. P. 491	65.7 39.6	T. P. 521	46 12 58.93 70 16 25.04	149 23 17 26	T. P. 520 T. P. 522	23.8 42.2
T. P. 491	46 13 15.30 70 16 06.80	198 14 345 22	T. P. 490 T. P. 492	39.6 94.4	T. P. 522	46 12 57.63 70 16 25.63	197 26 52 16	T. P. 521 T. P. 523	42.2 84.7
T. P. 492	46 13 12.34 70 16 05.69	165 22 349 20	T. P. 491 T. P. 493	94.4 66.0	T. P. 523	46 12 55.95 70 16 28.76	232 16 22 19	T. P. 522 T. P. 524	84.7 76.0
T. P. 493	46 13 10.24 70 16 05.12	169 20 33 47	T. P. 492 T. P. 494	66.0 33.1	T. P. 524	46 12 53.68 70 16 30.10	202 19 351 57	T. P. 523 T. P. 525	76.0 32.2
T. P. 494	46 13 09.35 70 16 05.98	213 47 117 27	T. P. 493 T. P. 495	33.1 69.2	T. P. 525	46 12 52.64 70 16 29.89	171 57 284 11	T. P. 524 T. P. 526	32.2 30.1
T. P. 495	46 13 10.38 70 16 08.84	297 27 142 22	T. P. 494 T. P. 496	69.2 41.0	T. P. 526	46 12 52.41 70 16 28.53	104 11 316 33	T. P. 525 T. P. 527	30.1 71.8
T. P. 496	46 13 11.43 70 16 10.01	322 22 60 26	T. P. 495 T. P. 497	41.0 17.8	T. P. 527	46 12 50.72 70 16 26.23	136 33 277 56	T. P. 526 T. P. 528	71.8 66.5
T. P. 497	46 13 11.15 70 16 10.74	240 26 357 07	T. P. 496 T. P. 498	17.8 37.2	T. P. 528	46 12 50.42 70 16 23.16	97 56 301 52	T. P. 527 T. P. 529	66.5 42.9
T. P. 498	46 13 09.95 70 16 10.65	177 07 18 49	T. P. 497 T. P. 499	37.2 85.4	T. P. 529	46 12 49.69 70 16 21.45	121 52 330 58	T. P. 528 T. P. 530	42.9 73.5
T. P. 499	46 13 07.33 70 16 11.93	198 49 339 28	T. P. 498 T. P. 500	85.4 16.6	T. P. 530	46 12 47.61 70 16 19.79	150 58 56 03	T. P. 529 T. P. 531	73.5 34.2
T. P. 500	46 13 06.82 70 16 11.66	159 28 213 44	T. P. 499 T. P. 501	16.6 32.0	T. P. 531	46 12 46.99 70 16 21.12	236 03 5 26	T. P. 530 T. P. 532	34.2 42.6
T. P. 501	46 13 07.69 70 16 10.84	33 44 257 09	T. P. 500 T. P. 502	32.0 38.8	T. P. 532	46 12 45.62 70 16 21.30	185 26 337 02	T. P. 531 T. P. 533	42.6 66.4
					T. P. 533	46 12 43.63 70 16 20.09	157 02 304 31	T. P. 532 T. P. 534	66.4 39.4

BOUNDARY TURNING POINTS AND REFERENCE MONUMENTS—SOUTHWEST BRANCH OF ST. JOHN RIVER—Continued

Station	Latitude and longitude	Azimuth	To station	Distance (meters)
	° ′ ″	° ′ ″		
T. P. 534	46 12 42.91 70 16 18.58	124 31 323 32	T. P. 533 T. P. 535	39.4 40.2
T. P. 535	46 12 41.86 70 16 17.46	143 32 14 42	T. P. 534 T. P. 536	40.2 48.8
T. P. 536	46 12 40.33 70 16 18.04	194 42 0 31	T. P. 535 T. P. 537	48.8 30.8
T P. 537	46 12 39.34 70 16 18.06	180 31 78 43	T. P. 536 T. P. 538	30.8 25.9
T. P. 538	46 12 39.17 70 16 19.24	258 43 161 07	T. P. 537 T. P. 539	25.9 35.6
T. P 539	46 12 40.26 70 16 19.78	341 07 95 52	T. P. 538 T. P. 540	35.6 17.3
T. P. 540	46 12 40.32 70 16 20.58	275 52 58 33	T. P. 539 T. P. 541	17.3 40.6
T. P. 541	46 12 39.64 70 16 22.20	238 33 6 50	T. P. 540 T. P. 542	40.6 27.8
T. P. 542	46 12 38.74 70 16 22.35	186 50 312 04	T. P. 541 T. P. 543	27.8 58.8
T. P. 543	46 12 37.46 70 16 20.32	132 04 341 30	T. P. 542 T. P. 544	58.8 21.0
T. P. 544	46 12 36.82 70 16 20.00	161 30 34 59	T. P. 543 T. P. 545	21.0 25.0
T. P. 545	46 12 36.16 70 16 20.67	214 59 86 54	T. P. 544 T. P. 546	25.0 46.5
T. P. 546	46 12 36.07 70 16 22.84	266 54 63 06	T. P. 545 T. P. 547	46.5 35.4
T. P. 547	46 12 35.56 70 16 24.31	243 06 44 14 122 04 40 297 40	T. P. 546 T. P. 548 Ref. Mon. C-68 Ref. Mon. S-67	35.4 61.2 855.2 135.1
Ref. Mon. C-68	46 12 50.26 70 16 58.12	12 28 301 28 00 302 04 10	Ref. Mon. C-69 Ref. Mon. S-67 T. P. 547	243.8 990.0 855.2
Ref. Mon. S-67	46 12 33.52 70 16 18.73	117 40 121 28 30	T. P. 547 Ref. Mon. C-68	135.1 990.0
Ref. Mon. C-69	46 12 42.55 70 17 00.58	192 28	Ref. Mon. C-68	243.8
T. P. 548	46 12 34.14 70 16 26.31	224 14 20 30	T. P. 547 T. P. 549	61.2 47.7
T. P. 549	46 12 32.69 70 16 27.09	200 30 52 13	T. P. 548 T. P. 550	47.7 177.4
T. P. 550	46 12 29.17 70 16 33.63	232 13 47 07	T. P. 549 T. P. 551	177.4 47.8
T. P. 551	46 12 28.11 70 16 35.26	227 07 62 20	T. P. 550 T. P. 552	47.8 47.5
T. P. 552	46 12 27.40 70 16 37.22	242 20 355 01	T. P. 551 T. P. 553	47.5 16.0
T. P. 553	46 12 26.88 70 16 37.16	175 01 25 04	T. P. 552 T. P. 554	16.0 97.5
T. P. 554	46 12 24.02 70 16 39.09	205 04 353 51	T. P. 553 T. P. 555	97.5 53.0
T. P. 555	46 12 22.32 70 16 38.82	173 51 9 54	T. P. 554 T. P. 556	53.0 108.3
T. P. 556	46 12 18.86 70 16 39.69	189 54 23 43	T. P. 555 T. P. 557	108.3 92.8
T. P. 557	46 12 16.11 70 16 41.43	203 43 11 46	T. P. 556 T. P. 558	92.8 23.2
T. P. 558	46 12 15.38 70 16 41.65	191 46 324 24	T. P. 557 T. P. 559	23.2 33.6
T. P. 559	46 12 14.49 70 16 40.74	144 24 25 46	T. P. 558 T. P. 560	33.6 27.9
T. P. 560	46 12 13.68 70 16 41.31	205 46 56 28	T. P. 559 T. P. 561	27.9 26.0
T. P. 561	46 12 13.21 70 16 42.32	236 28 88 35	T. P. 560 T. P. 562	26.0 50.2

Station	Latitude and longitude	Azimuth	To station	Distance (meters)
	° ′ ″	° ′ ″		
T. P. 562	46 12 13.17 70 16 44.66	268 35 32 22	T. P. 561 T. P. 563	50.2 99.6
T. P. 563	46 12 10.45 70 16 47.15	212 22 356 22	T. P. 562 T. P. 564	99.6 32.3
T. P. 564	46 12 09.40 70 16 47.05	176 22 22 47	T. P. 563 T. P. 565	32.3 89.9
T. P. 565	46 12 06.72 70 16 48.68	202 47 41 27	T. P. 564 T. P. 566	89.9 38.9
T. P. 566	46 12 05.77 70 16 49.88	221 27 72 39	T. P. 565 T. P. 567	38.9 100.3
T. P. 567	46 12 04.81 70 16 54.34	252 39 57 50	T. P. 566 T. P. 568	100.3 25.4
T. P. 568	46 12 04.37 70 16 55.34	237 50 353 42	T. P. 567 T. P. 569	25.4 47.6
T. P. 569	46 12 02.84 70 16 55.10	173 42 331 42	T. P. 568 T. P. 570	47.6 32.2
T. P. 570	46 12 01.92 70 16 54.39	151 42 347 03	T. P. 569 T. P. 571	32.2 36.6
T. P. 571	46 12 00.76 70 16 54.01	167 03 41 31 116 59 316 58	T. P. 570 T. P. 572 Ref. Mon. C-70 Ref. Mon. S-68	36.6 67.9 429.9 84.9
Ref. Mon. C-70	46 12 07.08 70 17 11.88	12 27 50 296 59 300 14 10	Ref. Mon. S-69 T. P. 571 Ref. Mon. S-68	1,324.6 429.9 510.5
Ref. Mon. S-68	46 11 58.75 70 16 51.31	120 14 20 136 58	Ref. Mon. C-70 T. P. 571	510.5 84.9
T. P. 572	46 11 59.11 70 16 56.11	221 31 60 44	T. P. 571 T. P. 573	67.9 86.5
T. P. 573	46 11 57.74 70 16 59.62	240 44 76 05	T. P. 572 T. P. 574	86.5 77.9
T. P. 574	46 11 57.14 70 17 03.15	256 05 49 54	T. P. 573 T. P. 575	77.9 30.1
T. P. 575	46 11 56.51 70 17 04.23	229 54 21 48	T. P. 574 T. P. 576	30.1 149.3
T. P. 576	46 11 52.02 70 17 06.81	201 48 78 55	T. P. 575 T. P. 577	149.3 62.6
T. P. 577	46 11 51.63 70 17 09.68	258 55 24 09	T. P. 576 T. P. 578	62.6 121.6
T. P. 578	46 11 48.04 70 17 12.00	204 09 356 19	T. P. 577 T. P. 579	121.6 49.2
T. P. 579	46 11 46.45 70 17 11.85	176 19 25 56	T. P. 578 T. P. 580	49.2 28.1
T. P. 580	46 11 45.63 70 17 12.43	205 56 340 16	T. P. 579 T. P. 581	28.1 46.9
T. P. 581	46 11 44.20 70 17 11.69	160 16 10 31	T. P. 580 T. P. 582	46.9 13.8
T. P. 582	46 11 43.76 70 17 11.80	190 31 76 18	T. P. 581 T. P. 583	13.8 31.5
T. P. 583	46 11 43.51 70 17 13.23	256 18 42 33	T. P. 582 T. P. 584	31.5 25.3
T. P. 584	46 11 42.91 70 17 14.03	222 33 79 07	T. P. 583 T. P. 585	25.3 26.0
T. P. 585	46 11 42.75 70 17 15.22	259 07 107 10	T. P. 584 T. P. 586	26.0 87.1
T P. 586	46 11 43.58 70 17 19.10	287 10 60 38	T. P. 585 T. P. 587	87.1 12.2
T. P. 587	46 11 43.39 70 17 19.60	240 38 23 40	T. P. 586 T. P. 588	12.2 29.2
T. P. 588	46 11 42.52 70 17 20.14	203 40 353 03	T. P. 587 T. P. 589	29.2 78.0
T. P. 589	46 11 40.02 70 17 19.70	173 03 335 24	T. P. 588 T. P. 590	78.0 53.0
T. P. 590	46 11 38.46 70 17 18.68	155 24 53 10	T. P. 589 T. P. 591	53.0 58.7

BOUNDARY TURNING POINTS AND REFERENCE MONUMENTS—SOUTHWEST BRANCH OF ST. JOHN RIVER—Continued

Station	Latitude and longitude	Azimuth	To station	Distance (meters)	Station	Latitude and longitude	Azimuth	To station	Distance (meters)
	° ′ ″	° ′ ″				° ′ ″	° ′ ″		
T. P. 591	46 11 37.32	233 10	T. P. 590	58.7	T. P. 619	46 11 07.01	95 16	T. P. 618	89.2
	70 17 20.87	124 07	T. P. 592	30.4		70 17 20.00	303 27	T. P. 620	97.2
T. P. 592	46 11 37.87	304 07	T. P. 591	30.4	T. P. 620	46 11 05.28	123 27	T. P. 619	97.2
	70 17 22.04	60 04	T. P. 593	28.3		70 17 16.22	261 44	T. P. 621	62.0
T. P. 593	46 11 37.41	240 04	T. P. 592	28.3	T. P. 621	46 11 05.57	81 44	T. P. 620	62.0
	70 17 23.18	15 22	T. P. 594	49.7		70 17 13.36	293 24	T. P. 622	41.8
T. P. 594	46 11 35.86	195 22	T. P. 593	49.7	T. P. 622	46 11 05.03	113 24	T. P. 621	41.8
	70 17 23.80	310 25	T. P. 595	39.7		70 17 11.57	319 15	T. P. 623	26.7
T. P. 595	46 11 35.03	130 25	T. P. 594	39.7	T. P. 623	46 11 04.37	139 15	T. P. 622	26.7
	70 17 22.39	6 30	T. P. 596	21.0		70 17 10.75	17 35	T. P. 624	63.7
T. P. 596	46 11 34.35	186 30	T. P. 595	21.0	T. P. 624	46 11 02.41	197 35	T. P. 623	63.7
	70 17 22.50	97 48	T. P. 597	47.6		70 17 11.65	356 13	T. P. 625	144.7
T. P. 597	46 11 34.56	277 48	T. P. 596	47.6	T. P. 625	46 10 57.73	176 13	T. P. 624	144.7
	70 17 24.70	57 36	T. P. 598	175.0		70 17 11.21	303 22	T. P. 626	78.2
T. P. 598	46 11 31.52	237 36	T. P. 597	175.0	T. P. 626	46 10 56.33	123 22	T. P. 625	78.2
	70 17 31.59	44 58	T. P. 599	57.2		70 17 08.16	342 52	T. P. 627	45.7
T. P. 599	46 11 30.21	224 58	T. P. 598	57.2	T. P. 627	46 10 54.92	162 52	T. P. 626	45.7
	70 17 33.47	71 09	T. P. 600	54.4		70 17 07.53	287 17	T. P. 628	35.7
T. P. 600	46 11 29.64	251 09	T. P. 599	54.4	T. P. 628	46 10 54.58	107 17	T. P. 627	35.7
	70 17 35.88	332 21	T. P. 601	38.8		70 17 05.94	305 55	T. P. 629	53.8
		24 02	Ref. Mon. 313	16.6	T. P. 629	46 10 53.56	125 55	T. P. 628	53.8
		298 13	Ref. Mon. 312	13.4		70 17 03.91	0 01	T. P. 630	42.9
Ref. Mon. 312	46 11 29.44	64 33	Ref. Mon. 313	20.6	T. P. 630	46 10 52.16	180 01	T. P. 629	42.9
	70 17 35.32	118 13	T. P. 600	13.4		70 17 03.91	66 22	T. P. 631	36.7
Ref. Mon. 313	46 11 29.15	204 02	T. P. 600	16.6	T. P. 631	46 10 51.69	246 22	T. P. 630	36.7
	70 17 36.19	244 33	Ref. Mon. 312	20.6		70 17 05.48	331 54	T. P. 632	75.0
		297 26	Ref. Mon. S-69	265.4	T. P. 632	46 10 49.54	151 54	T. P. 631	75.0
Ref. Mon. S-69	46 11 25.19	192 27 40	Ref. Mon. C-70	1,324.6		70 17 03.84	282 01	T. P. 633	32.5
	70 17 25.21	117 26	Ref. Mon. 313	265.4	T. P. 633	46 10 49.32	102 01	T. P. 632	32.5
T. P. 601	46 11 28.53	152 21	T. P. 600	38.8		70 17 02.35	272 44	T. P. 634	33.2
	70 17 35.04	358 15	T. P. 602	37.8	T. P. 634	46 10 49.27	92 44	T. P. 633	33.2
T. P. 602	46 11 27.31	178 15	T. P. 601	37.8		70 17 00.81	342 11	T. P. 635	26.3
	70 17 34.98	336 00	T. P. 603	27.5	T. P. 635	46 10 48.46	162 11	T. P. 634	26.3
T. P. 603	46 11 26.50	156 00	T. P. 602	27.5		70 17 00.43	319 06	T. P. 636	32.8
	70 17 34.46	8 36	T. P. 604	40.5	T. P. 636	46 10 47.66	139 06	T. P. 635	32.8
T. P. 604	46 11 25.20	188 36	T. P. 603	40.5		70 16 59.43	347 08	T. P. 637	36.6
	70 17 34.74	289 39	T. P. 605	42.5	T. P. 637	46 10 46.50	167 08	T. P. 636	36.6
T. P. 605	46 11 24.74	109 39	T. P. 604	42.5		70 16 59.05	358 22	T. P. 638	87.4
	70 17 32.88	241 16	T. P. 606	44.5	T. P. 638	46 10 43.68	178 22	T. P. 637	87.4
T. P. 606	46 11 25.43	61 16	T. P. 605	44.5		70 16 58.94	319 55	T. P. 639	72.7
	70 17 31.06	303 59	T. P. 607	17.4	T. P. 639	46 10 41.87	139 55	T. P. 638	72.7
T. P. 607	46 11 25.11	123 59	T. P. 606	17.4		70 16 56.76	283 33	T. P. 640	37.1
	70 17 30.39	16 26	T. P. 608	58.0	T. P. 640	46 10 41.59	103 33	T. P. 639	37.1
T. P. 608	46 11 23.31	196 26	T. P. 607	58.0		70 16 55.07	350 40	T. P. 641	51.2
	70 17 31.15	322 26	T. P. 609	92.7	T. P. 641	46 10 39.95	170 40	T. P. 640	51.2
T. P. 609	46 11 20.93	142 26	T. P. 608	92.7		70 16 54.69	314 34	T. P. 642	24.1
	70 17 28.52	293 10	T. P. 610	46.4	T. P. 642	46 10 39.41	134 34	T. P. 641	24.1
T. P. 610	46 11 20.34	113 10	T. P. 609	46.4		70 16 53.89	256 38	T. P. 643	44.4
	70 17 26.53	13 14	T. P. 611	42.6	T. P. 643	46 10 39.74	76 38	T. P. 642	44.4
T. P. 611	46 11 19.00	193 14	T. P. 610	42.6		70 16 51.87	303 37	T. P. 644	15.3
	70 17 26.98	349 34	T. P. 612	68.3	T. P. 644	46 10 39.46	123 37	T. P. 643	15.3
T. P. 612	46 11 16.82	169 34	T. P. 611	68.3		70 16 51.28	345 08	T. P. 645	54.2
	70 17 26.41	64 33	T. P. 613	52.5	T. P. 645	46 10 37.77	165 08	T. P. 644	54.2
T. P. 613	46 11 16.09	244 33	T. P. 612	52.5		70 16 50.63	355 19	T. P. 646	46.0
	70 17 28.62	355 05	T. P. 614	78.3	T. P. 646	46 10 36.28	175 19	T. P. 645	46.0
T. P. 614	46 11 13.57	175 05	T. P. 613	78.3		70 16 50.45	304 49	T. P. 647	41.8
	70 17 28.30	10 14	T. P. 615	106.2	T. P. 647	46 10 35.51	124 49	T. P. 646	41.8
T. P. 615	46 11 10.18	190 14	T. P. 614	106.2		70 16 48.85	342 59	T. P. 648	42.0
	70 17 29.18	334 59	T. P. 616	50.4	T. P. 648	46 10 34.21	162 59	T. P. 647	42.0
T. P. 616	46 11 08.70	154 59	T. P. 615	50.4		70 16 48.28	314 58	T. P. 649	33.2
	70 17 28.19	4 10	T. P. 617	57.0			48 22	Ref. Mon. C-72	292.0
T. P. 617	46 11 06.86	184 10	T. P. 616	57.0			227 23	Ref. Mon. S-70	133.8
	70 17 28.38	261 51	T. P. 618	91.9	Ref. Mon. C-72	46 10 27.93	137 58 40	Ref. Mon. C-71	1,157.0
T. P. 618	46 11 07.28	81 51	T. P. 617	91.9		70 16 58.46	228 03	Ref. Mon. S-70	425.8
	70 17 24.14	275 16	T. P. 619	89.2			228 22	T. P. 648	292.0

BOUNDARY TURNING POINTS AND REFERENCE MONUMENTS—SOUTHWEST BRANCH OF ST. JOHN RIVER—Continued

Station	Latitude and longitude	Azimuth	To station	Distance (meters)
Ref. Mon. S-70	46 10 37.14 / 70 16 43.69	47 23 / 48 04	T. P. 648 / Ref. Mon. C-72	133.8 / 425.8
Ref. Mon. C-71	46 10 55.76 / 70 17 34.57	317 58 20	Ref. Mon. C-72	1,157.0
T. P. 649	46 10 33.45 / 70 16 47.19	134 58 / 292 34	T. P. 648 / T. P. 650	33.2 / 18.8
T. P. 650	46 10 33.22 / 70 16 46.38	112 34 / 322 23	T. P. 649 / T. P. 651	18.8 / 170.5
T. P. 651	46 10 28.84 / 70 16 41.53	142 23 / 280 08	T. P. 650 / T. P. 652	170.5 / 51.8
T. P. 652	46 10 28.55 / 70 16 39.15	100 08 / 243 49	T. P. 651 / T. P. 653	51.8 / 36.8
T. P. 653	46 10 29.07 / 70 16 37.61	63 49 / 301 32	T. P. 652 / T. P. 654	36.8 / 58.7
T. P. 654	46 10 28.08 / 70 16 35.27	121 32 / 271 07	T. P. 653 / T. P. 655	58.7 / 36.1
T. P. 655	46 10 28.06 / 70 16 33.59	91 07 / 309 30	T. P. 654 / T. P. 656	36.1 / 29.9
T. P. 656	46 10 27.44 / 70 16 32.52	129 30 / 345 21	T. P. 655 / T. P. 657	29.9 / 36.9
T. P. 657	46 10 26.29 / 70 16 32.08	165 21 / 46 19	T. P. 656 / T. P. 658	36.9 / 59.0
T. P. 658	46 10 24.97 / 70 16 34.07	226 19 / 5 39	T. P. 657 / T. P. 659	59.0 / 18.0
T. P. 659	46 10 24.39 / 70 16 34.15	185 39 / 309 50	T. P. 658 / T. P. 660	18.0 / 55.6
T. P. 660	46 10 23.23 / 70 16 32.16	129 50 / 300 33	T. P. 659 / T. P. 661	55.6 / 79.8
T. P. 661	46 10 21.92 / 70 16 28.96	120 33 / 323 41	T. P. 660 / T. P. 662	79.8 / 48.0
T. P. 662	46 10 20.66 / 70 16 27.63	143 41 / 282 41	T. P. 661 / T. P. 663	48.0 / 47.7
T. P. 663	46 10 20.33 / 70 16 25.46	102 41 / 297 11	T. P. 662 / T. P. 664	47.7 / 43.4
T. P. 664	46 10 19.68 / 70 16 23.66	117 11 / 254 10	T. P. 663 / T. P. 665	43.4 / 70.7
T. P. 665	46 10 20.31 / 70 16 20.49	74 10 / 292 14	T. P. 664 / T. P. 666	70.7 / 51.2
T. P. 666	46 10 19.68 / 70 16 18.28	112 14 / 332 54 / 78 44 50 / 261 45	T. P. 665 / T. P. 667 / Ref. Mon. C-73 / Ref. Mon. S-71	51.2 / 78.0 / 546.8 / 187.2
Ref. Mon. C-73	46 10 16.22 / 70 16 43.28	258 44 30 / 259 30 30	T. P. 666 / Ref. Mon. S-71	546.8 / 733.8
Ref. Mon. S-71	46 10 20.55 / 70 16 09.64	79 30 50 / 81 45	Ref. Mon. C-73 / T. P. 666	733.8 / 187.2
T. P. 667	46 10 17.43 / 70 16 16.62	152 54 / 311 09	T. P. 666 / T. P. 668	78.0 / 52.9
T. P. 668	46 10 16.30 / 70 16 14.77	131 09 / 0 44	T. P. 667 / T. P. 669	52.9 / 18.0
T. P. 669	46 10 15.72 / 70 16 14.78	180 44 / 78 40	T. P. 668 / T. P. 670	18.0 / 30.5
T. P. 670	46 10 15.53 / 70 16 16.17	258 40 / 31 14	T. P. 669 / T. P. 671	30.5 / 20.5
T. P. 671	46 10 14.96 / 70 16 16.67	211 14 / 297 04	T. P. 670 / T. P. 672	20.5 / 116.2
T. P. 672	46 10 13.24 / 70 16 11.84	117 04 / 247 45	T. P. 671 / T. P. 673	116.2 / 38.6
T. P. 673	46 10 13.72 / 70 16 10.18	67 45 / 293 59	T. P. 672 / T. P. 674	38.6 / 72.2
T. P. 674	46 10 12.77 / 70 16 07.10	113 59 / 324 49	T. P. 673 / T. P. 675	72.2 / 117.8
T. P. 675	46 10 09.65 / 70 16 03.94	144 49 / 247 56	T. P. 674 / T. P. 676	117.8 / 30.0

Station	Latitude and longitude	Azimuth	To station	Distance (meters)
T. P. 676	46 10 10.01 / 70 16 02.65	67 56 / 275 18	T. P. 675 / T. P. 677	30.0 / 17.4
T. P. 677	46 10 09.96 / 70 16 01.84	95 18 / 342 24	T. P. 676 / T. P. 678	17.4 / 88.0
T. P. 678	46 10 07.24 / 70 16 00.60	162 24 / 324 39	T. P. 677 / T. P. 679	88.0 / 59.2
T. P. 679	46 10 05.68 / 70 15 59.00	144 39 / 301 54	T. P. 678 / T. P. 680	59.2 / 81.7
T. P. 680	46 10 04.28 / 70 15 55.76	121 54 / 331 29	T. P. 679 / T. P. 681	81.7 / 28.3
T. P. 681	46 10 03.48 / 70 15 55.14	151 29 / 11 43	T. P. 680 / T. P. 682	28.3 / 63.0
T. P. 682	46 10 01.48 / 70 15 55.73	191 43 / 334 15	T. P. 681 / T. P. 683	63.0 / 33.7
T. P. 683	46 10 00.50 / 70 15 55.05	154 15 / 341 21	T. P. 682 / T. P. 684	33.7 / 53.6
T. P. 684	46 09 58.85 / 70 15 54.25	161 21 / 356 52	T. P. 683 / T. P. 685	53.6 / 43.8
T. P. 685	46 09 57.44 / 70 15 54.14	176 52 / 12 58	T. P. 684 / T. P. 686	43.8 / 50.2
T. P. 686	46 09 55.85 / 70 15 54.66	192 58 / 354 06 / 33 48 / 240 51	T. P. 685 / T. P. 687 / Ref. Mon. C-74 / Ref. Mon. S-72	50.2 / 84.7 / 69.3 / 196.7
Ref. Mon. C-74	46 09 53.99 / 70 15 56.46	213 48 / 233 54	T. P. 686 / Ref. Mon. S-72	69.3 / 260.3
Ref. Mon. S-72	46 09 58.95 / 70 15 46.66	53 54 / 60 51	Ref. Mon. C-74 / T. P. 686	260.3 / 196.7
T. P. 687	46 09 53.12 / 70 15 54.26	174 06 / 303 49	T. P. 686 / T. P. 688	84.7 / 26.2
T. P. 688	46 09 52.65 / 70 15 53.24	123 49 / 275 33	T. P. 687 / T. P. 689	26.2 / 33.9
T. P. 689	46 09 52.54 / 70 15 51.67	95 33 / 297 34	T. P. 688 / T. P. 690	33.9 / 51.4
T. P. 690	46 09 51.77 / 70 15 49.55	117 34 / 258 25	T. P. 689 / T. P. 691	51.4 / 86.2
T. P. 691	46 09 52.33 / 70 15 45.61	78 25 / 297 16	T. P. 690 / T. P. 692	86.2 / 29.7
T. P. 692	46 09 51.89 / 70 15 44.38	117 16 / 352 52	T. P. 691 / T. P. 693	29.7 / 43.0
T. P. 693	46 09 50.51 / 70 15 44.13	172 52 / 317 48	T. P. 692 / T. P. 694	43.0 / 51.3
T. P. 694	46 09 49.28 / 70 15 42.53	137 48 / 271 18	T. P. 693 / T. P. 695	51.3 / 58.9
T. P. 695	46 09 49.24 / 70 15 39.78	91 18 / 310 08	T. P. 694 / T. P. 696	58.9 / 38.0
T. P. 696	46 09 48.44 / 70 15 38.43	130 08 / 295 55	T. P. 695 / T. P. 697	38.0 / 36.4
T. P. 697	46 09 47.93 / 70 15 36.90	115 55 / 324 59	T. P. 696 / T. P. 698	36.4 / 34.3
T. P. 698	46 09 47.02 / 70 15 35.98	144 59 / 338 15	T. P. 697 / T. P. 699	34.3 / 82.0
T. P. 699	46 09 44.55 / 70 15 34.57	158 15 / 319 49	T. P. 698 / T. P. 700	82.0 / 76.0
T. P. 700	46 09 42.67 / 70 15 32.28	139 49 / 21 55	T. P. 699 / T. P. 701	76.0 / 13.6
T. P. 701	46 09 42.26 / 70 15 32.52	201 55 / 85 00	T. P. 700 / T. P. 702	13.6 / 42.4
T. P. 702	46 09 42.14 / 70 15 34.48	265 00 / 11 26	T. P. 701 / T. P. 703	42.4 / 35.4
T. P. 703	46 09 41.02 / 70 15 34.81	191 26 / 324 02	T. P. 702 / T. P. 704	35.4 / 81.4
T. P. 704	46 09 38.88 / 70 15 32.58	144 02 / 296 55	T. P. 703 / T. P. 705	81.4 / 58.7

BOUNDARY TURNING POINTS AND REFERENCE MONUMENTS—SOUTHWEST BRANCH OF ST. JOHN RIVER—Continued

Station	Latitude and longitude	Azimuth	To station	Distance (meters)	Station	Latitude and longitude	Azimuth	To station	Distance (meters)
	° ′ ″	° ′ ″				° ′ ″	° ′ ″		
T. P. 705	46 09 38.02	116 55	T. P. 704	58.7	T. P. 734	46 09 14.41	131 21	T. P. 733	23.2
	70 15 30.14	337 22	T. P. 706	88.2		70 14 59.07	295 06	T. P. 735	95.2
T. P. 706	46 09 35.38	157 22	T. P. 705	88.2	T. P. 735	46 09 13.10	115 06	T. P. 734	95.2
	70 15 28.56	296 20	T. P. 707	25.4		70 14 55.05	325 06	T. P. 736	56.0
T. P. 707	46 09 35.02	116 20	T. P. 706	25.4	T. P. 736	46 09 11.62	145 06	T. P. 735	56.0
	70 15 27.50	292 22	T. P. 708	17.0		70 14 53.56	30 38	T. P. 737	34.9
T. P. 708	46 09 34.81	112 22	T. P. 707	17.0	T. P. 737	46 09 10.64	210 38	T. P. 736	34.9
	70 15 26.77	327 12	T. P. 709	28.1		70 14 54.38	15 45	T. P. 738	40.0
T. P. 709	46 09 34.05	147 12	T. P. 708	28.1	T. P. 738	46 09 09.39	195 45	T. P. 737	40.0
	70 15 26.06	304 40	T. P. 710	12.8		70 14 54.89	84 25	T. P. 739	29.7
T. P. 710	46 09 33.81	124 40	T. P. 709	12.8	T. P. 739	46 09 09.30	264 25	T. P. 738	29.7
	70 15 25.57	236 59	T. P. 711	36.3		70 14 56.27	2 53	T. P. 740	59.8
T. P. 711	46 09 34.45	56 59	T. P. 710	36.3	T. P. 740	46 09 07.37	182 53	T. P. 739	59.8
	70 15 24.15	260 41	T. P. 712	17.4		70 14 56.41	321 05	T. P. 741	19.8
T. P. 712	46 09 34.54	80 41	T. P. 711	17.4	T. P. 741	46 09 06.87	141 05	T. P. 740	19.8
	70 15 25.35	302 14	T. P. 713	19.2		70 14 55.83	287 07	T. P. 742	38.7
T. P. 713	46 09 34.21	122 14	T. P. 712	19.2	T. P. 742	46 09 06.50	107 07	T. P. 741	38.7
	70 15 22.59	21 54	T. P. 714	36.5		70 14 54.10	239 26	T. P. 743	35.8
T. P. 714	46 09 33.11	201 54	T. P. 713	36.5	T. P. 743	46 09 07.09	59 26	T. P. 742	35.8
	70 15 23.23	357 45	T. P. 715	26.9		70 14 52.67	261 37	T. P. 744	17.2
T. P. 715	46 09 32.24	177 45	T. P. 714	26.9	T. P. 744	46 09 07.17	81 37	T. P. 743	17.2
	70 15 23.18	323 34	T. P. 716	50.9		70 14 51.87	287 06	T. P. 745	24.9
T. P. 716	46 09 30.92	143 34	T. P. 715	50.9	T. P. 745	46 09 06.93	107 06	T. P. 744	24.9
	70 15 21.77	293 02	T. P. 717	41.5		70 14 50.76	313 51	T. P. 746	42.8
T. P. 717	46 09 30.39	113 02	T. P. 716	41.5	T. P. 746	46 09 05.97	133 51	T. P. 745	42.8
	70 15 19.99	264 31	T. P. 718	42.2		70 14 49.33	349 53	T. P. 747	54.4
T. P. 718	46 09 30.52	84 31	T. P. 717	42.2	T. P. 747	46 09 04.24	169 53	T. P. 746	54.4
	70 15 18.03	219 15	T. P. 719	22.8		70 14 48.88	313 55	T. P. 748	21.8
T. P. 719	46 09 31.09	39 15	T. P. 718	22.8	T. P. 748	46 09 03.75	133 55	T. P. 747	21.8
	70 15 17.36	273 42	T. P. 720	33.4		70 14 48.15	283 52	T. P. 749	24.7
T. P. 720	46 09 31.02	93 42	T. P. 719	33.4	T. P. 749	46 09 03.56	103 52	T. P. 748	24.7
	70 15 15.80	293 52	T. P. 721	98.6		70 14 47.03	259 08	T. P. 750	48.7
T. P. 721	46 09 29.73	113 52	T. P. 720	98.6	T. P. 750	46 09 03.85	79 08	T. P. 749	48.7
	70 15 11.60	321 12	T. P. 722	24.7		70 14 44.80	233 20	T. P. 751	52.3
T. P. 722	46 09 29.11	141 12	T. P. 721	24.7	T. P. 751	46 09 04.87	53 20	T. P. 750	52.3
	70 15 10.88	341 30	T. P. 723	62.1		70 14 42.85	203 31	T. P. 752	33.6
		54 51	Ref. Mon. C–75	69.6					
		249 01	Ref. Mon. S–73	179.0	T. P. 752	46 09 05.86	23 31	T. P. 751	33.6
Ref. Mon. C–75	46 09 27.81	234 51	T. P. 722	69.6		70 14 42.22	263 36	T. P. 753	28.4
	70 15 13.53	245 03	Ref. Mon. S–73	247.1	T. P. 753	46 09 05.97	83 36	T. P. 752	28.4
Ref. Mon. S–73	46 09 31.18	65 04	Ref. Mon. C–75	247.1		70 14 40.91	296 25	T. P. 754	23.1
	70 15 03.09	69 01	T. P. 722	179.0	T. P. 754	46 09 05.63	116 25	T. P. 753	23.1
T. P. 723	46 09 27.20	161 30	T. P. 722	62.1		70 14 39.95	329 30	T. P. 755	27.6
	70 15 09.96	359 23	T. P. 724	44.4	T. P. 755	46 09 04.86	149 30	T. P. 754	27.6
T. P. 724	46 09 25.76	179 23	T. P. 723	44.4		70 14 39.29	14 26	T. P. 756	63.6
	70 15 09.94	286 46	T. P. 725	82.5	T. P. 756	46 09 02.87	194 26	T. P. 755	63.6
T. P. 725	46 09 24.99	106 46	T. P. 724	82.5		70 14 40.03	302 03	T. P. 757	47.4
	70 15 06.26	316 20	T. P. 726	93.9	T. P. 757	46 09 02.06	122 03	T. P. 756	47.4
T. P. 726	46 09 22.79	136 20	T. P. 725	93.9		70 14 38.16	345 21	T. P. 758	42.8
	70 15 03.24	42 45	T. P. 727	19.7	T. P. 758	46 09 00.71	165 21	T. P. 757	42.8
T. P. 727	46 09 22.32	222 45	T. P. 726	19.7		70 14 37.66	326 42	T. P. 759	20.0
	70 15 03.86	330 55	T. P. 728	37.5	T. P. 759	46 09 00.17	146 42	T. P. 758	20.0
T. P. 728	46 09 21.26	150 55	T. P. 727	37.5		70 14 37.15	297 52	T. P. 760	46.2
	70 15 03.01	282 04	T. P. 729	39.0	T. P. 760	46 08 59.47	117 52	T. P. 759	46.2
T. P. 729	46 09 21.00	102 04	T. P. 728	39.0		70 14 35.24	269 30	T. P. 761	46.1
	70 15 01.23	327 44	T. P. 730	28.9	T. P. 761	46 08 59.49	89 30	T. P. 760	46.1
T. P. 730	46 09 20.20	147 44	T. P. 729	28.9		70 14 33.10	223 31	T. P. 762	41.0
	70 15 00.51	35 04	T. P. 731	122.8	T. P. 762	46 09 00.45	43 31	T. P. 761	41.0
T. P. 731	46 09 16.95	215 04	T. P. 730	122.8		70 14 31.78	190 52	T. P. 763	52.8
	70 15 03.80	348 21	T. P. 732	35.2	T. P. 763	46 09 02.13	10 52	T. P. 762	52.8
T. P. 732	46 09 15.83	168 21	T. P. 731	35.2		70 14 31.32	167 40	T. P. 764	32.4
	70 15 03.47	290 20	T. P. 733	82.2	T. P. 764	46 09 03.15	347 40	T. P. 763	32.4
P. 733	46 09 14.91	110 20	T. P. 732	82.2		70 14 31.64	226 48	T. P. 765	31.6
	70 14 59.88	311 21	T. P. 734	23.2					

BOUNDARY TURNING POINTS AND REFERENCE MONUMENTS—SOUTHWEST BRANCH OF ST. JOHN RIVER—Continued

Station	Latitude and longitude	Azimuth	To station	Distance (meters)	Station	Latitude and longitude	Azimuth	To station	Distance (meters)
	° ′ ″	° ′ ″				° ′ ″	° ′ ″		
T. P. 765	46 09 03.85	46 48	T. P. 764	31.6	T. P. 792	46 08 37.57	269 18	T. P. 791	5.9
	70 14 30.57	269 48	T. P. 766	48.0		70 14 22.29	40 14	T. P. 793	23.2
T. P. 766	46 09 03.86	89 48	T. P. 765	48.0	T. P. 793	46 08 36.99	220 14	T. P. 792	23.2
	70 14 28.33	319 28	T. P. 767	39.5		70 14 22.99	46 16	T. P. 794	50.2
T. P. 767	46 09 02.89	139 28	T. P. 766	39.5	T. P. 794	46 08 35.87	226 16	T. P. 793	50.2
	70 14 27.14	17 24	T. P. 768	20.7		70 14 24.68	345 37	T. P. 795	120.7
T. P. 768	46 09 02.25	197 24	T. P. 767	20.7	T. P. 795	46 08 32.08	165 37	T. P. 794	120.7
	70 14 27.43	351 19	T. P. 769	58.6		70 14 23.28	89 14	T. P. 796	8.9
T. P. 769	46 09 00.37	171 19	T. P. 768	58.6	T. P. 796	46 08 32.08	269 14	T. P. 795	8.9
	70 14 27.01	324 10	T. P. 770	26.6		70 14 23.70	46 38	T. P. 797	55.5
		47 41	Ref. Mon. C-76	199.3					
		219 57	Ref. Mon. S-74	124.1	T. P. 797	46 08 30.85	226 38	T. P. 796	55.5
Ref. Mon. C-76	46 08 56.02	224 43	Ref. Mon. S-74	322.7		70 14 25.58	334 59	T. P. 798	90.4
	70 14 33.88	227 41	T. P. 769	199.3	T. P. 798	46 08 28.19	154 59	T. P. 797	90.4
Ref. Mon. S-74	46 09 03.45	39 57	T. P. 769	124.1		70 14 23.79	21 50	T. P. 799	19.6
	70 14 23.30	44 43	Ref. Mon. C-76	322.7	T. P. 799	46 08 27.60	201 50	T. P. 798	19.6
T. P. 770	46 08 59.67	144 10	T. P. 769	26.6		70 14 24.13	59 34	T. P. 800	55.1
	70 14 26.29	16 30	T. P. 771	21.8	T. P. 800	46 08 26.70	239 34	T. P. 799	55.1
T. P. 771	46 08 59.00	196 30	T. P. 770	21.8		70 14 26.35	8 02	T. P. 801	23.7
	70 14 26.58	55 01	T. P. 772	28.4	T. P. 801	46 08 25.94	188 02	T. P. 800	23.7
T. P. 772	46 08 58.47	235 01	T. P. 771	28.4		70 14 26.50	284 58	T. P. 802	48.2
	70 14 27.66	11 13	T. P. 773	36.3	T. P. 802	46 08 25.54	104 58	T. P. 801	48.2
T. P. 773	46 08 57.31	191 13	T. P. 772	36.3		70 14 24.33	323 35	T. P. 803	19.8
	70 14 27.99	340 16	T. P. 774	18.9	T. P. 803	46 08 25.02	143 35	T. P. 802	19.8
T. P. 774	46 08 56.74	160 16	T. P. 773	18.9		70 14 23.78	354 44	T. P. 804	28.8
	70 14 27.70	303 11	T. P. 775	15.1	T. P. 804	46 08 24.09	174 44	T. P. 803	28.8
T. P. 775	46 08 56.47	123 11	T. P. 774	15.1		70 14 23.66	24 54	T. P. 805	53.8
	70 14 27.10	257 55	T. P. 776	25.3	T. P. 805	46 08 22.51	204 54	T. P. 804	53.8
T. P. 776	46 08 56.64	77 55	T. P. 775	25.3		70 14 24.72	113 03	T. P. 806	24.3
	70 14 25.95	278 54	T. P. 777	23.5	T. P. 806	46 08 22.82	293 03	T. P. 805	24.3
T. P. 777	46 08 56.52	98 54	T. P. 776	23.5		70 14 25.76	85 42	T. P. 807	21.4
	70 14 24.87	303 02	T. P. 778	35.1	T. P. 807	46 08 22.77	265 42	T. P. 806	21.4
T. P. 778	46 08 55.90	123 02	T. P. 777	35.1		70 14 26.75	11 25	T. P. 808	39.5
	70 14 23.50	327 34	T. P. 779	151.0	T. P. 808	46 08 21.51	191 25	T. P. 807	39.5
T. P. 779	46 08 51.78	147 34	T. P. 778	151.0		70 14 27.11	19 04	T. P. 809	19.3
	70 14 19.72	336 46	T. P. 780	111.0	T. P. 809	46 08 20.92	199 04	T. P. 808	19.3
T. P. 780	46 08 48.47	156 46	T. P. 779	111.0		70 14 27.41	308 53	T. P. 810	24.2
	70 14 17.68	311 07	T. P. 781	30.0	T. P. 810	46 08 20.43	128 53	T. P. 809	24.2
T. P. 781	46 08 47.83	131 07	T. P. 780	30.0		70 14 26.53	323 28	T. P. 811	29.7
	70 14 16.63	275 12	T. P. 782	32.8	T. P. 811	46 08 19.66	143 28	T. P. 810	29.7
T. P. 782	46 08 47.74	95 12	T. P. 781	32.8		70 14 25.71	335 14	T. P. 812	48.4
	70 14 15.10	290 55	T. P. 783	29.2	T. P. 812	46 08 18.23	155 14	T. P. 811	48.4
T. P. 783	46 08 47.40	110 55	T. P. 782	29.2		70 14 24.76	32 21	T. P. 813	27.6
	70 14 13.83	356 38	T. P. 784	41.3	T. P. 813	46 08 17.48	212 21	T. P. 812	27.6
T. P. 784	46 08 46.06	176 38	T. P. 783	41.3		70 14 25.45	339 07	T. P. 814	26.4
	70 14 13.72	23 37	T. P. 785	58.0	T. P. 814	46 08 16.68	159 07	T. P. 813	26.4
T. P. 785	46 08 44.34	203 37	T. P. 784	58.0		70 14 25.01	39 51	T. P. 815	16.3
	70 14 14.80	309 22	T. P. 786	55.3	T. P. 815	46 08 16.27	219 51	T. P. 814	16.3
T. P. 786	46 08 43.20	129 22	T. P. 785	55.3		70 14 25.50	134 11	T. P. 816	19.0
	70 14 12.81	7 10	T. P. 787	21.1	T. P. 816	46 08 16.70	314 11	T. P. 815	19.0
		246 07	Ref. Mon. S-75	302.0		70 14 26.13	105 55	T. P. 817	26.9
Ref. Mon. S-75	46 08 47.16	66 07	T. P. 786	302.0	T. P. 817	46 08 16.94	285 55	T. P. 816	26.9
	70 13 59.94	135 05 20	Ref. Mon. S-74	710.1		70 14 27.34	5 45	T. P. 818	28.6
T. P. 787	46 08 42.52	187 10	T. P. 786	21.1	T. P. 818	46 08 16.02	185 45	T. P. 817	28.6
	70 14 12.93	70 53	T. P. 788	78.7		70 14 27.47	20 13	T. P. 819	16.3
T. P. 788	46 08 41.69	250 53	T. P. 787	78.7	T. P. 819	46 08 15.53	200 13	T. P. 818	16.3
	70 14 16.40	43 38	T. P. 789	56.8		70 14 27.73	7 26	T. P. 820	36.5
T. P. 789	46 08 40.36	223 38	T. P. 788	56.8			109 23	Ref. Mon. C-77	102.9
	70 14 18.22	51 40	T. P. 790	41.7			292 53	Ref. Mon. S-76	195.4
T. P. 790	46 08 39.52	231 40	T. P. 789	41.7	Ref. Mon. C-77	46 08 16.63	289 23	T. P. 819	102.9
	70 14 19.74	38 59	T. P. 791	77.4		70 14 32.26	291 41	Ref. Mon. S-76	298.2
T. P. 791	46 08 37.57	218 59	T. P. 790	77.4	Ref. Mon. S-76	46 08 13.06	111 41	Ref. Mon. C-77	298.2
	70 14 22.01	89 18	T. P. 792	5.9		70 14 19.35	112 53	T. P. 819	195.4
					T. P. 820	46 08 14.35	187 26	T. P. 819	36.5
						70 14 27.95	313 46	T. P. 821	29.4

BOUNDARY TURNING POINTS AND REFERENCE MONUMENTS—SOUTHWEST BRANCH OF ST. JOHN RIVER—Continued

Station	Latitude and longitude	Azimuth	To station	Distance (meters)	Station	Latitude and longitude	Azimuth	To station	Distance (meters)
	° ′ ″	° ′ ″				° ′ ″	° ′ ″		
T. P. 821	46 08 13.69	133 46	T. P. 820	29.4	T. P. 853	46 07 51.28	182 25	T. P. 852	22.4
	70 14 26.96	354 20	T. P. 822	18.9		70 14 40.27	312 51	T. P. 854	34.8
T. P. 822	46 08 13.08	174 20	T. P. 821	18.9	T. P. 854	46 07 50.52	132 51	T. P. 853	34.8
	70 14 26.88	29 56	T. P. 823	14.8		70 14 39.08	351 27	T. P. 855	25.9
T. P. 823	46 08 12.67	209 56	T. P. 822	14.8	T. P. 855	46 07 49.69	171 27	T. P. 854	25.9
	70 14 27.22	105 16	T. P. 824	27.4		70 14 38.90	28 21	T. P. 856	67.4
T. P. 824	46 08 12.90	285 16	T. P. 823	27.4	T. P. 856	46 07 47.77	208 21	T. P. 855	67.4
	70 14 28.45	346 07	T. P. 825	27.3		70 14 40.40	353 37	T. P. 857	17.7
T. P. 825	46 08 12.04	166 07	T. P. 824	27.3	T. P. 857	46 07 47.20	173 37	T. P. 856	17.7
	70 14 28.15	85 58	T. P. 826	23.4		70 14 40.30	300 57	T. P. 858	14.9
T. P. 826	46 08 11.99	265 58	T. P. 825	23.4	T. P. 858	46 07 46.95	120 57	T. P. 857	14.9
	70 14 29.23	59 01	T. P. 827	13.7		70 14 39.71	321 54	T. P. 859	18.1
T. P. 827	46 08 11.76	239 01	T. P. 826	13.7	T. P. 859	46 07 46.49	141 54	T. P. 858	18.1
	70 14 29.78	354 39	T. P. 828	25.3		70 14 39.19	18 04	T. P. 860	30.7
T. P. 828	46 08 10.94	174 39	T. P. 827	25.3	T. P. 860	46 07 45.54	198 04	T. P. 859	30.7
	70 14 29.67	74 59	T. P. 829	21.8		70 14 39.63	321 58	T. P. 861	21.9
T. P. 829	46 08 10.76	254 59	T. P. 828	21.8	T. P. 861	46 07 44.98	141 58	T. P. 860	21.9
	70 14 30.65	29 27	T. P. 830	15.2		70 14 39.00	0 20	T. P. 862	33.6
T. P. 830	46 08 10.33	209 27	T. P. 829	15.2	T. P. 862	46 07 43.89	180 20	T. P. 861	33.6
	70 14 31.00	12 29	T. P. 831	23.5		70 14 39.01	35 30	T. P. 863	15.6
T. P. 831	46 08 09.59	192 29	T. P. 830	23.5	T. P. 863	46 07 43.48	215 30	T. P. 862	15.6
	70 14 31.24	20 52	T. P. 832	44.8		70 14 39.44	82 56	T. P. 864	18.3
T. P. 832	46 08 08.23	200 52	T. P. 831	44.8	T. P. 864	46 07 43.41	262 56	T. P. 863	18.3
	70 14 31.98	38 05	T. P. 833	13.4		70 14 40.28	133 13	T. P. 865	21.0
T. P. 833	46 08 07.89	218 05	T. P. 832	13.4	T. P. 865	46 07 43.88	313 13	T. P. 864	21.0
	70 14 32.36	93 19	T. P. 834	14.0		70 14 40.99	52 26	T. P. 866	15.1
T. P. 834	46 08 07.92	273 19	T. P. 833	14.0	T. P. 866	46 07 43.58	232 26	T. P. 865	15.1
	70 14 33.01	33 20	T. P. 835	19.4		70 14 41.55	80 44	T. P. 867	24.4
T. P. 835	46 08 07.40	213 20	T. P. 834	19.4	T. P. 867	46 07 43.45	260 44	T. P. 866	24.4
	70 14 33.51	335 52	T. P. 836	25.5		70 14 42.68	50 43	T. P. 868	11.4
T. P. 836	46 08 06.64	155 52	T. P. 835	25.5	T. P. 868	46 07 43.22	230 43	T. P. 867	11.4
	70 14 33.02	350 34	T. P. 837	21.8		70 14 43.09	30 48	T. P. 869	17.9
T. P. 837	46 08 05.95	170 34	T. P. 836	21.8	T. P. 869	46 07 42.72	210 48	T. P. 868	17.9
	70 14 32.86	267 28	T. P. 838	21.2		70 14 43.51	0 28	T. P. 870	37.9
T. P. 838	46 08 05.98	87 28	T. P. 837	21.2	T. P. 870	46 07 41.49	180 28	T. P. 869	37.9
	70 14 31.87	336 23	T. P. 839	16.4		70 14 43.53	35 58	T. P. 871	20.1
T. P. 839	46 08 05.49	156 23	T. P. 838	16.4	T. P. 871	46 07 40.96	215 58	T. P. 870	20.1
	70 14 31.56	22 07	T. P. 840	51.7		70 14 44.08	357 30	T. P. 872	11.9
T. P. 840	46 08 03.94	202 07	T. P. 839	51.7	T. P. 872	46 07 40.58	177 30	T. P. 871	11.9
	70 14 32.47	33 38	T. P. 841	103.8		70 14 44.05	274 27	T. P. 873	17.0
T. P. 841	46 08 01.14	213 38	T. P. 840	103.8	T. P. 873	46 07 40.53	94 27	T. P. 872	17.0
	70 14 35.15	12 15	T. P. 842	46.3		70 14 43.26	1 12	T. P. 874	30.6
T. P. 842	46 07 59.67	192 15	T. P. 841	46.3	T. P. 874	46 07 39.54	181 12	T. P. 873	30.6
	70 14 35.60	38 07	T. P. 843	17.0		70 14 43.29	319 12	T. P. 875	18.9
T. P. 843	46 07 59.24	218 07	T. P. 842	17.0	T. P. 875	46 07 39.08	139 12	T. P. 874	18.9
	70 14 36.09	8 16	T. P. 844	44.5		70 14 42.72	18 28	T. P. 876	17.1
T. P. 844	46 07 57.81	188 16	T. P. 843	44.5	T. P. 876	46 07 38.55	198 28	T. P. 875	17.1
	70 14 36.39	23 50	T. P. 845	31.7		70 14 42.97	94 46	T. P. 877	25.2
T. P. 845	46 07 56.87	203 50	T. P. 844	31.7	T. P. 877	46 07 38.62	274 46	T. P. 876	25.2
	70 14 36.99	294 53	T. P. 846	25.1		70 14 44.14	61 46	T. P. 878	10.3
T. P. 846	46 07 56.53	114 53	T. P. 845	25.1	T. P. 878	46 07 38.46	241 46	T. P. 877	10.3
	70 14 35.93	311 53	T. P. 847	22.2		70 14 44.56	319 13	T. P. 879	18.9
T. P. 847	46 07 56.05	131 53	T. P. 846	22.2	T. P. 879	46 07 38.00	139 13	T. P. 878	18.9
	70 14 35.16	348 45	T. P. 848	47.5		70 14 43.98	3 51	T. P. 880	11.4
T. P. 848	46 07 54.54	168 45	T. P. 847	47.5	T. P. 880	46 07 37.63	183 51	T. P. 879	11.4
	70 14 34.72	29 34	T. P. 849	75.3		70 14 44.02	73 37	T. P. 881	22.8
T. P. 849	46 07 52.42	209 34	T. P. 848	75.3	T. P. 881	46 07 37.42	253 37	T. P. 880	22.8
	70 14 36.45	78 55	T. P. 850	31.0		70 14 45.04	18 16	T. P. 882	11.5
T. P. 850	46 07 52.23	258 55	T. P. 849	31.0	T. P. 882	46 07 37.07	198 16	T. P. 881	11.5
	70 14 37.87	70 42	T. P. 851	27.1		70 14 45.21	326 39	T. P. 883	20.1
T. P. 851	46 07 51.94	250 42	T. P. 850	27.1	T. P. 883	46 07 36.53	146 39	T. P. 882	20.1
	70 14 39.06	94 54	T. P. 852	25.1		70 14 44.69	12 40	T. P. 884	8.8
T. P. 852	46 07 52.01	274 54	T. P. 851	25.1	T. P. 884	46 07 36.25	192 40	T. P. 883	8.8
	70 14 40.23	2 25	T. P. 853	22.4		70 14 44.78	34 17	T. P. 885	39.0

BOUNDARY TURNING POINTS AND REFERENCE MONUMENTS—SOUTHWEST BRANCH OF ST. JOHN RIVER—Continued

Station	Latitude and longitude	Azimuth	To station	Distance (meters)
T. P. 885	46 07 35.20 / 70 14 45.81	214 17 / 16 46	T. P. 884 / T. P. 886	39.0 / 27.0
T. P. 886	46 07 34.37 / 70 14 46.17	196 46 / 89 22	T. P. 885 / T. P. 887	27.0 / 31.9
T. P. 887	46 07 34.36 / 70 14 47.65	269 22 / 26 55	T. P. 886 / T. P. 888	31.9 / 20.1
T. P. 888	46 07 33.77 / 70 14 48.08	206 55 / 5 00	T. P. 887 / T. P. 889	20.1 / 21.4
T. P. 889	46 07 33.08 / 70 14 48.17	185 00 / 31 59	T. P. 888 / T. P. 890	21.4 / 10.6
T. P. 890	46 07 32.79 / 70 14 48.43	211 59 / 116 53	T. P. 889 / T. P. 891	10.6 / 16.5
T. P. 891	46 07 33.03 / 70 14 49.11	296 53 / 58 01	T. P. 890 / T. P. 892	16.5 / 23.6
T. P. 892	46 07 32.63 / 70 14 50.04	238 01 / 25 49	T. P. 891 / T. P. 893	23.6 / 11.8
T. P. 893	46 07 32.29 / 70 14 50.28	205 49 / 40 21	T. P. 892 / T. P. 894	11.8 / 22.8
T. P. 894	47 07 31.72 / 70 14 50.97	220 21 / 97 59 / 112 44 / 290 24	T. P. 893 / T. P. 895 / Ref. Mon. C–78 / Ref. Mon. S–77	22.8 / 19.2 / 160.6 / 161.8
Ref. Mon. C–78	46 07 33.73 / 70 14 57.87	291 33 / 292 44	Ref. Mon. S–77 / T. P. 894	322.4 / 160.6
Ref. Mon. S–77	46 07 29.90 / 70 14 43.91	110 24 / 111 34	T. P. 894 / Ref. Mon. C–78	161.8 / 322.4
T. P. 895	46 07 31.81 / 70 14 51.86	277 59 / 150 24	T. P. 894 / T. P. 896	19.2 / 22.9
T. P. 896	46 07 32.45 / 70 14 52.38	330 24 / 95 17	T. P. 895 / T. P. 897	22.9 / 12.4
T. P. 897	46 07 32.49 / 70 14 52.96	275 17 / 8 40	T. P. 896 / T. P. 898	12.4 / 36.5
T. P. 898	46 07 31.32 / 70 14 53.22	188 40 / 337 25	T. P. 897 / T. P. 899	36.5 / 32.4
T. P. 899	46 07 30.35 / 70 14 52.64	157 25 / 346 18	T. P. 898 / T. P. 900	32.4 / 37.3
T. P. 900	46 07 29.18 / 70 14 52.23	166 18 / 328 20	T. P. 899 / T. P. 901	37.3 / 33.4
T. P. 901	46 07 28.26 / 70 14 51.41	148 20 / 17 08	T. P. 900 / T. P. 902	33.4 / 14.1
T. P. 902	46 07 27.82 / 70 14 51.60	197 08 / 65 59	T. P. 901 / T. P. 903	14.1 / 26.8
T. P. 903	46 07 27.47 / 70 14 52.74	245 59 / 7 10	T. P. 902 / T. P. 904	26.8 / 19.2
T. P. 904	46 07 26.85 / 70 14 52.86	187 10 / 59 22	T. P. 903 / T. P. 905	19.2 / 12.6
T. P. 905	46 07 26.64 / 70 14 53.36	239 22 / 124 46	T. P. 904 / T. P. 906	12.6 / 27.8
T. P. 906	46 07 27.16 / 70 14 54.42	304 46 / 60 51	T. P. 905 / T. P. 907	27.8 / 14.1
T. P. 907	46 07 26.93 / 70 14 55.00	240 51 / 350 04	T. P. 906 / T. P. 908	14.1 / 23.0
T. P. 908	46 07 26.20 / 70 14 54.81	170 04 / 3 20	T. P. 907 / T. P. 909	23.0 / 21.3
T. P. 909	46 07 25.51 / 70 14 54.87	183 20 / 349 37	T. P. 908 / T. P. 910	21.3 / 25.9
T. P. 910	46 07 24.68 / 70 14 54.65	169 37 / 334 49	T. P. 909 / T. P. 911	25.9 / 25.6
T. P. 911	46 07 23.94 / 70 14 54.15	154 49 / 32 01	T. P. 910 / T. P. 912	25.6 / 30.7
T. P. 912	46 07 23.09 / 70 14 54.90	212 01 / 342 26	T. P. 911 / T. P. 913	30.7 / 35.3
T. P. 913	46 07 22.00 / 70 14 54.41	162 26 / 30 00	T. P. 912 / T. P. 914	35.3 / 32.7
T. P. 914	46 07 21.09 / 70 14 55.17	210 00 / 19 45	T. P. 913 / T. P. 915	32.7 / 19.7
T. P. 915	46 07 20.48 / 70 14 55.48	199 45 / 86 40	T. P. 914 / T. P. 916	19.7 / 28.9
T. P. 916	46 07 20.43 / 70 14 56.82	266 40 / 15 44	T. P. 915 / T. P. 917	28.9 / 55.2
T. P. 917	46 07 18.71 / 70 14 57.52	195 44 / 36 08	T. P. 916 / T. P. 918	55.2 / 48.4
T. P. 918	46 07 17.44 / 70 14 58.84	216 08 / 22 08	T. P. 917 / T. P. 919	48.4 / 58.2
T. P. 919	46 07 15.70 / 70 14 59.87	202 08 / 37 03	T. P. 918 / T. P. 920	58.2 / 52.6
T. P. 920	46 07 14.34 / 70 15 01.34	217 03 / 352 27	T. P. 919 / T. P. 921	52.6 / 20.0
T. P. 921	46 07 13.69 / 70 15 01.22	172 27 / 94 14	T. P. 920 / T. P. 922	20.0 / 12.8
T. P. 922	46 07 13.72 / 70 15 01.82	274 14 / 85 01	T. P. 921 / T. P. 923	12.8 / 43.1
T. P. 923	46 07 13.60 / 70 15 03.82	265 01 / 32 47	T. P. 922 / T. P. 924	43.1 / 21.5
T. P. 924	46 07 13.02 / 70 15 04.36	212 47 / 337 02	T. P. 923 / T. P. 925	21.5 / 29.0
T. P. 925	46 07 12.15 / 70 15 03.83	157 02 / 18 02	T. P. 924 / T. P. 926	29.0 / 25.6
T. P. 926	46 07 11.36 / 70 15 04.20	198 02 / 61 55	T. P. 925 / T. P. 927	25.6 / 13.7
T. P. 927	46 07 11.15 / 70 15 04.76	241 55 / 119 29	T. P. 926 / T. P. 928	13.7 / 14.6
T. P. 928	46 07 11.39 / 70 15 05.36	299 29 / 41 42 / 109 18 / 294 15	T. P. 927 / T. P. 929 / Ref. Mon. C–79 / Ref. Mon. S–78	14.6 / 24.0 / 117.0 / 218.4
Ref. Mon. C–79	46 07 12.64 / 70 15 10.50	289 18 / 292 31	T. P. 928 / Ref. Mon. S–78	117.0 / 335.1
Ref. Mon. S–78	46 07 08.48 / 70 14 56.08	112 31 / 114 15	Ref. Mon. C–79 / T. P. 928	335.1 / 218.4
T. P. 929	46 07 10.81 / 70 15 06.10	221 42 / 105 20	T. P. 928 / T. P. 930	24.0 / 16.5
T. P. 930	46 07 10.95 / 70 15 06.84	285 20 / 54 22	T. P. 929 / T. P. 931	16.5 / 18.2
T. P. 931	46 07 10.60 / 70 15 07.53	234 22 / 352 04	T. P. 930 / T. P. 932	18.2 / 13.6
T. P. 932	46 07 10.17 / 70 15 07.44	172 04 / 316 52	T. P. 931 / T. P. 933	13.6 / 22.4
T. P. 933	46 07 09.64 / 70 15 06.73	136 52 / 340 02	T. P. 932 / T. P. 934	22.4 / 16.6
T. P. 934	46 07 09.13 / 70 15 06.47	160 02 / 333 02	T. P. 933 / T. P. 935	16.6 / 28.9
T. P. 935	46 07 08.30 / 70 15 05.86	153 02 / 354 48	T. P. 934 / T. P. 936	28.9 / 43.8
T. P. 936	46 07 06.89 / 70 15 05.67	174 48 / 20 30	T. P. 935 / T. P. 937	43.8 / 34.2
T. P. 937	46 07 05.85 / 70 15 06.23	200 30 / 345 27	T. P. 936 / T. P. 938	34.2 / 25.0
T. P. 938	46 07 05.07 / 70 15 05.94	165 27 / 35 12	T. P. 937 / T. P. 939	25.0 / 22.2
T. P. 939	46 07 04.48 / 70 15 06.53	215 12 / 84 58	T. P. 938 / T. P. 940	22.2 / 12.6
T. P. 940	46 07 04.44 / 70 15 07.11	264 58 / 131 12	T. P. 939 / T. P. 941	12.6 / 20.0
T. P. 941	46 07 04.87 / 70 15 07.81	311 12 / 56 32	T. P. 940 / T. P. 942	20.0 / 21.2
T. P. 942	46 07 04.49 / 70 15 08.64	236 32 / 9 24	T. P. 941 / T. P. 943	21.2 / 37.3

BOUNDARY TURNING POINTS AND REFERENCE MONUMENTS—SOUTHWEST BRANCH OF ST. JOHN RIVER—Continued

Station	Latitude and longitude	Azimuth	To station	Distance (meters)	Station	Latitude and longitude	Azimuth	To station	Distance (meters)
T. P. 943	46 07 03.30 70 15 08.92	189 24 337 52	T. P. 942 T. P. 944	37.3 56.7	T. P. 974	46 06 48.66 70 15 17.47	27 14 262 59	T. P. 973 T. P. 975	13.9 8.0
T. P. 944	46 07 01.60 70 15 07.93	157 52 359 14	T. P. 943 T. P. 945	56.7 30.8	T. P. 975	46 06 48.69 70 15 17.10	82 59 5 00	T. P. 974 T. P. 976	8.0 14.1
T. P. 945	46 07 00.60 70 15 07.91	179 14 38 30	T. P. 944 T. P. 946	30.8 38.1	T. P. 976	46 06 48.24 70 15 17.16	185 00 301 08	T. P. 975 T. P. 977	14.1 10.2
T. P. 946	46 06 59.64 70 15 09.01	218 30 59 19	T. P. 945 T. P. 947	38.1 46.4	T. P. 977	46 06 48.06 70 15 16.75	121 08 327 54	T. P. 976 T. P. 978	10.2 20.6
T. P. 947	46 06 58.87 70 15 10.87	239 19 357 40	T. P. 946 T. P. 948	46.4 32.6	T. P. 978	46 06 47.50 70 15 16.24	147 54 4 57	T. P. 977 T P 979	20.6 13.0
T. P. 948	46 06 57.81 70 15 10.81	177 40 32 05	T. P. 947 T. P. 949	32.6 13.1	T. P. 979	46 06 47.08 70 15 16.29	184 57 276 21	T. P. 978 T. P. 980	13.0 13.7
T. P. 949	46 06 57.45 70 15 11.13	212 05 344 47	T. P. 948 T. P. 950	13.1 90.8	T. P. 980	46 06 47.03 70 15 15.66	96 21 296 12	T. P. 979 T. P. 981	13.7 14.0
T. P. 950	46 06 54.62 70 15 10.02	164 47 34 40	T. P. 949 T. P. 951	90.8 13.6	T. P. 981	46 06 46.83 70 15 15.08	116 12 310 59	T. P. 980 T. P. 982	14.0 12.2
T. P. 951	46 06 54.25 70 15 10.38	214 40 120 01	T. P. 950 T. P. 952	13.6 45.6	T. P. 982	46 06 46.57 70 15 14.65	130 59 349 38	T. P. 981 T. P. 983	12.2 19.5
T. P. 952	46 06 54.99 70 15 12.22	300 01 95 49	T. P. 951 T. P. 953	45.6 18.4	T. P. 983	46 06 45.95 70 15 14.48	169 38 14 44	T. P. 982 T. P. 984	19.5 33.2
T. P. 953	46 06 55.05 70 15 13.07	275 49 31 14	T. P. 952 T. P. 954	18.4 18.2	T. P. 984	46 06 44.91 70 15 14.88	194 44 345 54	T. P. 983 T P 985	33.2 12.8
T. P. 954	46 06 54.55 70 15 13.51	211 14 314 34	T. P. 953 T. P. 955	18.2 36.6	T. P. 985	46 06 44.51 70 15 14.73	165 54 58 34	T. P. 984 T. P. 986	12.8 14.2
T. P. 955	46 06 53.72 70 15 12.30	134 34 327 42	T. P. 954 T. P. 956	36.6 20.6	T. P. 986	46 06 44.27 70 15 15.30	238 34 80 19	T. P. 985 T. P. 987	14.2 13.5
T. P. 956	46 06 53.15 70 15 11.79	147 42 16 55	T. P. 955 T. P. 957	20.6 21.2	T. P. 987	46 06 44.20 70 15 15.92	260 19 139 56	T. P. 986 T. P. 988	13.5 12.5
T. P. 957	46 06 52.50 70 15 12.07	196 55 95 07	T. P. 956 T. P. 958	21.2 28.3	T. P. 988	46 06 44.51 70 15 16.29	319 56 24 11	T. P. 987 T. P. 989	12.5 41.0
T. P. 958	46 06 52.58 70 15 13.39	275 07 122 46	T. P. 957 T. P. 959	28.3 18.5	T. P. 989	46 06 43.29 70 15 17.07	204 11 279 50	T. P. 988 T. P, 990	41.0 12.5
T. P. 959	46 06 52.90 70 15 14.11	302 46 82 00	T. P. 958 T. P. 960	18.5 13.0	T. P. 990	46 06 43.22 70 15 16.50	99 50 339 32	T. P. 989 T. P. 991	12.5 10.2
T. P. 960	46 06 52.84 70 15 14.71	262 00 340 31	T. P. 959 T. P. 961	13.0 25.2	T. P. 991	46 06 42.92 70 15 16.33	159 32 53 44	T. P. 990 T. P. 992	10.2 20.5
T. P. 961	46 06 52.08 70 15 14.32	160 31 338 30	T. P. 960 T. P. 962	25.2 14.8	T. P. 992	46 06 42.52 70 15 17.10	233 44 354 20	T. P. 991 T. P. 993	20.5 12.4
T. P. 962	46 06 51.63 70 15 14.07	158 30 37 27	T. P. 961 T. P. 963	14.8 7.2	T. P. 993	46 06 42.12 70 15 17.05	174 20 267 55	T. P. 992 T. P. 994	12.4 13.9
T. P. 963	46 06 51.45 70 15 14.27	217 27 136 27	T P 962 T. P. 964	7.2 15.3	T. P. 994	46 06 42.14 70 15 16.40	87 55 318 32	T. P. 993 T. P. 995	13.9 7.3
T. P. 964	46 06 51.81 70 15 14.77	316 27 72 12	T. P. 963 T P 965	15.3 9.3	T. P. 995	46 06 41.96 70 15 16.17	138 32 30 04	T. P. 994 T. P. 996	7.3 18.3
T. P. 965	46 06 51.71 70 15 15.18	252 12 3 37	T. P. 964 T P 966	9.3 32.1	T. P. 996	46 06 41.45 70 15 16.60	210 04 96 03	T. P. 995 T. P. 997	18.3 17.6
T. P. 966	46 06 50.68 70 15 15.27	183 37 97 15	T. P. 965 T. P. 967	32.1 23.6	T. P. 997	46 06 41.51 70 15 17.42	276 03 21 21	T. P. 996 T. P. 998	17.6 10.8
T. P. 967	46 06 50.77 70 15 16.36	277 15 119 22	T. P. 966 T. P. 968	23.6 15.2	T. P. 998	46 06 41.18 70 15 17.60	201 21 321 42	T P 997 T. P. 999	10.8 17.3
T. P. 968	46 06 51.01 70 15 16.98	299 22 15 58	T. P. 967 T. P. 969	15.2 17.7	T. P. 999	46 06 40.74 70 15 17.10	141 42 0 12	T. P. 998 T. P. 1000	17.3 13.8
T. P. 969	46 06 50.46 70 15 17.20	195 58 63 38	T. P. 968 T. P. 970	17.7 23.9	T. P. 1000	46 06 40.30 70 15 17.10	180 12 53 20	T. P. 999 T. P. 1001	13.8 17.1
T. P. 970	46 06 50.12 70 15 18.20	243 38 25 32	T. P. 969 T. P. 971	23.9 14.4	T. P. 1001	46 06 39.97 70 15 17.74	233 20 93 10	T. P. 1000 T. P. 1002	17.1 21.3
T. P. 971	46 06 49.70 70 15 18.49	205 32 349 01	T. P. 970 T. P. 972	14.4 44.4	T. P. 1002	46 06 40.01 70 15 18.73	273 10 105 48	T. P. 1001 T. P. 1003	21.3 24.9
T. P. 972	46 06 48.29 70 15 18.10	169 01 277 19	T. P. 971 T. P. 973	44.4 7.2	T. P. 1003	46 06 40.22 70 15 19.84	285 48 45 58	T. P. 1002 T. P. 1004	24.9 8.9
T. P. 973	46 06 48.26 70 15 17.77	97 19 207 14	T. P. 972 T. P. 974	7.2 13.9	T. P. 1004	46 06 40.02 70 15 20.14	225 58 344 59	T. P. 1003 T. P. 1005	8.9 10.4

BOUNDARY TURNING POINTS AND REFERENCE MONUMENTS—SOUTHWEST BRANCH OF ST. JOHN RIVER—Continued

Station	Latitude and longitude	Azimuth	To station	Distance (meters)	Station	Latitude and longitude	Azimuth	To station	Distance (meters)
	° ′ ″	° ′ ″				° ′ ″	° ′ ″		
T. P. 1005	46 06 39.70 / 70 15 20.02	164 59 / 18 01	T. P. 1004 / T. P. 1006	10.4 / 17.9	T. P. 1025	46 06 30.78 / 70 15 19.52	93 58 / 332 19	T. P. 1024 / T. P. 1026	13.7 / 25.4
T. P. 1006	46 06 39.14 / 70 15 20.27	198 01 / 121 21	T. P. 1005 / T. P. 1007	17.9 / 11.1	T. P. 1026	46 06 30.06 / 70 15 18.97	152 19 / 312 12	T. P. 1025 / T. P. 1027	25.4 / 21.9
T. P. 1007	46 06 39.33 / 70 15 20.72	301 21 / 59 46	T. P. 1006 / T. P. 1008	11.1 / 10.2	T. P. 1027	46 06 29.58 / 70 15 18.21	132 12 / 330 45 / 21 32 / 201 39	T. P. 1026 / T. P. 1028 / Ref. Mon. C-81 / Ref. Mon. S-79	21.9 / 12.2 / 398.8 / 189.2
T. P. 1008	46 06 39.17 / 70 15 21.13	239 46 / 359 50	T. P. 1007 / T. P. 1009	10.2 / 42.6					
T. P 1009	46 06 37.79 / 70 15 21.12	179 50 / 267 55	T. P. 1008 / T. P. 1010	42.6 / 14.1	Ref. Mon. C-81	46 06 17.57 / 70 15 25.03	201 32 / 201 34 10	T. P. 1027 / Ref. Mon. S-79	398.8 / 588.0
T. P. 1010	46 06 37.80 / 70 15 20.47	87 55 / 259 15	T. P. 1009 / T. P. 1011	14.1 / 16.1	T. P. 1028	46 06 29.23 / 70 15 17.94	150 45 / 349 30	T. P. 1027 / T. P. 1029	12.2 / 18.0
T. P. 1011	46 06 37.90 / 70 15 19.73	79 15 / 305 32	T. P. 1010 / T. P. 1012	16.1 / 14.5	T. P. 1029	46 06 28.66 / 70 15 17.78	169 30 / 320 01	T. P. 1028 / T. P. 1030	18.0 / 16.9
T. P. 1012	46 06 37.63 / 70 15 19.18	125 32 / 337 34	T. P. 1011 / T. P. 1013	14.5 / 24.2	T. P. 1030	46 06 28.24 / 70 15 17.28	140 01 / 306 01	T. P. 1029 / T. P. 1031	16.9 / 54.3
T. P. 1013	46 06 36.90 / 70 15 18.75	157 34 / 61 31	T. P. 1012 / T. P. 1014	24.2 / 14.7	T. P. 1031	46 06 27.20 / 70 15 15.23	126 01 / 239 09	T. P. 1030 / T. P. 1032	54.3 / 46.7
T. P. 1014	46 06 36.68 / 70 15 19.35	241 31 / 30 38 / 108 12 / 294 39	T. P. 1013 / T. P. 1015 / Ref. Mon. C-80 / Ref. Mon. S-79	14.7 / 21.9 / 93.7 / 103.7	T. P. 1032	46 06 27.98 / 70 15 13.37	59 09 / 289 59	T. P. 1031 / T. P. 1033	46.7 / 25.4
Ref. Mon. C-80	46 06 37.62 / 70 15 23.50	288 12 / 291 35	T. P. 1014 / Ref. Mon. S-79	93.7 / 197.0	T. P. 1033	46 06 27.70 / 70 15 12.26	109 59 / 332 50	T. P. 1032 / T. P. 1034	25.4 / 16.8
Ref. Mon. S-79	46 06 35.28 / 70 15 14.96	21 34 20 / 21 39 / 111 35 / 114 39	Ref. Mon. C-81 / T. P. 1027 / Ref. Mon. C-80 / T. P. 1014	588.0 / 189.2 / 197.0 / 103.7	T. P. 1034	46 06 27.21 / 70 15 11.90	152 50 / 22 20	T. P. 1033 / T. P. 1035	16.8 / 29.8
T. P. 1015	46 06 36.06 / 70 15 19.87	210 38 / 14 14	T. P. 1014 / T. P. 1016	21.9 / 13.9	T. P. 1035	46 06 26.32 / 70 15 12.42	202 20 / 340 28	T. P. 1034 / T. P. 1036	29.8 / 32.5
T. P. 1016	46 06 35.63 / 70 15 20.03	194 14 / 350 24	T. P. 1015 / T. P. 1017	13.9 / 34.0	T. P. 1036	46 06 25.33 / 70 15 11.92	160 28 / 11 54	T. P. 1035 / T. P. 1037	32.5 / 8.6
T. P. 1017	46 06 34.54 / 70 15 19.76	170 24 / 42 56	T. P. 1016 / T. P. 1018	34.0 / 19.2	T. P. 1037	46 06 25.06 / 70 15 12.00	191 54 / 328 04	T. P. 1036 / T. P. 1038	8.6 / 14.9
T. P. 1018	46 06 34.09 / 70 15 20.37	222 56 / 20 53	T. P. 1017 / T. P. 1019	19.2 / 25.5	T. P. 1038	46 06 24.65 / 70 15 11.63	148 04 / 318 05	T. P. 1037 / T. P. 1039	14.9 / 32.8
T. P. 1019	46 06 33.31 / 70 15 20.80	200 53 / 40 04	T. P. 1018 / T. P. 1020	25.5 / 18.5	T. P. 1039	46 06 23.86 / 70 15 10.61	138 05 / 8 42	T. P. 1038 / T. P. 1040	32.8 / 41.8
T. P. 1020	46 06 32.86 / 70 15 21.35	220 04 / 340 15	T. P. 1019 / T. P. 1021	18.5 / 24.6	T. P. 1040	46 06 22.52 / 70 15 10.91	188 42 / 350 14	T. P. 1039 / T. P. 1041	41.8 / 97.4
T. P. 1021	46 06 32.10 / 70 15 20.96	160 15 / 304 12	T. P. 1020 / T. P. 1022	24.6 / 22.8	T. P. 1041	46 06 19.41 / 70 15 10.14	170 14 / 21 02	T. P. 1040 / T. P. 1042	97.4 / 138.6
T. P. 1022	46 06 31.69 / 70 15 20.09	124 12 / 13 51	T. P. 1021 / T. P. 1023	22.8 / 19.6	T. P. 1042	46 06 15.22 / 70 15 12.45	201 02 / 355 57	T. P. 1041 / T. P. 1043	138.6 / 283.6
T. P. 1023	46 06 31.07 / 70 15 20.30	193 51 / 338 11	T. P. 1022 / T. P. 1024	19.6 / 8.6	T. P. 1043	46 06 06.06 / 70 15 11.52	175 57 / 13 58	T. P. 1042 / T. P. 1044	283.6 / 167.2
T. P. 1024	46 06 30.82 / 70 15 20.16	158 11 / 273 58	T. P. 1023 / T. P. 1025	8.6 / 13.7	T. P. 1044	46 06 00.80 / 70 15 13.40	193 58 / 65 58	T. P. 1043 / T. P. 1045	167.2 / 155.1
					T. P. 1045	46 05 58.76 / 70 15 19.99	245 58 / 92 30	T. P. 1044 / Mon. 314	155.1 / 173.7

GEOGRAPHIC POSITIONS OF MONUMENTS MARKING THE INTERNATIONAL BOUNDARY FROM THE SOURCE OF THE SOUTHWEST BRANCH OF THE ST. JOHN RIVER TO THE HEAD OF HALLS STREAM

Station	Latitude and longitude	Azimuth	To station	Distance (meters)
	° ′ ″	° ′ ″		
Mon. 314	46 05 59.00 / 70 15 28.07	272 30 / 156 35 13	T. P. 1045 / Mon. 314-1	173.7 / 81.10
Mon. 314-1	46 06 01.41 / 70 15 29.57	336 35 12 / 100 40 17	Mon. 314 / Mon. 314-2	81.10 / 151.38
Mon. 314-2	46 06 02.32 / 70 15 36.50	280 40 12 / 117 40 16	Mon. 314-1 / Mon. 314-3	151.38 / 105.31
Mon. 314-3	46 06 03.90 / 70 15 40.84	297 40 13 / 74 49 15	Mon. 314-2 / Mon. 314-4	105.31 / 102.10
Mon. 314-4	46 06 03.04 / 70 15 45.43	254 49 12 / 50 21 13	Mon. 314-3 / Mon. 314-5	102.10 / 58.27
Mon. 314-5	46 06 01.83 / 70 15 47.52	230 21 12 / 103 11 12	Mon. 314-4 / Mon. 314-6	58.27 / 56.36
Mon. 314-6	46 06 02.25 / 70 15 50.07	283 11 10 / 116 42 10	Mon. 314-5 / Mon. 314-7	56.36 / 36.76
Mon. 314-7	46 06 02.78 / 70 15 51.60	296 42 09 / 74 32 08	Mon. 314-6 / Mon. 314-8	36.76 / 61.78
Mon. 314-8	46 06 02.25 / 70 15 54.37	254 32 06 / 113 00 05	Mon. 314-7 / Mon. 314-9	61.78 / 71.93
Mon. 314-9	46 06 03.16 / 70 15 57.46	293 00 03 / 78 55 01	Mon. 314-8 / Mon. 314-10	71.93 / 53.08
Mon. 314-10	46 06 02.83 / 70 15 59.88	258 54 59 / 110 39 56	Mon. 314-9 / Mon. 314-11	53.08 / 203.66
Mon. 314-11	46 06 05.16 / 70 16 08.75	290 39 50 / 79 59 45	Mon. 314-10 / Mon. 315	203.66 / 80.03
Mon. 315	46 06 04.71 / 70 16 12.42	259 59 42 / 77 08 55	Mon. 314-11 / Mon. 315-1	80.03 / 66.69
Mon. 315-1	46 06 04.23 / 70 16 15.45	257 08 53 / 120 34 55	Mon. 315 / Mon. 315-2	66.69 / 96.38
Mon. 315-2	46 06 05.82 / 70 16 19.31	300 34 52 / 112 23 21	Mon. 315-1 / Mon. 315-3	96.38 / 58.99
Mon. 315-3	46 06 06.54 / 70 16 21.85	292 23 19 / 143 09 26	Mon. 315-2 / Mon. 315-4	58.99 / 51.51
Mon. 315-4	46 06 07.88 / 70 16 23.29	323 09 25 / 88 50 19	Mon. 315-3 / Mon. 315-5	51.51 / 78.79
Mon. 315-5	46 06 07.83 / 70 16 26.96	268 50 16 / 52 02 39	Mon. 315-4 / Mon. 315-6	78.79 / 112.96
Mon. 315-6	46 06 05.58 / 70 16 31.10	232 02 36 / 83 49 25	Mon. 315-5 / Mon. 316	112.96 / 6.91
Mon. 316	46 06 05.55 / 70 16 31.42	263 49 25 / 72 32 25	Mon. 315-6 / Mon. 316-1	6.91 / 58.24
Mon. 316-1	46 06 04.99 / 70 16 34.01	252 32 23 / 58 51 54	Mon. 316 / Mon. 316-2	58.24 / 170.67
Mon. 316-2	46 06 02.13 / 70 16 40.81	238 51 49 / 65 14 44	Mon. 316-1 / Mon. 316-3	170.67 / 167.31
Mon. 316-3	46 05 59.86 / 70 16 47.88	245 14 39 / 90 18 58	Mon. 316-2 / Mon. 316-4	167.31 / 45.17
Mon. 316-4	46 05 59.87 / 70 16 49.99	270 18 56 / 105 37 21	Mon. 316-3 / Mon. 317	45.17 / 22.53
Mon. 317	46 06 00.06 / 70 16 51.00	285 37 21 / 104 41 46	Mon. 316-4 / Mon. 317-1	22.53 / 220.45
Mon. 317-1	46 06 01.88 / 70 17 00.93	284 41 39 / 76 43 00	Mon. 317 / Mon. 317-2	220.45 / 72.22
Mon. 317-2	46 06 01.34 / 70 17 04.20	256 42 58 / 53 50 10	Mon. 317-1 / Mon. 317-3	72.22 / 79.81
Mon. 317-3	46 05 59.81 / 70 17 07.20	233 50 07 / 83 39 24	Mon. 317-2 / Mon. 318	79.81 / 93.20
Mon. 318	46 05 59.74 / 70 17 11.54	268 39 21 / 17 55 23	Mon. 317-3 / Mon. 318-1	93.20 / 1.06
Mon. 318-1	46 05 59.71 / 70 17 11.55	197 55 23 / 314 54 46	Mon. 318 / Mon. 318-2	1.06 / 79.40
Mon. 318-2	46 05 57.90 / 70 17 08.94	134 54 48 / 333 23 12	Mon. 318-1 / Mon. 318-3	79.40 / 176.90
Mon. 318-3	46 05 52.77 / 70 17 05.25	153 23 15 / 33 25 41	Mon. 318-2 / Mon. 318-4	176.90 / 106.25
Mon. 318-4	46 05 49.90 / 70 17 07.97	213 25 39 / 65 01 07	Mon. 318-3 / Mon. 318-5	106.25 / 59.47
Mon. 318-5	46 05 49.09 / 70 17 10.48	245 01 05 / 46 44 33	Mon. 318-4 / Mon. 318-6	59.47 / 267.52
Mon. 318-6	46 05 43.15 / 70 17 19.55	226 44 26 / 62 27 58	Mon. 318-5 / Mon. 318-7	267.52 / 56.86
Mon. 318-7	46 05 42.30 / 70 17 21.90	242 27 56 / 57 07 29	Mon. 318-6 / Mon. 318-8	56.86 / 82.62
Mon. 318-8	46 05 40.85 / 70 17 25.13	237 07 27 / 18 03 01	Mon. 318-7 / Mon. 318-9	82.62 / 326.90
Mon. 318-9	46 05 30.78 / 70 17 29.84	198 02 58 / 2 01 37	Mon. 318-8 / Mon. 318-10	326.90 / 175.56
Mon. 318-10	46 05 25.10 / 70 17 30.13	182 01 37 / 352 38 19	Mon. 318-9 / Mon. 318-11	175.56 / 83.74
Mon. 318-11	46 05 22.41 / 70 17 29.63	172 38 19 / 16 32 02	Mon. 318-10 / Mon. 319	83.74 / 102.43
Mon. 319	46 05 19.23 / 70 17 30.99	196 32 01 / 1 17 55	Mon. 318-11 / Mon. 319-1	102.43 / 12.97
Mon. 319-1	46 05 18.81 / 70 17 31.00	181 17 55 / 8 16 28	Mon. 319 / Mon. 319-2	12.97 / 131.00
Mon. 319-2	46 05 14.61 / 70 17 31.88	188 16 27 / 31 35 27	Mon. 319-1 / Mon. 319-3	131.00 / 64.47
Mon. 319-3	46 05 12.83 / 70 17 33.45	211 35 26 / 48 17 57	Mon. 319-2 / Mon. 319-4	64.47 / 53.56
Mon. 319-4	46 05 11.68 / 70 17 35.31	228 17 56 / 27 13 40	Mon. 319-3 / Mon. 319-5	53.56 / 82.20
Mon. 319-5	46 05 09.31 / 70 17 37.06	207 13 39 / 51 49 36	Mon. 319-4 / Mon. 319-6	82.20 / 57.99
Mon. 319-6	46 05 08.15 / 70 17 39.19	231 49 34 / 70 59 08	Mon. 319-5 / Mon. 319-7	57.99 / 334.51
Mon. 319-7	46 05 04.62 / 70 17 53.91	250 58 57 / 61 06 23	Mon. 319-6 / Mon. 319-8	334.51 / 74.37
Mon. 319-8	46 05 03.46 / 70 17 56.94	241 06 21 / 49 51 48	Mon. 319-7 / Mon. 319-9	74.37 / 61.86
Mon. 319-9	46 05 02.16 / 70 17 59.14	229 51 46 / 73 12 38	Mon. 319-8 / Mon. 319-10	61.86 / 95.17
Mon. 319-10	46 05 01.27 / 70 18 03.38	253 12 35 / 51 01 28	Mon. 319-9 / Mon. 319-11	95.17 / 86.33
Mon. 319-11	46 04 59.52 / 70 18 06.50	231 01 26 / 33 39 56	Mon. 319-10 / Mon. 319-12	86.33 / 98.39
Mon. 319-12	46 04 56.86 / 70 18 09.04	213 39 54 / 15 52 02	Mon. 319-11 / Mon. 319-13	98.39 / 144.97
Mon. 319-13	46 04 52.35 / 70 18 10.89	195 52 01 / 351 36 11	Mon. 319-12 / Mon. 319-14	144.97 / 76.18
Mon. 319-14	46 04 49.91 / 70 18 10.37	171 36 11 / 304 15 16	Mon. 319-13 / Mon. 319-15	76.18 / 110.05
Mon. 319-15	46 04 47.90 / 70 18 06.14	124 15 19 / 311 20 12	Mon. 319-14 / Mon. 319-16	110.05 / 70.25
Mon. 319-16	46 04 46.40 / 70 18 03.68	131 20 14 / 314 37 08	Mon. 319-15 / Mon. 319-17	70.25 / 60.85
Mon. 319-17	46 04 45.01 / 70 18 01.66	134 37 09 / 7 20 21	Mon. 319-16 / Mon. 319-18	60.85 / 73.47

BOUNDARY MONUMENTS—SOURCE OF SOUTHWEST BRANCH OF ST. JOHN TO HEAD OF HALLS STREAM—Continued

Station	Latitude and longitude	Azimuth	To station	Distance (meters)	Station	Latitude and longitude	Azimuth	To station	Distance (meters)
Mon. 319–18	46 04 42.65 70 18 02.10	187 20 21 32 02 40	Mon. 319–17 Mon. 319–19	73.47 82.86	Mon. 320–16	46 03 40.42 70 18 26.92	116 50 54 256 52 23	Mon. 320–15 Mon. 320–17	106.11 41.68
Mon. 319–19	46 04 40.38 70 18 04.15	212 02 39 63 34 48	Mon. 319–18 Mon. 319–20	82.86 64.07	Mon. 320–17	46 03 40.72 70 18 25.04	76 52 24 243 01 29	Mon. 320–16 Mon. 320–18	41.68 53.63
Mon. 319–20	46 04 39.46 70 18 06.82	243 34 46 77 47 56	Mon. 319–19 Mon. 319–21	64.07 64.27	Mon. 320–18	46 03 41.51 70 18 22.81	63 01 31 272 05 07	Mon. 320–17 Mon. 320–19	53.63 33.14
Mon. 319–21	46 04 39.02 70 18 09.74	257 47 54 32 52 46	Mon. 319–20 Mon. 319–22	64.27 107.43	Mon. 320–19	46 03 41.47 70 18 21.27	92 05 08 237 46 49	Mon. 320–18 Mon. 320–20	33.14 65.68
Mon. 319–22	46 04 36.09 70 18 12.45	212 52 44 359 11 02	Mon. 319–21 Mon. 319–23	107.43 232.01	Mon. 320–20	46 03 42.60 70 18 18.69	57 46 51 238 23 39	Mon. 320–19 Mon. 320–21	65.68 112.13
Mon. 319–23	46 04 28.58 70 18 12.30	179 11 02 322 17 12	Mon. 319–22 Mon. 319–24	232.01 76.38	Mon. 320–21	46 03 44.51 70 18 14.24	58 23 42 287 40 37	Mon. 320–20 Mon. 320–22	112.13 22.89
Mon. 319–24	46 04 26.62 70 18 10.12	142 17 14 352 20 54	Mon. 319–23 Mon. 319–25	76.38 77.04	Mon. 320–22	46 03 44.28 70 18 13.23	107 40 38 0 49 20	Mon. 320–21 Mon. 320–23	22.89 52.98
Mon. 319–25	46 04 24.15 70 18 09.65	172 20 54 58 28 41	Mon. 319–24 Mon. 319–26	77.04 225.32	Mon. 320–23	46 03 42.57 70 18 13.26	180 49 20 313 33 43	Mon. 320–22 Mon. 320–24	52.98 147.63
Mon. 319–26	46 04 20.33 70 18 18.59	238 28 35 38 31 50	Mon. 319–25 Mon. 319–27	225.32 57.79	Mon. 320–24	46 03 39.27 70 18 08.29	133 33 47 251 15 25	Mon. 320–23 Mon. 320–25	147.63 50.11
Mon. 319–27	46 04 18.87 70 18 20.26	218 31 49 352 14 29	Mon. 319–26 Mon. 319–28	57.79 32.86	Mon. 320–25	46 03 39.79 70 18 06.08	71 15 27 306 50 53	Mon. 320–24 Mon. 320–26	50.11 67.79
Mon. 319–28	46 04 17.82 70 18 20.06	172 14 29 313 03 27	Mon. 319–27 Mon. 319–29	32.86 66.28	Mon. 320–26	46 03 38.48 70 18 03.56	126 50 55 245 16 13	Mon. 320–25 Mon. 320–27	67.79 80.35
Mon. 319–29	46 04 16.35 70 18 17.80	133 03 29 284 02 31	Mon. 319–28 Mon. 319–30	66.28 51.86	Mon. 320–27	46 03 39.57 70 18 00.16	65 16 15 271 07 33	Mon. 320–26 Mon. 320–28	80.35 49.31
Mon. 319–30	46 04 15.94 70 18 15.46	104 02 33 253 09 31	Mon. 319–29 Mon. 319–31	51.86 75.58	Mon. 320–28	46 03 39.54 70 17 57.87	91 07 34 293 29 28	Mon. 320–27 Mon. 321	49.31 37.11
Mon. 319–31	46 04 16.65 70 18 12.09	73 09 33 327 10 18	Mon. 319–30 Mon. 319–32	75.58 31.96	Mon. 321	46 03 39.06 70 17 56.28	113 29 29 294 19 40	Mon. 320–28 Mon. 321–1	37.11 63.75
Mon. 319–32	46 04 15.78 70 18 11.29	147 10 19 2 20 35	Mon. 319–31 Mon. 320	31.96 18.01	Mon. 321–1	46 03 38.20 70 17 53.58	114 19 42 278 22 56	Mon. 321 Mon. 321–2	63.75 88.78
Mon. 320	46 04 15.20 70 18 11.32	182 20 35 358 57 46	Mon. 319–32 Mon. 320–1	18.01 47.36	Mon. 321–2	46 03 37.79 70 17 49.50	98 22 59 240 37 08	Mon. 321–1 Mon. 321–3	88.78 64.95
Mon. 320–1	46 04 13.66 70 18 11.28	178 57 46 48 29 21	Mon. 320 Mon. 320–2	47.36 100.83	Mon. 321–3	46 03 38.82 70 17 46.86	60 37 10 271 16 02	Mon. 321–2 Mon. 321–4	64.95 84.65
Mon. 320–2	46 04 11.55 70 18 14.79	228 29 18 63 45 10	Mon. 320–1 Mon. 320–3	100.83 51.87	Mon. 321–4	46 03 38.76 70 17 42.92	91 16 05 289 23 16	Mon. 321–3 Mon. 321–5	84.65 66.92
Mon. 320–3	46 04 10.80 70 18 16.96	243 45 09 68 31 07	Mon. 320–2 Mon. 320–4	51.87 58.25	Mon. 321–5	46 03 38.04 70 17 39.99	109 23 18 255 44 18	Mon. 321–4 Mon. 321–6	66.92 45.19
Mon. 320–4	46 04 10.11 70 18 19.48	248 31 05 48 29 39	Mon. 320–3 Mon. 320–5	58.25 156.87	Mon. 321–6	46 03 38.40 70 17 37.95	75 44 19 279 19 14	Mon. 321–5 Mon. 321–7	45.19 84.59
Mon. 320–5	46 04 06.75 70 18 24.95	228 29 35 23 10 19	Mon. 320–4 Mon. 320–6	156.87 118.67	Mon. 321–7	46 03 37.96 70 17 34.06	99 19 17 223 03 13	Mon. 321–6 Mon. 321–8	84.59 108.10
Mon. 320–6	46 04 03.21 70 18 27.12	203 10 18 53 44 11	Mon. 320–5 Mon. 320–7	118.67 101.63	Mon. 321–8	46 03 40.51 70 17 30.63	43 03 15 253 10 48	Mon. 321–7 Mon. 321–9	108.10 40.57
Mon. 320–7	46 04 01.22 70 18 30.93	233 44 08 24 53 37	Mon. 320–6 Mon. 320–9	101.63 160.79	Mon. 321–9	46 03 40.89 70 17 28.82	73 10 49 230 23 40	Mon. 321–8 Mon. 321–10	40.57 161.40
Mon. 320–8	46 03 56.50 70 18 34.08	204 53 35 55 42 53	Mon. 320–7 Mon. 320–9	160.79 116.30	Mon. 321–10	46 03 44.23 70 17 23.04	50 23 44 263 24 01	Mon. 321–9 Mon. 321–11	161.40 123.62
Mon. 320–9	46 03 54.37 70 18 38.55	235 42 50 53 38 44	Mon. 320–8 Mon. 320–10	116.30 70.95	Mon. 321–11	46 03 44.69 70 17 17.33	83 24 05 230 49 11	Mon. 321–10 Mon. 321–12	123.62 60.55
Mon. 320–10	46 03 53.01 70 18 41.21	233 38 42 9 51 18	Mon. 320–9 Mon. 320–11	70.95 48.60	Mon. 321–12	46 03 45.92 70 17 15.14	50 49 13 262 52 50	Mon. 321–11 Mon. 321–13	60.55 82.81
Mon. 320–11	46 03 51.46 70 18 41.60	189 51 18 323 14 52	Mon. 320–10 Mon. 320–12	48.60 66.39	Mon. 321–13	46 03 46.26 70 17 11.32	82 52 53 290 34 13	Mon. 321–12 Mon. 321–14	82.81 56.44
Mon. 320–12	46 03 49.74 70 18 39.75	143 14 53 314 31 50	Mon. 320–11 Mon. 320–13	66.39 62.92	Mon. 321–14	46 03 45.62 70 17 08.86	110 34 15 257 14 54	Mon. 321–13 Mon. 321–15	56.44 75.14
Mon. 320–13	46 03 48.31 70 18 37.66	134 31 52 339 38 11	Mon. 320–12 Mon. 320–14	62.92 95.10	Mon. 321–15	46 03 46.15 70 17 05.45	77 14 56 325 47 48	Mon. 321–14 Mon. 321–16	75.14 77.78
Mon. 320–14	46 03 45.42 70 18 36.12	159 38 12 315 58 05	Mon. 320–13 Mon. 320–15	95.10 148.28	Mon. 321–16	46 03 44.07 70 17 03.42	145 47 49 292 18 42	Mon. 321–15 Mon. 321–17	77.78 42.54
Mon. 320–15	46 03 41.97 70 18 31.33	135 58 08 296 50 51	Mon. 320–14 Mon. 320–16	148.28 106.11	Mon. 321–17	46 03 43.54 70 17 01.59	112 18 43 339 08 24	Mon. 321–16 Mon. 321–18	42.54 37.62

BOUNDARY MONUMENTS—SOURCE OF SOUTHWEST BRANCH OF ST. JOHN TO HEAD OF HALLS STREAM—Continued

Station	Latitude and longitude	Azimuth	To station	Distance (meters)	Station	Latitude and longitude	Azimuth	To station	Distance (meters)
	° ′ ″	° ′ ″				° ′ ″	° ′ ″		
Mon. 321–18	46 03 42.41 / 70 17 00.97	159 08 25 / 1 05 06	Mon. 321–17 / Mon. 321–19	37.62 / 55.98	Mon. 322–21	46 03 01.97 / 70 16 56.90	250 30 05 / 33 41 02	Mon. 322–20 / Mon. 322–22	67.29 / 55.31
Mon. 321–19	46 03 40.59 / 70 17 01.02	181 05 06 / 327 32 29	Mon. 321–18 / Mon. 321–20	55.98 / 119.22	Mon. 322–22	46 03 00.48 / 70 16 58.32	213 41 01 / 46 07 28	Mon. 322–21 / Mon. 322–23	55.31 / 76.86
Mon. 321–20	46 03 37.34 / 70 16 58.04	147 32 31 / 245 35 25	Mon. 321–19 / Mon. 321–21	119.22 / 51.36	Mon. 322–23	46 02 58.75 / 70 17 00.90	226 07 26 / 76 33 17	Mon. 322–22 / Mon. 322–24	76.86 / 32.92
Mon. 321–21	46 03 38.02 / 70 16 55.86	65 35 27 / 272 50 16	Mon. 321–20 / Mon. 321–22	51.36 / 83.89	Mon. 322–24	46 02 58.50 / 70 17 02.39	256 33 16 / 42 17 36	Mon. 322–23 / Mon. 322–25	32.92 / 116.61
Mon. 321–22	46 03 37.89 / 70 16 51.96	92 50 19 / 231 14 15	Mon. 321–21 / Mon. 321–23	83.89 / 52.84	Mon. 322–25	46 02 55.71 / 70 17 06.04	222 17 33 / 28 34 59	Mon. 322–24 / Mon. 323	116.61 / 37.99
Mon. 321–23	46 03 38.96 / 70 16 50.05	51 14 17 / 271 48 19	Mon. 321–22 / Mon. 321–24	52.84 / 39.85	Mon. 323	46 02 54.63 / 70 17 06.88	208 34 58 / 33 08 37	Mon. 322–25 / Mon. 323–1	37.99 / 11.72
Mon. 321–24	46 03 38.92 / 70 16 48.19	91 48 20 / 249 47 17	Mon. 321–23 / Mon. 321–25	39.85 / 41.75	Mon. 323–1	46 02 54.31 / 70 17 07.18	213 08 37 / 71 15 57	Mon. 323 / Mon. 323–2	11.72 / 96.15
Mon. 321–25	46 03 39.39 / 70 16 46.37	69 47 18 / 330 13 39	Mon. 321–24 / Mon. 321–26	41.75 / 50.11	Mon. 323–2	46 02 53.31 / 70 17 11.42	251 15 54 / 46 00 42	Mon. 323–1 / Mon. 323–3	96.15 / 63.99
Mon. 321–26	46 03 37.98 / 70 16 45.21	150 13 40 / 36 10 26	Mon. 321–25 / Mon. 321–27	50.11 / 29.22	Mon. 323–3	46 02 51.88 / 70 17 13.56	226 00 40 / 63 38 00	Mon. 323–2 / Mon. 323–4	63.99 / 57.79
Mon. 321–27	46 03 37.21 / 70 16 46.02	216 10 25 / 337 13 05	Mon. 321–26 / Mon. 322	29.22 / 69.19	Mon. 323–4	46 02 51.04 / 70 17 15.96	243 37 58 / 32 08 03	Mon. 323–3 / Mon. 323–5	57.79 / 67.09
Mon. 322	46 03 35.15 / 70 16 44.77	157 13 07 / 340 23 45	Mon. 321–27 / Mon. 322–1	69.19 / 56.64	Mon. 323–5	46 02 49.20 / 70 17 17.62	212 08 02 / 73 29 03	Mon. 323–4 / Mon. 323–6	67.09 / 90.50
Mon. 322–1	46 03 33.42 / 70 16 43.88	160 23 46 / 56 19 50	Mon. 322 / Mon. 322–2	56.64 / 105.65	Mon. 323–6	46 02 48.37 / 70 17 21.66	253 29 00 / 58 50 35	Mon. 323–5 / Mon. 323–7	90.50 / 35.36
Mon. 322–2	46 03 31.52 / 70 16 47.98	236 19 47 / 2 38 15	Mon. 322–1 / Mon. 322–3	105.65 / 21.44	Mon. 323–7	46 02 47.78 / 70 17 23.07	238 50 34 / 33 09 16	Mon. 323–6 / Mon. 323–8	35.36 / 79.70
Mon. 322–3	46 03 30.83 / 70 16 48.02	182 38 15 / 336 08 07	Mon. 322–2 / Mon. 322–4	21.44 / 168.29	Mon. 323–8	46 02 45.62 / 70 17 25.10	213 09 15 / 8 50 36	Mon. 323–7 / Mon. 323–9	79.70 / 64.64
Mon. 322–4	46 03 25.84 / 70 16 44.85	156 08 09 / 349 53 49	Mon. 322–3 / Mon. 322–5	168.29 / 89.66	Mon. 323–9	46 02 43.55 / 70 17 25.56	188 50 36 / 51 09 18	Mon. 323–8 / Mon. 323–10	64.64 / 42.19
Mon. 322–5	46 03 22.98 / 70 16 44.12	169 53 50 / 30 25 47	Mon. 322–4 / Mon. 322–6	89.66 / 50.91	Mon. 323–10	46 02 42.69 / 70 17 27.09	231 09 17 / 352 28 54	Mon. 323–9 / Mon. 323–11	42.19 / 74.62
Mon. 322–6	46 03 21.56 / 70 16 45.32	210 25 46 / 77 01 20	Mon. 322–5 / Mon. 322–7	50.91 / 48.60	Mon. 323–11	46 02 40.30 / 70 17 26.63	172 28 54 / 39 25 03	Mon. 323–10 / Mon. 323–12	74.62 / 79.48
Mon. 322–7	46 03 21.21 / 70 16 47.52	257 01 18 / 46 32 33	Mon. 322–6 / Mon. 322–8	48.60 / 22.35	Mon. 323–12	46 02 38.31 / 70 17 28.98	219 25 01 / 71 51 49	Mon. 323–11 / Mon. 323–13	79.48 / 56.74
Mon. 322–8	46 03 20.71 / 70 16 48.28	226 32 33 / 4 40 54	Mon. 322–7 / Mon. 322–9	22.35 / 112.47	Mon. 323–13	46 02 37.73 / 70 17 31.49	251 51 47 / 42 15 56	Mon. 323–12 / Mon. 323–14	56.74 / 47.03
Mon. 322–9	46 03 17.08 / 70 16 48.71	184 40 53 / 55 09 26	Mon. 322–8 / Mon. 322–10	112.47 / 47.36	Mon. 323–14	46 02 36.61 / 70 17 32.96	222 15 55 / 50 38 30	Mon. 323–13 / Mon. 323–15	47.03 / 51.65
Mon. 322–10	46 03 16.20 / 70 16 50.52	235 09 25 / 95 18 40	Mon. 322–9 / Mon. 322–11	47.36 / 36.78	Mon. 323–15	46 02 35.55 / 70 17 34.82	230 38 29 / 16 13 24	Mon. 323–14 / Mon. 323–16	51.65 / 66.12
Mon. 322–11	46 03 16.31 / 70 16 52.22	275 18 39 / 41 50 42	Mon. 322–10 / Mon. 322–12	36.78 / 23.76	Mon. 323–16	46 02 33.49 / 70 17 35.67	196 13 23 / 37 34 08	Mon. 323–15 / Mon. 323–17	66.12 / 141.61
Mon. 322–12	46 03 15.74 / 70 16 52.96	221 50 41 / 338 13 38	Mon. 322–11 / Mon. 322–13	23.76 / 57.44	Mon. 323–17	46 02 29.86 / 70 17 39.69	217 34 05 / 33 46 44	Mon. 323–16 / Mon. 323–18	141.61 / 67.59
Mon. 322–13	46 03 14.01 / 70 16 51.96	158 13 39 / 19 54 00	Mon. 322–12 / Mon. 322–14	57.44 / 33.97	Mon. 323–18	46 02 28.04 / 70 17 41.44	213 46 43 / 75 52 25	Mon. 323–17 / Mon. 323–19	67.59 / 70.00
Mon. 322–14	46 03 12.98 / 70 16 52.50	199 54 00 / 22 42 21	Mon. 322–13 / Mon. 322–15	33.97 / 33.36	Mon. 323–19	46 02 27.48 / 70 17 44.59	255 52 23 / 157 22 37	Mon. 323–18 / Mon. 324	70.00 / 8.34
Mon. 322–15	46 03 11.98 / 70 16 53.10	202 42 20 / 317 09 11	Mon. 322–14 / Mon. 322–16	33.36 / 136.52	Mon. 324	46 02 27.73 / 70 17 44.74	337 22 37 / 73 28 47	Mon. 323–19 / Mon. 324–1	8.34 / 54.88
Mon. 322–16	46 03 08.74 / 70 16 48.78	137 09 14 / 25 16 17	Mon. 322–15 / Mon. 322–17	136.52 / 40.39	Mon. 324–1	46 02 27.23 / 70 17 47.19	253 28 45 / 101 18 29	Mon. 324 / Mon. 324–2	54.88 / 65.11
Mon. 322–17	46 03 07.56 / 70 16 49.58	205 16 16 / 61 05 49	Mon. 322–16 / Mon. 322–18	40.39 / 33.26	Mon. 324–2	46 02 27.64 / 70 17 50.16	281 18 27 / 67 50 41	Mon. 324–1 / Mon. 324–3	65.11 / 58.68
Mon. 322–18	46 03 07.04 / 70 16 50.94	241 05 48 / 32 44 51	Mon. 322–17 / Mon. 322–19	33.26 / 110.76	Mon. 324–3	46 02 26.92 / 70 17 52.69	247 50 39 / 2 35 23	Mon. 324–2 / Mon. 324–4	58.68 / 97.66
Mon. 322–19	46 03 04.02 / 70 16 53.72	212 44 49 / 6 35 10	Mon. 322–18 / Mon. 322–20	110.76 / 41.12	Mon. 324–4	46 02 23.76 / 70 17 52.89	182 35 23 / 41 23 06	Mon. 324–3 / Mon. 324–5	97.66 / 86.01
Mon. 322–20	46 03 02.70 / 70 16 53.94	186 35 10 / 70 30 07	Mon. 322–19 / Mon. 322–21	41.12 / 67.29	Mon. 324–5	46 02 21.67 / 70 17 55.54	221 23 04 / 53 58 17	Mon. 324–4 / Mon. 324–6	86.01 / 25.72

BOUNDARY MONUMENTS—SOURCE OF SOUTHWEST BRANCH OF ST. JOHN TO HEAD OF HALLS STREAM—Continued

Station	Latitude and longitude	Azimuth	To station	Distance (meters)	Station	Latitude and longitude	Azimuth	To station	Distance (meters)
	° ′ ″	° ′ ″				° ′ ″	° ′ ″		
Mon. 324–6	46 02 21.18 70 17 56.50	233 58 16 15 00 11	Mon. 324–5 Mon. 324–7	25.72 37.58	Mon. 325–4	46 01 34.46 70 18 17.95	227 14 50 50 28 17	Mon. 325–3 Mon. 325–5	107.98 71.66
Mon. 324–7	46 02 20.01 70 17 56.95	195 00 11 41 53 42	Mon. 324–6 Mon. 324–8	37.58 81.79	Mon. 325–5	46 01 32.98 70 18 20.52	230 28 15 39 50 12	Mon. 325–4 Mon. 325–6	71.66 62.53
Mon. 324–8	46 02 18.04 70 17 59.49	221 53 40 17 34 52	Mon. 324–7 Mon. 324–9	81.79 90.22	Mon. 325–6	46 01 31.43 70 18 22.38	219 50 11 52 55 08	Mon. 325–5 Mon. 325–7	62.53 65.61
Mon. 324–9	46 02 15.25 70 18 00.76	197 34 51 9 07 21	Mon. 324–8 Mon. 324–10	90.22 38.79	Mon. 325–7	46 01 30.15 70 18 24.81	232 55 06 74 31 03	Mon. 325–6 Mon. 325–8	65.61 88.81
Mon. 324–10	46 02 14.01 70 18 01.05	189 07 21 31 06 45	Mon. 324–9 Mon. 324–11	38.79 29.74	Mon. 325–8	46 01 29.38 70 18 28.79	254 31 00 60 53 58	Mon. 325–7 Mon. 325–9	88.81 97.91
Mon. 324–11	46 02 13.18 70 18 01.76	211 06 44 331 35 56	Mon. 324–10 Mon. 324–12	29.74 42.60	Mon. 325–9	46 01 27.84 70 18 32.77	240 53 55 74 32 53	Mon. 325–8 Mon. 325–10	97.91 96.12
Mon. 324–12	46 02 11.97 70 18 00.82	151 35 57 3 39 38	Mon. 324–11 Mon. 324–13	42.60 73.55	Mon. 325–10	46 01 27.01 70 18 37.08	254 32 50 54 57 48	Mon. 325–9 Mon. 325–11	96.12 165.18
Mon. 324–13	46 02 09.59 70 18 01.04	183 39 38 30 58 19	Mon. 324–12 Mon. 324–14	73.55 26.12	Mon. 325–11	46 01 23.94 70 18 43.36	234 57 43 45 12 41	Mon. 325–10 Mon. 325–12	165.18 70.20
Mon. 324–14	46 02 08.87 70 18 01.66	210 58 19 87 33 18	Mon. 324–13 Mon. 324–15	26.12 35.16	Mon. 325–12	46 01 22.34 70 18 45.68	225 12 39 67 19 38	Mon. 325–11 Mon. 325–13	70.20 44.17
Mon. 324–15	46 02 08.82 70 18 03.30	267 33 17 23 56 28	Mon. 324–14 Mon. 324–16	35.16 63.30	Mon. 325–13	46 01 21.78 70 18 47.57	247 19 37 53 24 36	Mon. 325–12 Mon. 325–14	44.17 46.08
Mon. 324–16	46 02 06.95 70 18 04.49	203 56 27 37 14 31	Mon. 324–15 Mon. 324–17	63.30 57.68	Mon. 325–14	46 01 20.89 70 18 49.29	233 24 35 73 49 34	Mon. 325–13 Mon. 325–15	46.08 43.46
Mon. 324–17	46 02 05.46 70 18 06.11	217 14 30 339 09 28	Mon. 324–16 Mon. 324–18	57.68 85.00	Mon. 325–15	46 01 20.50 70 18 51.24	253 49 33 20 52 32	Mon. 325–14 Mon. 325–16	43.46 71.42
Mon. 324–18	46 02 02.89 70 18 04.71	159 09 29 36 12 51	Mon. 324–17 Mon. 324–19	85.00 71.13	Mon. 325–16	46 01 18.34 70 18 52.42	200 52 31 67 01 00	Mon. 325–15 Mon. 325–17	71.42 32.41
Mon. 324–19	46 02 01.03 70 18 06.66	216 12 50 66 54 48	Mon. 324–18 Mon. 324–20	71.13 51.04	Mon. 325–17	46 01 17.93 70 18 53.80	247 00 59 51 36 28	Mon. 325–16 Mon. 325–18	32.41 44.12
Mon. 324–20	46 02 00.38 70 18 08.85	246 54 46 353 52 26	Mon. 324–19 Mon. 324–21	51.04 37.58	Mon. 325–18	46 01 17.04 70 18 55.41	231 36 27 15 10 26	Mon. 325–17 Mon. 325–19	44.12 111.36
Mon. 324–21	46 01 59.17 70 18 08.66	173 52 26 4 26 47	Mon. 324–20 Mon. 324–22	37.58 133.84	Mon. 325–19	46 01 13.56 70 18 56.77	195 10 25 56 29 24	Mon. 325–18 Mon. 325–20	111.36 43.81
Mon. 324–22	46 01 54.85 70 18 09.14	184 26 47 295 04 14	Mon. 324–21 Mon. 324–23	133.84 66.92	Mon. 325–20	46 01 12.78 70 18 58.47	236 29 23 41 17 52	Mon. 325–19 Mon. 325–21	43.81 73.57
Mon. 324–23	46 01 53.93 70 18 06.32	115 04 16 272 53 55	Mon. 324–22 Mon. 324–24	66.92 79.17	Mon. 325–21	46 01 10.99 70 19 00.72	221 17 50 67 43 19	Mon. 325–20 Mon. 325–22	73.57 44.42
Mon. 324–24	46 01 53.80 70 18 02.65	92 53 58 303 41 55	Mon. 324–23 Mon. 324–25	79.17 101.08	Mon. 325–22	46 01 10.44 70 19 02.63	247 43 18 95 06 18	Mon. 325–21 Mon. 325–23	44.42 44.52
Mon. 324–25	46 01 51.98 70 17 58.74	123 41 58 287 33 49	Mon. 324–24 Mon. 324–26	101.08 47.22	Mon. 325–23	46 01 10.57 70 19 04.70	275 06 17 45 37 47	Mon. 325–22 Mon. 325–24	44.52 68.10
Mon. 324–26	46 01 51.52 70 17 56.64	107 33 51 32 18 00	Mon. 324–25 Mon. 324–27	47.22 48.23	Mon. 325–24	46 01 09.03 70 19 06.96	225 37 45 340 44 15	Mon. 325–23 Mon. 326	68.10 17.34
Mon. 324–27	46 01 50.20 70 17 57.84	212 17 59 358 27 49	Mon. 324–26 Mon. 324–28	48.23 40.60	Mon. 326	46 01 08.50 70 19 06.70	160 44 15 318 11 01	Mon. 325–24 Mon. 326–1	17.34 38.48
Mon. 324–28	46 01 48.89 70 17 57.79	178 27 49 39 20 33	Mon. 324–27 Mon. 324–29	40.60 162.77	Mon. 326–1	46 01 07.57 70 19 05.50	138 11 02 279 41 00	Mon. 326 Mon. 326–2	38.48 89.66
Mon. 324–29	46 01 44.81 70 18 02.59	219 20 30 58 23 32	Mon. 324–28 Mon. 324–30	162.77 48.23	Mon. 326–2	46 01 07.08 70 19 01.40	99 41 03 291 19 25	Mon. 326–1 Mon. 326–3	89.66 25.84
Mon. 324–30	46 01 43.99 70 18 04.50	238 23 31 81 46 26	Mon. 324–29 Mon. 324–31	48.23 50.84	Mon. 326–3	46 01 06.78 70 19 00.28	111 19 26 267 30 24	Mon. 326–2 Mon. 326–4	25.84 37.64
Mon. 324–31	46 01 43.76 70 18 06.84	261 46 24 45 42 49	Mon. 324–30 Mon. 324–32	50.84 47.02	Mon. 326–4	46 01 06.83 70 18 58.53	87 30 25 313 32 29	Mon. 326–3 Mon. 326–5	37.64 43.10
Mon. 324–32	46 01 42.69 70 18 08.40	225 42 48 342 52 37	Mon. 324–31 Mon. 325	47.02 93.54	Mon. 326–5	46 01 05.87 70 18 57.08	133 32 30 346 03 59	Mon. 326–4 Mon. 326–6	43.10 99.35
Mon. 325	46 01 39.80 70 18 07.12	162 52 38 48 54 39	Mon. 324–32 Mon. 325–1	93.54 62.90	Mon. 326–6	46 01 02.74 70 18 55.96	166 04 00 10 07 59	Mon. 326–5 Mon. 326–7	99.35 57.95
Mon. 325–1	46 01 38.46 70 18 09.33	228 54 37 77 16 33	Mon. 325 Mon. 325–2	62.90 32.98	Mon. 326–7	46 01 00.90 70 18 56.44	190 07 59 313 46 29	Mon. 326–6 Mon. 326–8	57.95 110.03
Mon. 325–2	46 01 38.22 70 18 10.82	257 16 32 59 54 28	Mon. 325–1 Mon. 325–3	32.98 85.43	Mon. 326–8	46 00 58.43 70 18 52.74	133 46 32 240 46 03	Mon. 326–7 Mon. 326–9	110.03 94.84
Mon. 325–3	46 01 36.84 70 18 14.26	239 54 26 47 14 53	Mon. 325–2 Mon. 325–4	85.43 107.98	Mon. 326–9	46 00 59.93 70 18 48.90	60 46 06 258 23 07	Mon. 326–8 Mon. 326–10	94.84 59.13

BOUNDARY MONUMENTS—SOURCE OF SOUTHWEST BRANCH OF ST. JOHN TO HEAD OF HALLS STREAM—Continued

Station	Latitude and longitude	Azimuth	To station	Distance (meters)	Station	Latitude and longitude	Azimuth	To station	Distance (meters)
	° ′ ″	° ′ ″				° ′ ″	° ′ ″		
Mon. 326–10	46 01 00.32	78 23 09	Mon. 326–9	59.13	Mon. 327–17	46 00 11.12	132 11 42	Mon. 327–16	56.33
	70 18 46.20	332 48 46	Mon. 326–11	52.12		70 18 17.79	271 31 17	Mon. 327–18	102.16
Mon. 326–11	46 00 58.81	152 48 47	Mon. 326–10	52.12	Mon. 327–18	46 00 11.03	91 31 20	Mon. 327–17	102.16
	70 18 45.10	4 42 54	Mon. 326–12	87.65		70 18 13.04	349 11 13	Mon. 327–19	125.64
Mon. 326–12	46 00 55.98	184 42 54	Mon. 326–11	87.65	Mon. 327–19	46 00 07.03	169 11 14	Mon. 327–18	125.64
	70 18 45.43	277 52 32	Mon. 326–13	16.21		70 18 11.95	52 18 42	Mon. 327–20	53.79
Mon. 326–13	46 00 55.91	97 52 32	Mon. 326–12	16.21	Mon. 327–20	46 00 05.97	232 18 41	Mon. 327–19	53.79
	70 18 44.69	245 04 46	Mon. 326–14	62.27		70 18 13.92	74 18 45	Mon. 327–21	46.58
Mon. 326–14	46 00 56.76	65 04 48	Mon. 326–13	62.27	Mon. 327–21	46 00 05.56	254 18 43	Mon. 327–20	46.58
	70 18 42.06	307 57 02	Mon. 326–15	29.68		70 18 16.01	26 41 23	Mon. 327–22	31.57
Mon. 326–15	46 00 56.17	127 57 03	Mon. 326–14	29.68	Mon. 327–22	46 00 04.64	206 41 23	Mon. 327–21	31.57
	70 18 40.97	341 14 59	Mon. 326–16	67.85		70 18 16.67	327 53 57	Mon. 327–23	83.70
Mon. 326–16	46 00 54.09	161 15 00	Mon. 326–15	67.85	Mon. 327–23	46 00 02.35	147 53 59	Mon. 327–22	83.70
	70 18 39.96	13 02 03	Mon. 326–17	56.17		70 18 14.60	19 16 57	Mon. 327–24	29.56
Mon. 326–17	46 00 52.32	193 02 02	Mon. 326–16	56.17	Mon. 327–24	46 00 01.44	199 16 57	Mon. 327–23	29.56
	70 18 40.55	338 25 47	Mon. 326–18	31.60		70 18 15.06	324 37 36	Mon. 327–25	42.04
Mon. 326–18	46 00 51.37	158 25 47	Mon. 326–17	31.60	Mon. 327–25	46 00 00.34	144 37 37	Mon. 327–24	42.04
	70 18 40.01	345 47 02	Mon. 326–19	28.01		70 18 13.92	341 22 34	Mon. 327–26	117.62
Mon. 326–19	46 00 50.49	165 47 02	Mon. 326–18	28.01	Mon. 327–26	45 59 56.72	161 22 35	Mon. 327–25	117.62
	70 18 39.69	38 21 12	Mon. 326–20	62.49		70 18 12.18	317 34 50	Mon. 327–27	46.84
Mon. 326–20	46 00 48.90	218 21 10	Mon. 326–19	62.49	Mon. 327–27	45 59 55.60	137 34 51	Mon. 327–26	46.84
	70 18 41.49	347 37 38	Mon. 326–21	90.71		70 18 10.71	252 00 17	Mon. 327–28	40.21
Mon. 326–21	46 00 46.03	167 37 38	Mon. 326–20	90.71	Mon. 327–28	45 59 56.01	72 00 18	Mon. 327–27	40.21
	70 18 40.59	48 51 18	Mon. 326–22	64.20		70 18 08.93	279 03 02	Mon. 327–29	61.72
Mon. 326–22	46 00 44.66	228 51 16	Mon. 326–21	64.20	Mon. 327–29	45 59 55.69	99 03 04	Mon. 327–28	61.72
	70 18 42.84	1 03 50	Mon. 326–23	28.05		70 18 06.10	248 49 48	Mon. 327–30	49.78
Mon. 326–23	46 00 43.75	181 03 50	Mon. 326–22	28.05	Mon. 327–30	45 59 56.28	68 49 50	Mon. 327–29	49.78
	70 18 42.86	302 20 49	Mon. 327	20.55		70 18 03.94	304 15 58	Mon. 328	51.35
Mon. 327	46 00 43.40	122 20 50	Mon. 326–23	20.55	Mon. 328	45 59 55.34	124 15 59	Mon. 327–30	51.35
	70 18 42.05	299 20 31	Mon. 327–1	126.91		70 18 01.97	310 12 55	Mon. 328–1	51.47
Mon. 327–1	46 00 41.38	119 20 35	Mon. 327	126.91	Mon. 328–1	45 59 54.26	130 12 56	Mon. 328	51.47
	70 18 36.91	348 22 22	Mon. 327–2	49.30		70 18 00.15	242 18 26	Mon. 328–2	48.77
Mon. 327–2	46 00 39.82	168 22 22	Mon. 327–1	49.30	Mon. 328–2	45 59 55.00	62 18 27	Mon. 328–1	48.77
	70 18 36.45	323 21 33	Mon. 327–3	83.03		70 17 58.14	310 07 05	Mon. 328–3	46.18
Mon. 327–3	46 00 37.66	143 21 35	Mon. 327–2	83.03	Mon. 328–3	45 59 54.04	130 07 06	Mon. 328–2	46.18
	70 18 34.14	286 08 40	Mon. 327–4	45.86		70 17 56.50	334 49 32	Mon. 328–4	34.76
Mon. 327–4	46 00 37.25	106 08 41	Mon. 327–3	45.86	Mon. 328–4	45 59 53.02	154 49 32	Mon. 328–3	34.76
	70 18 32.10	234 21 21	Mon. 327–5	80.79		70 17 55.81	299 15 41	Mon. 328–5	52.39
Mon. 327–5	46 00 38.77	54 21 23	Mon. 327–4	80.79	Mon. 328–5	45 59 52.19	119 15 43	Mon. 328–4	52.39
	70 18 29.05	280 20 15	Mon. 327–6	42.65		70 17 53.69	250 19 29	Mon. 328–6	37.72
Mon. 327–6	46 00 38.52	100 20 16	Mon. 327–5	42.65	Mon. 328–6	45 59 52.60	70 19 30	Mon. 328–5	37.72
	70 18 27.10	326 12 44	Mon. 327–7	112.01		70 17 52.04	289 04 17	Mon. 328–7	48.95
Mon. 327–7	46 00 35.51	146 12 46	Mon. 327–6	112.01	Mon. 328–7	45 59 52.08	109 04 19	Mon. 328–6	48.95
	70 18 24.20	345 12 56	Mon. 327–8	144.75		70 17 49.89	297 57 14	Mon. 328–8	48.35
Mon. 327–8	46 00 30.98	165 12 57	Mon. 327–7	144.75	Mon. 328–8	45 59 51.35	117 57 15	Mon. 328–7	48.35
	70 18 22.48	348 21 36	Mon. 327–9	190.95		70 17 47.90	309 28 40	Mon. 328–9	54.47
Mon. 327–9	46 00 24.92	168 21 37	Mon. 327–8	190.95	Mon. 328–9	45 59 50.22	129 28 41	Mon. 328–8	54.47
	70 18 20.69	9 03 50	Mon. 327–10	96.46		70 17 45.95	339 28 25	Mon. 328–10	22.51
Mon. 327–10	46 00 21.83	189 03 49	Mon. 327–9	96.46	Mon. 328–10	45 59 49.54	159 28 25	Mon. 328–9	22.51
	70 18 21.40	47 23 44	Mon. 327–11	62.89		70 17 45.58	271 26 28	Mon. 328–11	44.75
Mon. 327–11	46 00 20.46	227 23 42	Mon. 327–10	62.89	Mon. 328–11	45 59 49.50	91 26 30	Mon. 328–10	44.75
	70 18 23.55	341 08 25	Mon. 327–12	50.24		70 17 43.50	279 28 46	Mon. 328–12	65.31
Mon. 327–12	46 00 18.92	161 08 26	Mon. 327–11	50.24	Mon. 328–12	45 59 49.16	99 28 48	Mon. 328–11	65.31
	70 18 22.80	349 27 45	Mon. 327–13	136.29		70 17 40.51	241 26 11	Mon. 328–13	95.11
Mon. 327–13	46 00 14.58	169 27 46	Mon. 327–12	136.29	Mon. 328–13	45 59 50.63	61 26 14	Mon. 328–12	95.11
	70 18 21.64	15 17 52	Mon. 327–14	41.62		70 17 36.63	265 10 03	Mon. 328–14	76.24
Mon. 327–14	46 00 13.28	195 17 52	Mon. 327–13	41.62	Mon. 328–14	45 59 50.84	85 10 06	Mon. 328–13	76.24
	70 18 22.15	312 29 34	Mon. 327–15	44.73		70 17 33.10	307 29 02	Mon. 328–15	46.64
Mon. 327–15	46 00 12.30	132 29 35	Mon. 327–14	44.73	Mon. 328–15	45 59 49.92	127 29 03	Mon. 328–14	46.64
	70 18 20.61	265 41 28	Mon. 327–16	19.11		70 17 31.38	52 22 19	Mon. 328–16	41.64
Mon. 327–16	46 00 12.34	85 41 29	Mon. 327–15	19.11	Mon. 328–16	45 59 49.10	232 22 18	Mon. 328–15	41.64
	70 18 19.73	312 11 41	Mon. 327–17	56.33		70 17 32.91	357 58 15	Mon. 328–17	36.37

BOUNDARY MONUMENTS—SOURCE OF SOUTHWEST BRANCH OF ST. JOHN TO HEAD OF HALLS STREAM—Continued

Station	Latitude and longitude	Azimuth	To station	Distance (meters)	Station	Latitude and longitude	Azimuth	To station	Distance (meters)
	° ′ ″	° ′ ″				° ′ ″	° ′ ″		
Mon. 328-17	45 59 47.92 70 17 32.85	177 58 15 325 03 36	Mon. 328-16 Mon. 328-18	36.37 66.28	Mon. 329-11	45 59 26.12 70 17 25.63	234 48 22 35 45 10	Mon. 329-10 Mon. 329-12	111.97 61.76
Mon. 328-18	45 59 46.16 70 17 31.08	145 03 37 291 50 36	Mon. 328-17 Mon. 328-19	66.28 51.19	Mon. 329-12	45 59 24.50 70 17 27.31	215 45 09 56 53 14	Mon. 329-11 Mon. 329-13	61.76 66.84
Mon. 328-19	45 59 45.54 70 17 28.88	111 50 38 267 30 56	Mon. 328-18 Mon. 328-20	51.19 30.89	Mon. 329-13	45 59 23.32 70 17 29.91	236 53 12 22 13 59	Mon. 329-12 Mon. 329-14	66.84 128.88
Mon. 328-20	45 59 45.58 70 17 27.44	87 30 57 13 43 21	Mon. 328-19 Mon. 328-21	30.89 55.91	Mon. 329-14	45 59 19.45 70 17 32.17	202 13 57 61 27 39	Mon. 329-13 Mon. 329-15	128.88 34.80
Mon. 328-21	45 59 43.83 70 17 28.06	193 43 21 67 25 57	Mon. 328-20 Mon. 328-22	55.91 45.25	Mon. 329-15	45 59 18.91 70 17 33.59	241 27 38 26 50 37	Mon. 329-14 Mon. 329-16	34.80 39.22
Mon. 328-22	45 59 43.26 70 17 30.00	247 25 56 3 58 02	Mon. 328-21 Mon. 328-23	45.25 33.40	Mon. 329-16	45 59 17.78 70 17 34.42	206 50 36 59 13 00	Mon. 329-15 Mon. 329-17	39.22 59.22
Mon. 328-23	45 59 42.18 70 17 30.11	183 58 02 317 03 32	Mon. 328-22 Mon. 328-24	33.40 34.32	Mon. 329-17	45 59 16.80 70 17 36.78	239 12 58 33 22 33	Mon. 329-16 Mon. 329-18	59.22 96.77
Mon. 328-24	45 59 41.37 70 17 29.02	137 03 33 250 44 57	Mon. 328-23 Mon. 328-25	34.32 31.09	Mon. 329-18	45 59 14.18 70 17 39.26	213 22 31 46 21 07	Mon. 329-17 Mon. 329-19	96.77 54.34
Mon. 328-25	45 59 41.70 70 17 27.66	70 44 58 248 37 29	Mon. 328-24 Mon. 328-26	31.09 141.72	Mon. 329-19	45 59 12.97 70 17 41.08	226 21 06 28 36 17	Mon. 329-18 Mon. 329-20	54.34 85.28
Mon. 328-26	45 59 43.38 70 17 21.52	68 37 33 339 11 13	Mon. 328-25 Mon. 328-27	141.72 68.69	Mon. 329-20	45 59 10.54 70 17 42.98	208 36 16 64 32 51	Mon. 329-19 Mon. 329-21	85.28 73.28
Mon. 328-27	45 59 41.30 70 17 20.39	159 11 14 47 26 37	Mon. 328-26 Mon. 328-28	68.69 56.13	Mon. 329-21	45 59 09.52 70 17 46.05	244 32 49 107 12 43	Mon. 329-20 Mon. 329-22	73.28 67.14
Mon. 328-28	45 59 40.07 70 17 22.31	227 26 36 329 46 34	Mon. 328-27 Mon. 328-29	56.13 46.58	Mon. 329-22	45 59 10.16 70 17 49.03	287 12 41 75 17 10	Mon. 329-21 Mon. 329-23	67.14 71.95
Mon. 328-29	45 59 38.76 70 17 21.22	149 46 35 258 35 28	Mon. 328-28 Mon. 328-30	46.58 72.03	Mon. 329-23	45 59 09.57 70 17 52.27	255 17 08 83 17 55	Mon. 329-22 Mon. 329-24	71.95 126.79
Mon. 328-30	45 59 39.22 70 17 17.94	78 35 30 241 07 12	Mon. 328-29 Mon. 328-31	72.03 51.57	Mon. 329-24	45 59 09.09 70 17 58.12	263 17 51 100 49 09	Mon. 329-23 Mon. 329-25	126.79 66.92
Mon. 328-31	45 59 40.03 70 17 15.84	61 07 14 263 01 09	Mon. 328-30 Mon. 328-32	51.57 47.57	Mon. 329-25	45 59 09.50 70 18 01.17	280 49 07 33 25 18	Mon. 329-24 Mon. 329-26	66.92 62.78
Mon. 328-32	45 59 40.22 70 17 13.65	83 01 11 224 52 37	Mon. 328-31 Mon. 328-33	47.57 24.48	Mon. 329-26	45 59 07.80 70 18 02.78	213 25 17 74 03 22	Mon. 329-25 Mon. 329-27	62.78 34.82
Mon. 328-33	45 59 40.78 70 17 12.84	44 52 37 237 46 16	Mon. 328-32 Mon. 328-34	24.48 125.46	Mon. 329-27	45 59 07.49 70 18 04.33	254 03 21 44 32 51	Mon. 329-26 Mon. 329-28	34.82 85.96
Mon. 328-34	45 59 42.95 70 17 07.91	57 46 19 232 25 59	Mon. 328-33 Mon. 328-35	125.46 26.93	Mon. 329-28	45 59 05.51 70 18 07.13	224 32 49 19 46 48	Mon. 329-27 Mon. 329-29	85.96 49.28
Mon. 328-35	45 59 43.48 70 17 06.92	52 26 00 250 26 17	Mon. 328-34 Mon. 328-36	26.93 58.24	Mon. 329-29	45 59 04.01 70 18 07.91	199 46 47 59 02 52	Mon. 329-28 Mon. 329-30	49.28 104.92
Mon. 328-36	45 59 44.11 70 17 04.37	70 26 19 11 58 37	Mon. 328-35 Mon. 329	58.24 11.41	Mon. 329-30	45 59 02.26 70 18 12.09	239 02 49 105 54 25	Mon. 329-29 Mon. 329-31	104.92 47.67
Mon. 329	45 59 43.74 70 17 04.48	191 58 37 40 42 48	Mon. 328-36 Mon. 329-1	11.41 72.33	Mon. 329-31	45 59 02.68 70 18 14.22	285 54 23 56 07 22	Mon. 329-30 Mon. 329-32	47.67 92.03
Mon. 329-1	45 59 41.97 70 17 06.67	220 42 46 52 06 33	Mon. 329 Mon. 329-2	72.33 94.45	Mon. 329-32	45 59 01.02 70 18 17.77	236 07 20 91 46 25	Mon. 329-31 Mon. 329-33	92.03 54.82
Mon. 329-2	45 59 40.09 70 17 10.13	232 06 31 30 18 07	Mon. 329-1 Mon. 329-3	94.45 39.64	Mon. 329-33	45 59 01.08 70 18 20.32	271 46 23 50 12 04	Mon. 329-32 Mon. 329-34	54.82 78.97
Mon. 329-3	45 59 38.98 70 17 11.06	210 18 06 55 31 29	Mon. 329-2 Mon. 329-4	39.64 115.99	Mon. 329-34	45 58 59.44 70 18 23.13	230 12 02 64 17 08	Mon. 329-33 Mon. 329-35	78.97 99.91
Mon. 329-4	45 59 36.86 70 17 15.51	235 31 26 10 16 08	Mon. 329-3 Mon. 329-5	115.99 56.43	Mon. 329-35	45 58 58.04 70 18 27.32	244 17 05 27 48 58	Mon. 329-34 Mon. 329-36	99.91 112.21
Mon. 329-5	45 59 35.06 70 17 15.97	190 16 08 307 02 07	Mon. 329-4 Mon. 329-6	56.43 86.64	Mon. 329-36	45 58 54.82 70 18 29.75	207 48 56 359 47 49	Mon. 329-35 Mon. 329-37	112.21 67.94
Mon. 329-6	45 59 33.37 70 17 12.76	127 02 09 41 02 27	Mon. 329-5 Mon. 329-7	86.64 30.80	Mon. 329-37	45 58 52.62 70 18 29.74	179 47 49 47 49 48	Mon. 329-36 Mon. 329-38	67.94 38.25
Mon. 329-7	45 59 32.62 70 17 13.70	221 02 26 47 42 32	Mon. 329-6 Mon. 329-8	30.80 85.74	Mon. 329-38	45 58 51.79 70 18 31.05	227 49 47 13 19 04	Mon. 329-37 Mon. 329-39	38.25 34.16
Mon. 329-8	45 59 30.75 70 17 16.65	227 42 30 59 21 35	Mon. 329-7 Mon. 329-9	85.74 108.98	Mon. 329-39	45 58 50.71 70 18 31.42	193 19 04 96 38 09	Mon. 329-38 Mon. 329-40	34.16 49.48
Mon. 329-9	45 59 28.95 70 17 21.00	239 21 32 19 29 56	Mon. 329-8 Mon. 329-10	108.98 24.12	Mon. 329-40	45 58 50.90 70 18 33.70	276 38 07 18 13 49	Mon. 329-39 Mon. 329-41	49.48 36.58
Mon. 329-10	45 59 28.21 70 17 21.38	199 29 56 54 48 25	Mon. 329-9 Mon. 329-11	24.12 111.97	Mon. 329-41	45 58 49.77 70 18 34.23	198 13 48 319 09 11	Mon. 329-40 Mon. 329-42	36.58 52.75

BOUNDARY MONUMENTS—SOURCE OF SOUTHWEST BRANCH OF ST. JOHN TO HEAD OF HALLS STREAM—Continued

Station	Latitude and longitude	Azimuth	To station	Distance (meters)	Station	Latitude and longitude	Azimuth	To station	Distance (meters)
	° ′ ″	° ′ ″				° ′ ″	° ′ ″		
Mon. 329–42	45 58 48.48 70 18 32.63	139 09 12 4 46 05	Mon. 329–41 Mon. 330	52.75 34.48	Mon. 330–30	45 57 52.48 70 18 57.32	2€0 39 04 21 17 24	Mon. 330–29 Mon. 330–31	96.39 40.24
Mon. 330	45 58 47.37 70 18 32.76	184 46 05 354 49 02	Mon. 329–42 Mon. 330–1	34.48 10.73	Mon. 330–31	45 57 51.26 70 18 58.00	201 17 23 63 04 37	Mon. 330–30 Mon. 330–32	40.24 37.63
Mon. 330–1	45 58 47.02 70 18 32.72	174 49 02 319 31 11	Mon. 330 Mon. 330–2	10.73 40.40	Mon. 330–32	45 57 50.71 70 18 59.56	243 04 36 0 33 37	Mon. 330–31 Mon. 331	37.63 38.13
Mon. 330–2	45 58 46.03 70 18 31.50	139 31 12 293 28 33	Mon. 330–1 Mon. 330–3	40.40 38.17	Mon. 331	45 57 49.48 70 18 59.57	180 33 37 354 50 03	Mon. 330–32 Mon. 331–1	38.13 73.43
Mon. 330–3	45 58 45.53 70 18 29.87	113 28 34 332 00 44	Mon. 330–2 Mon. 330–4	38.17 109.73	Mon. 331–1	45 57 47.11 70 18 59.27	174 50 03 275 16 53	Mon. 331 Mon. 331–2	73.43 53.25
Mon. 330–4	45 58 42.40 70 18 27.48	152 00 46 56 09 06	Mon. 330–3 Mon. 330–5	109.73 101.57	Mon. 331–2	45 57 46.95 70 18 56.80	95 16 55 267 32 57	Mon. 331–1 Mon. 331–3	53.25 145.61
Mon. 330–5	45 58 40.56 70 18 31.40	236 09 03 60 44 28	Mon. 330–4 Mon. 330–6	101.57 121.71	Mon. 331–3	45 57 47.15 70 18 50.05	87 33 02 329 02 24	Mon. 331–2 Mon. 331–4	145.61 112.37
Mon. 330–6	45 58 38.64 70 18 36.33	240 44 24 70 46 19	Mon. 330–5 Mon. 330–7	121.71 37.07	Mon. 331–4	45 57 44.03 70 18 47.36	149 02 26 252 19 50	Mon. 331–3 Mon. 331–5	112.37 137.00
Mon. 330–7	45 58 38.24 70 18 37.96	250 46 18 23 31 18	Mon. 330–6 Mon. 330–8	37.07 17.89	Mon. 331–5	45 57 45.38 70 18 41.30	72 19 54 241 00 07	Mon. 331–4 Mon. 331–6	137.00 61.82
Mon. 330–8	45 58 37.71 70 18 38.29	203 31 18 336 43 48	Mon. 330–7 Mon. 330–9	17.89 43.66	Mon. 331–6	45 57 46.35 70 18 38.79	61 00 09 269 56 17	Mon. 331–5 Mon. 331–7	61.82 63.11
Mon. 330–9	45 58 36.41 70 18 37.49	156 43 49 14 59 37	Mon. 330–8 Mon. 330–10	43.66 98.75	Mon. 331–7	45 57 46.35 70 18 35.86	89 56 19 211 15 22	Mon. 331–6 Mon. 331–8	63.11 50.07
Mon. 330–10	45 58 33.32 70 18 38.68	194 59 36 33 04 41	Mon. 330–9 Mon. 330–11	98.75 50.86	Mon. 331–8	45 57 47.74 70 18 34.65	31 15 23 226 07 50	Mon. 331–7 Mon. 331–9	50.07 70.23
Mon. 330–11	45 58 31.94 70 18 39.96	213 04 40 64 36 50	Mon. 330–10 Mon. 330–12	50.86 84.86	Mon. 331–9	45 57 49.31 70 18 32.30	46 07 52 217 02 14	Mon. 331–8 Mon. 331–10	70.23 23.54
Mon. 330–12	45 58 30.76 70 18 43.53	244 36 47 27 33 08	Mon. 330–11 Mon. 330–13	84.86 74.81	Mon. 331–10	45 57 49.92 70 18 31.64	37 02 14 252 15 06	Mon. 331–9 Mon. 331–11	23.54 80.39
Mon. 330–13	45 58 28.62 70 18 45.13	207 33 07 0 22 28	Mon. 330–12 Mon. 330–14	74.81 62.82	Mon. 331–11	45 57 50.72 70 18 28.09	72 15 09 221 16 56	Mon. 331–10 Mon. 331–12	80.39 55.74
Mon. 330–14	45 58 26.58 70 18 45.15	180 22 28 300 20 36	Mon. 330–13 Mon. 330–15	62.82 27.74	Mon. 331–12	45 57 52.07 70 18 26.38	41 16 57 259 32 51	Mon. 331–11 Mon. 331–13	55.74 29.01
Mon. 330–15	45 58 26.13 70 18 44.04	120 20 37 269 40 45	Mon. 330–14 Mon. 330–16	27.74 46.43	Mon. 331–13	45 57 52.24 70 18 25.05	79 32 52 242 03 52	Mon. 331–12 Mon. 331–14	29.01 132.11
Mon. 330–16	45 58 26.14 70 18 41.88	89 40 47 307 44 43	Mon. 330–15 Mon. 330–17	46.43 43.84	Mon. 331–14	45 57 54.25 70 18 19.63	62 03 56 275 46 40	Mon. 331–13 Mon. 331–15	132.11 27.44
Mon. 330–17	45 58 25.27 70 18 40.27	127 44 44 1 06 46	Mon. 330–16 Mon. 330–18	43.84 52.10	Mon. 331–15	45 57 54.16 70 18 18.36	95 46 41 276 51 14	Mon. 331–14 Mon. 331–16	27.44 54.03
Mon. 330–18	45 58 23.58 70 18 40.32	181 06 46 336 56 17	Mon. 330–17 Mon. 330–19	52.10 70.16	Mon. 331–16	45 57 53.95 70 18 15.87	96 51 16 343 41 25	Mon. 331–15 Mon. 331–17	54.03 34.50
Mon. 330–19	45 58 21.49 70 18 39.04	156 56 18 54 39 49	Mon. 330–18 Mon. 330–20	70.16 94.73	Mon. 331–17	45 57 52.88 70 18 15.42	163 41 25 14 10 52	Mon. 331–16 Mon. 331–18	34.50 36.27
Mon. 330–20	45 58 19.71 70 18 42.63	234 39 46 359 28 34	Mon. 330–19 Mon. 330–21	94.73 101.15	Mon. 331–18	45 57 51.74 70 18 15.84	194 10 52 298 53 25	Mon. 331–17 Mon. 331–19	36.27 43.79
Mon. 330–21	45 58 16.44 70 18 42.59	179 28 34 30 42 33	Mon. 330–20 Mon. 330–22	101.15 119.91	Mon. 331–19	45 57 51.05 70 18 14.05	118 53 26 247 32 54	Mon. 331–18 Mon. 331–20	43.79 27.80
Mon. 330–22	45 58 13.10 70 18 45.44	210 42 31 15 50 52	Mon. 330–21 Mon. 330–23	119.91 127.10	Mon. 331–20	45 57 51.40 70 18 12.86	67 32 55 291 54 05	Mon. 331–19 Mon. 331–21	27.80 58.12
Mon. 330–23	45 58 09.14 70 18.47.05	195 50 51 342 47 42	Mon. 330–22 Mon. 330–24	127.10 104.13	Mon. 331–21	45 57 50.69 70 18 10.36	111 54 07 246 43 06	Mon. 331–20 Mon. 331–22	58.12 64.66
Mon. 330–24	45 58 05.92 70 18 45.62	162 47 43 359 13 38	Mon. 330–23 Mon. 330–25	104.13 64.75	Mon. 331–22	45 57 51.52 70 18 07.60	66 43 08 262 40 02	Mon. 331–21 Mon. 331–23	64.66 64.49
Mon. 330–25	45 58 03.82 70 18 45.58	179 13 38 345 06 45	Mon. 330–24 Mon. 330–26	64.75 146.53	Mon. 331–23	45 57 51.79 70 18 04.63	82 40 04 316 08 46	Mon. 331–22 Mon. 331–24	64.49 36.53
Mon. 330–26	45 57 59.23 70 18 43.83	165 06 46 30 38 51	Mon. 330–25 Mon. 330–27	146.53 106.82	Mon. 331–24	45 57 50.94 70 18 03.46	136 08 47 317 08 30	Mon. 331–23 Mon. 331–25	36.53 71.03
Mon. 330–27	45 57 56.26 70 18 46.35	210 38 49 68 22 29	Mon. 330–26 Mon. 330–28	106.82 79.26	Mon. 331–25	45 57 49.25 70 18 01.21	137 08 32 273 24 40	Mon. 331–24 Mon. 331–26	71.03 61.50
Mon. 330–28	45 57 55.31 70 18 49.78	248 22 27 43 10 54	Mon. 330–27 Mon. 330–29	79.26 98.35	Mon. 331–26	45 57 49.13 70 17 58.36	93 24 42 328 57 21	Mon. 331–25 Mon. 331–27	61.50 85.34
Mon. 330–29	45 57 52.99 70 18 52.90	223 10 52 80 39 07	Mon. 330–28 Mon. 330–30	98.35 96.39	Mon. 331–27	45 57 46.76 70 17 56.32	148 57 22 239 18 38	Mon. 331–26 Mon. 331–28	85.34 64.66

BOUNDARY MONUMENTS—SOURCE OF SOUTHWEST BRANCH OF ST. JOHN TO HEAD OF HALLS STREAM—Continued

Station	Latitude and longitude	Azimuth	To station	Distance (meters)
Mon. 331–28	45 57 47.83 70 17 53.74	59 18 40 243 56 14	Mon. 331–27 Mon. 331–29	64.66 73.10
Mon. 331–29	45 57 48.87 70 17 50.68	63 56 16 295 38 39	Mon. 331–28 Mon. 332	73.10 120.55
Mon. 332	45 57 47.18 70 17 45.64	115 38 42 293 19 01	Mon. 331–29 Mon. 332–1	120.55 20.01
Mon. 332–1	45 57 46.93 70 17 44.78	113 19 02 269 25 37	Mon. 332 Mon. 332–2	20.01 69.88
Mon. 332–2	45 57 46.95 70 17 41.52	89 25 39 245 38 32	Mon. 332–1 Mon. 332–3	69.88 124.67
Mon. 332–3	45 57 48.61 70 17 36.25	65 38 36 274 45 34	Mon. 332–2 Mon. 332–4	124.67 99.09
Mon. 332–4	45 57 48.35 70 17 31.66	94 45 37 247 54 41	Mon. 332–3 Mon. 332–5	99.09 70.98
Mon. 332–5	45 57 49.21 70 17 28.61	67 54 43 289 03 47	Mon. 332–4 Mon. 332–6	70.98 128.58
Mon. 332–6	45 57 47.85 70 17 22.97	109 03 51 256 42 42	Mon. 332–5 Mon. 332–7	128.58 32.21
Mon. 332–7	45 57 48.09 70 17 21.51	76 42 43 190 24 33	Mon. 332–6 Mon. 332–8	32.21 46.52
Mon. 332–8	45 57 49.57 70 17 21.12	10 24 33 218 18 42	Mon 332–7 Mon. 332–9	46.52 48.54
Mon. 332–9	45 57 50.81 70 17 19.72	38 18 43 244 05 51	Mon. 332–8 Mon. 332–10	48.54 136.39
Mon. 332–10	45 57 52.74 70 17 14.02	64 05 55 275 48 45	Mon. 332–9 Mon. 332–11	136.39 127.86
Mon 332–11	45 57 52.32 70 17 08.12	95 48 49 263 54 32	Mon. 332–10 Mon. 332–12	127.86 59.63
Mon. 332–12	45 57 52.52 70 17 05.36	83 54 34 320 53 29	Mon. 332–11 Mon. 332–13	59.63 102.50
Mon. 332–13	45 57 49.95 70 17 02.36	140 53 31 257 52 55	Mon. 332–12 Mon. 332–14	102.50 61.17
Mon. 332–14	45 57 50.36 70 16 59.58	77 52 57 220 09 27	Mon. 332–13 Mon. 332–15	61.17 56.43
Mon. 332–15	45 57 51.76 70 16 57.89	40 09 28 291 57 10	Mon. 332–14 Mon. 332–16	56.43 72.91
Mon. 332–16	45 57 50.88 70 16 54.75	111 57 12 219 17 35	Mon. 332–15 Mon. 332–17	72.91 136.11
Mon. 332–17	45 57 54.29 70 16 50.75	39 17 38 184 02 07	Mon. 332–16 Mon. 332–18	136.11 57.05
Mon. 332–18	45 57 56.13 70 16 50.56	4 02 07 236 52 30	Mon. 332–17 Mon. 332–19	57.05 65.09
Mon. 332–19	45 57 57.28 70 16 48.03	56 52 32 268 45 43	Mon. 332–18 Mon. 332–20	65.09 37.27
Mon. 332–20	45 57 57.31 70 16 46.30	88 45 44 231 28 12	Mon. 332–19 Mon. 332–21	37.27 45.41
Mon. 332–21	45 57 58.23 70 16 44.65	51 28 13 240 31 05	Mon. 332–20 Mon. 332–22	45.41 97.07
Mon. 332–22	45 57 59.77 70 16 40.73	60 31 08 199 24 12	Mon. 332–21 Mon. 332–23	97.07 88.42
Mon 332–23	45 58 02.48 70 16 39.36	19 24 13 300 20 47	Mon. 332–22 Mon. 332–24	88.42 74.20
Mon. 332–24	45 58 01.26 70 16 36.39	120 20 49 269 55 52	Mon. 332–23 Mon. 332–25	74.20 40.69
Mon. 332–25	45 58 01.26 70 16 34.50	89 55 53 338 22 44	Mon. 332–24 Mon. 332–26	40.69 47.17
Mon. 332–26	45 57 59.84 70 16 33.69	158 22 45 306 43 24	Mon. 332–25 Mon. 332–27	47.17 65.33
Mon. 332–27	45 57 58.58 70 16 31.26	126 43 26 2 34 47	Mon. 332–26 Mon. 332–28	65.33 51.22
Mon. 332–28	45 57 56.92 70 16 31.37	182 34 47 309 44 08	Mon. 332–27 Mon. 332–29	51.22 27.88
Mon. 332–29	45 57 56.34 70 16 30.38	129 44 09 335 48 29	Mon. 332–28 Mon. 332–30	27.88 166.63
Mon. 332–30	45 57 51.42 70 16 27.20	155 48 31 253 56 45	Mon. 332–29 Mon. 332–31	166.63 75.64
Mon. 332–31	45 57 52.10 70 16 23.83	73 56 47 38 47 55	Mon. 332–30 Mon. 332–32	75.64 43.08
Mon. 332–32	45 57 51.01 70 16 25.08	218 47 54 65 20 02	Mon. 332–31 Mon. 332–33	43.08 162.61
Mon. 332–33	45 57 48.81 70 16 31.94	245 19 57 2 05 17	Mon. 332–32 Mon. 332–34	162.61 90.56
Mon. 332–34	45 57 45.88 70 16 32.10	182 05 17 348 17 08	Mon. 332–33 Mon. 332–35	90.56 72.03
Mon. 332–35	45 57 43.60 70 16 31.42	168 17 08 340 33 47	Mon. 332–34 Mon. 332–36	72.03 74.21
Mon. 332–36	45 57 41.33 70 16 30.27	160 33 48 269 36 08	Mon. 332–35 Mon. 332–37	74.21 43.50
Mon. 332–37	45 57 41.34 70 16 28.25	89 36 10 318 37 24	Mon. 332–36 Mon. 332–38	43.50 44.03
Mon. 332–38	45 57 40.27 70 16 26.90	138 37 25 259 26 51	Mon. 332–37 Mon. 332–39	44.03 40.42
Mon. 332–39	45 57 40.51 70 16 25.06	79 26 52 250 45 30	Mon. 332–38 Mon. 332–40	40.42 37.61
Mon. 332–40	45 57 40.91 70 16 23.41	70 45 31 274 02 02	Mon. 332–39 Mon. 332–41	37.61 56.09
Mon. 332–41	45 57 40.78 70 16 20.81	94 02 04 242 35 17	Mon. 332–40 Mon. 332–42	56.09 49.93
Mon. 332–42	45 57 41.52 70 16 18.75	62 35 19 227 48 14	Mon. 332–41 Mon. 332–43	49.93 122.50
Mon. 332–43	45 57 44.19 70 16 14.54	47 48 17 265 23 06	Mon. 332–42 Mon. 333	122.50 88.34
Mon. 333	45 57 44.42 70 16 10.45	85 23 10 188 33 11	Mon. 332–43 Mon. 333–1	88.34 2.45
Mon. 333–1	45 57 44.50 70 16 10.44	8 33 11 236 15 36	Mon. 333 Mon. 333–2	2.45 94.65
Mon. 333–2	45 57 46.20 70 16 06.78	56 15 39 258 28 27	Mon. 333–1 Mon. 333–3	94.65 35.97
Mon. 333–3	45 57 46.43 70 16 05.14	78 28 28 221 33 11	Mon. 333–2 Mon. 333–4	35.97 208.00
Mon. 333–4	45 57 51.48 70 15 58.74	41 33 16 315 57 04	Mon. 333–3 Mon. 333–5	208.00 28.60
Mon. 333–5	45 57 50.81 70 15 57.81	135 57 05 349 18 29	Mon. 333–4 Mon. 333–6	28.60 78.73
Mon. 333–6	45 57 48.30 70 15 57.13	169 18 29 6 58 19	Mon. 333–5 Mon. 333–7	78.73 57.39
Mon. 333–7	45 57 46.46 70 15 57.46	186 58 19 275 27 57	Mon. 333–6 Mon. 333–8	57.39 77.98
Mon. 333–8	45 57 46.22 70 15 53.85	95 28 00 0 44 09	Mon. 333–7 Mon. 333–9	77.98 55.02
Mon. 333–9	45 57 44.44 70 15 53.89	180 44 09 306 11 19	Mon. 333–8 Mon. 333–10	55.02 45.41
Mon. 333–10	45 57 43.57 70 15 52.18	126 11 20 270 45 48	Mon. 333–9 Mon. 333–11	45.41 44.11
Mon. 333–11	45 57 43.55 70 15 50.14	90 45 49 318 43 06	Mon. 333–10 Mon. 333–12	44.11 40.17
Mon. 333–12	45 57 42.57 70 15 48.90	138 43 07 340 32 55	Mon. 333–11 Mon. 333–13	40.17 101.86
Mon. 333–13	45 57 39.46 70 15 47.33	160 32 56 319 01 27	Mon. 333–12 Mon. 333–14	101.86 129.57
Mon. 333–14	45 57 36.29 70 15 43.38	139 01 30 281 01 45	Mon. 333–13 Mon. 333–15	129.57 59.52
Mon. 333–15	45 57 35.92 70 15 40.67	101 01 47 302 32 27	Mon. 333–14 Mon. 333–16	59.52 46.46

BOUNDARY MONUMENTS—SOURCE OF SOUTHWEST BRANCH OF ST. JOHN TO HEAD OF HALLS STREAM—Continued

Station	Latitude and longitude	Azimuth	To station	Distance (meters)	Station	Latitude and longitude	Azimuth	To station	Distance (meters)
	° ′ ″	° ′ ″				° ′ ″	° ′ ″		
Mon. 333–16	45 57 35.11 / 70 15 38.85	122 32 28 / 288 05 26	Mon. 333–15 / Mon. 333–17	46.46 / 97.05	Mon. 334–17	45 57 15.48 / 70 15 08.67	216 47 20 / 284 26 11	Mon. 334–16 / Mon. 334–18	51.80 / 29.96
Mon. 333–17	45 57 34.14 / 70 15 34.57	108 05 29 / 247 19 40	Mon. 333–16 / Mon. 333–18	97.05 / 21.36	Mon. 334–18	45 57 15.24 / 70 15 07.32	104 26 12 / 336 57 40	Mon. 334–17 / Mon. 334–19	29.96 / 124.99
Mon. 333–18	45 57 34.40 / 70 15 33.65	67 19 41 / 314 03 58	Mon. 333–17 / Mon. 333–19	21.36 / 77.48	Mon. 334–19	45 57 11.51 / 70 15 05.05	156 57 42 / 303 39 58	Mon. 334–18 / Mon. 334–20	124.99 / 105.53
Mon. 333–19	45 57 32.66 / 70 15 31.07	134 04 00 / 45 45 25	Mon. 333–18 / Mon. 333–20	77.48 / 220.86	Mon. 334–20	45 57 09.62 / 70 15 00.97	123 40 01 / 240 03 53	Mon. 334–19 / Mon. 334–21	105.53 / 21.13
Mon. 333–20	45 57 27.67 / 70 15 38.42	225 45 20 / 13 00 45	Mon. 333–19 / Mon. 333–21	220.86 / 26.85	Mon. 334–21	45 57 09.96 / 70 15 00.12	60 03 54 / 282 58 16	Mon. 334–20 / Mon. 334–22	21.13 / 22.38
Mon. 333–21	45 57 26.82 / 70 15 38.70	193 00 45 / 341 44 47	Mon. 333–20 / Mon. 333–22	26.85 / 90.75	Mon. 334–22	45 57 09.80 / 70 14 59.11	102 58 17 / 326 03 39	Mon. 334–21 / Mon. 334–23	22.38 / 25.78
Mon. 333–22	45 57 24.03 / 70 15 37.38	161 44 48 / 355 41 45	Mon. 333–21 / Mon. 333–23	90.75 / 34.62	Mon. 334–23	45 57 09.10 / 70 14 58.44	146 03 39 / 24 31 49	Mon. 334–22 / Mon. 334–24	25.78 / 42.85
Mon. 333–23	45 57 22.91 / 70 15 37.26	175 41 45 / 336 15 55	Mon. 333–22 / Mon. 333–24	34.62 / 79.21	Mon. 334–24	45 57 07.84 / 70 14 59.27	204 31 48 / 337 33 17	Mon. 334–23 / Mon. 334–25	42.85 / 41.12
Mon. 333–24	45 57 20.56 / 70 15 35.78	156 15 56 / 305 00 25	Mon. 333–23 / Mon. 333–25	79.21 / 68.14	Mon. 334–25	45 57 06.61 / 70 14 58.54	157 33 18 / 300 16 05	Mon. 334–24 / Mon. 334–26	41.12 / 57.49
Mon. 333–25	45 57 19.30 / 70 15 33.18	125 00 27 / 2 40 27	Mon. 333–24 / Mon. 333–26	68.14 / 75.42	Mon. 334–26	45 57 05.67 / 70 14 56.23	120 16 07 / 342 07 36	Mon. 334–25 / Mon. 334–27	57.49 / 62.63
Mon. 333–26	45 57 16.86 / 70 15 33.35	182 40 27 / 50 55 34	Mon. 333–25 / Mon. 333–27	75.42 / 176.30	Mon. 334–27	45 57 03.74 / 70 14 55.34	162 07 37 / 24 12 00	Mon. 334–26 / Mon. 334–28	62.63 / 84.86
Mon. 333–27	45 57 13.26 / 70 15 39.70	230 55 29 / 5 14 24	Mon. 333–26 / Mon. 333–28	176.30 / 33.76	Mon. 334–28	45 57 01.23 / 70 14 56.96	204 11 59 / 329 14 22	Mon. 334–27 / Mon. 334–29	84.86 / 79.13
Mon. 333–28	45 57 12.17 / 70 15 39.84	185 14 24 / 36 53 20	Mon. 333–27 / Mon. 333–29	33.76 / 52.71	Mon. 334–29	45 56 59.03 / 70 14 55.08	149 14 23 / 301 38 11	Mon. 334–28 / Mon. 334–30	79.13 / 59.97
Mon. 333–29	45 57 10.80 / 70 15 41.31	216 53 19 / 343 26 45	Mon. 333–28 / Mon. 334	52.71 / 55.21	Mon. 334–30	45 56 58.01 / 70 14 52.71	121 38 13 / 267 40 37	Mon. 334–29 / Mon. 334–31	59.97 / 44.27
Mon. 334	45 57 09.09 / 70 15 40.58	163 26 45 / 324 00 05	Mon. 333–29 / Mon. 334–1	55.21 / 19.03	Mon. 334–31	45 56 58.07 / 70 14 50.65	87 40 38 / 292 34 32	Mon. 334–30 / Mon. 334–32	44.27 / 70.37
Mon. 334–1	45 57 08.59 / 70 15 40.06	144 00 05 / 268 47 40	Mon. 334 / Mon. 334–2	19.03 / 38.34	Mon. 334–32	45 56 57.19 / 70 14 47.64	112 34 34 / 329 29 53	Mon. 334–31 / Mon. 335	70.37 / 49.32
Mon. 334–2	45 57 08.62 / 70 15 38.28	88 47 41 / 273 11 40	Mon. 334–1 / Mon. 334–3	38.34 / 47.18	Mon. 335	45 56 55.82 / 70 14 46.47	149 29 54 / 319 05 05	Mon. 334–32 / Mon. 335–1	49.32 / 71.54
Mon. 334–3	45 57 08.53 / 70 15 36.10	93 11 42 / 306 43 42	Mon. 334–2 / Mon. 334–4	47.18 / 46.04	Mon. 335–1	45 56 54.07 / 70 14 44.30	139 05 07 / 339 16 39	Mon. 335 / Mon. 335–2	71.54 / 75.31
Mon. 334–4	45 57 07.64 / 70 15 34.38	126 43 43 / 236 11 43	Mon. 334–3 / Mon. 334–5	46.04 / 109.45	Mon. 335–2	45 56 51.78 / 70 14 43.06	159 16 40 / 295 49 46	Mon. 335–1 / Mon. 335–3	75.31 / 153.38
Mon. 334–5	45 57 09.61 / 70 15 30.16	56 11 46 / 297 22 46	Mon. 334–4 / Mon. 334–6	109.45 / 124.46	Mon. 335–3	45 56 49.62 / 70 14 36.65	115 49 51 / 313 02 37	Mon. 335–2 / Mon. 335–4	153.38 / 62.16
Mon. 334–6	45 57 07.76 / 70 15 25.03	117 22 50 / 223 12 26	Mon. 334–5 / Mon. 334–7	124.46 / 59.75	Mon. 335–4	45 56 48.25 / 70 14 34.54	133 02 39 / 39 50 59	Mon. 335–3 / Mon. 335–5	62.16 / 57.07
Mon. 334–7	45 57 09.17 / 70 15 23.13	43 12 27 / 234 29 52	Mon. 334–6 / Mon. 334–8	59.75 / 54.42	Mon. 335–5	45 56 46.83 / 70 14 36.24	219 50 58 / 343 26 00	Mon. 335–4 / Mon. 335–6	57.07 / 47.38
Mon. 334–8	45 57 10.19 / 70 15 21.07	54 29 53 / 211 34 01	Mon. 334–7 / Mon. 334–9	54.42 / 53.19	Mon. 335–6	45 56 45.36 / 70 14 35.61	163 26 00 / 51 21 07	Mon. 335–5 / Mon. 335–7	47.38 / 97.55
Mon. 334–9	45 57 11.66 / 70 15 19.78	31 34 02 / 155 52 04	Mon. 334–8 / Mon. 334–10	53.19 / 67.10	Mon. 335–7	45 56 43.38 / 70 14 39.15	231 21 04 / 45 57 53	Mon. 335–6 / Mon. 335–8	97.55 / 66.28
Mon. 334–10	45 57 13.64 / 70 15 21.05	335 52 03 / 192 15 17	Mon. 334–9 / Mon. 334–11	67.10 / 73.28	Mon. 335–8	45 56 41.89 / 70 14 41.36	225 57 51 / 11 31 03	Mon. 335–7 / Mon. 335–9	66.28 / 22.22
Mon. 334–11	45 57 15.96 / 70 15 20.33	12 15 18 / 238 28 02	Mon. 334–10 / Mon. 334–12	73.28 / 104.02	Mon. 335–9	45 56 41.19 / 70 14 41.57	191 31 03 / 284 58 27	Mon. 335–8 / Mon. 335–10	22.22 / 74.13
Mon. 334–12	45 57 17.72 / 70 15 16.21	58 28 05 / 225 06 05	Mon. 334–11 / Mon. 334–13	104.02 / 67.75	Mon. 335–10	45 56 40.57 / 70 14 38.24	104 58 29 / 290 19 40	Mon. 335–9 / Mon. 335–11	74.13 / 85.86
Mon. 334–13	45 57 19.27 / 70 15 13.98	45 06 07 / 246 51 09	Mon. 334–12 / Mon. 334–14	67.75 / 41.05	Mon. 335–11	45 56 39.60 / 70 14 34.51	110 19 43 / 233 44 01	Mon. 335–10 / Mon. 335–12	85.86 / 41.58
Mon. 334–14	45 57 19.79 / 70 15 12.23	66 51 10 / 303 06 12	Mon. 334–13 / Mon. 334–15	41.05 / 106.71	Mon. 335–12	45 56 40.40 / 70 14 32.95	53 44 02 / 254 14 48	Mon. 335–11 / Mon. 335–13	41.58 / 44.24
Mon. 334–15	45 57 17.90 / 70 15 08.08	123 06 15 / 331 03 29	Mon. 334–14 / Mon. 334–16	106.71 / 38.07	Mon. 335–13	45 56 40.79 / 70 14 30.97	74 14 49 / 296 17 41	Mon. 335–12 / Mon. 335–14	44.24 / 30.10
Mon. 334–16	45 57 16.82 / 70 15 07.23	151 03 30 / 36 47 21	Mon. 334–15 / Mon. 334–17	38.07 / 51.80	Mon. 335–14	45 56 40.35 / 70 14 29.72	116 17 42 / 326 09 09	Mon. 335–13 / Mon. 335–15	30.10 / 74.83

BOUNDARY MONUMENTS—SOURCE OF SOUTHWEST BRANCH OF ST. JOHN TO HEAD OF HALLS STREAM—Continued

Station	Latitude and longitude	Azimuth	To station	Distance (meters)	Station	Latitude and longitude	Azimuth	To station	Distance (meters)
	° ′ ″	° ′ ″				° ′ ″	° ′ ″		
Mon. 335–15	45 56 38.34 70 14 27.79	146 09 10 252 39 17	Mon. 335–14 Mon. 335–16	74.83 64.62	Mon. 337–8	45 55 52.53 70 15 16.30	200 44 23 5 05 17	Mon. 337–7 Mon. 338	88.69 41.80
Mon. 335–16	45 56 38.96 70 14 24.92	72 39 19 287 52 50	Mon. 335–15 Mon. 335–17	64.62 41.94	Mon. 338	45 55 51.18 70 15 16.48	185 05 17 11 52 16	Mon. 337–8 Mon. 338–1	41.80 8.10
Mon. 335–17	45 56 38.55 70 14 23.07	107 52 51 356 49 09	Mon. 335–16 Mon. 335–18	41.94 41.02	Mon. 338–1	45 55 50.93 70 15 16.55	191 52 16 48 30 41	Mon. 338 Mon. 338–2	8.10 54.41
Mon. 335–18	45 56 37.22 70 14 22.96	176 49 09 52 42 57	Mon. 335–17 Mon. 335–19	41.02 121.08	Mon. 338–2	45 55 49.76 70 15 18.44	228 30 40 36 51 35	Mon. 338–1 Mon. 338–3	54.41 62.42
Mon. 335–19	45 56 34.85 70 14 27.44	232 42 54 1 54 11	Mon. 335–18 Mon. 335–20	121.08 98.37	Mon. 338–3	45 55 48.14 70 15 20.18	216 51 34 51 07 15	Mon. 338–2 Mon. 338–5	62.42 73.16
Mon. 335–20	45 56 31.66 70 14 27.59	181 54 11 314 24 08	Mon. 335–19 Mon. 335–21	98.37 78.72	Mon. 338–4	45 55 46.65 70 15 22.82	231 07 13 16 47 28	Mon. 338–3 Mon. 338–5	73.16 52.72
Mon. 335–21	45 56 29.88 70 14 24.98	134 24 10 33 59 42	Mon. 335–20 Mon. 335–22	78.72 47.94	Mon. 338–5	45 55 45.02 70 15 23.53	196 47 27 39 32 06	Mon. 338–4 Mon. 338–6	52.72 26.97
Mon. 335–22	45 56 28.59 70 14 26.22	213 59 41 24 36 12	Mon. 335–21 Mon. 335–23	47.94 43.43	Mon. 338–6	45 55 44.34 70 15 24.33	219 32 05 77 20 47	Mon. 338–5 Mon. 338–7	26.97 155.51
Mon. 335–23	45 56 27.31 70 14 27.06	204 36 11 343 11 54	Mon. 335–22 Mon. 336	43.43 38.77	Mon. 338–7	45 55 43.24 70 15 31.37	257 20 42 78 12 15	Mon. 338–6 Mon. 338–8	155.51 43.57
Mon. 336	45 56 26.11 70 14 26.54	163 11 54 334 25 13	Mon. 335–23 Mon. 336–1	38.77 20.28	Mon. 338–8	45 55 42.95 70 15 33.35	258 12 14 357 34 02	Mon. 338–7 Mon. 338–9	43.57 93.94
Mon. 336–1	45 56 25.52 70 14 26.13	154 25 13 324 42 01	Mon. 336 Mon. 336–2	20.28 64.88	Mon. 338–9	45 55 39.91 70 15 33.16	177 34 02 7 58 53	Mon. 338–8 Mon. 339	93.94 97.63
Mon. 336–2	45 56 23.80 70 14 24.39	144 42 02 21 45 50	Mon. 336–1 Mon. 336–3	64.88 25.02	Mon. 339	45 55 36.78 70 15 33.79	187 58 53 50 11 36	Mon. 338–9 Mon. 339–1	97.63 129.69
Mon. 336–3	45 56 23.05 70 14 24.82	201 45 50 43 44 15	Mon. 336–2 Mon. 336–4	25.02 104.31	Mon. 339–1	45 55 34.09 70 15 38.42	230 11 33 62 33 05	Mon. 339 Mon. 339–2	129.69 125.53
Mon. 336–4	45 56 20.61 70 14 28.17	223 44 13 52 31 19	Mon. 336–3 Mon. 336–5	104.31 198.92	Mon. 339–2	45 55 32.22 70 15 43.59	242 33 01 40 29 02	Mon. 339–1 Mon. 339–3	125.53 58.04
Mon. 336–5	45 56 16.69 70 14 35.50	232 31 14 26 45 53	Mon. 336–4 Mon. 336–6	198.92 65.87	Mon. 339–3	45 55 30.79 70 15 45.34	220 29 01 32 22 07	Mon. 339–2 Mon. 339–4	58.04 74.56
Mon. 336–6	45 56 14.78 70 14 36.88	206 45 52 11 25 51	Mon. 336–5 Mon. 336–7	65.87 33.59	Mon. 339–4	45 55 28.75 70 15 47.19	212 22 06 35 34 24	Mon. 339–3 Mon. 339–5	74.56 77.66
Mon. 336–7	45 56 13.72 70 14 37.18	191 25 51 68 11 33	Mon. 336–6 Mon. 336–8	33.59 39.47	Mon. 339–5	45 55 26.70 70 15 49.29	215 34 22 352 22 08	Mon. 339–4 Mon. 339–6	77.66 52.39
Mon. 336–8	45 56 13.24 70 14 38.89	248 11 32 124 12 04	Mon. 336–7 Mon. 336–9	39.47 43.52	Mon. 339–6	45 55 25.02 70 15 48.96	172 22 08 325 39 17	Mon. 339–5 Mon. 340	52.39 81.15
Mon. 336–9	45 56 14.03 70 14 40.56	304 12 03 57 52 11	Mon. 336–8 Mon. 336–10	43.52 55.11	Mon. 340	45 55 22.85 70 15 46.84	145 39 19 330 49 30	Mon. 339–6 Mon. 340–1	81.15 41.39
Mon. 336–10	45 56 13.08 70 14 42.72	237 52 09 60 54 14	Mon. 336–9 Mon. 336–11	55.11 64.63	Mon. 340–1	45 55 21.68 70 15 45.90	150 49 31 11 21 17	Mon. 340 Mon. 340–2	41.39 81.14
Mon. 336–11	45 56 12.06 70 14 45.34	240 54 12 68 58 20	Mon. 336–10 Mon. 336–12	64.63 122.83	Mon. 340–2	45 55 19.10 70 15 46.64	191 21 16 16 27 40	Mon. 340–1 Mon. 340–3	81.14 64.28
Mon. 336–12	45 56 10.64 70 14 50.67	248 58 16 45 58 29	Mon. 336–11 Mon. 336–13	122.83 76.78	Mon. 340–3	45 55 17.11 70 15 47.49	196 27 39 351 01 30	Mon. 340–2 Mon. 340–4	64.28 94.33
Mon. 336–13	45 56 08.91 70 14 53.23	225 58 27 38 11 13	Mon. 336–12 Mon. 337	76.78 51.45	Mon. 340–4	45 55 14.09 70 15 46.81	171 01 30 24 37 54	Mon. 340–3 Mon. 340–5	94.33 27.98
Mon. 337	45 56 07.60 70 14 54.70	218 11 12 40 43 31	Mon. 336–13 Mon. 337–1	51.45 56.13	Mon. 340–5	45 55 13.26 70 15 47.35	204 37 54 327 08 01	Mon. 340–4 Mon. 340–6	27.98 41.81
Mon. 337–1	45 56 06.22 70 14 56.40	220 43 30 54 04 44	Mon. 337 Mon. 337–2	56.13 181.47	Mon. 340–6	45 55 12.13 70 15 46.29	147 08 02 262 21 11	Mon. 340–5 Mon. 340–7	41.81 39.14
Mon. 337–2	45 56 02.77 70 15 03.23	234 04 39 70 01 50	Mon. 337–1 Mon. 337–3	181.47 103.45	Mon. 340–7	45 55 12.30 70 15 44.49	82 21 12 227 49 09	Mon. 340–6 Mon. 340–8	39.14 72.02
Mon. 337–3	45 56 01.63 70 15 07.74	250 01 47 46 08 47	Mon. 337–2 Mon. 337–4	103.45 112.71	Mon. 340–8	45 55 13.86 70 15 42.02	47 49 11 262 40 43	Mon. 340–7 Mon. 340–9	72.02 39.90
Mon. 337–4	45 55 59.10 70 15 11.51	226 08 44 42 15 14	Mon. 337–3 Mon. 337–5	112.71 57.33	Mon. 340–9	45 55 14.03 70 15 40.18	82 40 44 317 33 34	Mon. 340–8 Mon 340–10	39.90 25.09
Mon. 337–5	45 55 57.73 70 15 13.30	222 15 13 69 36 25	Mon. 337–4 Mon. 337–6	57.33 17.53	Mon. 340–10	45 55 13.43 70 15 39.40	137 33 35 325 52 20	Mon. 340–9 Mon. 340–11	25.09 94.47
Mon. 337–6	45 55 57.53 70 15 14.06	249 36 24 13 16 36	Mon. 337–5 Mon. 337–7	17.53 73.26	Mon. 340–11	45 55 10.90 70 15 36.94	145 52 22 344 33 04	Mon. 340–10 Mon. 340–12	94.47 73.15
Mon. 337–7	45 55 55.22 70 15 14.85	193 16 36 20 44 24	Mon. 337–6 Mon. 337–8	73.26 88.69	Mon. 340–12	45 55 08.61 70 15 36.03	164 33 05 304 23 56	Mon. 340–11 Mon. 340–13	73.15 43.34

BOUNDARY MONUMENTS—SOURCE OF SOUTHWEST BRANCH OF ST. JOHN TO HEAD OF HALLS STREAM—Continued

Station	Latitude and longitude	Azimuth	To station	Distance (meters)	Station	Latitude and longitude	Azimuth	To station	Distance (meters)
	° ′ ″	° ′ ″				° ′ ″	° ′ ″		
Mon. 340–13	45 55 07.82 / 70 15 34.37	124 23 57 / 293 35 31	Mon. 340–12 / Mon. 340–14	43.34 / 94.31	Mon. 341–16	45 54 31.66 / 70 15 20.06	148 52 56 / 354 57 49	Mon. 341–15 / Mon. 341–17	38.44 / 46.07
Mon. 340–14	45 55 06.60 / 70 15 30.36	113 35 34 / 300 40 29	Mon. 340–13 / Mon. 340–15	94.31 / 41.47	Mon. 341–17	45 54 30.17 / 70 15 19.87	174 57 49 / 313 33 24	Mon. 341–16 / Mon. 341–18	46.07 / 49.62
Mon. 340–15	45 55 05.91 / 70 15 28.71	120 40 30 / 347 00 08	Mon. 340–14 / Mon. 340–16	41.47 / 65.53	Mon. 341–18	45 54 29.07 / 70 15 18.20	133 33 25 / 340 19 18	Mon. 341–17 / Mon. 341–19	49.62 / 44.45
Mon. 340–16	45 55 03.84 / 70 15 28.02	167 00 08 / 52 54 55	Mon. 340–15 / Mon. 340–17	65.53 / 60.47	Mon. 341–19	45 54 27.71 / 70 15 17.51	160 19 19 / 290 41 59	Mon. 341–18 / Mon. 341–20	44.45 / 73.02
Mon. 340–17	45 55 02.66 / 70 15 30.26	232 54 53 / 342 22 52	Mon. 340–16 / Mon. 340–18	60.47 / 48.13	Mon. 341–20	45 54 26.87 / 70 15 14.34	110 42 01 / 8 39 59	Mon. 341–19 / Mon. 341–21	73.02 / 72.56
Mon. 340–18	45 55 01.18 / 70 15 29.59	162 22 52 / 341 20 59	Mon. 340–17 / Mon. 340–19	48.13 / 69.95	Mon. 341–21	45 54 24.55 / 70 15 14.84	188 39 59 / 16 02 27	Mon. 341–20 / Mon. 341–22	72.56 / 98.01
Mon. 340–19	45 54 59.03 / 70 15 28.55	161 21 00 / 6 32 04	Mon. 340–18 / Mon. 340–20	69.95 / 18.92	Mon. 341–22	45 54 21.50 / 70 15 16.10	196 02 26 / 359 28 17	Mon. 341–21 / Mon. 341–23	98.01 / 33.19
Mon. 340–20	45 54 58.42 / 70 15 28.65	186 32 04 / 27 29 51	Mon. 340–19 / Mon. 340–21	18.92 / 24.41	Mon. 341–23	45 54 20.42 / 70 15 16.09	179 28 17 / 336 27 08	Mon. 341–22 / Mon. 341–24	33.19 / 60.23
Mon. 340–21	45 54 57.72 / 70 15 29.17	207 29 51 / 8 43 44	Mon. 340–20 / Mon. 340–22	24.41 / 31.88	Mon. 341–24	45 54 18.64 / 70 15 14.97	156 27 09 / 8 26 54	Mon. 341–23 / Mon. 341–25	60.23 / 35.35
Mon. 340–22	45 54 56.70 / 70 15 29.40	188 43 44 / 77 57 50	Mon. 340–21 / Mon. 340–23	31.88 / 77.18	Mon. 341–25	45 54 17.50 / 70 15 15.21	188 26 54 / 13 30 32	Mon. 341–24 / Mon. 341–26	35.35 / 93.17
Mon. 340–23	45 54 56.18 / 70 15 32.90	257 57 47 / 26 56 05	Mon. 340–22 / Mon. 340–24	77.18 / 65.96	Mon. 341–26	45 54 14.57 / 70 15 16.22	193 30 31 / 319 46 27	Mon. 341–25 / Mon. 341–27	93.17 / 70.43
Mon. 340–24	45 54 54.27 / 70 15 34.28	206 56 04 / 340 47 00	Mon. 340–23 / Mon. 340–25	65.96 / 91.92	Mon. 341–27	45 54 12.83 / 70 15 14.11	139 46 29 / 25 01 49	Mon. 341–26 / Mon. 341–28	70.43 / 40.42
Mon. 340–25	45 54 51.46 / 70 15 32.88	160 47 01 / 11 05 43	Mon. 340–24 / Mon. 340–26	91.92 / 45.05	Mon. 341–28	45 54 11.64 / 70 15 14.90	205 01 48 / 22 54 20	Mon. 341–27 / Mon. 341–29	40.42 / 50.98
Mon. 340–26	45 54 50.03 / 70 15 33.28	191 05 43 / 343 30 32	Mon. 340–25 / Mon. 340–27	45.05 / 51.80	Mon. 341–29	45 54 10.12 / 70 15 15.82	202 54 19 / 11 00 14	Mon. 341–28 / Mon. 341–30	50.98 / 26.50
Mon. 340–27	45 54 48.42 / 70 15 32.60	163 30 32 / 358 28 23	Mon. 340–26 / Mon. 341	51.80 / 42.55	Mon. 341–30	45 54 09.28 / 70 15 16.06	191 00 14 / 40 28 45	Mon. 341–29 / Mon. 341–31	26.50 / 29.45
Mon. 341	45 54 47.04 / 70 15 32.55	178 28 23 / 353 38 12	Mon. 340–27 / Mon. 341–1	42.55 / 78.13	Mon. 341–31	45 54 08.55 / 70 15 16.95	220 28 44 / 84 17 33	Mon. 341–30 / Mon. 341–32	29.45 / 12.93
Mon. 341–1	45 54 44.53 / 70 15 32.14	173 38 12 / 16 19 55	Mon. 341 / Mon. 341–2	78.13 / 66.23	Mon. 341–32	45 54 08.51 / 70 15 17.54	264 17 33 / 49 37 28	Mon. 341–31 / Mon. 341–33	12.93 / 25.56
Mon. 341–2	45 54 42.47 / 70 15 33.01	196 19 54 / 30 43 01	Mon. 341–1 / Mon. 341–3	66.23 / 55.25	Mon. 341–33	45 54 07.97 / 70 15 18.45	229 37 27 / 49 27 22	Mon. 341–32 / Mon 341–34	25.56 / 71.17
Mon. 341–3	45 54 40.93 / 70 15 34.32	210 43 00 / 26 29 13	Mon. 341–2 / Mon. 341–4	55.25 / 35.23	Mon. 341–34	45 54 06.48 / 70 15 20.96	229 27 20 / 34 05 09	Mon. 341–33 / Mon. 341–35	71.17 / 82.46
Mon. 341–4	45 54 39.91 / 70 15 35.05	206 29 12 / 45 43 37	Mon. 341–3 / Mon. 341–5	35.23 / 44.30	Mon. 341–35	45 54 04.26 / 70 15 23.10	214 05 08 / 65 58 20	Mon. 341–34 / Mon. 341–36	82.46 / 64.29
Mon. 341–5	45 54 38.91 / 70 15 36.52	225 43 36 / 13 10 43	Mon. 341–4 / Mon. 341–6	44.30 / 32.54	Mon. 341–36	45 54 03.42 / 70 15 25.82	245 58 18 / 65 56 00	Mon. 341–35 / Mon. 342	64.29 / 46.97
Mon. 341–6	45 54 37.88 / 70 15 36.86	193 10 43 / 353 20 07	Mon. 341–5 / Mon. 341–7	32.54 / 74.16	Mon. 342	45 54 02.80 / 70 15 27.81	245 55 59 / 57 36 33	Mon. 341–36 / Mon. 342–1	46.97 / 14.10
Mon. 341–7	45 54 35.50 / 70 15 36.46	173 20 07 / 333 20 13	Mon. 341–6 / Mon. 341–8	74.16 / 42.12	Mon. 342–1	45 54 02.55 / 70 15 28.36	237 36 33 / 33 14 19	Mon. 342 / Mon. 342–2	14.10 / 108.97
Mon. 341–8	45 54 34.28 / 70 15 35.59	153 20 14 / 278 07 44	Mon. 341–7 / Mon. 341–9	42.12 / 65.23	Mon. 342–2	45 53 59.60 / 70 15 31.13	213 14 17 / 58 13 25	Mon. 342–1 / Mon. 342–3	108.97 / 61.96
Mon. 341–9	45 54 33.98 / 70 15 32.59	98 07 46 / 289 42 34	Mon. 341–8 / Mon. 341–10	65.23 / 27.56	Mon. 342–3	45 53 58.54 / 70 15 33.58	238 13 23 / 69 11 42	Mon. 342–2 / Mon. 342–4	61.96 / 76.30
Mon. 341–10	45 54 33.68 / 70 15 31.39	109 42 35 / 316 59 29	Mon. 341–9 / Mon. 341–11	27.56 / 45.68	Mon. 342–4	45 53 57.66 / 70 15 36.88	249 11 40 / 45 44 58	Mon. 342–3 / Mon. 342–5	76.30 / 55.69
Mon. 341–11	45 54 32.60 / 70 15 29.94	136 59 30 / 272 16 05	Mon. 341–10 / Mon. 341–12	45.68 / 44.61	Mon. 342–5	45 53 56.41 / 70 15 38.74	225 44 57 / 31 35 37	Mon. 342–4 / Mon. 342–6	55.69 / 63.63
Mon. 341–12	45 54 32.54 / 70 15 27.87	92 16 06 / 257 59 35	Mon. 341–11 / Mon. 341–13	44.61 / 45.02	Mon. 342–6	45 53 54.65 / 70 15 40.28	211 35 36 / 11 58 03	Mon. 342–5 / Mon. 342–7	63.63 / 81.00
Mon. 341–13	45 54 32.84 / 70 15 25.83	77 59 36 / 279 07 47	Mon. 341–12 / Mon. 341–14	45.02 / 54.16	Mon. 342–7	45 53 52.08 / 70 15 41.06	191 58 02 / 32 20 45	Mon. 342–6 / Mon. 342–8	81.00 / 110.18
Mon. 341–14	45 54 32.56 / 70 15 23.35	99 07 49 / 264 28 54	Mon. 341–13 / Mon. 341–15	54.16 / 51.37	Mon. 342–8	45 53 49.07 / 70 15 43.79	212 20 43 / 67 59 06	Mon. 342–7 / Mon. 342–9	110.18 / 131.87
Mon. 341–15	45 54 32.72 / 70 15 20.98	84 28 56 / 328 52 55	Mon. 341–14 / Mon. 341–16	51.37 / 38.44	Mon. 342–9	45 53 47.47 / 70 15 49.46	247 59 02 / 24 59 11	Mon. 342–8 / Mon. 342–10	131.87 / 160.88

BOUNDARY MONUMENTS—SOURCE OF SOUTHWEST BRANCH OF ST. JOHN TO HEAD OF HALLS STREAM—Continued

Station	Latitude and longitude	Azimuth	To station	Distance (meters)	Station	Latitude and longitude	Azimuth	To station	Distance (meters)
Mon. 342–10	45 53 42.75 / 70 15 52.62	204 59 09 / 26 03 56	Mon. 342–9 / Mon. 342–11	160.88 / 99.20	Mon. 343–8	45 52 57.11 / 70 16 24.89	219 47 10 / 17 50 21	Mon. 343–7 / Mon. 343–9	94.43 / 59.18
Mon. 342–11	45 53 39.86 / 70 15 54.64	206 03 55 / 55 19 34	Mon. 342–10 / Mon. 342–12	99.20 / 107.20	Mon. 343–9	45 52 55.28 / 70 16 25.73	197 50 20 / 23 21 01	Mon. 343–8 / Mon. 343–10	59.18 / 111.41
Mon. 342–12	45 53 37.88 / 70 15 58.73	235 19 31 / 354 23 44	Mon. 342–11 / Mon. 342–13	107.20 / 41.09	Mon. 343–10	45 52 51.97 / 70 16 27.78	203 21 00 / 2 05 17	Mon. 343–9 / Mon. 343–11	111.41 / 21.68
Mon. 342–13	45 53 36.56 / 70 15 58.54	174 23 44 / 304 05 33	Mon. 342–12 / Mon. 342–14	41.09 / 136.23	Mon. 343–11	45 52 51.27 / 70 16 27.82	182 05 17 / 353 16 51	Mon. 343–10 / Mon. 343–12	21.68 / 76.22
Mon. 342–14	45 53 34.09 / 70 15 53.31	124 05 37 / 293 49 19	Mon. 342–13 / Mon. 342–15	136.23 / 159.73	Mon. 343–12	45 52 48.82 / 70 16 27.40	173 16 51 / 19 08 31	Mon. 343–11 / Mon. 343–13	76.22 / 57.40
Mon. 342–15	45 53 32.00 / 70 15 46.53	113 49 24 / 231 03 42	Mon. 342–14 / Mon. 342–16	159.73 / 51.75	Mon. 343–13	45 52 47.06 / 70 16 28.28	199 08 30 / 58 11 46	Mon. 343–12 / Mon. 343–14	57.40 / 90.75
Mon. 342–16	45 53 33.05 / 70 15 44.66	51 03 43 / 308 40 20	Mon. 342–15 / Mon. 342–17	51.75 / 89.13	Mon. 343–14	45 52 45.51 / 70 16 31.85	238 11 43 / 51 47 35	Mon. 343–13 / Mon. 343–15	90.75 / 64.33
Mon. 342–17	45 53 31.25 / 70 15 41.44	128 40 22 / 296 56 11	Mon. 342–16 / Mon. 342–18	89.13 / 183.04	Mon. 343–15	45 52 44.22 / 70 16 34.20	231 47 33 / 65 03 12	Mon. 343–14 / Mon. 343–16	64.33 / 122.70
Mon. 342–18	45 53 28.56 / 70 15 33.87	116 56 16 / 50 17 10	Mon. 342–17 / Mon. 342–19	183.04 / 51.48	Mon. 343–16	45 52 42.55 / 70 16 39.36	245 03 08 / 27 28 16	Mon. 343–15 / Mon. 343–17	122.70 / 96.38
Mon. 342–19	45 53 27.50 / 70 15 35.70	230 17 09 / 40 52 15	Mon. 342–18 / Mon. 342–20	51.48 / 68.09	Mon. 343–17	45 52 39.78 / 70 16 41.42	207 28 15 / 42 24 47	Mon. 343–16 / Mon. 343–18	96.38 / 83.98
Mon. 342–20	45 53 25.83 / 70 15 37.77	220 52 14 / 344 04 42	Mon. 342–19 / Mon. 342–21	68.09 / 49.69	Mon. 343–18	45 52 37.77 / 70 16 44.04	222 24 45 / 75 29 40	Mon. 343–17 / Mon. 343–19	83.98 / 19.93
Mon. 342–21	45 53 24.28 / 70 15 37.14	164 04 42 / 45 51 51	Mon. 342–20 / Mon. 342–22	49.69 / 56.32	Mon. 343–19	45 52 37.61 / 70 16 44.94	255 29 39 / 44 04 59	Mon. 343–18 / Mon. 343–20	19.93 / 41.59
Mon. 342–22	45 53 23.01 / 70 15 39.01	225 51 50 / 51 47 52	Mon. 342–21 / Mon. 342–23	56.32 / 81.85	Mon. 343–20	45 52 36.64 / 70 16 46.28	224 04 58 / 70 57 47	Mon. 343–19 / Mon. 343–21	41.59 / 43.08
Mon. 342–23	45 53 21.37 / 70 15 42.00	231 47 50 / 13 06 51	Mon. 342–22 / Mon. 342–24	81.85 / 41.69	Mon. 343–21	45 52 36.18 / 70 16 48.17	250 57 46 / 41 21 35	Mon. 343–20 / Mon. 344	43.08 / 81.78
Mon. 342–24	45 53 20.06 / 70 15 42.44	193 06 51 / 37 13 51	Mon. 342–23 / Mon. 342–25	41.69 / 95.94	Mon. 344	45 52 34.20 / 70 16 50.68	221 21 33 / 41 21 33	Mon. 343–21 / Mon. 344–1	81.78 / 58.53
Mon. 342–25	45 53 17.58 / 70 15 45.13	217 13 49 / 66 45 53	Mon. 342–24 / Mon. 342–26	95.94 / 84.73	Mon. 344–1	45 52 32.77 / 70 16 52.47	221 21 32 / 1 13 50	Mon. 344 / Mon. 344–2	58.53 / 36.12
Mon. 342–26	45 53 16.50 / 70 15 48.74	246 45 50 / 66 42 52	Mon. 342–25 / Mon. 342–27	84.73 / 67.62	Mon. 344–2	45 52 31.60 / 70 16 52.50	181 13 50 / 3 06 02	Mon. 344–1 / Mon. 344–3	36.12 / 60.19
Mon. 342–27	45 53 15.63 / 70 15 51.62	246 42 50 / 39 03 45	Mon. 342–26 / Mon. 342–28	67.62 / 76.90	Mon. 344–3	45 52 29.66 / 70 16 52.66	183 06 02 / 16 07 08	Mon. 344–2 / Mon. 344–4	60.19 / 61.42
Mon. 342–28	45 53 13.70 / 70 15 53.87	219 03 43 / 64 35 25	Mon. 342–27 / Mon. 342–29	76.90 / 35.83	Mon. 344–4	45 52 27.75 / 70 16 53.45	196 07 07 / 42 11 24	Mon. 344–3 / Mon. 344–5	61.42 / 74.16
Mon. 342–29	45 53 13.20 / 70 15 55.37	244 35 24 / 45 00 17	Mon. 342–28 / Mon. 342–30	35.83 / 94.63	Mon. 344–5	45 52 25.97 / 70 16 55.76	222 11 22 / 71 05 27	Mon. 344–4 / Mon. 344–6	74.16 / 80.49
Mon. 342–30	45 53 11.03 / 70 15 58.47	225 00 14 / 61 29 47	Mon. 342–29 / Mon. 342–31	94.63 / 61.56	Mon. 344–6	45 52 25.12 / 70 16 59.29	251 05 24 / 38 10 23	Mon. 344–5 / Mon. 344–7	80.49 / 20.49
Mon. 342–31	45 53 10.08 / 70 16 00.98	241 29 45 / 79 17 35	Mon. 342–30 / Mon. 342–32	61.56 / 95.84	Mon. 344–7	45 52 24.60 / 70 16 59.87	218 10 23 / 39 30 03	Mon. 344–6 / Mon. 344–8	20.49 / 138.85
Mon. 342–32	45 53 09.50 / 70 16 05.35	259 17 32 / 35 06 51	Mon. 342–31 / Mon. 343	95.84 / 14.99	Mon. 344–8	45 52 21.13 / 70 17 03.97	219 30 00 / 30 22 40	Mon. 344–7 / Mon. 344–9	138.85 / 95.98
Mon. 343	45 53 09.11 / 70 16 05.75	215 06 51 / 34 01 29	Mon. 342–32 / Mon. 343–1	14.99 / 55.85	Mon. 344–9	45 52 18.45 / 70 17 06.22	210 22 38 / 90 57 59	Mon. 344–8 / Mon. 344–10	95.98 / 67.64
Mon. 343–1	45 53 07.61 / 70 16 07.20	214 01 28 / 53 27 24	Mon. 343 / Mon. 343–2	55.85 / 88.06	Mon. 344–10	45 52 18.48 / 70 17 09.36	270 57 57 / 57 25 42	Mon. 344–9 / Mon. 344–11	67.64 / 60.11
Mon. 343–2	45 53 05.91 / 70 16 10.48	233 27 22 / 64 10 18	Mon. 343–1 / Mon. 343–3	88.06 / 74.44	Mon. 344–11	45 52 17.44 / 70 17 11.70	237 25 40 / 48 17 55	Mon. 344–10 / Mon. 344–12	60.11 / 46.43
Mon. 343–3	45 53 04.86 / 70 16 13.59	244 10 16 / 70 26 29	Mon. 343–2 / Mon. 343–4	74.44 / 30.20	Mon. 344–12	45 52 16.44 / 70 17 13.31	228 17 54 / 76 09 33	Mon. 344–11 / Mon. 344–13	46.43 / 62.79
Mon. 343–4	45 53 04.53 / 70 16 14.91	250 26 28 / 39 57 17	Mon. 343–3 / Mon. 343–5	30.20 / 76.53	Mon. 344–13	45 52 15.95 / 70 17 16.14	256 09 31 / 59 03 03	Mon. 344–12 / Mon. 344–14	62.79 / 32.59
Mon. 343–5	45 53 02.63 / 70 16 17.19	219 57 15 / 47 07 16	Mon. 343–4 / Mon. 343–6	76.53 / 74.16	Mon. 344–14	45 52 15.41 / 70 17 17.43	239 03 02 / 39 16 46	Mon. 344–13 / Mon. 344–15	32.59 / 201.95
Mon. 343–6	45 53 01.00 / 70 16 19.71	227 07 14 / 47 16 44	Mon. 343–5 / Mon. 343–7	74.16 / 69.94	Mon. 344–15	45 52 10.34 / 70 17 23.36	219 16 42 / 33 01 13	Mon. 344–14 / Mon. 344–16	201.95 / 55.61
Mon. 343–7	45 52 59.46 / 70 16 22.09	227 16 42 / 39 47 12	Mon. 343–6 / Mon. 343–8	69.94 / 94.43	Mon. 344–16	45 52 08.83 / 70 17 24.77	213 01 12 / 86 28 18	Mon. 344–15 / Mon. 344–17	55.61 / 49.71

BOUNDARY MONUMENTS—SOURCE OF SOUTHWEST BRANCH OF ST. JOHN TO HEAD OF HALLS STREAM—Continued

Station	Latitude and longitude	Azimuth	To station	Distance (meters)
Mon. 344–17	45 52 08.74 / 70 17 27.07	266 28 17 / 48 50 30	Mon. 344–16 / Mon. 344–18	49.71 / 49.45
Mon. 344–18	45 52 07.68 / 70 17 28.79	228 50 29 / 37 26 23	Mon. 344–17 / Mon. 344–19	49.45 / 87.20
Mon. 344–19	45 52 05.44 / 70 17 31.25	217 26 22 / 46 54 03	Mon. 344–18 / Mon. 344–20	87.20 / 45.81
Mon. 344–20	45 52 04.42 / 70 17 32.80	226 54 02 / 59 13 26	Mon. 344–19 / Mon. 344–21	45.81 / 104.98
Mon. 344–21	45 52 02.68 / 70 17 36.98	239 13 23 / 39 21 58	Mon. 344–20 / Mon. 345	104.98 / 134.85
Mon. 345	45 51 59.31 / 70 17 40.95	219 21 56 / 41 27 10	Mon. 344–21 / Mon. 345–1	134.85 / 18.60
Mon. 345–1	45 51 58.86 / 70 17 41.52	221 27 10 / 50 33 33	Mon. 345 / Mon. 345–2	18.60 / 180.62
Mon. 345–2	45 51 55.14 / 70 17 47.98	230 33 28 / 53 25 44	Mon. 345–1 / Mon. 345–3	180.62 / 84.65
Mon. 345–3	45 51 53.50 / 70 17 51.14	233 25 42 / 62 47 17	Mon. 345–2 / Mon. 345–4	84.65 / 137.71
Mon. 345–4	45 51 51.46 / 70 17 56.81	242 47 13 / 70 01 17	Mon. 345–3 / Mon. 345–5	137.71 / 165.61
Mon. 345–5	45 51 49.63 / 70 18 04.03	250 01 12 / 65 14 16	Mon. 345–4 / Mon. 345–6	165.61 / 255.49
Mon. 345–6	45 51 46.17 / 70 18 14.78	245 14 08 / 13 16 31	Mon. 345–5 / Mon. 345–7	255.49 / 49.56
Mon. 345–7	45 51 44.60 / 70 18 15.31	193 16 31 / 28 59 47	Mon. 345–6 / Mon. 345–8	49.56 / 87.63
Mon. 345–8	45 51 42.12 / 70 18 17.28	208 59 46 / 40 19 09	Mon. 345–7 / Mon. 345–9	87.63 / 134.67
Mon. 345–9	45 51 38.80 / 70 18 21.32	220 19 06 / 27 27 52	Mon. 345–8 / Mon. 345–10	134.67 / 67.64
Mon. 345–10	45 51 36.85 / 70 18 22.77	207 27 51 / 45 07 38	Mon. 345–9 / Mon. 345–11	67.64 / 67.97
Mon. 345–11	45 51 35.30 / 70 18 25.00	225 07 36 / 63 55 22	Mon. 345–10 / Mon. 345–12	67.97 / 54.19
Mon. 345–12	45 51 34.53 / 70 18 27.26	243 55 20 / 41 52 01	Mon. 345–11 / Mon. 345–13	54.19 / 96.37
Mon 345–13	45 51 32.20 / 70 18 30.24	221 51 59 / 75 46 27	Mon. 345–12 / Mon. 345–14	96.37 / 178.17
Mon. 345–14	45 51 30.79 / 70 18 38.24	255 46 21 / 94 41 19	Mon. 345–13 / Mon. 345–15	178.17 / 122.74
Mon 345–15	45 51 31.11 / 70 18 43.91	274 41 15 / 71 25 02	Mon. 345–14 / Mon. 345–16	122.74 / 91.46
Mon. 345–16	45 51 30.17 / 70 18 47.93	251 24 59 / 70 47 03	Mon. 345–15 / Mon. 345–17	91.46 / 135.14
Mon. 345–17	45 51 28.73 / 70 18 53.85	250 46 59 / 53 03 34	Mon. 345–16 / Mon. 345–18	135.14 / 263.29
Mon. 345–18	45 51 23.60 / 70 19 03.60	233 03 27 / 69 23 37	Mon. 345–17 / Mon. 345–19	263.29 / 85.92
Mon. 345–19	45 51 22.62 / 70 19 07.33	249 23 34 / 74 59 15	Mon. 345–18 / Mon. 345–20	85.92 / 65.41
Mon. 345–20	45 51 22.07 / 70 19 10.26	254 59 13 / 59 12 05	Mon. 345–19 / Mon. 345–21	65.41 / 81.83
Mon. 345–21	45 51 20.72 / 70 19 13.52	239 12 03 / 112 56 38	Mon. 345–20 / Mon. 345–22	81.83 / 156.29
Mon. 345–22	45 51 22.69 / 70 19 20.19	292 56 33 / 54 37 01	Mon. 345–21 / Mon. 345–23	156.29 / 33.04
Mon. 345–23	45 51 22.07 / 70 19 21.44	234 37 00 / 50 40 53	Mon. 345–22 / Mon. 345–24	33.04 / 131.28
Mon. 345–24	45 51 19.37 / 70 19 26.14	230 40 50 / 84 59 42	Mon. 345–23 / Mon. 345–25	131.28 / 84.15
Mon. 345–25	45 51 19.14 / 70 19 30.03	264 59 39 / 76 24 08	Mon. 345–24 / Mon. 345–26	84.15 / 97.05
Mon. 345–26	45 51 18.40 / 70 19 34.40	256 24 05 / 81 22 45	Mon. 345–25 / Mon. 345–27	97.05 / 103.58
Mon. 345–27	45 51 17.89 / 70 19 39.15	261 22 42 / 114 29 47	Mon. 345–26 / Mon. 345–28	103.58 / 68.90
Mon. 345–28	45 51 18.82 / 70 19 42.06	294 29 45 / 75 32 49	Mon. 345–27 / Mon. 345–29	68.90 / 44.34
Mon. 345–29	45 51 18.46 / 70 19 44.05	255 32 48 / 73 14 53	Mon. 345–28 / Mon. 345–30	44.34 / 56.31
Mon. 345–30	45 51 17.94 / 70 19 46.54	253 14 51 / 6 03 55	Mon. 345–29 / Mon. 345–31	56.31 / 44.78
Mon. 345–31	45 51 16.49 / 70 19 46.76	186 03 55 / 2 25 48	Mon. 345–30 / Mon. 345–32	44.78 / 45.52
Mon. 345–32	45 51 15.02 / 70 19 46.85	182 25 48 / 79 57 28	Mon. 345–31 / Mon. 345–33	45.52 / 63.66
Mon. 345–33	45 51 14.66 / 70 19 49.76	259 57 26 / 105 38 19	Mon. 345–32 / Mon. 345–34	63.66 / 74.98
Mon. 345–34	45 51 15.32 / 70 19 53.11	285 38 16 / 55 38 38	Mon. 345–33 / Mon. 345–35	74.98 / 135.60
Mon. 345–35	45 51 12.84 / 70 19 58.30	235 38 34 / 46 58 45	Mon. 345–34 / Mon. 345–36	135.60 / 48.43
Mon. 345–36	45 51 11.77 / 70 19 59.94	226 58 44 / 57 11 43	Mon. 345–35 / Mon. 345–37	48.43 / 19.79
Mon. 345–37	45 51 11.42 / 70 20 00.71	237 11 42 / 86 32 46	Mon. 345–36 / Mon. 345–38	19.79 / 59.24
Mon. 345–38	45 51 11.30 / 70 20 03.45	266 32 44 / 104 19 19	Mon. 345–37 / Mon. 346	59.24 / 67.30
Mon. 346	45 51 11.84 / 70 20 06.48	284 19 16 / 125 06 59	Mon. 345–38 / Mon. 346–1	67.30 / 26.50
Mon. 346–1	45 51 12.34 / 70 20 07.48	305 06 58 / 85 23 00	Mon. 346 / Mon. 346–2	26.50 / 85.59
Mon. 346–2	45 51 12.12 / 70 20 11.43	265 22 57 / 79 52 13	Mon. 346–1 / Mon. 346–3	85.59 / 71.25
Mon. 346–3	45 51 11.71 / 70 20 14.68	259 52 11 / 54 42 39	Mon. 346–2 / Mon. 346–4	71.25 / 94.87
Mon. 346–4	45 51 09.94 / 70 20 18.27	234 42 36 / 89 48 59	Mon. 346–3 / Mon. 346–5	94.87 / 107.45
Mon. 346–5	45 51 09.92 / 70 20 23.25	269 48 55 / 72 30 37	Mon. 346–4 / Mon. 346–6	107.45 / 128.67
Mon. 346–6	45 51 08.67 / 70 20 28.94	252 30 33 / 86 36 23	Mon. 346–5 / Mon. 346–7	128.67 / 76.10
Mon. 346–7	45 51 08.53 / 70 20 32.46	266 36 20 / 117 03 16	Mon. 346–6 / Mon. 346–8	76.10 / 16.74
Mon. 346–8	45 51 08.77 / 70 20 33.15	297 03 16 / 32 58 12	Mon. 346–7 / Mon. 346–9	16.74 / 36.55
Mon. 346–9	45 51 07.78 / 70 20 34.08	212 58 11 / 18 56 01	Mon. 346–8 / Mon. 346–10	36.55 / 28.82
Mon. 346–10	45 51 06.90 / 70 20 34.51	198 56 01 / 43 58 21	Mon. 346–9 / Mon. 346–11	28.82 / 32.74
Mon. 346–11	45 51 06.13 / 70 20 35.56	223 58 20 / 30 42 11	Mon. 346–10 / Mon. 346–12	32.74 / 75.04
Mon. 346–12	45 51 04.04 / 70 20 37.34	210 42 10 / 15 11 08	Mon. 346–11 / Mon. 346–13	75.04 / 121.40
Mon. 346–13	45 51 00.25 / 70 20 38.81	195 11 07 / 62 47 47	Mon. 346–12 / Mon. 346–14	121.40 / 111.97
Mon. 346–14	45 50 58.59 / 70 20 43.43	242 47 44 / 64 47 25	Mon. 346–13 / Mon. 346–15	111.97 / 131.73
Mon. 346–15	45 50 56.77 / 70 20 48.95	244 47 21 / 37 08 04	Mon. 346–14 / Mon. 346–16	131.73 / 60.11
Mon. 346–16	45 50 55.22 / 70 20 50.63	217 08 03 / 44 09 53	Mon. 346–15 / Mon. 346–17	60.11 / 110.82
Mon. 346–17	45 50 52.65 / 70 20 54.21	224 09 51 / 52 07 35	Mon. 346–16 / Mon. 347	110.82 / 81.89

BOUNDARY MONUMENTS—SOURCE OF SOUTHWEST BRANCH OF ST. JOHN TO HEAD OF HALLS STREAM—Continued

Station	Latitude and longitude	Azimuth	To station	Distance (meters)	Station	Latitude and longitude	Azimuth	To station	Distance (meters)
	° ′ ″	° ′ ″				° ′ ″	° ′ ″		
Mon. 347	45 50 51.02 / 70 20 57.21	232 07 33 / 53 37 40	Mon. 346-17 / Mon. 347-1	81.89 / 64.58	Mon. 347-31	45 50 07.86 / 70 21 37.15	261 53 36 / 113 07 16	Mon. 347-30 / Mon. 347-32	23.52 / 69.63
Mon. 347-1	45 50 49.78 / 70 20 59.62	233 37 38 / 9 54 13	Mon. 347 / Mon. 347-2	64.58 / 89.68	Mon. 347-32	45 50 08.74 / 70 21 40.11	293 07 14 / 92 52 42	Mon. 347-31 / Mon. 347-33	69.63 / 59.02
Mon. 347-2	45 50 46.92 / 70 21 00.33	189 54 12 / 7 00 36	Mon. 347-1 / Mon. 347-3	89.68 / 51.13	Mon. 347-33	45 50 08.84 / 70 21 42.84	272 52 40 / 105 48 21	Mon. 347-32 / Mon. 347-34	59.02 / 37.94
Mon. 347-3	45 50 45.27 / 70 21 00.62	187 00 36 / 316 27 07	Mon. 347-2 / Mon. 347-4	51.13 / 25.66	Mon. 347-34	45 50 09.17 / 70 21 44.54	285 48 20 / 59 30 01	Mon. 347-33 / Mon. 348	37.94 / 14.06
Mon. 347-4	45 50 44.67 / 70 20 59.80	136 27 08 / 34 29 39	Mon. 347-3 / Mon. 347-5	25.66 / 40.40	Mon. 348	45 50 08.94 / 70 21 45.10	239 30 01 / 61 31 16	Mon. 347-34 / Mon. 348-1	14.06 / 103.49
Mon. 347-5	45 50 43.59 / 70 21 00.86	214 29 38 / 30 52 52	Mon. 347-4 / Mon. 347-6	40.40 / 100.91	Mon. 348-1	45 50 07.34 / 70 21 49.31	241 31 13 / 50 19 38	Mon. 348 / Mon. 348-2	103.49 / 41.66
Mon. 347-6	45 50 40.79 / 70 21 03.26	210 52 50 / 52 52 11	Mon. 347-5 / Mon. 347-7	100.91 / 40.17	Mon. 348-2	45 50 06.48 / 70 21 50.80	230 19 37 / 61 59 03	Mon. 348-1 / Mon. 348-3	41.66 / 84.01
Mon. 347-7	45 50 40.00 / 70 21 04.75	232 52 10 / 48 33 14	Mon. 347-6 / Mon. 347-8	40.17 / 36.87	Mon. 348-3	45 50 05.20 / 70 21 54.23	241 59 01 / 107 27 30	Mon. 348-2 / Mon. 348-4	84.01 / 60.92
Mon. 347-8	45 50 39.21 / 70 21 06.03	228 33 13 / 69 38 00	Mon. 347-7 / Mon. 347-9	36.87 / 48.23	Mon. 348-4	45 50 05.79 / 70 21 56.93	287 27 28 / 108 30 59	Mon. 348-3 / Mon. 348-5	60.92 / 36.72
Mon. 347-9	45 50 38.67 / 70 21 08.13	249 37 58 / 33 47 09	Mon. 347-8 / Mon. 347-10	48.23 / 69.39	Mon. 348-5	45 50 06.17 / 70 21 58.54	288 30 58 / 83 45 29	Mon. 348-4 / Mon. 348-6	36.72 / 113.35
Mon. 347-10	45 50 36.80 / 70 21 09.92	213 47 08 / 26 55 32	Mon. 347-9 / Mon. 347-11	69.39 / 100.08	Mon. 348-6	45 50 05.77 / 70 22 03.76	263 45 25 / 160 43 00	Mon. 348-5 / Mon. 348-7	113.35 / 37.98
Mon. 347-11	45 50 33.91 / 70 21 12.02	206 55 30 / 30 41 32	Mon. 347-10 / Mon. 347-12	100.08 / 38.45	Mon. 348-7	45 50 06.93 / 70 22 04.34	340 43 00 / 162 30 34	Mon. 348-6 / Mon. 348-8	37.98 / 70.84
Mon. 347-12	45 50 32.84 / 70 21 12.93	210 41 31 / 311 12 15	Mon. 347-11 / Mon. 347-13	38.45 / 67.37	Mon. 348-8	45 50 09.12 / 70 22 05.33	342 30 33 / 114 14 06	Mon. 348-7 / Mon. 348-9	70.84 / 75.24
Mon. 347-13	45 50 31.40 / 70 21 10.58	131 12 17 / 333 38 37	Mon. 347-12 / Mon. 347-14	67.37 / 28.58	Mon. 348-9	45 50 10.12 / 70 22 08.51	294 14 04 / 70 58 38	Mon. 348-8 / Mon. 348-10	75.24 / 24.08
Mon. 347-14	45 50 30.57 / 70 21 09.99	153 38 37 / 10 00 15	Mon. 347-13 / Mon. 347-15	28.58 / 38.51	Mon. 348-10	45 50 09.87 / 70 22 09.56	250 58 37 / 61 07 12	Mon. 348-9 / Mon. 348-11	24.08 / 117.65
Mon. 347-15	45 50 29.34 / 70 21 10.30	190 00 15 / 359 07 42	Mon. 347-14 / Mon. 347-16	38.51 / 31.15	Mon. 348-11	45 50 08.03 / 70 22 14.34	241 07 09 / 63 14 49	Mon. 348-10 / Mon. 348-12	117.65 / 66.47
Mon. 347-16	45 50 28.34 / 70 21 10.28	179 07 42 / 346 35 15	Mon. 347-15 / Mon. 347-17	31.15 / 23.46	Mon. 348-12	45 50 07.06 / 70 22 17.08	243 14 47 / 37 26 29	Mon. 348-11 / Mon. 348-13	66.47 / 43.62
Mon. 347-17	45 50 27.60 / 70 21 10.02	166 35 15 / 55 00 18	Mon. 347-16 / Mon. 347-18	23.46 / 124.37	Mon. 348-13	45 50 05.94 / 70 22 18.31	217 26 28 / 20 59 12	Mon. 348-12 / Mon. 348-14	43.62 / 33.66
Mon. 347-18	45 50 25.29 / 70 21 14.75	235 00 15 / 85 46 50	Mon. 347-17 / Mon. 347-19	124.37 / 56.19	Mon. 348-14	45 50 04.92 / 70 22 18.87	200 59 12 / 42 50 57	Mon. 348-13 / Mon. 348-15	33.66 / 30.14
Mon. 347-19	45 50 25.15 / 70 21 17.34	265 46 48 / 56 19 42	Mon. 347-18 / Mon. 347-20	56.19 / 47.69	Mon. 348-15	45 50 04.20 / 70 22 19.82	222 50 56 / 28 36 42	Mon. 348-14 / Mon. 348-16	30.14 / 56.48
Mon. 347-20	45 50 24.30 / 70 21 19.18	236 19 41 / 60 14 06	Mon. 347-19 / Mon. 347-21	47.69 / 86.31	Mon. 348-16	45 50 02.60 / 70 22 21.08	208 36 41 / 298 52 29	Mon. 348-15 / Mon. 348-17	56.48 / 42.26
Mon. 347-21	45 50 22.91 / 70 21 22.65	240 14 03 / 38 19 47	Mon. 347-20 / Mon. 347-22	86.31 / 108.62	Mon. 348-17	45 50 01.93 / 70 22 19.36	118 52 30 / 319 45 18	Mon. 348-16 / Mon. 348-18	42.26 / 196.11
Mon. 347-22	45 50 20.15 / 70 21 25.78	218 19 45 / 341 33 42	Mon. 347-21 / Mon. 347-23	108.62 / 112.55	Mon. 348-18	45 49 57.08 / 70 22 13.49	139 45 22 / 27 14 10	Mon. 348-17 / Mon. 348-19	196.18 / 91.51
Mon. 347-23	45 50 16.69 / 70 21 24.13	161 33 43 / 40 51 35	Mon. 347-22 / Mon. 347-24	112.55 / 79.68	Mon. 348-19	45 49 54.45 / 70 22 15.43	207 14 09 / 306 17 00	Mon. 348-18 / Mon. 348-20	91.58 / 99.04
Mon. 347-24	45 50 14.74 / 70 21 26.54	220 51 33 / 38 40 02	Mon. 347-23 / Mon. 347-25	79.68 / 48.40	Mon. 348-20	45 49 52.55 / 70 22 11.74	126 17 03 / 45 51 54	Mon. 348-19 / Mon. 348-21	99.04 / 125.74
Mon. 347-25	45 50 13.51 / 70 21 27.94	218 40 01 / 59 55 37	Mon. 347-24 / Mon. 347-26	48.40 / 60.93	Mon. 348-21	45 49 49.71 / 70 22 15.92	225 51 51 / 49 28 47	Mon. 348-20 / Mon. 348-22	125.74 / 73.71
Mon. 347-26	45 50 12.52 / 70 21 30.39	239 55 35 / 53 36 00	Mon. 347-25 / Mon. 347-27	60.93 / 36.58	Mon. 348-22	45 49 48.16 / 70 22 18.51	229 28 45 / 29 58 43	Mon. 348-21 / Mon. 348-23	73.71 / 133.18
Mon. 347-27	45 50 11.82 / 70 21 31.75	233 35 59 / 31 28 25	Mon. 347-26 / Mon. 347-28	36.58 / 66.46	Mon. 348-23	45 49 44.43 / 70 22 21.60	209 58 41 / 7 14 44	Mon. 348-22 / Mon. 348-24	133.18 / 102.02
Mon. 347-28	45 50 09.99 / 70 21 33.36	211 28 24 / 71 02 20	Mon. 347-27 / Mon. 347-29	66.46 / 35.31	Mon. 348-24	45 49 41.15 / 70 22 22.19	187 14 44 / 49 20 50	Mon. 348-23 / Mon. 348-25	102.02 / 42.77
Mon. 347-29	45 50 09.61 / 70 21 34.90	251 02 19 / 26 13 28	Mon. 347-28 / Mon. 347-30	35.31 / 56.80	Mon. 348-25	45 49 40.25 / 70 22 23.69	229 20 49 / 70 01 57	Mon. 348-24 / Mon. 348-26	42.77 / 15.86
Mon. 347-30	45 50 07.96 / 70 21 36.07	206 13 27 / 81 53 37	Mon. 347-29 / Mon. 347-31	56.80 / 23.52	Mon. 348-26	45 49 40.07 / 70 22 24.38	250 01 57 / 85 52 06	Mon. 348-25 / Mon. 348-27	15.86 / 93.13

BOUNDARY MONUMENTS—SOURCE OF SOUTHWEST BRANCH OF ST. JOHN TO HEAD OF HALLS STREAM—Continued

Station	Latitude and longitude	Azimuth	To station	Distance (meters)	Station	Latitude and longitude	Azimuth	To station	Distance (meters)
	° ′ ″	° ′ ″				° ′ ″	° ′ ″		
Mon. 348–27	45 49 39.85 70 22 28.69	265 52 03 80 45 15	Mon. 348–26 Mon. 348–28	93.13 82.90	Mon. 350–6	45 48 44.19 70 23 27.57	184 48 24 50 16 37	Mon. 350–5 Mon. 350–7	40.39 78.79
Mon. 348–28	45 49 39.42 70 22 32.48	260 45 12 60 49 26	Mon. 348–27 Mon. 348–29	82.90 89.45	Mon. 350–7	45 48 42.56 70 23 30.38	230 16 35 48 53 47	Mon. 350–6 Mon. 351	78.79 443.25
Mon. 348–29	45 49 38.01 70 22 36.10	240 49 23 53 07 41	Mon. 348–28 Mon. 348–30	89.45 67.63	Mon. 351	45 48 33.12 70 23 45.85	228 53 36 40 15 14	Mon. 350–7 Mon. 351–A	443.25 45.75
Mon. 348–30	45 49 36.70 70 22 38.60	233 07 39 32 57 59	Mon. 348–29 Mon. 348–31	67.63 62.30	Mon. 351–A	45 48 31.99 70 23 47.22	220 15 13 40 15 13	Mon. 351 Mon. 351–B	45.75 19.61
Mon. 348–31	45 49 35.00 70 22 40.17	212 57 58 53 32 21	Mon. 348–30 Mon 348–32	62.30 134.00	Mon. 351–B	45 48 31.50 70 23 47.80	220 15 12 40 15 12	Mon. 351–A Mon. 352	19.61 81.57
Mon. 348–32	45 49 32.42 70 22 45.16	233 32 17 50 53 45	Mon. 348–31 Mon. 348–33	134.00 139.58	Mon. 352	45 48 29.49 70 23 50.24	220 15 10 22 24 04	Mon. 351–B Mon. 352–1	81.57 95.46
Mon. 348–33	45 49 29.57 70 22 50.18	230 53 41 38 32 14	Mon. 348–32 Mon. 348–34	139.58 103.73	Mon. 352–1	45 48 26.63 70 23 51.93	202 24 03 341 33 12	Mon. 352 Mon. 353	95.46 55.92
Mon. 348–34	45 49 26.94 70 22 53.18	218 32 12 32 05 49	Mon. 348–33 Mon. 348–35	103.73 84.82	Mon. 353	45 48 24.91 70 23 51.11	161 33 12 341 44 42	Mon. 352–1 Mon. 353–1	55.92 70.81
Mon. 348–35	45 49 24.62 70 22 55.26	212 05 47 21 25 27	Mon. 348–34 Mon. 348–36	84.82 68.72	Mon. 353–1	45 48 22.73 70 23 50.08	161 44 43 7 32 13	Mon. 353 Mon. 353–2	70.81 78.64
Mon. 348–36	45 49 22.54 70 22 56.43	201 25 26 60 07 09	Mon. 348–35 Mon. 348–37	68.72 60.56	Mon. 353–2	45 48 20.21 70 23 50.56	187 32 13 22 48 48	Mon. 353–1 Mon. 353–3	78.64 73.65
Mon. 348–37	45 49 21.57 70 22 58.86	240 07 07 46 32 52	Mon. 348–36 Mon. 348–38	60.56 88.26	Mon. 353–3	45 48 18.01 70 23 51.88	202 48 47 31 30 15	Mon. 353–2 Mon. 353–4	73.65 102.66
Mon. 348–38	45 49 19.60 70 23 01.83	226 32 50 61 24 39	Mon. 348–37 Mon. 349	88.26 36.37	Mon. 353–4	45 48 15.17 70 23 54.36	211 30 13 1 24 04	Mon. 353–3 Mon. 353–5	102.66 39.20
Mon. 349	45 49 19.04 70 23 03.31	241 24 38 64 42 29	Mon. 348–38 Mon. 349–1	36.37 29.98	Mon. 353–5	45 48 13.90 70 23 54.41	181 24 04 305 14 56	Mon. 353–4 Mon. 353–6	39.20 82.49
Mon. 349–1	45 49 18.62 70 23 04.56	244 42 28 38 06 16	Mon. 349 Mon. 349–2	29.98 73.96	Mon. 353–6	45 48 12.36 70 23 51.29	125 14 57 312 31 56	Mon. 353–5 Mon. 353–7	82.49 133.89
Mon. 349–2	45 49 16.74 70 23 06.68	218 06 14 39 56 49	Mon. 349–1 Mon. 349–3	73.96 54.91	Mon. 353–7	45 48 09.43 70 23 46.72	132 31 59 9 49 11	Mon. 353–6 Mon. 354	133.89 16.32
Mon. 349–3	45 49 15.37 70 23 08.31	219 56 48 54 18 38	Mon. 349–2 Mon 349–4	54.91 113.26	Mon. 354	45 48 08.91 70 23 46.85	189 49 11 15 45 26	Mon. 353–7 Mon. 354–1	16.32 40.48
Mon. 349–4	45 49 13.23 70 23 12.57	234 18 35 22 58 13	Mon. 349–3 Mon. 349–5	113.26 53.86	Mon. 354–1	45 48 07.65 70 23 47.36	195 45 26 33 18 54	Mon. 354 Mon. 354–2	40.48 67.36
Mon. 349–5	45 49 11.63 70 23 13.55	202 58 12 46 56 17	Mon. 349–4 Mon. 349–6	53.86 162.47	Mon. 354–2	45 48 05.83 70 23 49.07	213 18 53 5 48 12	Mon. 354–1 Mon. 354–3	67.36 180.56
Mon. 349–6	45 49 08.04 70 23 19.04	226 56 13 0 45 27	Mon. 349–5 Mon. 349–7	162.47 90.83	Mon. 354–3	45 48 00.01 70 23 49.92	185 48 11 313 02 58	Mon. 354–2 Mon. 354–4	180.56 46.74
Mon. 349–7	45 49 05.09 70 23 19.10	180 45 27 8 24 16	Mon. 349–6 Mon. 349–8	90.83 127.15	Mon. 354–4	45 47 58.97 70 23 48.34	133 02 59 286 57 55	Mon. 354–3 Mon. 354–5	46.74 40.90
Mon. 349–8	45 49 01.02 70 23 19.96	188 24 16 359 18 01	Mon. 349–7 Mon. 349–9	127.15 73.84	Mon. 354–5	45 47 58.59 70 23 46.52	106 57 56 22 15 55	Mon. 354–4 Mon. 355	40.90 7.51
Mon. 349–9	45 48 58.63 70 23 19.92	179 18 01 322 05 44	Mon. 349–8 Mon. 349–10	73.84 42.57	Mon. 355	45 47 58.36 70 23 46.66	202 15 55 22 08 27	Mon. 354–5 Mon. 355–1	7.51 95.28
Mon. 349–10	45 48 57.54 70 23 18.71	142 05 45 351 12 54	Mon. 349–9 Mon. 349–11	42.57 51.47	Mon. 355–1	45 47 55.50 70 23 48.32	202 08 26 40 04 31	Mon. 355 Mon. 355–2	95.28 139.25
Mon. 349–11	45 48 55.89 70 23 18.34	171 12 54 358 18 48	Mon. 349–10 Mon. 349–12	51.47 120.13	Mon. 355–2	45 47 52.05 70 23 52.47	220 04 28 46 16 03	Mon. 355–1 Mon. 355–3	139.25 172.24
Mon. 349–12	45 48 52.00 70 23 18.18	178 18 48 40 44 24	Mon. 349–11 Mon. 350	120.13 12.70	Mon. 355–3	45 47 48.20 70 23 58.23	226 15 59 71 04 18	Mon. 355–2 Mon. 355–4	172.24 93.36
Mon. 350	45 48 51.69 70 23 18.56	220 44 24 31 35 12	Mon. 349–12 Mon. 350–1	12.70 45.78	Mon. 355–4	45 47 47.22 70 24 02.32	251 04 15 66 37 12	Mon. 355–3 Mon. 355–5	93.36 111.66
Mon. 350–1	45 48 50.43 70 23 19.68	211 35 11 54 11 35	Mon. 350 Mon. 350–2	45.78 28.26	Mon. 355–5	45 47 45.78 70 24 07.07	246 37 09 92 41 16	Mon. 355–4 Mon. 355–6	111.66 92.50
Mon. 350–2	45 48 49.89 70 23 20.74	234 11 34 77 35 47	Mon. 350–1 Mon. 350–3	28.26 32.01	Mon. 355–6	45 47 45.92 70 24 11.35	272 41 13 90 46 08	Mon. 355–5 Mon. 355–7	92.50 18.71
Mon 350–3	45 48 49.67 70 23 22.18	257 35 46 63 51 42	Mon. 350–2 Mon. 350–4	32.01 108.25	Mon. 355–7	45 47 45.93 70 24 12.21	270 46 08 123 48 29	Mon. 355–6 Mon. 356	18.71 37.29
Mon. 350–4	45 48 48.12 70 23 26.69	243 51 39 10 57 30	Mon. 350–3 Mon. 350–5	108.25 82.75	Mon. 356	45 47 46.60 70 24 13.65	303 48 28 111 26 33	Mon. 355–7 Mon. 356–1	37.29 25.37
Mon. 350–5	45 48 45.49 70 23 27.42	190 57 30 4 48 24	Mon. 350–4 Mon. 350–6	82.75 40.39	Mon. 356–1	45 47 46.90 70 24 14.74	291 26 32 91 00 01	Mon. 356 Mon. 356–2	25.37 32.17

BOUNDARY MONUMENTS—SOURCE OF SOUTHWEST BRANCH OF ST. JOHN TO HEAD OF HALLS STREAM—Continued

Station	Latitude and longitude	Azimuth	To station	Distance (meters)
	° ′ ″	° ′ ″		
Mon. 356-2	45 47 46.92 / 70 24 16.23	271 00 00 / 117 56 26	Mon. 356-1 / Mon. 356-3	32.17 / 125.00
Mon. 356-3	45 47 48.82 / 70 24 21.34	297 56 22 / 136 45 32	Mon. 356-2 / Mon. 356-4	125.00 / 151.86
Mon. 356-4	45 47 52.40 / 70 24 26.16	316 45 29 / 69 28 53	Mon. 356-3 / Mon. 356-5	151.86 / 48.74
Mon. 356-5	45 47 51.84 / 70 24 28.27	249 28 51 / 91 20 43	Mon. 356-4 / Mon. 356-6	48.74 / 88.85
Mon. 356-6	45 47 51.91 / 70 24 32.39	271 20 40 / 58 35 49	Mon. 356-5 / Mon. 356-7	88.85 / 64.62
Mon. 356-7	45 47 50.82 / 70 24 34.94	238 35 47 / 70 40 19	Mon. 356-6 / Mon. 356-8	64.62 / 72.46
Mon. 356-8	45 47 50.04 / 70 24 38.11	250 40 17 / 57 13 15	Mon. 356-7 / Mon. 357	72.46 / 41.03
Mon. 357	45 47 49.33 / 70 24 39.70	237 13 14 / 61 29 10	Mon. 356-8 / Mon. 357-1	41.03 / 70.96
Mon. 357-1	45 47 48.23 / 70 24 42.59	241 29 08 / 68 54 02	Mon. 357 / Mon. 357-2	70.96 / 209.21
Mon. 357-2	45 47 45.79 / 70 24 51.63	248 53 55 / 73 57 26	Mon. 357-1 / Mon. 357-3	209.21 / 111.69
Mon. 357-3	45 47 44.79 / 70 24 56.60	253 57 22 / 93 06 24	Mon. 357-2 / Mon. 357-4	111.69 / 91.15
Mon. 357-4	45 47 44.95 / 70 25 00.81	273 06 21 / 64 28 53	Mon. 357-3 / Mon. 357-5	91.15 / 49.28
Mon. 357-5	45 47 44.26 / 70 25 02.87	244 28 52 / 25 55 51	Mon. 357-4 / Mon. 358	49.28 / 19.03
Mon. 358	45 47 43.71 / 70 25 03.26	205 55 51 / 21 36 12	Mon. 357-5 / Mon. 358-1	19.03 / 100.39
Mon. 358-1	45 47 40.69 / 70 25 04.97	201 36 11 / 23 44 52	Mon. 358 / Mon. 358-2	100.39 / 68.45
Mon. 358-2	45 47 38.66 / 70 25 06.24	203 44 51 / 314 28 57	Mon. 358-1 / Mon. 358-3	68.45 / 85.95
Mon. 358-3	45 47 36.71 / 70 25 03.41	134 28 59 / 250 29 26	Mon. 358-2 / Mon. 358-4	85.95 / 32.02
Mon. 358-4	45 47 37.05 / 70 25 02.01	70 29 27 / 334 16 13	Mon. 358-3 / Mon. 358-5	32.02 / 47.01
Mon. 358-5	45 47 35.68 / 70 25 01.06	154 16 14 / 334 06 19	Mon. 358-4 / Mon. 358-6	47.01 / 115.58
Mon. 358-6	45 47 32.31 / 70 24 58.73	154 06 21 / 312 44 07	Mon. 358-5 / Mon. 358-7	115.58 / 32.84
Mon. 358-7	45 47 31.59 / 70 24 57.61	132 44 08 / 321 08 16	Mon. 358-6 / Mon. 358-8	32.84 / 46.09
Mon. 358-8	45 47 30.43 / 70 24 56.27	141 08 17 / 330 54 26	Mon. 358-7 / Mon. 358-9	46.09 / 42.01
Mon. 358-9	45 47 29.24 / 70 24 55.32	150 54 26 / 347 15 18	Mon. 358-8 / Mon. 359	42.01 / 72.89
Mon. 359	45 47 26.94 / 70 24 54.58	167 15 18 / 345 20 22	Mon. 358-9 / Mon. 359-1	72.89 / 64.53
Mon. 359-1	45 47 24.92 / 70 24 53.82	165 20 23 / 16 27 22	Mon. 359 / Mon. 359-2	64.53 / 93.64
Mon. 359-2	45 47 22.01 / 70 24 55.05	196 27 21 / 1 14 01	Mon. 359-1 / Mon. 359-3	93.64 / 68.29
Mon. 359-3	45 47 19.80 / 70 24 55.12	181 14 01 / 13 08 10	Mon. 359-2 / Mon. 359-4	68.29 / 159.21
Mon. 359-4	45 47 14.78 / 70 24 56.80	193 08 09 / 353 33 05	Mon. 359-3 / Mon. 359-5	159.21 / 32.04
Mon. 359-5	45 47 13.74 / 70 24 56.63	173 33 05 / 356 52 26	Mon. 359-4 / Mon. 359-6	32.04 / 33.90
Mon. 359-6	45 47 12.65 / 70 24 56.54	176 52 26 / 31 44 58	Mon. 359-5 / Mon. 359-7	33.90 / 84.37
Mon. 359-7	45 47 10.32 / 70 24 58.60	211 44 57 / 2 56 08	Mon. 359-6 / Mon. 359-8	84.37 / 84.77
Mon. 359-8	45 47 07.58 / 70 24 58.80	182 56 08 / 333 39 09	Mon. 359-7 / Mon. 359-9	84.77 / 107.04
Mon. 359-9	45 47 04.48 / 70 24 56.60	153 39 11 / 292 45 47	Mon. 359-8 / Mon. 359-10	107.04 / 27.59
Mon. 359-10	45 47 04.13 / 70 24 55.42	112 45 48 / 256 43 00	Mon. 359-9 / Mon. 360	27.59 / 77.80
Mon. 360	45 47 04.71 / 70 24 51.92	76 43 02 / 257 27 34	Mon. 359-10 / Mon. 360-1	77.80 / 47.42
Mon. 360-1	45 47 05.04 / 70 24 49.77	77 27 36 / 280 50 41	Mon. 360 / Mon. 360-2	47.42 / 53.89
Mon. 360-2	45 47 04.71 / 70 24 47.32	100 50 43 / 262 18 48	Mon. 360-1 / Mon. 360-3	53.89 / 72.82
Mon. 360-3	45 47 05.03 / 70 24 43.98	82 18 50 / 260 13 38	Mon. 360-2 / Mon. 360-4	72.82 / 46.70
Mon. 360-4	45 47 05.29 / 70 24 41.85	80 13 40 / 308 28 22	Mon. 360-3 / Mon. 360-5	46.70 / 84.19
Mon. 360-5	45 47 03.59 / 70 24 38.80	128 28 24 / 349 13 36	Mon. 360-4 / Mon. 360-6	84.19 / 30.14
Mon. 360-6	45 47 02.63 / 70 24 38.54	169 13 36 / 334 17 00	Mon. 360-5 / Mon. 360-7	30.14 / 60.74
Mon. 360-7	45 47 00.86 / 70 24 37.32	154 17 01 / 320 56 07	Mon. 360-6 / Mon. 360-8	60.74 / 33.14
Mon. 360-8	45 47 00.02 / 70 24 36.35	140 56 08 / 336 13 26	Mon. 360-7 / Mon. 360-9	33.14 / 73.93
Mon. 360-9	45 46 57.83 / 70 24 34.97	156 13 27 / 346 24 09	Mon. 360-8 / Mon. 360-10	73.93 / 102.08
Mon. 360-10	45 46 54.62 / 70 24 33.86	166 24 10 / 1 28 35	Mon. 360-9 / Mon. 360-11	102.08 / 85.05
Mon. 360-11	45 46 51.86 / 70 24 33.96	181 28 35 / 320 25 24	Mon. 360-10 / Mon. 360-12	85.05 / 68.79
Mon. 360-12	45 46 50.15 / 70 24 31.94	140 25 25 / 334 13 14	Mon. 360-11 / Mon. 361	68.79 / 16.99
Mon. 361	45 46 49.65 / 70 24 31.59	154 13 14 / 6 23 23	Mon. 360-12 / Mon. 361-1	16.99 / 21.09
Mon. 361-1	45 46 48.97 / 70 24 31.70	186 23 23 / 18 32 23	Mon. 361 / Mon. 361-2	21.09 / 32.10
Mon. 361-2	45 46 47.99 / 70 24 32.18	198 32 23 / 328 11 22	Mon. 361-1 / Mon. 361-3	32.10 / 69.03
Mon. 361-3	45 46 46.09 / 70 24 30.49	148 11 23 / 339 30 20	Mon. 361-2 / Mon. 361-4	69.03 / 108.13
Mon. 361-4	45 46 42.81 / 70 24 28.74	159 30 21 / 341 33 14	Mon. 361-3 / Mon. 361-5	108.13 / 58.29
Mon. 361-5	45 46 41.01 / 70 24 27.88	161 33 14 / 334 39 05	Mon. 361-4 / Mon. 362	58.29 / 72.32
Mon. 362	45 46 38.90 / 70 24 26.45	154 39 06 / 10 05 27	Mon. 361-5 / Mon. 362-1	72.32 / 3.20
Mon. 362-1	45 46 38.80 / 70 24 26.48	190 05 27 / 305 58 59	Mon. 362 / Mon. 362-2	3.20 / 51.19
Mon. 362-2	45 46 37.82 / 70 24 24.56	125 59 00 / 299 23 33	Mon. 362-1 / Mon. 362-3	51.19 / 42.82
Mon. 362-3	45 46 37.14 / 70 24 22.83	119 23 34 / 347 14 09	Mon. 362-2 / Mon. 362-4	42.82 / 41.81
Mon. 362-4	45 46 35.82 / 70 24 22.40	167 14 09 / 24 34 46	Mon. 362-3 / Mon. 362-5	41.81 / 55.95
Mon. 362-5	45 46 34.17 / 70 24 23.48	204 34 45 / 40 45 26	Mon. 362-4 / Mon. 362-6	55.95 / 42.73
Mon. 362-6	45 46 33.12 / 70 24 24.77	220 45 25 / 17 17 09	Mon. 362-5 / Mon. 362-7	42.73 / 52.35
Mon. 362-7	45 46 31.50 / 70 24 25.49	197 17 08 / 27 48 56	Mon. 362-6 / Mon. 362-8	52.35 / 89.66
Mon. 362-8	45 46 28.94 / 70 24 27.43	207 48 55 / 13 26 49	Mon. 362-7 / Mon. 362-9	89.66 / 88.07

BOUNDARY MONUMENTS—SOURCE OF SOUTHWEST BRANCH OF ST. JOHN TO HEAD OF HALLS STREAM—Continued

Station	Latitude and longitude	Azimuth	To station	Distance (meters)	Station	Latitude and longitude	Azimuth	To station	Distance (meters)
	° ′ ″	° ′ ″				° ′ ″	° ′ ″		
Mon. 362–9	45 46 26.16	193 26 48	Mon. 362–8	88.07	Mon. 366–4	45 45 26.06	99 12 37	Mon. 366–3	141.84
	70 24 28.38	23 34 48	Mon. 363	58.52		70 23 56.25	270 11 43	Mon. 366–5	67.49
Mon. 363	45 46 24.42	203 34 47	Mon. 362–9	58.52	Mon. 366–5	45 45 26.06	90 11 45	Mon. 366–4	67.49
	70 24 29.46	21 34 30	Mon. 363–1	16.70		70 23 53.13	293 34 07	Mon. 366–6	137.39
Mon. 363–1	45 46 23.92	201 34 30	Mon. 363	16.70	Mon. 366–6	45 45 24.28	113 34 11	Mon. 366–5	137.39
	70 24 29.75	353 12 30	Mon. 363–2	63.87		70 23 47.30	327 32 44	Mon. 366–7	38.56
Mon. 363–2	45 46 21.87	173 12 30	Mon. 363–1	63.87	Mon. 366–7	45 45 23.22	147 32 45	Mon. 366–6	38.56
	70 24 29.40	347 01 31	Mon. 363–3	52.12		70 23 46.34	341 43 28	Mon. 366–8	46.32
Mon. 363–3	45 46 20.22	167 01 31	Mon. 363–2	52.12	Mon. 366–8	45 45 21.80	161 43 28	Mon. 366–7	46.32
	70 24 28.85	316 14 32	Mon. 363–4	83.10		70 23 45.67	320 17 06	Mon. 366–9	65.42
Mon. 363–4	45 46 18.28	136 14 34	Mon. 363–3	83.10	Mon. 366–9	45 45 20.17	140 17 07	Mon. 366–8	65.42
	70 24 26.19	318 41 36	Mon. 363–5	67.55		70 23 43.74	345 31 21	Mon. 366–10	70.10
Mon. 363–5	45 46 16.64	138 41 37	Mon. 363–4	67.55	Mon. 366–10	45 45 17.97	165 31 22	Mon. 366–9	70.10
	70 24 24.13	340 06 39	Mon. 363–6	44.57		70 23 42.92	326 42 29	Mon. 366–11	35.78
Mon. 363–6	45 46 15.28	160 06 40	Mon. 363–5	44.57	Mon. 366–11	45 45 17.00	146 42 30	Mon. 366–10	35.78
	70 24 23.43	333 08 42	Mon. 363–7	50.71		70 23 42.02	311 14 38	Mon. 366–12	50.47
Mon. 363–7	45 46 13.81	153 08 43	Mon. 363–6	50.71	Mon. 366–12	45 45 15.92	131 14 39	Mon. 366–11	50.47
	70 24 22.37	344 59 45	Mon. 363–8	45.97		70 23 40.26	318 45 22	Mon. 367	13.50
Mon. 363–8	45 46 12.37	164 59 45	Mon. 363–7	45.97	Mon. 367	45 45 15.59	138 45 22	Mon. 366–12	13.50
	70 24 21.82	45 20 48	Mon. 363–9	58.33		70 23 39.85	325 40 18	Mon. 367–1	16.42
Mon. 363–9	45 46 11.05	225 20 47	Mon. 363–8	58.33	Mon. 367–1	45 45 15.15	145 40 18	Mon. 367	16.42
	70 24 23.74	14 03 49	Mon. 363–10	122.14		70 23 39.42	313 50 56	Mon. 367–2	180.79
Mon. 363–10	45 46 07.21	194 03 48	Mon. 363–9	122.14	Mon. 367–2	45 45 11.10	133 51 00	Mon. 367–1	180.79
	70 24 25.11	358 00 52	Mon. 364	33.21		70 23 33.39	320 52 26	Mon. 367–3	82.22
Mon. 364	45 46 06.13	178 00 52	Mon. 363–10	33.21	Mon. 367–3	45 45 09.03	140 52 28	Mon. 367–2	82.22
	70 24 25.06	358 24 17	Mon. 364–1	70.32		70 23 30.99	326 27 51	Mon. 367–4	64.96
Mon. 364–1	45 46 03.86	178 24 17	Mon. 364	70.32	Mon. 367–4	45 45 07.28	146 27 52	Mon. 367–3	64.96
	70 24 24.97	11 46 35	Mon. 364–2	47.40		70 23 29.33	298 47 49	Mon. 367–5	18.81
Mon. 364–2	45 46 02.35	191 46 35	Mon. 364–1	47.40	Mon. 367–5	45 45 06.98	118 47 50	Mon. 367–4	18.81
	70 24 25.42	0 27 49	Mon. 364–3	139.04		70 23 28.56	321 49 58	Mon. 367–6	97.24
Mon. 364–3	45 45 57.85	180 27 49	Mon. 364–2	139.04	Mon. 367–6	45 45 04.51	141 50 00	Mon. 367–5	97.24
	70 24 25.47	355 06 53	Mon. 364–4	143.33		70 23 25.78	310 51 52	Mon. 367–7	99.19
Mon. 364–4	45 45 53.22	175 06 53	Mon. 364–3	143.33	Mon. 367–7	45 45 02.41	130 51 54	Mon. 367–6	99.19
	70 24 24.90	28 54 47	Mon. 364–5	106.27		70 23 22.32	314 40 43	Mon. 367–8	55.45
Mon. 364–5	45 45 50.21	208 54 45	Mon. 364–4	106.27	Mon. 367–8	45 45 01.14	134 40 44	Mon. 367–7	55.45
	70 24 27.28	3 01 31	Mon. 365	27.39		70 23 20.49	357 11 43	Mon. 367–9	58.00
Mon. 365	45 45 49.33	183 01 31	Mon. 364–5	27.39	Mon. 367–9	45 44 59.27	177 11 43	Mon. 367–8	58.00
	70 24 27.35	9 57 08	Mon. 365–1	42.25		70 23 20.36	24 27 17	Mon. 367–10	38.29
Mon. 365–1	45 45 47.98	189 57 08	Mon. 365	42.25	Mon. 367–10	45 44 58.14	204 27 16	Mon. 367–9	38.29
	70 24 27.69	356 01 28	Mon. 365–2	77.70		70 23 21.09	16 38 00	Mon. 367–11	26.81
Mon. 365–2	45 45 45.47	176 01 28	Mon. 365–1	77.70	Mon. 367–11	45 44 57.31	196 38 00	Mon. 367–10	26.81
	70 24 27.44	324 09 50	Mon. 365–3	73.89		70 23 21.45	340 49 14	Mon. 367–12	30.94
Mon. 365–3	45 45 43.52	144 37 55	Mon. 365–2	73.89	Mon. 367–12	45 44 56.36	160 49 14	Mon. 367–11	30.94
	70 24 25.46	309 17 39	Mon. 365–4	103.43		70 23 20.98	314 57 39	Mon. 367–13	59.18
Mon. 365–4	45 45 41.39	129 17 42	Mon. 365–3	103.43	Mon. 367–13	45 44 55.00	134 57 40	Mon. 367–12	59.18
	70 24 21.75	327 50 45	Mon. 365–5	55.99		70 23 19.04	8 42 33	Mon. 367–14	28.31
Mon. 365–5	45 45 39.86	147 50 46	Mon. 365–4	55.99	Mon. 367–14	45 44 54.10	188 42 33	Mon. 367–13	28.31
	70 24 20.38	322 15 07	Mon. 365–6	203.46		70 23 19.24	34 35 01	Mon. 367–15	57.19
Mon. 365–6	45 45 34.65	142 15 11	Mon. 365–5	203.46	Mon. 367–15	45 44 52.57	214 35 00	Mon. 367–14	57.19
	70 24 14.61	324 09 50	Mon. 365–7	72.26		70 23 20.74	26 37 27	Mon. 367–16	62.19
Mon. 365–7	45 45 32.75	144 09 51	Mon. 365–6	72.26	Mon. 367–16	45 44 50.77	206 37 26	Mon. 367–15	62.19
	70 24 12.65	310 58 06	Mon. 365–8	42.25		70 23 22.03	32 20 33	Mon. 368	42.57
Mon. 365–8	45 45 31.85	130 58 07	Mon. 365–7	42.25	Mon. 368	45 44 49.60	212 20 32	Mon. 367–16	42.57
	70 24 11.18	316 32 34	Mon. 366	37.09		70 23 23.09	47 59 53	Mon. 368–1	126.20
Mon. 366	45 45 30.98	136 32 35	Mon. 365–8	37.09	Mon. 368–1	45 44 46.87	227 59 50	Mon. 368	126.20
	70 24 10.00	319 35 47	Mon. 366–1	112.57		70 23 27.42	62 15 14	Mon. 368–2	63.27
Mon. 366–1	45 45 28.20	139 35 49	Mon. 366	112.57	Mon. 368–2	45 44 45.92	242 15 12	Mon. 368–1	63.27
	70 24 06.62	318 22 37	Mon. 366–2	54.13		70 23 30.01	68 50 51	Mon. 368–3	82.54
Mon. 366–2	45 45 26.89	138 22 38	Mon. 366–1	54.13	Mon. 368–3	45 44 44.95	248 50 48	Mon. 368–2	82.54
	70 24 04.96	273 32 07	Mon. 366–3	48.30		70 23 33.58	12 49 01	Mon. 368–4	20.17
Mon. 366–3	45 45 26.80	93 32 09	Mon. 366–2	48.30	Mon. 368–4	45 44 44.31	192 49 01	Mon. 368–3	20.17
	70 24 02.73	279 12 32	Mon. 366–4	141.84		70 23 33.78	33 08 49	Mon. 368–5	40.53

104709—25†——15

BOUNDARY MONUMENTS—SOURCE OF SOUTHWEST BRANCH OF ST. JOHN TO HEAD OF HALLS STREAM—Continued

Station	Latitude and longitude	Azimuth	To station	Distance (meters)	Station	Latitude and longitude	Azimuth	To station	Distance (meters)
	° ′ ″	° ′ ″				° ′ ″	° ′ ″		
Mon. 368–5	45 44 43.22 / 70 23 34.81	213 08 48 / 19 37 29	Mon. 368–4 / Mon. 368–6	40.53 / 33.94	Mon. 369–11	45 44 15.40 / 70 23 27.18	97 24 56 / 255 57 21	Mon. 369–10 / Mon. 369–12	50.57 / 49.29
Mon. 368–6	45 44 42.18 / 70 23 35.33	199 37 29 / 47 24 09	Mon. 368–5 / Mon. 368–7	33.94 / 47.13	Mon. 369–12	45 44 15.79 / 70 23 24.97	75 57 23 / 306 26 36	Mon. 369–11 / Mon. 369–13	49.29 / 29.08
Mon. 368–7	45 44 41.15 / 70 23 36.94	227 24 08 / 28 21 40	Mon. 368–6 / Mon. 368–8	47.13 / 19.13	Mon. 369–13	45 44 15.23 / 70 23 23.89	126 26 37 / 51 23 20	Mon. 369–12 / Mon. 369–14	29.08 / 42.58
Mon. 368–8	45 44 40.60 / 70 23 37.36	208 21 40 / 345 29 30	Mon. 368–7 / Mon. 368–9	19.13 / 23.52	Mon. 369–14	45 44 14.37 / 70 23 25.42	231 23 19 / 58 15 14	Mon. 369–13 / Mon. 369–15	42.58 / 52.10
Mon. 368–9	45 44 39.86 / 70 23 37.09	165 29 30 / 50 25 31	Mon. 368–8 / Mon. 368–10	23.52 / 23.97	Mon. 369–15	45 44 13.48 / 70 23 27.48	238 15 13 / 349 11 32	Mon. 369–14 / Mon. 370	52.10 / 70.95
Mon. 368–10	45 44 39.37 / 70 23 37.94	230 25 30 / 92 42 49	Mon. 368–9 / Mon. 368–11	23.97 / 35.61	Mon. 370	45 44 11.22 / 70 23 26.86	169 11 32 / 350 39 45	Mon. 369–15 / Mon. 370–1	70.95 / 27.16
Mon. 368–11	45 44 39.42 / 70 23 39.59	272 42 48 / 70 07 48	Mon. 368–10 / Mon. 368–12	35.61 / 37.93	Mon. 370–1	45 44 10.35 / 70 23 26.66	170 39 45 / 290 35 58	Mon. 370 / Mon. 370–2	27.16 / 65.91
Mon. 368–12	45 44 39.01 / 70 23 41.24	250 07 47 / 10 01 40	Mon. 368–11 / Mon. 368–13	37.93 / 34.83	Mon. 370–2	45 44 09.60 / 70 23 23.80	110 36 00 / 268 43 59	Mon. 370–1 / Mon. 370–3	65.91 / 95.39
Mon. 368–13	45 44 37.90 / 70 23 41.52	190 01 40 / 46 55 56	Mon. 368–12 / Mon. 368–14	34.83 / 25.60	Mon. 370–3	45 44 09.67 / 70 23 19.39	88 44 02 / 238 40 58	Mon. 370–2 / Mon. 370–4	95.39 / 53.24
Mon. 368–14	45 44 37.33 / 70 23 42.38	226 55 55 / 351 06 22	Mon. 368–13 / Mon. 368–15	25.60 / 76.92	Mon. 370–4	45 44 10.56 / 70 23 17.29	58 41 00 / 217 30 29	Mon. 370–3 / Mon. 370–5	53.24 / 28.61
Mon. 368–15	45 44 34.87 / 70 23 41.83	171 06 22 / 34 07 53	Mon. 368–14 / Mon. 368–16	76.92 / 28.01	Mon. 370–5	45 44 11.30 / 70 23 16.48	37 30 30 / 251 39 50	Mon. 370–4 / Mon. 370–6	28.61 / 26.80
Mon. 368–16	45 44 34.12 / 70 23 42.56	214 07 52 / 3 42 10	Mon. 368–15 / Mon. 368–17	28.01 / 25.63	Mon. 370–6	45 44 11.57 / 70 23 15.30	71 39 51 / 297 37 12	Mon. 370–5 / Mon. 370–7	26.80 / 57.99
Mon. 368–17	45 44 33.29 / 70 23 42.64	183 42 10 / 330 57 57	Mon. 368–16 / Mon. 368–18	25.63 / 49.04	Mon. 370–7	45 44 10.70 / 70 23 12.93	117 37 14 / 265 58 10	Mon. 370–6 / Mon. 370–8	57.99 / 37.56
Mon. 368–18	45 44 31.90 / 70 23 41.53	150 57 58 / 281 06 20	Mon. 368–17 / Mon. 368–19	49.04 / 81.15	Mon. 370–8	45 44 10.79 / 70 23 11.20	85 58 11 / 260 11 11	Mon. 370–7 / Mon. 370–9	37.56 / 31.85
Mon. 368–19	45 44 31.39 / 70 23 37.85	101 06 23 / 334 25 10	Mon. 368–18 / Mon. 368–20	81.15 / 59.26	Mon. 370–9	45 44 10.96 / 70 23 09.74	80 11 12 / 296 33 23	Mon. 370–8 / Mon. 370–10	31.85 / 22.24
Mon. 368–20	45 44 29.66 / 70 23 36.67	154 25 11 / 56 17 15	Mon. 368–19 / Mon. 368–21	59.26 / 71.81	Mon. 370–10	45 44 10.64 / 70 23 08.82	116 33 23 / 329 12 54	Mon. 370–9 / Mon. 371	22.24 / 46.46
Mon. 368–21	45 44 28.37 / 70 23 39.43	236 17 13 / 8 23 57	Mon. 368–20 / Mon. 368–22	71.81 / 34.02	Mon. 371	45 44 09.35 / 70 23 07.72	149 12 55 / 330 32 12	Mon. 370–10 / Mon. 371–1	46.46 / 13.31
Mon. 368–22	45 44 27.28 / 70 23 39.66	188 23 57 / 9 58 03	Mon. 368–21 / Mon. 368–23	34.02 / 29.40	Mon. 371–1	45 44 08.97 / 70 23 07.42	150 32 12 / 55 00 23	Mon. 371 / Mon. 371–2	13.31 / 65.06
Mon. 368–23	45 44 26.34 / 70 23 39.90	189 58 03 / 6 33 03	Mon. 368–22 / Mon. 368–24	29.40 / 50.39	Mon. 371–2	45 44 07.77 / 70 23 09.88	235 00 21 / 41 01 54	Mon. 371–1 / Mon. 371–3	65.06 / 43.27
Mon. 368–24	45 44 24.72 / 70 23 40.16	186 33 03 / 332 12 43	Mon. 368–23 / Mon. 369	50.39 / 38.21	Mon. 371–3	45 44 06.71 / 70 23 11.20	221 01 53 / 1 17 00	Mon. 371–2 / Mon. 371–4	43.27 / 52.01
Mon. 369	45 44 23.63 / 70 23 39.34	152 12 44 / 323 05 54	Mon. 368–24 / Mon. 369–1	38.21 / 29.30	Mon. 371–4	45 44 05.02 / 70 23 11.25	181 17 00 / 300 30 28	Mon. 371–3 / Mon. 371–5	52.01 / 44.32
Mon. 369–1	45 44 22.87 / 70 23 38.53	143 05 55 / 294 17 03	Mon. 369 / Mon. 369–2	29.30 / 24.13	Mon. 371–5	45 44 04.30 / 70 23 09.49	120 30 29 / 244 42 14	Mon. 371–4 / Mon. 371–6	44.32 / 35.19
Mon. 369–2	45 44 22.55 / 70 23 37.51	114 17 03 / 275 25 53	Mon. 369–1 / Mon. 369–3	24.13 / 60.18	Mon. 371–6	45 44 04.78 / 70 23 08.02	64 42 15 / 243 16 50	Mon. 371–5 / Mon. 371–7	35.19 / 55.10
Mon. 369–3	45 44 22.36 / 70 23 34.74	95 25 55 / 293 02 38	Mon. 369–2 / Mon. 369–4	60.18 / 40.56	Mon. 371–7	45 44 05.58 / 70 23 05.74	63 16 52 / 283 58 29	Mon. 371–6 / Mon. 371–8	55.10 / 23.86
Mon. 369–4	45 44 21.85 / 70 23 33.01	113 02 39 / 329 54 58	Mon. 369–3 / Mon. 369–5	40.56 / 15.27	Mon. 371–8	45 44 05.40 / 70 23 04.67	103 58 30 / 320 23 07	Mon. 371–7 / Mon. 371–9	23.86 / 23.99
Mon. 369–5	45 44 21.42 / 70 23 32.66	149 54 58 / 32 02 59	Mon. 369–4 / Mon. 369–6	15.27 / 86.07	Mon. 371–9	45 44 04.80 / 70 23 03.96	140 23 08 / 16 46 44	Mon. 371–8 / Mon. 371–10	23.99 / 30.88
Mon. 369–6	45 44 19.06 / 70 23 34.77	212 02 57 / 327 48 46	Mon. 369–5 / Mon. 369–7	86.07 / 59.11	Mon. 371–10	45 44 03.84 / 70 23 04.37	196 46 44 / 36 09 18	Mon. 371–9 / Mon. 371–11	30.88 / 37.86
Mon. 369–7	45 44 17.44 / 70 23 33.31	147 48 47 / 290 31 30	Mon. 369–6 / Mon. 369–8	59.11 / 20.00	Mon. 371–11	45 44 02.85 / 70 23 05.41	216 09 17 / 60 15 50	Mon. 371–10 / Mon. 371–12	37.86 / 103.09
Mon. 369–8	45 44 17.21 / 70 23 32.45	110 31 31 / 296 33 08	Mon. 369–7 / Mon. 369–9	20.00 / 50.47	Mon. 371–12	45 44 01.20 / 70 23 09.55	240 15 47 / 82 13 16	Mon. 371–11 / Mon. 371–13	103.09 / 21.06
Mon. 369–9	45 44 16.48 / 70 23 30.36	116 33 09 / 325 15 04	Mon. 369–8 / Mon. 369–10	50.47 / 32.61	Mon. 371–13	45 44 01.10 / 70 23 10.51	262 13 15 / 34 45 43	Mon. 371–12 / Mon. 371–14	21.06 / 13.51
Mon. 369–10	45 44 15.61 / 70 23 29.50	145 15 05 / 277 24 54	Mon. 369–9 / Mon. 369–11	32.61 / 50.57	Mon. 371–14	45 44 00.74 / 70 23 10.87	214 45 43 / 350 51 11	Mon. 371–13 / Mon. 371–15	13.51 / 57.39

BOUNDARY MONUMENTS—SOURCE OF SOUTHWEST BRANCH OF ST. JOHN TO HEAD OF HALLS STREAM—Continued

Station	Latitude and longitude	Azimuth	To station	Distance (meters)	Station	Latitude and longitude	Azimuth	To station	Distance (meters)
	° ′ ″	° ′ ″				° ′ ″	° ′ ″		
Mon. 371–15	45 43 58.91	170 51 11	Mon. 371–14	57.39	Mon. 374–16	45 43 24.20	173 01 41	Mon. 374–15	105.38
	70 23 10.44	16 10 36	Mon. 371–16	34.47		70 23 53.30	27 26 38	Mon. 374–17	24.27
Mon. 371–16	45 43 57.84	196 10 36	Mon. 371–15	34.47	Mon. 374–17	45 43 23.50	207 26 38	Mon. 374–16	24.27
	70 23 10.89	45 02 17	Mon. 371–17	63.14		70 23 53.81	62 36 33	Mon. 374–18	96.20
Mon. 371–17	45 43 56.39	225 02 16	Mon. 371–16	63.14	Mon. 374–18	45 43 22.07	242 36 30	Mon. 374–17	96.20
	70 23 12.96	46 21 19	Mon. 372	19.59		70 23 57.76	34 24 18	Mon. 374–19	53.80
Mon. 372	45 43 55.95	226 21 19	Mon. 371–17	19.59	Mon. 374–19	45 43 20.63	214 24 17	Mon. 374–18	53.80
	70 23 13.61	52 19 19	Mon. 372–1	6.01		70 23 59.17	54 07 01	Mon. 374–20	76.78
Mon. 372–1	45 43 55.83	232 19 19	Mon. 372	6.01	Mon. 374–20	45 43 19.17	234 06 59	Mon. 374–19	76.78
	70 23 13.83	26 43 33	Mon. 372–2	79.21		70 24 02.05	63 49 37	Mon. 374–21	56.38
Mon. 372–2	45 43 53.54	206 43 32	Mon. 372–1	79.21	Mon. 374–21	45 43 18.36	243 49 35	Mon. 374–20	56.38
	70 23 15.48	42 24 15	Mon. 372–3	40.04		70 24 04.39	320 42 09	Mon. 374–22	51.73
Mon. 372–3	45 43 52.58	222 24 14	Mon. 372–2	40.04	Mon. 374–22	45 43 17.07	140 42 10	Mon. 374–21	51.73
	70 23 16.73	36 08 57	Mon. 373	231.95		70 24 02.87	296 16 42	Mon. 374–23	34.40
Mon. 373	45 43 46.52	216 08 52	Mon. 372–3	231.95	Mon. 374–23	45 43 16.58	116 16 43	Mon. 374–22	34.40
	70 23 23.06	34 27 58	Mon. 373–1	132.79		70 24 01.44	330 37 14	Mon. 374–24	44.58
Mon. 373–1	45 43 42.97	214 27 55	Mon. 373	132.79	Mon. 374–24	45 43 15.32	150 37 15	Mon. 374–23	44.58
	70 23 26.53	85 48 26	Mon. 373–2	82.09		70 24 00.43	5 34 43	Mon. 374–25	33.23
Mon. 373–2	45 43 42.78	265 48 23	Mon. 373–1	82.09	Mon. 374–25	45 43 14.25	185 34 43	Mon. 374–24	33.23
	70 23 30.32	136 04 58	Mon. 373–3	42.17		70 24 00.58	62 26 09	Mon. 374–26	43.87
Mon. 373–3	45 43 43.76	316 04 57	Mon. 373–2	42.17	Mon. 374–26	45 43 13.59	242 26 08	Mon. 374–25	43.87
	70 23 31.67	106 22 15	Mon. 373–4	34.95		70 24 02.38	17 37 31	Mon. 374–27	72.01
Mon. 373–4	45 43 44.08	286 22 14	Mon. 373–3	34.95	Mon. 374–27	45 43 11.36	197 37 30	Mon. 374–26	72.01
	70 23 33.22	140 55 21	Mon. 373–5	62.91		70 24 03.39	78 26 46	Mon. 375	49.84
Mon. 373–5	45 43 45.66	320 55 20	Mon. 373–4	62.91	Mon. 375	45 43 11.04	258 26 44	Mon. 374–27	49.84
	70 23 35.06	109 55 47	Mon. 373–6	35.71		70 24 05.65	82 17 03	Mon. 375–1	28.68
Mon. 373–6	45 43 46.06	289 55 46	Mon. 373–5	35.71	Mon. 375–1	45 43 10.92	262 17 02	Mon. 375	28.68
	70 23 36.61	100 49 26	Mon. 373–7	177.26		70 24 06.96	62 25 03	Mon. 375–2	27.86
Mon. 373–7	45 43 47.14	280 49 20	Mon. 373–6	177.26	Mon. 375–2	45 43 10.50	242 25 02	Mon. 375–1	27.86
	70 23 44.66	59 39 08	Mon. 374	115.25		70 24 08.10	76 21 37	Mon. 375–3	71.79
Mon. 374	45 43 45.25	239 39 05	Mon. 373–7	115.25	Mon. 375–3	45 43 09.95	256 21 35	Mon. 375–2	71.79
	70 23 49.26	53 58 08	Mon. 374–1	8.78		70 24 11.33	60 52 42	Mon. 375–4	25.22
Mon. 374–1	45 43 45.08	233 58 08	Mon. 374	8.78	Mon. 375–4	45 43 09.55	240 52 41	Mon. 375–3	25.22
	70 23 49.59	33 04 04	Mon. 374–2	75.83		70 24 12.35	19 28 47	Mon. 375–5	15.56
Mon. 374–2	45 43 43.02	213 04 03	Mon. 374–1	75.83	Mon. 375–5	45 43 09.08	199 28 47	Mon. 375–4	15.56
	70 23 51.50	354 07 52	Mon. 374–3	92.68		70 24 12.59	21 47 47	Mon. 375–6	46.86
Mon. 374–3	45 43 40.04	174 07 52	Mon. 374–2	92.68	Mon. 375–6	45 43 07.67	201 47 46	Mon. 375–5	46.86
	70 23 51.06	349 23 33	Mon. 374–4	83.95		70 24 13.39	51 13 40	Mon. 375–7	58.72
Mon. 374–4	45 43 37.37	169 23 34	Mon. 374–3	83.95	Mon. 375–7	45 43 06.48	231 13 38	Mon. 375–6	58.72
	70 23 50.35	31 15 09	Mon. 374–5	34.57		70 24 15.51	74 44 44	Mon. 375–8	201.92
Mon. 374–5	45 43 36.41	211 15 08	Mon. 374–4	34.57	Mon. 375–8	45 43 04.76	254 44 37	Mon. 375–7	201.92
	70 23 51.18	67 43 39	Mon. 374–6	46.47		70 24 24.52	51 47 35	Mon. 375–9	79.82
Mon. 374–6	45 43 35.84	247 43 38	Mon. 374–5	46.47	Mon. 375–9	45 43 03.16	231 47 33	Mon. 375–8	79.82
	70 23 53.16	26 53 07	Mon. 374–7	19.28		70 24 27.42	44 30 42	Mon. 375–10	38.49
Mon. 374–7	45 43 35.28	206 53 07	Mon. 374–6	19.28	Mon. 375–10	45 43 02.27	224 30 41	Mon. 375–9	38.49
	70 23 53.57	349 15 34	Mon. 374–8	47.28		70 24 28.66	24 11 58	Mon. 376	46.85
Mon. 374–8	45 43 33.78	169 15 34	Mon. 374–7	47.28	Mon. 376	45 43 00.88	204 11 57	Mon. 375–10	46.85
	70 23 53.16	339 24 57	Mon. 374–9	27.63		70 24 29.55	19 43 32	Mon. 376–1	13.39
Mon. 374–9	45 43 32.94	159 24 57	Mon. 374–8	27.63	Mon. 376–1	45 43 00.48	199 43 32	Mon. 376	13.39
	70 23 52.71	333 57 18	Mon. 374–10	31.08		70 24 29.76	88 58 50	Mon. 376–2	18.69
Mon. 374–10	45 43 32.04	153 57 18	Mon. 374–9	31.08	Mon. 376–2	45 43 00.46	268 58 49	Mon. 376–1	18.69
	70 23 52.08	277 16 37	Mon. 374–11	23.04		70 24 30.63	86 05 49	Mon. 376–3	74.74
Mon. 374–11	45 43 31.94	97 16 38	Mon. 374–10	23.04	Mon. 376–3	45 43 00.30	266 05 47	Mon. 376–2	74.74
	70 23 51.02	336 52 57	Mon. 374–12	34.89		70 24 34.08	90 26 50	Mon. 376–4	42.00
Mon. 374–12	45 43 30.90	156 52 57	Mon. 374–11	34.89	Mon. 376–4	45 43 00.31	270 26 49	Mon. 376–3	42.00
	70 23 50.39	43 18 14	Mon. 374–13	28.98		70 24 36.02	71 52 09	Mon. 376–5	95.86
Mon. 374–13	45 43 30.22	223 18 13	Mon. 374–12	28.98	Mon. 376–5	45 42 59.34	251 52 06	Mon. 376–4	95.86
	70 23 51.31	4 01 28	Mon. 374–14	58.37		70 24 40.23	90 35 16	Mon. 376–6	31.99
Mon. 374–14	45 43 28.33	184 01 28	Mon. 374–13	58.37	Mon. 376–6	45 42 59.36	270 35 15	Mon. 376–5	31.99
	70 23 51.50	65 56 37	Mon. 374–15	56.58		70 24 41.71	105 09 35	Mon. 376–7	98.99
Mon. 374–15	45 43 27.59	245 56 35	Mon. 374–14	56.58	Mon. 376–7	45 43 00.19	285 09 32	Mon 376–6	98.90
	70 23 53.89	353 01 41	Mon. 374–16	105.38		70 24 46.13	84 54 12	Mon. 376–8	58.61

BOUNDARY MONUMENTS—SOURCE OF SOUTHWEST BRANCH OF ST. JOHN TO HEAD OF HALLS STREAM—Continued

Station	Latitude and longitude	Azimuth	To station	Distance (meters)	Station	Latitude and longitude	Azimuth	To station	Distance (meters)
	° ′ ″	° ′ ″				° ′ ″	° ′ ″		
Mon. 376-8	45 43 00.02 70 24 48.82	264 54 10 34 22 31	Mon. 376-7 Mon. 377	58.61 9.77	Mon. 378-24	45 42 37.26 70 25 48.19	231 15 59 27 03 45	Mon. 378-23 Mon. 378-25	25.71 25.72
Mon. 377	45 42 59.76 70 24 49.08	214 22 31 13 58 03	Mon. 376-8 Mon. 377-1	9.77 37.34	Mon. 378-25	45 42 36.52 70 25 48.73	207 03 45 338 55 31	Mon. 378-24 Mon. 379	25.72 103.18
Mon. 377-1	45 42 58.59 70 24 49.50	193 58 03 31 53 09	Mon. 377 Mon. 377-2	37.34 13.75	Mon. 379	45 42 33.40 70 25 47.02	158 55 32 335 57 37	Mon. 378-25 Mon. 379-1	103.18 57.49
Mon. 377-2	45 42 58.21 70 24 49.83	211 53 09 342 03 36	Mon. 377-1 Mon. 377-3	13.75 62.21	Mon. 379-1	45 42 31.70 70 25 45.94	155 57 38 1 18 02	Mon. 379 Mon. 379-2	57.49 77.92
Mon. 377-3	45 42 56.30 70 24 48.95	162 03 37 37 20 51	Mon. 377-2 Mon. 377-4	62.21 15.35	Mon. 379-2	45 42 29.18 70 25 46.02	181 18 02 287 17 28	Mon. 379-1 Mon. 379-3	77.92 32.45
Mon. 377-4	45 42 55.90 70 24 49.38	217 20 51 78 34 15	Mon. 377-3 Mon. 377-5	15.35 41.96	Mon. 379-3	45 42 28.87 70 25 44.58	107 17 29 244 19 57	Mon. 379-2 Mon. 379-4	32.45 82.72
Mon. 377-5	45 42 55.63 70 24 51.28	258 34 14 40 14 49	Mon. 377-4 Mon. 378	41.96 20.64	Mon. 379-4	45 42 30.03 70 25 41.14	64 19 59 256 14 29	Mon. 379-3 Mon. 379-5	82.72 58.18
Mon. 378	45 42 55.12 70 24 51.90	220 14 49 40 48 39	Mon. 377-5 Mon. 378-1	20.64 59.55	Mon. 379-5	45 42 30.48 70 25 38.52	76 14 31 304 58 32	Mon. 379-4 Mon. 379-6	58.18 118.62
Mon. 378-1	45 42 53.66 70 24 53.70	220 48 38 62 17 25	Mon. 378 Mon. 378-2	59.55 74.28	Mon. 379-6	45 42 28.27 70 25 34.03	124 58 35 340 16 42	Mon. 379-5 Mon. 379-7	118.62 26.91
Mon. 378-2	45 42 52.54 70 24 56.74	242 17 23 66 05 10	Mon. 378-1 Mon. 378-3	74.28 47.74	Mon. 379-7	45 42 27.45 70 25 33.61	160 16 42 30 15 51	Mon. 379-6 Mon. 379-8	26.91 36.64
Mon. 378-3	45 42 51.91 70 24 58.75	246 05 09 56 30 56	Mon. 378-2 Mon. 378-4	47.74 61.37	Mon. 379-8	45 42 26.43 70 25 34.47	210 15 50 63 06 59	Mon. 379-7 Mon. 380	36.64 4.12
Mon. 378-4	45 42 50.82 70 25 01.12	236 30 54 63 31 11	Mon. 378-3 Mon. 378-5	61.37 73.23	Mon. 380	45 42 26.37 70 25 34.64	243 06 59 61 40 22	Mon. 379-8 Mon. 380-1	4.12 18.53
Mon. 378-5	45 42 49.76 70 25 04.15	243 31 09 42 11 26	Mon. 378-4 Mon. 378-6	73.23 49.82	Mon. 380-1	45 42 26.08 70 25 35.39	241 40 21 106 58 05	Mon. 380 Mon. 380-2	18.53 103.84
Mon. 378-6	45 42 48.56 70 25 05.70	222 11 25 66 11 12	Mon. 378-5 Mon. 378-7	49.82 104.22	Mon. 380-2	45 42 27.07 70 25 39.98	286 58 02 100 44 50	Mon. 380-1 Mon. 380-3	103.84 27.82
Mon. 378-7	45 42 47.20 70 25 10.11	246 11 09 73 53 56	Mon. 378-6 Mon. 378-8	104.22 62.49	Mon. 380-3	45 42 27.23 70 25 41.24	280 44 49 103 24 38	Mon. 380-2 Mon. 380-4	27.82 57.82
Mon. 378-8	45 42 46.64 70 25 12.88	253 53 54 61 12 41	Mon. 378-7 Mon. 378-9	62.49 37.93	Mon. 380-4	45 42 27.67 70 25 43.84	283 24 36 62 29 28	Mon. 380-3 Mon. 380-5	57.82 53.46
Mon. 378-9	45 42 46.05 70 25 14.42	241 12 40 70 53 27	Mon. 378-8 Mon. 378-10	37.93 164.49	Mon. 380-5	45 42 26.87 70 25 46.04	242 29 26 95 42 21	Mon. 380-4 Mon. 380-6	53.46 50.05
Mon. 378-10	45 42 44.30 70 25 21.61	250 53 22 87 53 09	Mon. 378-9 Mon. 378-11	164.49 26.67	Mon. 380-6	45 42 27.03 70 25 48.34	275 42 19 44 07 16	Mon. 380-5 Mon. 380-7	50.05 41.88
Mon. 378-11	45 42 44.27 70 25 22.84	267 53 08 46 49 25	Mon. 378-10 Mon. 378-12	26.67 56.15	Mon. 380-7	45 42 26.06 70 25 49.69	224 07 15 88 56 14	Mon. 380-6 Mon. 380-8	41.88 66.69
Mon. 378-12	45 42 43.03 70 25 24.73	226 49 24 75 53 41	Mon. 378-11 Mon. 378-13	56.15 38.96	Mon. 380-8	45 42 26.02 70 25 52.77	268 56 12 75 35 44	Mon. 380-7 Mon. 380-9	66.69 46.14
Mon. 378-13	45 42 42.72 70 25 26.48	255 53 40 83 32 57	Mon. 378-12 Mon. 378-14	38.96 59.60	Mon. 380-9	45 42 25.64 70 25 54.84	255 35 43 45 08 17	Mon. 380-8 Mon. 380-10	46.14 31.39
Mon. 378-14	45 42 42.50 70 25 29.22	263 32 55 102 27 00	Mon. 378-13 Mon. 378-15	59.60 60.27	Mon. 380-10	45 42 24.93 70 25 55.86	225 08 16 58 57 22	Mon. 380-9 Mon. 380-11	31.39 122.84
Mon. 378-15	45 42 42.92 70 25 31.94	282 26 58 79 15 57	Mon. 378-14 Mon. 378-16	60.27 62.40	Mon. 380-11	45 42 22.87 70 26 00.73	238 57 18 58 56 30	Mon. 380-10 Mon. 380-12	122.84 47.35
Mon. 378-16	45 42 42.55 70 25 34.77	259 15 55 51 00 42	Mon. 378-15 Mon. 378-17	62.40 21.38	Mon. 380-12	45 42 22.08 70 26 02.60	238 56 29 65 46 43	Mon. 380-11 Mon. 380-13	47.35 48.67
Mon. 378-17	45 42 42.11 70 25 35.54	231 00 41 56 21 16	Mon. 378-16 Mon. 378-18	21.38 115.96	Mon. 380-13	45 42 21.44 70 26 04.66	245 46 42 60 14 58	Mon. 380-12 Mon. 380-14	48.67 29.14
Mon. 378-18	45 42 40.03 70 25 40.00	236 21 13 72 14 12	Mon. 378-17 Mon. 378-19	115.96 28.72	Mon. 380-14	45 42 20.97 70 26 05.82	240 14 57 84 25 15	Mon. 380-13 Mon. 380-15	29.14 49.82
Mon. 378-19	45 42 39.74 70 25 41.27	252 14 11 31 21 58	Mon. 378-18 Mon. 378-20	28.72 19.14	Mon. 380-15	45 42 20.81 70 26 08.12	264 25 13 55 23 33	Mon. 380-14 Mon. 380-16	49.82 174.18
Mon. 378-20	45 42 39.22 70 25 41.73	211 21 58 65 57 45	Mon. 378-19 Mon. 378-21	19.14 38.06	Mon. 380-16	45 42 17.61 70 26 14.74	235 23 28 69 34 56	Mon. 380-15 Mon. 380-17	174.18 77.77
Mon. 378-21	45 42 38.71 70 25 43.34	245 57 44 32 46 31	Mon. 378-20 Mon. 378-22	38.06 40.69	Mon. 380-17	45 42 16.73 70 26 18.11	249 34 54 56 01 26	Mon. 380-16 Mon. 380-18	77.77 75.23
Mon. 378-22	45 42 37.60 70 25 44.36	212 46 30 95 05 16	Mon. 378-21 Mon. 378-23	40.69 63.15	Mon. 380-18	45 42 15.37 70 26 21.00	236 01 24 54 46 59	Mon. 380-17 Mon. 380-19	75.23 56.30
Mon. 378-23	45 42 37.78 70 25 47.26	275 05 14 51 16 00	Mon. 378-22 Mon. 378-24	63.15 25.71	Mon. 380-19	45 42 14.31 70 26 23.12	234 46 57 116 36 35	Mon. 380-18 Mon. 380-20	56.30 29.42

BOUNDARY MONUMENTS—SOURCE OF SOUTHWEST BRANCH OF ST. JOHN TO HEAD OF HALLS STREAM—Continued

Station	Latitude and longitude	Azimuth	To station	Distance (meters)	Station	Latitude and longitude	Azimuth	To station	Distance (meters)
Mon. 380–20	45 42 14.74	296 36 34	Mon. 380–19	29.42	Mon. 382–6	45 42 25.57	272 58 54	Mon. 382–5	47.32
	70 26 24.34	128 23 13	Mon. 380–21	43.44		70 27 28.69	61 53 52	Mon. 382–7	67.63
Mon. 380–21	45 42 15.62	308 23 12	Mon. 380–20	43.44	Mon. 382–7	45 42 24.54	241 53 50	Mon. 382–6	67.63
	70 26 25.91	119 39 53	Mon. 380–22	32.73		70 27 31.45	50 23 45	Mon. 382–8	40.12
Mon. 380–22	45 42 16.14	299 39 52	Mon. 380–21	32.73	Mon. 382–8	45 42 23.71	230 23 44	Mon. 382–7	40.12
	70 26 27.23	155 42 34	Mon. 380–23	88.71		70 27 32.88	91 12 37	Mon. 382–9	100.87
Mon. 380–23	45 42 18.76	335 42 33	Mon. 380–22	88.71	Mon. 382–9	45 42 23.78	271 12 34	Mon. 382–8	100.87
	70 26 28.92	141 09 16	Mon. 381	11.38		70 27 37.54	37 14 22	Mon. 382–10	77.99
Mon. 381	45 42 19.05	321 09 16	Mon. 380–23	11.38	Mon. 382–10	45 42 21.77	217 14 20	Mon. 382–9	77.99
	70 26 29.24	146 05 33	Mon. 381–1	27.54		70 27 39.72	58 37 05	Mon. 382–11	82.91
Mon. 381–1	45 42 19.79	326 05 32	Mon. 381	27.54	Mon. 382–11	45 42 20.37	238 37 03	Mon. 382–10	82.91
	70 26 29.96	42 13 04	Mon. 381–2	22.89		70 27 42.99	89 03 44	Mon. 382–12	65.07
Mon. 381–2	45 42 19.24	222 13 03	Mon. 381–1	22.89	Mon. 382–12	45 42 20.34	269 03 42	Mon. 382–11	65.07
	70 26 30.67	72 21 42	Mon. 381–3	64.86		70 27 46.00	113 15 20	Mon. 382–13	81.80
Mon. 381–3	45 42 18.60	252 21 40	Mon. 381–2	64.86	Mon. 382–13	45 42 21.39	293 15 18	Mon. 382–12	81.80
	70 26 33.52	59 03 09	Mon. 381–4	80.80		70 27 49.48	118 09 52	Mon. 382–14	78.76
Mon. 381–4	45 42 17.26	239 03 07	Mon. 381–3	80.80	Mon. 382–14	45 42 22.59	298 09 50	Mon. 382–13	78.76
	70 26 36.73	35 44 46	Mon. 381–5	44.80		70 27 52.69	90 27 20	Mon. 382–15	31.12
Mon. 381–5	45 42 16.08	215 44 45	Mon. 381–4	44.80	Mon. 382–15	45 42 22.60	270 27 19	Mon. 382–14	31.12
	70 26 37.94	49 41 43	Mon. 381–6	85.81		70 27 54.12	113 53 47	Mon. 382–16	75.36
Mon. 381–6	45 42 14.28	229 41 41	Mon. 381–5	85.81	Mon. 382–16	45 42 23.59	293 53 45	Mon. 382–15	75.36
	70 26 40.96	66 08 15	Mon. 381–7	30.07		70 27 57.31	128 47 10	Mon. 382–17	14.27
Mon. 381–7	45 42 13.89	246 08 14	Mon. 381–6	30.07	Mon. 382–17	45 42 23.88	308 47 10	Mon. 382–16	14.27
	70 26 42.23	82 25 18	Mon. 381–8	65.34		70 27 57.82	51 03 26	Mon. 383	6.09
Mon. 381–8	45 42 13.61	262 25 16	Mon. 381–7	65.34	Mon. 383	45 42 23.75	231 03 26	Mon. 382–17	6.09
	70 26 45.23	99 55 03	Mon. 381–9	44.31		70 27 58.04	53 09 09	Mon. 383–1	99.77
Mon. 381–9	45 42 13.85	279 55 02	Mon. 381–8	44.31	Mon. 383–1	45 42 21.81	233 09 06	Mon. 383	99.77
	70 26 47.25	71 10 49	Mon. 381–10	33.08		70 28 01.73	27 57 37	Mon. 383–2	95.66
Mon. 381–10	45 42 13.51	251 10 48	Mon. 381–9	33.08	Mon. 383–2	45 42 19.08	207 57 36	Mon. 383–1	95.66
	70 26 48.69	122 09 53	Mon. 381–11	123.74		70 28 03.81	0 40 28	Mon. 383–3	54.52
Mon. 381–11	45 42 15.64	302 09 49	Mon. 381–10	123.74	Mon. 383–3	45 42 17.31	180 40 28	Mon. 383–2	54.52
	70 26 53.54	98 34 31	Mon. 381–12	35.02		70 28 03.84	48 37 50	Mon. 383–4	80.63
Mon. 381–12	45 42 15.81	278 34 30	Mon. 381–11	35.02	Mon. 383–4	45 42 15.58	228 37 48	Mon. 383–3	80.63
	70 26 55.14	103 08 36	Mon. 381–13	81.33		70 28 06.63	62 49 11	Mon. 383–5	200.13
Mon. 381–13	45 42 16.41	283 08 33	Mon. 381–12	81.33	Mon. 383–5	45 42 12.62	242 49 05	Mon. 383–4	200.13
	70 26 58.80	88 24 09	Mon. 381–14	47.03		70 28 14.86	33 21 59	Mon. 383–6	46.68
Mon. 381–14	45 42 16.37	268 24 07	Mon. 381–13	47.03	Mon. 383–6	45 42 11.36	213 21 58	Mon. 383–5	46.68
	70 27 00.97	62 01 44	Mon. 381–15	48.22		70 28 16.05	338 01 52	Mon. 383–7	44.77
Mon. 381–15	45 42 15.64	242 01 43	Mon. 381–14	48.22	Mon. 383–7	45 42 10.02	158 01 53	Mon. 383–6	44.77
	70 27 02.94	67 17 50	Mon. 381–16	50.96		70 28 15.28	319 52 17	Mon. 383–8	145.85
Mon. 381–16	45 42 15.00	247 17 48	Mon. 381–15	50.96	Mon. 383–8	45 42 06.40	139 52 20	Mon. 383–7	145.85
	70 27 05.11	24 38 55	Mon. 381–17	15.99		70 28 10.93	53 10 45	Mon. 383–9	113.29
Mon. 381–17	45 42 14.53	204 38 55	Mon. 381–16	15.99	Mon. 383–9	45 42 04.20	233 10 42	Mon. 383–8	113.29
	70 27 05.42	138 59 02	Mon. 381–18	62.47		70 28 15.12	51 01 37	Mon. 383–10	104.22
Mon. 381–18	45 42 16.05	318 59 01	Mon. 381–17	62.47	Mon. 383–10	45 42 02.08	231 01 34	Mon. 383–9	104.22
	70 27 07.32	141 22 09	Mon. 381–19	111.04		70 28 18.87	55 44 30	Mon. 383–11	160.48
Mon. 381–19	45 42 18.86	321 22 07	Mon. 381–18	111.04	Mon. 383–11	45 41 59.16	235 44 26	Mon. 383–10	160.48
	70 27 10.52	131 46 15	Mon. 381–20	158.89		70 28 25.00	52 02 23	Mon. 383–12	190.69
Mon. 381–20	45 42 22.29	311 46 11	Mon. 381–19	158.89	Mon. 383–12	45 41 55.36	232 02 18	Mon 383–11	190.69
	70 27 16.00	145 58 20	Mon. 382	41.70		70 28 31.95	19 12 46	Mon. 383–13	31.23
Mon. 382	45 42 23.41	325 58 19	Mon. 381–20	41.70	Mon. 383–13	45 41 54.40	199 12 46	Mon. 383–12	31.23
	70 27 17.08	145 25 38	Mon. 382–1	45.86		70 28 32.42	354 39 14	Mon. 383–14	65.76
Mon. 382–1	45 42 24.63	325 25 37	Mon. 382	45.86	Mon. 383–14	45 41 52.28	174 39 14	Mon. 383–13	65.76
	70 27 18.28	100 33 47	Mon. 382–2	67.38		70 28 32.14	41 18 12	Mon. 383–15	124.35
Mon. 382–2	45 42 25.03	280 33 45	Mon. 382–1	67.38	Mon. 383–15	45 41 49.25	221 18 09	Mon. 383–14	124.35
	70 27 21.34	116 00 52	Mon. 382–3	50.98		70 28 35.94	60 34 08	Mon. 383–16	117.21
Mon. 382–3	45 42 25.76	296 00 50	Mon. 382–2	50.98	Mon. 383–16	45 41 47.39	240 34 05	Mon. 383–15	117.21
	70 27 23.46	81 00 54	Mon. 382–4	24.13		70 28 40.65	83 04 05	Mon. 383–17	30.63
Mon. 382–4	45 42 25.64	261 00 53	Mon. 382–3	24.13	Mon. 383–17	45 41 47.27	263 04 04	Mon. 383–16	30.63
	70 27 24.56	84 02 56	Mon. 382–5	42.33		70 28 42.06	22 12 04	Mon. 383–18	47.08
Mon. 382–5	45 42 25.49	264 02 55	Mon. 382–4	42.33	Mon. 383–18	45 41 45.86	202 12 03	Mon. 383–17	47.08
	70 27 26.51	92 58 56	Mon. 382–6	47.32		70 28 42.88	48 38 03	Mon. 383–19	115.79

BOUNDARY MONUMENTS—SOURCE OF SOUTHWEST BRANCH OF ST. JOHN TO HEAD OF HALLS STREAM—Continued

Station	Latitude and longitude	Azimuth	To station	Distance (meters)	Station	Latitude and longitude	Azimuth	To station	Distance (meters)
	° ′ ″	° ′ ″				° ′ ″	° ′ ″		
Mon. 383–19	45 41 43.38 / 70 28 46.90	228 38 00 / 26 54 25	Mon. 383–18 / Mon. 383–20	115.79 / 50.98	Mon. 384–7	45 41 10.75 / 70 29 51.56	244 56 05 / 333 42 43	Mon. 384–6 / Mon. 384–8	48.90 / 34.73
Mon. 383–20	45 41 41.91 / 70 28 47.96	206 54 24 / 71 04 01	Mon. 383–19 / Mon. 383–21	50.98 / 60.10	Mon. 384–8	45 41 09.74 / 70 29 50.85	153 42 44 / 306 22 28	Mon. 384–7 / Mon. 385	34.73 / 30.28
Mon. 383–21	45 41 41.27 / 70 28 50.59	251 03 59 / 48 40 01	Mon. 383–20 / Mon. 383–22	60.10 / 66.77	Mon. 385	45 41 09.16 / 70 29 49.72	126 22 29 / 334 24 06	Mon. 384–8 / Mon. 385–1	30.28 / 17.03
Mon. 383–22	45 41 39.85 / 70 28 52.91	228 39 59 / 62 53 01	Mon. 383–21 / Mon. 383–23	66.77 / 164.58	Mon. 385–1	45 41 08.66 / 70 29 49.38	154 24 06 / 54 20 25	Mon. 385 / Mon. 385–2	17.03 / 59.70
Mon. 383–23	45 41 37.42 / 70 28 59.68	242 52 56 / 109 28 59	Mon. 383–22 / Mon. 383–24	164.58 / 45.50	Mon. 385–2	45 41 07.54 / 70 29 51.62	234 20 23 / 62 15 11	Mon. 385–1 / Mon. 385–3	59.70 / 411.59
Mon. 383–24	45 41 37.91 / 70 29 01.66	289 28 58 / 73 09 01	Mon. 383–23 / Mon. 383–25	45.50 / 23.24	Mon. 385–3	45 41 01.33 / 70 30 08.45	242 14 59 / 54 01 02	Mon. 385–2 / Mon. 385–4	411.59 / 60.87
Mon. 383–25	45 41 37.69 / 70 29 02.69	253 09 00 / 38 07 04	Mon. 383–24 / Mon. 383–26	23.24 / 33.30	Mon. 385–4	45 41 00.17 / 70 30 10.73	234 01 00 / 26 36 50	Mon. 385–3 / Mon. 385–5	60.87 / 62.86
Mon. 383–26	45 41 36.84 / 70 29 03.64	218 07 03 / 102 51 07	Mon. 383–25 / Mon. 383–27	33.30 / 76.33	Mon. 385–5	45 40 58.35 / 70 30 12.03	206 36 49 / 0 42 21	Mon. 385–4 / Mon. 385–6	62.86 / 23.72
Mon. 383–27	45 41 37.39 / 70 29 07.08	282 51 05 / 49 42 09	Mon. 383–26 / Mon. 383–28	76.33 / 20.95	Mon. 385–6	45 40 57.58 / 70 30 12.04	180 42 21 / 330 29 42	Mon. 385–5 / Mon. 385–7	23.72 / 50.44
Mon. 383–28	45 41 36.95 / 70 29 07.82	229 42 08 / 9 34 12	Mon. 383–27 / Mon. 383–29	20.95 / 85.03	Mon. 385–7	45 40 56.16 / 70 30 10.90	150 29 43 / 344 11 03	Mon. 385–6 / Mon. 385–8	50.44 / 37.19
Mon. 383–29	45 41 34.24 / 70 29 08.47	189 34 12 / 42 09 47	Mon. 383–28 / Mon. 383–30	85.03 / 145.58	Mon. 385–8	45 40 55.00 / 70 30 10.43	164 11 03 / 65 08 59	Mon. 385–7 / Mon. 385–9	37.19 / 66.45
Mon. 383–30	45 41 30.74 / 70 29 12.99	222 09 44 / 54 31 50	Mon. 383–29 / Mon. 383–31	145.58 / 57.15	Mon. 385–9	45 40 54.10 / 70 30 13.22	245 08 57 / 62 57 04	Mon. 385–8 / Mon. 385–10	66.45 / 48.27
Mon. 383–31	45 41 29.67 / 70 29 15.14	234 31 48 / 62 21 24	Mon. 383–30 / Mon. 383–32	57.15 / 87.19	Mon. 385–10	45 40 53.39 / 70 30 15.20	242 57 03 / 101 20 04	Mon. 385–9 / Mon. 385–11	48.27 / 60.04
Mon. 383–32	45 41 28.36 / 70 29 18.71	242 21 22 / 31 29 28	Mon. 383–31 / Mon. 383–33	87.19 / 43.61	Mon. 385–11	45 40 53.77 / 70 30 17.92	281 20 02 / 55 58 45	Mon. 385–10 / Mon. 385–12	60.04 / 68.50
Mon. 383–33	45 41 27.15 / 70 29 19.76	211 29 27 / 61 37 34	Mon. 383–32 / Mon. 383–34	43.61 / 111.36	Mon. 385–12	45 40 52.53 / 70 30 20.54	235 58 43 / 90 39 07	Mon. 385–11 / Mon. 385–13	68.50 / 66.19
Mon. 383–34	45 41 25.44 / 70 29 24.29	241 37 31 / 0 10 08	Mon. 383–33 / Mon. 383–35	111.36 / 23.56	Mon. 385–13	45 40 52.55 / 70 30 23.60	270 39 05 / 62 30 53	Mon. 385–12 / Mon. 385–14	66.19 / 68.50
Mon. 383–35	45 41 24.68 / 70 29 24.29	180 10 08 / 79 02 45	Mon. 383–34 / Mon. 383–36	23.56 / 51.78	Mon. 385–14	45 40 51.53 / 70 30 26.41	242 30 51 / 58 57 32	Mon. 385–13 / Mon. 385–15	68.50 / 120.83
Mon. 383–36	45 41 24.36 / 70 29 26.64	259 02 43 / 35 19 21	Mon. 383–35 / Mon. 383–37	51.78 / 34.22	Mon. 385–15	45 40 49.51 / 70 30 31.20	238 57 29 / 70 57 33	Mon. 385–14 / Mon. 385–16	120.83 / 49.60
Mon. 383–37	45 41 23.45 / 70 29 27.56	215 19 20 / 62 48 58	Mon. 383–36 / Mon. 383–38	34.22 / 62.51	Mon. 385–16	45 40 48.99 / 70 30 33.36	250 57 31 / 31 09 41	Mon. 385–15 / Mon. 385–17	49.60 / 56.49
Mon. 383–38	45 41 22.53 / 70 29 30.12	242 48 56 / 111 10 04	Mon. 383–37 / Mon. 383–39	62.51 / 31.15	Mon. 385–17	45 40 47.42 / 70 30 34.71	211 09 40 / 71 48 26	Mon. 385–16 / Mon. 385–18	56.49 / 53.22
Mon. 383–39	45 41 22.89 / 70 29 31.47	291 10 03 / 62 47 11	Mon. 383–38 / Mon. 383–40	31.15 / 90.93	Mon. 385–18	45 40 46.88 / 70 30 37.05	251 48 24 / 59 17 33	Mon. 385–17 / Mon. 385–19	53.22 / 96.91
Mon. 383–40	45 41 21.54 / 70 29 35.20	242 47 08 / 62 09 17	Mon. 383–39 / Mon. 383–41	90.93 / 69.06	Mon. 385–19	45 40 45.28 / 70 30 40.90	239 17 30 / 1 34 02	Mon. 385–18 / Mon. 385–20	96.91 / 112.29
Mon. 383–41	45 41 20.50 / 70 29 38.03	242 09 15 / 81 24 24	Mon. 383–40 / Mon. 383–42	69.06 / 30.38	Mon. 385–20	45 40 41.64 / 70 30 41.04	181 34 02 / 47 53 52	Mon. 385–19 / Mon. 385–21	112.29 / 60.70
Mon. 383–42	45 41 20.35 / 70 29 39.41	261 24 23 / 61 14 03	Mon. 383–41 / Mon. 384	30.38 / 29.16	Mon. 385–21	45 40 40.33 / 70 30 43.12	227 53 51 / 61 35 17	Mon. 385–20 / Mon. 385–22	60.70 / 41.95
Mon. 384	45 41 19.90 / 70 29 40.60	241 14 02 / 63 19 40	Mon. 383–42 / Mon. 384–1	29.16 / 25.48	Mon. 385–22	45 40 39.68 / 70 30 44.83	241 35 16 / 28 51 23	Mon. 385–21 / Mon. 385–23	41.95 / 101.11
Mon. 384–1	45 41 19.53 / 70 29 41.65	243 19 39 / 8 38 36	Mon. 384 / Mon. 384–2	25.48 / 116.24	Mon. 385–23	45 40 36.81 / 70 30 47.08	208 51 21 / 57 27 33	Mon. 385–22 / Mon. 385–24	101.11 / 48.17
Mon. 384–2	45 41 15.80 / 70 29 42.45	188 38 35 / 53 13 29	Mon. 384–1 / Mon. 384–3	116.24 / 32.87	Mon. 385–24	45 40 35.97 / 70 30 48.96	237 27 32 / 37 53 38	Mon. 385–23 / Mon. 385–25	48.17 / 49.40
Mon. 384–3	45 41 15.17 / 70 29 43.67	233 13 28 / 63 02 22	Mon. 384–2 / Mon. 384–4	32.87 / 83.41	Mon. 385–25	45 40 34.71 / 70 30 50.36	217 53 37 / 49 54 49	Mon. 385–24 / Mon. 385–26	49.40 / 177.92
Mon. 384–4	45 41 13.94 / 70 29 47.11	243 02 20 / 57 22 24	Mon. 384–3 / Mon. 384–5	83.41 / 45.84	Mon. 385–26	45 40 31.00 / 70 30 56.65	229 54 45 / 28 59 37	Mon. 385–25 / Mon. 385–27	177.92 / 49.74
Mon. 384–5	45 41 13.14 / 70 29 48.89	237 22 23 / 14 10 03	Mon. 384–4 / Mon. 384–6	45.84 / 54.72	Mon. 385–27	45 40 29.59 / 70 30 57.76	208 59 36 / 59 42 10	Mon. 385–26 / Mon. 385–28	49.74 / 118.24
Mon. 384–6	45 41 11.42 / 70 29 49.51	194 10 03 / 64 56 06	Mon. 384–5 / Mon. 384–7	54.72 / 48.90	Mon. 385–28	45 40 27.66 / 70 31 02.48	239 42 07 / 53 08 16	Mon. 385–27 / Mon. 385–29	118.24 / 41.93

BOUNDARY MONUMENTS—SOURCE OF SOUTHWEST BRANCH OF ST. JOHN TO HEAD OF HALLS STREAM—Continued

Station	Latitude and longitude	Azimuth	To station	Distance (meters)	Station	Latitude and longitude	Azimuth	To station	Distance (meters)
	° ′ ″	° ′ ″				° ′ ″	° ′ ″		
Mon. 385–29	45 40 26.84 / 70 31 04.03	233 08 15 / 32 28 17	Mon. 385–28 / Mon. 385–30	41 93 / 107. 23	Mon. 387–23	45 40 15.96 / 70 32 04.20	271 19 44 / 41 08 54	Mon. 387–22 / Mon. 387–24	56. 61 / 58. 89
Mon. 385–30	45 40 23.91 / 70 31 06.69	212 28 15 / 301 23 41	Mon. 385–29 / Mon. 386	107. 23 / 2. 47	Mon. 387–24	45 40 14.52 / 70 32 05.99	221 08 53 / 29 28 11	Mon. 387–23 / Mon. 387–25	58. 89 / 100. 35
Mon. 386	45 40 23.87 / 70 31 06.59	121 23 41 / 344 00 58	Mon. 385–30 / Mon. 386–1	2. 47 / 63. 99	Mon. 387–25	45 40 11.69 / 70 32 08.27	209 28 10 / 68 30 38	Mon. 387–24 / Mon. 387–26	100. 35 / 70. 15
Mon. 386–1	45 40 21.88 / 70 31 05.78	164 00 59 / 59 02 30	Mon. 386 / Mon. 386–2	63. 99 / 82. 86	Mon. 387–26	45 40 10.86 / 70 32 11.29	248 30 36 / 74 57 49	Mon. 387–25 / Mon. 387–27	70. 15 / 67. 01
Mon. 386–2	45 40 20.50 / 70 31 09.06	239 02 28 / 44 52 20	Mon. 386–1 / Mon. 386–3	82. 86 / 117. 86	Mon. 387–27	45 40 10.30 / 70 32 14.28	254 57 47 / 53 27 29	Mon. 387–26 / Mon. 388	67. 01 / 45. 30
Mon. 386–3	45 40 17.79 / 70 31 12.90	224 52 17 / 34 29 30	Mon. 386–2 / Mon. 386–4	117. 86 / 20. 02	Mon. 388	45 40 09.42 / 70 32 15.96	233 27 28 / 61 10 04	Mon. 387–27 / Mon. 388–1	45. 30 / 90. 85
Mon. 386–4	45 40 17.26 / 70 31 13.42	214 29 30 / 337 23 16	Mon. 386–3 / Mon. 386–5	20. 02 / 30. 95	Mon. 388–1	45 40 08.00 / 70 32 19.64	241 10 01 / 38 59 32	Mon. 388 / Mon. 388–2	90. 85 / 146. 50
Mon. 386–5	45 40 16.33 / 70 31 12.88	157 23 16 / 343 23 11	Mon. 386–4 / Mon. 387	30. 95 / 79. 75	Mon. 388–2	45 40 04.32 / 70 32 23.89	218 59 29 / 57 19 57	Mon. 388–1 / Mon. 388–3	146. 50 / 150. 21
Mon. 387	45 40 13.86 / 70 31 11.82	163 23 12 / 286 37 57	Mon. 386–5 / Mon. 387–1	79. 75 / 2. 01	Mon. 388–3	45 40 01.69 / 70 32 29.74	237 19 53 / 56 50 06	Mon. 388–2 / Mon. 388–4	150. 21 / 92. 65
Mon. 387–1	45 40 13.84 / 70 31 11.73	106 37 57 / 359 11 08	Mon. 387 / Mon. 387–2	2. 01 / 65. 44	Mon. 388–4	45 40 00.05 / 70 32 33.32	236 50 03 / 64 42 36	Mon. 388–3 / Mon. 388–5	92. 65 / 33. 18
Mon. 387–2	45 40 11.72 / 70 31 11.69	179 11 08 / 62 16 55	Mon. 387–1 / Mon. 387–3	65. 44 / 20. 32	Mon. 388–5	45 39 59.59 / 70 32 34.70	244 42 35 / 107 31 51	Mon. 388–4 / Mon. 388–6	33. 18 / 174. 55
Mon. 387–3	45 40 11.41 / 70 31 12.52	242 16 54 / 64 20 18	Mon. 387–2 / Mon. 387–4	20. 32 / 25. 45	Mon. 388–6	45 40 01.29 / 70 32 42.39	287 31 46 / 84 01 41	Mon. 388–5 / Mon. 388–7	174. 55 / 31. 92
Mon. 387–4	45 40 11.06 / 70 31 13.58	244 20 17 / 4 19 37	Mon. 387–3 / Mon. 387–5	25. 45 / 63. 35	Mon. 388–7	45 40 01.18 / 70 32 43.86	264 01 40 / 45 31 06	Mon. 388–6 / Mon. 388–8	31. 92 / 42. 80
Mon. 387–5	45 40 09.01 / 70 31 13.80	184 19 37 / 61 13 33	Mon. 387–4 / Mon. 387–6	63. 35 / 56. 28	Mon. 388–8	45 40 00.21 / 70 32 45.27	225 31 05 / 44 45 37	Mon. 388–7 / Mon. 388–9	42. 80 / 52. 79
Mon. 387–6	45 40 08.13 / 70 31 16.08	241 13 31 / 97 53 24	Mon. 387–5 / Mon. 387–7	56. 28 / 48. 57	Mon. 388–9	45 39 59.00 / 70 32 46.99	224 45 36 / 61 15 09	Mon. 388–8 / Mon. 388–10	52. 79 / 63. 63
Mon. 387–7	45 40 08.35 / 70 31 18.30	277 53 22 / 59 58 30	Mon. 387–6 / Mon. 387–8	48. 57 / 134. 12	Mon. 388–10	45 39 58.01 / 70 32 49.57	241 15 07 / 98 22 36	Mon. 388–9 / Mon. 389	63. 63 / 51. 94
Mon. 387–8	45 40 06.17 / 70 31 23.67	239 58 26 / 92 33 53	Mon. 387–7 / Mon. 387–9	134. 12 / 33. 60	Mon. 389	45 39 58.25 / 70 32 51.94	278 22 34 / 105 21 24	Mon. 388–10 / Mon. 389–1	51. 94 / 50. 63
Mon. 387–9	45 40 06.22 / 70 31 25.22	272 33 52 / 37 54 15	Mon. 387–8 / Mon. 387–10	33. 60 / 104. 66	Mon. 389–1	45 39 58.69 / 70 32 54.19	285 21 22 / 115 32 17	Mon. 389 / Mon. 389–2	50. 63 / 437. 96
Mon. 387–10	45 40 03.55 / 70 31 28.19	217 54 13 / 48 25 04	Mon. 387–9 / Mon. 387–11	104. 66 / 120. 20	Mon. 389–2	45 40 04.80 / 70 33 12.45	295 32 04 / 47 53 16	Mon. 389–1 / Mon. 389–3	437. 96 / 102. 60
Mon. 387–11	45 40 00.96 / 70 31 32.34	228 25 01 / 62 27 52	Mon. 387–10 / Mon. 387–12	120. 20 / 116. 09	Mon. 389–3	45 40 02.58 / 70 33 15.96	227 53 13 / 66 37 28	Mon. 389–2 / Mon. 389–4	102. 60 / 123. 01
Mon. 387–12	45 39 59.22 / 70 31 37.10	242 27 49 / 115 58 40	Mon. 387–11 / Mon. 387–13	116. 09 / 73. 55	Mon. 389–4	45 40 00.99 / 70 33 21.18	246 37 24 / 53 46 29	Mon. 389–3 / Mon. 389–5	123. 01 / 47. 62
Mon. 387–13	45 40 00.27 / 70 31 40.15	295 58 38 / 134 12 32	Mon. 387–12 / Mon. 387–14	73. 55 / 83. 66	Mon. 389–5	45 40 00.08 / 70 33 22.95	233 46 28 / 114 19 31	Mon. 389–4 / Mon. 389–6	47. 62 / 54. 90
Mon. 387–14	45 40 02.16 / 70 31 42.92	314 12 30 / 156 43 10	Mon. 387–13 / Mon. 387–15	83. 66 / 33. 17	Mon. 389–6	45 40 00.81 / 70 33 25.26	294 19 29 / 106 36 24	Mon. 389–5 / Mon. 389–7	54. 90 / 30. 01
Mon. 387–15	45 40 03.14 / 70 31 43.53	336 43 10 / 130 05 14	Mon. 387–14 / Mon. 387–16	33. 17 / 81. 56	Mon. 389–7	45 40 01.09 / 70 33 26.59	286 36 23 / 114 09 29	Mon. 389–6 / Mon. 389–8	30. 01 / 50. 85
Mon. 387–16	45 40 04.85 / 70 31 46.41	310 05 12 / 159 32 26	Mon. 387–15 / Mon. 387–17	81. 56 / 46. 42	Mon. 389–8	45 40 01.77 / 70 33 28.74	294 09 27 / 54 45 38	Mon. 389–7 / Mon. 389–9	50. 85 / 112. 94
Mon. 387–17	45 40 06.26 / 70 31 47.16	339 32 25 / 134 17 21	Mon. 387–16 / Mon. 387–18	46. 42 / 63. 56	Mon. 389–9	45 39 59.66 / 70 33 33.00	234 45 35 / 31 33 18	Mon. 389–8 / Mon. 389–10	112. 94 / 87. 74
Mon. 387–18	45 40 07.69 / 70 31 49.26	314 17 19 / 148 17 11	Mon. 387–17 / Mon. 387–19	63. 56 / 99. 25	Mon. 389–10	45 39 57.23 / 70 33 35.12	211 33 16 / 39 56 51	Mon. 389–9 / Mon. 389–11	87. 74 / 71. 95
Mon. 387–19	45 40 10.43 / 70 31 51.67	328 17 09 / 131 07 04	Mon. 387–18 / Mon. 387–20	99. 25 / 90. 31	Mon. 389–11	45 39 55.45 / 70 33 37.25	219 56 49 / 45 16 10	Mon. 389–10 / Mon. 389–12	71. 95 / 88. 93
Mon. 387–20	45 40 12.35 / 70 31 54.81	311 07 02 / 123 01 55	Mon. 387–19 / Mon. 387–21	90. 31 / 68. 52	Mon. 389–12	45 39 53.42 / 70 33 40.17	225 16 08 / 339 20 44	Mon. 389–11 / Mon. 390	88. 93 / 72. 55
Mon. 387–21	45 40 13.56 / 70 31 57.47	303 01 53 / 129 12 55	Mon. 387–20 / Mon. 387–22	68. 52 / 115. 04	Mon. 390	45 39 51.22 / 70 33 38.99	159 20 45 / 348 12 38	Mon. 389–12 / Mon. 390–1	72. 55 / 12. 55
Mon. 387–22	45 40 15.92 / 70 32 01.58	309 12 52 / 91 19 46	Mon. 387–21 / Mon. 387–23	115. 04 / 56. 61	Mon. 390–1	45 39 50.82 / 70 33 38.87	168 12 38 / 58 29 03	Mon. 390 / Mon. 390–2	12. 55 / 78. 14

BOUNDARY MONUMENTS—SOURCE OF SOUTHWEST BRANCH OF ST. JOHN TO HEAD OF HALLS STREAM—Continued

Station	Latitude and longitude	Azimuth	To station	Distance (meters)
Mon. 390-2	45 39 49.50 70 33 41.95	238 29 01 63 42 06	Mon. 390-1 Mon. 390-3	78.14 228.88
Mon. 390-3	45 39 46.22 70 33 51.43	243 41 59 1 17 24	Mon. 390-2 Mon. 390-4	228.88 87.41
Mon. 390-4	45 39 43.38 70 33 51.52	181 17 24 331 18 42	Mon. 390-3 Mon. 390-5	87.41 111.65
Mon. 390-5	45 39 40.21 70 33 49.04	151 18 44 319 48 32	Mon. 390-4 Mon. 390-6	111.65 102.26
Mon. 390-6	45 39 37.68 70 33 45.99	139 48 34 19 01 49	Mon. 390-5 Mon. 390-7	102.26 75.45
Mon. 390-7	45 39 35.37 70 33 47.13	199 01 48 35 19 14	Mon. 390-6 Mon. 390-8	75.45 34.64
Mon. 390-8	45 39 34.46 70 33 48.06	215 19 13 15 15 42	Mon. 390-7 Mon. 390-9	34.64 144.91
Mon. 390-9	45 39 29.93 70 33 49.82	195 15 41 54 01 45	Mon. 390-8 Mon. 390-10	144.91 53.32
Mon. 390-10	45 39 28.91 70 33 51.81	234 01 44 50 35 09	Mon. 390-9 Mon. 390-11	53.32 141.80
Mon. 390-11	45 39 26.00 70 33 56.87	230 35 05 8 55 58	Mon. 390-10 Mon. 390-12	141.80 67.83
Mon. 390-12	45 39 23.83 70 33 57.36	188 55 58 340 46 50	Mon. 390-11 Mon. 390-13	67.83 144.71
Mon. 390-13	45 39 19.40 70 33 55.15	160 46 52 16 57 15	Mon. 390-12 Mon. 390-14	144.71 56.77
Mon. 390-14	45 39 17.64 70 33 55.92	196 57 14 67 17 06	Mon. 390-13 Mon. 390-15	56.77 92.79
Mon. 390-15	45 39 16.48 70 33 59.87	247 17 03 56 25 36	Mon. 390-14 Mon. 390-16	92.79 89.51
Mon. 390-16	45 39 14.88 70 34 03.32	236 25 34 27 32 18	Mon. 390-15 Mon. 391	89.51 74.23
Mon. 391	45 39 12.75 70 34 04.90	207 32 17 26 13 44	Mon. 390-16 Mon. 391-1	74.23 154.03
Mon. 391-1	45 39 08.28 70 34 08.04	206 13 42 44 26 21	Mon. 391 Mon. 391-2	154.03 189.43
Mon. 391-2	45 39 03.90 70 34 14.17	224 26 17 54 54 52	Mon. 391-1 Mon. 391-3	189.43 63.42
Mon. 391-3	45 39 02.72 70 34 16.57	234 54 50 40 33 45	Mon. 391-2 Mon. 391-4	63.42 71.14
Mon. 391-4	45 39 00.96 70 34 18.70	220 33 43 62 48 54	Mon. 391-3 Mon. 391-5	71.14 93.43
Mon. 391-5	45 38 59.58 70 34 22.54	242 48 51 47 34 56	Mon. 391-4 Mon. 391-6	93.43 42.52
Mon. 391-6	45 38 58.65 70 34 23.99	227 34 55 5 17 35	Mon. 391-5 Mon. 391-7	42.52 57.36
Mon. 391-7	45 38 56.80 70 34 24.23	185 17 34 9 28 21	Mon. 391-6 Mon. 392	57.36 15.98
Mon. 392	45 38 56.29 70 34 24.36	189 28 20 352 48 16	Mon. 391-7 Mon. 392-1	15.98 11.34
Mon. 392-1	45 38 55.93 70 34 24.29	172 48 16 71 24 33	Mon. 392 Mon. 392-2	11.34 29.20
Mon. 392-2	45 38 55.63 70 34 25.57	251 24 32 68 31 33	Mon. 392-1 Mon. 392-3	29.20 78.06
Mon. 392-3	45 38 54.70 70 34 28.92	248 31 31 86 23 03	Mon. 392-2 Mon. 392-4	78.06 113.74
Mon. 392-4	45 38 54.47 70 34 34.16	266 22 59 20 36 48	Mon. 392-3 Mon. 392-5	113.74 158.35
Mon. 392-5	45 38 49.67 70 34 36.74	200 36 46 50 58 48	Mon. 392-4 Mon. 392-6	158.35 83.94
Mon. 392-6	45 38 47.96 70 34 39.75	230 58 46 359 46 18	Mon. 392-5 Mon. 392-7	83.94 89.01
Mon. 392-7	45 38 45.07 70 34 39.73	179 46 18 43 58 03	Mon. 392-6 Mon. 392-8	89.01 155.11
Mon. 392-8	45 38 41.46 70 34 44.71	223 57 59 30 00 03	Mon. 392-7 Mon. 392-9	155.11 96.71
Mon. 392-9	45 38 38.74 70 34 46.94	210 00 01 33 58 03	Mon. 392-8 Mon. 392-10	96.71 56.16
Mon. 392-10	45 38 37.24 70 34 48.39	213 58 02 53 48 18	Mon. 392-9 Mon. 392-11	56.16 156.73
Mon. 392-11	45 38 34.24 70 34 54.23	233 48 14 59 36 48	Mon. 392-10 Mon. 392-12	156.73 53.73
Mon. 392-12	45 38 33.36 70 34 56.37	239 36 46 87 36 18	Mon. 392-11 Mon. 392-13	53.73 85.36
Mon. 392-13	45 38 33.24 70 35 00.31	267 36 15 81 41 48	Mon. 392-12 Mon. 392-14	85.36 57.99
Mon. 392-14	45 38 32.97 70 35 02.96	261 41 46 10 10 18	Mon. 392-13 Mon. 392-15	57.99 66.91
Mon. 392-15	45 38 30.84 70 35 03.50	190 10 18 9 12 33	Mon. 392-14 Mon. 392-16	66.91 87.80
Mon. 392-16	45 38 28.03 70 35 04.15	189 12 33 336 01 33	Mon. 392-15 Mon. 392-17	87.80 57.18
Mon. 392-17	45 38 26.34 70 35 03.08	156 01 34 14 31 16	Mon. 392-16 Mon. 393	57.18 54.03
Mon. 393	45 38 24.64 70 35 03.70	194 31 16 20 12 15	Mon. 392-17 Mon. 393-1	54.03 78.96
Mon. 393-1	45 38 22.24 70 35 04.96	200 12 14 324 36 48	Mon. 393 Mon. 393-2	78.96 33.99
Mon. 393-2	45 38 21.35 70 35 04.06	144 36 49 19 22 18	Mon. 393-1 Mon. 393-3	33.99 34.59
Mon. 393-3	45 38 20.29 70 35 04.59	199 22 18 50 14 03	Mon. 393-2 Mon. 393-4	34.59 160.22
Mon. 393-4	45 38 16.97 70 35 10.27	230 13 59 58 18 48	Mon. 393-3 Mon. 393-5	160.22 41.27
Mon. 393-5	45 38 16.27 70 35 11.89	238 18 47 11 45 03	Mon. 393-4 Mon. 393-6	41.27 254.69
Mon. 393-6	45 38 08.19 70 35 14.29	191 45 01 45 13 33	Mon. 393-5 Mon. 393-7	254.69 71.41
Mon. 393-7	45 38 06.56 70 35 16.63	225 13 31 55 40 48	Mon. 393-6 Mon. 393-8	71.41 240.13
Mon. 393-8	45 38 02.18 70 35 25.78	235 40 41 29 09 18	Mon. 393-7 Mon. 393-9	240.13 110.65
Mon. 393-9	45 37 59.05 70 35 28.27	209 09 16 5 17 48	Mon. 393-8 Mon. 393-10	110.65 53.40
Mon. 393-10	45 37 57.32 70 35 28.50	185 17 48 353 33 33	Mon. 393-9 Mon. 393-11	53.40 89.82
Mon. 393-11	45 37 54.43 70 35 28.03	173 33 33 10 51 48	Mon. 393-10 Mon. 393-12	89.82 139.18
Mon. 393-12	45 37 50.01 70 35 29.25	190 51 47 47 43 03	Mon. 393-11 Mon. 393-13	139.18 155.36
Mon. 393-13	45 37 46.62 70 35 34.55	227 42 59 92 55 48	Mon. 393-12 Mon. 393-14	155.36 244.98
Mon. 393-14	45 37 47.03 70 35 45.84	272 55 40 99 06 18	Mon. 393-13 Mon. 393-15	244.98 98.52
Mon. 393-15	45 37 47.53 70 35 50.33	279 06 15 57 44 33	Mon. 393-14 Mon. 393-16	98.52 34.79
Mon. 393-16	45 37 46.93 70 35 51.69	237 44 32 33 11 53	Mon. 393-15 Mon. 394	34.79 102.78
Mon. 394	45 37 44.15 70 35 54.29	213 11 51 44 00 47	Mon. 393-16 Mon. 394-1	102.78 83.85
Mon. 394-1	45 37 42.19 70 35 56.98	224 00 45 51 50 32	Mon. 394 Mon. 394-2	83.85 189.31
Mon. 394-2	45 37 38.41 70 36 03.85	231 50 27 74 32 02	Mon. 394-1 Mon. 394-3	189.31 219.85
Mon. 394-3	45 37 36.51 70 36 13.63	254 31 55 85 17 02	Mon. 394-2 Mon. 394-4	219.85 145.22

BOUNDARY MONUMENTS—SOURCE OF SOUTHWEST BRANCH OF ST. JOHN TO HEAD OF HALLS STREAM—Continued

Station	Latitude and longitude	Azimuth	To station	Distance (meters)	Station	Latitude and longitude	Azimuth	To station	Distance (meters)
	° ′ ″	° ′ ″				° ′ ″	° ′ ″		
Mon. 394-4	45 37 36.12	265 16 57	Mon. 394-3	145.22	Mon. 396-5	45 36 33.40	234 35 44	Mon. 396-4	56.21
	70 36 20.31	55 37 32	Mon. 394-5	187.28		70 37 56.59	94 05 15	Mon. 396-6	79.46
Mon. 394-5	45 37 32.70	235 37 28	Mon. 394-4	187.28	Mon. 396-6	45 36 33.58	274 05 12	Mon. 396-5	79.46
	70 36 27.45	7 57 47	Mon. 394-6	77.26		70 38 00.24	119 57 45	Mon. 396-7	191.88
Mon. 394-6	45 37 30.22	187 57 47	Mon. 394-5	77.26	Mon. 396-7	45 36 36.69	299 57 40	Mon. 396-6	191.88
	70 36 27.94	359 48 31	Mon. 394-7	59.66		70 38 07.92	79 30 00	Mon. 396-8	95.44
Mon. 394-7	45 37 28.28	179 48 31	Mon. 394-6	59.66	Mon. 396-8	45 36 36.12	259 29 57	Mon. 396-7	95.44
	70 36 27.93	0 13 02	Mon. 394-8	72.00		70 38 12.25	54 16 45	Mon. 396-9	150.43
Mon. 394-8	45 37 25.95	180 13 02	Mon. 394-7	72.00	Mon. 396-9	45 36 33.28	234 16 41	Mon. 396-8	150.43
	70 36 27.95	25 23 32	Mon. 394-9	246.95		70 38 17.88	62 25 45	Mon. 396-10	252.13
Mon. 394-9	45 37 18.73	205 23 29	Mon. 394-8	246.95	Mon. 396-10	45 36 29.50	242 25 38	Mon. 396-9	252.13
	70 36 32.83	49 52 02	Mon. 394-10	49.35		70 38 28.20	56 17 30	Mon. 396-11	68.54
Mon. 394-10	45 37 17.70	229 52 01	Mon. 394-9	49.35	Mon. 396-11	45 36 28.27	236 17 28	Mon. 396-10	68.54
	70 36 34.58	75 17 17	Mon. 394-11	144.81		70 38 30.83	80 26 00	Mon. 396-12	45.90
Mon. 394-11	45 37 16.51	255 17 12	Mon. 394-10	144.81	Mon. 396-12	45 36 28.02	260 25 59	Mon. 396-11	45.90
	70 36 41.04	47 04 32	Mon. 394-12	68.36		70 38 32.92	60 49 15	Mon. 396-13	87.95
Mon. 394-12	45 37 15.00	227 04 30	Mon. 394-11	68.36	Mon. 396-13	45 36 26.63	240 49 12	Mon. 396-12	87.95
	70 36 43.35	23 16 32	Mon. 394-13	107.60		70 38 36.46	85 13 30	Mon. 396-14	78.85
Mon. 394-13	45 37 11.80	203 16 31	Mon. 394-12	107.60	Mon. 396-14	45 36 26.42	265 13 27	Mon. 396-13	78.85
	70 36 45.31	51 20 58	Mon. 395	68.83		70 38 40.09	61 10 45	Mon. 396-15	39.27
Mon. 395	45 37 10.40	231 20 56	Mon. 394-13	68.83	Mon. 396-15	45 36 25.80	241 10 44	Mon. 396-14	39.27
	70 36 47.79	57 31 51	Mon. 395-1	76.49		70 38 41.67	61 59 45	Mon. 396-16	21.84
Mon. 395-1	45 37 09.07	237 31 49	Mon. 395	76.49	Mon. 396-16	45 36 25.47	241 59 44	Mon. 396-15	21.84
	70 36 50.77	62 00 30	Mon. 395-2	123.34		70 38 42.56	44 33 33	Mon. 397	35.42
Mon. 395-2	45 37 07.20	242 00 26	Mon. 395-1	123.34	Mon. 397	45 36 24.66	224 33 32	Mon. 396-16	35.42
	70 36 55.80	56 34 30	Mon. 395-3	56.01		70 38 43.71	39 43 01	Mon. 397-1	45.78
Mon. 395-3	45 37 06.20	236 34 28	Mon. 395-2	56.01	Mon. 397-1	45 36 23.52	219 43 00	Mon. 397	45.78
	70 36 57.96	358 22 00	Mon. 395-4	60.05		70 38 45.06	12 25 22	Mon. 397-2	123.74
Mon. 395-4	45 37 04.26	178 22 00	Mon. 395-3	60.05	Mon. 397-2	45 36 19.60	192 25 21	Mon. 397-1	123.74
	70 36 57.88	45 24 15	Mon. 395-5	180.56		70 38 46.29	14 47 22	Mon. 397-3	172.31
Mon. 395-5	45 37 00.15	225 24 12	Mon. 395-4	180.56	Mon. 397-3	45 36 14.20	194 47 21	Mon. 397-2	172.31
	70 37 03.81	18 02 30	Mon. 395-6	60.05		70 38 48.32	41 45 42	Mon. 397-4	56.43
Mon. 395-6	45 36 58.30	198 02 29	Mon. 395-5	60.05	Mon. 397-4	45 36 12.84	221 45 41	Mon. 397-3	56.43
	70 37 04.67	41 17 45	Mon. 395-7	90.99		70 38 50.05	29 54 12	Mon. 397-5	246.88
Mon. 395-7	45 36 56.09	221 17 43	Mon. 395-6	90.99	Mon. 397-5	45 36 05.91	209 54 08	Mon. 397-4	246.88
	70 37 07.44	11 15 15	Mon. 395-8	79.87		70 38 55.73	29 51 12	Mon. 397-6	60.46
Mon. 395-8	45 36 53.55	191 15 14	Mon. 395-7	79.87	Mon. 397-6	45 36 04.21	209 51 11	Mon. 397-5	60.46
	70 37 08.16	40 18 30	Mon. 395-9	60.05		70 38 57.12	40 47 42	Mon. 397-7	145.71
Mon. 395-9	45 36 52.07	220 18 29	Mon. 395-8	60.05	Mon. 397-7	45 36 00.64	220 47 39	Mon. 397-6	145.71
	70 37 09.95	357 24 15	Mon. 395-10	208.87		70 39 01.51	45 02 12	Mon. 397-8	111.85
Mon. 395-10	45 36 45.31	177 24 15	Mon. 395-9	208.87	Mon. 397-8	45 35 58.08	225 02 09	Mon. 397-7	111.85
	70 37 09.52	32 24 00	Mon. 395-11	60.66		70 39 05.17	321 32 42	Mon. 397-9	133.21
Mon. 395-11	45 36 43.65	212 23 59	Mon. 395-10	60.66	Mon. 397-9	45 35 54.70	141 32 39	Mon. 397-8	133.21
	70 37 11.02	78 06 00	Mon. 395-12	142.15		70 39 01.34	330 00 17	Mon. 397-10	30.63
Mon. 395-12	45 36 42.70	258 05 55	Mon. 395-11	142.15	Mon. 397-10	45 35 53.84	150 00 17	Mon. 397-9	30.63
	70 37 17.44	70 38 45	Mon. 395-13	189.66		70 39 00.64	12 11 12	Mon. 397-11	70.94
Mon. 395-13	45 36 40.66	250 38 39	Mon. 395-12	189.66	Mon. 397-11	45 35 51.60	192 11 12	Mon. 397-10	70.94
	70 37 25.70	112 15 45	Mon. 395-14	104.74		70 39 01.33	32 30 12	Mon. 397-12	222.09
Mon. 395-14	45 36 41.95	292 15 42	Mon. 395-13	104.74	Mon. 397-12	45 35 45.53	212 30 08	Mon. 397-11	222.09
	70 37 30.17	61 03 00	Mon. 395-15	44.69		70 39 06.83	46 15 57	Mon. 397-13	77.99
Mon. 395-15	45 36 41.25	241 02 59	Mon. 395-14	44.69	Mon. 397-13	45 35 43.78	226 15 55	Mon. 397-12	77.99
	70 37 31.98	48 45 54	Mon. 396	199.61		70 39 09.43	27 48 58	Mon. 398	93.31
Mon. 396	45 36 36.98	228 45 49	Mon. 395-15	199.61	Mon. 398	45 35 41.11	207 48 57	Mon. 397-13	93.31
	70 37 38.90	12 58 43	Mon. 396-1	7.12		70 39 11.44	27 21 19	Mon. 398-1	231.84
Mon. 396-1	45 36 36.76	192 58 43	Mon. 396	7.12	Mon. 398-1	45 35 34.44	207 21 16	Mon. 398	231.84
	70 37 38.98	97 09 15	Mon. 396-2	89.37		70 39 16.36	39 43 18	Mon. 398-2	269.60
Mon. 396-2	45 36 37.12	277 09 12	Mon. 396-1	89.37	Mon. 398-2	45 35 27.72	219 43 12	Mon. 398-1	269.60
	70 37 43.07	86 06 15	Mon. 396-3	133.45		70 39 24.31	46 54 48	Mon. 398-3	75.73
Mon. 396-3	45 36 36.83	266 06 11	Mon. 396-2	133.45	Mon. 398-3	45 35 26.04	226 54 33	Mon. 398-2	75.73
	70 37 49.21	57 14 45	Mon. 396-4	135.47		70 39 26.86	62 44 33	Mon. 398-4	197.31
Mon. 396-4	45 36 34.45	237 14 41	Mon. 396-3	135.47	Mon. 398-4	45 35 23.12	242 44 27	Mon. 398-3	197.31
	70 37 54.47	54 35 45	Mon. 396-5	56.21		70 39 34.95	358 55 03	Mon. 398-5	263.54

BOUNDARY MONUMENTS—SOURCE OF SOUTHWEST BRANCH OF ST. JOHN TO HEAD OF HALLS STREAM—Continued

Station	Latitude and longitude	Azimuth	To station	Distance (meters)	Station	Latitude and longitude	Azimuth	To station	Distance (meters)
	° ′ ″	° ′ ″				° ′ ″	° ′ ″		
Mon. 398–5	45 35 14.58 70 39 34.72	178 55 03 34 48 18	Mon. 398–4 Mon. 398–6	263.54 91.28	Mon. 400–9	45 34 01.82 70 41 09.05	149 09 43 348 12 26	Mon. 400–8 Mon. 400–10	133.22 57.09
Mon. 398–6	45 35 12.16 70 39 37.12	214 48 16 48 14 18	Mon. 398–5 Mon. 398–7	91.28 50.29	Mon. 400–10	45 34 00.01 70 41 08.51	168 12 26 48 28 41	Mon. 400–9 Mon. 400–11	57.09 70.65
Mon. 398–7	45 35 11.07 70 39 38.85	228 14 17 45 34 03	Mon. 398–6 Mon. 398–8	50.29 164.59	Mon. 400–11	45 33 58.49 70 41 10.95	228 28 39 357 28 26	Mon. 400–10 Mon. 400–12	70.65 110.74
Mon. 398–8	45 35 07.34 70 39 44.28	225 33 59 67 48 18	Mon. 398–7 Mon. 398–9	164.59 122.38	Mon. 400–12	45 33 54.90 70 41 10.72	177 28 26 50 39 56	Mon. 400–11 Mon. 400–13	110.74 144.56
Mon. 398–9	45 35 05.84 70 39 49.50	247 48 14 60 15 03	Mon. 398–8 Mon. 398–10	122.38 57.36	Mon. 400–13	45 33 51.94 70 41 15.88	230 39 52 79 33 26	Mon. 400–12 Mon. 400–14	144.56 94.75
Mon. 398–10	45 35 04.92 70 39 51.80	240 15 01 349 29 03	Mon. 398–9 Mon. 398–11	57.36 117.54	Mon. 400–14	45 33 51.38 70 41 20.18	259 33 23 08 08 26	Mon. 400–13 Mon. 400–15	94.75 76.13
Mon. 398–11	45 35 01.18 70 39 50.81	169 29 04 26 51 33	Mon. 398–10 Mon. 398–12	117.54 96.94	Mon. 400–15	45 33 49.07 70 41 21.38	200 08 25 14 26 41	Mon. 400–14 Mon. 400–16	76.13 55.47
Mon. 398–12	45 34 58.38 70 39 52.83	206 51 32 72 54 33	Mon. 398–11 Mon. 398–13	96.94 114.51	Mon. 400–16	45 33 47.33 70 41 22.02	194 26 40 14 26 41	Mon. 400–15 Mon. 400–17	55.47 99.61
Mon. 398–13	45 34 57.29 70 39 57.88	252 54 29 49 34 39	Mon. 398–12 Mon. 399	114.51 150.09	Mon. 400–17	45 33 44.20 70 41 23.17	194 26 40 334 09 11	Mon. 400–16 Mon. 400–18	99.61 196.99
Mon. 399	45 34 54.13 70 40 03.15	229 34 35 50 42 24	Mon. 398–13 Mon. 399–1	150.09 459.28	Mon. 400–18	45 33 38.46 70 41 19.21	154 09 14 329 56 11	Mon. 400–17 Mon. 400–19	196.99 71.67
Mon. 399–1	45 34 44.71 70 40 19.54	230 42 12 42 45 10	Mon. 399 Mon. 399–2	459.28 71.05	Mon. 400–19	45 33 36.45 70 41 17.55	149 56 12 294 39 11	Mon. 400–18 Mon. 400–20	71.67 79.77
Mon. 399–2	45 34 43.02 70 40 21.76	222 45 08 24 04 24	Mon. 399–1 Mon. 399–3	71.05 71.25	Mon. 400–20	45 33 35.37 70 41 14.21	114 39 13 305 56 56	Mon. 400–19 Mon. 400–21	79.77 45.75
Mon. 399–3	45 34 40.92 70 40 23.10	204 04 23 349 00 25	Mon. 399–2 Mon. 399–4	71.25 192.69	Mon. 400–21	45 33 34.50 70 41 12.50	125 56 57 332 02 56	Mon. 400–20 Mon. 401	45.75 127.36
Mon. 399–4	45 34 34.79 70 40 21.41	169 00 26 39 50 54	Mon. 399–3 Mon. 399–5	192.69 202.00	Mon. 401	45 33 30.86 70 41 09.75	152 02 58 331 02 02	Mon. 400–21 Mon. 401–1	127.36 191.76
Mon. 399–5	45 34 29.76 70 40 27.38	219 50 50 57 16 55	Mon. 399–4 Mon. 399–6	202.00 118.61	Mon. 401–1	45 33 25.42 70 41 05.46	151 02 05 315 36 50	Mon. 401 Mon. 401–2	191.76 174.24
Mon. 399–6	45 34 27.69 70 40 31.98	237 16 52 21 38 54	Mon. 399–5 Mon. 399–7	118.61 144.72	Mon. 401–2	45 33 21.39 70 40 59.85	135 36 54 308 31 50	Mon. 401–1 Mon. 401–3	174.24 362.16
Mon. 399–7	45 34 23.33 70 40 34.44	201 38 52 38 25 40	Mon. 399–6 Mon. 399–8	144.72 168.81	Mon. 401–3	45 33 14.08 70 40 46.78	128 31 59 319 00 48	Mon. 401–2 Mon. 401–4	362.16 235.80
Mon. 399–8	45 34 19.05 70 40 39.28	218 25 37 42 42 10	Mon. 399–7 Mon. 399–9	168.81 77.12	Mon. 401–4	45 33 08.32 70 40 39.66	139 00 53 28 24 50	Mon. 401–3 Mon. 401–5	235.80 68.00
Mon. 399–9	45 34 17.21 70 40 41.70	222 42 07 19 06 54	Mon. 399–8 Mon. 399–10	77.12 100.19	Mon. 401–5	45 33 06.38 70 40 41.15	208 24 49 68 19 38	Mon. 401–4 Mon. 401–6	68.00 103.01
Mon. 399–10	45 34 14.14 70 40 43.21	199 06 53 70 04 24	Mon. 399–9 Mon. 399–11	100.19 96.75	Mon. 401–6	45 33 05.15 70 40 45.56	248 19 35 44 27 20	Mon. 401–5 Mon. 401–7	103.01 110.66
Mon. 399–11	45 34 13.08 70 40 47.40	250 04 21 82 40 40	Mon. 399–10 Mon. 399–12	96.75 108.70	Mon. 401–7	45 33 02.59 70 40 49.13	224 27 17 98 02 50	Mon. 401–6 Mon. 401–8	110.66 65.40
Mon. 399–12	45 34 12.63 70 40 52.38	262 40 37 64 49 18	Mon. 399–11 Mon. 400	108.70 227.52	Mon. 401–8	45 33 02.89 70 40 52.12	278 02 48 114 54 50	Mon. 401–7 Mon. 401–9	65.40 68.81
Mon. 400	45 34 09.49 70 41 01.87	244 49 11 66 11 32	Mon. 399–12 Mon. 400–1	227.52 76.54	Mon. 401–9	45 33 03.82 70 40 55.00	294 54 48 93 44 38	Mon. 401–8 Mon. 401–10	68.81 208.66
Mon. 400–1	45 34 08.49 70 41 05.10	246 11 30 111 40 56	Mon. 400 Mon. 400–2	76.54 176.54	Mon 401–10	45 33 04.27 70 41 04.59	273 44 31 70 49 38	Mon. 401–9 Mon. 401–11	208.66 68.21
Mon. 400–2	45 34 10.60 70 41 12.67	291 40 51 89 15 11	Mon. 400–1 Mon. 400–3	176.54 52.03	Mon. 401–11	45 33 03.54 70 41 07.56	250 49 36 43 30 38	Mon. 401–10 Mon. 401–12	68.21 241.44
Mon. 400–3	45 34 10.58 70 41 15.06	269 15 09 80 41 56	Mon. 400–2 Mon. 400–4	52.03 59.52	Mon. 401–12	45 32 57.87 70 41 15.23	223 30 33 34 07 20	Mon. 401–11 Mon. 401–13	241.44 312.46
Mon. 400–4	45 34 10.27 70 41 17.77	260 41 54 29 33 56	Mon. 400–3 Mon. 400–5	59.52 69.04	Mon. 401–13	45 32 49.49 70 41 23.31	214 07 14 14 12 38	Mon. 401–12 Mon. 402	312.46 23.06
Mon. 400–5	45 34 08.32 70 41 19.34	209 33 55 349 51 26	Mon. 400–4 Mon. 400–6	69.04 51.83	Mon. 402	45 32 48.77 70 41 23.57	194 12 38 21 19 47	Mon. 401–13 Mon. 402–1	23.06 168.99
Mon. 400–6	45 34 06.67 70 41 18.92	169 51 26 308 09 11	Mon. 400–5 Mon. 400–7	51.83 66.00	Mon. 402–1	45 32 43.67 70 41 26.40	201 19 45 36 05 25	Mon. 402 Mon. 402–2	168.99 200.26
Mon. 400–7	45 34 05.35 70 41 16.53	128 09 13 266 49 26	Mon. 400–6 Mon. 400–8	66.00 94.14	Mon. 402–2	45 32 38.43 70 41 31.84	216 05 21 23 24 47	Mon. 402–1 Mon. 402–3	200.26 126.18
Mon. 400–8	45 34 05.52 70 41 12.20	86 49 29 329 09 41	Mon. 400–7 Mon. 400–9	94.14 133.22	Mon. 402–3	45 32 34.68 70 41 34.15	203 24 45 45 36 15	Mon. 402–2 Mon. 402–4	126.18 85.30

BOUNDARY MONUMENTS—SOURCE OF SOUTHWEST BRANCH OF ST. JOHN TO HEAD OF HALLS STREAM—Continued

Station	Latitude and longitude	Azimuth	To station	Distance (meters)	Station	Latitude and longitude	Azimuth	To station	Distance (meters)
	° ′ ″	° ′ ″				° ′ ″	° ′ ″		
Mon. 402-4	45 32 32.75 / 70 41 36.96	225 36 13 / 48 41 25	Mon. 402-3 / Mon. 402-5	85.30 / 83.01	Mon. 404-7	45 31 10.06 / 70 42 42.99	226 36 45 / 75 05 12	Mon. 404-6 / Mon. 404-8	26.78 / 79.73
Mon. 402-5	45 32 30.97 / 70 41 39.83	228 41 23 / 54 20 25	Mon. 402-4 / Mon. 402-6	83.01 / 196.90	Mon. 404-8	45 31 09.40 / 70 42 46.54	255 05 10 / 68 34 30	Mon. 404-7 / Mon. 404-9	79.73 / 177.14
Mon. 402-6	45 32 27.25 / 70 41 47.20	234 20 20 / 29 41 59	Mon. 402-5 / Mon. 402-7	196.90 / 103.63	Mon. 404-9	45 31 07.30 / 70 42 54.14	248 34 25 / 114 44 25	Mon. 404-8 / Mon. 404-10	177.14 / 53.34
Mon. 402-7	45 32 24.34 / 70 41 49.57	209 41 57 / 358 32 37	Mon. 402-6 / Mon. 402-8	103.63 / 160.88	Mon. 404-10	45 31 08.03 / 70 42 56.37	294 44 23 / 95 37 51	Mon. 404-9 / Mon. 404-11	53.34 / 52.73
Mon. 402-8	45 32 19.13 / 70 41 49.38	178 32 37 / 19 26 48	Mon. 402-7 / Mon. 402-9	160.88 / 379.51	Mon. 404-11	45 31 08.20 / 70 42 58.79	275 37 49 / 52 38 13	Mon. 404-10 / Mon. 404-12	52.73 / 130.84
Mon. 402-9	45 32 07.54 / 70 41 55.21	199 26 44 / 46 46 46	Mon. 402-8 / Mon. 402-10	379.51 / 99.60	Mon. 404-12	45 31 05.62 / 70 43 03.58	232 38 10 / 31 38 34	Mon. 404-11 / Mon. 404-13	130.84 / 78.11
Mon. 402-10	45 32 05.33 / 70 41 58.55	226 46 44 / 28 40 30	Mon. 402-9 / Mon. 402-11	99.60 / 189.26	Mon. 404-13	45 31 03.47 / 70 43 05.47	211 38 33 / 57 18 30	Mon. 404-12 / Mon. 404-14	78.11 / 213.59
Mon. 402-11	45 31 59.95 / 70 42 02.74	208 40 27 / 35 22 48	Mon. 402-10 / Mon. 402-12	189.26 / 99.81	Mon. 404-14	45 30 59.73 / 70 43 13.75	237 18 24 / 41 32 36	Mon. 404-13 / Mon. 404-15	213.59 / 166.38
Mon. 402-12	45 31 57.31 / 70 42 05.40	215 22 46 / 353 39 57	Mon. 402-11 / Mon. 402-13	99.81 / 103.26	Mon. 404-15	45 30 55.70 / 70 43 18.84	221 32 32 / 27 05 04	Mon. 404-14 / Mon. 404-16	166.38 / 212.71
Mon. 402-13	45 31 53.99 / 70 42 04.87	173 39 57 / 311 17 46	Mon. 402-12 / Mon. 402-14	103.26 / 176.77	Mon. 404-16	45 30 49.56 / 70 43 23.30	207 05 01 / 12 01 45	Mon. 404-15 / Mon. 404-17	212.71 / 402.26
Mon. 402-14	45 31 50.21 / 70 41 58.75	131 17 50 / 2 36 52	Mon. 402-13 / Mon. 402-15	176.77 / 42.96	Mon. 404-17	45 30 36.82 / 70 43 27.16	192 01 42 / 358 31 55	Mon. 404-16 / Mon. 404-18	402.26 / 129.01
Mon. 402-15	45 31 48.82 / 70 41 58.84	182 36 52 / 49 12 37	Mon. 402-14 / Mon. 402-16	42.96 / 48.07	Mon. 404-18	45 30 32.64 / 70 43 27.01	178 31 55 / 342 20 12	Mon. 404-17 / Mon. 404-19	129.01 / 171.82
Mon. 402-16	45 31 47.80 / 70 42 00.52	229 12 36 / 99 21 07	Mon. 402-15 / Mon. 403	48.07 / 11.38	Mon. 404-19	45 30 27.34 / 70 43 24.61	162 20 14 / 350 22 12	Mon. 404-18 / Mon. 404-20	171.82 / 110.90
Mon. 403	45 31 47.86 / 70 42 01.04	279 21 07 / 83 56 35	Mon. 402-16 / Mon. 403-1	11.38 / 207.61	Mon. 404-20	45 30 23.80 / 70 43 23.75	170 22 13 / 317 33 17	Mon. 404-19 / Mon. 404-21	110.90 / 61.01
Mon. 403-1	45 31 47.15 / 70 42 10.55	263 56 28 / 64 32 13	Mon. 403 / Mon. 403-2	207.61 / 44.49	Mon. 404-21	45 30 22.34 / 70 43 21.86	137 33 18 / 289 16 46	Mon. 404-20 / Mon. 404-22	61.01 / 153.24
Mon. 403-2	45 31 46.53 / 70 42 12.40	244 32 12 / 61 24 14	Mon. 403-1 / Mon. 403-3	44.49 / 215.49	Mon. 404-22	45 30 20.70 / 70 43 15.19	109 16 51 / 302 05 55	Mon. 404-21 / Mon. 404-23	153.24 / 170.31
Mon. 403-3	45 31 43.19 / 70 42 21.12	241 24 08 / 51 32 47	Mon. 403-2 / Mon. 403-4	215.49 / 116.50	Mon. 404-23	45 30 17.77 / 70 43 08.54	122 02 59 / 294 46 10	Mon. 404-22 / Mon. 404-24	170.31 / 74.05
Mon. 403-4	45 31 40.84 / 70 42 25.33	231 32 44 / 23 55 40	Mon. 403-3 / Mon. 403-5	116.50 / 56.42	Mon. 404-24	45 30 16.77 / 70 43 05.45	114 46 12 / 292 35 29	Mon. 404-23 / Mon. 404-25	74.05 / 66.36
Mon. 403-5	45 31 39.17 / 70 42 26.38	203 55 39 / 6 28 52	Mon. 403-4 / Mon. 403-6	56.42 / 88.71	Mon. 404-25	45 30 15.94 / 70 43 02.63	112 35 31 / 261 29 23	Mon. 404-24 / Mon. 404-26	66.36 / 112.18
Mon. 403-6	45 31 36.32 / 70 42 26.84	186 28 51 / 10 20 20	Mon. 403-5 / Mon. 403-7	88.71 / 73.16	Mon. 404-26	45 30 16.48 / 70 42 57.52	81 29 27 / 323 28 08	Mon. 404-25 / Mon. 404-27	112.18 / 87.65
Mon. 403-7	45 31 33.99 / 70 42 27.45	190 20 20 / 46 49 06	Mon. 403-6 / Mon. 403-8	73.16 / 67.25	Mon. 404-27	45 30 14.20 / 70 42 55.11	143 28 10 / 318 40 08	Mon. 404-26 / Mon. 405	87.65 / 90.78
Mon. 403-8	45 31 32.50 / 70 42 29.71	226 49 04 / 55 28 35	Mon. 403-7 / Mon. 403-9	67.25 / 63.15	Mon. 405	45 30 11.99 / 70 42 52.35	138 40 10 / 269 40 06	Mon. 404-27 / Mon. 405-1	90.78 / 4.68
Mon. 403-9	45 31 31.34 / 70 42 32.10	235 28 33 / 54 00 07	Mon. 403-8 / Mon. 403-10	63.15 / 83.42	Mon. 405-1	45 30 11.99 / 70 42 52.14	89 40 06 / 296 52 25	Mon. 405 / Mon. 405-2	4.68 / 93.96
Mon. 403-10	45 31 29.75 / 70 42 35.22	234 00 05 / 11 09 22	Mon. 403-9 / Mon. 404	83.42 / 263.53	Mon. 405-2	45 30 10.62 / 70 42 48.28	116 52 28 / 325 19 27	Mon. 405-1 / Mon. 405-3	93.96 / 80.59
Mon. 404	45 31 21.38 / 70 42 37.56	191 09 20 / 7 41 08	Mon. 403-10 / Mon. 404-1	263.53 / 4.43	Mon. 405-3	45 30 08.47 / 70 42 46.16	145 19 29 / 314 30 18	Mon. 405-2 / Mon. 405-4	80.59 / 71.18
Mon. 404-1	45 31 21.23 / 70 42 37.59	187 41 08 / 28 51 13	Mon. 404 / Mon. 404-2	4.43 / 74.08	Mon. 405-4	45 30 06.85 / 70 42 43.82	134 30 20 / 12 22 00	Mon. 405-3 / Mon. 405-5	71.18 / 20.07
Mon. 404-2	45 31 19.13 / 70 42 39.24	208 51 12 / 1 50 09	Mon. 404-1 / Mon. 404-3	74.08 / 99.86	Mon. 405-5	45 30 06.22 / 70 42 44.02	192 22 00 / 29 31 50	Mon. 405-4 / Mon. 405-6	20.07 / 53.76
Mon. 404-3	45 31 15.90 / 70 42 39.39	181 50 09 / 23 11 44	Mon. 404-2 / Mon. 404-4	99.86 / 57.58	Mon. 405-6	45 30 04.70 / 70 42 45.24	209 31 49 / 23 14 29	Mon. 405-5 / Mon. 405-7	53.76 / 47.49
Mon. 404-4	45 31 14.18 / 70 42 40.43	203 11 43 / 27 43 01	Mon. 404-3 / Mon. 404-5	57.58 / 49.32	Mon. 405-7	45 30 03.29 / 70 42 46.11	203 14 28 / 339 08 39	Mon. 405-6 / Mon. 405-8	47.49 / 189.15
Mon. 404-5	45 31 12.77 / 70 42 41.49	207 43 00 / 11 29 23	Mon. 404-4 / Mon. 404-6	49.32 / 66.43	Mon. 405-8	45 29 57.56 / 70 42 43.00	159 08 41 / 1 17 04	Mon. 405-7 / Mon. 405-9	189.15 / 96.19
Mon. 404-6	45 31 10.66 / 70 42 42.10	191 29 23 / 46 36 46	Mon. 404-5 / Mon. 404-7	66.43 / 26.78	Mon. 405-9	45 29 54.45 / 70 42 43.10	181 17 04 / 15 43 19	Mon. 405-8 / Mon. 405-10	96.19 / 142.81

BOUNDARY MONUMENTS—SOURCE OF SOUTHWEST BRANCH OF ST. JOHN TO HEAD OF HALLS STREAM—Continued

Station	Latitude and longitude	Azimuth	To station	Distance (meters)	Station	Latitude and longitude	Azimuth	To station	Distance (meters)
	° ′ ″	° ′ ″				° ′ ″	° ′ ″		
Mon. 405–10	45 29 50.00 / 70 42 44.89	195 43 18 / 27 55 44	Mon. 405–9 / Mon. 405–11	142.81 / 75.05	Mon. 408	45 28 00.02 / 70 41 36.25	193 22 30 / 8 20 57	Mon. 407–9 / Mon. 408–1	360.65 / 24.34
Mon. 405–11	45 29 47.85 / 70 42 46.50	207 55 43 / 30 42 09	Mon. 405–10 / Mon. 405–12	75.05 / 146.24	Mon. 408–1	45 27 59.24 / 70 41 36.41	188 20 57 / 338 21 57	Mon. 408 / Mon. 408–2	24.34 / 262.79
Mon. 405–12	45 29 43.78 / 70 42 49.94	210 42 06 / 40 29 49	Mon. 405–11 / Mon. 405–13	146.24 / 210.76	Mon. 408–2	45 27 51.33 / 70 41 31.95	158 22 00 / 304 02 17	Mon. 408–1 / Mon. 408–3	262.79 / 110.08
Mon. 405–13	45 29 38.58 / 70 42 56.25	220 29 44 / 34 20 16	Mon. 405–12 / Mon. 405–14	210.76 / 230.37	Mon. 408–3	45 27 49.33 / 70 41 27.75	124 02 20 / 276 47 32	Mon. 408–2 / Mon. 408–4	110.08 / 117.95
Mon. 405–14	45 29 32.42 / 70 43 02.23	214 20 12 / 21 37 56	Mon. 405–13 / Mon. 405–15	230.37 / 240.49	Mon. 408–4	45 27 48.88 / 70 41 22.36	96 47 36 / 274 52 21	Mon. 408–3 / Mon. 408–5	117.95 / 239.97
Mon. 405–15	45 29 25.18 / 70 43 06.31	201 37 53 / 344 16 58	Mon. 405–14 / Mon. 406	240.49 / 282.53	Mon. 408–5	45 27 48.22 / 70 41 11.35	94 52 29 / 286 23 59	Mon. 408–4 / Mon. 408–6	239.97 / 180.38
Mon. 406	45 29 16.37 / 70 43 02.79	164 17 00 / 345 57 02	Mon. 405–15 / Mon. 406–1	282.53 / 150.76	Mon. 408–6	45 27 46.57 / 70 41 03.39	106 24 05 / 294 32 39	Mon. 408–5 / Mon. 408–7	180.38 / 82.60
Mon. 406–1	45 29 11.64 / 70 43 01.10	165 57 03 / 316 30 38	Mon. 406 / Mon. 406–2	150.76 / 92.03	Mon. 408–7	45 27 45.46 / 70 40 59.93	114 32 41 / 319 42 56	Mon. 408–6 / Mon. 408–8	82.60 / 73.33
Mon. 406–2	45 29 09.47 / 70 42 58.19	136 30 40 / 305 53 07	Mon. 406–1 / Mon. 406–3	92.03 / 234.42	Mon. 408–8	45 27 43.65 / 70 40 57.75	139 42 58 / 327 59 00	Mon. 408–7 / Mon. 408–9	73.33 / 44.83
Mon. 406–3	45 29 05.02 / 70 42 49.44	125 53 13 / 316 11 28	Mon. 406–2 / Mon. 406–4	234.42 / 160.80	Mon. 408–9	45 27 42.42 / 70 40 56.65	147 59 01 / 356 42 46	Mon. 408–8 / Mon. 408–10	44.83 / 68.06
Mon. 406–4	45 29 01.26 / 70 42 44.32	136 11 32 / 303 45 09	Mon. 406–3 / Mon. 406–5	160.80 / 114.02	Mon. 408–10	45 27 40.22 / 70 40 56.48	176 42 46 / 348 35 51	Mon. 408–9 / Mon. 408–11	68.06 / 298.60
Mon. 406–5	45 28 59.21 / 70 42 39.95	123 45 12 / 321 43 07	Mon. 406–4 / Mon. 406–6	114.02 / 389.19	Mon. 408–11	45 27 30.74 / 70 40 53.76	168 35 53 / 358 18 41	Mon. 408–10 / Mon. 409	298.60 / 199.51
Mon. 406–6	45 28 49.32 / 70 42 28.85	141 43 15 / 306 39 16	Mon. 406–5 / Mon. 406–7	389.19 / 262.64	Mon. 409	45 27 24.28 / 70 40 53.49	178 18 41 / 356 54 24	Mon. 408–11 / Mon. 409–1	199.51 / 72.81
Mon. 406–7	45 28 44.24 / 70 42 19.15	126 39 23 / 242 24 06	Mon. 406–6 / Mon. 406–8	262.64 / 74.08	Mon. 409–1	45 27 21.92 / 70 40 53.31	176 54 24 / 9 47 37	Mon. 409 / Mon. 409–2	72.81 / 251.69
Mon. 406–8	45 28 45.35 / 70 42 16.13	62 24 08 / 278 54 20	Mon. 406–7 / Mon. 406–9	74.08 / 60.34	Mon. 409–2	45 27 13.89 / 70 40 55.28	189 47 36 / 0 57 24	Mon. 409–1 / Mon. 409–3	251.69 / 126.25
Mon. 406–9	45 28 45.04 / 70 42 13.38	98 54 22 / 286 00 46	Mon. 406–8 / Mon. 406–10	60.34 / 98.50	Mon. 409–3	45 27 09.80 / 70 40 55.37	180 57 24 / 330 38 10	Mon. 409–2 / Mon. 409–4	126.25 / 56.86
Mon. 406–10	45 28 44.16 / 70 42 09.02	106 00 49 / 278 32 59	Mon. 406–9 / Mon. 406–11	98.50 / 85.78	Mon. 409–4	45 27 08.20 / 70 40 54.09	150 38 11 / 277 03 05	Mon. 409–3 / Mon. 409–5	56.86 / 216.58
Mon. 406–11	45 28 43.75 / 70 42 05.12	98 33 02 / 249 24 14	Mon. 406–10 / Mon. 406–12	85.78 / 75.70	Mon. 409–5	45 27 07.33 / 70 40 44.20	97 03 12 / 264 52 44	Mon. 409–4 / Mon. 409–6	216.58 / 150.85
Mon. 406–12	45 28 44.61 / 70 42 01.85	69 24 16 / 277 53 11	Mon. 406–11 / Mon. 406–13	75.70 / 36.33	Mon. 409–6	45 27 07.77 / 70 40 37.29	84 52 49 / 280 57 18	Mon. 409–5 / Mon. 409–7	150.85 / 108.69
Mon. 406–13	45 28 44.45 / 70 42 00.20	97 53 12 / 302 37 02	Mon. 406–12 / Mon. 406–14	36.33 / 63.77	Mon. 409–7	45 27 07.10 / 70 40 32.38	100 57 22 / 299 30 44	Mon. 409–6 / Mon. 409–8	108.69 / 310.17
Mon. 406–14	45 28 43.34 / 70 41 57.72	122 37 04 / 313 32 44	Mon. 406–13 / Mon. 407	63.77 / 206.94	Mon. 409–8	45 27 02.15 / 70 40 19.95	119 30 53 / 293 21 59	Mon. 409–7 / Mon. 409–9	310.17 / 164.36
Mon. 407	45 28 38.72 / 70 41 50.82	133 32 49 / 316 12 42	Mon. 406–14 / Mon. 407–1	206.94 / 45.62	Mon. 409–9	45 27 00.04 / 70 40 13.01	113 22 04 / 312 31 43	Mon. 409–8 / Mon. 409–10	164.36 / 113.54
Mon. 407–1	45 28 37.66 / 70 41 49.36	136 12 43 / 324 43 26	Mon. 407 / Mon. 407–2	45.62 / 140.48	Mon. 409–10	45 26 57.56 / 70 40 09.16	132 31 46 / 295 06 37	Mon. 409–9 / Mon. 409–11	113.54 / 216.58
Mon. 407–2	45 28 33.94 / 70 41 45.63	144 43 29 / 306 25 15	Mon. 407–1 / Mon. 407–3	140.48 / 180.94	Mon. 409–11	45 26 54.58 / 70 40 00.14	115 06 43 / 316 10 42	Mon. 409–10 / Mon. 409–12	216.58 / 79.66
Mon. 407–3	45 28 30.46 / 70 41 38.92	126 25 20 / 290 50 03	Mon. 407–2 / Mon. 407–4	180.94 / 116.13	Mon. 409–12	45 26 52.72 / 70 39 57.60	136 10 44 / 316 19 58	Mon. 409–11 / Mon. 409–13	79.66 / 184.13
Mon. 407–4	45 28 29.12 / 70 41 33.93	110 50 07 / 320 44 31	Mon. 407–3 / Mon. 407–5	116.13 / 56.86	Mon. 409–13	45 26 48.40 / 70 39 51.75	136 20 02 / 326 11 38	Mon. 409–12 / Mon. 409–14	184.13 / 55.46
Mon. 407–5	45 28 27.70 / 70 41 32.27	140 44 32 / 359 33 40	Mon. 407–4 / Mon. 407–6	56.86 / 51.03	Mon. 409–14	45 26 46.91 / 70 39 50.33	146 11 39 / 312 52 38	Mon. 409–13 / Mon. 409–15	55.46 / 50.20
Mon. 407–6	45 28 26.04 / 70 41 32.25	179 33 40 / 359 51 00	Mon. 407–5 / Mon. 407–7	51.03 / 90.14	Mon. 409–15	45 26 45.80 / 70 39 48.63	132 52 39 / 286 53 56	Mon. 409–14 / Mon. 409–16	50.20 / 99.03
Mon. 407–7	45 28 23.12 / 70 41 32.24	179 51 00 / 358 19 46	Mon. 407–6 / Mon. 407–8	90.14 / 112.12	Mon. 409–16	45 26 44.87 / 70 39 44.27	106 53 59 / 271 04 07	Mon. 409–15 / Mon. 409–17	99.03 / 566.68
Mon. 407–8	45 28 19.49 / 70 41 32.09	178 19 46 / 1 33 04	Mon. 407–7 / Mon. 407–9	112.12 / 250.27	Mon. 409–17	45 26 44.52 / 70 39 18.20	91 04 25 / 279 49 57	Mon. 409–16 / Mon. 409–18	566.68 / 102.45
Mon. 407–9	45 28 11.39 / 70 41 32.40	181 33 04 / 13 22 32	Mon. 407–8 / Mon. 408	250.27 / 360.65	Mon. 409–18	45 26 43.96 / 70 39 13.56	99 50 00 / 286 10 04	Mon. 409–17 / Mon. 409–19	102.45 / 141.80

BOUNDARY MONUMENTS—SOURCE OF SOUTHWEST BRANCH OF ST. JOHN TO HEAD OF HALLS STREAM—Continued

Station	Latitude and longitude	Azimuth	To station	Distance (meters)	Station	Latitude and longitude	Azimuth	To station	Distance (meters)
	° ′ ″	° ′ ″				° ′ ″	° ′ ″		
Mon. 409–19	45 26 42.68 / 70 39 07.29	106 10 08 / 285 33 57	Mon. 409–18 / Mon. 410	141.80 / 53.07	Mon. 411–14	45 25 25.29 / 70 37 45.45	129 36 57 / 338 27 29	Mon. 411–13 / Mon. 411–15	48.79 / 70.03
Mon. 410	45 26 42.22 / 70 39 04.94	105 33 59 / 298 17 21	Mon. 409–19 / Mon. 410–1	53.07 / 5.27	Mon. 411–15	45 25 23.18 / 70 37 44.27	158 27 30 / 318 36 28	Mon. 411–14 / Mon. 411–16	70.03 / 61.42
Mon. 410–1	45 26 42.14 / 70 39 04.72	118 17 21 / 337 53 29	Mon. 410 / Mon. 410–2	5.27 / 103.86	Mon. 411–16	45 25 21.69 / 70 37 42.40	138 36 29 / 20 41 27	Mon. 411–15 / Mon. 412	61.42 / 5.94
Mon. 410–2	45 26 39.02 / 70 39 02.92	157 53 30 / 355 59 44	Mon. 410–1 / Mon. 410–3	103.86 / 140.40	Mon. 412	45 25 21.51 / 70 37 42.50	200 41 27 / 1 15 19	Mon. 411–16 / Mon. 412–1	5.94 / 56.50
Mon. 410–3	45 26 34.48 / 70 39 02.47	175 59 44 / 329 35 19	Mon. 410–2 / Mon. 410–4	140.40 / 357.07	Mon. 412–1	45 25 19.68 / 70 37 42.55	181 15 19 / 8 39 41	Mon. 412 / Mon. 412–2	56.50 / 55.85
Mon. 410–4	45 26 24.51 / 70 38 54.16	149 35 25 / 333 14 41	Mon. 410–3 / Mon. 410–5	357.07 / 283.38	Mon. 412–2	45 25 17.90 / 70 37 42.94	188 39 41 / 329 50 44	Mon. 412–1 / Mon. 412–3	55.85 / 42.11
Mon. 410–5	45 26 16.31 / 70 38 48.29	153 14 45 / 311 50 06	Mon. 410–4 / Mon. 410–6	283.38 / 145.92	Mon. 412–3	45 25 16.72 / 70 37 41.97	149 50 45 / 2 08 48	Mon. 412–2 / Mon. 412–4	42.11 / 57.29
Mon. 410–6	45 26 13.16 / 70 38 43.28	131 50 10 / 290 01 46	Mon. 410–5 / Mon. 410–7	145.92 / 141.92	Mon. 412–4	45 25 14.86 / 70 37 42.06	182 08 48 / 47 42 07	Mon. 412–3 / Mon. 412–5	57.29 / 56.86
Mon. 410–7	45 26 11.58 / 70 38 37.15	110 01 50 / 294 30 10	Mon. 410–6 / Mon. 410–8	141.92 / 45.08	Mon. 412–5	45 25 13.62 / 70 37 44.00	227 42 06 / 37 55 45	Mon. 412–4 / Mon. 412–6	56.86 / 43.12
Mon. 410–8	45 26 10.98 / 70 38 35.26	114 30 11 / 8 22 29	Mon. 410–7 / Mon. 410–9	45.08 / 77.39	Mon. 412–6	45 25 12.52 / 70 37 45.22	217 55 44 / 35 05 39	Mon. 412–5 / Mon. 412–7	43.12 / 19.84
Mon. 410–9	45 26 08.50 / 70 38 35.78	188 22 29 / 19 05 57	Mon. 410–8 / Mon. 410–10	77.39 / 135.54	Mon. 412–7	45 25 11.99 / 70 37 45.74	215 05 39 / 354 45 32	Mon. 412–6 / Mon. 412–8	19.84 / 76.52
Mon. 410–10	45 26 04.35 / 70 38 37.82	199 05 56 / 351 53 45	Mon. 410–9 / Mon. 410–11	135.54 / 95.98	Mon. 412–8	45 25 09.53 / 70 37 45.42	174 45 32 / 69 25 49	Mon. 412–7 / Mon. 412–9	76.52 / 98.65
Mon. 410–11	45 26 01.27 / 70 38 37.20	171 53 45 / 333 40 07	Mon. 410–10 / Mon. 410–12	95.98 / 66.09	Mon. 412–9	45 25 08.40 / 70 37 49.67	249 25 46 / 53 51 58	Mon. 412–8 / Mon. 412–10	98.65 / 50.33
Mon. 410–12	45 25 59.35 / 70 38 35.85	153 40 08 / 319 21 36	Mon. 410–11 / Mon. 410–13	66.09 / 86.70	Mon. 412–10	45 25 07.44 / 70 37 51.54	233 51 57 / 324 18 28	Mon. 412–9 / Mon. 412–11	50.33 / 24.90
Mon. 410–13	45 25 57.22 / 70 38 33.26	139 21 38 / 327 14 36	Mon. 410–12 / Mon. 410–14	86.70 / 223.66	Mon. 412–11	45 25 06.79 / 70 37 50.87	144 18 28 / 1 11 43	Mon. 412–10 / Mon. 412–12	24.90 / 33.18
Mon. 410–14	45 25 51.13 / 70 38 27.69	147 14 40 / 311 36 41	Mon. 410–13 / Mon. 410–15	223.66 / 312.59	Mon. 412–12	45 25 05.71 / 70 37 50.90	181 11 43 / 61 04 04	Mon. 412–11 / Mon. 412–13	33.18 / 50.60
Mon. 410–15	45 25 44.41 / 70 38 16.94	131 36 49 / 313 03 20	Mon. 410–14 / Mon. 411	312.59 / 60.25	Mon. 412–13	45 25 04.92 / 70 37 52.94	241 04 03 / 60 23 53	Mon. 412–12 / Mon. 412–14	50.60 / 33.56
Mon. 411	45 25 43.08 / 70 38 14.91	133 03 22 / 272 40 20	Mon. 410–15 / Mon. 411–1	60.25 / 1.04	Mon. 412–14	45 25 04.38 / 70 37 54.28	240 23 52 / 2 10 05	Mon. 412–13 / Mon. 412–15	33.56 / 94.12
Mon. 411–1	45 25 43.07 / 70 38 14.86	92 40 20 / 343 50 21	Mon. 411 / Mon. 411–2	1.04 / 99.57	Mon. 412–15	45 25 01.34 / 70 37 54.44	182 10 05 / 343 28 35	Mon. 412–14 / Mon. 412–16	94.12 / 74.16
Mon. 411–2	45 25 39.97 / 70 38 13.59	163 50 22 / 307 59 19	Mon. 411–1 / Mon. 411–3	99.57 / 53.64	Mon. 412–16	45 24 59.03 / 70 37 53.47	163 28 36 / 19 04 09	Mon. 412–15 / Mon. 412–17	74.16 / 49.38
Mon. 411–3	45 25 38.91 / 70 38 11.64	127 59 20 / 293 45 55	Mon. 411–2 / Mon. 411–4	53.64 / 36.44	Mon. 412–17	45 24 57.52 / 70 37 54.22	199 04 08 / 68 19 31	Mon. 412–16 / Mon. 412–18	49.38 / 78.64
Mon. 411–4	45 25 38.43 / 70 38 10.11	113 45 56 / 275 53 07	Mon. 411–3 / Mon. 411–5	36.44 / 182.77	Mon. 412–18	45 24 56.58 / 70 37 57.58	248 19 29 / 99 21 33	Mon. 412–17 / Mon. 412–19	78.64 / 186.69
Mon. 411–5	45 25 37.82 / 70 38 01.74	95 53 13 / 291 28 43	Mon. 411–4 / Mon. 411–6	182.77 / 80.74	Mon. 412–19	45 24 57.56 / 70 38 06.05	279 21 27 / 43 48 50	Mon. 412–18 / Mon. 412–20	186.69 / 48.14
Mon. 411–6	45 25 36.86 / 70 37 58.29	111 28 45 / 272 01 18	Mon. 411–5 / Mon. 411–7	80.74 / 140.38	Mon. 412–20	45 24 56.44 / 70 38 07.58	223 48 49 / 357 27 14	Mon. 412–19 / Mon. 412–21	48.14 / 32.78
Mon. 411–7	45 25 36.70 / 70 37 51.84	92 01 23 / 314 12 31	Mon. 411–6 / Mon. 411–8	140.38 / 72.45	Mon. 412–21	45 24 55.38 / 70 38 07.51	177 27 14 / 48 34 05	Mon. 412–20 / Mon. 412–22	32.78 / 68.55
Mon. 411–8	45 25 35.07 / 70 37 49.45	134 12 33 / 359 43 22	Mon. 411–7 / Mon. 411–9	72.45 / 39.69	Mon. 412–22	45 24 53.91 / 70 38 09.88	228 34 03 / 356 54 56	Mon. 412–21 / Mon. 412–23	68.55 / 93.51
Mon. 411–9	45 25 33.78 / 70 37 49.44	179 43 22 / 7 52 43	Mon. 411–8 / Mon. 411–10	39.69 / 54.87	Mon. 412–23	45 24 50.88 / 70 38 09.64	176 54 56 / 9 18 56	Mon. 412–22 / Mon. 412–24	93.51 / 69.56
Mon. 411–10	45 25 32.02 / 70 37 49.78	187 52 43 / 3 29 20	Mon. 411–9 / Mon. 411–11	54.87 / 38.47	Mon. 412–24	45 24 48.66 / 70 38 10.16	189 18 56 / 2 04 49	Mon. 412–23 / Mon. 412–25	69.56 / 65.17
Mon. 411–11	45 25 30.78 / 70 37 49.89	183 29 20 / 341 55 55	Mon. 411–10 / Mon. 411–12	38.47 / 84.20	Mon. 412–25	45 24 46.55 / 70 38 10.27	182 04 49 / 339 22 39	Mon. 412–24 / Mon. 412–26	65.17 / 77.53
Mon. 411–12	45 25 28.18 / 70 37 48.69	161 55 56 / 330 30 20	Mon. 411–11 / Mon. 411–13	84.20 / 66.80	Mon. 412–26	45 24 44.20 / 70 38 09.02	159 22 40 / 340 01 07	Mon. 412–25 / Mon. 412–27	77.53 / 48.37
Mon. 411–13	45 25 26.30 / 70 37 47.18	150 30 21 / 309 36 56	Mon. 411–12 / Mon. 411–14	66.80 / 48.79	Mon. 412–27	45 24 42.73 / 70 38 08.26	160 01 07 / 354 13 11	Mon. 412–26 / Mon. 412–28	48.37 / 64.16

BOUNDARY MONUMENTS—SOURCE OF SOUTHWEST BRANCH OF ST. JOHN TO HEAD OF HALLS STREAM—Continued

Station	Latitude and longitude	Azimuth	To station	Distance (meters)	Station	Latitude and longitude	Azimuth	To station	Distance (meters)
Mon. 412–28	45 24 40.66 / 70 38 07.96	174 13 11 / 21 14 24	Mon. 412–27 / Mon. 412–29	64.16 / 16.81	Mon. 414–8	45 23 59.85 / 70 37 44.48	278 21 25 / 42 00 15	Mon. 414–7 / Mon. 414–9	168.63 / 84.94
Mon. 412–29	45 24 40.16 / 70 38 08.24	201 14 24 / 315 12 17	Mon. 412–28 / Mon. 412–30	16.81 / 46.48	Mon. 414–9	45 23 57.80 / 70 37 47.09	222 00 13 / 76 17 35	Mon. 414–8 / Mon. 414–10	84.94 / 34.98
Mon. 412–30	45 24 39.09 / 70 38 06.73	135 12 18 / 337 48 41	Mon. 412–29 / Mon. 413	46.48 / 61.59	Mon. 414–10	45 23 57.54 / 70 37 48.65	256 17 34 / 104 29 15	Mon. 414–9 / Mon. 414–11	34.98 / 75.44
Mon. 413	45 24 37.24 / 70 38 05.66	157 48 41 / 334 09 03	Mon. 412–30 / Mon. 413–1	61.59 / 75.06	Mon. 414–11	45 23 58.15 / 70 37 52.01	284 29 13 / 68 22 16	Mon. 414–10 / Mon. 414–12	75.44 / 33.40
Mon. 413–1	45 24 35.05 / 70 38 04.16	154 09 04 / 310 47 28	Mon. 413 / Mon. 413–2	75.06 / 89.94	Mon. 414–12	45 23 57.75 / 70 37 53.44	248 22 15 / 50 32 18	Mon. 414–11 / Mon. 414–13	33.40 / 24.09
Mon. 413–2	45 24 33.15 / 70 38 01.03	130 47 30 / 343 50 08	Mon. 413–1 / Mon. 413–3	89.94 / 58.91	Mon. 414–13	45 23 57.25 / 70 37 54.30	230 32 17 / 57 00 37	Mon. 414–12 / Mon. 414–14	24.09 / 82.52
Mon. 413–3	45 24 31.32 / 70 38 00.27	163 50 09 / 293 25 39	Mon. 413–2 / Mon. 413–4	58.91 / 25.84	Mon. 414–14	45 23 55.80 / 70 37 57.48	237 00 34 / 64 35 14	Mon. 414–13 / Mon. 414–15	82.52 / 85.95
Mon. 413–4	45 24 30.98 / 70 37 59.18	113 25 40 / 285 04 33	Mon. 413–3 / Mon. 413–5	25.84 / 35.93	Mon. 414–15	45 23 54.60 / 70 38 01.05	244 35 11 / 46 56 46	Mon. 414–14 / Mon. 414–16	85.95 / 151.27
Mon. 413–5	45 24 30.68 / 70 37 57.59	105 04 34 / 291 01 18	Mon. 413–4 / Mon. 413–6	35.93 / 51.06	Mon. 414–16	45 23 51.26 / 70 38 06.13	226 56 42 / 33 24 07	Mon. 414–15 / Mon. 414–17	151.27 / 157.75
Mon. 413–6	45 24 30.09 / 70 37 55.40	111 01 20 / 327 27 32	Mon. 413–5 / Mon. 413–7	51.06 / 42.38	Mon. 414–17	45 23 46.99 / 70 38 10.12	213 24 04 / 17 25 35	Mon. 414–16 / Mon. 414–18	157.75 / 64.58
Mon. 413–7	45 24 28.93 / 70 37 54.35	147 27 33 / 333 25 41	Mon. 413–6 / Mon. 413–8	42.38 / 79.26	Mon. 414–18	45 23 44.99 / 70 38 11.01	197 25 34 / 35 30 32	Mon. 414–17 / Mon. 414–19	64.58 / 68.55
Mon. 413–8	45 24 26.64 / 70 37 52.72	153 25 42 / 304 44 20	Mon. 413–7 / Mon. 413–9	79.26 / 54.08	Mon. 414–19	45 23 43.19 / 70 38 12.84	215 30 30 / 357 13 04	Mon. 414–18 / Mon. 414–20	68.55 / 81.78
Mon. 413–9	45 24 25.64 / 70 37 50.67	124 44 21 / 277 19 52	Mon. 413–8 / Mon. 413–10	54.08 / 129.08	Mon. 414–20	45 23 40.54 / 70 38 12.66	177 13 04 / 5 56 32	Mon. 414–19 / Mon. 414–21	81.78 / 210.56
Mon. 413–10	45 24 25.10 / 70 37 44.78	97 19 56 / 286 48 17	Mon 413–9 / Mon. 413–11	129.08 / 150.78	Mon. 414–21	45 23 33.76 / 70 38 13.66	185 56 31 / 25 25 25	Mon. 414–20 / Mon. 414–22	210.56 / 85.40
Mon. 413–11	45 24 23.69 / 70 37 38.15	106 48 22 / 292 40 46	Mon. 413–10 / Mon 413–12	150.78 / 64.98	Mon. 414–22	45 23 31.26 / 70 38 15.34	205 25 23 / 40 28 04	Mon. 414–21 / Mon. 414–23	85.40 / 63.77
Mon. 413–12	45 24 22.88 / 70 37 35.39	112 40 48 / 276 19 01	Mon. 413–11 / Mon. 413–13	64.98 / 115.59	Mon. 414–23	45 23 29.69 / 70 38 17.25	220 28 02 / 24 49 04	Mon. 414–22 / Mon. 414–24	63.77 / 111.54
Mon. 413–13	45 24 22.47 / 70 37 30.10	96 19 05 / 307 52 38	Mon. 113–12 / Mon. 413–14	115.59 / 64.96	Mon. 414–24	45 23 26.41 / 70 38 19.40	204 49 02 / 7 20 02	Mon. 414–23 / Mon. 414–25	111.54 / 118.22
Mon. 413–14	45 24 21.18 / 70 37 27.75	127 52 40 / 326 24 43	Mon. 413–13 / Mon. 413–15	64.96 / 90.14	Mon. 414–25	45 23 22.61 / 70 38 20.09	187 20 01 / 19 17 41	Mon. 414–24 / Mon. 414–26	118.22 / 42.51
Mon. 413–15	45 24 18.74 / 70 37 25.45	146 24 45 / 341 00 08	Mon. 413–14 / Mon. 413–16	90.14 / 102.22	Mon. 414–26	45 23 21.31 / 70 38 20.74	199 17 41 / 37 49 34	Mon. 414–25 / Mon. 414–27	42.51 / 46.56
Mon. 413–16	45 24 15.61 / 70 37 23.92	161 00 09 / 323 49 02	Mon. 413–15 / Mon. 413–17	102.22 / 61.74	Mon. 414–27	45 23 20.12 / 70 38 22.05	217 49 33 / 310 43 23	Mon. 414–26 / Mon. 414–28	46.56 / 59.72
Mon. 413–17	45 24 14.00 / 70 37 22.25	143 49 03 / 333 12 26	Mon. 413–16 / Mon. 413–18	61.74 / 50.85	Mon. 414–28	45 23 18.86 / 70 38 19.97	130 43 24 / 296 33 36	Mon. 414–27 / Mon. 414–29	59.72 / 63.81
Mon. 413–18	45 24 12.53 / 70 37 21.20	153 12 27 / 322 33 32	Mon. 413–17 / Mon. 413–19	50.85 / 91.15	Mon. 414–29	45 23 17.93 / 70 38 17.35	116 33 38 / 331 16 40	Mon. 414–28 / Mon. 414–30	63.81 / 72.67
Mon. 413–19	45 24 10.18 / 70 37 18.65	142 33 33 / 21 44 03	Mon. 413–18 / Mon. 414	91.15 / 36.21	Mon. 414–30	45 23 15.87 / 70 38 15.74	151 16 41 / 358 52 45	Mon. 414–29 / Mon. 414–31	72.67 / 47.32
Mon. 414	45 24 09.09 / 70 37 19.27	201 44 02 / 25 54 30	Mon. 413–19 / Mon. 414–1	36.21 / 30.59	Mon. 414–31	45 23 14.34 / 70 38 15.70	178 52 45 / 297 58 49	Mon. 414–30 / Mon. 414–32	47.32 / 28.58
Mon. 414–1	45 24 08.20 / 70 37 19.88	205 54 30 / 32 37 33	Mon. 414 / Mon. 414–2	30.59 / 103.24	Mon. 414–32	45 23 13.90 / 70 38 14.54	117 58 50 / 318 41 47	Mon. 414–31 / Mon. 414–33	28.58 / 47.77
Mon. 414–2	45 24 05.39 / 70 37 22.44	212 37 31 / 43 53 01	Mon. 414–1 / Mon. 414–3	103.24 / 86.64	Mon. 414–33	45 23 12.74 / 70 38 13.09	138 41 48 / 332 13 06	Mon. 414–32 / Mon. 414–34	47.77 / 103.44
Mon. 414–3	45 24 03.36 / 70 37 25.20	223 52 59 / 15 59 39	Mon. 414–2 / Mon. 414–4	86.64 / 72.27	Mon. 414–34	45 23 09.77 / 70 38 10.87	152 13 08 / 316 04 20	Mon. 414–33 / Mon. 414–35	103.44 / 98.51
Mon. 414–4	45 24 01.11 / 70 37 26.12	195 59 38 / 76 08 08	Mon. 414–3 / Mon. 414–5	72.27 / 78.87	Mon. 414–35	45 23 07.48 / 70 38 07.73	136 04 22 / 358 50 52	Mon. 414–34 / Mon. 414–36	98.51 / 53.99
Mon. 414–5	45 24 00.50 / 70 37 29.64	256 08 05 / 76 40 55	Mon. 414–4 / Mon. 414–6	78.87 / 60.87	Mon. 414–36	45 23 05.73 / 70 38 07.68	178 50 52 / 23 16 07	Mon. 414–35 / Mon. 414–37	53.99 / 44.07
Mon. 414–6	45 24 00.05 / 70 37 32.36	256 40 53 / 72 25 28	Mon. 414–5 / Mon. 414–7	60.87 / 101.51	Mon. 414–37	45 23 04.42 / 70 38 08.48	203 16 07 / 333 08 06	Mon. 414–36 / Mon. 414–38	44.07 / 82.80
Mon. 414–7	45 23 59.05 / 70 37 36.81	252 25 25 / 98 21 30	Mon. 414–6 / Mon. 414–8	101.51 / 168.63	Mon. 414–38	45 23 02.02 / 70 38 06.76	153 08 07 / 24 58 28	Mon. 414–37 / Mon. 414–39	82.80 / 47.11

BOUNDARY MONUMENTS—SOURCE OF SOUTHWEST BRANCH OF ST. JOHN TO HEAD OF HALLS STREAM—Continued

Station	Latitude and longitude	Azimuth	To station	Distance (meters)	Station	Latitude and longitude	Azimuth	To station	Distance (meters)
Mon. 414–39	45 23 00.64 / 70 38 07.67	204 58 27 / 92 42 27	Mon. 414–38 / Mon. 414–40	47.11 / 46.71	Mon. 417–4	45 22 50.40 / 70 39 39.64	344 29 53 / 158 16 25	Mon. 417–3 / Mon. 417–5	80.45 / 88.31
Mon. 414–40	45 23 00.71 / 70 38 09.82	272 42 26 / 40 00 33	Mon. 414–39 / Mon. 414–41	46.71 / 43.87	Mon. 417–5	45 22 53.06 / 70 39 41.14	338 16 24 / 167 01 21	Mon. 417–4 / Mon. 417–6	88.31 / 110.00
Mon. 414–41	45 22 59.62 / 70 38 11.11	220 00 32 / 36 15 35	Mon. 414–40 / Mon. 415	43.87 / 78.53	Mon. 417–6	45 22 56.53 / 70 39 42.27	347 01 20 / 196 37 50	Mon. 417–5 / Mon. 417–7	110.00 / 62.35
Mon. 415	45 22 57.57 / 70 38 13.25	216 15 34 / 50 02 17	Mon. 414–41 / Mon. 415–1	78.53 / 43.15	Mon. 417–7	45 22 58.46 / 70 39 41.45	16 37 51 / 191 46 46	Mon. 417–6 / Mon. 417–8	62.35 / 27.01
Mon. 415–1	45 22 56.67 / 70 38 14.77	230 02 16 / 68 45 57	Mon. 415 / Mon. 415–2	43.15 / 161.01	Mon. 417–8	45 22 59.32 / 70 39 41.20	11 46 46 / 175 42 05	Mon. 417–7 / Mon. 417–9	27.01 / 286.48
Mon. 415–2	45 22 54.78 / 70 38 21.66	248 45 52 / 69 50 49	Mon. 415–1 / Mon. 415–3	161.01 / 119.19	Mon. 417–9	45 23 08.57 / 70 39 42.19	355 42 04 / 151 51 52	Mon. 417–8 / Mon. 417–10	286.48 / 86.53
Mon. 415–3	45 22 53.46 / 70 38 26.81	249 50 45 / 73 41 39	Mon. 415–2 / Mon. 415–4	119.19 / 47.68	Mon. 417–10	45 23 11.04 / 70 39 44.06	331 51 51 / 115 52 49	Mon. 417–9 / Mon. 418	86.53 / 18.70
Mon. 415–4	45 22 53.02 / 70 38 28.91	253 41 38 / 48 48 33	Mon. 415–3 / Mon. 415–5	47.68 / 57.58	Mon. 418	45 23 11.31 / 70 39 44.84	295 52 49 / 149 24 19	Mon. 417–10 / Mon. 418–1	18.70 / 13.94
Mon. 415–5	45 22 51.79 / 70 38 30.90	228 48 32 / 53 18 35	Mon. 415–4 / Mon. 415–6	57.58 / 203.38	Mon. 418–1	45 23 11.70 / 70 39 45.16	329 24 19 / 105 58 19	Mon. 418 / Mon. 418–2	13.94 / 97.76
Mon. 415–6	45 22 47.86 / 70 38 38.40	233 18 30 / 59 28 28	Mon. 415–5 / Mon. 415–7	203.38 / 87.26	Mon. 418–2	45 23 12.57 / 70 39 49.48	285 58 16 / 135 56 34	Mon. 418–1 / Mon. 418–3	97.76 / 58.68
Mon. 415–7	45 22 46.42 / 70 38 41.85	239 28 25 / 55 29 37	Mon. 415–6 / Mon. 415–8	87.26 / 137.99	Mon. 418–3	45 23 13.94 / 70 39 51.36	315 56 33 / 135 45 22	Mon. 418–2 / Mon. 418–4	58.68 / 132.97
Mon. 415–8	45 22 43.89 / 70 38 47.08	235 29 33 / 82 47 01	Mon. 415–7 / Mon. 415–9	137.99 / 38.36	Mon. 418–4	45 23 17.02 / 70 39 55.62	315 45 19 / 125 14 43	Mon. 418–3 / Mon. 418–5	132.97 / 124.26
Mon. 415–9	45 22 43.73 / 70 38 48.83	262 47 00 / 63 09 41	Mon. 415–8 / Mon. 416	38.36 / 193.58	Mon. 418–5	45 23 19.34 / 70 40 00.29	305 14 39 / 122 41 46	Mon. 418–4 / Mon. 418–6	124.26 / 352.82
Mon. 416	45 22 40.90 / 70 38 56.77	243 09 36 / 61 06 24	Mon. 415–9 / Mon. 416–1	193.58 / 171.08	Mon. 418–6	45 23 25.52 / 70 40 13.94	302 41 36 / 132 48 35	Mon. 418–5 / Mon. 418–7	352.82 / 74.96
Mon. 416–1	45 22 38.22 / 70 39 03.65	241 06 19 / 88 31 00	Mon. 416 / Mon. 416–2	171.08 / 50.57	Mon. 418–7	45 23 27.17 / 70 40 16.46	312 48 33 / 127 14 11	Mon. 418–6 / Mon. 418–8	74.96 / 107.69
Mon. 416–2	45 22 38.18 / 70 39 05.97	268 30 58 / 65 47 00	Mon. 416–1 / Mon. 416–3	50.57 / 60.19	Mon. 418–8	45 23 29.28 / 70 40 20.40	307 14 09 / 125 23 49	Mon. 418–7 / Mon. 418–9	107.69 / 231.23
Mon. 416–3	45 22 37.38 / 70 39 08.50	245 46 58 / 122 03 34	Mon. 416–2 / Mon. 416–4	60.19 / 65.32	Mon. 418–9	45 23 33.62 / 70 40 29.07	305 23 43 / 110 36 48	Mon. 418–8 / Mon. 418–10	231.23 / 95.61
Mon. 416–4	45 22 38.50 / 70 39 11.04	302 03 32 / 135 19 51	Mon. 416–3 / Mon. 416–5	65.32 / 41.44	Mon. 418–10	45 23 34.71 / 70 40 33.18	290 36 45 / 122 32 34	Mon. 418–9 / Mon. 418–11	95.61 / 187.65
Mon. 416–5	45 22 39.46 / 70 39 12.38	315 19 50 / 89 31 12	Mon. 416–4 / Mon. 416–6	41.44 / 98.20	Mon. 418–11	45 23 37.98 / 70 40 40.46	302 32 29 / 129 10 53	Mon. 418–10 / Mon. 418–12	187.65 / 84.75
Mon. 416–6	45 22 39.43 / 70 39 16.89	269 31 09 / 102 18 32	Mon. 416–5 / Mon. 416–7	98.20 / 74.51	Mon. 418–12	45 23 39.71 / 70 40 43.48	309 10 51 / 90 37 43	Mon. 418–11 / Mon. 418–13	84.75 / 76.87
Mon. 416–7	45 22 39.95 / 70 39 20.24	282 18 30 / 93 58 46	Mon. 416–6 / Mon. 416–8	74.51 / 75.20	Mon. 418–13	45 23 39.74 / 70 40 47.01	270 37 40 / 103 36 56	Mon. 418–12 / Mon. 418–14	76.87 / 123.51
Mon. 416–8	45 22 40.12 / 70 39 23.69	273 58 44 / 82 07 52	Mon. 416–7 / Mon. 416–9	75.20 / 91.52	Mon. 418–14	45 23 40.68 / 70 40 52.53	283 36 52 / 113 05 39	Mon. 418–13 / Mon. 418–15	123.51 / 188.93
Mon. 416–9	45 22 39.71 / 70 39 27.85	262 07 49 / 93 23 05	Mon. 416–8 / Mon. 416–10	91.52 / 126.18	Mon. 418–15	45 23 43.08 / 70 41 00.52	293 05 33 / 69 44 43	Mon. 418–14 / Mon. 419	188.93 / 108.61
Mon. 416–10	45 22 39.95 / 70 39 33.64	273 23 01 / 104 24 13	Mon. 416–9 / Mon. 416–11	126.18 / 116.14	Mon. 419	45 23 41.86 / 70 41 05.20	249 44 39 / 69 44 27	Mon. 418–15 / Mon. 419–1	108.61 / 50.50
Mon. 416–11	45 22 40.89 / 70 39 38.81	284 24 09 / 123 51 03	Mon. 416–10 / Mon. 416–12	116.14 / 25.42	Mon. 419–1	45 23 41.30 / 70 41 07.38	249 44 25 / 44 09 12	Mon. 419 / Mon. 419–2	50.50 / 29.03
Mon. 416–12	45 22 41.35 / 70 39 39.78	303 51 02 / 108 30 00	Mon. 416–11 / Mon. 416–13	25.42 / 25.37	Mon. 419–2	45 23 40.62 / 70 41 08.31	224 09 11 / 41 28 03	Mon. 419–1 / Mon. 419–3	29.03 / 183.85
Mon. 416–13	45 22 41.61 / 70 39 40.89	288 29 59 / 171 41 06	Mon. 416–12 / Mon. 417	25.37 / 24.98	Mon. 419–3	45 23 36.16 / 70 41 13.91	221 27 59 / 60 20 26	Mon. 419–2 / Mon. 419–4	183.85 / 91.62
Mon. 417	45 22 42.41 / 70 39 41.06	351 41 06 / 196 46 06	Mon. 416–13 / Mon. 417–1	24.98 / 17.71	Mon. 419–4	45 23 34.69 / 70 41 17.57	240 20 23 / 97 12 45	Mon. 419–3 / Mon. 419–5	91.62 / 33.62
Mon. 417–1	45 22 42.96 / 70 39 40.82	16 46 06 / 208 10 08	Mon. 417 / Mon. 417–2	17.71 / 102.42	Mon. 419–5	45 23 34.83 / 70 41 19.10	277 12 44 / 99 53 51	Mon. 419–4 / Mon. 419–6	33.62 / 191.00
Mon. 417–2	45 22 45.88 / 70 39 38.60	28 10 10 / 178 58 34	Mon. 417–1 / Mon. 417–3	102.42 / 61.91	Mon. 419–6	45 23 35.89 / 70 41 27.75	279 53 45 / 67 02 52	Mon. 419–5 / Mon. 419–7	191.00 / 58.40
Mon. 417–3	45 22 47.89 / 70 39 38.65	358 58 34 / 164 29 54	Mon. 417–2 / Mon. 417–4	61.91 / 80.45	Mon. 419–7	45 23 35.16 / 70 41 30.22	247 02 50 / 55 06 02	Mon. 419–6 / Mon. 419–8	58.40 / 84.72

BOUNDARY MONUMENTS—SOURCE OF SOUTHWEST BRANCH OF ST. JOHN TO HEAD OF HALLS STREAM—Continued

Station	Latitude and longitude	Azimuth	To station	Distance (meters)	Station	Latitude and longitude	Azimuth	To station	Distance (meters)
	° ′ ″	° ′ ″				° ′ ″	° ′ ″		
Mon. 419-8	45 23 33.59	235 06 00	Mon. 419-7	84.72	Mon. 421-6	45 23 54.37	300 02 53	Mon. 421-5	227.69
	70 41 33.42	86 58 07	Mon. 419-9	321.63		70 43 44.56	132 02 37	Mon. 421-7	125.00
Mon. 419-9	45 23 33.04	266 57 57	Mon. 419-8	321.63	Mon. 421-7	45 23 57.08	312 02 34	Mon. 421-6	125.00
	70 41 48.18	115 24 34	Mon. 419-10	94.43		70 43 48.82	164 18 10	Mon. 421-8	84.35
Mon. 419-10	45 23 34.35	295 24 31	Mon. 419-9	94.43	Mon. 421-8	45 23 59.71	344 18 09	Mon. 421-7	84.35
	70 41 52.10	155 41 03	Mon. 419-11	59.51		70 43 49.87	147 50 48	Mon. 421-9	153.89
Mon. 419-11	45 23 36.10	335 41 02	Mon. 419-10	59.51	Mon. 421-9	45 24 03.94	327 50 45	Mon. 421-8	153.89
	70 41 53.23	180 39 19	Mon. 419-12	60.37		70 43 53.64	160 16 40	Mon. 421-10	103.23
Mon. 419-12	45 23 38.06	0 39 19	Mon. 419-11	60.37	Mon. 421-10	45 24 07.08	340 16 39	Mon. 421-9	103.23
	70 41 53.20	139 34 11	Mon. 419-13	28.81		70 43 55.24	187 45 18	Mon. 421-11	119.19
Mon. 419-13	45 23 38.77	319 34 11	Mon. 419-12	28.81	Mon. 421-11	45 24 10.91	7 45 18	Mon. 421-10	119.19
	70 41 54.06	126 02 53	Mon. 419-14	99.10		70 43 54.50	202 41 58	Mon. 421-12	173.29
Mon. 419-14	45 23 40.66	306 02 50	Mon. 419-13	99.10	Mon. 421-12	45 24 16.09	22 42 00	Mon. 421-11	173.29
	70 41 57.74	90 24 57	Mon. 419-15	54.49		70 43 51.42	130 46 03	Mon. 421-13	165.40
Mon. 419-15	45 23 40.67	270 24 55	Mon. 419-14	54.49	Mon. 421-13	45 24 19.59	310 45 59	Mon. 421-12	165.40
	70 42 00.25	62 30 06	Mon. 419-16	250.89		70 43 57.19	116 44 38	Mon. 421-14	230.21
Mon. 419-16	45 23 36.92	242 29 59	Mon. 419-15	250.89	Mon. 421-14	45 24 22.94	296 44 31	Mon. 421-13	230.21
	70 42 10.48	93 23 45	Mon. 420	30.14		70 44 06.64	130 09 13	Mon. 422	140.28
Mon. 420	45 23 36.98	273 23 44	Mon. 419-16	30.14	Mon. 422	45 24 25.87	310 09 10	Mon. 421-14	140.28
	70 42 11.86	93 32 48	Mon. 420-1	24.49		70 44 11.57	130 07 50	Mon. 422-1	68.25
Mon. 420-1	45 23 37.03	273 32 47	Mon. 420	24.49	Mon. 422-1	45 24 27.30	310 07 48	Mon. 422	68.25
	70 42 12.99	91 52 02	Mon. 420-2	92.16		70 44 13.97	142 31 46	Mon. 422-2	197.86
Mon. 420-2	45 23 37.12	271 51 59	Mon. 420-1	92.16	Mon. 422-2	45 24 32.38	322 31 42	Mon. 422-1	197.86
	70 42 17.22	75 49 09	Mon. 420-3	196.87		70 44 19.50	128 56 50	Mon. 422-3	253.80
Mon. 420-3	45 23 35.56	255 49 03	Mon. 420-2	196.87	Mon. 422-3	45 24 37.55	308 56 44	Mon. 422-2	253.80
	70 42 26.00	49 07 47	Mon. 420-4	74.71		70 44 28.58	115 00 37	Mon. 422-4	127.60
Mon. 420-4	45 23 33.98	229 07 45	Mon. 420-3	74.71	Mon. 422-4	45 24 39.30	295 00 33	Mon. 422-3	127.60
	70 42 28.59	5 53 39	Mon. 420-5	73.18		70 44 33.90	136 34 59	Mon. 422-5	158.76
Mon. 420-5	45 23 31.62	185 53 39	Mon. 420-4	73.18	Mon. 422-5	45 24 43.03	316 34 55	Mon. 422-4	158.76
	70 42 28.94	60 53 51	Mon. 420-6	152.78		70 44 38.92	180 27 44	Mon. 422-6	166.36
Mon. 420-6	45 23 29.21	240 53 47	Mon. 420-5	152.78	Mon. 422-6	45 24 48.42	0 27 44	Mon. 422-5	166.36
	70 42 35.08	46 47 00	Mon. 420-7	71.64		70 44 38.86	154 50 33	Mon. 422-7	96.99
Mon. 420-7	45 23 27.62	226 46 58	Mon. 420-6	71.64	Mon. 422-7	45 24 51.27	334 50 32	Mon. 422-6	96.99
	70 42 37.48	80 45 12	Mon. 420-8	92.16		70 44 40.75	142 39 32	Mon. 422-8	85.06
Mon. 420-8	45 23 27.14	260 45 09	Mon. 420-7	92.16	Mon. 422-8	45 24 53.46	322 39 30	Mon. 422-7	85.06
	70 42 41.66	67 07 24	Mon. 420-9	86.65		70 44 43.12	151 28 35	Mon. 422-9	57.84
Mon. 420-9	45 23 26.05	247 07 21	Mon. 420-8	86.65	Mon. 422-9	45 24 55.10	331 28 34	Mon. 422-8	57.84
	70 42 45.33	130 19 30	Mon. 420-10	126.11		70 44 44.40	173 30 00	Mon. 422-10	116.85
Mon. 420-10	45 23 28.70	310 19 27	Mon. 420-9	126.11	Mon. 422-10	45 24 58.86	353 30 00	Mon. 422-9	116.85
	70 42 49.75	130 17 11	Mon. 420-11	133.35		70 44 45.00	208 17 05	Mon. 422-11	162.11
Mon. 420-11	45 23 31.49	310 17 08	Mon. 420-10	133.35	Mon. 422-11	45 25 03.49	28 17 07	Mon. 422-10	162.11
	70 42 54.42	114 27 27	Mon. 420-12	251.06		70 44 41.47	183 12 22	Mon. 422-12	112.27
Mon. 420-12	45 23 34.86	294 27 20	Mon. 420-11	251.06	Mon. 422-12	45 25 07.12	3 12 22	Mon. 422-11	112.27
	70 43 04.93	130 29 02	Mon. 420-13	175.25		70 44 41.18	187 48 27	Mon. 422-13	188.55
Mon. 420-13	45 23 38.54	310 28 57	Mon. 420-12	175.25	Mon. 422-13	45 25 13.17	7 48 28	Mon. 422-12	188.55
	70 43 11.06	122 22 11	Mon. 420-14	151.86		70 44 40.00	173 58 33	Mon. 423	104.42
Mon. 420-14	45 23 41.18	302 22 06	Mon. 420-13	151.86	Mon. 423	45 25 16.53	353 58 33	Mon. 422-13	104.42
	70 43 16.95	106 51 01	Mon. 420-15	92.90		70 44 40.51	131 55 46	Mon. 423-1	71.85
Mon. 420-15	45 23 42.05	286 50 58	Mon. 420-14	92.90	Mon. 423-1	45 25 18.09	311 55 44	Mon. 423	71.85
	70 43 21.04	127 39 13	Mon. 421	0.98		70 44 42.97	115 45 55	Mon. 423-2	193.46
Mon. 421	45 23 42.07	307 39 13	Mon. 420-15	0.98	Mon. 423-2	45 25 20.81	295 45 49	Mon. 423-1	193.46
	70 43 21.08	125 18 42	Mon. 421-1	70.90		70 44 50.98	104 31 06	Mon. 423-3	180.90
Mon. 421-1	45 23 43.40	305 18 40	Mon. 421	70.90	Mon. 423-3	45 25 22.28	284 31 00	Mon. 423-2	180.90
	70 43 23.74	108 35 20	Mon. 421-2	95.97		70 44 59.04	127 44 10	Mon. 423-4	85.09
Mon. 421-2	45 23 44.39	288 35 17	Mon. 421-1	95.97	Mon. 423-4	45 25 23.97	307 44 08	Mon. 423-3	85.09
	70 43 27.92	130 02 57	Mon. 421-3	57.46		70 45 02.13	138 17 31	Mon. 423-5	73.34
Mon. 421-3	45 23 45.59	310 02 56	Mon. 421-2	57.46	Mon. 423-5	45 25 25.74	318 17 29	Mon. 423-4	73.34
	70 43 29.94	151 34 20	Mon. 421-4	120.11		70 45 04.38	163 37 19	Mon. 423-6	125.27
Mon. 421-4	45 23 49.01	331 34 18	Mon. 421-3	120.11	Mon. 423-6	45 25 29.64	343 37 18	Mon. 423-5	125.27
	70 43 32.57	129 02 22	Mon. 421-5	81.91		70 45 06.00	166 43 58	Mon. 423-7	164.57
Mon. 421-5	45 23 50.68	309 02 20	Mon. 421-4	81.91	Mon. 423-7	45 25 34.82	346 43 57	Mon. 423-6	164.57
	70 43 35.50	120 02 59	Mon. 421-6	227.69		70 45 07.74	141 01 57	Mon. 423-8	95.09

BOUNDARY MONUMENTS—SOURCE OF SOUTHWEST BRANCH OF ST. JOHN TO HEAD OF HALLS STREAM—Continued

Station	Latitude and longitude	Azimuth	To station	Distance (meters)	Station	Latitude and longitude	Azimuth	To station	Distance (meters)
	° ′ ″	° ′ ″				° ′ ″	° ′ ″		
Mon. 423-8	45 25 37.22 / 70 45 10.49	321 01 55 / 129 53 08	Mon. 423-7 / Mon. 423-9	95.09 / 132.99	Mon. 425-8	45 25 36.95 / 70 47 26.08	271 24 41 / 128 20 35	Mon. 425-7 / Mon. 425-9	85.34 / 46.90
Mon. 423-9	45 25 39.98 / 70 45 15.18	309 53 05 / 133 36 13	Mon. 423-8 / Mon. 423-10	132.99 / 101.81	Mon. 425-9	45 25 37.89 / 70 47 27.77	308 20 34 / 141 28 42	Mon. 425-8 / Mon. 425-10	46.90 / 142.07
Mon. 423-10	45 25 42.26 / 70 45 18.58	313 36 10 / 103 27 18	Mon. 423-9 / Mon. 423-11	101.81 / 66.64	Mon. 425-10	45 25 41.49 / 70 47 31.84	321 28 39 / 106 19 40	Mon. 425-9 / Mon. 425-11	142.07 / 62.10
Mon. 423-11	45 25 42.76 / 70 45 21.56	283 27 16 / 83 27 24	Mon. 423-10 / Mon. 423-12	66.64 / 172.93	Mon. 425-11	45 25 42.06 / 70 47 34.58	286 19 38 / 100 01 07	Mon. 425-10 / Mon. 425-12	62.10 / 37.30
Mon. 423-12	45 25 42.12 / 70 45 29.46	263 27 18 / 69 40 26	Mon. 423-11 / Mon. 423-13	172.93 / 73.66	Mon. 425-12	45 25 42.27 / 70 47 36.27	280 01 06 / 93 10 27	Mon. 425-11 / Mon. 425-13	37.30 / 78.31
Mon. 423-13	45 25 41.29 / 70 45 32.64	249 40 24 / 52 39 33	Mon. 423-12 / Mon. 423-14	73.66 / 165.48	Mon. 425-13	45 25 42.41 / 70 47 39.86	273 10 24 / 74 51 03	Mon. 425-12 / Mon. 425-14	78.31 / 127.34
Mon. 423-14	45 25 38.04 / 70 45 38.69	232 39 28 / 69 49 06	Mon. 423-13 / Mon. 423-15	165.48 / 121.92	Mon. 425-14	45 25 41.33 / 70 47 45.52	254 50 59 / 49 23 50	Mon. 425-13 / Mon. 425-15	127.34 / 207.31
Mon. 423-15	45 25 36.68 / 70 45 43.95	249 49 03 / 65 27 20	Mon. 423-14 / Mon. 423-16	121.92 / 196.41	Mon. 425-15	45 25 36.96 / 70 47 52.76	229 23 45 / 55 33 53	Mon. 425-14 / Mon. 425-16	207.31 / 65.57
Mon. 423-16	45 25 34.03 / 70 45 52.17	245 27 14 / 73 31 21	Mon. 423-15 / Mon. 423-17	196.41 / 39.27	Mon. 425-16	45 25 35.76 / 70 47 55.24	235 33 51 / 27 13 55	Mon. 425-15 / Mon. 425-17	65.57 / 89.16
Mon. 423-17	45 25 33.67 / 70 45 53.90	253 31 19 / 117 24 56	Mon. 423-16 / Mon. 423-18	39.27 / 68.62	Mon. 425-17	45 25 33.19 / 70 47 57.12	207 13 54 / 355 36 52	Mon. 425-16 / Mon. 425-18	89.16 / 183.89
Mon. 423-18	45 25 34.70 / 70 45 56.70	297 24 55 / 143 01 21	Mon. 423-17 / Mon. 424	68.62 / 53.00	Mon. 425-18	45 25 27.25 / 70 47 56.48	175 36 52 / 32 09 30	Mon. 425-17 / Mon. 425-19	183.89 / 178.12
Mon. 424	45 25 36.07 / 70 45 58.17	323 01 20 / 142 57 31	Mon. 423-18 / Mon. 424-1	53.00 / 170.67	Mon. 425-19	45 25 22.36 / 70 48 00.84	212 09 27 / 23 45 15	Mon. 425-18 / Mon. 425-20	178.12 / 131.82
Mon. 424-1	45 25 40.48 / 70 46 02.90	322 57 28 / 136 12 12	Mon. 424 / Mon. 424-2	170.67 / 72.24	Mon. 425-20	45 25 18.46 / 70 48 03.28	203 45 13 / 33 45 51	Mon. 425-19 / Mon. 425-21	131.82 / 127.53
Mon. 424-2	45 25 42.17 / 70 46 05.20	316 12 10 / 113 56 29	Mon. 424-1 / Mon. 424-3	72.24 / 58.09	Mon. 425-21	45 25 15.02 / 70 48 06.54	213 45 49 / 17 52 17	Mon. 425-20 / Mon. 425-22	127.53 / 207.13
Mon. 424-3	45 25 42.93 / 70 46 07.64	293 56 27 / 90 58 27	Mon. 424-2 / Mon. 424-4	58.09 / 102.34	Mon. 425-22	45 25 08.64 / 70 48 09.46	197 52 15 / 17 16 33	Mon. 425-21 / Mon. 425-23	207.13 / 120.79
Mon. 424-4	45 25 42.99 / 70 46 12.35	270 58 24 / 96 18 23	Mon. 424-3 / Mon. 424-5	102.34 / 332.91	Mon. 425-23	45 25 04.90 / 70 48 11.11	197 16 32 / 56 47 02	Mon. 425-22 / Mon. 426	120.79 / 30.89
Mon. 424-5	45 25 44.17 / 70 46 27.57	276 18 12 / 115 33 13	Mon. 424-4 / Mon. 424-6	332.91 / 280.33	Mon. 426	45 25 04.35 / 70 48 12.30	236 47 01 / 56 36 55	Mon. 425-23 / Mon. 426-1	30.89 / 44.16
Mon. 424-6	45 25 48.09 / 70 46 39.21	295 33 05 / 106 46 16	Mon. 424-5 / Mon. 424-7	280.33 / 45.14	Mon. 426-1	45 25 03.56 / 70 48 14.00	236 36 54 / 74 50 31	Mon. 426 / Mon. 426-2	44.16 / 163.54
Mon. 424-7	45 25 48.51 / 70 46 41.19	286 46 15 / 94 31 56	Mon. 424-6 / Mon. 424-8	45.14 / 82.86	Mon. 426-2	45 25 02.18 / 70 48 21.26	254 50 26 / 67 45 25	Mon. 426-1 / Mon. 426-3	163.54 / 207.39
Mon. 424-8	45 25 48.72 / 70 46 44.99	274 31 53 / 90 55 20	Mon. 424-7 / Mon. 424-9	82.86 / 74.65	Mon. 426-3	45 24 59.64 / 70 48 30.08	247 45 19 / 87 36 00	Mon. 426-2 / Mon. 426-4	207.39 / 122.73
Mon. 424-9	45 25 48.76 / 70 46 48.43	270 55 18 / 116 32 45	Mon. 424-8 / Mon. 424-10	74.65 / 51.19	Mon. 426-4	45 24 59.47 / 70 48 35.72	267 35 56 / 79 17 47	Mon. 426-3 / Mon. 426-5	122.73 / 158.36
Mon. 424-10	45 25 49.50 / 70 46 50.54	296 32 43 / 124 23 23	Mon. 424-9 / Mon. 424-11	51.19 / 38.92	Mon. 426-5	45 24 58.52 / 70 48 42.88	259 17 42 / 16 11 46	Mon. 426-4 / Mon. 426-6	158.36 / 62.43
Mon. 424-11	45 25 50.22 / 70 46 52.01	304 23 21 / 138 12 50	Mon. 424-10 / Mon. 425	38.92 / 105.52	Mon. 426-6	45 24 56.58 / 70 48 43.68	196 11 45 / 12 55 40	Mon. 426-5 / Mon. 426-7	62.43 / 112.07
Mon. 425	45 25 52.76 / 70 46 55.25	318 12 48 / 43 21 39	Mon. 424-11 / Mon. 425-1	105.52 / 85.26	Mon. 426-7	45 24 53.04 / 70 48 44.83	192 55 39 / 4 14 19	Mon. 426-6 / Mon. 426-8	112.07 / 189.73
Mon. 425-1	45 25 50.76 / 70 46 57.94	223 21 37 / 32 19 18	Mon. 425 / Mon. 425-2	85.26 / 104.11	Mon. 426-8	45 24 46.91 / 70 48 45.48	184 14 19 / 21 39 21	Mon. 426-7 / Mon. 426-9	189.73 / 81.92
Mon. 425-2	45 25 47.91 / 70 47 00.50	212 19 16 / 37 32 01	Mon. 425-1 / Mon. 425-3	104.11 / 139.95	Mon. 426-9	45 24 44.44 / 70 48 46.87	201 39 20 / 17 26 40	Mon. 426-8 / Mon. 426-10	81.92 / 98.37
Mon. 425-3	45 25 44.31 / 70 47 04.42	217 31 58 / 36 04 58	Mon. 425-2 / Mon. 425-4	139.95 / 63.33	Mon. 426-10	45 24 41.41 / 70 48 48.22	197 26 39 / 55 47 44	Mon. 426-9 / Mon. 426-11	98.37 / 42.03
Mon. 425-4	45 25 42.65 / 70 47 06.14	216 04 57 / 42 18 43	Mon. 425-3 / Mon. 425-5	63.33 / 149.52	Mon. 426-11	45 24 40.64 / 70 48 49.82	235 47 43 / 35 01 13	Mon. 426-10 / Mon. 426-12	42.03 / 70.96
Mon. 425-5	45 25 39.07 / 70 47 10.77	222 18 40 / 53 22 49	Mon. 425-4 / Mon. 425-6	149.52 / 179.47	Mon. 426-12	45 24 38.76 / 70 48 51.70	215 01 12 / 31 18 50	Mon. 426-11 / Mon. 426-13	70.96 / 141.00
Mon. 425-6	45 25 35.60 / 70 47 17.40	233 22 44 / 110 52 13	Mon. 425-5 / Mon. 425-7	179.47 / 110.62	Mon. 426-13	45 24 34.86 / 70 48 55.07	211 18 48 / 56 18 46	Mon 426-12 / Mon. 426-14	141.00 / 65.17
Mon. 425-7	45 25 36.88 / 70 47 22.15	290 52 10 / 91 24 44	Mon. 425-6 / Mon. 425-8	110.62 / 85.34	Mon. 426-14	45 24 33.69 / 70 48 57.56	236 18 44 / 38 06 34	Mon. 426-13 / Mon. 426-15	65.17 / 82.22

BOUNDARY MONUMENTS—SOURCE OF SOUTHWEST BRANCH OF ST. JOHN TO HEAD OF HALLS STREAM—Continued

Station	Latitude and longitude	Azimuth	To station	Distance (meters)
	° ′ ″	° ′ ″		
Mon. 426–15	45 24 31.59	218 06 32	Mon. 426–14	82.22
	70 48 59.89	56 25 22	Mon. 426–16	95.62
Mon. 426–16	45 24 29.88	236 25 19	Mon. 426–15	95.62
	70 49 03.56	18 55 21	Mon. 426–17	105.07
Mon. 426–17	45 24 26.66	198 55 20	Mon. 426–16	105.07
	70 49 05.12	19 47 20	Mon. 426–18	104.76
Mon. 426–18	45 24 23.47	199 47 19	Mon. 426–17	104.76
	70 49 06.76	23 09 57	Mon. 426–19	155.01
Mon. 426–19	45 24 18.85	203 09 55	Mon. 426–18	155.01
	70 49 09.56	20 52 10	Mon. 426–20	26.80
Mon. 426–20	45 24 18.04	200 52 10	Mon. 426–19	26.80
	70 49 10.00	41 52 10	Mon. 426–21	148.80
Mon. 426–21	45 24 14.45	221 52 07	Mon. 426–20	148.80
	70 49 14.57	48 47 42	Mon. 427	124.58
Mon. 427	45 24 11.79	228 47 38	Mon. 426–21	124.58
	70 49 18.88	47 42 33	Mon. 427–1	124.43
Mon. 427–1	45 24 09.08	227 42 30	Mon. 427	124.43
	70 49 23.11	42 29 32	Mon. 427–2	241.65
Mon. 427–2	45 24 03.31	222 29 27	Mon. 427–1	241.65
	70 49 30.61	59 25 35	Mon. 427–3	46.05
Mon. 427–3	45 24 02.55	239 25 34	Mon. 427–2	46.05
	70 49 32.44	51 33 29	Mon. 427–4	64.07
Mon. 427–4	45 24 01.26	231 33 27	Mon. 427–3	64.07
	70 49 34.74	353 00 52	Mon. 427–5	97.77
Mon. 427–5	45 23 58.12	173 00 52	Mon. 427–4	97.77
	70 49 34.20	14 16 52	Mon 427–6	116.30
Mon. 427–6	45 23 54.46	194 16 51	Mon. 427–5	116.30
	70 49 35.51	345 40 30	Mon. 427–7	16.18
Mon. 427–7	45 23 53.96	165 40 30	Mon. 427–6	16.18
	70 49 35.33	315 54 59	Mon. 427–8	103.79
Mon. 427–8	45 23 51.54	135 55 01	Mon. 427–7	103.79
	70 49 32.01	332 32 33	Mon. 427–9	116.00
Mon. 427–9	45 23 48.21	152 32 35	Mon. 427–8	116.00
	70 49 29.55	0 16 43	Mon. 427–10	184.68
Mon. 427–10	45 23 42.22	180 16 43	Mon. 427–9	184.68
	70 49 29.59	12 28 08	Mon. 427–11	105.89
Mon. 427–11	45 23 38.88	192 28 07	Mon. 427–10	105.89
	70 49 30.64	21 26 39	Mon. 427–12	55.17
Mon. 427–12	45 23 37.21	201 26 38	Mon. 427–11	55.17
	70 49 31.57	27 30 09	Mon. 427–13	63.77
Mon. 427–13	45 23 35.38	207 30 08	Mon. 427–12	63.77
	70 49 32.92	312 21 15	Mon. 427–14	107.69
Mon. 427–14	45 23 33.03	132 21 18	Mon. 427–13	107.69
	70 49 29.26	323 17 07	Mon. 427–15	51.32
Mon. 427–15	45 23 31.70	143 17 08	Mon. 427–14	51.32
	70 49 27.85	16 20 27	Mon. 427–16	55.51
Mon. 427–16	45 23 29.97	196 20 27	Mon. 427–15	55.51
	70 49 28.57	352 48 38	Mon. 428	12.82
Mon. 428	45 23 29.56	172 48 38	Mon. 427–16	12.82
	70 49 28.50	352 57 44	Mon. 428–1	48.69
Mon. 428–1	45 23 28.00	172 57 44	Mon. 428	48.69
	70 49 28.22	310 00 53	Mon. 428–2	43.10
Mon. 428–2	45 23 27.10	130 00 54	Mon. 428–1	43.10
	70 49 26.70	291 20 42	Mon. 428–3	86.12
Mon. 428–3	45 23 26.08	111 20 45	Mon. 428–2	86.12
	70 49 23.02	265 18 29	Mon. 428–4	98.36
Mon. 428–4	45 23 26.34	85 18 32	Mon. 428–3	98.36
	70 49 18.51	274 07 22	Mon. 428–5	309.14
Mon. 428–5	45 23 25.62	94 07 32	Mon. 428–4	309.14
	70 49 04.34	299 52 47	Mon. 428–6	71.24
Mon. 428–6	45 23 24.47	119 52 49	Mon. 428–5	71.24
	70 49 01.50	321 49 27	Mon. 428–7	226.29
Mon. 428–7	45 23 18.71	141 49 32	Mon. 428–6	226.29
	70 48 55.07	315 46 16	Mon. 428–8	106.08
Mon. 428–8	45 23 16.25	135 46 18	Mon. 428–7	106.08
	70 48 51.67	338 03 36	Mon. 428–9	78.10
Mon. 428–9	45 23 13.90	158 03 37	Mon. 428–8	78.10
	70 48 50.32	352 28 17	Mon. 428–10	86.95
Mon. 428–10	45 23 11.11	172 28 17	Mon. 428–9	86.95
	70 48 49.80	332 43 43	Mon. 428–11	50.35
Mon. 428–11	45 23 09.66	152 43 44	Mon. 428–10	50.35
	70 48 48.74	355 05 55	Mon. 429	143.19
Mon. 429	45 23 05.04	175 05 56	Mon. 428–11	143.19
	70 48 48.18	353 39 53	Mon. 429–1	71.59
Mon. 429–1	45 23 02.73	173 39 53	Mon. 429	71.59
	70 48 47.81	343 18 03	Mon. 429–2	65.78
Mon. 429–2	45 23 00.69	163 18 04	Mon. 429–1	65.78
	70 48 46.94	320 40 09	Mon. 429–3	256.07
Mon. 429–3	45 22 54.28	140 40 14	Mon. 429–2	256.07
	70 48 39.48	354 05 24	Mon. 429–4	51.09
Mon. 429–4	45 22 52.63	174 05 24	Mon. 429–3	51.09
	70 48 39.24	340 26 12	Mon. 429–5	144.40
Mon. 429–5	45 22 48.22	160 26 14	Mon. 429–4	144.40
	70 48 37.02	315 19 04	Mon. 429–6	194.58
Mon. 429–6	45 22 43.74	135 19 08	Mon. 429–5	194.58
	70 48 30.73	315 57 53	Mon. 429–7	34.57
Mon. 429–7	45 22 42.94	135 57 54	Mon. 429–6	34.57
	70 48 29.63	328 12 44	Mon. 429–8	137.56
Mon. 429–8	45 22 39.15	148 12 47	Mon. 429–7	137.56
	70 48 26.30	343 48 36	Mon. 430	61.80
Mon. 430	45 22 37.23	163 48 37	Mon. 429–8	61.80
	70 48 25.51	344 30 33	Mon. 430–1	278.45
Mon. 430–1	45 22 28.54	164 30 35	Mon. 430	278.45
	70 48 22.09	1 51 04	Mon. 430–2	40.93
Mon. 430–2	45 22 27.21	181 51 04	Mon. 430–1	40.93
	70 48 22.15	340 50 00	Mon. 430–3	181.51
Mon. 430–3	45 22 21.66	160 50 02	Mon. 430–2	181.51
	70 48 19.41	1 32 36	Mon. 430–4	150.97
Mon. 430–4	45 22 16.77	181 32 36	Mon. 430–3	150.97
	70 48 19.60	328 51 45	Mon. 430–5	132.56
Mon. 430–5	45 22 13.10	148 51 47	Mon. 430–4	132.56
	70 48 16.45	355 19 11	Mon. 430–6	97.44
Mon. 430–6	45 22 09.95	175 19 11	Mon. 430–5	97.44
	70 48 16.08	341 44 55	Mon. 430–7	127.80
Mon. 430–7	45 22 06.02	161 44 56	Mon. 430–6	127.80
	70 48 14.24	328 35 00	Mon. 430–8	94.74
Mon. 430–8	45 22 03.40	148 35 02	Mon. 430–7	94.74
	70 48 11.98	355 09 36	Mon. 430–9	205.45
Mon. 430–9	45 21 56.77	175 09 37	Mon. 430–8	205.45
	70 48 11.18	21 11 23	Mon. 430–10	51.80
Mon. 430–10	45 21 55.20	201 11 22	Mon. 430–9	51.80
	70 48 12.04	26 05 44	Mon. 430–11	26.84
Mon. 430–11	45 21 54.42	206 05 44	Mon. 430–10	26.84
	70 48 12.58	66 26 12	Mon. 431	2.23
Mon. 431	45 21 54.39	246 26 12	Mon. 430–11	2.23
	70 48 12.68	67 24 30	Mon. 431–1	218.17
Mon. 431–1	45 21 51.68	247 24 23	Mon. 431	218.17
	70 48 21.93	71 41 33	Mon. 431–2	94.16
Mon. 431–2	45 21 50.72	251 41 30	Mon. 431–1	94.16
	70 48 26.04	53 33 13	Mon. 431–3	174.10
Mon. 431–3	45 21 47.37	233 33 08	Mon. 431–2	174.10
	70 48 32.48	4 01 04	Mon. 431–4	80.20
Mon. 431–4	45 21 44.78	184 01 04	Mon. 431–3	80.20
	70 48 32.73	353 40 37	Mon. 431–5	52.06

BOUNDARY MONUMENTS—SOURCE OF SOUTHWEST BRANCH OF ST. JOHN TO HEAD OF HALLS STREAM—Continued

Station	Latitude and longitude	Azimuth	To station	Distance (meters)
	° ′ ″	° ′ ″		
Mon. 431–5	45 21 43.10 / 70 48 32.47	173 40 37 / 20 14 50	Mon. 431–4 / Mon. 431–6	52.06 / 105.62
Mon. 431–6	45 21 39.89 / 70 48 34.15	200 14 49 / 22 56 22	Mon. 431–5 / Mon. 431–7	105.62 / 121.63
Mon. 431–7	45 21 36.26 / 70 48 36.33	202 56 21 / 6 19 29	Mon. 431–6 / Mon. 432	121.63 / 142.08
Mon. 432	45 21 31.69 / 70 48 37.05	186 19 29 / 6 14 02	Mon. 431–7 / Mon. 432–1	142.08 / 83.18
Mon. 432–1	45 21 29.01 / 70 48 37.46	186 14 02 / 49 18 02	Mon. 432 / Mon. 432–2	83.18 / 64.80
Mon. 432–2	45 21 27.64 / 70 48 39.72	229 18 00 / 58 53 48	Mon. 432–1 / Mon. 432–3	64.80 / 76.33
Mon. 432–3	45 21 26.37 / 70 48 42.72	238 53 46 / 80 45 16	Mon. 432–2 / Mon. 432–4	76.33 / 86.04
Mon. 432–4	45 21 25.92 / 70 48 46.62	260 45 13 / 100 19 16	Mon. 432–3 / Mon. 432–5	86.04 / 96.07
Mon. 432–5	45 21 26.48 / 70 48 50.97	280 19 13 / 111 30 43	Mon. 432–4 / Mon. 432–6	96.07 / 19.32
Mon. 432–6	45 21 26.70 / 70 48 51.79	291 30 42 / 38 30 28	Mon. 432–5 / Mon. 432–7	19.32 / 23.84
Mon. 432–7	45 21 26.10 / 70 48 52.47	218 30 28 / 34 09 46	Mon. 432–6 / Mon. 432–8	23.84 / 65.15
Mon. 432–8	45 21 24.36 / 70 48 54.16	214 09 45 / 344 38 51	Mon. 432–7 / Mon. 432–9	65.15 / 57.59
Mon. 432–9	45 21 22.56 / 70 48 53.46	164 38 52 / 349 07 45	Mon. 432–8 / Mon. 432–10	57.59 / 97.61
Mon. 432–10	45 21 19.45 / 70 48 52.61	169 07 46 / 356 39 32	Mon. 432–9 / Mon. 432–11	97.61 / 41.02
Mon. 432–11	45 21 18.12 / 70 48 52.50	176 39 32 / 332 24 25	Mon. 432–10 / Mon. 432–12	41.02 / 120.16
Mon. 432–12	45 21 14.68 / 70 48 49.94	152 24 27 / 321 37 57	Mon. 432–11 / Mon. 432–13	120.16 / 137.61
Mon. 432–13	45 21 11.18 / 70 48 46.02	141 37 59 / 335 58 45	Mon. 432–12 / Mon. 432–14	137.61 / 109.04
Mon. 432–14	45 21 07.95 / 70 48 43.98	155 58 46 / 291 22 43	Mon. 432–13 / Mon. 433	109.04 / 76.91
Mon. 433	45 21 07.05 / 70 48 40.69	111 22 45 / 291 21 54	Mon. 432–14 / Mon. 433–1	76.91 / 108.55
Mon. 433–1	45 21 05.76 / 70 48 36.04	111 21 57 / 17 35 00	Mon. 433 / Mon. 433–2	108.55 / 55.54
Mon. 433–2	45 21 04.05 / 70 48 36.82	197 34 59 / 4 57 20	Mon. 433–1 / Mon. 433–3	55.54 / 138.03
Mon. 433–3	45 20 59.60 / 70 48 37.36	184 57 20 / 13 08 21	Mon. 433–2 / Mon. 433–4	138.03 / 45.67
Mon. 433–4	45 20 58.16 / 70 48 37.84	193 08 21 / 352 37 04	Mon. 433–3 / Mon. 433–5	45.67 / 81.40
Mon. 433–5	45 20 55.54 / 70 48 37.36	172 37 04 / 40 07 22	Mon. 433–4 / Mon. 433–6	81.40 / 29.02
Mon. 433–6	45 20 54.82 / 70 48 38.22	220 07 21 / 46 26 05	Mon. 433–5 / Mon. 433–7	29.02 / 65.42
Mon. 433–7	45 20 53.36 / 70 48 40.40	226 26 03 / 37 18 46	Mon. 433–6 / Mon. 434	65.42 / 177.56
Mon. 434	45 20 48.79 / 70 48 45.34	217 18 43 / 37 20 38	Mon. 433–7 / Mon. 434–1	177.56 / 47.43
Mon 434–1	45 20 47.57 / 70 48 46.66	217 20 37 / 65 16 49	Mon. 434 / Mon. 434–2	47.43 / 62.24
Mon. 434–2	45 20 46.72 / 70 48 49.26	245 16 47 / 82 55 23	Mon. 434–1 / Mon. 434–3	62.24 / 179.17
Mon. 434–3	45 20 46.01 / 70 48 57.43	262 55 17 / 74 37 49	Mon. 434–2 / Mon. 434–4	179.17 / 35.35
Mon. 434–4	45 20 45.71 / 70 48 58.99	254 37 48 / 41 32 22	Mon. 434–3 / Mon. 434–5	35.35 / 127.10
Mon. 434–5	45 20 42.62 / 70 49 02.86	221 32 19 / 42 26 23	Mon. 434–4 / Mon. 434–6	127.10 / 50.69
Mon. 434–6	45 20 41.41 / 70 49 04.44	222 26 22 / 27 13 51	Mon. 434–5 / Mon. 434–7	50.69 / 58.45
Mon. 434–7	45 20 39.72 / 70 49 05.66	207 13 50 / 31 51 49	Mon. 434–6 / Mon. 434–8	58.45 / 20.55
Mon. 434–8	45 20 39.16 / 70 49 06.16	211 51 49 / 2 59 23	Mon. 434–7 / Mon. 434–9	20.55 / 34.98
Mon. 434–9	45 20 38.03 / 70 49 06.24	182 59 23 / 359 44 47	Mon. 434–8 / Mon. 434–10	34.98 / 16.62
Mon. 434–10	45 20 37.49 / 70 49 06.24	179 44 47 / 29 09 19	Mon. 434–9 / Mon. 434–11	16.62 / 287.33
Mon. 434–11	45 20 29.36 / 70 49 12.67	209 09 14 / 10 07 43	Mon. 434–10 / Mon. 434–12	287.33 / 86.06
Mon. 434–12	45 20 26.62 / 70 49 13.37	190 07 43 / 8 29 12	Mon. 434–11 / Mon. 434–13	86.06 / 49.85
Mon. 434–13	45 20 25.02 / 70 49 13.70	188 29 12 / 345 01 03	Mon. 434–12 / Mon. 435	49.85 / 38.07
Mon. 435	45 20 23.83 / 70 49 13.25	165 01 03 / 339 55 34	Mon. 434–13 / Mon. 435–1	38.07 / 90.08
Mon. 435–1	45 20 21.09 / 70 49 11.83	159 55 35 / 310 16 11	Mon. 435 / Mon. 435–2	90.08 / 68.27
Mon. 435–2	45 20 19.66 / 70 49 09.44	130 16 13 / 328 57 36	Mon. 435–1 / Mon. 435–3	68.27 / 106.38
Mon. 435–3	45 20 16.71 / 70 49 06.92	148 57 38 / 33 50 39	Mon. 435–2 / Mon. 435–4	106.38 / 42.43
Mon. 435–4	45 20 15.57 / 70 49 08.01	213 50 38 / 13 50 32	Mon. 435–3 / Mon. 435–5	42.43 / 242.61
Mon. 435–5	45 20 07.94 / 70 49 10.67	193 50 30 / 324 32 30	Mon. 435–4 / Mon. 435–6	242.61 / 46.11
Mon. 435–6	45 20 06.72 / 70 49 09.44	144 32 31 / 346 24 22	Mon. 435–5 / Mon. 435–7	46.11 / 88.72
Mon. 435–7	45 20 03.93 / 70 49 08.48	166 24 23 / 351 41 31	Mon. 435–6 / Mon. 435–8	88.72 / 195.82
Mon. 435–8	45 19 57.65 / 70 49 07.19	171 41 32 / 310 25 28	Mon. 435–7 / Mon. 435–9	195.82 / 127.10
Mon. 435–9	45 19 54.98 / 70 49 02.74	130 25 31 / 343 46 04	Mon. 435–8 / Mon. 436	127.10 / 5.54
Mon. 436	45 19 54.81 / 70 49 02.67	163 46 04 / 343 37 43	Mon. 435–9 / Mon. 436–1	5.54 / 119.21
Mon. 436–1	45 19 51.10 / 70 49 01.13	163 37 44 / 290 07 45	Mon. 436 / Mon. 436–2	119.21 / 95.89
Mon. 436–2	45 19 50.03 / 70 48 56.99	110 07 48 / 314 04 34	Mon. 436–1 / Mon. 436–3	95.89 / 84.78
Mon. 436–3	45 19 48.12 / 70 48 54.20	134 04 36 / 348 01 16	Mon. 436–2 / Mon. 436–4	84.78 / 73.69
Mon. 436–4	45 19 45.79 / 70 48 53.50	168 01 16 / 330 00 32	Mon. 436–3 / Mon. 436–5	73.69 / 53.23
Mon. 436–5	45 19 44.30 / 70 48 52.27	150 00 33 / 319 15 22	Mon. 436–4 / Mon. 436–6	53.23 / 123.94
Mon. 436–6	45 19 41.25 / 70 48 48.56	139 15 25 / 296 24 06	Mon. 436–5 / Mon. 436–7	123.94 / 33.98
Mon. 436–7	45 19 40.76 / 70 48 47.16	116 24 07 / 274 08 09	Mon. 436–6 / Mon. 436–8	33.98 / 91.64
Mon. 436–8	45 19 40.54 / 70 48 42.96	94 08 12 / 255 25 14	Mon. 436–7 / Mon. 437	91.64 / 49.62
Mon. 437	45 19 40.96 / 70 48 40.76	75 25 16 / 255 23 59	Mon. 436–8 / Mon. 437–1	49.62 / 177.04
Mon. 437–1	45 19 42.40 / 70 48 32.89	75 24 05 / 315 25 01	Mon. 437 / Mon. 437–2	177.04 / 108.58
Mon. 437–2	45 19 39.90 / 70 48 29.39	135 25 04 / 17 53 02	Mon. 437–1 / Mon. 437–3	108.58 / 49.67

BOUNDARY MONUMENTS—SOURCE OF SOUTHWEST BRANCH OF ST. JOHN TO HEAD OF HALLS STREAM—Continued

Station	Latitude and longitude	Azimuth	To station	Dis-tance (meters)	Station	Latitude and longitude	Azimuth	To station	Dis-tance (meters)
	° ′ ″	° ′ ″				° ′ ″	° ′ ″		
Mon. 437-3	45 19 38.36 / 70 48 30.09	197 53 02 / 21 51 03	Mon. 437-2 / Mon. 437-4	49.67 / 59.06	Mon. 439-7	45 18 32.67 / 70 48 51.03	237 50 41 / 89 05 04	Mon. 439-6 / Mon. 439-8	99.74 / 32.13
Mon. 437-4	45 19 36.59 / 70 48 31.10	201 51 02 / 0 22 08	Mon. 437-3 / Mon. 437-5	59.06 / 194.90	Mon. 439-8	45 18 32.66 / 70 48 52.51	269 05 03 / 27 38 59	Mon. 439-7 / Mon. 439-9	32.13 / 103.72
Mon. 437-5	45 19 30.28 / 70 48 31.16	180 22 08 / 332 43 34	Mon. 437-4 / Mon. 438	194.90 / 87.45	Mon. 439-9	45 18 29.68 / 70 48 54.72	207 38 57 / 327 54 13	Mon. 439-8 / Mon. 439-10	103.72 / 34.88
Mon. 438	45 19 27.76 / 70 48 29.32	152 43 35 / 334 13 24	Mon. 437-5 / Mon. 438-1	87.45 / 74.66	Mon. 439-10	45 18 28.72 / 70 48 53.87	147 54 14 / 340 41 35	Mon. 439-9 / Mon. 439-11	34.88 / 19.28
Mon. 438-1	45 19 25.58 / 70 48 27.83	154 13 25 / 356 26 05	Mon. 438 / Mon. 438-2	74.66 / 80.45	Mon. 439-11	45 18 28.14 / 70 48 53.58	160 41 35 / 298 30 21	Mon. 439-10 / Mon. 439-12	19.28 / 113.21
Mon. 438-2	45 19 22.98 / 70 48 27.60	176 26 05 / 322 26 00	Mon. 438-1 / Mon. 438-3	80.45 / 44.79	Mon. 439-12	45 18 26.38 / 70 48 49.01	118 30 24 / 329 11 15	Mon. 439-11 / Mon. 439-13	113.21 / 18.36
Mon. 438-3	45 19 21.83 / 70 48 26.34	142 26 01 / 336 56 20	Mon. 438-2 / Mon. 438-4	44.79 / 128.90	Mon. 439-13	45 18 25.87 / 70 48 48.58	149 11 16 / 327 09 35	Mon. 439-12 / Mon. 439-14	18.36 / 110.10
Mon. 438-4	45 19 17.99 / 70 48 24.02	156 56 22 / 0 20 41	Mon. 438-3 / Mon. 438-5	128.90 / 41.14	Mon. 439-14	45 18 22.88 / 70 48 45.84	147 09 37 / 338 48 48	Mon. 439-13 / Mon. 440	110.10 / 36.71
Mon. 438-5	45 19 16.66 / 70 48 24.04	180 20 41 / 18 39 51	Mon. 438-4 / Mon. 438-6	41.14 / 45.10	Mon. 440	45 18 21.77 / 70 48 45.23	158 48 48 / 339 03 27	Mon. 439-14 / Mon. 440-1	36.71 / 42.94
Mon. 438-6	45 19 15.27 / 70 48 24.70	198 39 51 / 19 39 53	Mon. 438-5 / Mon. 438-7	45.10 / 36.56	Mon. 440-1	45 18 20.47 / 70 48 44.53	159 03 28 / 10 15 16	Mon. 440 / Mon. 440-2	42.94 / 58.72
Mon. 438-7	45 19 14.16 / 70 48 25.26	199 39 52 / 70 59 53	Mon. 438-6 / Mon. 438-8	36.56 / 23.77	Mon. 440-2	45 18 18.60 / 70 48 45.01	190 15 16 / 348 23 39	Mon. 440-1 / Mon. 440-3	58.72 / 148.63
Mon. 438-8	45 19 13.90 / 70 48 26.30	250 59 52 / 66 41 42	Mon. 438-7 / Mon. 438-9	23.77 / 22.55	Mon. 440-3	45 18 13.88 / 70 48 43.63	168 23 40 / 18 08 43	Mon. 440-2 / Mon. 440-4	148.63 / 91.71
Mon. 438-9	45 19 13.62 / 70 48 27.25	246 41 41 / 1 11 06	Mon. 438-8 / Mon. 438-10	22.55 / 98.42	Mon. 440-4	45 18 11.06 / 70 48 44.94	198 08 42 / 20 32 41	Mon. 440-3 / Mon. 440-5	91.71 / 117.15
Mon. 438-10	45 19 10.43 / 70 48 27.34	181 11 06 / 29 35 27	Mon. 438-9 / Mon. 438-11	98.42 / 36.87	Mon. 440-5	45 18 07.51 / 70 48 46.83	200 32 40 / 42 30 42	Mon. 440-4 / Mon. 440-6	117.15 / 46.15
Mon. 438-11	45 19 09.39 / 70 48 28.18	209 35 27 / 7 25 18	Mon. 438-10 / Mon. 438-12	36.87 / 57.29	Mon. 440-6	45 18 06.40 / 70 48 48.26	222 30 41 / 51 37 56	Mon. 440-5 / Mon. 440-7	46.15 / 70.06
Mon. 438-12	45 19 07.55 / 70 48 28.52	187 25 18 / 29 24 21	Mon. 438-11 / Mon. 438-13	57.29 / 57.59	Mon. 440-7	45 18 05.00 / 70 48 50.78	231 37 54 / 24 44 51	Mon. 440-6 / Mon. 440-8	70.06 / 107.04
Mon. 438-13	45 19 05.93 / 70 48 29.81	209 24 20 / 7 23 53	Mon. 438-12 / Mon. 438-14	57.59 / 184.66	Mon. 440-8	45 18 01.85 / 70 48 52.84	204 44 50 / 51 28 27	Mon. 440-7 / Mon. 440-9	107.04 / 187.91
Mon. 438-14	45 19 00.00 / 70 48 30.91	187 23 52 / 355 56 45	Mon. 438-13 / Mon. 438-15	184.66 / 120.06	Mon. 440-9	45 17 58.06 / 70 48 59.59	231 28 22 / 11 49 49	Mon. 440-8 / Mon. 440-10	187.91 / 52.63
Mon. 438-15	45 18 56.12 / 70 48 30.52	175 56 45 / 11 19 11	Mon. 438-14 / Mon. 438-16	120.06 / 96.29	Mon. 440-10	45 17 56.39 / 70 49 00.08	191 49 48 / 3 52 07	Mon. 440-9 / Mon. 440-11	52.63 / 52.97
Mon. 438-16	45 18 53.06 / 70 48 31.38	191 19 10 / 22 11 33	Mon. 438-15 / Mon. 438-17	96.29 / 137.13	Mon. 440-11	45 17 54.68 / 70 49 00.25	183 52 07 / 20 36 23	Mon. 440-10 / Mon. 440-12	52.97 / 29.71
Mon. 438-17	45 18 48.95 / 70 48 33.76	202 11 31 / 345 12 17	Mon. 438-16 / Mon. 438-18	137.13 / 104.21	Mon. 440-12	45 17 53.77 / 70 49 00.73	200 36 23 / 62 33 59	Mon. 440-11 / Mon. 440-13	29.71 / 61.62
Mon. 438-18	45 18 45.68 / 70 48 32.54	165 12 18 / 357 08 14	Mon. 438-17 / Mon. 438-19	104.21 / 51.19	Mon. 440-13	45 17 52.85 / 70 49 03.24	242 33 57 / 134 15 01	Mon. 440-12 / Mon. 440-14	61.62 / 49.85
Mon. 438-19	45 18 44.03 / 70 48 32.42	177 08 14 / 359 27 05	Mon. 438-18 / Mon. 438-20	51.19 / 36.09	Mon. 440-14	45 17 53.98 / 70 49 04.88	314 15 00 / 165 57 47	Mon. 440-13 / Mon. 440-15	49.85 / 42.37
Mon. 438-20	45 18 42.86 / 70 48 32.41	179 27 05 / 42 21 57	Mon. 438-19 / Mon. 439	36.09 / 15.24	Mon. 440-15	45 17 55.31 / 70 49 05.35	345 57 47 / 95 19 38	Mon. 440-14 / Mon. 441	42.37 / 35.17
Mon. 439	45 18 42.49 / 70 48 32.88	222 21 57 / 42 18 48	Mon. 438-20 / Mon. 439-1	15.24 / 28.46	Mon. 441	45 17 55.42 / 70 49 06.95	275 19 36 / 95 19 46	Mon. 440-15 / Mon. 441-1	35.17 / 52.11
Mon. 439-1	45 18 41.81 / 70 48 33.76	222 18 47 / 78 11 13	Mon. 439 / Mon. 439-2	28.46 / 108.93	Mon. 441-1	45 17 55.58 / 70 49 09.33	275 19 44 / 120 18 32	Mon. 441 / Mon. 441-2	52.11 / 58.20
Mon. 439-2	45 18 41.09 / 70 48 38.65	258 11 10 / 46 00 46	Mon. 439-1 / Mon. 439-3	108.93 / 61.50	Mon. 441-2	45 17 56.53 / 70 49 11.64	300 18 30 / 62 56 38	Mon. 441-1 / Mon. 441-3	58.20 / 96.90
Mon. 439-3	45 18 39.70 / 70 48 40.68	226 00 45 / 47 35 16	Mon. 439-2 / Mon. 439-4	61.50 / 62.11	Mon. 441-3	45 17 55.10 / 70 49 15.60	242 56 35 / 58 36 58	Mon. 441-2 / Mon. 441-4	96.90 / 49.67
Mon. 439-4	45 18 38.35 / 70 48 42.79	227 35 14 / 32 44 10	Mon. 439-3 / Mon. 439-5	62.11 / 76.49	Mon. 441-4	45 17 54.26 / 70 49 17.55	238 36 57 / 87 01 28	Mon. 441-3 / Mon. 441-5	49.67 / 68.56
Mon. 439-5	45 18 36.26 / 70 48 44.68	212 44 09 / 43 02 20	Mon. 439-4 / Mon. 439-6	76.49 / 78.94	Mon. 441-5	45 17 54.14 / 70 49 20.69	267 01 26 / 53 30 59	Mon. 441-4 / Mon. 441-6	68.56 / 51.19
Mon. 439-6	45 18 34.39 / 70 48 47.16	223 02 18 / 57 50 44	Mon. 439-5 / Mon. 439-7	78.94 / 99.74	Mon. 441-6	45 17 53.16 / 70 49 22.58	233 30 58 / 65 50 13	Mon. 441-5 / Mon. 441-7	51.19 / 35.35

BOUNDARY MONUMENTS—SOURCE OF SOUTHWEST BRANCH OF ST. JOHN TO HEAD OF HALLS STREAM—Continued

Station	Latitude and longitude	Azimuth	To station	Distance (meters)
Mon. 441-7	45 17 52.69 / 70 49 24.06	245 50 12 / 32 14 03	Mon. 441-6 / Mon. 441-8	35.35 / 27.73
Mon. 441-8	45 17 51.93 / 70 49 24.74	212 14 03 / 76 23 16	Mon. 441-7 / Mon. 441-9	27.73 / 34.43
Mon. 441-9	45 17 51.67 / 70 49 26.27	256 23 15 / 131 41 08	Mon. 441-8 / Mon. 441-10	34.43 / 65.21
Mon. 441-10	45 17 53.07 / 70 49 28.51	311 41 06 / 81 38 20	Mon. 441-9 / Mon. 441-11	65.21 / 79.05
Mon. 441-11	45 17 52.70 / 70 49 32.10	261 38 17 / 48 31 07	Mon. 441-10 / Mon. 442	79.05 / 104.52
Mon. 442	45 17 50.46 / 70 49 35.69	228 31 04 / 44 33 58	Mon. 441-11 / Mon. 442-1	104.52 / 74.92
Mon. 442-1	45 17 48.73 / 70 49 38.10	224 33 56 / 67 20 07	Mon. 442 / Mon. 442-2	74.92 / 27.36
Mon. 442-2	45 17 48.39 / 70 49 39.26	247 20 06 / 94 39 24	Mon. 442-1 / Mon. 442-3	27.36 / 44.40
Mon. 442-3	45 17 48.51 / 70 49 41.29	274 39 23 / 55 49 48	Mon. 442-2 / Mon. 442-4	44.40 / 85.05
Mon. 442-4	45 17 46.96 / 70 49 44.52	235 49 46 / 91 15 36	Mon. 442-3 / Mon. 442-5	85.05 / 41.00
Mon. 442-5	45 17 46.99 / 70 49 46.40	271 15 35 / 62 24 50	Mon. 442-4 / Mon. 442-6	41.00 / 44.63
Mon. 442-6	45 17 46.32 / 70 49 48.22	242 24 48 / 36 35 15	Mon. 442-5 / Mon. 442-7	44.63 / 44.67
Mon. 442-7	45 17 45.16 / 70 49 49.44	216 35 14 / 57 32 29	Mon. 442-6 / Mon. 442-8	44.67 / 60.41
Mon. 442-8	45 17 44.11 / 70 49 51.78	237 32 27 / 67 35 18	Mon. 442-7 / Mon. 442-9	60.41 / 19.32
Mon. 442-9	45 17 43.87 / 70 49 52.60	247 35 18 / 61 49 18	Mon. 442-8 / Mon. 442-10	19.32 / 36.69
Mon. 442-10	45 17 43.31 / 70 49 54.08	241 49 17 / 79 51 48	Mon. 442-9 / Mon. 442-11	36.69 / 41.56
Mon. 442-11	45 17 43.07 / 70 49 55.96	259 51 47 / 74 38 46	Mon. 442-10 / Mon. 442-12	41.56 / 89.83
Mon. 442-12	45 17 42.30 / 70 49 59.94	254 38 43 / 88 08 03	Mon. 442-11 / Mon. 442-13	89.83 / 40.28
Mon. 442-13	45 17 42.26 / 70 50 01.79	268 08 02 / 45 02 08	Mon. 442-12 / Mon. 442-14	40.28 / 116.34
Mon. 442-14	45 17 39.59 / 70 50 05.56	225 02 05 / 59 35 02	Mon. 442-13 / Mon. 442-15	116.34 / 63.03
Mon. 442-15	45 17 38.56 / 70 50 08.06	239 35 00 / 91 51 45	Mon. 442-14 / Mon. 442-16	63.03 / 36.69
Mon. 442-16	45 17 38.60 / 70 50 09.74	271 51 44 / 24 20 29	Mon. 442-15 / Mon. 443	36.69 / 16.48
Mon. 443	45 17 38.11 / 70 50 10.05	204 20 29 / 25 27 23	Mon. 442-16 / Mon. 443-1	16.48 / 28.88
Mon. 443-1	45 17 37.27 / 70 50 10.62	205 27 23 / 319 28 58	Mon. 443 / Mon. 443-2	28.88 / 53.88
Mon. 443-2	45 17 35.94 / 70 50 09.02	139 28 59 / 304 11 42	Mon. 443-1 / Mon. 443-3	53.88 / 50.23
Mon. 443-3	45 17 35.03 / 70 50 07.11	124 11 43 / 324 40 38	Mon. 443-2 / Mon. 443-4	50.23 / 55.39
Mon. 443-4	45 17 33.56 / 70 50 05.64	144 40 39 / 315 02 06	Mon. 443-3 / Mon. 443-5	55.39 / 56.62
Mon. 443-5	45 17 32.26 / 70 50 03.80	135 02 07 / 317 57 14	Mon. 443-4 / Mon. 443-6	56.62 / 87.72
Mon. 443-6	45 17 30.15 / 70 50 01.11	137 57 16 / 321 04 56	Mon. 443-5 / Mon. 443-7	87.72 / 67.89
Mon. 443-7	45 17 28.44 / 70 49 59.15	141 04 57 / 296 05 05	Mon. 443-6 / Mon. 443-8	67.89 / 64.26
Mon. 443-8	45 17 27.53 / 70 49 56.50	116 05 07 / 259 47 45	Mon. 443-7 / Mon. 443-9	64.26 / 83.49
Mon. 443-9	45 17 28.01 / 70 49 52.73	79 47 48 / 302 53 11	Mon. 443-8 / Mon. 443-10	83.49 / 59.11
Mon. 443-10	45 17 26.97 / 70 49 50.45	122 53 13 / 348 05 46	Mon. 443-9 / Mon. 443-11	59.11 / 63.30
Mon. 443-11	45 17 24.96 / 70 49 49.86	168 05 46 / 351 33 13	Mon. 443-10 / Mon. 443-12	63.30 / 47.75
Mon. 443-12	45 17 23.43 / 70 49 49.53	171 33 13 / 355 09 56	Mon. 443-11 / Mon. 443-13	47.75 / 118.66
Mon. 443-13	45 17 19.60 / 70 49 49.07	175 09 56 / 6 13 57	Mon. 443-12 / Mon. 443-14	118.66 / 206.78
Mon. 443-14	45 17 12.94 / 70 49 50.10	186 13 56 / 15 53 07	Mon. 443-13 / Mon. 443-15	206.78 / 77.21
Mon. 443-15	45 17 10.54 / 70 49 51.07	195 53 07 / 20 00 55	Mon. 443-14 / Mon. 444	77.21 / 137.33
Mon. 444	45 17 06.36 / 70 49 53.23	200 00 54 / 12 48 41	Mon. 443-15 / Mon. 444-1	137.33 / 93.06
Mon. 444-1	45 17 03.42 / 70 49 54.18	192 48 40 / 5 55 35	Mon. 444 / Mon. 444-2	93.06 / 263.77
Mon. 444-2	45 16 54.92 / 70 49 55.43	185 55 34 / 5 33 06	Mon. 444-1 / Mon. 444-3	263.77 / 326.52
Mon. 444-3	45 16 44.39 / 70 49 56.88	185 33 05 / 61 36 34	Mon. 444-2 / Mon. 444-4	326.52 / 74.10
Mon. 444-4	45 16 43.25 / 70 49 59.87	241 36 32 / 49 21 38	Mon. 444-3 / Mon. 444-5	74.10 / 112.23
Mon. 444-5	45 16 40.88 / 70 50 03.77	229 21 35 / 51 37 47	Mon. 444-4 / Mon. 444-6	112.23 / 67.91
Mon. 444-6	45 16 39.52 / 70 50 06.22	231 37 45 / 42 05 15	Mon. 444-5 / Mon. 444-7	67.91 / 204.13
Mon. 444-7	45 16 34.61 / 70 50 12.49	222 05 11 / 36 30 15	Mon. 444-6 / Mon. 444-8	204.13 / 29.86
Mon. 444-8	45 16 33.83 / 70 50 13.31	216 30 15 / 2 43 38	Mon. 444-7 / Mon. 444-9	29.86 / 81.85
Mon. 444-9	45 16 31.18 / 70 50 13.49	182 43 38 / 55 59 18	Mon. 444-8 / Mon. 444-10	81.85 / 52.94
Mon. 444-10	45 16 30.22 / 70 50 15.50	235 59 16 / 16 35 28	Mon. 444-9 / Mon. 444-11	52.94 / 143.27
Mon. 444-11	45 16 25.78 / 70 50 17.38	196 35 27 / 8 04 49	Mon. 444-10 / Mon. 444-11	143.27 / 53.20
Mon. 444-12	45 16 24.07 / 70 50 17.72	188 04 49 / 4 48 03	Mon. 444-11 / Mon. 444-13	53.20 / 75.96
Mon. 444-13	45 16 21.62 / 70 50 18.01	184 48 03 / 14 41 01	Mon. 444-12 / Mon. 444-14	75.96 / 157.69
Mon. 444-14	45 16 16.68 / 70 50 19.85	194 41 00 / 21 20 39	Mon. 444-13 / Mon. 444-15	157.69 / 197.58
Mon. 444-15	45 16 10.72 / 70 50 23.14	201 20 36 / 5 28 49	Mon. 444-14 / Mon. 444-16	197.58 / 59.12
Mon. 444-16	45 16 08.81 / 70 50 23.40	185 28 49 / 37 36 47	Mon. 444-15 / Mon. 445	59.12 / 75.16
Mon. 445	45 16 06.88 / 70 50 25.51	217 36 45 / 37 40 15	Mon. 444-16 / Mon. 445-1	75.16 / 126.71
Mon. 445-1	45 16 03.63 / 70 50 29.06	217 40 13 / 20 10 58	Mon. 445 / Mon. 445-2	126.71 / 40.17
Mon. 445-2	45 16 02.41 / 70 50 29.70	200 10 58 / 36 29 12	Mon. 445-1 / Mon. 445-3	40.17 / 32.37
Mon. 445-3	45 16 01.57 / 70 50 30.58	216 29 11 / 44 20 13	Mon. 445-2 / Mon. 445-4	32.37 / 136.48
Mon. 445-4	45 15 58.41 / 70 50 34.95	224 20 10 / 50 42 06	Mon. 445-3 / Mon. 445-5	136.48 / 137.70
Mon. 445-5	45 15 55.58 / 70 50 39.84	230 42 03 / 66 38 00	Mon. 445-4 / Mon. 445-6	137.70 / 207.53
Mon. 445-6	45 15 52.92 / 70 50 48.58	246 37 54 / 50 42 37	Mon. 445-5 / Mon. 446	207.53 / 8.24

BOUNDARY MONUMENTS—SOURCE OF SOUTHWEST BRANCH OF ST. JOHN TO HEAD OF HALLS STREAM—Continued

Station	Latitude and longitude	Azimuth	To station	Distance (meters)	Station	Latitude and longitude	Azimuth	To station	Distance (meters)
	° ′ ″	° ′ ″				° ′ ″	° ′ ″		
Mon. 446	45 15 52.75	230 42 37	Mon 445-6	8.24	Mon. 449-6	45 14 14.25	99 54 17	Mon. 449-5	46.67
	70 50 48.87	51 11 49	Mon. 446-1	215.56		70 50 19.04	265 14 21	Mon. 449-7	77.77
Mon. 446-1	45 15 48.37	231 11 43	Mon. 446	215.56	Mon. 449-7	45 14 14.46	85 14 23	Mon. 449-6	77.77
	70 50 56.58	52 19 49	Mon. 446-2	46.49		70 50 15.49	260 21 51	Mon. 449-8	33.58
Mon. 446-2	45 15 47.45	232 19 48	Mon. 446-1	46.49	Mon. 449-8	45 14 14.64	80 21 52	Mon. 449-7	33.58
	70 50 58.27	336 55 52	Mon. 446-3	60.57		70 50 13.97	347 05 54	Mon. 450	0.59
Mon. 446-3	45 15 45.64	156 55 53	Mon. 446-2	60.57	Mon. 450	45 14 14.62	167 05 54	Mon. 449-8	0.59
	70 50 57.18	344 56 37	Mon. 446-4	71.29		70 50 13.96	352 39 38	Mon. 450-1	43.06
Mon. 446-4	45 15 43.42	164 56 38	Mon. 446-3	71.29	Mon. 450-1	45 14 13.24	172 39 38	Mon. 450	43.06
	70 50 56.33	355 51 12	Mon. 446-5	99.09		70 50 13.71	20 42 57	Mon. 450-2	180.50
Mon. 446-5	45 15 40.21	175 51 12	Mon. 446-4	99.09	Mon. 450-2	45 14 07.77	200 42 55	Mon. 450-1	180.50
	70 50 56.00	347 50 31	Mon. 446-6	60.54		70 50 16.64	19 21 24	Mon. 450-3	48.56
Mon. 446-6	45 15 38.30	167 50 31	Mon. 446-5	60.54	Mon. 450-3	45 14 06.28	199 21 23	Mon. 450-2	48.56
	70 50 55.41	358 41 34	Mon. 446-7	179.48		70 50 17.38	42 36 47	Mon. 450-4	55.89
Mon. 446-7	45 15 32.48	178 41 34	Mon. 446-6	179.48	Mon. 450-4	45 14 04.95	222 36 46	Mon. 450-3	55.89
	70 50 55.23	20 26 46	Mon. 446-8	290.15		70 50 19.11	67 48 20	Mon. 450-5	116.36
Mon. 446-8	45 15 23.68	200 26 43	Mon. 446-7	290.15	Mon. 450-5	45 14 03.53	247 48 17	Mon. 450-4	116.36
	70 50 59.88	15 25 35	Mon. 446-9	67.06		70 50 24.05	77 18 26	Mon. 450-6	80.93
Mon. 446-9	45 15 21.58	195 25 34	Mon. 446-8	67.06	Mon. 450-6	45 14 02.95	257 18 23	Mon. 450-5	80.93
	70 51 00.69	328 01 20	Mon. 447	163.40		70 50 27.67	98 06 09	Mon. 450-7	87.96
Mon. 447	45 15 17.09	148 01 23	Mon. 446-9	163.40	Mon. 450-7	45 14 03.35	278 06 06	Mon. 450-6	87.96
	70 50 56.72	325 33 24	Mon. 447-1	36.19		70 50 31.66	102 55 40	Mon. 450-8	148.57
Mon 447-1	45 15 16.13	145 33 25	Mon. 447	36.19	Mon. 450-8	45 14 04.43	282 55 35	Mon. 450-7	148.57
	70 50 55.79	310 07 00	Mon. 447-2	174.12		70 50 38.30	87 21 17	Mon. 450-9	215.51
Mon. 447-2	45 15 12.49	130 07 04	Mon. 447-1	174.12	Mon. 450-9	45 14 04.11	267 21 10	Mon. 450-8	215.51
	70 50 49.68	357 08 48	Mon. 447-3	41.04		70 50 48.17	54 25 56	Mon. 450-10	123.08
Mon. 447-3	45 15 11.16	177 08 48	Mon. 447-2	41.04	Mon. 450-10	45 14 01.79	234 25 53	Mon. 450-9	123.08
	70 50 49.58	17 41 53	Mon. 447-4	47.43		70 50 52.76	63 10 39	Mon. 450-11	77.88
Mon. 447-4	45 15 09.70	197 41 52	Mon. 447-3	47.43	Mon. 450-11	45 14 00.65	243 10 37	Mon. 450-10	77.88
	70 50 50.25	17 37 45	Mon. 447-5	343.37		70 50 55.94	60 46 09	Mon. 450-12	129.92
Mon. 447-5	45 14 59.10	197 37 42	Mon. 447-4	343.37	Mon. 450-12	45 13 58.60	240 46 05	Mon. 450-11	129.92
	70 50 55.02	352 23 23	Mon. 447-6	56.28		70 51 01.14	62 58 19	Mon. 450-13	76.96
Mon. 447-6	45 14 57.29	172 23 23	Mon. 447-5	56.28	Mon. 450-13	45 13 57.46	242 58 17	Mon. 450-12	76.96
	70 50 54.67	12 45 14	Mon. 447-7	139.60		70 51 04.29	47 58 51	Mon. 450-14	60.77
Mon. 447-7	45 14 52.88	192 45 13	Mon. 447-6	139.60	Mon. 450-14	45 13 56.15	227 58 50	Mon. 450-13	60.77
	70 50 56.09	12 45 43	Mon. 448	125.94		70 51 06.36	71 15 33	Mon. 451	23.52
Mon. 448	45 14 48.90	192 45 42	Mon. 447-7	125.94	Mon. 451	45 13 55.90	251 15 32	Mon. 450-14	23.52
	70 50 57.36	11 08 52	Mon. 448-1	34.07		70 51 07.38	71 33 05	Mon. 451-1	51.45
Mon. 448-1	45 14 47.82	191 08 52	Mon. 448	34.07	Mon. 451-1	45 13 55.38	251 33 03	Mon. 451	51.45
	70 50 57.66	355 40 40	Mon. 448-2	150.39		70 51 09.62	72 09 03	Mon. 451-2	53.57
Mon. 448-2	45 14 42.96	175 40 40	Mon. 448-1	150.39	Mon. 451-2	45 13 54.84	252 09 01	Mon. 451-1	53.57
	70 50 57.14	341 20 38	Mon. 448-3	98.18		70 51 11.95	77 04 01	Mon. 451-3	39.96
Mon. 448-3	45 14 39.95	161 20 39	Mon. 448-2	98.18	Mon. 451-3	45 13 54.55	257 04 00	Mon. 451-2	39.96
	70 50 55.70	318 26 29	Mon. 448-4	220.83		70 51 13.74	48 23 00	Mon. 451-4	78.36
Mon. 448-4	45 14 34.60	138 26 34	Mon. 448-3	220.83	Mon. 451-4	45 13 52.87	228 22 58	Mon. 451-3	78.36
	70 50 48.99	307 51 04	Mon. 448-5	172.00		70 51 16.42	50 15 58	Mon. 451-5	133.02
Mon. 448-5	45 14 31.18	127 51 08	Mon. 448-4	172.00	Mon. 451-5	45 13 50.11	230 15 55	Mon. 451-4	133.02
	70 50 42.76	334 34 01	Mon. 448-6	37.41		70 51 21.11	68 49 25	Mon. 451-6	44.79
Mon. 448-6	45 14 30.08	154 34 01	Mon. 448-5	37.41	Mon. 451-6	45 13 49.59	248 49 24	Mon. 451-5	44.79
	70 50 42.02	326 17 45	Mon. 449	114.97		70 51 23.03	50 04 24	Mon. 451-7	76.54
Mon. 449	45 14 26.98	146 17 47	Mon. 448-6	114.97	Mon. 451-7	45 13 48.00	230 04 22	Mon. 451-6	76.54
	70 50 39.10	326 17 05	Mon. 449-1	41.35		70 51 25.72	357 39 22	Mon. 451-8	31.19
Mon. 449-1	45 14 25.87	146 17 06	Mon. 449	41.35	Mon. 451-8	45 13 46.99	177 39 22	Mon. 451-7	31.19
	70 50 38.05	303 48 36	Mon. 449-2	127.11		70 51 25.66	54 44 22	Mon. 451-9	94.48
Mon. 449-2	45 14 23.58	123 48 39	Mon. 449-1	127.11	Mon. 451-9	45 13 45.22	234 44 19	Mon. 451-8	94.48
	70 50 33.21	326 38 36	Mon. 449-3	72.38		70 51 29.20	92 25 19	Mon. 451-10	51.92
Mon. 449-3	45 14 21.62	146 38 37	Mon. 449-2	72.38	Mon. 451-10	45 13 45.29	272 25 17	Mon. 451-9	51.92
	70 50 31.38	317 30 01	Mon. 449-4	257.21		70 51 31.57	112 38 17	Mon. 451-11	60.80
Mon. 449-4	45 14 15.48	137 30 07	Mon. 449-3	257.21	Mon. 451-11	45 13 46.05	292 38 15	Mon. 451-10	60.80
	70 50 23.42	301 11 03	Mon. 449-5	57.83		70 51 34.15	106 03 15	Mon. 451-12	232.08
Mon. 449-5	45 14 14.51	121 11 05	Mon. 449-4	57.83	Mon. 451-12	45 13 48.13	286 03 08	Mon. 451-11	232.08
	70 50 21.15	279 54 15	Mon. 449-6	46.67		70 51 44.37	130 12 08	Mon. 451-13	54.83

BOUNDARY MONUMENTS—SOURCE OF SOUTHWEST BRANCH OF ST. JOHN TO HEAD OF HALLS STREAM—Continued

Station	Latitude and longitude	Azimuth	To station	Distance (meters)	Station	Latitude and longitude	Azimuth	To station	Distance (meters)
	° ′ ″	° ′ ″				° ′ ″	° ′ ″		
Mon. 451-13	45 13 49.28 / 70 51 46.29	310 12 07 / 127 57 07	Mon. 451-12 / Mon. 451-14	54.83 / 121.99	Mon. 455-1	45 14 28.28 / 70 53 45.92	345 57 15 / 121 53 45	Mon. 455 / Mon. 455-2	34.46 / 77.95
Mon. 451-14	45 13 51.71 / 70 51 50.70	307 57 04 / 109 35 04	Mon. 451-13 / Mon. 451-15	121.99 / 105.61	Mon. 455-2	45 14 29.61 / 70 53 48.95	301 53 43 / 133 24 56	Mon. 455-1 / Mon. 455-3	77.95 / 63.92
Mon. 451-15	45 13 52.86 / 70 51 55.26	289 35 01 / 96 29 01	Mon. 451-14 / Mon. 451-16	105.61 / 150.59	Mon. 455-3	45 14 31.04 / 70 53 51.08	313 24 54 / 208 10 57	Mon. 455-2 / Mon. 455-4	63.92 / 38.99
Mon. 451-16	45 13 53.41 / 70 52 02.12	276 28 56 / 112 45 56	Mon. 451-15 / Mon. 451-17	150.59 / 196.29	Mon. 455-4	45 14 32.15 / 70 53 50.24	28 10 58 / 219 04 47	Mon. 455-3 / Mon. 455-5	38.99 / 45.31
Mon. 451-17	45 13 55.87 / 70 52 10.42	292 45 50 / 120 47 50	Mon. 451-16 / Mon. 451-18	196.29 / 96.26	Mon. 455-5	45 14 33.29 / 70 53 48.93	39 04 48 / 162 29 15	Mon. 455-4 / Mon. 455-6	45.31 / 63.12
Mon. 451-18	45 13 57.46 / 70 52 14.21	300 47 47 / 113 59 47	Mon. 451-17 / Mon. 451-19	96.26 / 69.62	Mon. 455-6	45 14 35.24 / 70 53 49.80	342 29 14 / 99 01 38	Mon. 455-5 / Mon. 455-7	63.12 / 93.30
Mon. 451-19	45 13 58.38 / 70 52 17.12	293 59 45 / 118 37 45	Mon. 451-18 / Mon. 451-20	69.62 / 168.53	Mon. 455-7	45 14 35.71 / 70 53 54.02	279 01 35 / 146 56 08	Mon. 455-6 / Mon. 455-8	93.30 / 37.69
Mon. 451-20	45 14 01.00 / 70 52 23.90	298 37 40 / 113 01 40	Mon. 451-19 / Mon. 451-21	168.53 / 178.89	Mon. 455-8	45 14 36.74 / 70 53 54.97	326 56 07 / 165 49 38	Mon. 455-7 / Mon. 455-9	37.69 / 72.59
Mon. 451-21	45 14 03.26 / 70 52 31.45	293 01 35 / 69 18 35	Mon. 451-20 / Mon. 452	178.89 / 2.42	Mon. 455-9	45 14 39.02 / 70 53 55.78	345 49 37 / 185 21 02	Mon. 455-8 / Mon. 455-10	72.59 / 250.31
Mon. 452	45 14 03.23 / 70 52 31.56	249 18 35 / 69 16 43	Mon. 451-21 / Mon. 452-1	2.42 / 134.12	Mon. 455-10	45 14 47.09 / 70 53 54.71	5 21 03 / 193 35 42	Mon. 455-9 / Mon. 455-11	250.31 / 68.10
Mon. 452-1	45 14 01.70 / 70 52 37.31	249 16 39 / 74 01 01	Mon. 452 / Mon. 452-2	134.12 / 54.28	Mon. 455-11	45 14 49.23 / 70 53 53.98	13 35 43 / 186 02 14	Mon. 455-10 / Mon. 455-12	68.10 / 148.02
Mon. 452-2	45 14 01.21 / 70 52 39.70	254 00 59 / 83 41 38	Mon. 452-1 / Mon. 452-3	54.28 / 193.19	Mon. 455-12	45 14 54.00 / 70 53 53.26	6 02 14 / 208 04 35	Mon. 455-11 / Mon. 455-13	148.02 / 105.73
Mon. 452-3	45 14 00.53 / 70 52 48.50	263 41 32 / 134 46 04	Mon. 452-2 / Mon. 452-4	193.19 / 140.13	Mon. 455-13	45 14 57.02 / 70 53 50.98	28 04 37 / 200 31 03	Mon. 455-12 / Mon. 456	105.73 / 191.68
Mon. 452-4	45 14 03.72 / 70 52 53.06	314 46 01 / 89 05 50	Mon. 452-3 / Mon. 452-5	140.13 / 158.42	Mon. 456	45 15 02.84 / 70 53 47.90	20 31 05 / 205 52 48	Mon. 455-13 / Mon. 456-1	191.68 / 60.19
Mon. 452-5	45 14 03.64 / 70 53 00.32	269 05 45 / 157 14 29	Mon. 452-4 / Mon. 452-6	158.42 / 103.13	Mon. 456-1	45 15 04.59 / 70 53 46.70	25 52 49 / 200 58 49	Mon. 456 / Mon. 456-2	60.19 / 127.86
Mon. 452-6	45 14 06.72 / 70 53 02.15	337 14 28 / 69 26 43	Mon. 452-5 / Mon. 453	103.13 / 80.32	Mon. 456-2	45 15 08.46 / 70 53 44.60	20 58 50 / 149 34 50	Mon. 456-1 / Mon. 456-3	127.86 / 94.26
Mon. 453	45 14 05.81 / 70 53 05.60	249 26 40 / 90 04 04	Mon. 452-6 / Mon. 453-1	80.32 / 33.26	Mon. 456-3	45 15 11.09 / 70 53 46.78	329 34 48 / 118 19 18	Mon. 456-2 / Mon. 456-4	94.26 / 69.40
Mon. 453-1	45 14 05.81 / 70 53 07.12	270 04 03 / 140 23 14	Mon. 453 / Mon. 453-2	33.26 / 79.90	Mon. 456-4	45 15 12.16 / 70 53 49.59	298 19 16 / 136 46 16	Mon. 456-3 / Mon. 456-5	69.40 / 174.15
Mon. 453-2	45 14 07.80 / 70 53 09.46	320 23 12 / 126 37 51	Mon. 453-1 / Mon. 453-3	79.90 / 156.36	Mon. 456-5	45 15 16.27 / 70 53 55.06	316 46 12 / 155 34 12	Mon. 456-4 / Mon. 456-6	174.15 / 51.78
Mon. 453-3	45 14 10.82 / 70 53 15.21	306 37 47 / 139 15 10	Mon. 453-2 / Mon. 453-4	156.36 / 63.03	Mon. 456-6	45 15 17.79 / 70 53 56.04	335 34 11 / 173 51 11	Mon. 456-5 / Mon. 456-7	51.78 / 33.77
Mon. 453-4	45 14 12.37 / 70 53 17.10	319 15 09 / 137 21 13	Mon. 453-3 / Mon. 453-5	63.03 / 179.00	Mon. 456-7	45 15 18.88 / 70 53 56.20	353 51 11 / 203 19 11	Mon. 456-6 / Mon. 456-8	33.77 / 49.80
Mon. 453-5	45 14 16.64 / 70 53 22.66	317 21 09 / 167 10 31	Mon. 453-4 / Mon. 453-6	179.00 / 95.32	Mon. 456-8	45 15 20.36 / 70 53 55.30	23 19 12 / 162 51 12	Mon. 456-7 / Mon. 456-9	49.80 / 61.07
Mon. 453-6	45 14 19.65 / 70 53 23.63	347 10 30 / 111 14 50	Mon. 453-5 / Mon. 454	95.32 / 20.94	Mon. 456-9	45 15 22.25 / 70 53 56.13	342 51 11 / 180 40 11	Mon. 456-8 / Mon. 456-10	61.07 / 209.31
Mon. 454	45 14 19.90 / 70 53 24.52	291 14 50 / 109 25 15	Mon. 453-6 / Mon. 454-1	20.94 / 117.81	Mon. 456-10	45 15 29.03 / 70 53 56.02	0 40 11 / 156 50 11	Mon. 456-9 / Mon. 456-11	209.31 / 16.36
Mon. 454-1	45 14 21.16 / 70 53 29.61	289 25 11 / 79 16 12	Mon. 454 / Mon. 454-2	117.81 / 91.71	Mon. 456-11	45 15 29.52 / 70 53 56.31	336 50 11 / 160 56 11	Mon. 456-10 / Mon. 456-12	16.36 / 25.55
Mon. 454-2	45 14 20.61 / 70 53 33.74	259 16 09 / 90 45 52	Mon. 454-1 / Mon. 454-3	91.71 / 38.42	Mon. 456-12	45 15 30.30 / 70 53 56.69	340 56 11 / 145 02 11	Mon. 456-11 / Mon. 457	25.55 / 10.00
Mon. 454-3	45 14 20.63 / 70 53 35.50	270 45 51 / 132 35 52	Mon. 454-2 / Mon. 454-4	38.42 / 122.68	Mon. 457	45 15 30.57 / 70 53 56.96	325 02 11 / 136 45 46	Mon. 456-12 / Mon. 457-1	10.00 / 37.90
Mon. 454-4	45 14 23.32 / 70 53 39.64	312 35 49 / 123 52 50	Mon. 454-3 / Mon. 454-5	122.68 / 50.60	Mon. 457-1	45 15 31.46 / 70 53 58.15	316 45 45 / 98 58 30	Mon. 457 / Mon. 457-2	37.90 / 99.84
Mon. 454-5	45 14 24.23 / 70 53 41.57	303 52 49 / 123 32 25	Mon. 454-4 / Mon. 454-6	50.60 / 70.38	Mon. 457-2	45 15 31.96 / 70 54 02.67	278 58 27 / 134 47 49	Mon. 457-1 / Mon. 457-3	99.84 / 165.53
Mon. 454-6	45 14 25.49 / 70 53 44.26	303 32 23 / 152 09 34	Mon. 454-5 / Mon. 455	70.38 / 59.47	Mon. 457-3	45 15 35.74 / 70 54 08.06	314 47 45 / 121 16 03	Mon. 457-2 / Mon. 457-4	165.53 / 53.97
Mon. 455	45 14 27.20 / 70 53 45.54	332 09 33 / 165 57 15	Mon. 454-6 / Mon. 455-1	59.47 / 34.46	Mon. 457-4	45 15 36.65 / 70 54 10.17	301 16 01 / 126 47 51	Mon. 457-3 / Mon. 457-5	53.97 / 105.85

BOUNDARY MONUMENTS—SOURCE OF SOUTHWEST BRANCH OF ST. JOHN TO HEAD OF HALLS STREAM—Continued

Station	Latitude and longitude	Azimuth	To station	Distance (meters)	Station	Latitude and longitude	Azimuth	To station	Distance (meters)
	° ′ ″	° ′ ″				° ′ ″	° ′ ″		
Mon. 457-5	45 15 38.70 / 70 54 14.06	306 47 48 / 81 07 40	Mon. 457-4 / Mon. 457-6	105.85 / 108.68	Mon. 460-4	45 16 38.72 / 70 55 01.15	2 41 21 / 120 05 37	Mon. 460-3 / Mon. 460-5	69.64 / 38.40
Mon. 457-6	45 15 38.16 / 70 54 18.98	261 07 37 / 122 56 57	Mon. 457-5 / Mon. 457-7	108.68 / 43.02	Mon. 460-5	45 16 39.35 / 70 55 02.68	300 05 36 / 107 10 12	Mon. 460-4 / Mon. 460-6	38.40 / 151.00
Mon. 457-7	45 15 38.92 / 70 54 20.64	302 56 56 / 101 11 49	Mon. 457-6 / Mon. 457-8	43.02 / 58.43	Mon. 460-6	45 16 40.79 / 70 55 09.29	287 10 07 / 114 36 53	Mon. 460-5 / Mon. 460-7	151.00 / 54.37
Mon. 457-8	45 15 39.29 / 70 54 23.27	281 11 47 / 142 30 49	Mon. 457-7 / Mon. 457-9	58.43 / 102.75	Mon. 460-7	45 16 41.53 / 70 55 11.56	294 36 51 / 119 10 02	Mon. 460-6 / Mon. 460-8	54.37 / 162.81
Mon. 457-9	45 15 41.93 / 70 54 26.14	322 30 47 / 210 45 39	Mon. 457-8 / Mon. 457-10	102.75 / 74.88	Mon. 460-8	45 16 44.10 / 70 55 18.08	299 09 57 / 158 23 11	Mon. 460-7 / Mon. 460-9	162.81 / 47.43
Mon. 457-10	45 15 44.01 / 70 54 24.38	30 45 40 / 196 04 12	Mon. 457-9 / Mon. 457-11	74.88 / 75.76	Mon. 460-9	45 16 45.52 / 70 55 18.88	338 23 10 / 169 39 31	Mon. 460-8 / Mon. 460-10	47.43 / 148.13
Mon. 457-11	45 15 46.37 / 70 54 23.42	16 04 13 / 179 56 38	Mon. 457-10 / Mon. 457-12	75.76 / 57.49	Mon. 460-10	45 16 50.24 / 70 55 20.10	349 39 30 / 237 22 24	Mon. 460-9 / Mon. 460-11	148.13 / 85.74
Mon. 457-12	45 15 48.23 / 70 54 23.42	359 56 38 / 190 58 10	Mon. 457-11 / Mon. 457-13	57.49 / 54.52	Mon. 460-11	45 16 51.74 / 70 55 16.79	57 22 26 / 186 02 07	Mon. 460-10 / Mon. 460-12	85.74 / 52.18
Mon. 457-13	45 15 49.97 / 70 54 22.95	10 58 10 / 160 49 34	Mon. 457-12 / Mon. 457-14	54.52 / 34.78	Mon. 460-12	45 16 53.42 / 70 55 16.54	6 02 07 / 190 25 13	Mon. 460-11 / Mon. 460-13	52.18 / 58.89
Mon. 457-14	45 15 51.03 / 70 54 23.47	340 49 34 / 198 28 15	Mon. 457-13 / Mon. 458	34.78 / 35.69	Mon. 460-13	45 16 55.30 / 70 55 16.05	10 25 13 / 191 02 55	Mon. 460-12 / Mon. 460-14	58.89 / 371.07
Mon. 458	45 15 52.13 / 70 54 22.95	18 28 15 / 198 31 56	Mon. 457-14 / Mon. 458-1	35.69 / 46.96	Mon. 460-14	45 17 07.10 / 70 55 12.79	11 02 58 / 227 17 35	Mon. 460-13 / Mon. 460-15	371.07 / 104.85
Mon. 458-1	45 15 53.57 / 70 54 22.27	18 31 56 / 221 36 41	Mon. 458 / Mon. 458-2	46.96 / 63.87	Mon. 460-15	45 17 09.40 / 70 55 09.25	47 17 38 / 178 50 35	Mon. 460-14 / Mon. 460-16	104.85 / 158.97
Mon. 458-2	45 15 55.12 / 70 54 20.32	41 36 42 / 163 38 58	Mon. 458-1 / Mon. 458-3	63.87 / 75.72	Mon. 460-16	45 17 14.55 / 70 55 09.40	358 50 35 / 226 43 07	Mon. 460-15 / Mon. 460-17	158.97 / 80.71
Mon. 458-3	45 15 57.47 / 70 54 21.30	343 38 57 / 143 42 07	Mon. 458-2 / Mon. 458-4	75.72 / 105.61	Mon. 460-17	45 17 16.34 / 70 55 06.70	46 43 09 / 202 26 46	Mon. 460-16 / Mon. 461	80.71 / 39.19
Mon. 458-4	45 16 00.23 / 70 54 24.17	323 42 05 / 139 56 55	Mon. 458-3 / Mon. 458-5	105.61 / 68.45	Mon. 461	45 17 17.51 / 70 55 06.02	22 26 47 / 198 02 22	Mon. 460-17 / Mon. 461-1	39.19 / 55.58
Mon. 458-5	45 16 01.92 / 70 54 26.19	319 56 54 / 152 53 07	Mon. 458-4 / Mon. 458-6	68.45 / 103.52	Mon. 461-1	45 17 19.22 / 70 55 05.23	18 02 23 / 215 47 19	Mon. 461 / Mon. 461-2	55.58 / 163.70
Mon. 458-6	45 16 04.91 / 70 54 28.35	332 53 06 / 164 47 43	Mon. 458-5 / Mon. 458-7	103.52 / 57.72	Mon. 461-2	45 17 23.53 / 70 55 00.83	35 47 22 / 225 37 13	Mon. 461-1 / Mon 461-3	163.70 / 104.15
Mon. 458-7	45 16 06.71 / 70 54 29.05	344 47 43 / 146 11 48	Mon. 458-6 / Mon. 459	57.72 / 130.34	Mon. 461-3	45 17 25.89 / 70 54 57.42	45 37 15 / 247 49 06	Mon. 461-2 / Mon. 461-4	104.15 / 40.88
Mon. 459	45 16 10.22 / 70 54 32.37	326 11 46 / 133 33 29	Mon. 458-7 / Mon. 459-1	130.34 / 15.66	Mon. 461-4	45 17 26.39 / 70 54 55.68	67 49 07 / 189 26 58	Mon. 461-3 / Mon. 461-5	40.88 / 82.59
Mon. 459-1	45 16 10.57 / 70 54 32.89	313 33 29 / 101 39 59	Mon. 459 / Mon. 459-2	15.66 / 98.05	Mon. 461-5	45 17 29.03 / 70 54 55.06	9 26 59 / 184 42 45	Mon. 461-4 / Mon. 461-6	82.59 / 52.34
Mon. 459-2	45 16 11.21 / 70 54 37.30	281 39 56 / 105 37 58	Mon. 459-1 / Mon. 459-3	98.05 / 124.05	Mon. 461-6	45 17 30.72 / 70 54 54.86	4 42 45 / 261 26 01	Mon. 461-5 / Mon. 461-7	52.34 / 68.01
Mon. 459-3	45 16 12.30 / 70 54 42.78	285 37 54 / 169 28 54	Mon. 459-2 / Mon. 459-4	124.05 / 142.67	Mon. 461-7	45 17 31.04 / 70 54 51.78	81 26 03 / 180 38 30	Mon. 461-6 / Mon. 461-8	68.01 / 66.83
Mon. 459-4	45 16 16.84 / 70 54 43.97	349 28 53 / 159 12 43	Mon. 459-3 / Mon. 459-5	142.67 / 74.25	Mon. 461-8	45 17 33.21 / 70 54 51.74	0 38 30 / 190 59 22	Mon. 461-7 / Mon. 462	66.83 / 63.22
Mon. 459-5	45 16 19.09 / 70 54 45.18	339 12 42 / 127 51 32	Mon. 459-4 / Mon. 459-6	74.25 / 154.10	Mon. 462	45 17 35.22 / 70 54 51.19	10 59 23 / 189 46 21	Mon. 461-8 / Mon. 462-1	63.22 / 225.80
Mon. 459-6	45 16 22.15 / 70 54 50.76	307 51 28 / 159 49 23	Mon. 459-5 / Mon. 459-7	154.10 / 103.38	Mon. 462-1	45 17 42.43 / 70 54 49.43	9 46 22 / 210 59 50	Mon. 462 / Mon. 462-2	225.80 / 84.16
Mon. 459-7	45 16 25.30 / 70 54 52.40	339 49 22 / 135 23 17	Mon. 459-6 / Mon. 459-8	103.38 / 93.88	Mon. 462-2	45 17 44.76 / 70 54 47.44	30 59 51 / 213 25 52	Mon. 462-1 / Mon. 462-3	84.16 / 85.12
Mon. 459-8	45 16 27.46 / 70 54 55.42	315 23 14 / 157 01 07	Mon. 459-7 / Mon. 460	93.88 / 101.01	Mon. 462-3	45 17 47.06 / 70 54 45.29	33 25 54 / 170 53 19	Mon. 462-2 / Mon. 462-4	85.12 / 64.07
Mon. 460	45 16 30.47 / 70 54 57.23	337 01 06 / 157 01 33	Mon. 459-8 / Mon. 460-1	101.01 / 81.95	Mon. 462-4	45 17 49.11 / 70 54 45.76	350 53 19 / 161 39 07	Mon. 462-3 / Mon. 462-5	64.07 / 405.97
Mon. 460-1	45 16 32.92 / 70 54 58.70	337 01 32 / 136 40 58	Mon. 460 / Mon. 460-2	81.95 / 61.04	Mon. 462-5	45 18 01.60 / 70 54 51.62	341 39 03 / 137 42 17	Mon. 462-4 / Mon. 462-6	405.97 / 190.13
Mon. 460-2	45 16 34.36 / 70 55 00.62	316 40 57 / 167 13 33	Mon. 460-1 / Mon. 460-3	61.04 / 66.96	Mon. 462-6	45 18 06.15 / 70 54 57.49	317 42 13 / 141 09 46	Mon. 462-5 / Mon. 463	190.13 / 183.19
Mon. 460-3	45 16 36.47 / 70 55 01.30	347 13 33 / 182 41 21	Mon. 460-2 / Mon. 460-4	66.96 / 69.64	Mon. 463	45 18 10.77 / 70 55 02.76	321 09 42 / 140 37 35	Mon. 462-6 / Mon. 463-1	183.19 / 339.73

BOUNDARY MONUMENTS—SOURCE OF SOUTHWEST BRANCH OF ST. JOHN TO HEAD OF HALLS STREAM—Continued

Station	Latitude and longitude	Azimuth	To station	Distance (meters)	Station	Latitude and longitude	Azimuth	To station	Distance (meters)
	° ′ ″	° ′ ″				° ′ ″	° ′ ″		
Mon. 463–1	45 18 19.28	320 37 28	Mon. 463	339.73	Mon. 465–11	45 19 45.91	301 54 54	Mon. 465–10	62.62
	70 55 12.66	196 50 47	Mon. 463–2	136.82		70 56 46.95	119 34 28	Mon. 465–12	205.83
Mon. 463–2	45 18 23.52	16 50 48	Mon. 463–1	136.82	Mon. 465–12	45 19 49.20	299 34 22	Mon. 465–11	205.83
	70 55 10.84	169 33 39	Mon. 463–3	85.16		70 56 55.17	158 30 44	Mon. 465–13	69.08
Mon. 463–3	45 18 26.23	349 33 38	Mon. 463–2	85.16	Mon. 465–13	45 19 51.28	338 30 43	Mon. 465–12	69.08
	70 55 11.54	139 04 14	Mon. 463–4	78.24		70 56 56.33	122 43 31	Mon. 465–14	100.62
Mon. 463–4	45 18 28.15	319 04 12	Mon. 463–3	78.24	Mon. 465–14	45 19 53.05	302 43 28	Mon. 465–13	100.62
	70 55 13.90	203 29 48	Mon. 463–5	122.00		70 57 00.22	214 29 54	Mon. 465–15	78.39
Mon. 463–5	45 18 31.77	23 29 50	Mon. 463–4	122.00	Mon. 465–15	45 19 55.14	34 29 55	Mon. 465–14	78.39
	70 55 11.66	181 39 01	Mon. 463–6	68.41		70 56 58.18	159 52 16	Mon. 465–16	60.67
Mon. 463–6	45 18 33.99	1 39 01	Mon. 463–5	68.41	Mon. 465–16	45 19 56.98	339 52 15	Mon. 465–15	60.67
	70 55 11.57	203 42 50	Mon. 463–7	287.79		70 56 59.14	152 49 14	Mon. 466	298.70
Mon. 463–7	45 18 42.52	23 42 54	Mon. 463–6	287.79	Mon. 466	45 20 05.59	332 49 10	Mon. 465–16	298.70
	70 55 06.26	134 13 45	Mon. 463–8	262.97		70 57 05.40	184 54 34	Mon. 466–1	89.33
Mon. 463–8	45 18 48.47	314 13 39	Mon. 463–7	262.97	Mon. 466–1	45 20 08.48	4 54 34	Mon. 466	89.33
	70 55 14.91	113 14 55	Mon. 463–9	89.01		70 57 05.05	186 01 23	Mon. 466–2	86.01
Mon. 463–9	45 18 49.60	293 14 52	Mon. 463–8	89.01	Mon. 466–2	45 20 11.25	6 01 23	Mon. 466–1	86.01
	70 55 18.66	105 45 42	Mon. 464	154.10		70 57 04.64	196 02.29	Mon. 466–3	64.24
Mon. 464	45 18 50.96	285 45 38	Mon. 463–9	154.10	Mon. 466–3	45 20 13.25	16 02 30	Mon. 466–2	64.24
	70 55 25.47	109 46 44	Mon. 464–1	71.51		70 57 03.82	196 58 28	Mon. 466–4	67.03
Mon. 464–1	45 18 51.74	289 46 42	Mon. 464	71.51	Mon. 466–4	45 20 15.32	16 58 29	Mon. 466–3	67.03
	70 55 28.56	127 35 16	Mon. 464–2	99.99		70 57 02.92	153 18 05	Mon. 466–5	106.43
Mon. 464–2	45 18 53.72	307 35 13	Mon. 464–1	99.99	Mon. 466–5	45 20 18.40	333 18 03	Mon. 466–4	106.43
	70 55 32.20	77 23 07	Mon. 464–3	27.61		70 57 05.12	130 24 53	Mon. 466–6	71.50
Mon. 464–3	45 18 53.52	257 23 06	Mon. 464–2	27.61	Mon. 466–6	45 20 19.90	310 24 51	Mon. 466–5	71.50
	70 55 33.44	93 28 03	Mon. 464–4	139.53		70 57 07.62	120 14 51	Mon. 466–7	75.35
Mon. 464–4	45 18 53.80	273 27 58	Mon. 464–3	139.53	Mon. 466–7	45 20 21.13	300 14 49	Mon. 466–6	75.35
	70 55 39.83	165 46 45	Mon. 464–5	119.11		70 57 10.61	88 55 49	Mon. 466–8	61.73
Mon. 464–5	45 18 57.54	345 46 44	Mon. 464–4	119.11	Mon. 466–8	45 20 21.10	268 55 47	Mon. 466–7	61.73
	70 55 41.18	121 06 31	Mon. 464–6	107.75		70 57 13.45	62 23 20	Mon. 466–9	109.64
Mon. 464–6	45 18 59.34	301 06 28	Mon. 464–5	107.75	Mon. 466–9	45 20 19.45	242 23 17	Mon. 466–8	109.64
	70 55 45.41	111 48 57	Mon. 464–7	54.30		70 57 17.91	86 28 22	Mon. 466–10	73.43
Mon. 464–7	45 18 59.99	291 48 55	Mon. 464–6	54.30	Mon. 466–10	45 20 19.30	266 28 20	Mon. 466–9	73.43
	70 55 47.72	169 05 42	Mon. 464–8	252.91		70 57 21.27	62 12 42	Mon. 466–11	123.65
Mon. 464–8	45 19 08.04	349 05 41	Mon. 464–7	252.91	Mon. 466–11	45 20 17.44	242 12 39	Mon. 466–10	123.65
	70 55 49.92	100 59 55	Mon. 464–9	71.62		70 57 26.30	97 46 07	Mon. 466–12	52.99
Mon. 464–9	45 19 08.48	280 59 53	Mon. 464–8	71.62	Mon. 466–12	45 20 17.67	277 46 05	Mon. 466–11	52.99
	70 55 53.15	104 12 42	Mon. 464–10	28.19		70 57 28.71	62 48 39	Mon. 467	92.62
Mon. 464–10	45 19 08.70	284 12 41	Mon. 464–9	28.19	Mon. 467	45 20 16.30	242 48 36	Mon. 466–12	92.62
	70 55 54.40	99 47 55	Mon. 465	195.78		70 57 32.49	38 27 06	Mon. 467–1	95.85
Mon. 465	45 19 09.78	279 47 49	Mon. 464–10	195.78	Mon. 467–1	45 20 13.86	218 27 04	Mon. 467	95.85
	70 56 03.26	100 39 26	Mon. 465–1	326.05		70 57 35.23	74 54 40	Mon. 467–2	159.51
Mon. 465–1	45 19 11.74	280 39 16	Mon. 465	326.05	Mon. 467–2	45 20 12.52	254 54 35	Mon. 467–1	159.51
	70 56 17.97	99 55 13	Mon. 465–2	91.09		70 57 42.30	37 49 51	Mon. 467–3	158.16
Mon. 465–2	45 19 12.24	279 55 10	Mon. 465–1	91.09	Mon. 467–3	45 20 08.47	217 49 48	Mon. 467–2	158.16
	70 56 22.09	159 52 04	Mon. 465–3	384.49		70 57 46.76	41 01 40	Mon. 467–4	59.07
Mon. 465–3	45 19 23.94	339 52 00	Mon. 465–2	384.49	Mon. 467–4	45 20 07.03	221 01 39	Mon. 467–3	59.07
	70 56 28.17	107 29 49	Mon. 465–4	114.61		70 57 48.54	35 29 46	Mon. 467–5	145.21
Mon. 465–4	45 19 25.05	287 29 45	Mon. 465–3	114.61	Mon. 467–5	45 20 03.20	215 29 43	Mon. 467–4	145.21
	70 56 33.19	107 55 03	Mon. 465–5	122.03		70 57 52.41	57 29 40	Mon. 467–6	153.02
Mon. 465–5	45 19 26.27	287 54 59	Mon. 465–4	122.03	Mon. 467–6	45 20 00.54	237 29 36	Mon. 467–5	153.02
	70 56 38.52	145 55 33	Mon. 465–6	157.57		70 57 58.34	108 53 17	Mon. 467–7	28.98
Mon. 465–6	45 19 30.50	325 55 30	Mon. 465–5	157.57	Mon. 467–7	45 20 00.84	288 53 16	Mon. 467–6	28.98
	70 56 42.57	146 18 02	Mon. 465–7	86.76		70 57 59.60	107 43 56	Mon. 467–8	19.81
Mon. 465–7	45 19 32.84	326 18 01	Mon. 465–6	86.76	Mon. 467–8	45 20 01.04	287 43 55	Mon. 467–7	19.81
	70 56 44.78	191 51 31	Mon. 465–8	127.34		70 58 00.46	31 04 31	Mon. 467–9	36.84
Mon. 465–8	45 19 36.87	11 51 32	Mon. 465–7	127.34	Mon. 467–9	45 20 00.01	211 04 30	Mon. 467–8	36.84
	70 56 43.58	207 37 57	Mon. 465–9	68.22		70 58 01.34	40 48 02	Mon. 467–10	38.77
Mon. 465–9	45 19 38.83	27 37 58	Mon. 465–8	68.22	Mon. 467–10	45 19 59.06	220 48 01	Mon. 467–9	38.77
	70 56 42.13	164 23 06	Mon. 465–10	192.63		70 58 02.50	26 23 13	Mon. 467–11	93.51
Mon. 465–10	45 19 44.84	344 23 04	Mon. 465–9	192.63	Mon. 467–11	45 19 56.35	206 23 12	Mon. 467–10	93.51
	70 56 44.51	121 54 56	Mon. 465–11	62.62		70 58 04.41	84 05 23	Mon. 467–12	103.17

BOUNDARY MONUMENTS—SOURCE OF SOUTHWEST BRANCH OF ST. JOHN TO HEAD OF HALLS STREAM—Continued

Station	Latitude and longitude	Azimuth	To station	Distance (meters)	Station	Latitude and longitude	Azimuth	To station	Distance (meters)
	° ′ ″	° ′ ″				° ′ ″	° ′ ″		
Mon. 467–12	45 19 56.00 / 70 58 09.12	264 05 20 / 135 12 11	Mon. 467–11 / Mon. 467–13	103.17 / 126.70	Mon. 469–7	45 20 24.42 / 70 59 51.61	298 28 09 / 129 34 15	Mon. 469–6 / Mon. 469–8	140.80 / 249.60
Mon. 467–13	45 19 58.92 / 70 58 13.22	315 12 08 / 100 25 40	Mon. 467–12 / Mon. 467–14	126.70 / 64.16	Mon. 469–8	45 20 29.57 / 71 00 00.44	309 34 09 / 131 24 13	Mon. 469–7 / Mon. 469–9	249.60 / 30.47
Mon. 467–14	45 19 59.29 / 70 58 16.12	280 25 38 / 79 23 35	Mon. 467–13 / Mon. 467–15	64.16 / 92.33	Mon. 469–9	45 20 30.22 / 71 00 01.49	311 24 12 / 133 32 12	Mon. 469–8 / Mon. 469–10	30.47 / 64.05
Mon. 467–15	45 19 58.74 / 70 58 20.29	259 23 32 / 122 46 23	Mon. 467–14 / Mon. 467–16	92.33 / 148.37	Mon. 469–10	45 20 31.65 / 71 00 03.63	313 32 10 / 160 53 44	Mon. 469–9 / Mon. 469–11	64.05 / 135.13
Mon. 467–16	45 20 01.34 / 70 58 26.02	302 46 19 / 83 48 45	Mon. 467–15 / Mon. 467–17	148.37 / 260.51	Mon. 469–11	45 20 35.79 / 71 00 05.66	340 53 43 / 151 21 19	Mon. 469–10 / Mon. 469–12	135.13 / 59.57
Mon. 467–17	45 20 00.44 / 70 58 37.91	263 48 37 / 8 24 23	Mon. 467–16 / Mon. 467–18	260.51 / 39.91	Mon. 469–12	45 20 37.48 / 71 00 06.97	331 21 18 / 174 38 18	Mon. 469–11 / Mon. 469–13	59.57 / 57.31
Mon. 467–18	45 19 59.16 / 70 58 38.18	188 24 23 / 49 10 54	Mon. 467–17 / Mon. 467–19	39.91 / 64.90	Mon. 469–13	45 20 39.33 / 71 00 07.22	354 38 18 / 90 19 10	Mon. 469–12 / Mon. 469–14	57.31 / 68.86
Mon. 467–19	45 19 57.78 / 70 58 40.44	229 10 52 / 60 00 04	Mon. 467–18 / Mon. 467–20	64.90 / 36.75	Mon. 469–14	45 20 39.34 / 71 00 10.38	270 19 08 / 121 26 48	Mon. 469–13 / Mon. 469–15	68.86 / 37.61
Mon. 467–20	45 19 57.19 / 70 58 41.90	240 00 03 / 84 49 20	Mon. 467–19 / Mon. 468	36.75 / 122.39	Mon. 469–15	45 20 39.97 / 71 00 11.85	301 26 47 / 130 59 55	Mon. 469–14 / Mon. 469–16	37.61 / 173.83
Mon. 468	45 19 56.83 / 70 58 47.50	264 49 16 / 89 14 47	Mon. 467–20 / Mon. 468–1	122.39 / 23.20	Mon. 469–16	45 20 43.67 / 71 00 17.88	310 59 51 / 118 30 41	Mon. 469–15 / Mon. 469–17	173.83 / 533.32
Mon. 468–1	45 19 56.82 / 70 58 48.56	269 14 46 / 83 52 14	Mon. 468 / Mon. 468–2	23.20 / 80.04	Mon. 469–17	45 20 51.91 / 71 00 39.41	298 30 25 / 93 22 01	Mon. 469–16 / Mon. 470	533.32 / 21.90
Mon. 468–2	45 19 56.54 / 70 58 52.22	263 52 11 / 80 23 44	Mon. 468–1 / Mon. 468–3	80.04 / 41.70	Mon. 470	45 20 51.96 / 71 00 40.41	273 22 00 / 44 59 02	Mon. 469–17 / Mon. 470–1	21.90 / 53.73
Mon. 468–3	45 19 56.32 / 70 58 54.10	260 23 43 / 135 13 25	Mon. 468–2 / Mon. 468–4	41.70 / 66.44	Mon. 470–1	45 20 50.72 / 71 00 42.16	224 59 01 / 354 53 58	Mon. 470 / Mon. 470–2	53.73 / 45.84
Mon. 468–4	45 19 57.85 / 70 58 56.25	315 13 23 / 89 27 35	Mon. 468–3 / Mon. 468–5	66.44 / 98.57	Mon. 470–2	45 20 49.24 / 71 00 41.97	174 53 58 / 22 15 39	Mon. 470–1 / Mon. 470–3	45.84 / 43.19
Mon. 468–5	45 19 57.82 / 70 59 00.78	269 27 32 / 61 33 32	Mon. 468–4 / Mon. 468–6	98.57 / 97.12	Mon. 470–3	45 20 47.95 / 71 00 42.72	202 15 39 / 20 08 01	Mon. 470–2 / Mon. 470–4	43.19 / 59.16
Mon. 468–6	45 19 56.32 / 70 59 04.70	241 33 29 / 64 02 57	Mon. 468–5 / Mon. 468–7	97.12 / 79.67	Mon. 470–4	45 20 46.15 / 71 00 43.66	200 08 00 / 18 59 28	Mon. 470–3 / Mon. 470–5	59.16 / 78.60
Mon. 468–7	45 19 55.19 / 70 59 07.99	244 02 55 / 155 15 04	Mon. 468–6 / Mon. 468–8	79.67 / 131.36	Mon. 470–5	45 20 43.74 / 71 00 44.83	198 59 27 / 38 37 58	Mon. 470–4 / Mon. 470–6	78.60 / 94.75
Mon. 468–8	45 19 59.06 / 70 59 10.52	335 15 02 / 101 52 17	Mon. 468–7 / Mon. 468–9	131.36 / 99.95	Mon. 470–6	45 20 41.35 / 71 00 47.55	218 37 56 / 27 40 54	Mon. 470–5 / Mon. 470–7	94.75 / 62.04
Mon. 468–9	45 19 59.72 / 70 59 15.01	281 52 14 / 122 06 31	Mon. 468–8 / Mon 468–10	99.95 / 202.77	Mon. 470–7	45 20 39.57 / 71 00 48.87	207 40 53 / 324 58 56	Mon. 470–6 / Mon. 470–8	62.04 / 59.18
Mon. 468–10	45 20 03.21 / 70 59 22.90	302 06 25 / 155 09 27	Mon. 468–9 / Mon. 468–11	202.77 / 185.15	Mon. 470–8	45 20 38.00 / 71 00 47.31	144 58 57 / 358 36 18	Mon. 470–7 / Mon. 470–9	59.18 / 282.31
Mon. 468–11	45 20 08.65 / 70 59 26.47	335 09 24 / 166 34 23	Mon. 468–10 / Mon. 468–12	185.15 / 56.38	Mon. 470–9	45 20 28.85 / 71 00 47.00	178 36 18 / 322 20 29	Mon. 470–8 / Mon. 470–10	282.31 / 164.53
Mon. 468–12	45 20 10.43 / 70 59 27.07	346 34 23 / 183 12 47	Mon. 468–11 / Mon. 468–13	56.38 / 92.86	Mon. 470–10	45 20 24.64 / 71 00 42.38	142 20 33 / 0 29 03	Mon. 470–9 / Mon. 470–11	164.53 / 26.64
Mon. 468–13	45 20 13.43 / 70 59 26.83	3 12 47 / 158 17 04	Mon. 468–12 / Mon. 468–14	92.86 / 134.13	Mon. 470–11	45 20 23.77 / 71 00 42.39	180 29 03 / 323 59 11	Mon. 470–10 / Mon. 470–12	26.64 / 35.94
Mon. 468–14	45 20 17.47 / 70 59 29.11	338 17 03 / 114 16 45	Mon. 468–13 / Mon. 469	134.13 / 24.23	Mon. 470–12	45 20 22.83 / 71 00 41.42	143 59 12 / 36 08 50	Mon. 470–11 / Mon. 470–13	35.94 / 56.29
Mon. 469	45 20 17.79 / 70 59 30.12	294 16 45 / 82 52 01	Mon. 468–14 / Mon. 469–1	24.23 / 60.21	Mon. 470–13	45 20 21.36 / 71 00 42.94	216 08 49 / 333 09 00	Mon. 470–12 / Mon. 470–14	56.29 / 127.26
Mon. 469–1	45 20 17.55 / 70 59 32.87	262 51 59 / 97 34 56	Mon. 469 / Mon. 469–2	60.21 / 94.23	Mon. 470–14	45 20 17.68 / 71 00 40.30	153 09 01 / 63 13 52	Mon. 470–13 / Mon. 470–15	127.26 / 72.45
Mon. 469–2	45 20 17.95 / 70 59 37.16	277 34 53 / 104 33 55	Mon. 469–1 / Mon. 469–3	94.23 / 59.35	Mon. 470–15	45 20 16.62 / 71 00 43.28	243 13 50 / 1 53 41	Mon. 470–14 / Mon. 470–16	72.45 / 79.75
Mon. 469–3	45 20 18.44 / 70 59 39.80	284 33 53 / 146 38 15	Mon. 469–2 / Mon. 469–4	59.35 / 40.98	Mon. 470–16	45 20 14.04 / 71 00 43.40	181 53 41 / 347 12 48	Mon. 470–15 / Mon. 470–17	79.75 / 69.06
Mon. 469–4	45 20 19.54 / 70 59 40.83	326 38 14 / 133 01 41	Mon. 469–3 / Mon. 469–5	40.98 / 45.15	Mon. 470–17	45 20 11.86 / 71 00 42.69	167 12 49 / 320 42 34	Mon. 470–16 / Mon. 470–18	69.06 / 47.17
Mon. 469–5	45 20 20.54 / 70 59 42.35	313 01 40 / 124 00 14	Mon. 469–4 / Mon. 469–6	45.15 / 93.89	Mon. 470–18	45 20 10.68 / 71 00 41.32	140 42 35 / 359 24 52	Mon. 470–17 / Mon. 470–19	47.17 / 161.05
Mon. 469–6	45 20 22.24 / 70 59 45.92	304 00 12 / 118 28 13	Mon. 469–5 / Mon. 469–7	93.89 / 140.80	Mon. 470–19	45 20 05.46 / 71 00 41.25	179 24 52 / 34 27 08	Mon. 470–18 / Mon. 470–20	161.05 / 47.77

BOUNDARY MONUMENTS—SOURCE OF SOUTHWEST BRANCH OF ST. JOHN TO HEAD OF HALLS STREAM—Continued

Station	Latitude and longitude	Azimuth	To station	Distance (meters)
Mon. 470–20	45 20 04.18 / 71 00 42.49	214 27 07 / 89 21 06	Mon. 470–19 / Mon. 470–21	47.77 / 51.95
Mon. 470–21	45 20 04.17 / 71 00 44.87	269 21 04 / 16 36 12	Mon. 470–20 / Mon. 470–22	51.95 / 61.92
Mon. 470–22	45 20 02.24 / 71 00 45.69	196 36 11 / 306 12 38	Mon. 470–21 / Mon. 470–23	61.92 / 40.86
Mon. 470–23	45 20 01.46 / 71 00 44.17	126 12 39 / 277 07 29	Mon. 470–22 / Mon. 470–24	40.86 / 264.53
Mon. 470–24	45 20 00.40 / 71 00 32.12	97 07 38 / 306 49 54	Mon. 470–23 / Mon. 470–25	264.53 / 57.91
Mon. 470–25	45 19 59.27 / 71 00 29.99	126 49 56 / 306 38 52	Mon. 470–24 / Mon. 470–26	57.91 / 50.42
Mon. 470–26	45 19 58.30 / 71 00 28.13	126 38 53 / 276 40 03	Mon. 470–25 / Mon. 470–27	50.42 / 46.21
Mon. 470–27	45 19 58.12 / 71 00 26.02	96 40 04 / 316 48 42	Mon. 470–26 / Mon. 470–28	46.21 / 117.14
Mon. 470–28	45 19 55.36 / 71 00 22.34	136 48 45 / 316 19 43	Mon. 470–27 / Mon. 470–29	117.14 / 149.17
Mon. 470–29	45 19 51.86 / 71 00 17.61	136 19 46 / 339 52 05	Mon. 470–28 / Mon. 471	149.17 / 70.25
Mon. 471	45 19 49.73 / 71 00 16.50	159 52 06 / 321 03 33	Mon. 470–29 / Mon. 471–1	70.25 / 74.71
Mon. 471–1	45 19 47.85 / 71 00 14.34	141 03 35 / 5 39 33	Mon. 471 / Mon. 471–2	74.71 / 58.36
Mon. 471–2	45 19 45.96 / 71 00 14.61	185 39 33 / 318 26 31	Mon. 471–1 / Mon. 471–3	58.36 / 119.69
Mon. 471–3	45 19 43.06 / 71 00 10.96	138 26 34 / 284 58 52	Mon. 471–2 / Mon. 471–4	119.69 / 48.66
Mon. 471–4	45 19 42.66 / 71 00 08.80	104 58 54 / 33 05 32	Mon. 471–3 / Mon. 471–5	48.66 / 41.58
Mon. 471–5	45 19 41.53 / 71 00 09.85	213 05 31 / 58 17 44	Mon. 471–4 / Mon. 471–6	41.58 / 83.93
Mon. 471–6	45 19 40.10 / 71 00 13.13	238 17 42 / 59 58 46	Mon. 471–5 / Mon. 471–7	83.93 / 77.16
Mon. 471–7	45 19 38.85 / 71 00 16.19	239 58 44 / 20 38 15	Mon. 471–6 / Mon. 471–8	77.16 / 353.16
Mon. 471–8	45 19 28.14 / 71 00 21.91	200 38 11 / 29 46 09	Mon. 471–7 / Mon. 471–9	353.16 / 186.57
Mon. 471–9	45 19 23.00 / 71 00 26.16	209 46 06 / 34 17 54	Mon. 471–8 / Mon. 471–10	186.57 / 123.23
Mon. 471–10	45 19 19.60 / 71 00 29.35	214 17 52 / 33 13 16	Mon. 471–9 / Mon. 471–11	123.23 / 94.91
Mon. 471–11	45 19 17.03 / 71 00 31.74	213 13 14 / 9 47 42	Mon. 471–10 / Mon. 471–12	94.91 / 127.93
Mon. 471–12	45 19 12.94 / 71 00 32.74	189 47 41 / 322 00 12	Mon. 471–11 / Mon. 471–13	127.93 / 17.07
Mon. 471–13	45 19 12.51 / 71 00 32.25	142 00 12 / 333 06 15	Mon. 471–12 / Mon. 471–14	17.07 / 46.62
Mon. 471–14	45 19 11.16 / 71 00 31.29	153 06 16 / 32 28 29	Mon. 471–13 / Mon. 471–15	46.62 / 58.13
Mon. 471–15	45 19 09.57 / 71 00 32.72	212 28 28 / 57 19 26	Mon. 471–14 / Mon. 471–16	58.13 / 16.99
Mon. 471–16	45 19 09.28 / 71 00 33.38	237 19 25 / 60 18 39	Mon. 471–15 / Mon. 471–17	16.99 / 69.88
Mon. 471–17	45 19 08.16 / 71 00 36.16	240 18 37 / 73 59 55	Mon. 471–16 / Mon. 471–18	69.88 / 65.43
Mon. 471–18	45 19 07.57 / 71 00 39.05	253 59 53 / 61 08 51	Mon. 471–17 / Mon. 471–19	65.43 / 73.41
Mon. 471–19	45 19 06.42 / 71 00 42.00	241 08 49 / 21 08 15	Mon. 471–18 / Mon. 471–20	73.41 / 48.21
Mon. 471–20	45 19 04.97 / 71 00 42.80	201 08 14 / 50 43 24	Mon. 471–19 / Mon. 471–21	48.21 / 68.05
Mon. 471–21	45 19 03.57 / 71 00 45.22	230 43 22 / 55 42 47	Mon. 471–20 / Mon. 472	68.05 / 139.46
Mon. 472	45 19 01.03 / 71 00 50.51	235 42 43 / 88 59 02	Mon. 471–21 / Mon. 472–1	139.46 / 83.82
Mon. 472–1	45 19 00.98 / 71 00 54.36	268 58 59 / 87 31 59	Mon. 472 / Mon. 472–2	83.82 / 17.29
Mon. 472–2	45 19 00.96 / 71 00 55.15	267 31 58 / 61 18 58	Mon. 472–1 / Mon. 472–3	17.29 / 117.87
Mon. 472–3	45 18 59.12 / 71 00 59.90	241 18 55 / 7 54 10	Mon. 472–2 / Mon. 472–4	117.87 / 90.61
Mon. 472–4	45 18 56.22 / 71 01 00.47	187 54 10 / 82 30 50	Mon. 472–3 / Mon 472–5	90.61 / 34.43
Mon. 472–5	45 18 56.07 / 71 01 02.04	262 30 49 / 78 50 29	Mon. 472–4 / Mon. 472–6	34.43 / 113.10
Mon. 472–6	45 18 55.36 / 71 01 07.13	258 50 25 / 98 23 35	Mon. 472–5 / Mon. 472–7	113.10 / 104.75
Mon. 472–7	45 18 55.86 / 71 01 11.89	278 23 31 / 57 12 51	Mon. 472–6 / Mon 472–8	104.75 / 65.59
Mon. 472–8	45 18 54.71 / 71 01 14.42	237 12 49 / 83 12 19	Mon 472–7 / Mon. 472–9	65.59 / 71.28
Mon. 472–9	45 18 54.43 / 71 01 17.67	263 12 17 / 36 55 17	Mon. 472–8 / Mon. 472–10	71.28 / 83.03
Mon. 472–10	45 18 52.28 / 71 01 19.96	216 55 15 / 90 11 30	Mon. 472–9 / Mon. 472–11	83.03 / 62.10
Mon. 472–11	45 18 52.29 / 71 01 22.81	270 11 28 / 126 33 58	Mon. 472–10 / Mon. 472–12	62.10 / 90.46
Mon. 472–12	45 18 54.04 / 71 01 26.15	306 33 56 / 117 17 16	Mon. 472–11 / Mon. 472–13	90.46 / 12.82
Mon. 472–13	45 18 54.23 / 71 01 26.67	297 17 16 / 141 15 06	Mon. 472–12 / Mon. 472–14	12.82 / 62.87
Mon. 472–14	45 18 55.81 / 71 01 28.48	321 15 05 / 76 35 45	Mon. 472–13 / Mon. 472–15	62.87 / 45.95
Mon. 472–15	45 18 55.47 / 71 01 30.53	256 35 43 / 74 28 43	Mon. 472–14 / Mon. 473	45.95 / 67.22
Mon. 473	45 18 54.89 / 71 01 33.50	254 28 41 / 68 00 50	Mon. 472–15 / Mon. 473–1	67.22 / 108.61
Mon. 473–1	45 18 53.57 / 71 01 38.13	248 00 47 / 69 28 02	Mon. 473 / Mon. 473–2	108.61 / 33.86
Mon. 473–2	45 18 53.18 / 71 01 39.58	249 28 01 / 21 29 31	Mon. 473–1 / Mon. 473–3	33.86 / 59.18
Mon. 473–3	45 18 51.40 / 71 01 40.58	201 29 30 / 56 11 00	Mon. 473–2 / Mon. 473–4	59.18 / 327.44
Mon. 473–4	45 18 45.50 / 71 01 53.07	236 10 51 / 21 01 36	Mon. 473–3 / Mon. 473–5	327.44 / 134.16
Mon. 473–5	45 18 41.44 / 71 01 55.28	201 01 34 / 34 52 19	Mon. 473–4 / Mon. 473–6	134.16 / 167.87
Mon. 473–6	45 18 36.98 / 71 01 59.68	214 52 16 / 83 37 16	Mon. 473–5 / Mon. 473–7	167.87 / 61.60
Mon. 473–7	45 18 36.76 / 71 02 02.49	263 37 14 / 58 57 44	Mon. 473–6 / Mon. 473–8	61.60 / 23.96
Mon. 473–8	45 18 36.36 / 71 02 03.44	238 57 43 / 141 16 43	Mon. 473–7 / Mon. 473–9	23.96 / 47.58
Mon. 473–9	45 18 37.56 / 71 02 04.80	321 16 42 / 112 10 27	Mon. 473–8 / Mon. 473–10	47.58 / 36.07
Mon. 473–10	45 18 38.00 / 71 02 06.33	292 10 26 / 159 04 56	Mon. 473–9 / Mon 473–11	36.07 / 26.05
Mon. 473–11	45 18 38.79 / 71 02 06.76	339 04 56 / 88 49 11	Mon. 473–10 / Mon. 473–12	26.05 / 115.90
Mon. 473–12	45 18 38.71 / 71 02 12.08	268 49 07 / 132 58 52	Mon. 473–11 / Mon. 473–13	115.90 / 315.71
Mon. 473–13	45 18 45.68 / 71 02 22.68	312 58 45 / 42 19 30	Mon. 473–12 / Mon. 473–14	315.71 / 30.30

BOUNDARY MONUMENTS—SOURCE OF SOUTHWEST BRANCH OF ST. JOHN TO HEAD OF HALLS STREAM—Continued

Station	Latitude and longitude	Azimuth	To station	Distance (meters)
Mon. 473–14	45 18 44.96 / 71 02 23.62	222 19 30 / 106 32 00	Mon. 473–13 / Mon. 473–15	30.30 / 51.75
Mon. 473–15	45 18 45.44 / 71 02 25.90	286 31 58 / 112 59 13	Mon. 473–14 / Mon. 473–16	51.75 / 61.84
Mon. 473–16	45 18 46.22 / 71 02 28.51	292 59 11 / 121 48 41	Mon. 473–15 / Mon. 473–17	61.84 / 75.04
Mon. 473–17	45 18 47.50 / 71 02 31.44	301 48 39 / 68 40 09	Mon. 473–16 / Mon. 473–18	75.04 / 77.57
Mon. 473–18	45 18 46.59 / 71 02 34.75	248 40 07 / 108 38 22	Mon. 473–17 / Mon. 473–19	77.57 / 95.98
Mon. 473–19	45 18 47.58 / 71 02 38.93	288 38 19 / 88 33 49	Mon. 473–18 / Mon. 473–20	95.98 / 140.65
Mon. 473–20	45 18 47.47 / 71 02 45.38	268 33 44 / 76 16 44	Mon. 473–19 / Mon. 473–21	140.65 / 51.04
Mon. 473–21	45 18 47.07 / 71 02 47.66	256 16 42 / 102 21 57	Mon. 473–20 / Mon. 473–22	51.04 / 50.90
Mon. 473–22	45 18 47.43 / 71 02 49.94	282 21 55 / 70 26 25	Mon. 473–21 / Mon. 473–23	50.90 / 438.79
Mon. 473–23	45 18 42.67 / 71 03 08.92	250 26 11 / 36 28 26	Mon. 473–22 / Mon. 473–24	438.79 / 41.28
Mon. 473–24	45 18 41.59 / 71 02 10.05	216 28 25 / 85 38 10	Mon. 473–23 / Mon. 473–25	41.28 / 74.49
Mon. 473–25	45 18 41.41 / 71 03 13.46	265 38 08 / 105 03 23	Mon. 473–24 / Mon. 473–26	74.49 / 43.68
Mon. 473–26	45 18 41.78 / 71 03 15.40	285 03 22 / 133 31 22	Mon. 473–25 / Mon. 474	43.68 / 142.52
Mon. 474	45 18 44.96 / 71 03 20.14	313 31 19 / 133 57 44	Mon. 473–26 / Mon. 474–1	142.52 / 81.56
Mon. 474–1	45 18 46.79 / 71 03 22.84	313 57 42 / 102 37 42	Mon. 474 / Mon. 474–2	81.56 / 120.01
Mon. 474–2	45 18 47.64 / 71 03 28.21	282 37 38 / 110 01 23	Mon. 474–1 / Mon. 474–3	120.01 / 22.37
Mon. 474–3	45 18 47.89 / 71 03 29.18	290 01 22 / 119 21 52	Mon. 474–2 / Mon. 474–4	22.37 / 140.90
Mon. 474–4	45 18 50.13 / 71 03 34.81	299 21 48 / 71 25 03	Mon. 474–3 / Mon. 474–5	140.90 / 74.70
Mon. 474–5	45 18 49.36 / 71 03 38.06	251 25 01 / 55 16 01	Mon. 474–4 / Mon. 474–6	74.70 / 30.27
Mon. 474–6	45 18 48.80 / 71 03 39.21	235 16 00 / 31 23 00	Mon. 474–5 / Mon. 474–7	30.27 / 62.33
Mon. 474–7	45 18 47.07 / 71 03 40.70	211 22 59 / 66 29 29	Mon. 474–6 / Mon. 474–8	62.33 / 41.55
Mon. 474–8	45 18 46.54 / 71 03 42.44	246 29 28 / 88 22 43	Mon. 474–7 / Mon. 474–9	41.55 / 88.77
Mon. 474–9	45 18 46.46 / 71 03 46.52	268 22 40 / 147 34 40	Mon. 474–8 / Mon. 474–10	88.77 / 41.12
Mon. 474–10	45 18 47.58 / 71 03 47.53	327 34 39 / 55 06 24	Mon. 474–9 / Mon. 474–11	41.12 / 61.55
Mon. 474–11	45 18 46.44 / 71 03 49.85	235 06 22 / 77 32 37	Mon. 474–10 / Mon. 474–12	61.55 / 63.28
Mon. 474–12	45 18 46.00 / 71 03 52.69	257 32 35 / 57 43 35	Mon. 474–11 / Mon. 474–13	63.28 / 57.57
Mon. 474–13	45 18 45.00 / 71 03 54.92	237 43 33 / 101 36 33	Mon. 474–12 / Mon. 474–14	57.57 / 68.49
Mon. 474–14	45 18 45.45 / 71 03 58.00	281 36 31 / 30 23 46	Mon. 474–13 / Mon. 474–15	68.49 / 63.41
Mon. 474–15	45 18 43.68 / 71 03 59.47	210 23 45 / 306 33 30	Mon. 474–14 / Mon. 474–16	63.41 / 74.04
Mon. 474–16	45 18 42.25 / 71 03 56.74	126 33 32 / 54 50 17	Mon. 474–15 / Mon. 474–17	74.04 / 43.37
Mon. 474–17	45 18 41.44 / 71 03 58.37	234 50 16 / 92 59 01	Mon. 474–16 / Mon. 474–18	43.37 / 31.79
Mon. 474–18	45 18 41.49 / 71 03 59.83	272 59 00 / 32 26 15	Mon. 474–17 / Mon. 474–19	31.79 / 60.91
Mon. 474–19	45 18 39.83 / 71 04 01.33	212 26 14 / 115 13 29	Mon. 474–18 / Mon. 474–20	60.91 / 46.74
Mon. 474–20	45 18 40.47 / 71 04 03.27	295 13 28 / 24 59 43	Mon. 474–19 / Mon. 474–21	46.74 / 42.48
Mon. 474–21	45 18 39.23 / 71 04 04.09	204 59 42 / 20 11 57	Mon. 474–20 / Mon. 474–22	42.48 / 28.70
Mon. 474–22	45 18 38.35 / 71 04 04.55	200 11 57 / 71 16 57	Mon. 474–21 / Mon. 747–23	28.70 / 115.05
Mon. 474–23	45 18 37.16 / 71 04 09.55	251 16 53 / 349 14 08	Mon. 474–22 / Mon. 474–24	115.05 / 63.82
Mon. 474–24	45 18 35.13 / 71 04 09.00	169 14 08 / 54 41 38	Mon. 474–23 / Mon. 474–25	63.82 / 39.86
Mon. 474–25	45 18 34.38 / 71 04 10.50	234 41 37 / 101 20 22	Mon. 474–24 / Mon. 474–26	39.86 / 37.01
Mon. 474–26	45 18 34.62 / 71 04 12.16	281 20 21 / 69 03 51	Mon. 474–25 / Mon. 474–27	37.01 / 50.02
Mon. 474–27	45 18 34.04 / 71 04 14.31	249 03 49 / 112 13 49	Mon. 474–26 / Mon. 474–28	50.02 / 39.37
Mon. 474–28	45 18 34.52 / 71 04 15.98	292 13 48 / 49 19 48	Mon. 474–27 / Mon. 474–29	39.37 / 178.23
Mon. 474–29	45 18 30.76 / 71 04 22.18	229 19 44 / 63 01 14	Mon. 474–28 / Mon. 474–30	178.23 / 118.12
Mon. 474–30	45 18 29.02 / 71 04 27.02	243 01 11 / 60 54 56	Mon. 474–29 / Mon. 474–31	118.12 / 61.41
Mon. 474–31	45 18 28.06 / 71 04 29.48	240 54 54 / 36 47 54	Mon. 474–30 / Mon. 474–32	61.41 / 90.63
Mon. 474–32	45 18 25.70 / 71 04 31.97	216 47 52 / 90 18 37	Mon. 474–31 / Mon. 474–33	90.63 / 133.80
Mon. 474–33	45 18 25.73 / 71 04 38.11	270 18 33 / 45 54 18	Mon. 474–32 / Mon. 474–34	133.80 / 54.05
Mon. 474–34	45 18 24.51 / 71 04 39.89	225 54 17 / 47 42 32	Mon. 474–33 / Mon. 474–35	54.05 / 20.53
Mon. 474–35	45 18 24.06 / 71 04 40.59	227 42 32 / 95 33 17	Mon. 474–34 / Mon. 474–36	20.53 / 66.34
Mon. 474–36	45 18 24.27 / 71 04 43.62	275 33 15 / 54 57 15	Mon. 474–35 / Mon. 474–37	66.34 / 40.25
Mon. 474–37	45 18 23.52 / 71 04 45.14	234 57 14 / 123 11 59	Mon. 474–36 / Mon. 474–38	40.25 / 121.86
Mon. 474–38	45 18 25.68 / 71 04 49.82	303 11 56 / 45 15 41	Mon. 474–37 / Mon. 474–39	121.86 / 37.82
Mon. 474–39	45 18 24.82 / 71 04 51.05	225 15 40 / 91 33 10	Mon. 474–38 / Mon. 474–40	37.82 / 24.14
Mon. 474–40	45 18 24.84 / 71 04 52.16	271 33 09 / 56 38 39	Mon. 474–39 / Mon. 474–41	24.14 / 101.00
Mon. 474–41	45 18 23.04 / 71 04 56.03	236 38 36 / 90 40 06	Mon. 474–40 / Mon. 474–42	101.00 / 84.05
Mon. 474–42	45 18 23.07 / 71 04 59.89	270 40 03 / 22 10 48	Mon. 474–41 / Mon. 474–43	84.05 / 71.82
Mon. 474–43	45 18 20.92 / 71 05 01.13	202 10 47 / 68 16 47	Mon. 474–42 / Mon. 475	71.82 / 76.58
Mon. 475	45 18 20.00 / 71 05 04.40	248 16 45 / 93 05 13	Mon. 474–43 / Mon. 475–1	76.58 / 32.13
Mon. 475–1	45 18 20.06 / 71 05 05.87	273 05 12 / 133 16 45	Mon. 475 / Mon. 475–2	32.13 / 34.77
Mon. 475–2	45 18 20.83 / 71 05 07.03	313 16 44 / 96 30 27	Mon. 475–1 / Mon. 475–3	34.77 / 78.77
Mon. 475–3	45 18 21.12 / 71 05 10.63	276 30 24 / 19 19 18	Mon. 475–2 / Mon. 475–4	78.77 / 47.09
Mon. 475–4	45 18 19.68 / 71 05 11.34	199 19 17 / 75 02 46	Mon. 475–3 / Mon. 475–5	47.09 / 80.73

BOUNDARY MONUMENTS—SOURCE OF SOUTHWEST BRANCH OF ST. JOHN TO HEAD OF HALLS STREAM—Continued

Station	Latitude and longitude	Azimuth	To station	Distance (meters)	Station	Latitude and longitude	Azimuth	To station	Distance (meters)
Mon. 475–5	45 18 19.00 / 71 05 14.92	255 02 43 / 349 37 02	Mon. 475–4 / Mon. 475–6	80.73 / 52.89	Mon. 476–28	45 17 29.78 / 71 06 17.12	188 50 31 / 41 25 17	Mon. 476–27 / Mon. 476–29	32.13 / 48.57
Mon. 475–6	45 18 17.32 / 71 05 14.48	169 37 02 / 81 52 41	Mon. 475–5 / Mon. 475–7	52.89 / 84.54	Mon. 476–29	45 17 28.61 / 71 06 18.60	221 25 16 / 98 58 52	Mon. 476–28 / Mon. 476–30	48.57 / 102.60
Mon. 475–7	45 18 16.93 / 71 05 18.33	261 52 39 / 99 10 37	Mon. 475–6 / Mon. 476	84.54 / 115.49	Mon. 476–30	45 17 29.12 / 71 06 23.25	278 58 49 / 62 23 45	Mon. 476–29 / Mon. 476–31	102.60 / 59.10
Mon. 476	45 18 17.52 / 71 05 23.56	279 10 34 / 59 01 54	Mon. 475–7 / Mon. 476–1	115.49 / 37.92	Mon. 476–31	45 17 28.24 / 71 06 25.65	242 23 43 / 16 40 13	Mon. 476–30 / Mon. 476–32	59.10 / 145.26
Mon. 476–1	45 18 16.89 / 71 05 25.05	239 01 53 / 50 36 33	Mon. 476 / Mon. 476–2	37.92 / 74.57	Mon. 476–32	45 17 23.73 / 71 06 27.57	196 40 11 / 62 42 17	Mon. 476–31 / Mon. 476–33	145.26 / 68.28
Mon. 476–2	45 18 15.36 / 71 05 27.70	230 36 31 / 80 01 21	Mon. 476–1 / Mon. 476–3	74.57 / 166.86	Mon. 476–33	45 17 22.72 / 71 06 30.35	242 42 15 / 13 28 55	Mon. 476–32 / Mon. 476–34	68.28 / 325.49
Mon. 476–3	45 18 14.42 / 71 05 35.24	260 01 16 / 46 07 47	Mon. 476–2 / Mon. 476–4	166.86 / 232.31	Mon. 476–34	45 17 12.46 / 71 06 33.83	193 28 52 / 14 15 27	Mon. 476–33 / Mon. 477	325.49 / 67.74
Mon. 476–4	45 18 09.21 / 71 05 42.93	226 07 42 / 70 12 58	Mon. 476–3 / Mon. 476–5	232.31 / 74.87	Mon. 477	45 17 10.34 / 71 06 34.60	194 15 26 / 41 09 52	Mon. 476–34 / Mon. 477–1	67.74 / 181.07
Mon. 476–5	45 18 08.39 / 71 05 46.16	250 12 56 / 85 37 22	Mon. 476–4 / Mon. 476–6	74.87 / 40.09	Mon. 477–1	45 17 05.92 / 71 06 40.07	221 09 48 / 30 37 33	Mon. 477 / Mon. 477–2	181.07 / 66.45
Mon. 476–6	45 18 08.29 / 71 05 47.99	265 37 20 / 98 27 50	Mon. 476–5 / Mon. 476–7	40.09 / 57.74	Mon. 477–2	45 17 04.07 / 71 06 41.62	210 37 32 / 294 39 02	Mon. 477–1 / Mon. 477–3	66.45 / 60.20
Mon. 476–7	45 18 08.56 / 71 05 50.62	278 27 48 / 56 44 34	Mon. 476–6 / Mon. 476–8	57.74 / 43.65	Mon. 477–3	45 17 03.26 / 71 06 39.11	114 39 04 / 356 33 44	Mon. 477–2 / Mon. 477–4	60.20 / 62.29
Mon. 476–8	45 18 07.79 / 71 05 52.29	236 44 33 / 23 15 04	Mon. 476–7 / Mon. 476–9	43.65 / 40.85	Mon. 477–4	45 17 01.24 / 71 06 38.94	176 33 44 / 344 07 24	Mon. 477–3 / Mon. 477–5	62.29 / 54.84
Mon. 476–9	45 18 06.57 / 71 05 53.03	203 15 03 / 82 46 49	Mon. 476–8 / Mon. 476–10	40.85 / 56.37	Mon. 477–5	45 16 59.54 / 71 06 38.25	164 07 25 / 321 08 05	Mon. 477–4 / Mon. 477–6	54.84 / 109.83
Mon. 476–10	45 18 06.34 / 71 05 55.60	262 46 47 / 10 58 23	Mon. 476–9 / Mon. 476–11	56.37 / 89.75	Mon. 477–6	45 16 56.76 / 71 06 35.09	141 08 07 / 273 51 42	Mon. 477–5 / Mon. 477–7	109.83 / 67.86
Mon. 476–11	45 18 03.49 / 71 05 56.38	190 58 22 / 330 17 52	Mon. 476–10 / Mon. 476–12	89.75 / 37.68	Mon. 477–7	45 16 56.62 / 71 06 31.98	93 51 44 / 256 18 04	Mon. 477–6 / Mon. 477–8	67.86 / 231.57
Mon. 476–12	45 18 02.43 / 71 05 55.53	150 17 53 / 8 01 29	Mon. 476–11 / Mon. 476–13	37.68 / 40.56	Mon. 477–8	45 16 58.39 / 71 06 21.66	76 18 11 / 2 06 51	Mon. 477–7 / Mon. 477–9	231.57 / 25.37
Mon. 476–13	45 18 01.13 / 71 05 55.79	188 01 29 / 68 33 15	Mon. 476–12 / Mon. 476–14	40.56 / 44.25	Mon. 477–9	45 16 57.57 / 71 06 21.70	182 06 51 / 28 08 16	Mon. 477–8 / Mon. 477–10	25.37 / 86.44
Mon. 476–14	45 18 00.60 / 71 05 57.68	248 33 14 / 29 25 44	Mon. 476–13 / Mon. 476–15	44.25 / 113.55	Mon. 477–10	45 16 55.10 / 71 06 23.57	208 08 15 / 46 08 35	Mon. 477–9 / Mon. 477–11	86.44 / 50.29
Mon. 476–15	45 17 57.40 / 71 06 00.24	209 25 42 / 45 32 22	Mon. 476–14 / Mon. 476–16	113.55 / 116.43	Mon. 477–11	45 16 53.97 / 71 06 25.24	226 08 34 / 348 37 54	Mon. 477–10 / Mon. 477–12	50.29 / 75.38
Mon. 476–16	45 17 54.76 / 71 06 04.05	225 32 19 / 48 39 04	Mon. 476–15 / Mon. 476–17	116.43 / 101.70	Mon. 477–12	45 16 51.58 / 71 06 24.56	168 37 54 / 10 31 29	Mon. 477–11 / Mon. 477–13	75.38 / 66.86
Mon. 476–17	45 17 52.58 / 71 06 07.56	228 39 01 / 44 49 21	Mon. 476–16 / Mon. 476–18	101.70 / 100.24	Mon. 477–13	45 16 49.45 / 71 06 25.12	190 31 29 / 354 31 49	Mon. 477–12 / Mon. 477–14	66.86 / 34.52
Mon. 476–18	45 17 50.28 / 71 06 10.80	224 49 19 / 34 52 04	Mon. 476–17 / Mon. 476–19	100.24 / 69.62	Mon. 477–14	45 16 48.34 / 71 06 24.96	174 31 49 / 52 02 19	Mon. 477–13 / Mon. 477–15	34.52 / 53.36
Mon. 476–19	45 17 48.43 / 71 06 12.63	214 52 03 / 45 24 19	Mon. 476–18 / Mon. 476–20	69.62 / 163.16	Mon. 477–15	45 16 47.27 / 71 06 26.89	232 02 18 / 8 34 26	Mon. 477–14 / Mon. 477–16	53.36 / 153.30
Mon. 476–20	45 17 44.72 / 71 06 17.96	225 24 15 / 30 44 55	Mon. 476–19 / Mon. 476–21	163.16 / 55.40	Mon. 477–16	45 16 42.36 / 71 06 27.94	188 34 25 / 39 46 12	Mon. 477–15 / Mon. 477–17	153.30 / 186.46
Mon. 476–21	45 17 43.17 / 71 06 19.26	210 44 54 / 44 17 35	Mon. 476–20 / Mon. 476–22	55.40 / 56.26	Mon. 477–17	45 16 37.72 / 71 06 33.41	219 46 08 / 92 29 46	Mon. 477–16 / Mon. 477–18	186.46 / 64.82
Mon. 476–22	45 17 41.87 / 71 06 21.06	224 17 34 / 8 23 50	Mon. 476–21 / Mon. 476–23	56.26 / 84.24	Mon. 477–18	45 16 37.81 / 71 06 36.38	272 29 44 / 41 08 06	Mon. 477–17 / Mon. 477–19	64.82 / 21.21
Mon. 476–23	45 17 39.17 / 71 06 21.63	188 23 50 / 345 40 10	Mon. 476–22 / Mon. 476–24	84.24 / 74.95	Mon. 477–19	45 16 37.30 / 71 06 37.02	221 08 06 / 19 13 45	Mon. 477–18 / Mon. 477–20	21.21 / 28.22
Mon. 476–24	45 17 36.82 / 71 06 20.78	165 40 11 / 316 34 57	Mon. 476–23 / Mon. 476–25	74.95 / 128.73	Mon. 477–20	45 16 36.43 / 71 06 37.45	199 13 45 / 341 33 30	Mon. 477–19 / Mon. 477–21	28.22 / 66.25
Mon. 476–25	45 17 33.79 / 71 06 16.72	136 35 00 / 342 53 56	Mon. 476–24 / Mon. 476–26	128.73 / 36.93	Mon. 477–21	45 16 34.40 / 71 06 36.49	161 33 31 / 41 33 37	Mon. 477–20 / Mon. 477–22	66.25 / 63.07
Mon. 476–26	45 17 32.64 / 71 06 16.22	162 53 56 / 14 37 47	Mon. 476–25 / Mon. 476–27	36.93 / 58.39	Mon. 477–22	45 16 32.87 / 71 06 38.41	221 33 36 / 50 17 32	Mon. 477–21 / Mon. 477–23	63.07 / 56.93
Mon. 476–27	45 17 30.81 / 71 06 16.90	194 37 46 / 8 50 31	Mon. 476–26 / Mon. 476–28	58.39 / 32.13	Mon. 477–23	45 16 31.69 / 71 06 40.42	230 17 31 / 110 08 08	Mon. 477–22 / Mon. 477–24	56.93 / 81.14

BOUNDARY MONUMENTS—SOURCE OF SOUTHWEST BRANCH OF ST. JOHN TO HEAD OF HALLS STREAM—Continued

Station	Latitude and longitude	Azimuth	To station	Distance (meters)	Station	Latitude and longitude	Azimuth	To station	Distance (meters)
	° ′ ″	° ′ ″				° ′ ″	° ′ ″		
Mon. 477–24	45 16 32.59 / 71 06 43.91	290 08 06 / 47 33 56	Mon. 477–23 / Mon. 477–25	81.14 / 50.22	Mon. 478–6	45 15 18.82 / 71 07 28.88	195 44 13 / 41 22 41	Mon. 478–5 / Mon. 478–7	95.90 / 101.06
Mon. 477–25	45 16 31.50 / 71 06 45.61	227 33 55 / 56 46 09	Mon. 477–24 / Mon. 477–26	50.22 / 108.64	Mon. 478–7	45 15 16.36 / 71 07 31.95	221 22 39 / 109 24 50	Mon. 478–6 / Mon. 478–8	101.06 / 53.92
Mon. 477–26	45 16 29.57 / 71 06 49.78	236 46 06 / 104 54 47	Mon. 477–25 / Mon. 477–27	108.64 / 65.16	Mon. 478–8	45 15 16.94 / 71 07 34.28	289 24 48 / 40 38 18	Mon. 478–7 / Mon. 478–9	53.92 / 104.44
Mon. 477–27	45 16 30.11 / 71 06 52.67	284 54 45 / 68 38 28	Mon. 477–26 / Mon. 477–28	65.16 / 119.02	Mon. 478–9	45 15 14.38 / 71 07 37.40	220 38 16 / 129 23 16	Mon. 478–8 / Mon. 478–10	104.44 / 46.00
Mon. 477–28	45 16 28.71 / 71 06 57.75	248 38 24 / 51 48 43	Mon. 477–27 / Mon. 477–29	119.02 / 83.98	Mon. 478–10	45 15 15.32 / 71 07 39.03	309 23 15 / 56 11 43	Mon. 478–9 / Mon. 478–11	46.00 / 95.21
Mon. 477–29	45 16 27.02 / 71 07 00.78	231 48 41 / 6 53 22	Mon. 477–28 / Mon. 477–30	83.98 / 100.61	Mon. 478–11	45 15 13.61 / 71 07 42.66	236 11 40 / 17 33 20	Mon. 478–10 / Mon. 478–12	95.21 / 77.61
Mon. 477–30	45 16 23.79 / 71 07 01.34	186 53 22 / 25 41 10	Mon. 477–29 / Mon. 477–31	100.61 / 58.62	Mon. 478–12	45 15 11.21 / 71 07 43.73	197 33 19 / 42 16 40	Mon. 478–11 / Mon. 478–13	77.61 / 79.82
Mon. 477–31	45 16 22.08 / 71 07 02.50	205 41 09 / 345 03 49	Mon. 477–30 / Mon. 477–32	58.62 / 149.60	Mon. 478–13	45 15 09.30 / 71 07 46.19	222 16 38 / 27 22 02	Mon. 478–12 / Mon. 478–14	79.82 / 135.74
Mon. 477–32	45 16 17.40 / 71 07 00.73	165 03 50 / 357 35 30	Mon. 477–31 / Mon. 477–33	149.60 / 106.93	Mon. 478–14	45 15 05.39 / 71 07 49.06	207 22 00 / 342 17 16	Mon. 478–13 / Mon. 478–15	135.74 / 81.53
Mon. 477–33	45 16 13.94 / 71 07 00.52	177 35 30 / 7 42 59	Mon. 477–32 / Mon. 477–34	106.93 / 113.23	Mon. 478–15	45 15 02.88 / 71 07 47.92	162 17 17 / 15 22 48	Mon. 478–14 / Mon. 478–16	81.53 / 72.98
Mon. 477–34	45 16 10.30 / 71 07 01.22	187 42 58 / 33 32 01	Mon. 477–33 / Mon. 477–35	113.23 / 152.76	Mon. 478–16	45 15 00.60 / 71 07 48.81	195 22 47 / 48 51 55	Mon. 478–15 / Mon. 478–17	72.98 / 50.89
Mon. 477–35	45 16 06.18 / 71 07 05.09	213 31 58 / 48 35 41	Mon. 477–34 / Mon. 477–36	152.76 / 83.89	Mon. 478–17	45 14 59.51 / 71 07 50.56	228 51 54 / 353 46 51	Mon. 478–16 / Mon. 478–18	50.89 / 62.91
Mon. 477–36	45 16 04.38 / 71 07 07.98	228 35 39 / 42 13 55	Mon. 477–35 / Mon. 477–37	83.89 / 99.79	Mon. 478–18	45 14 57.48 / 71 07 50.25	173 46 51 / 350 10 28	Mon. 478–17 / Mon. 478–19	62.91 / 77.67
Mon. 477–37	45 16 01.98 / 71 07 11.06	222 13 53 / 27 33 29	Mon. 477–36 / Mon. 477–38	99.79 / 82.31	Mon. 478–19	45 14 55.01 / 71 07 49.64	170 10 28 / 29 43 56	Mon. 478–18 / Mon. 478–20	77.67 / 141.10
Mon. 477–38	45 15 59.62 / 71 07 12.80	207 33 28 / 16 15 46	Mon. 477–37 / Mon. 477–39	82.31 / 154.10	Mon. 478–20	45 14 51.04 / 71 07 52.85	209 43 54 / 6 59 23	Mon. 478–19 / Mon. 478–21	141.10 / 97.75
Mon. 477–39	45 15 54.83 / 71 07 14.78	196 15 45 / 350 00 41	Mon. 477–38 / Mon. 477–40	154.10 / 103.56	Mon. 478–21	45 14 47.89 / 71 07 53.40	186 59 23 / 33 12 57	Mon. 478–20 / Mon. 478–22	97.75 / 111.79
Mon. 477–40	45 15 51.52 / 71 07 13.96	170 00 42 / 23 33 53	Mon. 477–39 / Mon. 477–41	103.56 / 67.49	Mon. 478–22	45 14 44.86 / 71 07 56.21	213 12 55 / 37 00 50	Mon. 478–21 / Mon. 478–23	111.79 / 98.32
Mon. 477–41	45 15 49.52 / 71 07 15.20	203 33 52 / 307 53 35	Mon. 477–40 / Mon. 477–42	67.49 / 108.65	Mon. 478–23	45 14 42.32 / 71 07 58.92	217 00 48 / 32 50 39	Mon. 478–22 / Mon. 478–24	98.32 / 64.83
Mon. 477–42	45 15 47.36 / 71 07 11.26	127 53 38 / 28 02 09	Mon. 477–41 / Mon. 477–43	108.65 / 72.54	Mon. 478–24	45 14 40.56 / 71 08 00.53	212 50 38 / 59 37 22	Mon. 478–23 / Mon. 478–25	64.83 / 95.96
Mon. 477–43	45 15 45.29 / 71 07 12.83	208 02 08 / 341 55 03	Mon. 477–42 / Mon. 477–44	72.54 / 48.84	Mon. 478–25	45 14 38.98 / 71 08 04.33	239 37 19 / 73 20 07	Mon. 478–24 / Mon. 478–26	95.96 / 35.28
Mon. 477–44	45 15 43.78 / 71 07 12.13	161 55 03 / 7 11 23	Mon. 477–43 / Mon. 477–45	48.84 / 50.59	Mon. 478–26	45 14 38.66 / 71 08 05.88	253 20 06 / 65 33 06	Mon. 478–25 / Mon. 478–27	35.28 / 48.01
Mon. 477–45	45 15 42.16 / 71 07 12.42	187 11 23 / 82 01 31	Mon. 477–44 / Mon. 477–46	50.59 / 40.73	Mon. 478–27	45 14 38.01 / 71 08 07.88	245 33 05 / 81 38 03	Mon. 478–26 / Mon. 478–28	48.01 / 60.37
Mon. 477–46	45 15 41.97 / 71 07 14.27	262 01 30 / 40 46 19	Mon. 477–45 / Mon. 477–47	40.73 / 68.63	Mon. 478–28	45 14 37.73 / 71 08 10.62	261 38 01 / 98 16 54	Mon. 478–27 / Mon. 478–29	60.37 / 109.75
Mon. 477–47	45 15 40.29 / 71 07 16.33	220 46 17 / 28 11 11	Mon. 477–46 / Mon. 477–48	68.63 / 99.50	Mon. 478–29	45 14 38.24 / 71 08 15.60	278 16 50 / 67 52 52	Mon. 478–28 / Mon. 478–30	109.75 / 98.27
Mon. 477–48	45 15 37.45 / 71 07 18.48	208 11 09 / 43 35 38	Mon. 477–47 / Mon. 478	99.50 / 125.87	Mon. 478–30	45 14 37.04 / 71 08 19.78	247 52 49 / 43 22 33	Mon. 478–29 / Mon. 478–31	98.27 / 114.08
Mon. 478	45 15 34.50 / 71 07 22.47	223 35 35 / 43 26 00	Mon. 477–48 / Mon. 478–1	125.87 / 151.46	Mon. 478–31	45 14 34.36 / 71 08 23.37	223 22 30 / 90 20 04	Mon. 478–30 / Mon. 478–32	114.08 / 87.92
Mon. 478–1	45 15 30.93 / 71 07 27.24	223 25 56 / 56 25 57	Mon. 478 / Mon. 478–2	151.46 / 22.29	Mon. 478–32	45 14 34.37 / 71 08 27.40	270 20 01 / 72 23 33	Mon. 478–31 / Mon. 478–33	87.92 / 95.15
Mon. 478–2	45 15 30.53 / 71 07 28.09	236 25 56 / 15 47 09	Mon. 478–1 / Mon. 478–3	22.29 / 103.77	Mon. 478–33	45 14 33.44 / 71 08 31.56	252 23 30 / 90 39 05	Mon. 478–32 / Mon. 478–34	95.15 / 155.85
Mon. 478–3	45 15 27.30 / 71 07 29.39	195 47 08 / 346 05 49	Mon. 478–2 / Mon. 478–4	103.77 / 43.71	Mon. 478–34	45 14 33.50 / 71 08 38.70	270 39 00 / 54 14 27	Mon. 478–33 / Mon. 478–35	155.85 / 54.74
Mon. 478–4	45 15 25.92 / 71 07 28.91	166 05 49 / 348 12 01	Mon. 478–3 / Mon. 478–5	43.71 / 129.79	Mon. 478–35	45 14 32.46 / 71 08 40.74	234 14 26 / 48 52 16	Mon. 478–34 / Mon. 479	54.74 / 177.47
Mon. 478–5	45 15 21.81 / 71 07 27.69	168 12 02 / 15 44 14	Mon. 478–4 / Mon. 478–6	129.79 / 95.90	Mon. 479	45 14 28.68 / 71 08 46.87	228 52 12 / 13 50 32	Mon. 478–35 / Mon. 479–1	177.47 / 32.40

BOUNDARY MONUMENTS—SOURCE OF SOUTHWEST BRANCH OF ST. JOHN TO HEAD OF HALLS STREAM—Continued

Station	Latitude and longitude	Azimuth	To station	Distance (meters)	Station	Latitude and longitude	Azimuth	To station	Distance (meters)
	° ′ ″	° ′ ″				° ′ ″	° ′ ″		
Mon. 479-1	45 14 27.66 / 71 08 47.22	193 50 32 / 31 35 54	Mon. 479 / Mon. 479-2	32.40 / 93.06	Mon. 480-16	45 14 54.72 / 71 09 31.16	288 29 49 / 117 17 49	Mon. 480-15 / Mon. 480-17	88.80 / 90.63
Mon. 479-2	45 14 25.09 / 71 08 49.46	211 35 52 / 340 52 18	Mon. 479-1 / Mon. 479-3	93.06 / 57.64	Mon. 480-17	45 14 56.06 / 71 09 34.86	297 17 46 / 86 09 41	Mon. 480-16 / Mon. 480-18	90.63 / 58.39
Mon. 479-3	45 14 23.33 / 71 08 48.59	160 52 19 / 72 28 20	Mon. 479-2 / Mon. 479-4	57.64 / 107.22	Mon. 480-18	45 14 55.93 / 71 09 37.53	266 09 39 / 130 19 14	Mon. 480-17 / Mon. 480-19	58.39 / 105.68
Mon. 479-4	45 14 22.28 / 71 08 53.28	252 28 17 / 98 19 02	Mon. 479-3 / Mon. 479-5	107.22 / 37.78	Mon. 480-19	45 14 58.15 / 71 09 41.22	310 19 11 / 131 45 55	Mon. 480-18 / Mon. 480-20	105.68 / 69.56
Mon. 479-5	45 14 22.46 / 71 08 55.00	278 19 01 / 140 56 18	Mon. 479-4 / Mon. 479-6	37.78 / 34.11	Mon. 480-20	45 14 59.65 / 71 09 43.60	311 45 54 / 142 08 47	Mon. 480-19 / Mon. 480-21	69.56 / 38.19
Mon. 479-6	45 14 23.32 / 71 08 55.98	320 56 17 / 208 17 03	Mon. 479-5 / Mon. 479-7	34.11 / 29.71	Mon. 480-21	45 15 00.63 / 71 09 44.68	322 08 46 / 126 35 46	Mon. 480-20 / Mon. 481	38.19 / 48.32
Mon. 479-7	45 14 24.17 / 71 08 55.33	28 17 03 / 194 37 28	Mon. 479-6 / Mon. 479-8	29.71 / 33.77	Mon. 481	45 15 01.56 / 71 09 46.45	306 35 45 / 28 20 51	Mon. 480-21 / Mon. 481-1	48.32 / 94.40
Mon. 479-8	45 14 25.22 / 71 08 54.94	14 37 28 / 207 35 20	Mon. 479-7 / Mon. 479-9	33.77 / 43.93	Mon. 481-1	45 14 58.87 / 71 09 48.51	208 20 50 / 56 15 59	Mon. 481 / Mon. 481-2	94.40 / 35.10
Mon. 479-9	45 14 26.49 / 71 08 54.01	27 35 21 / 224 40 16	Mon. 479-8 / Mon. 479-10	43.93 / 47.35	Mon. 481-2	45 14 58.24 / 71 09 49.85	236 15 58 / 36 33 31	Mon. 481-1 / Mon. 481-3	35.10 / 79.28
Mon. 479-10	45 14 27.58 / 71 08 52.48	44 40 17 / 166 52 24	Mon. 479-9 / Mon. 479-11	47.35 / 34.16	Mon. 481-3	45 14 56.17 / 71 09 52.02	216 33 29 / 106 05 47	Mon. 481-2 / Mon. 481-4	79.28 / 95.02
Mon. 479-11	45 14 28.66 / 71 08 52.84	346 52 24 / 138 11 07	Mon. 479-10 / Mon. 479-12	34.16 / 46.02	Mon. 481-4	45 14 57.03 / 71 09 56.20	286 05 44 / 31 48 18	Mon. 481-3 / Mon. 481-5	95.02 / 73.36
Mon. 479-12	45 14 29.77 / 71 08 54.25	318 11 06 / 175 49 48	Mon. 479-11 / Mon. 479-13	46.02 / 48.43	Mon. 481-5	45 14 55.01 / 71 09 57.98	211 48 17 / 52 18 41	Mon. 481-4 / Mon. 481-6	73.36 / 29.51
Mon. 479-13	45 14 31.33 / 71 08 54.41	355 49 48 / 168 09 21	Mon. 479-12 / Mon. 479-14	48.43 / 56.11	Mon. 481-6	45 14 54.42 / 71 09 59.05	232 18 40 / 41 19 23	Mon. 481-5 / Mon. 481-7	29.51 / 101.74
Mon. 479-14	45 14 33.11 / 71 08 54.94	348 09 21 / 137 46 56	Mon. 479-13 / Mon. 479-15	56.11 / 64.01	Mon. 481-7	45 14 51.95 / 71 10 02.13	221 19 21 / 8 53 12	Mon. 481-6 / Mon. 481-8	101.74 / 22.20
Mon. 479-15	45 14 34.65 / 71 08 56.91	317 46 54 / 132 58 21	Mon. 479-14 / Mon. 480	64.01 / 89.10	Mon. 481-8	45 14 51.24 / 71 10 02.28	188 53 12 / 48 23 06	Mon. 481-7 / Mon. 481-9	22.20 / 80.32
Mon. 480	45 14 36.61 / 71 08 59.90	312 58 19 / 132 43 35	Mon. 479-15 / Mon. 480-1	89.10 / 3.35	Mon. 481-9	45 14 49.51 / 71 10 05.04	228 23 04 / 95 46 16	Mon. 481-8 / Mon. 481-10	80.32 / 47.06
Mon. 480-1	45 14 36.69 / 71 09 00.01	312 43 35 / 116 17 30	Mon. 480 / Mon. 480-2	3.35 / 55.95	Mon. 481-10	45 14 49.66 / 71 10 07.18	275 46 14 / 41 31 13	Mon. 481-9 / Mon. 481-11	47.06 / 27.00
Mon. 480-2	45 14 37.49 / 71 09 02.31	296 17 28 / 100 54 23	Mon. 480-1 / Mon. 480-3	55.95 / 55.68	Mon. 481-11	45 14 49.01 / 71 10 08.00	221 31 13 / 25 52 33	Mon. 481-10 / Mon. 481-12	27.00 / 46.97
Mon. 480-3	45 14 37.83 / 71 09 04.82	280 54 21 / 140 55 15	Mon. 480-2 / Mon. 480-4	55.68 / 111.81	Mon. 481-12	45 14 47.64 / 71 10 08.94	205 52 32 / 39 28 03	Mon. 481-11 / Mon. 481-13	46.97 / 30.10
Mon. 480-4	45 14 40.64 / 71 09 08.05	320 55 13 / 119 48 06	Mon. 480-3 / Mon. 480-5	111.81 / 86.54	Mon. 481-13	45 14 46.89 / 71 10 09.82	219 28 03 / 128 55 53	Mon. 481-12 / Mon. 481-14	30.10 / 62.63
Mon. 480-5	45 14 42.04 / 71 09 11.49	299 48 04 / 139 14 50	Mon. 480-4 / Mon. 480-6	86.54 / 126.71	Mon. 481-14	45 14 48.16 / 71 10 12.06	308 55 51 / 42 37 25	Mon. 481-13 / Mon. 481-15	62.63 / 32.08
Mon. 480-6	45 14 45.15 / 71 09 15.28	319 14 47 / 108 53 58	Mon. 480-5 / Mon. 480-7	126.71 / 88.58	Mon. 481-15	45 14 47.40 / 71 10 13.05	222 37 24 / 119 58 01	Mon. 481-14 / Mon. 481-16	32.08 / 39.39
Mon. 480-7	45 14 46.08 / 71 09 19.13	288 53 55 / 139 25 04	Mon. 480-6 / Mon. 480-8	88.58 / 58.20	Mon. 481-16	45 14 48.04 / 71 10 14.62	299 58 00 / 37 46 24	Mon. 481-15 / Mon. 481-17	39.39 / 85.95
Mon. 480-8	45 14 47.51 / 71 09 20.86	319 25 03 / 91 12 29	Mon. 480-7 / Mon. 480-9	58.20 / 59.12	Mon. 481-17	45 14 45.83 / 71 10 17.03	217 46 22 / 92 43 25	Mon. 481-16 / Mon. 481-18	85.95 / 85.20
Mon. 480-9	45 14 47.55 / 71 09 23.57	271 12 27 / 202 52 50	Mon. 480-8 / Mon. 480-10	59.12 / 55.47	Mon. 481-18	45 14 45.96 / 71 10 20.93	272 43 22 / 106 34 39	Mon. 481-17 / Mon. 481-19	85.20 / 59.34
Mon. 480-10	45 14 49.20 / 71 09 22.58	22 52 51 / 147 27 49	Mon. 480-9 / Mon. 480-11	55.47 / 71.18	Mon. 481-19	45 14 46.51 / 71 10 23.54	286 34 37 / 110 08 04	Mon. 481-18 / Mon. 481-20	59.34 / 47.74
Mon. 480-11	45 14 51.15 / 71 09 24.34	327 27 48 / 92 52 00	Mon. 480-10 / Mon. 480-12	71.18 / 56.69	Mon. 481-20	45 14 47.05 / 71 10 25.60	290 08 03 / 23 48 19	Mon. 481-19 / Mon. 481-21	47.74 / 61.24
Mon. 480-12	45 14 51.24 / 71 09 26.94	272 51 58 / 156 36 53	Mon. 480-11 / Mon. 480-13	56.69 / 21.48	Mon. 481-21	45 14 45.23 / 71 10 26.73	203 48 18 / 54 23 52	Mon. 481-20 / Mon. 481-22	61.24 / 63.15
Mon. 480-13	45 14 51.88 / 71 09 27.33	336 36 53 / 201 07 10	Mon. 480-12 / Mon. 480-14	21.48 / 37.00	Mon. 481-22	45 14 44.04 / 71 10 29.08	234 23 50 / 90 23 03	Mon. 481-21 / Mon. 481-23	63.15 / 27.68
Mon. 480-14	45 14 53.00 / 71 09 26.72	21 07 10 / 152 43 55	Mon. 480-13 / Mon. 480-15	37.00 / 27.95	Mon. 481-23	45 14 44.05 / 71 10 30.35	270 23 02 / 32 56 32	Mon. 481-22 / Mon. 481-24	27.68 / 41.60
Mon. 480-15	45 14 53.80 / 71 09 27.30	332 43 55 / 108 29 52	Mon. 480-14 / Mon. 480-16	27.95 / 88.80	Mon. 481-24	45 14 42.92 / 71 10 31.39	212 56 31 / 58 28 53	Mon. 481-23 / Mon. 481-25	41.60 / 25.59

BOUNDARY MONUMENTS—SOURCE OF SOUTHWEST BRANCH OF ST. JOHN TO HEAD OF HALLS STREAM—Continued

Station	Latitude and longitude	Azimuth	To station	Distance (meters)
Mon. 481–25	45 14 42.48 / 71 10 32.39	238 28 52 / 45 12 25	Mon. 481–24 / Mon. 481–26	25.59 / 59.19
Mon. 481–26	45 14 41.13 / 71 10 34.32	225 12 24 / 37 45 58	Mon. 481–25 / Mon. 481–27	59.19 / 63.97
Mon. 481–27	45 14 39.49 / 71 10 36.11	217 45 57 / 70 33 34	Mon. 481–26 / Mon. 481–28	63.97 / 57.68
Mon. 481–28	45 14 38.87 / 71 10 38.61	250 33 32 / 15 41 48	Mon. 481–27 / Mon. 481–29	57.68 / 38.89
Mon. 481–29	45 14 37.66 / 71 10 39.09	195 41 48 / 23 37 01	Mon. 481–28 / Mon. 481–30	38.89 / 77.50
Mon. 481–30	45 14 35.36 / 71 10 40.51	203 37 00 / 40 55 08	Mon. 481–29 / Mon. 481–31	77.50 / 49.83
Mon. 481–31	45 14 34.14 / 71 10 42.01	220 55 07 / 24 26 13	Mon. 481–30 / Mon. 481–32	49.83 / 95.66
Mon. 481–32	45 14 31.32 / 71 10 43.82	204 26 12 / 6 55 35	Mon. 481–31 / Mon. 481–33	95.66 / 64.24
Mon. 481–33	45 14 29.25 / 71 10 44.18	186 55 35 / 66 34 50	Mon. 481–32 / Mon. 481–34	64.24 / 63.36
Mon. 481–34	45 14 28.44 / 71 10 46.85	246 34 48 / 29 39 07	Mon. 481–33 / Mon. 481–35	63.36 / 81.38
Mon. 481–35	45 14 26.14 / 71 10 48.69	209 39 06 / 30 40 20	Mon. 481–34 / Mon. 482	81.38 / 73.90
Mon. 482	45 14 24.08 / 71 10 50.42	210 40 19 / 108 45 06	Mon. 481–35 / Mon. 482–1	73.90 / 87.44
Mon. 482–1	45 14 25.00 / 71 10 54.22	288 45 03 / 88 15 03	Mon. 482 / Mon. 482–2	87.44 / 54.08
Mon. 482–2	45 14 24.94 / 71 10 56.70	268 15 01 / 149 47 21	Mon. 482–1 / Mon. 482–3	54.08 / 29.75
Mon. 482–3	45 14 25.78 / 71 10 57.38	329 47 21 / 131 47 41	Mon. 482–2 / Mon. 482–4	29.75 / 38.11
Mon. 482–4	45 14 26.60 / 71 10 58.68	311 47 40 / 187 05 55	Mon. 482–3 / Mon. 482–5	38.11 / 79.40
Mon. 482–5	45 14 29.15 / 71 10 58.23	7 05 55 / 133 11 15	Mon. 482–4 / Mon. 482–6	79.40 / 37.91
Mon. 482–6	45 14 29.99 / 71 10 59.50	313 11 14 / 185 39 14	Mon. 482–5 / Mon. 482–7	37.91 / 45.60
Mon. 482–7	45 14 31.46 / 71 10 59.30	5 39 14 / 161 22 14	Mon. 482–6 / Mon. 482–8	45.60 / 22.18
Mon. 482–8	45 14 32.14 / 71 10 59.62	341 22 14 / 199 51 31	Mon. 482–7 / Mon. 482–9	22.18 / 38.48
Mon. 482–9	45 14 33.32 / 71 10 59.02	19 51 31 / 149 28 06	Mon. 482–8 / Mon. 482–10	38.48 / 124.10
Mon. 482–10	45 14 36.78 / 71 11 01.91	329 28 04 / 104 00 13	Mon. 482–9 / Mon. 482–11	124.10 / 54.97
Mon. 482–11	45 14 37.21 / 71 11 04.36	284 00 11 / 162 13 25	Mon. 482–10 / Mon. 482–12	54.97 / 25.51
Mon. 482–12	45 14 38.00 / 71 11 04.72	342 13 25 / 196 37 36	Mon. 482–11 / Mon. 482–13	25.51 / 32.41
Mon. 482–13	45 14 39.00 / 71 11 04.29	16 37 36 / 173 49 04	Mon. 482–12 / Mon. 482–14	32.41 / 38.43
Mon. 482–14	45 14 40.24 / 71 11 04.48	353 49 04 / 183 09 08	Mon. 482–13 / Mon. 482–15	38.43 / 57.80
Mon. 482–15	45 14 42.11 / 71 11 04.34	3 09 08 / 81 03 38	Mon. 482–14 / Mon. 482–16	57.80 / 43.96
Mon. 482–16	45 14 41.89 / 71 11 06.33	261 03 37 / 122 22 35	Mon. 482–15 / Mon. 482–17	43.96 / 40.55
Mon. 482–17	45 14 42.59 / 71 11 07.90	302 22 34 / 21 56 04	Mon. 482–16 / Mon. 482–18	40.55 / 90.81
Mon. 482–18	45 14 39.86 / 71 11 09.45	201 56 03 / 79 03 57	Mon. 482–17 / Mon. 482–19	90.81 / 53.27
Mon. 482–19	45 14 39.54 / 71 11 11.85	259 03 55 / 105 09 33	Mon. 482–18 / Mon. 482–20	53.27 / 67.79
Mon. 482–20	45 14 40.11 / 71 11 14.85	285 09 31 / 136 54 52	Mon. 482–19 / Mon. 482–21	67.79 / 102.42
Mon. 482–21	45 14 42.53 / 71 11 18.06	316 54 50 / 198 39 29	Mon. 482–20 / Mon. 482–22	102.42 / 37.19
Mon. 482–22	45 14 43.68 / 71 11 17.51	18 39 29 / 204 36 58	Mon. 482–21 / Mon. 482–23	37.19 / 66.35
Mon. 482–23	45 14 45.63 / 71 11 16.24	24 36 59 / 161 51 59	Mon. 482–22 / Mon. 482–24	66.35 / 42.70
Mon. 482–24	45 14 46.94 / 71 11 16.85	341 51 59 / 198 40 35	Mon. 482–23 / Mon. 482–25	42.70 / 27.08
Mon. 482–25	45 14 47.78 / 71 11 16.46	18 40 35 / 165 33 48	Mon. 482–24 / Mon. 482–26	27.08 / 126.39
Mon. 482–26	45 14 51.74 / 71 11 17.90	345 33 47 / 115 39 27	Mon. 482–25 / Mon. 482–27	126.39 / 42.02
Mon. 482–27	45 14 52.33 / 71 11 19.64	295 39 26 / 92 03 23	Mon. 482–26 / Mon. 482–28	42.02 / 61.32
Mon. 482–28	45 14 52.40 / 71 11 22.45	272 03 21 / 49 39 21	Mon. 482–27 / Mon. 482–29	61.32 / 36.31
Mon. 482–29	45 14 51.64 / 71 11 23.72	229 39 20 / 99 53 20	Mon. 482–28 / Mon. 482–30	36.31 / 36.08
Mon. 482–30	45 14 51.84 / 71 11 25.35	279 53 19 / 98 06 02	Mon. 482–29 / Mon. 482–31	36.08 / 48.64
Mon. 482–31	45 14 52.06 / 71 11 27.55	278 06 00 / 111 44 26	Mon. 482–30 / Mon. 482–32	48.64 / 52.04
Mon. 482–32	45 14 52.69 / 71 11 29.77	291 44 24 / 155 12 19	Mon. 482–31 / Mon. 482–33	52.04 / 69.92
Mon. 482–33	45 14 54.74 / 71 11 31.11	335 12 18 / 173 47 39	Mon. 482–32 / Mon. 482–34	69.92 / 48.64
Mon. 482–34	45 14 56.31 / 71 11 31.36	353 47 39 / 201 21 11	Mon. 482–33 / Mon. 482–35	48.64 / 61.62
Mon. 482–35	45 14 58.17 / 71 11 30.33	21 21 12 / 138 45 17	Mon. 482–34 / Mon. 482–36	61.62 / 21.50
Mon. 482–36	45 14 58.69 / 71 11 30.98	318 45 17 / 106 27 38	Mon. 482–35 / Mon. 482–37	21.50 / 137.93
Mon. 482–37	45 14 59.96 / 71 11 37.04	286 27 34 / 88 32 10	Mon. 482–36 / Mon. 482–38	137.93 / 26.21
Mon. 482–38	45 14 59.94 / 71 11 38.24	268 32 09 / 152 39 27	Mon. 482–37 / Mon. 482–39	26.21 / 53.99
Mon. 482–39	45 15 01.49 / 71 11 39.38	332 39 26 / 130 14 49	Mon. 482–38 / Mon. 482–40	53.99 / 53.75
Mon. 482–40	45 15 02.62 / 71 11 41.26	310 14 48 / 134 08 59	Mon. 482–39 / Mon. 482–41	53.75 / 100.11
Mon. 482–41	45 15 04.88 / 71 11 44.56	314 08 57 / 197 43 44	Mon. 482–40 / Mon. 482–42	100.11 / 69.87
Mon. 482–42	45 15 07.03 / 71 11 43.58	17 43 44 / 156 46 43	Mon. 482–41 / Mon. 483	69.87 / 118.05
Mon. 483	45 15 10.55 / 71 11 45.71	336 46 42 / 122 14 02	Mon. 482–42 / Mon. 483–1	118.05 / 60.96
Mon. 483–1	45 15 11.60 / 71 11 48.08	302 14 00 / 199 14 20	Mon. 483 / Mon. 483–2	60.96 / 32.87
Mon. 483–2	45 15 12.60 / 71 11 47.58	19 14 20 / 163 56 52	Mon. 483–1 / Mon. 483–3	32.87 / 45.32
Mon. 483–3	45 15 14.02 / 71 11 48.16	343 56 52 / 168 25 41	Mon. 483–2 / Mon. 483–4	45.32 / 19.10
Mon. 483–4	45 15 14.62 / 71 11 48.33	348 25 41 / 114 12 26	Mon. 483–3 / Mon. 483–5	19.10 / 20.91
Mon. 483–5	45 15 14.90 / 71 11 49.21	294 12 25 / 102 58 05	Mon. 483–4 / Mon. 483–6	20.91 / 57.43
Mon. 483–6	45 15 15.32 / 71 11 51.77	282 58 04 / 25 52 05	Mon. 483–5 / Mon. 483–7	57.43 / 31.48
Mon. 483–7	45 15 14.40 / 71 11 52.40	205 52 04 / 93 18 47	Mon. 483–6 / Mon. 483–8	31.48 / 31.72

BOUNDARY MONUMENTS—SOURCE OF SOUTHWEST BRANCH OF ST. JOHN TO HEAD OF HALLS STREAM—Continued

Station	Latitude and longitude	Azimuth	To station	Distance (meters)
	° ′ ″	° ′ ″		
Mon. 483-8	45 15 14.46 / 71 11 53.86	273 18 46 / 121 40 22	Mon. 483-7 / Mon. 483-9	31.72 / 34.09
Mon. 483-9	45 15 15.04 / 71 11 55.19	301 40 21 / 113 03 42	Mon. 483-8 / Mon. 483-10	34.09 / 46.65
Mon. 483-10	45 15 15.63 / 71 11 57.15	293 03 41 / 30 41 36	Mon. 483-9 / Mon. 483-11	46.65 / 41.48
Mon. 483-11	45 15 14.48 / 71 11 58.12	210 41 35 / 33 31 35	Mon. 483-10 / Mon. 483-12	41.48 / 46.67
Mon. 483-12	45 15 13.22 / 71 11 59.31	213 31 34 / 91 03 13	Mon. 483-11 / Mon. 483-13	46.67 / 34.97
Mon. 483-13	45 15 13.24 / 71 12 00.91	271 03 12 / 36 26 48	Mon. 483-12 / Mon. 483-14	34.97 / 42.55
Mon. 483-14	45 15 12.13 / 71 12 02.07	216 26 47 / 107 04 43	Mon. 483-13 / Mon. 483-15	42.55 / 25.93
Mon. 483-15	45 15 12.37 / 71 12 03.21	287 04 43 / 142 05 07	Mon. 483-14 / Mon. 483-16	25.93 / 37.44
Mon. 483-16	45 15 13.33 / 71 12 04.26	322 05 06 / 162 44 15	Mon. 483-15 / Mon. 483-17	37.44 / 48.40
Mon. 483-17	45 15 14.83 / 71 12 04.92	342 44 15 / 98 52 47	Mon. 483-16 / Mon. 483-18	48.40 / 53.13
Mon. 483-18	45 15 15.09 / 71 12 07.33	278 52 45 / 114 53 12	Mon. 483-17 / Mon. 483-19	53.13 / 44.89
Mon. 483-19	45 15 15.71 / 71 12 09.19	294 53 11 / 96 57 08	Mon. 483-18 / Mon. 483-20	44.89 / 41.30
Mon. 483-20	45 15 15.87 / 71 12 11.07	276 57 07 / 38 43 18	Mon. 483-19 / Mon. 483-21	41.30 / 49.47
Mon. 483-21	45 15 14.62 / 71 12 12.49	218 43 17 / 53 24 12	Mon. 483-20 / Mon. 483-22	49.47 / 87.08
Mon. 483-22	45 15 12.94 / 71 12 15.70	233 24 09 / 10 59 07	Mon. 483-21 / Mon. 483-23	87.08 / 42.25
Mon. 483-23	45 15 11.59 / 71 12 16.07	190 59 07 / 75 01 29	Mon. 483-22 / Mon. 483-24	42.25 / 61.26
Mon. 483-24	45 15 11.08 / 71 12 18.78	255 01 27 / 37 39 31	Mon. 483-23 / Mon. 484	61.26 / 25.59
Mon. 484	45 15 10.42 / 71 12 19.50	217 39 30 / 37 39 00	Mon. 483-24 / Mon. 484-1	25.59 / 55.62
Mon. 484-1	45 15 09.00 / 71 12 21.06	217 38 59 / 117 52 36	Mon. 484 / Mon. 484-2	55.62 / 95.08
Mon. 484-2	45 15 10.44 / 71 12 24.91	297 52 33 / 101 58 12	Mon. 484-1 / Mon. 484-3	95.08 / 45.35
Mon. 484-3	45 15 10.74 / 71 12 26.95	281 58 11 / 130 23 06	Mon. 484-2 / Mon. 484-4	45.35 / 27.97
Mon. 484-4	45 15 11.33 / 71 12 27.92	310 23 05 / 26 46 43	Mon. 484-3 / Mon. 484-5	27.97 / 92.93
Mon. 484-5	45 15 08.64 / 71 12 29.84	206 46 42 / 51 39 47	Mon. 484-4 / Mon. 484-6	92.93 / 32.41
Mon. 484-6	45 15 07.99 / 71 12 31.01	231 39 46 / 15 27 58	Mon. 484-5 / Mon. 484-7	32.41 / 95.25
Mon. 484-7	45 15 05.02 / 71 12 32.18	195 27 57 / 64 45 36	Mon. 484-6 / Mon. 484-8	95.25 / 53.96
Mon. 484-8	45 15 04.27 / 71 12 34.41	244 45 34 / 42 02 18	Mon. 484-7 / Mon. 484-9	53.96 / 75.16
Mon. 484-9	45 15 02.46 / 71 12 36.72	222 02 16 / 98 12 41	Mon. 484-8 / Mon. 484-10	75.16 / 75.31
Mon. 484-10	45 15 02.81 / 71 12 40.14	278 12 39 / 49 32 24	Mon. 484-9 / Mon. 484-11	75.31 / 28.84
Mon. 484-11	45 15 02.20 / 71 12 41.14	229 32 23 / 30 28 16	Mon. 484-10 / Mon. 484-12	28.84 / 40.37
Mon. 484-12	45 15 01.08 / 71 12 42.08	210 28 15 / 82 10 53	Mon. 484-11 / Mon. 484-13	40.37 / 41.57
Mon. 484-13	45 15 00.90 / 71 12 43.97	262 10 52 / 112 06 37	Mon. 484-12 / Mon. 484-14	41.57 / 55.38
Mon. 484-14	45 15 01.57 / 71 12 46.33	292 06 35 / 47 18 30	Mon. 484-13 / Mon. 484-15	55.38 / 38.04
Mon. 484-15	45 15 00.74 / 71 12 47.61	227 18 29 / 125 50 39	Mon. 484-14 / Mon. 484-16	38.04 / 104.72
Mon. 484-16	45 15 02.72 / 71 12 51.50	305 50 36 / 92 55 17	Mon. 484-15 / Mon. 484-17	104.72 / 43.38
Mon. 484-17	45 15 02.79 / 71 12 53.49	272 55 16 / 60 16 31	Mon. 484-16 / Mon. 484-18	43.38 / 61.15
Mon. 484-18	45 15 01.81 / 71 12 55.92	240 16 29 / 90 15 54	Mon. 484-17 / Mon. 484-19	61.15 / 158.07
Mon. 484-19	45 15 01.84 / 71 13 03.17	270 15 49 / 139 24 40	Mon. 484-18 / Mon. 484-20	158.07 / 65.69
Mon. 484-20	45 15 03.45 / 71 13 05.13	319 24 39 / 156 04 06	Mon. 484-19 / Mon. 484-21	65.69 / 27.76
Mon. 484-21	45 15 04.27 / 71 13 05.64	336 04 06 / 76 32 31	Mon. 484-20 / Mon. 484-22	27.76 / 34.18
Mon. 484-22	45 15 04.02 / 71 13 07.17	256 32 30 / 34 10 14	Mon. 484-21 / Mon. 484-23	34.18 / 48.28
Mon. 484-23	45 15 02.72 / 71 13 08.41	214 10 13 / 30 23 47	Mon. 484-22 / Mon. 484-24	48.28 / 21.31
Mon. 484-24	45 15 02.12 / 71 13 08.91	210 23 47 / 97 29 13	Mon. 484-23 / Mon. 484-25	21.31 / 73.05
Mon. 484-25	45 15 02.43 / 71 13 12.23	277 29 11 / 100 07 35	Mon. 484-24 / Mon. 484-26	73.05 / 90.34
Mon. 484-26	45 15 02.95 / 71 13 16.30	280 07 32 / 185 38 30	Mon. 484-25 / Mon. 484-27	90.34 / 64.89
Mon. 484-27	45 15 05.04 / 71 13 16.01	5 38 30 / 163 01 22	Mon. 484-26 / Mon. 484-28	64.89 / 72.51
Mon. 484-28	45 15 07.29 / 71 13 16.98	343 01 21 / 117 34 06	Mon. 484-27 / Mon. 484-29	72.51 / 65.49
Mon. 484-29	45 15 08.27 / 71 13 19.65	297 34 04 / 187 44 40	Mon. 484-28 / Mon. 484-30	65.49 / 93.64
Mon. 484-30	45 15 11.28 / 71 13 19.07	7 44 40 / 122 13 30	Mon. 484-29 / Mon. 484-31	93.64 / 65.81
Mon. 484-31	45 15 12.41 / 71 13 21.62	302 13 28 / 37 33 32	Mon. 484-30 / Mon. 484-32	65.81 / 104.69
Mon. 484-32	45 15 09.72 / 71 13 24.55	217 33 30 / 53 22 52	Mon. 484-31 / Mon. 484-33	104.69 / 75.19
Mon. 484-33	45 15 08.27 / 71 13 27.32	233 22 50 / 78 22 04	Mon. 484-32 / Mon. 484-34	75.19 / 54.52
Mon. 484-34	45 15 07.92 / 71 13 29.77	258 22 02 / 44 52 28	Mon. 484-33 / Mon. 484-35	54.52 / 56.39
Mon. 484-35	45 15 06.62 / 71 13 31.59	224 52 27 / 80 28 14	Mon. 484-34 / Mon. 484-36	56.39 / 22.83
Mon. 484-36	45 15 06.50 / 71 13 32.62	260 28 13 / 52 27 21	Mon. 484-35 / Mon. 484-37	22.83 / 46.34
Mon. 484-37	45 15 05.58 / 71 13 34.31	232 27 20 / 65 40 24	Mon. 484-36 / Mon. 484-38	46.34 / 50.45
Mon. 484-38	45 15 04.91 / 71 13 36.42	245 40 22 / 19 05 51	Mon. 484-37 / Mon. 484-39	50.45 / 44.19
Mon. 484-39	45 15 03.56 / 71 13 37.08	199 05 51 / 39 47 11	Mon. 484-38 / Mon. 484-40	44.19 / 49.05
Mon. 484-40	45 15 02.34 / 71 13 38.52	219 47 10 / 10 05 13	Mon. 484-39 / Mon. 484-41	49.05 / 28.96
Mon. 484-41	45 15 01.41 / 71 13 38.75	190 05 13 / 44 23 19	Mon. 484-40 / Mon. 484-42	28.96 / 38.68
Mon. 484-42	45 15 00.52 / 71 13 39.99	224 23 18 / 60 22 20	Mon. 484-41 / Mon. 484-43	38.68 / 63.90
Mon. 484-43	45 14 59.50 / 71 13 42.54	240 22 18 / 31 55 41	Mon. 484-42 / Mon. 484-44	63.90 / 51.76
Mon. 484-44	45 14 58.07 / 71 13 43.79	211 55 40 / 106 00 35	Mon. 484-43 / Mon. 484-45	51.76 / 59.41

BOUNDARY MONUMENTS—SOURCE OF SOUTHWEST BRANCH OF ST. JOHN TO HEAD OF HALLS STREAM—Continued

Station	Latitude and longitude	Azimuth	To station	Distance (meters)	Station	Latitude and longitude	Azimuth	To station	Distance (meters)
	° ′ ″	° ′ ″				° ′ ″	° ′ ″		
Mon. 484–45	45 14 58.60 71 13 46.41	286 00 33 44 09 39	Mon. 484–44 Mon. 484–46	59.41 50.87	Mon. 485–3	45 15 51.90 71 14 28.59	312 56 34 130 15 58	Mon. 485–2 Mon. 485–4	162.50 105.47
Mon. 484–46	45 14 57.42 71 13 48.04	224 09 38 94 23 37	Mon. 484–45 Mon. 484–47	50.87 43.29	Mon. 485–4	45 15 54.10 71 14 32.29	310 15 55 145 13 01	Mon. 485–3 Mon. 485–5	105.47 212.54
Mon. 484–47	45 14 57.53 71 13 50.02	274 23 36 113 06 03	Mon. 484–46 Mon. 484–48	43.29 53.29	Mon. 485–5	45 15 59.76 71 14 37.85	325 12 57 150 16 47	Mon. 485–4 Mon. 485–6	212.54 104.04
Mon. 484–48	45 14 58.21 71 13 52.26	293 06 01 140 58 39	Mon. 484–47 Mon. 484–49	53.29 66.31	Mon. 485–6	45 16 02.69 71 14 40.21	330 16 46 141 05 35	Mon. 485–5 Mon. 486	104.04 122.95
Mon. 484–49	45 14 59.88 71 13 54.18	320 58 38 158 08 17	Mon. 484–48 Mon. 484–50	66.31 101.93	Mon. 486	45 16 05.79 71 14 43.76	321 05 33 141 04 51	Mon. 485–6 Mon. 486–1	122.95 87.24
Mon. 484–50	45 15 02.94 71 13 55.92	338 08 16 147 08 02	Mon. 484–49 Mon. 484–51	101.93 32.03	Mon. 486–1	45 16 07.98 71 14 46.27	321 04 49 72 58 01	Mon. 486 Mon. 486–2	87.24 110.97
Mon. 484–51	45 15 03.81 71 13 56.72	327 08 01 92 05 13	Mon. 484–50 Mon. 484–52	32.03 67.63	Mon. 486–2	45 16 06.93 71 14 51.14	252 57 58 112 40 43	Mon. 486–1 Mon. 486–3	110.97 41.00
Mon. 484–52	45 15 03.89 71 13 59.82	272 05 11 151 50 17	Mon. 484–51 Mon. 484–53	67.63 66.40	Mon. 486–3	45 16 07.44 71 14 52.87	292 40 42 52 09 47	Mon. 486–2 Mon. 486–4	41.00 57.95
Mon. 484–53	45 15 05.79 71 14 01.25	331 50 16 198 17 14	Mon. 484–52 Mon. 484–54	66.40 24.58	Mon. 486–4	45 16 06.29 71 14 54.97	232 09 46 37 28 56	Mon. 486–3 Mon. 486–5	57.95 49.02
Mon. 484–54	45 15 06.54 71 14 00.90	18 17 14 238 43 38	Mon. 484–53 Mon. 484–55	24.58 39.29	Mon. 486–5	45 16 05.03 71 14 56.34	217 28 55 61 22 58	Mon. 486–4 Mon. 486–6	49.02 32.99
Mon. 484–55	45 15 07.20 71 13 59.36	58 43 39 209 46 40	Mon. 484–54 Mon. 484–56	39.29 85.30	Mon. 486–6	45 16 04.52 71 14 57.67	241 22 57 110 32 27	Mon. 486–5 Mon. 486–7	32.99 57.95
Mon. 484–56	45 15 09.60 71 13 57.42	29 46 41 200 54 26	Mon. 484–55 Mon. 484–57	85.30 157.29	Mon. 486–7	45 16 05.18 71 15 00.16	290 32 25 158 20 08	Mon. 486–6 Mon. 486–8	57.95 77.38
Mon. 484–57	45 15 14.36 71 13 54.84	20 54 28 142 02 55	Mon. 484–56 Mon. 484–58	157.29 109.55	Mon. 486–8	45 16 07.51 71 15 01.47	338 20 07 189 07 04	Mon. 486–7 Mon. 486–9	77.38 45.26
Mon. 484–58	45 15 17.16 71 13 57.93	322 02 53 160 51 57	Mon. 484–57 Mon. 484–59	109.55 73.68	Mon. 486–9	45 16 08.96 71 15 01.14	9 07 04 115 13 51	Mon. 486–8 Mon. 486–10	45.26 32.68
Mon. 484–59	45 15 19.42 71 13 59.04	340 51 56 172 26 41	Mon. 484–58 Mon. 484–60	73.68 108.18	Mon. 486–10	45 16 09.41 71 15 02.49	295 13 50 163 28 20	Mon. 486–9 Mon. 486–11	32.68 49.88
Mon. 484–60	45 15 22.89 71 13 59.69	352 26 41 178 28 13	Mon. 484–59 Mon. 484–61	108.18 73.48	Mon. 486–11	45 16 10.96 71 15 03.14	343 28 20 112 49 01	Mon. 486–10 Mon. 486–12	49.88 62.58
Mon. 484–61	45 15 25.27 71 13 59.78	358 28 13 150 41 08	Mon. 484–60 Mon. 484–62	73.48 81.07	Mon. 486–12	45 16 11.74 71 15 05.79	292 48 59 95 56 26	Mon. 486–11 Mon. 486–13	62.58 32.99
Mon. 484–62	45 15 27.56 71 14 01.60	330 41 07 116 02 17	Mon. 484–61 Mon. 484–63	81.07 53.52	Mon. 486–13	45 16 11.85 71 15 07.30	275 56 25 158 46 36	Mon. 486–12 Mon. 486–14	32.99 45.32
Mon. 484–63	45 15 28.32 71 14 03.81	296 02 15 158 57 22	Mon. 484–62 Mon. 484–64	53.52 60.84	Mon. 486–14	45 16 13.22 71 15 08.05	338 46 35 119 14 00	Mon. 486–13 Mon. 486–15	45.32 61.66
Mon. 484–64	45 15 30.16 71 14 04.81	338 57 21 141 24 12	Mon. 484–63 Mon. 484–65	60.84 54.37	Mon. 486–15	45 16 14.20 71 15 10.52	299 13 58 136 21 23	Mon. 486–14 Mon. 486–16	61.66 82.31
Mon. 484–65	45 15 31.54 71 14 06.37	321 24 11 149 33 47	Mon. 484–64 Mon. 484–66	54.37 67.19	Mon. 486–16	45 16 16.12 71 15 13.12	316 21 21 123 01 00	Mon. 486–15 Mon. 486–17	82.31 115.91
Mon. 484–66	45 15 33.41 71 14 07.93	329 33 46 182 37 05	Mon. 484–65 Mon. 484–67	67.19 44.49	Mon. 486–17	45 16 18.17 71 15 17.58	303 00 57 113 43 32	Mon. 486–16 Mon. 486–18	115.91 94.95
Mon. 484–67	45 15 34.85 71 14 07.83	2 37 05 160 38 55	Mon. 484–66 Mon. 484–68	44.49 154.52	Mon. 486–18	45 16 19.41 71 15 21.57	293 43 29 149 08 44	Mon. 486–17 Mon. 486–19	94.95 25.59
Mon. 484–68	45 15 39.57 71 14 10.18	340 38 53 128 45 13	Mon. 484–67 Mon. 484–69	154.52 39.50	Mon. 486–19	45 16 20.12 71 15 22.17	329 08 44 161 07 41	Mon. 486–18 Mon. 486–20	25.59 94.83
Mon. 484–69	45 15 40.37 71 14 11.60	308 45 12 108 11 05	Mon. 484–68 Mon. 484–70	39.50 82.77	Mon. 486–20	45 16 23.03 71 15 23.58	341 07 40 126 06 17	Mon. 486–19 Mon. 486–21	94.83 42.22
Mon. 484–70	45 15 41.21 71 14 15.20	288 11 02 95 56 56	Mon. 484–69 Mon. 484–71	82.77 77.75	Mon. 486–21	45 16 23.83 71 15 25.14	306 06 16 45 52 34	Mon. 486–20 Mon. 486–22	42.22 51.48
Mon. 484–71	45 15 41.47 71 14 18.75	275 56 54 102 47 54	Mon. 484–70 Mon. 484–72	77.75 116.77	Mon. 486–22	45 16 22.67 71 15 26.84	225 52 33 64 32 21	Mon. 486–21 Mon. 486–23	51.48 36.07
Mon. 484–72	45 15 42.31 71 14 23.97	282 47 51 188 21 26	Mon. 484–71 Mon. 485	116.77 5.18	Mon. 486–23	45 16 22.17 71 15 28.33	244 32 20 50 47 23	Mon. 486–22 Mon. 486–24	36.07 148.59
Mon. 485	45 15 42.47 71 14 23.94	8 21 26 188 14 24	Mon. 484–72 Mon. 485–1	5.18 89.80	Mon. 486–24	45 16 19.13 71 15 33.61	230 47 19 81 18 29	Mon. 486–23 Mon. 486–25	148.59 21.89
Mon. 485–1	45 15 45.35 71 14 23.35	8 14 24 182 52 55	Mon. 485 Mon. 485–2	89.80 91.37	Mon. 486–25	45 16 19.02 71 15 34.61	261 18 28 124 16 51	Mon. 486–24 Mon. 486–26	21.89 34.22
Mon. 485–2	45 15 48.31 71 14 23.14	2 52 55 132 56 38	Mon. 485–1 Mon. 485–3	91.37 162.50	Mon. 486–26	45 16 19.64 71 15 35.90	304 16 50 164 54 26	Mon. 486–25 Mon. 486–27	34.22 41.62

BOUNDARY MONUMENTS—SOURCE OF SOUTHWEST BRANCH OF ST. JOHN TO HEAD OF HALLS STREAM—Continued

Station	Latitude and longitude	Azimuth	To station	Distance (meters)	Station	Latitude and longitude	Azimuth	To station	Distance (meters)
	° ′ ″	° ′ ″				° ′ ″	° ′ ″		
Mon. 486–27	45 16 20.94 / 71 15 36.40	344 54 26 / 206 25 23	Mon. 486–26 / Mon. 486–28	41.62 / 49.32	Mon. 487–3	45 17 14.96 / 71 15 55.39	315 05 25 / 167 02 43	Mon. 487–2 / Mon. 487–4	27.51 / 129.67
Mon. 486–28	45 16 22.38 / 71 15 35.39	26 25 24 / 155 56 45	Mon. 486–27 / Mon. 486–29	49.32 / 45.01	Mon. 487–4	45 17 19.06 / 71 15 56.72	347 02 42 / 149 21 05	Mon. 487–3 / Mon. 487–5	129.67 / 112.61
Mon. 486–29	45 16 23.71 / 71 15 36.24	335 56 44 / 155 56 44	Mon. 486–28 / Mon. 486–30	45.01 / 36.07	Mon. 487–5	45 17 22.20 / 71 15 59.36	329 21 03 / 185 10 56	Mon. 487–4 / Mon. 487–6	112.61 / 121.80
Mon. 486–30	45 16 24.77 / 71 15 36.91	335 56 44 / 162 58 21	Mon. 486–29 / Mon. 486–31	36.07 / 54.87	Mon. 487–6	45 17 26.12 / 71 15 58.85	5 10 56 / 163 18 24	Mon. 487–5 / Mon. 487–7	121.80 / 108.96
Mon. 486–31	45 16 26.47 / 71 15 37.65	342 58 20 / 195 20 31	Mon. 486–30 / Mon. 486–32	54.87 / 74.23	Mon. 487–7	45 17 29.51 / 71 16 00.29	343 18 23 / 205 28 27	Mon. 487–6 / Mon. 487–8	108.96 / 64.49
Mon. 486–32	45 16 28.79 / 71 15 36.75	15 20 32 / 118 34 27	Mon. 486–31 / Mon. 486–33	74.23 / 65.06	Mon. 487–8	45 17 31.39 / 71 15 59.02	25 28 28 / 203 38 50	Mon. 487–7 / Mon. 487–9	64.49 / 34.55
Mon. 486–33	45 16 29.80 / 71 15 39.37	298 34 25 / 147 21 58	Mon. 486–32 / Mon. 486–34	65.06 / 58.57	Mon. 487–9	45 17 32.42 / 71 15 58.38	23 38 50 / 220 54 18	Mon. 487–8 / Mon. 487–10	34.55 / 143.94
Mon. 486–34	45 16 31.40 / 71 15 40.82	327 21 57 / 126 27 42	Mon. 486–33 / Mon. 486–35	58.57 / 110.67	Mon. 487–10	45 17 35.94 / 71 15 54.05	40 54 21 / 147 39 50	Mon. 487–9 / Mon. 487–11	143.94 / 73.90
Mon. 486–35	45 16 33.53 / 71 15 44.90	306 27 39 / 110 52 11	Mon. 486–34 / Mon. 486–36	110.67 / 34.01	Mon. 487–11	45 17 37.96 / 71 15 55.87	327 39 49 / 116 43 17	Mon. 487–10 / Mon. 487–12	73.90 / 49.81
Mon. 486–36	45 16 33.92 / 71 15 46.36	290 52 10 / 186 19 31	Mon. 486–35 / Mon. 486–37	34.01 / 64.85	Mon. 487–12	45 17 38.69 / 71 15 57.91	296 43 15 / 125 01 48	Mon. 487–11 / Mon. 487–13	49.81 / 74.82
Mon. 486–37	45 16 36.01 / 71 15 46.03	6 19 31 / 149 10 21	Mon. 486–36 / Mon. 486–38	64.85 / 35.45	Mon. 487–13	45 17 40.08 / 71 16 00.72	305 01 46 / 93 52 09	Mon. 487–12 / Mon. 487–14	74.82 / 56.54
Mon. 486–38	45 16 37.00 / 71 15 46.86	329 10 20 / 146 56 11	Mon. 486–37 / Mon. 486–39	35.45 / 77.54	Mon. 487–14	45 17 40.20 / 71 16 03.31	273 52 07 / 120 18 25	Mon. 487–13 / Mon. 487–15	56.54 / 54.62
Mon. 486–39	45 16 39.10 / 71 15 48.80	326 56 10 / 188 07 53	Mon. 486–38 / Mon. 486–40	77.54 / 79.14	Mon. 487–15	45 17 41.10 / 71 16 05.48	300 18 24 / 117 52 17	Mon. 487–14 / Mon. 487–16	54.62 / 57.44
Mon. 486–40	45 16 41.64 / 71 15 48.29	8 07 53 / 175 05 20	Mon. 486–39 / Mon. 486–41	79.14 / 65.91	Mon. 487–16	45 17 41.97 / 71 16 07.80	297 52 16 / 125 35 44	Mon. 487–15 / Mon. 487–17	57.44 / 70.86
Mon. 486–41	45 16 43.76 / 71 15 48.55	355 05 20 / 196 27 24	Mon. 486–40 / Mon. 486–42	65.91 / 49.95	Mon. 487–17	45 17 43.30 / 71 16 10.45	305 35 42 / 94 54 15	Mon. 487–16 / Mon. 487–18	70.86 / 80.66
Mon. 486–42	45 16 45.32 / 71 15 47.90	16 27 24 / 171 01 29	Mon. 486–41 / Mon. 486–43	49.95 / 34.84	Mon. 487–18	45 17 43.53 / 71 16 14.14	274 54 13 / 128 57 42	Mon. 487–17 / Mon. 487–19	80.66 / 33.31
Mon. 486–43	45 16 46.43 / 71 15 48.15	351 01 29 / 147 10 01	Mon. 486–42 / Mon. 486–44	34.84 / 54.31	Mon. 487–19	45 17 44.20 / 71 16 15.33	308 57 41 / 118 05 04	Mon. 487–18 / Mon. 487–20	33.31 / 74.22
Mon. 486–44	45 16 47.91 / 71 15 49.50	327 10 00 / 143 16 30	Mon. 486–43 / Mon. 486–45	54.31 / 44.97	Mon. 487–20	45 17 45.34 / 71 16 18.33	298 05 02 / 108 38 30	Mon. 487–19 / Mon. 487–21	74.22 / 64.77
Mon. 486–45	45 16 49.08 / 71 15 50.73	323 16 29 / 185 32 05	Mon. 486–44 / Mon. 486–46	44.97 / 189.35	Mon. 487–21	45 17 46.01 / 71 16 21.15	288 38 28 / 137 06 56	Mon. 487–20 / Mon. 487–22	64.77 / 82.73
Mon. 486–46	45 16 55.18 / 71 15 49.90	5 32 06 / 142 51 13	Mon. 486–45 / Mon. 486–47	189.35 / 56.72	Mon. 487–22	45 17 47.97 / 71 16 23.73	317 06 55 / 60 30 34	Mon. 487–21 / Mon. 488	82.73 / 2.45
Mon. 486–47	45 16 56.65 / 71 15 51.47	322 51 12 / 165 56 25	Mon. 486–46 / Mon. 486–48	56.72 / 65.86	Mon. 488	45 17 47.93 / 71 16 23.83	240 30 34 / 60 12 20	Mon. 487–22 / Mon. 488–1	2.45 / 101.92
Mon. 486–48	45 16 58.72 / 71 15 52.20	345 56 25 / 183 42 40	Mon. 486–47 / Mon. 486–49	65.86 / 77.55	Mon. 488–1	45 17 46.29 / 71 16 27.89	240 12 17 / 39 28 50	Mon. 488 / Mon. 488–2	101.92 / 47.46
Mon. 486–49	45 17 01.22 / 71 15 51.97	3 42 40 / 179 53 05	Mon. 486–48 / Mon. 486–50	77.55 / 104.35	Mon. 488–2	45 17 45.10 / 71 16 29.28	219 28 49 / 78 01 42	Mon. 488–1 / Mon. 488–3	47.46 / 48.37
Mon. 486–50	45 17 04.60 / 71 15 51.98	359 53 05 / 196 35 25	Mon. 486–49 / Mon. 486–51	104.35 / 30.83	Mon. 488–3	45 17 44.78 / 71 16 31.45	258 01 40 / 46 11 34	Mon. 488–2 / Mon. 488–4	48.37 / 102.57
Mon. 486–51	45 17 05.56 / 71 15 51.58	16 35 25 / 154 55 11	Mon. 486–50 / Mon. 486–52	30.83 / 43.16	Mon. 488–4	45 17 42.48 / 71 16 34.84	226 11 32 / 73 43 09	Mon. 488–3 / Mon. 488–5	102.57 / 76.37
Mon. 486–52	45 17 06.82 / 71 15 52.42	334 55 10 / 183 52 00	Mon. 486–51 / Mon. 486–53	43.16 / 38.78	Mon. 488–5	45 17 41.78 / 71 16 38.21	253 43 07 / 112 10 17	Mon. 488–4 / Mon. 488–6	76.37 / 51.44
Mon. 486–53	45 17 08.08 / 71 15 52.30	3 52 00 / 167 05 30	Mon. 486–52 / Mon. 486–54	38.78 / 115.45	Mon. 488–6	45 17 42.41 / 71 16 40.39	292 10 15 / 77 38 45	Mon. 488–5 / Mon. 488–7	51.44 / 45.75
Mon. 486–54	45 17 11.72 / 71 15 53.48	347 05 29 / 150 14 44	Mon. 486–53 / Mon. 487	115.45 / 14.16	Mon. 488–7	45 17 42.10 / 71 16 42.44	347 38 44 / 47 38 28	Mon. 488–6 / Mon. 488–8	45.75 / 46.07
Mon. 487	45 17 12.12 / 71 15 53.80	330 14 44 / 150 12 19	Mon. 486–54 / Mon. 487–1	14.16 / 29.34	Mon. 488–8	45 17 41.09 / 71 16 44.01	227 38 27 / 72 30 30	Mon. 488–7 / Mon. 488–9	46.07 / 65.14
Mon. 487–1	45 17 12.95 / 71 15 54.47	330 12 19 / 179 15 47	Mon. 487 / Mon. 487–2	29.34 / 42.79	Mon. 488–9	45 17 40.46 / 71 16 46.86	252 30 28 / 95 45 49	Mon. 488–8 / Mon. 488–10	65.14 / 110.54
Mon. 487–2	45 17 14.33 / 71 15 54.50	359 15 47 / 135 05 26	Mon. 487–1 / Mon. 487–3	42.79 / 27.51	Mon. 488–10	45 17 40.82 / 71 16 51.90	275 45 45 / 155 02 46	Mon. 488–9 / Mon. 488–11	110.54 / 70.23

BOUNDARY MONUMENTS—SOURCE OF SOUTHWEST BRANCH OF ST. JOHN TO HEAD OF HALLS STREAM—Continued

Station	Latitude and longitude	Azimuth	To station	Distance (meters)
	° ′ ″	° ′ ″		
Mon. 488–11	45 17 42.88 / 71 16 53.26	335 02 45 / 184 45 19	Mon. 488–10 / Mon. 488–12	70.23 / 42.39
Mon. 488–12	45 17 44.25 / 71 16 53.10	4 45 19 / 140 00 45	Mon. 488–11 / Mon. 488–13	42.39 / 32.82
Mon. 488–13	45 17 45.06 / 71 16 54.07	320 00 44 / 160 23 24	Mon. 488–12 / Mon. 488–14	32.82 / 51.92
Mon. 488–14	45 17 46.64 / 71 16 54.87	340 23 23 / 133 07 30	Mon. 488–13 / Mon. 488–15	51.92 / 147.03
Mon. 488–15	45 17 49.90 / 71 16 59.80	313 07 26 / 205 48 53	Mon. 488–14 / Mon. 488–16	147.03 / 101.00
Mon. 488–16	45 17 52.85 / 71 16 57.78	25 48 54 / 178 14 50	Mon. 488–15 / Mon. 488–17	101.00 / 55.48
Mon. 488–17	45 17 54.64 / 71 16 57.86	358 14 50 / 189 15 41	Mon. 488–16 / Mon. 488–18	55.48 / 77.68
Mon. 488–18	45 17 57.13 / 71 16 57.28	9 15 41 / 158 12 08	Mon. 488–17 / Mon. 488–19	77.68 / 46.09
Mon. 488–19	45 17 58.51 / 71 16 58.07	338 12 08 / 117 54 50	Mon. 488–18 / Mon. 489	46.09 / 52.37
Mon. 489	45 17 59.31 / 71 17 00.19	297 54 49 / 117 53 28	Mon. 488–19 / Mon. 489–1	52.37 / 68.59
Mon. 489–1	45 18 00.35 / 71 17 02.97	297 53 26 / 164 10 49	Mon. 489 / Mon. 489–2	68.59 / 34.97
Mon. 489–2	45 18 01.44 / 71 17 03.41	344 10 49 / 216 07 02	Mon. 489–1 / Mon. 489–3	34.97 / 83.92
Mon. 489–3	45 18 03.63 / 71 17 01.14	36 07 04 / 159 05 17	Mon. 489–2 / Mon. 489–4	83.92 / 120.35
Mon. 489–4	45 18 07.27 / 71 17 03.11	339 05 16 / 135 15 19	Mon. 489–3 / Mon. 489–5	120.35 / 66.55
Mon. 489–5	45 18 08.80 / 71 17 05.26	315 15 17 / 20 13 55	Mon. 489–4 / Mon. 489–6	66.55 / 127.69
Mon. 489–6	45 18 04.92 / 71 17 07.29	200 13 53 / 35 01 42	Mon. 489–5 / Mon. 489–7	127.69 / 86.92
Mon. 489–7	45 18 02.62 / 71 17 09.58	215 01 40 / 43 13 21	Mon. 489–6 / Mon. 489–8	86.92 / 42.40
Mon. 489–8	45 18 01.62 / 71 17 10.91	223 13 20 / 115 10 25	Mon. 489–7 / Mon. 489–9	42.40 / 106.05
Mon. 489–9	45 18 03.08 / 71 17 15.32	295 10 22 / 102 21 48	Mon. 489–8 / Mon. 489–10	106.05 / 72.07
Mon. 489–10	45 18 03.58 / 71 17 18.55	282 21 46 / 35 22 26	Mon. 489–9 / Mon. 489–11	72.07 / 118.75
Mon. 489–11	45 18 00.44 / 71 17 21.70	215 22 24 / 87 40 44	Mon. 489–10 / Mon. 489–12	118.75 / 85.12
Mon. 489–12	45 18 00.33 / 71 17 25.60	267 40 41 / 48 38 11	Mon. 489–11 / Mon. 489–13	85.12 / 70.50
Mon. 489–13	45 17 58.82 / 71 17 28.03	228 38 09 / 8 36 54	Mon. 489–12 / Mon. 489–14	70.50 / 64.21
Mon. 489–14	45 17 56.76 / 71 17 28.48	188 36 54 / 34 20 55	Mon. 489–13 / Mon. 489–15	64.21 / 41.02
Mon. 489–15	45 17 55.67 / 71 17 29.54	214 20 54 / 81 34 04	Mon. 489–14 / Mon. 489–16	41.02 / 146.52
Mon. 489–16	45 17 54.97 / 71 17 36.19	261 33 59 / 109 23 20	Mon. 489–15 / Mon. 489–17	146.52 / 47.03
Mon. 489–17	45 17 55.48 / 71 17 38.22	289 23 19 / 79 02 24	Mon. 489–16 / Mon. 489–18	47.03 / 76.12
Mon. 489–18	45 17 55.01 / 71 17 41.66	259 02 22 / 104 42 53	Mon. 489–17 / Mon. 489–19	76.12 / 71.31
Mon. 489–19	45 17 55.60 / 71 17 44.82	284 42 51 / 122 05 02	Mon. 489–18 / Mon. 489–20	71.31 / 94.69
Mon. 489–20	45 17 57.22 / 71 17 48.50	302 04 59 / 41 40 04	Mon. 489–19 / Mon. 489–21	94.69 / 161.46
Mon. 489–21	45 17 53.32 / 71 17 53.43	221 40 00 / 16 11 06	Mon. 489–20 / Mon. 489–22	161.46 / 28.89
Mon. 489–22	45 17 52.42 / 71 17 53.80	196 11 06 / 44 38 32	Mon. 489–21 / Mon. 489–23	28.89 / 120.42
Mon. 489–23	45 17 49.64 / 71 17 57.68	224 38 29 / 64 13 25	Mon. 489–22 / Mon. 490	120.42 / 6.76
Mon. 490	45 17 49.55 / 71 17 57.96	244 13 25 / 64 14 06	Mon. 489–23 / Mon. 490–1	6.76 / 10.71
Mon. 490–1	45 17 49.40 / 71 17 58.40	244 14 06 / 79 22 36	Mon. 490 / Mon. 490–2	10.71 / 42.06
Mon. 490–2	45 17 49.15 / 71 18 00.30	259 22 35 / 36 25 35	Mon. 490–1 / Mon. 490–3	42.06 / 72.78
Mon. 490–3	45 17 47.25 / 71 18 02.29	216 25 34 / 130 12 04	Mon. 490–2 / Mon. 490–4	72.78 / 47.73
Mon. 490–4	45 17 48.25 / 71 18 03.96	310 12 03 / 35 14 03	Mon. 490–3 / Mon. 490–5	47.73 / 175.74
Mon. 490–5	45 17 43.60 / 71 18 08.61	215 14 00 / 19 36 45	Mon. 490–4 / Mon. 490–6	175.74 / 75.05
Mon. 490–6	45 17 41.31 / 71 18 09.77	199 36 44 / 25 52 59	Mon. 490–5 / Mon. 490–7	75.05 / 99.67
Mon. 490–7	45 17 38.40 / 71 18 11.77	205 52 58 / 13 34 28	Mon. 490–6 / Mon. 490–8	99.67 / 107.61
Mon. 490–8	45 17 35.01 / 71 18 12.92	193 34 27 / 62 24 27	Mon. 490–7 / Mon. 490–9	107.61 / 129.97
Mon. 490–9	45 17 33.06 / 71 18 18.21	242 24 23 / 21 46 38	Mon. 490–8 / Mon. 490–10	129.97 / 95.16
Mon. 490–10	45 17 30.20 / 71 18 19.83	201 46 37 / 32 34 37	Mon. 490–9 / Mon. 490–11	95.16 / 214.82
Mon. 490–11	45 17 24.34 / 71 18 25.14	212 34 33 / 352 43 03	Mon. 490–10 / Mon. 490–12	214.82 / 54.43
Mon. 490–12	45 17 22.59 / 71 18 24.82	172 43 03 / 19 52 03	Mon. 490–11 / Mon. 490–13	54.43 / 155.11
Mon. 490–13	45 17 17.86 / 71 18 27.24	199 52 01 / 30 17 46	Mon. 490–12 / Mon. 490–14	155.11 / 93.26
Mon. 490–14	45 17 15.26 / 71 18 29.40	210 17 44 / 69 39 29	Mon. 490–13 / Mon. 490–15	93.26 / 94.21
Mon. 490–15	45 17 14.19 / 71 18 33.45	249 39 26 / 42 46 26	Mon. 490–14 / Mon. 490–16	94.21 / 35.00
Mon. 490–16	45 17 13.36 / 71 18 34.54	222 46 25 / 86 14 20	Mon. 490–15 / Mon. 491	35.00 / 79.54
Mon. 491	45 17 13.19 / 71 18 38.19	266 14 17 / 86 11 09	Mon. 490–16 / Mon. 491–1	79.54 / 16.72
Mon. 491–1	45 17 13.16 / 71 18 38.95	266 11 08 / 64 02 12	Mon. 491 / Mon. 491–2	16.72 / 91.39
Mon. 491–2	45 17 11.86 / 71 18 42.72	244 02 09 / 107 45 43	Mon. 491–1 / Mon. 491–3	91.39 / 61.23
Mon. 491–3	45 17 12.46 / 71 18 45.40	287 45 41 / 109 50 38	Mon. 491–2 / Mon. 491–4	61.23 / 33.60
Mon. 491–4	45 17 12.83 / 71 18 46.85	289 50 37 / 104 53 10	Mon. 491–3 / Mon. 491–5	33.60 / 41.80
Mon. 491–5	45 17 13.18 / 71 18 48.70	284 53 09 / 73 55 59	Mon. 491–4 / Mon. 491–6	41.80 / 58.58
Mon. 491–6	45 17 12.66 / 71 18 51.28	253 55 57 / 96 00 08	Mon. 491–5 / Mon. 491–7	58.58 / 61.30
Mon. 491–7	45 17 12.86 / 71 18 54.08	276 00 06 / 71 55 15	Mon. 491–6 / Mon. 491–8	61.30 / 81.01
Mon. 491–8	45 17 12.05 / 71 18 57.61	251 55 12 / 24 46 20	Mon. 491–7 / Mon. 491–9	81.01 / 71.92
Mon. 491–9	45 17 09.94 / 71 18 59.00	204 46 19 / 56 25 59	Mon. 491–8 / Mon. 491–10	71.92 / 114.56
Mon. 491–10	45 17 07.88 / 71 19 03.38	236 25 56 / 26 42 04	Mon. 491–9 / Mon. 491–11	114.56 / 62.79
Mon. 491–11	45 17 06.07 / 71 19 04.67	206 42 03 / 42 09 02	Mon. 491–10 / Mon. 491–12	62.79 / 151.81

BOUNDARY MONUMENTS—SOURCE OF SOUTHWEST BRANCH OF ST. JOHN TO HEAD OF HALLS STREAM—Continued

Station	Latitude and longitude	Azimuth	To station	Distance (meters)	Station	Latitude and longitude	Azimuth	To station	Distance (meters)
	° ′ ″	° ′ ″				° ′ ″	° ′ ″		
Mon. 491-12	45 17 02.42 / 71 19 09.35	222 08 59 / 18 52 40	Mon. 491-11 / Mon. 491-13	151.81 / 110.64	Mon. 494-1	45 16 19.57 / 71 20 53.69	267 17 53 / 29 55 26	Mon. 494 / Mon. 494-2	32.36 / 159.43
Mon. 491-13	45 16 59.03 / 71 19 10.99	198 52 39 / 78 56 34	Mon. 491-12 / Mon. 491-14	110.64 / 40.17	Mon. 494-2	45 16 15.09 / 71 20 57.34	209 55 23 / 42 00 45	Mon. 494-1 / Mon. 494-3	159.43 / 189.76
Mon. 491-14	45 16 58.78 / 71 19 12.80	258 56 33 / 33 27 16	Mon. 491-13 / Mon. 491-15	40.17 / 87.41	Mon. 494-3	45 16 10.53 / 71 21 03.16	222 00 41 / 95 31 33	Mon. 494-2 / Mon. 494-4	189.76 / 42.33
Mon. 491-15	45 16 56.42 / 71 19 15.01	213 27 14 / 50 28 32	Mon. 491-14 / Mon. 491-16	87.41 / 58.15	Mon. 494-4	45 16 10.66 / 71 21 05.09	275 31 32 / 56 40 26	Mon. 494-3 / Mon 494-5	42.33 / 170.74
Mon. 491-16	45 16 55.22 / 71 19 17.07	230 28 31 / 77 27 52	Mon. 491-15 / Mon. 492	58.15 / 88.52	Mon. 494-5	45 16 07.62 / 71 21 11.64	236 40 21 / 80 40 31	Mon. 494-4 / Mon. 494-6	170.74 / 62.57
Mon. 492	45 16 54.59 / 71 19 21.03	257 27 50 / 77 26 38	Mon. 491-16 / Mon. 492-1	88.52 / 216.34	Mon. 494-6	45 16 07.29 / 71 21 14.47	260 40 29 / 89 48 34	Mon. 494-5 / Mon. 494-7	62.57 / 174.84
Mon. 492-1	45 16 53.07 / 71 19 30.72	257 26 31 / 87 00 06	Mon. 492 / Mon. 492-2	216.34 / 152.35	Mon. 494-7	45 16 07.27 / 71 21 22.49	269 48 28 / 113 38 58	Mon. 494-6 / Mon. 494-8	174.84 / 238.41
Mon 492-2	45 16 52.81 / 71 19 37.70	267 00 01 / 72 17 09	Mon. 492-1 / Mon. 492-3	152.35 / 162.69	Mon. 494-8	45 16 10.37 / 71 21 32.51	293 38 51 / 128 31 26	Mon. 494-7 / Mon. 494-9	238.41 / 112.88
Mon. 492-3	45 16 51.21 / 71 19 44.81	252 17 04 / 55 50 51	Mon. 492-2 / Mon. 492-4	162.69 / 54.66	Mon. 494-9	45 16 12.65 / 71 21 36.56	308 31 23 / 116 10 06	Mon. 494-8 / Mon. 494-10	112.88 / 60.43
Mon. 492-4	45 16 50.21 / 71 19 46.88	235 50 50 / 76 00 58	Mon. 492-3 / Mon. 492-5	54.66 / 58.22	Mon. 494-10	45 16 13.51 / 71 21 39.05	296 10 04 / 26 47 43	Mon. 494-9 / Mon. 494-11	60.43 / 59.05
Mon. 492-5	45 16 49.76 / 71 19 49.48	256 00 56 / 79 40 05	Mon. 492-4 / Mon 492-6	58.22 / 76.62	Mon. 494-11	45 16 11.80 / 71 21 40.27	206 47 42 / 9 46 09	Mon. 494-10 / Mon. 494-12	59.05 / 111.37
Mon. 492-6	45 16 49.31 / 71 19 52.94	259 40 02 / 39 21 48	Mon. 492-5 / Mon. 492-7	76.62 / 111.21	Mon. 494-12	45 16 08.25 / 71 21 41.14	189 46 08 / 43 22 21	Mon. 494-11 / Mon. 495	111.37 / 107.28
Mon 492-7	45 16 46.53 / 71 19 56.17	219 21 46 / 350 21 54	Mon. 492-6 / Mon. 492-8	111.21 / 60.39	Mon. 495	45 16 05.72 / 71 21 44.52	223 22 19 / 43 22 49	Mon. 494-12 / Mon. 495-1	107.28 / 64.80
Mon. 492-8	45 16 44.60 / 71 19 55.71	170 21 54 / 39 22 15	Mon. 492-7 / Mon. 492-9	60.39 / 108.16	Mon. 495-1	45 16 04.20 / 71 21 46.56	223 22 48 / 53 24 13	Mon. 495 / Mon. 495-2	64.80 / 66.33
Mon. 492-9	45 16 41.89 / 71 19 58.85	219 22 13 / 9 55 49	Mon. 492-8 / Mon. 492-10	108.16 / 89.24	Mon. 495-2	45 16 02.92 / 71 21 49.00	233 24 11 / 10 29 46	Mon. 495-1 / Mon. 495-3	66.33 / 73.67
Mon. 492-10	45 16 39.04 / 71 19 59.56	189 55 48 / 28 26 28	Mon. 492-9 / Mon. 492-11	89.24 / 65.44	Mon. 495-3	45 16 00.57 / 71 21 49.61	190 29 46 / 338 04 40	Mon. 495-2 / Mon. 495-4	73.67 / 194.04
Mon. 492-11	45 16 37.18 / 71 20 00.99	208 26 27 / 359 37 39	Mon. 492-10 / Mon. 492-12	65.44 / 116.90	Mon. 495-4	45 15 54.74 / 71 21 46.29	158 04 42 / 334 54 30	Mon. 495-3 / Mon. 495-5	194.04 / 67.01
Mon. 492-12	45 16 33.39 / 71 20 00.96	179 37 39 / 37 11 18	Mon. 492-11 / Mon. 493	116.90 / 3.68	Mon. 495-5	45 15 52.78 / 71 21 44.97	154 34 31 / 320 14 31	Mon. 495-4 / Mon. 496	67.01 / 20.17
Mon. 493	45 16 33.29 / 71 20 01.06	217 11 18 / 37 11 18	Mon. 492-12 / Mon. 493-1	3.68 / 55.67	Mon. 496	45 15 52.27 / 71 21 44.38	140 14 31 / 320 13 48	Mon. 495-5 / Mon. 496-1	20.17 / 191.32
Mon. 493-1	45 16 31.86 / 71 20 02.60	217 11 17 / 29 30 56	Mon. 493 / Mon. 493-2	55.67 / 242.48	Mon. 496-1	45 15 47.51 / 71 21 38.76	140 13 52 / 328 59 17	Mon. 496 / Mon. 496-2	191.32 / 131.67
Mon. 493-2	45 16 25.02 / 71 20 08.08	209 30 52 / 53 21 40	Mon. 493-1 / Mon. 493-3	242.48 / 22.42	Mon. 496-2	45 15 43.86 / 71 21 35.65	148 59 19 / 350 30 38	Mon. 496-1 / Mon. 496-3	131.67 / 296.55
Mon. 493-3	45 16 24.59 / 71 20 08.91	233 21 39 / 51 02 49	Mon. 493-2 / Mon. 493-4	22.42 / 118.30	Mon. 496-3	45 15 34.38 / 71 21 33.41	170 30 40 / 330 32 09	Mon. 496-2 / Mon. 496-4	296.55 / 123.53
Mon. 493-4	45 16 22.18 / 71 20 13.13	231 02 46 / 81 44 03	Mon. 493-3 / Mon. 493-5	118.30 / 168.79	Mon. 496-4	45 15 30.90 / 71 21 30.62	150 32 11 / 334 54 44	Mon. 496-3 / Mon. 496-5	123.53 / 122.32
Mon. 493-5	45 16 21.39 / 71 20 20.79	261 43 58 / 70 57 00	Mon. 493-4 / Mon. 493-6	168.79 / 156.18	Mon. 496-5	45 15 27.31 / 71 21 28.24	154 54 46 / 332 59 46	Mon. 496-4 / Mon. 496-6	122.32 / 114.62
Mon. 493-6	45 16 19.74 / 71 20 27.56	250 56 55 / 59 23 37	Mon. 493-5 / Mon. 493-7	156.18 / 175.84	Mon. 496-6	45 15 24.00 / 71 21 25.86	152 59 48 / 12 01 18	Mon. 496-5 / Mon. 496-7	114.62 / 144.67
Mon. 493-7	45 16 16.84 / 71 20 34.50	239 23 32 / 89 35 29	Mon. 493-6 / Mon. 493-8	175.84 / 153.87	Mon. 496-7	45 15 19.42 / 71 21 27.24	192 01 17 / 324 58 47	Mon. 496-6 / Mon. 496-8	144.67 / 86.91
Mon. 493-8	45 16 16.81 / 71 20 41.56	269 35 24 / 102 44 30	Mon. 493-7 / Mon 493-9	153.87 / 35.38	Mon. 496-8	45 15 17.11 / 71 21 24.95	144 58 49 / 8 59 49	Mon. 496-7 / Mon. 496-9	86.91 / 86.14
Mon. 493-9	45 16 17.06 / 71 20 43.14	282 44 29 / 102 39 46	Mon. 493-8 / Mon. 493-10	35.38 / 86.89	Mon. 496-9	45 15 14.35 / 71 21 25.57	188 59 49 / 29 13 19	Mon. 496-8 / Mon. 496-10	86.14 / 91.95
Mon. 493-10	45 16 17.68 / 71 20 47.03	282 39 43 / 125 47 01	Mon. 493-9 / Mon. 493-11	86.89 / 104.75	Mon. 496-10	45 15 11.75 / 71 21 27.63	209 13 17 / 27 55 17	Mon. 496-9 / Mon. 497	91.95 / 175.20
Mon. 493-11	45 16 19.66 / 71 20 50.93	305 46 59 / 87 17 21	Mon. 493-10 / Mon. 494	104.75 / 27.76	Mon. 497	45 15 06.74 / 71 21 31.39	207 55 14 / 27 57 23	Mon. 496-10 / Mon. 497-1	175.20 / 110.06
Mon. 494	45 16 19.62 / 71 20 52.20	267 17 20 / 87 17 54	Mon. 493-11 / Mon. 494-1	27.76 / 32.36	Mon. 497-1	45 15 03.59 / 71 21 33.76	207 57 21 / 42 33 04	Mon. 497 / Mon. 497-2	110.06 / 54.69

BOUNDARY MONUMENTS—SOURCE OF SOUTHWEST BRANCH OF ST. JOHN TO HEAD OF HALLS STREAM—Continued

Station	Latitude and longitude	Azimuth	To station	Distance (meters)	Station	Latitude and longitude	Azimuth	To station	Distance (meters)
	° ′ ″	° ′ ″				° ′ ″	° ′ ″		
Mon. 497-2	45 15 02.29 / 71 21 35.45	222 33 03 / 55 42 34	Mon. 497-1 / Mon. 497-3	54.69 / 262.32	Mon. 500-17	45 14 02.31 / 71 23 14.95	318 27 29 / 122 42 53	Mon. 500-16 / Mon. 500-18	118.57 / 218.33
Mon. 497-3	45 14 57.50 / 71 21 45.39	235 42 27 / 28 53 56	Mon. 497-2 / Mon. 497-4	262.32 / 115.80	Mon. 500-18	45 14 06.13 / 71 23 23.37	302 42 47 / 151 09 31	Mon. 500-17 / Mon. 500-19	218.33 / 192.27
Mon. 497-4	45 14 54.22 / 71 21 47.96	208 53 54 / 66 52 35	Mon. 497-3 / Mon. 498	115.80 / 156.19	Mon. 500-19	45 14 11.58 / 71 23 27.62	331 09 28 / 135 10 17	Mon. 500-18 / Mon. 501	192.27 / 143.26
Mon. 498	45 14 52.23 / 71 21 54.54	246 52 30 / 66 54 29	Mon. 497-4 / Mon. 498-1	156.19 / 96.77	Mon. 501	45 14 14.88 / 71 23 32.25	315 10 14 / 152 29 29	Mon. 500-19 / Mon. 501-1	143.26 / 165.78
Mon. 498-1	45 14 51.00 / 71 21 58.63	246 54 26 / 88 19 55	Mon. 498 / Mon. 498-2	96.77 / 93.81	Mon. 501-1	45 14 19.64 / 71 23 35.76	332 29 27 / 192 26 38	Mon. 501 / Mon. 501-2	165.78 / 82.08
Mon. 498-2	45 14 50.91 / 71 22 02.93	268 19 52 / 32 42 55	Mon. 498-1 / Mon. 498-3	93.81 / 34.43	Mon. 501-2	45 14 22.23 / 71 23 34.95	12 26 39 / 132 43 40	Mon. 501-1 / Mon. 501-3	82.08 / 61.13
Mon. 498-3	45 14 49.97 / 71 22 03.78	212 42 54 / 30 20 48	Mon. 498-2 / Mon. 498-4	34.43 / 56.00	Mon. 501-3	45 14 23.58 / 71 23 37.01	312 43 39 / 137 11 21	Mon. 501-2 / Mon. 501-4	61.13 / 167.97
Mon 498-4	45 14 48.41 / 71 22 05.08	210 20 47 / 49 35 16	Mon. 498-3 / Mon. 498-5	56.00 / 52.16	Mon. 501-4	45 14 27.57 / 71 23 42.24	317 11 17 / 125 40 39	Mon. 501-3 / Mon. 501-5	167.97 / 179.38
Mon. 498-5	45 14 47.31 / 71 22 06.90	229 35 15 / 87 13 39	Mon. 498-4 / Mon. 499	52.16 / 56.83	Mon. 501-5	45 14 30.96 / 71 23 48.93	305 40 34 / 104 58 00	Mon. 501-4 / Mon. 501-6	179.38 / 116.07
Mon. 499	45 14 47.22 / 71 22 09.50	267 13 37 / 87 14 44	Mon. 498-5 / Mon. 499-1	56.83 / 286.01	Mon. 501-6	45 14 31.93 / 71 23 54.07	284 57 56 / 89 26 28	Mon. 501-5 / Mon. 501-7	116.07 / 146.74
Mon. 499-1	45 14 46.78 / 71 22 22.60	267 14 35 / 44 03 35	Mon. 499 / Mon. 499-2	286.01 / 122.62	Mon. 501-7	45 14 31.88 / 71 24 00.80	269 26 23 / 105 30 00	Mon. 501-6 / Mon. 501-8	146.74 / 204.18
Mon. 499-2	45 14 43.92 / 71 22 26.51	224 03 32 / 76 45 32	Mon. 499-1 / Mon. 499-3	122.62 / 101.07	Mon. 501-8	45 14 33.65 / 71 24 09.82	285 29 54 / 68 51 20	Mon. 501-7 / Mon. 501-9	204.18 / 152.39
Mon. 499-3	45 14 43.17 / 71 22 31.02	256 45 29 / 80 47 29	Mon. 499-2 / Mon. 499-4	101.07 / 98.27	Mon. 501-9	45 14 31.87 / 71 24 16.33	248 51 15 / 78 33 52	Mon. 501-8 / Mon. 501-10	152.39 / 143.50
Mon. 499-4	45 14 42.66 / 71 22 35.47	260 47 26 / 37 56 26	Mon. 499-3 / Mon. 500	98.27 / 100.26	Mon. 501-10	45 14 30.95 / 71 24 22.78	258 33 47 / 62 17 53	Mon. 501-9 / Mon. 501-11	143.50 / 149.38
Mon. 500	45 14 40.10 / 71 22 38.29	217 56 24 / 37 56 46	Mon. 499-4 / Mon. 500-1	100.26 / 87.09	Mon. 501-11	45 14 28.70 / 71 24 28.84	242 17 49 / 9 14 10	Mon. 501-10 / Mon. 502	149.38 / 91.08
Mon. 500-1	45 14 37.88 / 71 22 40.75	217 56 44 / 67 01 28	Mon. 500 / Mon. 500-2	87.09 / 78.30	Mon. 502	45 14 25.79 / 71 24 29.52	189 14 10 / 9 12 56	Mon. 501-11 / Mon. 502-1	91.08 / 45.31
Mon. 500-2	45 14 36.89 / 71 22 44.06	247 01 26 / 29 53 57	Mon. 500-1 / Mon. 500-3	78.30 / 85.27	Mon. 502-1	45 14 24.34 / 71 24 29.85	189 12 56 / 38 00 56	Mon. 502 / Mon. 502-2	45.31 / 100.96
Mon. 500-3	45 14 34.49 / 71 22 46.00	209 53 56 / 0 44 00	Mon. 500-2 / Mon. 500-4	85.27 / 45.38	Mon. 502-2	45 14 21.76 / 71 24 32.70	218 00 54 / 66 40 54	Mon. 502-1 / Mon. 502-3	100.96 / 48.84
Mon. 500-4	45 14 33.02 / 71 22 46.03	180 44 00 / 3 19 14	Mon. 500-3 / Mon. 500-5	45.38 / 78.37	Mon. 502-3	45 14 21.14 / 71 24 34.75	246 40 52 / 72 27 52	Mon. 502-2 / Mon. 502-4	48.84 / 64.53
Mon. 500-5	45 14 30.49 / 71 22 46.24	183 19 14 / 7 58 38	Mon. 500-4 / Mon. 500-6	78.37 / 35.75	Mon. 502-4	45 14 20.50 / 71 24 37.58	252 27 50 / 103 05 50	Mon. 502-3 / Mon. 502-5	64.53 / 89.14
Mon. 500-6	45 14 29.34 / 71 22 46.47	187 58 38 / 33 27 12	Mon. 500-5 / Mon. 500-7	35.75 / 99.52	Mon. 502-5	45 14 21.16 / 71 24 41.56	283 05 47 / 59 09 47	Mon. 502-4 / Mon. 502-6	89.14 / 86.85
Mon. 500-7	45 14 26.65 / 71 22 48.98	213 27 10 / 13 01 34	Mon. 500-6 / Mon. 500-8	99.52 / 221.99	Mon. 502-6	45 14 19.72 / 71 24 44.98	239 09 45 / 22 22 45	Mon. 502-5 / Mon. 502-7	86.85 / 106.45
Mon. 500-8	45 14 19.65 / 71 22 51.28	193 01 32 / 28 33 21	Mon. 500-7 / Mon. 500-9	221.99 / 138.56	Mon. 502-7	45 14 16.53 / 71 24 46.83	202 22 44 / 354 07 14	Mon. 502-6 / Mon. 502-8	106.45 / 104.63
Mon. 500-9	45 14 15.70 / 71 22 54.31	208 33 19 / 33 39 48	Mon. 500-8 / Mon. 500-10	138.56 / 107.30	Mon. 502-8	45 14 13.16 / 71 24 46.34	174 07 14 / 24 54 14	Mon. 502-7 / Mon. 502-9	104.63 / 129.97
Mon. 500-10	45 14 12.81 / 71 22 57.04	213 39 46 / 16 01 00	Mon. 500-9 / Mon. 500-11	107.30 / 165.74	Mon. 502-9	45 14 09.34 / 71 24 48.85	204 54 12 / 109 47 12	Mon. 502-8 / Mon. 502-10	129.97 / 81.80
Mon. 500-11	45 14 07.65 / 71 22 59.14	196 00 58 / 28 37 27	Mon. 500-10 / Mon. 500-12	165.74 / 65.67	Mon. 502-10	45 14 10.24 / 71 24 52.38	289 47 10 / 81 07 40	Mon. 502-9 / Mon. 502-11	81.80 / 225.34
Mon. 500-12	45 14 05.78 / 71 23 00.58	208 37 26 / 28 37 05	Mon. 500-11 / Mon. 500-13	65.67 / 86.64	Mon. 502-11	45 14 09.11 / 71 25 02.58	261 07 33 / 37 15 33	Mon. 502-10 / Mon. 502-12	225.34 / 112.72
Mon. 500-13	45 14 03.32 / 71 23 02.48	208 37 03 / 35 59 52	Mon. 500-12 / Mon. 500-14	86.64 / 91.28	Mon. 502-12	45 14 06.20 / 71 25 05.71	217 15 31 / 48 21 31	Mon. 502-11 / Mon. 502-13	112.72 / 164.81
Mon. 500-14	45 14 00.93 / 71 23 04.94	215 59 50 / 60 54 04	Mon. 500-13 / Mon. 500-15	91.28 / 105.35	Mon. 502-13	45 14 02.66 / 71 25 11.36	228 21 27 / 22 31 57	Mon. 502-12 / Mon. 502-14	164.81 / 149.80
Mon. 500-15	45 13 59.27 / 71 23 09.16	240 54 01 / 95 56 15	Mon. 500-14 / Mon. 500-16	105.35 / 47.95	Mon. 502-14	45 13 58.17 / 71 25 13.99	202 31 55 / 55 44 55	Mon. 502-13 / Mon. 502-15	149.80 / 31.54
Mon. 500-16	45 13 59.43 / 71 23 11.34	275 56 13 / 138 27 32	Mon. 500-15 / Mon. 500-17	47.95 / 118.57	Mon. 502-15	45 13 57.60 / 71 25 15.19	235 44 54 / 53 15 54	Mon. 502-14 / Mon. 502-16	31.54 / 70.86

BOUNDARY MONUMENTS—SOURCE OF SOUTHWEST BRANCH OF ST. JOHN TO HEAD OF HALLS STREAM—Continued

Station	Latitude and longitude	Azimuth	To station	Distance (meters)	Station	Latitude and longitude	Azimuth	To station	Distance (meters)
	° ′ ″	° ′ ″				° ′ ″	° ′ ″		
Mon. 502-16	45 13 56.23 71 25 17.79	233 15 52 143 34 52	Mon. 502-15 Mon. 502-17	70.86 80.01	Mon. 503-15	45 14 18.23 71 26 11.26	291 41 53 115 23 46	Mon. 503-14 Mon. 503-16	52.57 129.28
Mon. 502-17	45 13 58.31 71 25 19.97	323 34 50 121 12 20	Mon. 502-16 Mon. 502-18	80.01 180.32	Mon. 503-16	45 14 20.03 71 26 16.61	295 23 43 99 59 18	Mon. 503-15 Mon. 504	129.28 137.63
Mon. 502-18	45 14 01.34 71 25 27.04	301 12 15 102 25 15	Mon. 502-17 Mon. 503	180.32 22.69	Mon. 504	45 14 20.80 71 26 22.83	279 59 14 99 57 09	Mon. 503-16 Mon. 504-1	137.63 44.99
Mon. 503	45 14 01.50 71 25 28.06	282 25 14 102 23 55	Mon. 502-18 Mon. 503-1	22.69 24.91	Mon. 504-1	45 14 21.06 71 26 24.86	279 57 08 44 15 58	Mon. 504 Mon. 504-2	44.99 80.64
Mon. 503-1	45 14 01.67 71 25 29.17	282 23 54 66 14 44	Mon. 503 Mon. 503-2	24.91 107.20	Mon. 504-2	45 14 19.18 71 26 27.44	224 15 56 93 31 26	Mon. 504-1 Mon. 504-3	80.64 119.46
Mon. 503-2	45 14 00.27 71 25 33.67	246 14 41 118 02 51	Mon. 503-1 Mon. 503-3	107.20 85.43	Mon. 504-3	45 14 19.42 71 26 32.91	273 31 22 61 11 42	Mon. 504-2 Mon. 504-4	119.46 36.28
Mon. 503-3	45 14 01.57 71 25 37.12	298 02 49 152 35 14	Mon. 503-2 Mon. 503-4	85.43 59.39	Mon. 504-4	45 14 18.86 71 26 34.36	241 11 41 61 19 01	Mon. 504-3 Mon. 504-5	36.28 45.28
Mon. 503-4	45 14 03.28 71 25 38.38	332 35 13 100 50 28	Mon. 503-3 Mon. 503-5	59.39 51.65	Mon. 504-5	45 14 18.15 71 26 36.18	241 19 00 23 12 40	Mon. 504-4 Mon. 504-6	45.28 40.34
Mon. 503-5	45 14 03.60 71 25 40.70	280 50 26 43 32 36	Mon. 503-4 Mon. 503-6	51.65 58.53	Mon. 504-6	45 14 16.95 71 26 36.91	203 12 39 12 35 24	Mon. 504-5 Mon. 504-7	40.34 136.74
Mon. 503-6	45 14 02.22 71 25 42.55	223 32 35 96 17 55	Mon. 503-5 Mon. 503-7	58.53 95.60	Mon. 504-7	45 14 12.63 71 26 38.28	192 35 23 343 59 53	Mon. 504-6 Mon. 505	136.74 32.89
Mon. 503-7	45 14 02.56 71 25 46.91	276 17 52 161 50 17	Mon. 503-6 Mon. 503-8	95.60 131.56	Mon. 505	45 14 11.60 71 26 37.86	163 59 53 343 55 47	Mon. 504-7 Mon. 505-1	32.89 30.85
Mon. 503-8	45 14 06.61 71 25 48.79	341 50 16 180 43 46	Mon. 503-7 Mon. 503-9	131.56 98.30	Mon. 505-1	45 14 10.64 71 26 37.47	163 55 47 18 34 04	Mon. 505 Mon. 506	30.85 79.23
Mon. 503-9	45 14 09.79 71 25 48.73	0 43 46 121 43 56	Mon. 503-8 Mon. 503-10	98.30 64.85	Mon. 506	45 14 08.21 71 26 38.63	198 34 03 18 35 51	Mon. 505-1 Mon. 506-1	79.23 7.15
Mon. 503-10	45 14 19.90 71 25 51.26	301 43 54 101 15 14	Mon. 503-9 Mon. 503-11	64.85 79.23	Mon. 506-1	45 14 07.99 71 26 38.73	198 35 51 37 38 18	Mon. 506 Mon. 506-2	7.15 38.55
Mon. 503-11	45 14 11.40 71 25 54.82	281 15 11 129 34 51	Mon. 503-10 Mon. 503-12	79.23 109.59	Mon. 506-2	45 14 07.00 71 26 39.81	217 38 17 330 40 04	Mon. 506-1 Mon. 506-3	38.55 33.24
Mon. 503-12	45 14 13.66 71 25 58.69	309 34 48 136 52 43	Mon. 503-11 Mon. 503-13	109.59 208.79	Mon. 506-3	45 14 06.07 71 26 39.06	150 40 05 330 36 22	Mon. 506-2 Mon. 507	33.24 17.26
Mon. 503-13	45 14 18.60 71 26 05.24	316 52 38 69 35 18	Mon. 503-12 Mon. 503-14	208.79 87.96	Mon. 507	45 14 05.58 71 26 38.68	150 36 22 276 53	Mon. 506-3 T. P. 1	17.26 9.9
Mon. 503-14	45 14 17.60 71 26 09.02	249 35 15 111 41 55	Mon. 503-13 Mon. 503-15	87.96 52.57					

GEOGRAPHIC POSITIONS OF BOUNDARY TURNING POINTS AND REFERENCE MONUMENTS DEFINING THE INTERNATIONAL BOUNDARY THROUGH HALLS STREAM

Station	Latitude and longitude	Azimuth	To station	Distance (meters)	Station	Latitude and longitude	Azimuth	To station	Distance (meters)
	° ′ ″	° ′				° ′ ″	° ′		
T. P. 1	45 14 05.54 71 26 38.23	96 53 240 50	Mon. 507 T. P. 2	9.9 40.4	T. P. 28	45 13 56.89 71 26 17.51	128 38 338 45	T. P. 27 T. P. 29	22.8 35.5
T. P. 2	45 14 06.18 71 26 36.61	60 50 285 10	T. P. 1 T. P. 3	40.4 18.1	T. P. 29	45 13 55.82 71 26 16.92	158 45 283 59	T. P. 28 T. P. 30	35.5 33.3
T. P. 3	45 14 06.03 71 26 35.81	105 10 219 03	T. P. 2 T. P. 4	18.1 10.7	T. P. 30	45 13 55.56 71 26 15.44	103 59 250 45	T. P. 29 T. P. 31	33.3 22.6
T. P. 4	45 14 06.30 71 26 35.50	39 03 274 09	T. P. 3 T. P. 5	10.7 16.0	T. P. 31	45 13 55.80 71 26 14.46	70 45 298 58	T. P. 30 T. P. 32	22.6 14.5
T. P. 5	45 14 06.26 71 26 34.77	94 09 252 08	T. P. 4 T. P. 6	16.0 15.9	T. P. 32	45 13 55.57 71 26 13.88	118 58 2 48	T. P. 31 T. P. 33	14.5 22.3
T. P. 6	45 14 06.42 71 26 34.07	72 08 277 32	T. P. 5 T. P. 7	15.9 32.9	T. P. 33	45 13 54.85 71 26 13.93	182 48 307 18	T. P. 32 T. P. 34	22.3 87.8
T. P. 7	45 14 06.28 71 26 32.57	97 32 252 16	T. P. 6 T. P. 8	32.9 45.2	T. P. 34	45 13 53.13 71 26 10.73	127 18 224 32	T. P. 33 T. P. 35	87.8 14.0
T. P, 8	45 14 06.72 71 26 30.60	72 16 285 45	T. P. 7 T. P. 9	45.2 51.5	T. P. 35	45 13 53.45 71 26 10.28	44 32 200 09	T. P. 34 T. P. 36	14.0 36.9
T. P. 9	45 14 06.27 71 26 28.33	105 45 261 41	T. P. 8 T. P. 10	51.5 10.9	T. P. 36	45 13 54.57 71 26 09.70	20 09 271 26	T. P. 35 T. P. 37	36.9 13.9
T. P. 10	45 14 06.32 71 26 27.84	81 41 313 45	T. P. 9 T. P. 11	10.9 35.7	T. P. 37	45 13 54.56 71 26 09.06	91 26 337 10	T. P. 36 T. P. 38	13.9 61.9
T. P. 11	45 14 05.52 71 26 26.66	133 45 323 56	T. P. 10 T. P. 12	35.7 27.2	T. P. 38	45 13 52.72 71 26 07.96	157 10 321 34	T. P. 37 T. P. 39	61.9 46.6
T. P. 12	45 14 04.81 71 26 25.92	143 56 276 01	T. P. 11 T. P. 13	27.2 12.7	T. P. 39	45 13 51.54 71 26 06.63	141 34 304 48	T. P. 38 T. P. 40	46.6 42.7
T. P. 13	45 14 04.77 71 26 25.34	96 01 317 18	T. P. 12 T. P. 14	12.7 27.5	T. P. 40	45 13 50.74 71 26 05.03	124 48 313 58	T. P. 39 T. P. 41	42.7 54.2
T. P. 14	45 14 04.12 71 26 24.49	137 18 357 08	T. P. 13 T. P. 15	27.5 37.0	T. P. 41	45 13 49.52 71 26 03.24	133 58 348 27	T. P. 40 T. P. 42	54.2 12.4
T. P. 15	45 14 02.92 71 26 24.40	177 08 320 59	T. P. 14 T. P. 16	37.0 35.6	T. P. 42	45 13 49.13 71 26 03.13	168 27 278 29	T. P. 41 T. P. 43	12.4 10.7
T. P. 16	45 14 02.02 71 26 23.37	140 59 344 01	T. P. 15 T. P. 17	35.6 23.8	T. P. 43	45 13 49.08 71 26 02.64	98 29 358 30	T. P. 42 T. P. 44	10.7 17.7
T. P. 17	45 14 01.28 71 26 23.07	164 01 305 50	T. P. 16 T. P. 18	23.8 25.3	T. P. 44	45 13 48.51 71 26 02.62	178 30 258 26 268 42	T. P. 43 Ref. Mon. 509 T. P. 45	17.7 13.7 23.9
T. P. 18	45 14 00.80 71 26 22.13	125 50 2 53	T. P. 17 T. P. 19	25.3 14.8	Ref. Mon. 509	45 13 48.60 71 26 02.00	78 26 138 26	T. P. 44 Run	13.7 83.8
T. P. 19	45 14 00.32 71 26 22.16	182 53 312 48	T. P. 18 T. P. 20	14.8 10.8	T. P. 45	45 13 48.53 71 26 01.52	88 42 242 27	T. P. 44 T. P. 46	23.9 17.7
T. P. 20	45 14 00.08 71 26 21.80	132 48 293 34	T. P. 19 T. P. 21	10.8 20.6	T. P. 46	45 13 48.80 71 26 00.80	62 27 341 22	T. P. 45 T. P. 47	17.7 35.1
T. P. 21	45 13 59.81 71 26 20.94	113 34 338 49	T. P. 20 T. P. 22	20.6 13.1	T. P. 47	45 13 47.72 71 26 00.29	161 22 357 04	T. P. 46 T. P. 48	35.1 11.3
T. P. 22	45 13 59.42 71 26 20.72	158 49 308 36	T. P. 21 T. P. 23	13.1 15.7	T. P. 48	45 13 47.35 71 26 00.26	177 04 303 23	T. P. 47 T. P. 49	11.3 19.1
T. P. 23	45 13 59.10 71 26 20.16	128 36 355 41 14 54	T. P. 22 T. P. 24 Ref. Mon. 508	15.7 14.0 10.7	T. P. 49	45 13 47.01 71 25 59.53	123 23 354 30	T. P. 48 T. P. 50	19.1 17.2
Ref. Mon. 508	45 13 58.76 71 26 20.28	194 54 263 42 313 56	T. P. 23 Bog T. P. 24	10.7 111.0 5.3	T. P. 50	45 13 46.46 71 25 59.45	174 30 275 36	T. P. 49 T. P. 51	17.2 21.3
T. P. 24	45 13 58.64 71 26 20.11	133 56 175 41 5 18	Ref. Mon. 508 T. P. 23 T. P. 25	5.3 14.0 26.6	T. P. 51	45 13 46.39 71 25 58.48	95 36 335 32	T. P. 50 T. P. 52	21.3 26.3
T. P. 25	45 13 57.78 71 26 20.22	185 18 325 10	T. P. 24 T. P. 26	26.6 16.9	T. P. 52	45 13 45.62 71 25 57.98	155 32 280 03	T. P. 51 T. P. 53	26.3 29.1
T. P. 26	45 13 57.33 71 26 19.78	145 10 269 09	T. P. 25 T. P. 27	16.9 31.6	T. P. 53	45 13 45.46 71 25 56.67	100 03 330 42	T. P. 52 T. P. 54	29.1 38.6
T. P. 27	45 13 57.35 71 26 18.33	89 09 308 38	T. P. 26 T. P 28	31.6 22.8	T. P. 54	45 13 44.37 71 25 55.80	150 42 15 21	T. P. 53 T. P. 55	38.6 35.1
					T. P. 55	45 13 43.27 71 25 56.23	195 21 291 16	T. P. 54 T. P. 56	35.1 14.2

BOUNDARY TURNING POINTS AND REFERENCE MONUMENTS—HALLS STREAM—Contd.

Station	Latitude and longitude	Azimuth	To station	Distance (meters)
T. P. 56	45 13 43.10	111 16	T. P. 55	14.2
	71 25 55.62	323 32	T. P. 57	20.9
T. P. 57	45 13 42.56	143 32	T. P. 56	20.9
	71 25 55.05	271 08	T. P. 58	12.6
T. P. 58	45 13 42.55	91 08	T. P. 57	12.6
	71 25 54.47	318 10	T. P. 59	9.2
T. P. 59	45 13 42.33	138 10	T. P. 58	9.2
	71 25 54.19	272 36	T. P. 60	25.2
T. P. 60	45 13 42.29	92 36	T. P. 59	25.2
	71 25 53.04	335 09	T. P. 61	14.3
T. P. 61	45 13 41.87	155 09	T. P. 60	14.3
	71 25 52.77	305 49	T. P. 62	25.1
T. P. 62	45 13 41.39	125 49	T. P. 61	25.1
	71 25 51.84	220 53	T. P. 63	19.9
T. P. 63	45 13 41.88	40 53	T. P. 62	19.9
	71 25 51.24	300 33	T. P. 64	13.1
T. P. 64	45 13 41.66	120 33	T. P. 63	13.1
	71 25 50.72	292 54	T. P. 65	19.6
T. P. 65	45 13 41.41	112 54	T. P. 64	19.6
	71 25 49.89	233 22	T. P. 66	21.5
T. P. 66	45 13 41.82	53 22	T. P. 65	21.5
	71 25 49.10	320 32	T. P. 67	51.8
T. P. 67	45 13 40.53	140 32	T. P. 66	51.8
	71 25 47.59	299 53	T. P. 68	54.4
T. P. 68	45 13 39.65	119 53	T. P. 67	54.4
	71 25 45.43	320 49	T. P. 69	18.5
T. P. 69	45 13 39.19	140 49	T. P. 68	18.5
	71 25 44.90	283 57	T. P. 70	11.0
T. P. 70	45 13 39.10	103 57	T. P. 69	11.0
	71 25 44.41	313 31	T. P. 71	22.1
T. P. 71	45 13 38.61	133 31	T. P. 70	22.1
	71 25 43.67	356 02	T. P. 72	18.7
T. P. 72	45 13 38.01	176 02	T. P. 71	18.7
	71 25 43.61	303 58	T. P. 73	12.6
T. P. 73	45 13 37.78	123 58	T. P. 72	12.6
	71 25 43.13	259 58	T. P. 74	17.7
		293 39	Ref. Mon. 510	6.1
Ref. Mon. 510	45 13 37.70	17 47	Labor	183.0
	71 25 42.88	113 39	T. P. 73	6.1
		245 01	T. P. 74	13.1
T. P. 74	45 13 37.88	65 01	Ref. Mon. 510	13.1
	71 25 42.34	79 58	T. P. 73	17.7
		325 16	T. P. 75	18.6
T. P. 75	45 13 37.39	145 16	T. P. 74	18.6
	71 25 41.85	300 59	T. P. 76	23.5
T. P. 76	45 13 37.00	120 59	T. P. 75	23.5
	71 25 40.93	339 31	T. P. 77	11.2
T. P. 77	45 13 36.66	159 31	T. P. 76	11.2
	71 25 40.75	301 36	T. P. 78	49.3
T. P. 78	45 13 35.82	121 36	T. P. 77	49.3
	71 25 38.82	333 20	T. P. 79	13.3
T. P. 79	45 13 35.44	153 20	T. P. 78	13.3
	71 25 38.55	308 13	T. P. 80	41.4
T. P. 80	45 13 34.61	128 13	T. P. 79	41.4
	71 25 37.06	18 35	T. P. 81	37.4
T. P. 81	45 13 33.46	198 35	T. P. 80	37.4
	71 25 37.61	355 19	T. P. 82	31.5
T. P. 82	45 13 32.44	175 19	T. P. 81	31.5
	71 25 37.49	7 28	T. P. 83	29.0
T. P. 83	45 13 31.51	187 28	T. P. 82	29.0
	71 25 37.66	322 42	T. P. 84	21.9
T. P. 84	45 13 30.94	142 42	T. P. 83	21.9
	71 25 37.05	276 28	T. P. 85	27.8
T. P. 85	45 13 30.84	96 28	T. P. 84	27.8
	71 25 35.78	291 36	T. P. 86	27.3
T. P. 86	45 13 30.51	111 36	T. P. 85	27.3
	71 25 34.62	316 06	T. P. 87	30.4
T. P. 87	45 13 29.80	136 06	T. P. 86	30.4
	71 25 33.66	254 04	T. P. 88	43.7
T. P. 88	45 13 30.19	74 04	T. P. 87	43.7
	71 25 31.73	272 45	T. P. 89	39.7
T. P. 89	45 13 30.13	92 45	T. P. 88	39.7
	71 25 29.91	316 58	T. P. 90	14.9
T. P. 90	45 13 29.78	136 58	T. P. 89	14.9
	71 25 29.44	289 27	T. P. 91	47.9
		322 22	Ref. Mon. 510-1	65.4
Ref. Mon. 510-1	45 13 28.10	142 22	T. P. 90	65.4
	71 25 27.61	188 13	T. P. 91	36.3
		308 52	Ref. Mon. 510-2	260.1
T. P. 91	45 13 29.26	8 13	Ref. Mon. 510-1	36.3
	71 25 27.38	109 27	T. P. 90	47.9
		239 47	T. P. 92	35.1
T. P. 92	45 13 29.83	59 47	T. P. 91	35.1
	71 25 25.99	306 01	T. P. 93	32.0
T. P. 93	45 13 29.22	126 01	T. P. 92	32.0
	71 25 24.80	293 37	T. P. 94	45.6
T. P. 94	45 13 28.63	113 37	T. P. 93	45.6
	71 25 22.88	322 42	T. P. 95	44.2
T. P. 95	45 13 27.49	142 42	T. P. 94	44.2
	71 25 21.65	260 41	T. P. 96	19.4
T. P. 96	45 13 27.59	80 41	T. P. 95	19.4
	71 25 20.77	328 15	T. P. 97	21.4
T. P. 97	45 13 27.00	148 15	T. P. 96	21.4
	71 25 20.25	296 04	T. P. 98	23.0
T. P. 98	45 13 26.67	116 04	T. P. 97	23.0
	71 25 19.30	303 58	T. P. 99	35.4
T. P. 99	45 13 26.03	123 58	T. P. 98	35.4
	71 25 17.96	263 21	T. P. 100	28.1
T. P. 100	45 13 26.14	83 21	T. P. 99	28.1
	71 25 16.68	321 14	T. P. 101	18.2
T. P. 101	45 13 25.68	141 14	T. P. 100	18.2
	71 25 16.16	359 13	T. P. 102	38.1
T. P. 102	45 13 24.45	43 14	Ref. Mon. 510-2	69.6
	71 25 16.14	179 13	T. P. 101	38.1
		306 03	T. P. 103	62.2
Ref. Mon. 510-2	45 13 22.81	223 14	T. P. 102	69.6
	71 25 18.33	261 48	T. P. 103	98.9
		308 06	Ref. Mon. 510-3	301.4
T. P. 103	45 13 23.27	81 48	Ref. Mon. 510-2	98.9
	71 25 13.85	126 03	T. P. 102	62.2
		20 27	T. P. 104	22.3
T. P. 104	45 13 22.59	200 27	T. P. 103	22.3
	71 25 14.21	354 06	T. P. 105	11.5
T. P. 105	45 13 22.22	174 06	T. P. 104	11.5
	71 25 14.16	298 37	T. P. 106	72.0
T. P. 106	45 13 21.10	118 37	T. P. 105	72.0
	71 25 11.26	329 13	T. P. 107	27.1
T. P. 107	45 13 20.35	149 13	T. P. 106	27.1
	71 25 10.62	341 45	T. P. 108	23.1
T. P. 108	45 13 19.64	161 45	T. P. 107	23.1
	71 25 10.29	296 00	T. P. 109	66.3
		325 01	Ref. Mon. 510-3	107.5
Ref. Mon. 510-3	45 13 16.79	145 01	T. P. 108	107.5
	71 25 07.46	128 06	Ref. Mon. 510-2	301.4
		178 03	T. P. 109	59.0
T. P. 109	45 13 18.70	116 00	T. P. 108	66.3
	71 25 07.55	358 03	Ref. Mon. 510-3	59.0
		282 33	T. P. 110	22.6
T. P. 110	45 13 18.54	102 33	T. P. 109	22.6
	71 25 06.54	268 01	T. P. 111	39.8
T. P. 111	45 13 18.59	88 01	T. P. 110	39.8
	71 25 04.72	346 43	T. P. 112	21.0

BOUNDARY TURNING POINTS AND REFERENCE MONUMENTS—HALLS STREAM—Contd.

Station	Latitude and longitude	Azimuth	To station	Distance (meters)	Station	Latitude and longitude	Azimuth	To station	Distance (meters)
	° ′ ″	° ′				° ′ ″	° ′		
T. P. 112	45 13 17.93 71 25 04.50	166 43 329 40	T. P. 111 T. P. 113	21.0 60.2	T. P. 137	45 13 01.28 71 24 31.15	75 36 279 31	T. P. 136 T. P. 138	96.7 44.0
T. P. 113	45 13 16.25 71 25 03.11	149 40 347 42	T. P. 112 T. P. 114	60.2 36.1	T. P. 138	45 13 01.04 71 24 29.17	99 31 315 23 321 41	T. P. 137 T. P. 139 Ref. Mon. 510-8	44.0 99.1 84.9
T. P. 114	45 13 15.11 71 25 02.76	167 42 0 15	T. P. 113 T. P. 115	36.1 50.5	Ref. Mon. 510-8	45 12 58.88 71 24 26.76	97 33 141 41 282 53	Ref. Mon. 510-7 T. P. 138 T. P. 139	217.9 84.9 17.4
T. P. 115	45 13 13.47 71 25 02.77	180 15 324 23	T. P. 114 T. P. 116	50.5 67.9	T. P. 139	45 12 58.75 71 24 25.97	102 53 135 23 287 14	Ref. Mon. 510-8 T. P. 138 T. P. 140	17.4 99.1 71.3
T. P. 116	45 13 11.68 71 25 00.96	144 23 309 48	T. P. 115 T. P. 117	67.9 33.9	T. P. 140	45 12 58.07 71 24 22.85	107 14 235 12	T. P. 139 T. P. 141	71.3 29.2
T. P. 117	45 13 10.98 71 24 59.77	129 48 344 25	T. P. 116 T. P. 118	33.9 75.9	T. P. 141	45 12 58.61 71 24 21.75	55 12 318 43	T. P. 140 T. P. 142	29.2 28.9
T. P. 118	45 13 08.61 71 24 58.83	164 25 45 03	T. P. 117 T. P. 119	75.9 28.0	T. P. 142	45 12 57.91 71 24 20.88	138 43 291 21	T. P. 141 T. P. 143	28.9 19.7
T. P. 119	45 13 07.97 71 24 59.74	225 03 23 49	T. P. 118 T. P. 120	28.0 15.7	T. P. 143	45 12 57.68 71 24 20.04	111 21 330 10	T. P. 142 T. P. 144	19.7 48.1
T. P. 120	45 13 07.50 71 25 00.03	203 49 325 47	T. P. 119 T. P. 121	15.7 41.4	T. P. 144	45 12 56.33 71 24 18.94	150 10 282 03	T. P. 143 T. P. 145	48.1 74.8
T. P. 121	45 13 06.39 71 24 58.96	41 23 145 47 290 30	Ref. Mon. 510-4 T. P. 120 T. P. 122	44.4 41.4 16.6	T. P. 145	45 12 55.82 71 24 15.59	102 03 313 34	T. P. 144 T. P. 146	74.8 19.5
Ref. Mon. 510-4	45 13 05.31 71 25 00.30	185 06 221 23 238 36	Ridge T. P. 121 T. P. 122	237.2 44.4 52.6	T. P. 146	45 12 55.39 71 24 14.94	133 34 270 32	T. P. 145 T. P. 147	19.5 36.3
T. P. 122	45 13 06.19 71 24 58.25	58 36 110 30 318 15	Ref. Mon. 510-4 T. P. 121 T. P. 123	52.6 16.6 31.6	T. P. 147	45 12 55.38 71 24 13.28	90 32 337 57 232 10	T. P. 146 T. P. 148 Ref. Mon. 510-9	36.3 112.6 27.7
T. P. 123	45 13 05.43 71 24 57.29	138 15 284 02	T. P. 122 T. P. 124	31.6 20.4	Ref. Mon. 510-9	45 12 55.93 71 24 12.28	52 10 341 57 350 29	T. P. 147 Ref. Mon. 510-10 T. P. 148	27.7 310.8 123.1
T. P. 124	45 13 05.27 71 24 56.38	104 02 297 38	T. P. 123 T. P. 125	20.4 83.3	T. P. 148	45 12 52.00 71 24 11.34	157 57 170 29 295 59	T. P. 147 Ref. Mon. 510-9 T. P. 149	112.6 123.1 36.0
T. P. 125	45 13 04.02 71 24 52.99	31 33 117 38 308 41	Ref. Mon. 510-5 T. P. 124 T. P. 126	78.9 83.3 47.1	T. P. 149	45 12 51.49 71 24 09.86	115 59 349 52	T. P. 148 T. P. 150	36.0 54.1
Ref. Mon. 510-5	45 13 01.84 71 24 54.88	211 33 270 18	T. P. 125 Ref. Mon. 510-6	78.9 246.7	T. P. 150	45 12 49.76 71 24 09.42	169 52 78 29	T. P. 149 T. P. 151	54.1 18.1
T. P. 126	45 13 03.07 71 24 51.30	128 41 276 02	T. P. 125 T. P. 127	47.1 46.1	T. P. 151	45 12 49.64 71 24 10.23	258 29 322 14	T. P. 150 T. P. 152	18.1 38.1
T. P. 127	45 13 02.91 71 24 49.20	96 02 242 21	T. P. 126 T. P. 128	46.1 24.1	T. P. 152	45 12 48.66 71 24 09.16	142 14 290 54	T. P. 151 T. P. 153	38.1 20.4
T. P. 128	45 13 03.27 71 24 48.22	62 21 291 34	T. P. 127 T. P. 129	24.1 62.7	T. P. 153	45 12 48.43 71 24 08.29	110 54 29 31	T. P. 152 T. P. 154	20.4 33.9
T. P. 129	45 13 02.52 71 24 45.54	111 34 274 37	T. P. 128 T. P. 130	62.7 31.1	T. P. 154	45 12 47.48 71 24 09.05	209 31 3 48	T. P. 153 T. P. 155	33.9 46.4
T. P. 130	45 13 02.44 71 24 44.12	94 37 228 14 328 33	T. P. 129 T. P. 131 Ref. Mon. 510-6	31.1 51.1 23.3	T. P. 155	45 12 45.98 71 24 09.19	183 48 248 11 350 24	T. P. 154 Ref. Mon. 510-10 T. P. 156	46.4 31.4 45.6
Ref. Mon. 510-6	45 13 01.80 71 24 43.57	90 18 148 33 205 41	Ref. Mon. 510-5 T. P. 130 T. P. 131	246.7 23.3 59.8	Ref. Mon. 510-10	45 12 46.35 71 24 07.86	20 51 68 11 324 35	T. P. 156 T. P. 155 Ref. Mon. 510-11	60.6 31.4 188.0
T. P. 131	45 13 03.55 71 24 42.38	25 41 48 14 290 24	Ref. Mon. 510-6 T. P. 130 T. P. 132	59.8 51.1 36.5	T. P. 156	45 12 44.52 71 24 08.85	170 24 200 51 324 02	T. P. 155 Ref. Mon. 510-10 T. P. 157	45.6 60.6 45.9
T. P. 132	45 13 03.14 71 24 40.81	110 24 319 50	T. P. 131 T. P. 133	36.5 28.7	T. P. 157	45 12 43.32 71 24 07.61	144 02 1 17	T. P. 156 T. P. 158	45.9 59.1
T. P. 133	45 13 02.43 71 24 39.96	139 50 271 44	T. P. 132 T. P. 134	28.7 11.9	T. P. 158	45 12 41.41 71 24 07.69	181 17 313 57	T. P. 157 T. P. 159	59.1 66.3
T. P. 134	45 13 02.42 71 24 39.41	91 44 338 48	T. P. 133 T. P. 135	11.9 30.0	T. P. 159	45 12 39.92 71 24 05.50	133 57 231 23 332 17	T. P. 158 Ref. Mon. 510-11 T. P. 160	66.3 73.1 83.9
T. P. 135	45 13 01.51 71 24 38.91	158 48 292 14	T. P. 134 T. P. 136	30.0 81.9	Ref. Mon. 510-11	45 12 41.39 71 24 02.87	51 23 144 35	T. P. 159 Ref. Mon. 510-10	73.1 188.0
T. P. 136	45 13 00.50 71 24 35.44	51 04 112 14 255 36	Ref. Mon. 510-7 T. P. 135 T. P. 137	33.9 81.9 96.7	T. P. 160	45 12 37.51 71 24 03.71	152 17 289 26	T. P. 159 T. P. 161	83.9 23.8
Ref. Mon. 510-7	45 12 59.81 71 24 36.65	112 07 231 04	Ref. Mon. 510-6 T. P. 136	163.0 33.9					

BOUNDARY TURNING POINTS AND REFERENCE MONUMENTS—HALLS STREAM—Contd.

Station	Latitude and longitude	Azimuth	To station	Distance (meters)
	° ′ ″	° ′		
T. P. 161	45 12 37.25 71 24 02.68	109 26 0 43	T. P. 160 T. P. 162	23.8 27.5
T. P. 162	45 12 36.36 71 24 02.69	180 43 344 55	T. P. 161 T. P. 163	27.5 28.6
T. P. 163	45 12 35.47 71 24 02.35	164 55 253 33	T. P. 162 T. P. 164	28.6 24.4
T. P. 164	45 12 35.69 71 24 01.28	73 33 349 38	T. P. 163 T. P. 165	24.4 14.6
T. P. 165	45 12 35.23 71 24 01.16	169 38 55 38	T. P. 164 T. P. 166	14.6 43.2
T. P. 166	45 12 34.44 71 24 02.79	235 38 295 57	T. P. 165 T. P. 167	43.2 35.5
T. P. 167	45 12 33.94 71 24 01.33	115 57 9 36	T. P. 166 T. P. 168	35.5 28.7
T. P. 168	45 12 33.02 71 24 01.55	189 36 261 39	T. P. 167 T. P. 169	28.7 26.8
T. P. 169	45 12 33.15 71 24 00.34	81 39 340 58	T. P. 168 T. P. 170	26.8 38.1
T. P. 170	45 12 31.98 71 23 59.77	160 58 278 18	T. P. 169 T. P. 171	38.1 33.4
T. P. 171	45 12 31.82 71 23 58.26	98 18 355 12	T. P. 170 T. P. 172	33.4 28.7
T. P. 172	45 12 30.89 71 23 58.15	175 12 59 48	T. P. 171 T. P. 173	28.7 31.2
T. P. 173	45 12 30.38 71 23 59.38	239 48 348 42	T. P. 172 T. P. 174	31.2 63.2
T. P. 174	45 12 28.37 71 23 58.81	168 42 233 34	T. P. 173 T. P. 175	63.2 15.5
T. P. 175	45 12 28.67 71 23 58.24	53 34 288 35 309 42	T. P. 174 Ref. Mon. 510-12 T. P. 176	15.5 43.9 26.6
Ref. Mon. 510-12	45 12 28.22 71 23 56.33	81 51 108 35 342 45	T. P. 176 T. P. 175 Ref. Mon. 510-13	21.3 43.9 292.1
T. P. 176	45 12 28.12 71 23 57.30	129 42 47 02 261 51	T. P. 175 T. P. 177 Ref. Mon. 510-12	26.6 26.3 21.3
T. P. 177	45 12 27.54 71 23 58.18	227 02 321 19	T. P. 176 T. P. 178	26.3 16.0
T. P. 178	45 12 27.14 71 23 57.72	141 19 351 40	T. P. 177 T. P. 179	16.0 53.6
T. P. 179	45 12 25.42 71 23 57.36	171 40 282 44	T. P. 178 T. P. 180	53.6 31.3
T. P. 180	45 12 25.20 71 23 55.96	102 44 336 02	T. P. 179 T. P. 181	31.3 23.9
T. P. 181	45 12 24.49 71 23 55.52	156 02 28 05	T. P. 180 T. P. 182	23.9 26.7
T. P. 182	45 12 23.73 71 23 56.10	208 05 303 22	T. P. 181 T. P. 183	26.7 18.2
T. P. 183	45 12 23.41 71 23 55.40	123 22 358 55	T. P. 182 T. P. 184	18.2 37.1
T. P. 184	45 12 22.21 71 23 55.37	178 55 303 03	T. P. 183 T. P. 185	37.1 28.0
T. P. 185	45 12 21.72 71 23 54.29	123 03 5 53	T. P. 184 T. P. 186	28.0 35.6
T. P. 186	45 12 20.57 71 23 54.46	185 53 330 41	T. P. 185 T. P. 187	35.6 38.5
T. P. 187	45 12 19.48 71 23 53.59	150 41 16 17	T. P. 186 T. P. 188	38.5 28.8
T. P. 188	45 12 18.58 71 23 53.96	196 17 1 38 241 55	T. P. 187 T. P. 189 Ref. Mon. 510-13	28.8 64.2 39.6
Ref. Mon. 510-13	45 12 19.18 71 23 52.36	61 55 354 32	T. P. 188 Ref. Mon. 510-14	39.6 205.2
T. P. 189	45 12 16.50 71 23 54.04	181 38 347 56	T. P. 188 T. P. 190	64.2 55.1
T. P. 190	45 12 14.75 71 23 53.51	167 56 329 02	T. P. 189 T. P. 191	55.1 39.1
T. P. 191	45 12 13.66 71 23 52.59	149 02 352 26	T. P. 190 T. P. 192	39.1 21.5
T. P. 192	45 12 12.97 71 23 52.46	172 26 12 26 300 03	T. P. 191 T. P. 193 Ref. Mon. 510-14	21.5 42.9 25.3
Ref. Mon. 510-14	45 12 12.56 71 23 51.46	46 48 120 03 174 32	T. P. 193 T. P. 192 Ref. Mon. 510-13	42.7 25.3 205.2
T. P. 193	45 12 11.62 71 23 52.88	192 26 226 48 41 07	T. P. 192 Ref. Mon. 510-14 T. P. 194	42.9 42.7 49.2
T. P. 194	45 12 10.41 71 23 54.36	221 07 34 35	T. P. 193 T. P. 195	49.2 42.2
T. P. 195	45 12 09.29 71 23 55.46	214 35 42 20	T. P. 194 T. P. 196	42.2 49.5
T. P. 196	45 12 08.10 71 23 56.99	222 20 70 40 48 45	T. P. 195 T. P. 197 Ref. Mon. 510-15	49.5 57.4 42.5
Ref. Mon. 510-15	45 12 07.20 71 23 58.46	112 05 222 41 228 45	T. P. 197 Ref. Mon. 510-14 T. P. 196	24.0 225.2 42.5
T. P. 197	45 12 07.49 71 23 59.48	250 40 292 05 92 45	T. P. 196 Ref. Mon. 510-15 T. P. 198	57.4 24.0 41.1
T. P. 198	45 12 07.55 71 24 01.36	272 45 34 24	T. P. 197 T. P. 199	41.1 58.2
T. P. 199	45 12 06.00 71 24 02.87	214 24 316 24	T. P. 198 T. P. 200	58.2 13.3
T. P. 200	45 12 05.69 71 24 02.45	136 24 343 50	T. P. 199 T. P. 201	13.3 18.7
T. P. 201	45 12 05.11 71 24 02.21	163 50 10 25	T. P. 200 T. P. 202	18.7 15.3
T. P. 202	45 12 04.62 71 24 02.34	190 25 318 57	T. P. 201 T. P. 203	15.3 14.1
T. P. 203	45 12 04.27 71 24 01.91	138 57 6 24	T. P. 202 T. P. 204	14.1 12.4
T. P. 204	45 12 03.87 71 24 01.97	186 24 309 40	T. P. 203 T. P. 205	12.4 11.8
T. P. 205	45 12 03.63 71 24 01.55	129 40 8 12	T. P. 204 T. P. 206	11.8 23.0
T. P. 206	45 12 02.89 71 24 01.70	188 12 6 56	T. P. 205 T. P. 207	23.0 44.0
T. P. 207	45 12 01.48 71 24 01.94	186 56 58 09	T. P. 206 T. P. 208	44.0 46.4
T. P. 208	45 12 00.69 71 24 03.74	238 09 70 38	T. P. 207 T. P. 209	46.4 39.7
T. P. 209	45 12 00.26 71 24 05.45	250 38 114 17	T. P. 208 T. P. 210	39.7 32.5
T. P. 210	45 12 00.69 71 24 06.81	294 17 192 30	T. P. 209 T. P. 211	32.5 22.4
T. P. 211	45 12 01.40 71 24 06.59	12 30 142 19	T. P. 210 T. P. 212	22.4 15.2
T. P. 212	45 12 01.79 71 24 07.02	322 19 57 36	T. P. 211 T. P. 213	15.2 22.9
T. P. 213	45 12 01.39 71 24 07.91	237 36 104 08	T. P. 212 T. P. 214	22.9 19.7
T. P. 214	45 12 01.55 71 24 08.79	284 08 91 38	T. P. 213 T. P. 215	19.7 24.5
T. P. 215	45 12 01.57 71 24 09.91	271 38 5 17	T. P. 214 T. P. 216	24.5 24.6

BOUNDARY TURNING POINTS AND REFERENCE MONUMENTS—HALLS STREAM—Contd.

Station	Latitude and longitude	Azimuth	To station	Distance (meters)	Station	Latitude and longitude	Azimuth	To station	Distance (meters)
	° ′ ″	° ′				° ′ ″	° ′		
T. P. 216	45 12 00.78 71 24 10.01	185 17 54 50	T. P. 215 T. P. 217	24.6 67.7	T. P. 244	45 11 42.96 71 24 17.58	152 11 338 51	T. P. 243 T. P. 245	44.3 25.6
T. P. 217	45 11 59.52 71 24 12.55	234 50 21 55	T. P. 216 T. P. 218	67.7 21.6	T. P. 245	45 11 42.19 71 24 17.15	158 51 39 50	T. P. 244 T. P. 246	25.6 54.2
T. P. 218	45 11 58.87 71 24 12.92	201 55 343 02	T. P. 217 T. P. 219	21.6 26.3	T. P. 246	45 11 40.84 71 24 18.74	219 50 29 24	T. P. 245 T. P. 247	54.2 47.7
T. P. 219	45 11 58.05 71 24 12.57	163 02 35 36	T. P. 218 T. P. 220	26.3 21.6	T. P. 247	45 11 39.49 71 24 19.81	209 24 10 44	T. P. 246 T. P. 248	47.7 33.9
T. P. 220	45 11 57.48 71 24 13.15	215 36 291 55	T. P. 219 T. P. 221	21.6 26.8	T. P. 248	45 11 38.41 71 24 20.10	190 44 308 28 351 09	T. P. 247 Ref. Mon. 510-18 T. P. 249	33.9 68.9 42.1
T. P. 221	45 11 57.15 71 24 12.01	111 55 53 41 335 55	T. P. 220 T. P. 222 Ref. Mon. 510-16	26.8 35.9 98.2	Ref. Mon. 510-18	45 11 37.03 71 24 17.63	44 31 91 32 128 28	Ref. Mon. 510-19 T. P. 249 T. P. 248	439.8 47.5 68.9
Ref. Mon. 510-16	45 11 54.25 71 24 10.17	3 07 134 44 155 55	Ref. Mon. 510-17 T. P. 222 T. P. 221	229.0 97.1 98.2	T. P. 249	45 11 37.07 71 24 19.80	171 09 26 38 271 32	T. P. 248 T. P. 250 Ref. Mon. 510-18	42.1 36.4 47.5
T. P. 222	45 11 56.47 71 24 13.33	233 41 30 41 314 44	T. P. 221 T. P. 223 Ref. Mon. 510-16	35.9 29.4 97.1	T. P. 250	45 11 36.02 71 24 20.55	206 38 55 33	T. P. 249 T. P. 251	36.4 45.7
T. P. 223	45 11 55.65 71 24 14.02	210 41 49 40	T. P. 222 T. P. 224	29.4 23.7	T. P. 251	45 11 35.18 71 24 22.28	235 33 83 13	T. P. 250 T. P. 252	45.7 40.2
T. P. 224	45 11 55.15 71 24 14.85	229 40 99 05	T. P. 223 T. P. 225	23.7 18.4	T. P. 252	45 11 35.03 71 24 24.11	263 13 148 47	T. P. 251 T. P. 253	40.2 21.0
T. P. 225	45 11 55.25 71 24 15.68	279 05 76 17	T. P. 224 T. P. 226	18.4 26.7	T. P. 253	45 11 35.61 71 24 24.61	328 47 62 10	T. P. 252 T. P. 254	21.0 25.1
T. P. 226	45 11 55.05 71 24 16.87	256 17 347 35	T. P. 225 T. P. 227	26.7 12.6	T. P. 254	45 11 35.23 71 24 25.62	242 10 19 57	T. P. 253 T. P. 255	25.1 29.4
T. P. 227	45 11 54.65 71 24 16.74	167 35 55 31	T. P. 226 T. P. 228	12.6 41.3	T. P. 255	45 11 34.33 71 24 26.08	199 57 342 16	T. P. 254 T. P. 256	29.4 42.6
T. P. 228	45 11 53.89 71 24 18.30	235 31 22 46	T. P. 227 T. P. 229	41.3 26.0	T. P. 256	45 11 33.01 71 24 25.48	162 16 357 09	T. P. 255 T. P. 257	42.6 51.1
T. P. 229	45 11 53.11 71 24 18.76	202 46 56 56	T. P. 228 T. P. 230	26.0 70.3	T. P. 257	45 11 31.36 71 24 25.36	177 09 75 46	T. P. 256 T. P. 258	51.1 39.1
T. P. 230	45 11 51.87 71 24 21.46	236 56 98 08	T. P. 229 T. P. 231	70.3 36.5	T. P. 258	45 11 31.05 71 24 27.10	255 46 46 04	T. P. 257 T. P. 259	39.1 49.9
T. P. 231	45 11 52.04 71 24 23.12	278 08 354 13	T. P. 230 T. P. 232	36.5 24.4	T. P. 259	45 11 29.93 71 24 28.75	226 04 353 47	T. P. 258 T. P. 260	49.9 23.6
T. P. 232	45 11 51.25 71 24 23.01	174 13 295 57	T. P. 231 T. P. 233	24.4 23.6	T. P. 260	45 11 29.17 71 24 28.63	173 47 47 44	T. P. 259 T. P. 261	23.6 24.1
T. P. 233	45 11 50.91 71 24 22.04	115 57 332 13	T. P. 232 T. P. 234	23.6 20.0	T. P. 261	45 11 28.64 71 24 29.45	227 44 337 28	T. P. 260 T. P. 262	24.1 85.7
T. P. 234	45 11 50.34 71 24 21.61	152 13 6 32	T. P. 233 T. P. 235	20.0 33.2	T. P. 262	45 11 26.08 71 24 27.94	106 16 157 28 292 57	Ref. Mon. 510-19 T. P. 261 T. P. 263	86.6 85.7 19.8
T. P. 235	45 11 49.27 71 24 21.78	186 32 268 01	T. P. 234 T. P. 236	33.2 25.9	Ref. Mon. 510-19	45 11 26.87 71 24 31.75	58 54 286 16	Ref. Mon. 510-20 T. P. 262	740.7 86.6
T. P. 236	45 11 49.30 71 24 20.60	88 01 341 09	T. P. 235 T. P. 237	25.9 18.1	T. P. 263	45 11 25.83 71 24 27.10	112 57 326 15	T. P. 262 T. P. 264	19.8 18.0
T. P. 237	45 11 48.75 71 24 20.33	161 09 293 00	T. P. 236 T. P. 238	18.1 26.8	T. P. 264	45 11 25.35 71 24 26.64	146 15 11 54	T. P. 263 T. P. 265	18.0 38.7
T. P. 238	45 11 48.41 71 24 19.19	113 00 30 51 284 36	T. P. 237 T. P. 239 Ref. Mon. 510-17	26.8 42.0 190.7	T. P. 265	45 11 24.12 71 24 27.01	191 54 28 08	T. P. 264 T. P. 266	38.7 54.8
Ref. Mon. 510-17	45 11 46.84 71 24 10.74	104 36 183 07	T. P. 238 Ref. Mon. 510-16	190.7 229.0	T. P. 266	45 11 22.56 71 24 28.19	208 08 71 02	T. P. 265 T. P. 267	54.8 37.7
T. P. 239	45 11 47.24 71 24 20.18	210 51 357 57	T. P. 238 T. P. 240	42.0 39.4	T. P. 267	45 11 22.16 71 24 29.82	251 02 30 31	T. P. 266 T. P. 268	37.7 51.3
T. P. 240	45 11 45.96 71 24 20.12	177 57 296 46	T. P. 239 T. P. 241	39.4 11.0	T. P. 268	45 11 20.73 71 24 31.02	210 31 33 36	T. P. 267 T. P. 269	51.3 63.2
T. P. 241	45 11 45.80 71 24 19.67	116 46 356 34	T. P. 240 T. P. 242	11.0 20.1	T. P. 269	45 11 19.02 71 24 32.62	213 36 25 44	T. P. 268 T. P. 270	63.2 53.5
T. P. 242	45 11 45.15 71 24 19.61	176 34 319 58	T. P. 241 T. P. 243	20.1 37.2	T. P. 270	45 11 17.46 71 24 33.69	205 44 18 59	T. P. 269 T. P. 271	53.5 44.2
T. P. 243	45 11 44.23 71 24 18.51	139 58 332 11	T. P. 242 T. P. 244	37.2 44.3	T. P. 271	45 11 16.11 71 24 34.35	198 59 29 59	T. P. 270 T. P. 272	44.2 31.9

BOUNDARY TURNING POINTS AND REFERENCE MONUMENTS—HALLS STREAM—Contd.

Station	Latitude and longitude	Azimuth	To station	Distance (meters)
	° ′ ″	° ′		
T. P. 272	45 11 15.21 / 71 24 35.08	209 59 / 62 52	T. P. 271 / T. P. 273	31.9 / 38.3
T. P. 273	45 11 14.64 / 71 24 36.64	242 52 / 11 47	T. P. 272 / T. P. 274	38.3 / 40.5
T. P. 274	45 11 13.36 / 71 24 37.02	191 47 / 35 38	T. P. 273 / T. P. 275	40.5 / 41.9
T. P. 275	45 11 12.26 / 71 24 38.14	215 38 / 46 26	T. P. 274 / T. P. 276	41.9 / 72.9
T. P. 276	45 11 10.63 / 71 24 40.56	226 26 / 105 02 / 82 30	T. P. 275 / Ref. Mon. 510–20 / T. P. 277	72.9 / 457.5 / 75.4
Ref. Mon. 510–20	45 11 14.47 / 71 25 00.80	285 02 / 342 33	T. P. 276 / Ref. Mon. 510–21	457.5 / 248.6
T. P. 277	45 11 10.31 / 71 24 43.98	262 30 / 58 39	T. P. 276 / T. P. 278	75.4 / 47.9
T. P. 278	45 11 09.50 / 71 24 45.85	238 39 / 65 17	T. P. 277 / T. P. 279	47.9 / 94.3
T. P. 279	45 11 08.23 / 71 24 49.78	245 17 / 53 39	T. P. 278 / T. P. 280	94.3 / 48.2
T. P. 280	45 11 07.30 / 71 24 51.55	233 39 / 43 29	T. P. 279 / T. P. 281	48.2 / 75.4
T. P. 281	45 11 05.53 / 71 24 53.93	223 29 / 6 23	T. P. 280 / T. P. 282	75.4 / 86.9
T. P. 282	45 11 02.73 / 71 24 54.37	186 23 / 152 15 / 15 31	T. P. 281 / Ref. Mon. 510–21 / T. P. 283	86.9 / 141.4 / 87.0
Ref. Mon. 510–21	45 11 06.79 / 71 24 57.39	15 05 / 332 15	Ref. Mon. 510–22 / T. P. 282	350.7 / 141.4
T. P. 283	45 11 00.02 / 71 24 55.43	195 31 / 27 04	T. P. 282 / T. P. 284	87.0 / 95.4
T. P. 284	45 10 57.27 / 71 24 57.42	207 04 / 347 34	T. P. 283 / T. P. 285	95.4 / 53.3
T. P. 285	45 10 55.58 / 71 24 56.90	167 34 / 94 07 / 10 49	T. P. 284 / Ref. Mon. 510–22 / T. P. 286	53.3 / 102.2 / 95.7
Ref. Mon. 510–22	45 10 55.82 / 71 25 01.57	274 07 / 348 13	T. P. 285 / Ref. Mon. 510–23	102.2 / 240.5
T. P. 286	45 10 52.53 / 71 24 57.72	190 49 / 21 43	T. P. 285 / T. P. 287	95.7 / 58.7
T. P. 287	45 10 50.76 / 71 24 58.72	201 43 / 322 21	T. P. 286 / T. P. 288	58.7 / 58.1
T. P. 288	45 10 49.27 / 71 24 57.09	142 21 / 261 43	T. P. 287 / T. P. 289	58.1 / 58.5
T. P. 289	45 10 49.55 / 71 24 54.44	68 31 / 81 43 / 334 08	Ref. Mon. 510–23 / T. P. 288 / T. P. 290	114.5 / 58.5 / 35.1
Ref. Mon. 510–23	45 10 48.19 / 71 24 59.32	168 13 / 248 31	Ref. Mon. 510–22 / T. P. 289	240.5 / 114.5
T. P. 290	45 10 48.53 / 71 24 53.74	154 08 / 33 00	T. P. 289 / T. P. 291	35.1 / 44.2
T. P. 291	45 10 47.33 / 71 24 54.84	213 00 / 341 19	T. P. 290 / T. P. 292	44.2 / 32.2
T. P. 292	45 10 46.34 / 71 24 54.37	161 19 / 326 30	T. P. 291 / T. P. 293	32.2 / 62.0
T. P. 293	45 10 44.67 / 71 24 52.80	146 30 / 42 38	T. P. 292 / T. P. 294	62.0 / 57.1
T. P. 294	45 10 43.31 / 71 24 54.57	222 38 / 36 24	T. P. 293 / T. P. 295	57.1 / 28.6
T. P. 295	45 10 42.57 / 71 24 55.35	216 24 / 49 01	T. P. 294 / T. P. 296	28.6 / 45.8
T. P. 296	45 10 41.58 / 71 24 56.94	229 01 / 25 32	T. P. 295 / T. P. 297	45.8 / 77.3
T. P. 297	45 10 39.33 / 71 24 58.46	205 32 / 109 11 / 4 58	T. P. 296 / Ref. Mon. 510–24 / T. P. 298	77.3 / 96.8 / 144.4

Station	Latitude and longitude	Azimuth	To station	Distance (meters)
	° ′ ″	° ′		
Ref. Mon. 510–24	45 10 40.36 / 71 25 02.65	16 43 / 289 11	Knoll / T. P. 297	314.3 / 96.8
T. P. 298	45 10 34.67 / 71 24 59.03	184 58 / 23 05	T. P. 297 / T. P. 299	144.4 / 93.4
T. P. 299	45 10 31.89 / 71 25 00.71	203 05 / 56 24	T. P. 298 / T. P. 300	93.4 / 47.3
T. P. 300	45 10 31.04 / 71 25 02.52	236 24 / 49 39	T. P. 299 / T. P. 301	47.3 / 58.5
T. P. 301	45 10 29.81 / 71 25 04.56	292 19 / 229 39 / 15 41	Ref. Mon. 510–25 / T. P. 300 / T. P. 302	171.6 / 58.5 / 115.6
Ref. Mon. 510–25	45 10 27.70 / 71 24 57.29	112 19 / 113 25	T. P. 301 / Knoll	171.6 / 226.1
T. P. 302	45 10 26.20 / 71 25 05.98	195 41 / 355 13	T. P. 301 / T. P. 303	115.6 / 74.7
T. P. 303	45 10 23.79 / 71 25 05.69	175 13 / 55 21	T. P. 302 / T. P. 304	74.7 / 52.4
T. P. 304	45 10 22.82 / 71 25 07.67	235 21 / 343 06	T. P. 303 / T. P. 305	52.4 / 92.0
T. P. 305	45 10 19.97 / 71 25 06.45	163 06 / 43 57	T. P. 304 / T. P. 306	92.0 / 83.6
T. P. 306	45 10 18.02 / 71 25 09.11	223 57 / 19 22	T. P. 305 / T. P. 307	83.6 / 42.7
T. P. 307	45 10 16.71 / 71 25 09.76	199 22 / 339 47	T. P. 306 / T. P. 308	42.7 / 82.6
T. P. 308	45 10 14.20 / 71 25 08.45	159 47 / 31 59	T. P. 307 / T. P. 309	82.6 / 31.9
T. P. 309	45 10 13.32 / 71 25 09.22	211 59 / 76 58	T. P. 308 / T. P. 310	31.9 / 23.9
T. P. 310	45 10 13.15 / 71 25 10.29	256 58 / 37 25	T. P. 309 / T. P. 311	23.9 / 32.0
T. P. 311	45 10 12.33 / 71 25 11.18	217 25 / 114 16 / 68 11	T. P. 310 / Ref. Mon. 510–26 / T. P. 312	32.0 / 79.2 / 40.4
Ref. Mon. 510–26	45 10 13.38 / 71 25 14.48	119 42 / 294 16	Robert's West Base / T. P. 311	279.1 / 79.2
T. P. 312	45 10 11.84 / 71 25 12.89	248 11 / 8 26	T. P. 311 / T. P. 313	40.4 / 19.4
T. P. 313	45 10 11.22 / 71 25 13.02	188 26 / 58 54	T. P. 312 / T. P. 314	19.4 / 28.1
T. P. 314	45 10 10.75 / 71 25 14.12	238 54 / 23 12	T. P. 313 / T. P. 315	28.1 / 58.7
T. P. 315	45 10 09.00 / 71 25 15.18	203 12 / 59 40	T. P. 314 / T. P. 316	58.7 / 68.5
T. P. 316	45 10 07.88 / 71 25 17.89	239 40 / 43 29	T. P. 315 / T. P. 317	68.5 / 39.8
T. P. 317	45 10 06.94 / 71 25 19.14	223 29 / 2 46	T. P. 316 / T. P. 318	39.8 / 34.6
T. P. 318	45 10 05.82 / 71 25 19.22	182 46 / 40 37 / 6 39	T. P. 317 / T. P. 319 / Ref. Mon. 510–27	34.6 / 33.9 / 30.0
Ref. Mon. 510–27	45 10 04.86 / 71 25 19.38	53 00 / 186 39	King / T. P. 318	433.7 / 30.0
T. P. 319	45 10 04.99 / 71 25 20.23	220 37 / 22 13	T. P. 318 / T. P. 320	33.9 / 69.7
T. P. 320	45 10 02.90 / 71 25 21.44	202 13 / 35 16	T. P. 319 / T. P. 321	69.7 / 38.7
T. P. 321	45 10 01.88 / 71 25 22.46	215 16 / 85 31	T. P. 320 / T. P. 322	38.7 / 18.2
T. P. 322	45 10 01.83 / 71 25 23.29	265 31 / 7 44	T. P. 321 / T. P. 323	18.2 / 12.0
T. P. 323	45 10 01.45 / 71 25 23.37	187 44 / 67 22	T. P. 322 / T. P. 324	12.0 / 32.0
T. P. 324	45 10 01.05 / 71 25 24.72	247 22 / 8 08	T. P. 323 / T. P. 325	32.0 / 54.0

BOUNDARY TURNING POINTS AND REFERENCE MONUMENTS—HALLS STREAM—Contd.

Station	Latitude and longitude	Azimuth	To station	Distance (meters)
	° ′ ″	° ′		
T. P. 325	45 09 59.32 / 71 25 25.07	188 08 / 97 14	T. P. 324 / T. P. 326	54.0 / 43.3
T. P. 326	45 09 59.50 / 71 25 27.04	277 14 / 54 17	T. P. 325 / T. P. 327	43.3 / 35.2
T. P. 327	45 09 58.83 / 71 25 28.35	234 17 / 104 34	T. P. 326 / T. P. 328	35.2 / 22.1
T. P. 328	45 09 59.01 / 71 25 29.33	284 34 / 73 24	T. P. 327 / T. P. 329	22.1 / 38.4
T. P. 329	45 09 58.66 / 71 25 31.02	253 24 / 355 54	T. P. 328 / T. P. 330	38.4 / 27.8
T. P. 330	45 09 57.76 / 71 25 30.93	175 54 / 53 30 / 241 14	T. P. 329 / T. P. 331 / Ref. Mon. 511	27.8 / 23.1 / 17.4
Ref. Mon. 511	45 09 58.03 / 71 25 30.23	61 14 / 65 26	T. P. 330 / King	17.4 / 120.4
T. P. 331	45 09 57.31 / 71 25 31.77	233 30 / 345 00	T. P. 330 / T. P. 332	23.1 / 102.6
T. P. 332	45 09 54.10 / 71 25 30.55	165 00 / 327 44	T. P. 331 / T. P. 333	102.6 / 39.3
T. P. 333	45 09 53.02 / 71 25 29.59	147 44 / 282 57	T. P. 332 / T. P. 334	39.3 / 27.8
T. P. 334	45 09 52.82 / 71 25 28.35	102 57 / 206 35	T. P. 333 / T. P. 335	27.8 / 48.2
T. P. 335	45 09 54.21 / 71 25 27.36	26 35 / 330 28	T. P. 334 / T. P. 336	48.2 / 43.1
T. P. 336	45 09 53.00 / 71 25 26.39	150 28 / 34 26	T. P. 335 / T. P. 337	43.1 / 34.9
T. P. 337	45 09 52.07 / 71 25 27.29	214 26 / 342 38	T. P. 336 / T. P. 338	34.9 / 60.6
T. P. 338	45 09 50.20 / 71 25 26.46	162 38 / 70 11	T. P. 337 / T. P. 339	60.6 / 59.1
T. P. 339	45 09 49.55 / 71 25 29.01	250 11 / 14 17	T. P. 338 / T. P. 340	59.1 / 65.8
T. P. 340	45 09 47.48 / 71 25 29.76	194 17 / 337 22	T. P. 339 / T. P. 341	65.8 / 66.8
T. P. 341	45 09 45.48 / 71 25 28.58	157 22 / 298 57	T. P. 340 / T. P. 342	66.8 / 29.7
T. P. 342	45 09 45.01 / 71 25 27.39	118 57 / 28 46	T. P. 341 / T. P. 343	29.7 / 36.0
T. P. 343	45 09 43.99 / 71 25 28.18	208 46 / 318 06	T. P. 342 / T. P. 344	36.0 / 47.6
T. P. 344	45 09 42.84 / 71 25 26.72	138 06 / 23 30	T. P. 343 / T. P. 345	47.6 / 24.6
T. P. 345	45 09 42.11 / 71 25 27.17	203 30 / 71 32	T. P. 344 / T. P. 346	24.6 / 31.2
T. P. 346	45 09 41.79 / 71 25 28.53	251 32 / 13 40	T. P. 345 / T. P. 347	31.2 / 27.4
T. P. 347	45 09 40.93 / 71 25 28.83	193 40 / 354 09	T. P. 346 / T. P. 348	27.4 / 44.2
T. P. 348	45 09 39.51 / 71 25 28.63	174 09 / 298 40	T. P. 347 / T. P. 349	44.2 / 50.5
T. P. 349	45 09 38.73 / 71 25 26.60	118 40 / 36 33	T. P. 348 / T. P. 350	50.5 / 29.4
T. P. 350	45 09 37.96 / 71 25 27.40	216 33 / 122 53	T. P. 349 / T. P. 351	29.4 / 43.0
T. P. 351	45 09 38.72 / 71 25 29.05	302 53 / 48 47	T. P. 350 / T. P. 352	43.0 / 22.7
T. P. 352	45 09 38.24 / 71 25 29.83	228 47 / 342 08	T. P. 351 / T. P. 353	22.7 / 27.7
T. P. 353	45 09 37.39 / 71 25 29.44	162 08 / 271 05	T. P. 352 / T. P. 354	27.7 / 42.8
T. P. 354	45 09 37.37 / 71 25 27.48	91 05 / 343 31	T. P. 353 / T. P. 355	42.8 / 14.1
T. P. 355	45 09 36.93 / 71 25 27.30	163 31 / 44 54	T. P. 354 / T. P. 356	14.1 / 46.8
T. P. 356	45 09 35.86 / 71 25 28.81	224 54 / 301 20 / 90 32	T. P. 355 / T. P. 357 / Ref. Mon. 511-1	46.8 / 41.6 / 42.0
Ref. Mon. 511-1	45 09 35.85 / 71 25 30.74	155 26 / 270 32	Culvert / T. P. 356	189.0 / 42.0
T. P. 357	45 09 35.14 / 71 25 27.20	121 20 / 22 47	T. P. 356 / T. P. 358	41.6 / 116.9
T. P. 358	45 09 31.65 / 71 25 29.27	202 47 / 45 20	T. P. 357 / T. P. 359	116.9 / 85.3
T. P. 359	45 09 29.71 / 71 25 32.05	225 20 / 25 16	T. P. 358 / T. P. 360	85.3 / 48.8
T. P. 360	45 09 28.28 / 71 25 33.00	205 16 / 86 26	T. P. 359 / T. P. 361	48.8 / 36.0
T. P. 361	45 09 28.20 / 71 25 34.65	266 26 / 352 07 / 12 57	T. P. 360 / T. P. 362 / Ref. Mon. 511-2	36.0 / 25.7 / 23.8
Ref. Mon. 511-2	45 09 27.45 / 71 25 34.89	17 47 / 192 57	Ref. Mon. 511-3 / T. P. 361	110.4 / 23.8
T. P. 362	45 09 27.38 / 71 25 34.48	172 07 / 297 42	T. P. 361 / T. P. 363	25.7 / 62.2
T. P. 363	45 09 26.44 / 71 25 31.96	117 42 / 21 54	T. P. 362 / T. P. 364	62.2 / 49.3
T. P. 364	45 09 24.96 / 71 25 32.80	201 54 / 294 05	T. P. 363 / T. P. 365	49.3 / 32.0
T. P. 365	45 09 24.54 / 71 25 31.46	114 05 / 13 10	T. P. 364 / T. P. 366	32.0 / 17.0
T. P. 366	45 09 24.00 / 71 25 31.64	193 10 / 81 46	T. P. 365 / T. P. 367	17.0 / 41.0
T. P. 367	45 09 23.81 / 71 25 33.50	261 46 / 350 03	T. P. 366 / T. P. 368	41.0 / 50.0
T. P. 368	45 09 22.21 / 71 25 33.10	170 03 / 66 24	T. P. 367 / T. P. 369	50.0 / 26.3
T. P. 369	45 09 21.87 / 71 25 34.20	246 24 / 124 40	T. P. 368 / T. P. 370	26.3 / 48.9
T. P. 370	45 09 22.77 / 71 25 36.04	304 40 / 20 38	T. P. 369 / T. P. 371	48.9 / 27.7
T. P. 371	45 09 21.93 / 71 25 36.49	181 12 / 200 38 / 306 11	Ref. Mon. 511-3 / T. P. 370 / T. P. 372	65.3 / 27.7 / 45.8
Ref. Mon. 511-3	45 09 24.04 / 71 25 36.43	1 12 / 197 47	T. P. 371 / Ref. Mon. 511-2	65.3 / 110.4
T. P. 372	45 09 21.05 / 71 25 34.81	126 11 / 32 19	T. P. 371 / T. P. 373	45.8 / 55.9
T. P. 373	45 09 19.52 / 71 25 36.18	212 19 / 342 17	T. P. 372 / T. P. 374	55.9 / 46.9
T. P. 374	45 09 18.07 / 71 25 35.53	162 17 / 22 31	T. P. 373 / T. P. 375	46.9 / 56.7
T. P. 375	45 09 16.39 / 71 25 36.52	202 31 / 356 10	T. P. 374 / T. P. 376	56.7 / 58.8
T. P. 376	45 09 14.49 / 71 25 36.34	176 10 / 8 32	T. P. 375 / T. P. 377	58.8 / 65.8
T. P. 377	45 09 12.38 / 71 25 36.79	188 32 / 354 58	T. P. 376 / T. P. 378	65.8 / 41.5
T. P. 378	45 09 11.04 / 71 25 36.62	174 58 / 15 42	T. P. 377 / T. P. 379	41.5 / 35.4
T. P. 379	45 09 09.93 / 71 25 37.06	195 42 / 31 56	T. P. 378 / T. P. 380	35.4 / 157.6
T. P. 380	45 09 05.60 / 71 25 40.88	211 56 / 48 24	T. P. 379 / T. P. 381	157.6 / 59.8
T. P. 381	45 09 04.31 / 71 25 42.93	228 24 / 67 35	T. P. 380 / T. P. 382	59.8 / 65.3
T. P 382	45 09 03.50 / 71 25 45.69	247 35 / 95 15	T. P. 381 / T. P. 383	65.3 / 70.0

BOUNDARY TURNING POINTS AND REFERENCE MONUMENTS—HALLS STREAM—Contd.

Station	Latitude and longitude	Azimuth	To station	Distance (meters)
T. P. 383	45 09 03.71 71 25 48.88	275 15 52 24	T. P. 382 T. P. 384	70.0 46.4
T. P. 384	45 09 02.79 71 25 50.56	232 24 9 36	T. P. 383 T. P. 385	46.4 89.1
T. P. 385	45 08 59.94 71 25 51.24	189 36 59 13	T. P. 384 T. P. 386	89.1 81.6
T. P. 386	45 08 58.59 71 25 54.45	239 13 79 40	T. P. 385 T. P. 387	81.6 42.3
T. P. 387	45 08 58.34 71 25 56.35	259 40 29 51	T. P. 386 T. P. 388	42.3 71.5
T. P. 388	45 08 56.33 71 25 57.98	209 51 51 55	T. P. 387 T. P. 389	71.5 105.5
T. P. 389	45 08 54.23 71 26 01.78	231 55 13 10 278 07	T. P. 388 T. P. 390 Ref. Mon. 511-4	105.5 83.7 51.3
Ref. Mon. 511-4	45 08 53.99 71 25 59.45	98 07 357 42	T. P. 389 Bird	51.3 323.6
T. P. 390	45 08 51.59 71 26 02.65	193 10 350 16	T. P. 389 T. P. 391	83.7 57.9
T. P. 391	45 08 49.74 71 26 02.20	170 16 11 47	T. P. 390 T. P. 392	57.9 62.5
T. P. 392	45 08 47.76 71 26 02.78	191 47 347 37	T. P. 391 T. P. 393	62.5 94.3
T. P. 393	45 08 44.78 71 26 01.86	167 37 3 44	T. P. 392 T. P. 394	94.3 44.9
T. P. 394	45 08 43.33 71 26 01.99	183 44 63 56	T. P. 393 T. P. 395	44.9 31.3
T. P. 395	45 08 42.88 71 26 03.28	243 56 161 09	T. P. 394 T. P. 396	31.3 37.9
T. P. 396	45 08 44.04 71 26 03.84	341 09 114 11	T. P. 395 T. P. 397	37.9 33.9
T. P. 397	45 08 44.48 71 26 05.25	318 37 294 11 12 24	Ref. Mon. 511-5 T. P. 396 T. P. 398	30.2 33.9 44.9
Ref. Mon. 511-5	45 08 43.75 71 26 04.34	52 56 138 37	Duran T. P. 397	340.1 30.2
T. P. 398	45 08 43.06 71 26 05.69	192 24 348 34	T. P. 397 T. P. 399	44.9 68.3
T. P. 399	45 08 40.89 71 26 05.07	168 34 26 10	T. P. 398 T. P. 400	68.3 57.4
T. P. 400	45 08 39.22 71 26 06.23	206 10 52 18	T. P. 399 T. P. 401	57.4 40.7
T. P. 401	45 08 38.41 71 26 07.70	232 18 9 44	T. P. 400 T. P. 402	40.7 110.5
T. P. 402	45 08 34.88 71 26 08.56	189 44 358 27	T. P. 401 T. P. 403	110.5 50.0
T. P. 403	45 08 33.26 71 26 08.50	178 27 17 31	T. P. 402 T. P. 404	50.0 71.3
T. P. 404	45 08 31.06 71 26 09.48	197 31 79 38	T. P. 403 T. P. 405	71.3 31.2
T. P. 405	45 08 30.88 71 26 10.88	259 38 142 35	T. P. 404 T. P. 406	31.2 57.5
T. P. 406	45 08 32.36 71 26 12.48	322 35 101 00	T. P. 405 T. P. 407	57.5 39.5
T. P. 407	45 08 32.61 71 26 14.26	281 00 55 52	T. P. 406 T. P. 408	39.5 83.9
T. P. 408	45 08 31.09 71 26 17.44	235 52 0 29	T. P. 407 T. P. 409	83.9 40.4
T. P. 409	45 08 29.78 71 26 17.46	180 29 327 52	T. P. 408 T. P. 410	40.4 150.2
T. P. 410	45 08 25.66 71 26 13.80	147 52 323 25	T. P. 409 T. P. 411	150.2 106.8
T. P. 411	45 08 22.88 71 26 10.89	143 25 300 29	T. P. 410 T. P. 412	106.8 101.1
T. P. 412	45 08 21.22 71 26 06.90	120 29 320 47	T. P. 411 T. P. 413	101.1 86.7
T. P. 413	45 08 19.04 71 26 04.39	140 47 295 22	T. P. 412 T. P. 414	86.7 135.6
T. P. 414	45 08 17.16 71 25 58.78	115 22 4 33	T. P. 413 T. P. 415	135.6 72.9
T. P. 415	45 08 14.80 71 25 59.04	184 33 308 15	T. P. 414 T. P. 416	72.9 110.3
T. P. 416	45 08 12.59 71 25 55.08	128 15 328 39	T. P. 415 T. P. 417	110.3 36.3
T. P. 417	45 08 11.59 71 25 54.22	148 39 224 00 351 41	T. P. 416 Ref. Mon. 511-6 T. P. 418	36.3 15.3 155.9
Ref. Mon. 511-6	45 08 11.95 71 25 53.73	44 00 147 04	T. P. 417 Duran	15.3 925.5
T. P. 418	45 08 06.59 71 25 53.19	171 41 328 24	T. P. 417 T. P. 419	155.9 110.3
T. P. 419	45 08 03.55 71 25 50.55	148 24 315 39	T. P. 418 T. P. 420	110.3 84.2
T. P. 420	45 08 01.60 71 25 47.86	135 39 288 19	T. P. 419 T. P. 421	84.2 52.9
T. P. 421	45 08 01.06 71 25 45.56	108 19 345 02	T. P. 420 T. P. 422	52.9 39.3
T. P. 422	45 07 59.83 71 25 45.10	165 02 13 14	T. P. 421 T. P. 423	39.3 72.0
T. P. 423	45 07 57.56 71 25 45.85	193 14 338 02	T. P. 422 T. P. 424	72.0 115.3
T. P. 424	45 07 54.09 71 05 43.88	158 02 283 02	T. P. 423 T. P. 425	115.3 36.0
T. P. 425	45 07 53.83 71 25 42.27	103 02 345 55	T. P. 424 T. P. 426	36.0 190.0
T. P. 426	45 07 47.86 71 25 40.15	165 55 298 43 157 13	T. P. 425 T. P. 427 Ref. Mon. 511-7	190.0 25.4 51.5
Ref. Mon. 511-7	45 07 49.40 71 25 41.06	337 13 339 30	T. P. 426 Cliff	51.5 654.5
T. P. 427	45 07 47.46 71 25 39.13	118 43 234 31	T. P. 426 T. P. 428	25.4 35.2
T. P. 428	45 07 48.12 71 25 37.82	54 31 323 03	T. P. 427 T. P. 429	35.2 65.9
T. P. 429	45 07 46.41 71 25 36.01	143 03 21 39	T. P. 428 T. P. 430	65.9 145.9
T. P. 430	45 07 42.02 71 25 38.47	201 39 346 46	T. P. 429 T. P. 431	145.9 105.6
T. P. 431	45 07 38.69 71 25 37.36	166 46 7 14	T. P. 430 T. P. 432	105.6 34.9
T. P. 432	45 07 37.57 71 25 37.56	187 14 38 42	T. P. 431 T. P. 433	34.9 163.1
T. P. 433	45 07 33.45 71 25 42.23	218 42 14 58	T. P. 432 T. P. 434	163.1 102.1
T. P. 434	45 07 30.26 71 25 43.44	194 58 67 58	T. P. 433 T. P. 435	102.1 77.8
T. P. 435	45 07 29.31 71 25 46.74	247 58 0 50	T. P. 434 T. P. 436	77.8 58.7
T. P. 436	45 07 27.41 71 25 46.78	180 50 315 59	T. P. 435 T. P. 437	58.7 79.5
T. P. 437	45 07 25.56 71 25 44.25	135 59 41 29	T. P. 436 T. P. 438	79.5 72.5
T. P. 438	45 07 23.80 71 25 46.45	221 29 21 29	T. P. 437 T. P. 439	72.5 106.4
T. P. 439	45 07 20.59 71 25 48.23	201 29 51 24 359 04	T. P. 438 T. P. 440 Ref. Mon. 511-8	106.4 175.5 37.9
Ref. Mon. 511-8	45 07 19.36 71 25 48.20	179 04 230 47	T. P. 439 Cliff	37.9 497.1

BOUNDARY TURNING POINTS AND REFERENCE MONUMENTS—HALLS STREAM—Contd.

Station	Latitude and longitude	Azimuth	To station	Distance (meters)
T. P. 440	45 07 17.04 / 71 25 54.50	231 24 / 24 11	T. P. 439 / T. P. 441	175.5 / 102.8
T. P. 441	45 07 14.00 / 71 25 56.43	204 11 / 50 24	T. P. 440 / T. P. 442	102.8 / 112.1
T. P. 442	45 07 11.69 / 71 26 00.38	230 24 / 83 47	T. P. 441 / T. P. 443	112.1 / 38.6
T. P. 443	45 07 11.55 / 71 26 02.14	263 47 / 110 13	T. P. 442 / T. P. 444	38.6 / 64.7
T. P. 444	45 07 12.27 / 71 26 04.91	290 13 / 50 41	T. P. 443 / T. P. 445	64.7 / 149.5
T. P. 445	45 07 09.20 / 71 26 10.20	230 41 / 334 57	T. P. 444 / T. P. 446	149.5 / 81.1
T. P. 446	45 07 06.83 / 71 26 08.63	154 57 / 30 25	T. P. 445 / T. P. 447	81.1 / 46.1
T. P. 447	45 07 05.54 / 71 26 09.70	210 25 / 58 05	T. P. 446 / T. P. 448	46.1 / 77.7
T. P. 448	45 07 04.21 / 71 26 12.72	238 05 / 88 26	T. P. 447 / T. P. 449	77.7 / 105.5
T. P. 449	45 07 04.12 / 71 26 17.54	268 26 / 56 12	T. P. 448 / T. P. 450	105.5 / 92.0
T. P. 450	45 07 02.46 / 71 26 21.04	236 12 / 36 51	T. P. 449 / T. P. 451	92.0 / 117.2
T. P. 451	45 06 59.42 / 71 26 24.26	216 51 / 44 47	T. P. 450 / T. P. 452	117.2 / 65.3
T. P. 452	45 06 57.92 / 71 26 26.36	224 47 / 13 59	T. P 451 / T. P. 453	65.3 / 80.4
T. P. 453	45 06 55.39 / 71 26 27.25	193 59 / 27 45	T. P. 452 / T. P. 454	80.4 / 61.3
T. P. 454	45 06 53.63 / 71 26 28.55	207 45 / 9 05	T. P. 453 / T. P. 455	61.3 / 31.3
T. P. 455	45 06 52.63 / 71 26 28.78	189 05 / 315 21	T. P. 454 / T. P. 456	31.3 / 93.0
T. P. 456	45 06 50.49 / 71 26 25.79	135 21 / 47 32	T. P. 455 / T. P. 457	93.0 / 42.0
T. P. 457	45 06 49.57 / 71 26 27.21	227 32 / 73 30	T. P. 456 / T. P. 458	42.0 / 59.1
T. P. 458	45 06 49.02 / 71 26 29.80	253 30 / 41 18	T. P. 457 / T. P. 459	59.1 / 65.4
T. P. 459	45 06 47.43 / 71 26 31.78	221 18 / 75 03	T. P. 458 / T. P. 460	65.4 / 37.4
T. P. 460	45 06 47.12 / 71 26 33.43	255 03 / 90 57	T. P. 459 / T. P. 461	37.4 / 90.1
T. P. 461	45 06 47.17 / 71 26 37.55	270 57 / 52 56	T. P. 460 / T. P. 462	90.1 / 89.2
T. P. 462	45 06 45.42 / 71 26 40.80	232 56 / 129 09 / 238 59	T. P. 461 / T. P. 463 / Ref. Mon. 511–9	89.2 / 129.3 / 74.0
Ref. Mon. 511–9	45 06 46.66 / 71 26 37.90	58 59 / 100 45	T. P. 462 / Paquette	74.0 / 436.8
T. P. 463	45 06 48.07 / 71 26 45.39	309 09 / 118 25	T. P. 462 / T. P. 464	129.3 / 56.7
T. P. 464	45 06 48.94 / 71 26 47.67	298 25 / 83 28	T. P. 463 / T. P. 465	56.7 / 98.7
T. P. 465	45 06 48.58 / 71 26 52.16	263 28 / 62 40	T. P. 464 / T. P. 466	98.7 / 91.2
T. P. 466	45 06 47.22 / 71 26 55.87	242 40 / 36 24	T. P. 465 / T. P. 467	91.2 / 65.1
T. P. 467	45 06 45.52 / 71 26 57.64	216 24 / 348 51	T. P. 466 / T. P. 468	65.1 / 131.0
T. P. 468	45 06 41.36 / 71 26 56.48	168 51 / 43 35	T. P. 467 / T. P. 469	131.0 / 98.8
T. P. 469	45 06 39.04 / 71 26 59.60	223 35 / 67 10	T. P. 468 / T. P. 470	98.8 / 75.9
T. P. 470	45 06 38.09 / 71 27 02.80	247 10 / 23 15	T. P. 469 / T. P. 471	75.9 / 49.5
T. P. 471	45 06 36.62 / 71 27 03.69	203 15 / 329 30	T. P. 470 / T. P. 472	49.5 / 27.9
T. P. 472	45 06 35.84 / 71 27 03.04	149 30 / 24 44	T. P. 471 / T. P. 473	27.9 / 56.7
T. P. 473	45 06 34.17 / 71 27 04.13	204 44 / 3 35	T. P. 472 / T. P. 474	56.7 / 26.8
T. P. 474	45 06 33.30 / 71 27 04.21	183 35 / 325 05	T. P. 473 / T. P. 475	26.8 / 31.8
T. P. 475	45 06 32.46 / 71 27 03.38	145 05 / 228 27	T. P. 474 / T. P. 476	31.8 / 87.2
T. P. 476	45 06 34.33 / 71 27 00.39	48 27 / 308 10	T. P. 475 / T. P. 477	87.2 / 41.7
T. P. 477	45 06 33.50 / 71 26 58.89	128 10 / 339 25	T. P. 476 / T. P. 478	41.7 / 117.5
T. P. 478	45 06 29.94 / 71 26 57.00	159 25 / 10 12	T. P. 477 / T. P. 479	117.5 / 39.4
T. P. 479	45 06 28.68 / 71 26 57.32	190 12 / 69 06	T. P. 478 / T. P. 480	39.4 / 82.4
T. P. 480	45 06 27.73 / 71 27 00.84	249 06 / 42 50	T. P. 479 / T. P. 481	82.4 / 83.6
T. P. 481	45 06 25.74 / 71 27 03.44	222 50 / 0 10	T. P. 480 / T. P. 482	83.6 / 50.8
T. P. 482	45 06 24.09 / 71 27 03.45	180 10 / 308 19	T. P. 481 / T. P. 483	50.8 / 50.7
T. P. 483	45 06 23.07 / 71 27 01.63	128 19 / 40 13	T. P. 482 / T. P. 484	50.7 / 57.6
T. P. 484	45 06 21.65 / 71 27 03.33	220 13 / 16 45	T. P. 483 / T. P. 485	57.6 / 43.5
T. P. 485	45 06 20.30 / 71 27 03.90	196 45 / 40 45	T. P. 484 / T. P. 486	43.5 / 66.5
T. P. 486	45 06 18.67 / 71 27 05.89	220 45 / 327 30	T. P. 485 / T. P. 487	66.5 / 39.1
T. P. 487	45 06 17.60 / 71 27 04.93	147 30 / 285 39	T. P. 486 / T. P. 488	39.1 / 63.7
T. P. 488	45 06 17.04 / 71 27 02.12	105 39 / 216 19	T. P. 487 / T. P. 489	63.7 / 65.2
T. P. 489	45 06 18.74 / 71 27 00.35	36 19 / 322 10	T. P. 488 / T. P. 490	65.2 / 45.2
T. P. 490	45 06 17.59 / 71 26 59.08	142 10 / 12 23	T. P. 489 / T. P. 491	45.2 / 38.3
T. P. 491	45 06 16.38 / 71 26 59.46	192 23 / 52 55	T. P. 490 / T. P. 492	38.3 / 49.1
T. P. 492	45 06 15.42 / 71 27 01.26	232 55 / 42 14 / 9 54	T. P. 491 / T. P. 493 / Ref. Mon. 511–10	49.1 / 113.1 / 20.7
Ref. Mon. 511–10	45 06 14.76 / 71 27 01.42	56 37 / 189 54	Cedar tablet / T. P. 492	1,137.1 / 20.7
T. P. 493	45 06 12.71 / 71 27 04.74	222 14 / 17 23	T. P. 492 / T. P. 494	113.1 / 48.7
T. P. 494	45 06 11.20 / 71 27 05.40	197 23 / 39 13	T. P. 493 / T. P. 495	48.7 / 81.5
T. P. 495	45 06 09.15 / 71 27 07.76	219 13 / 54 33	T. P. 494 / T. P. 496	81.5 / 88.8
T. P. 496	45 06 07.48 / 71 27 11.07	234 33 / 104 04	T. P. 495 / T. P. 497	88.8 / 45.2
T. P. 497	45 06 07.84 / 71 27 13.08	284 04 / 72 00	T. P. 496 / T. P. 498	45.2 / 34.1
T. P. 498	45 06 07.50 / 71 27 14.56	252 00 / 47 33	T. P. 497 / T. P. 499	34.1 / 61.3
T. P. 499	45 06 06.16 / 71 27 16.63	227 33 / 75 19	T. P. 498 / T. P. 500	61.3 / 89.2

BOUNDARY TURNING POINTS AND REFERENCE MONUMENTS—HALLS STREAM—Contd.

Station	Latitude and longitude	Azimuth	To station	Distance (meters)	Station	Latitude and longitude	Azimuth	To station	Distance (meters)
	° ′ ″	° ′				° ′ ″	° ′		
T. P. 500	45 06 05.43 71 27 20.57	255 19 37 17	T. P. 499 T. P. 501	89.2 65.9	Ref. Mon. 511–13	45 05 14.56 71 28 05.98	38 53 296 23 333 35	Cone T. P. 528 T. P. 529	1,281.6 70.2 73.7
T. P. 501	45 06 03.73 71 27 22.39	217 17 11 31	T. P. 500 T. P. 502	65.9 120.1	T. P. 529	45 05 12.42 71 28 04.48	153 35 220 51 5 07	Ref. Mon. 511–13 T. P. 528 T. P. 530	73.7 46.0 70.1
T. P. 502	45 05 59.92 71 27 23.49	191 31 48 59 114 11	T. P. 501 T. P. 503 Ref. Mon. 511–11	120.1 28.2 66.7	T. P. 530	45 05 10.16 71 28 04.77	185 07 335 07	T. P. 529 T. P. 531	70.1 51.9
Ref. Mon. 511–11	45 06 00.80 71 27 26.27	64 19 294 11	Cedar tablet T. P. 502	450.4 66.7	T. P. 531	45 05 08.63 71 28 03.77	155 07 0 03	T. P. 530 T. P. 532	51.9 45.0
T. P. 503	45 05 59.31 71 27 24.46	228 59 66 17	T. P. 502 T. P. 504	28.2 162.6	T. P. 532	45 05 07.17 71 28 03.77	180 03 49 25	T. P. 531 T. P. 533	45.0 32.1
T. P. 504	45 05 57.19 71 27 31.27	246 17 35 52	T. P. 503 T. P. 505	162.6 43.2	T. P. 533	45 05 06.49 71 28 04.89	229 25 72 08	T. P. 532 T. P. 534	32.1 41.4
T. P. 505	45 05 56.06 71 27 32.43	215 52 19 20	T. P. 504 T. P. 506	43.2 169.5	T. P. 534	45 05 06.08 71 28 06.69	252 08 27 58	T. P. 533 T. P. 535	41.4 80.5
T. P. 506	45 05 50.88 71 27 35.00	199 20 13 01	T. P. 505 T. P. 507	169.5 95.4	T. P. 535	45 05 03.78 71 28 08.41	207 58 5 10	T. P. 534 T. P. 536	80.5 28.8
T. P. 507	45 05 47.87 71 27 35.98	193 01 347 11	T. P. 506 T. P. 508	95.4 59.9	T. P. 536	45 05 02.85 71 28 08.53	185 10 293 05	T. P. 535 T. P. 537	28.8 43.6
T. P. 508	45 05 45.98 71 27 35.37	167 11 317 34	T. P. 507 T. P. 509	59.9 83.2	T. P. 537	45 05 02.30 71 28 06.70	113 05 344 57	T. P. 536 T. P. 538	43.6 27.7
T. P. 509	45 05 43.99 71 27 32.80	137 34 335 21	T. P. 508 T. P. 510	83.2 38.4	T. P. 538	45 05 01.43 71 28 06.37	164 57 77 33	T. P. 537 T. P. 539	27.7 44.2
T. P. 510	45 05 42.86 71 27 32.07	155 21 52 23	T. P. 509 T. P. 511	38.4 35.5	T. P. 539	45 05 01.12 71 28 08.35	257 33 100 49	T. P. 538 T. P. 540	44.2 75.9
T. P. 511	45 05 42.16 71 27 33.36	232 23 91 39	T. P. 510 T. P. 512	35.5 110.0	T. P. 540	45 05 01.59 71 28 11.76	280 49 66 28	T. P. 539 T. P. 541	75.9 78.3
T. P. 512	45 05 42.26 71 27 38.39	271 39 71 43	T. P. 511 T. P. 513	110.0 33.2	T. P. 541	45 05 00.58 71 28 15.05	246 28 104 43	T. P. 540 T. P. 542	78.3 73.3
T. P. 513	45 05 41.92 71 27 39.83	251 43 47 10	T. P. 512 T. P. 514	33.2 38.2	T. P. 542	45 05 01.18 71 28 18.29	284 43 100 03	T. P. 541 T. P. 543	73.3 109.7
T. P. 514	45 05 41.08 71 27 41.11	227 10 28 41	T. P. 513 T. P. 515	38.2 199.5	T. P. 543	45 05 01.80 71 28 23.23	280 03 77 16	T. P. 542 T. P. 544	109.7 70.0
T. P. 515	45 05 35.41 71 27 45.49	208 41 83 17	T. P. 514 T. P. 516	199.5 34.9	T. P. 544	45 05 01.30 71 28 26.35	257 16 96 11	T. P. 543 T. P. 545	70.0 79.4
T. P. 516	45 05 35.28 71 27 47.07	263 17 111 16	T. P. 515 T. P. 517	34.9 115.9	T. P. 545	45 05 01.58 71 28 29.96	276 11 136 23	T. P. 544 T. P. 546	79.4 84.1
T. P. 517	45 05 36.64 71 27 52.01	291 16 77 04	T. P. 516 T. P. 518	115.9 40.2	T. P. 546	45 05 03.55 71 28 32.61	316 23 65 38	T. P. 545 T. P. 547	84.1 58.8
T. P. 518	45 05 36.35 71 27 53.80	257 04 22 32 289 37	T. P. 517 T. P. 519 Ref. Mon. 511–12	40.2 100.6 175.3	T. P. 547	45 05 02.76 71 28 35.06	245 38 358 34	T. P. 546 T. P. 548	58.8 60.2
Ref. Mon. 511–12	45 05 34.45 71 27 46.25	37 30 109 37	Cone T. P. 518	2,031.1 175.3	T. P. 548	45 05 00.81 71 28 34.99	178 34 40 04	T. P. 547 T. P. 549	60.2 70.3
T. P. 519	45 05 33.34 71 27 55.56	202 32 25 15	T. P. 518 T. P. 520	100.6 53.0	T. P. 549	45 04 59.07 71 28 37.06	220 04 80 14 240 08	T. P. 548 T. P. 550 Ref. Mon. 511–14	70.3 46.7 62.5
T. P. 520	45 05 31.79 71 27 56.59	205 15 38 11	T. P. 519 T. P. 521	53.0 50.9	Ref. Mon. 511–14	45 05 00.08 71 28 34.58	18 00 60 08	Cone T. P. 549	579.0 62.5
T. P. 521	45 05 30.49 71 27 58.03	218 11 22 43	T. P. 520 T. P. 522	50.9 52.3	T. P. 550	45 04 58.81 71 28 39.16	260 14 164 38	T. P. 549 T. P. 551	46.7 131.9
T. P. 522	45 05 28.93 71 27 58.95	202 43 353 53	T. P. 521 T. P. 523	52.3 34.0	T. P. 551	45 05 02.93 71 28 40.76	344 38 119 24	T. P. 550 T. P. 552	131.9 62.4
T. P. 523	45 05 27.83 71 27 58.78	173 53 6 19	T. P. 522 T. P. 524	34.0 82.3	T. P. 552	45 05 03.92 71 28 43.25	299 24 18 50	T. P. 551 T. P. 553	62.4 93.0
T. P. 524	45 05 25.18 71 27 59.19	186 19 13 01	T. P. 523 T. P. 525	82.3 163.9	T. P. 553	45 05 01.07 71 28 44.62	198 50 87 24	T. P. 552 T. P. 554	93.0 88.1
T. P. 525	45 05 20.01 71 28 00.88	193 01 333 19	T. P. 524 T. P. 526	163.9 161.7	T. P. 554	45 05 00.94 71 28 48.65	267 24 69 00	T. P. 553 T. P. 555	88.1 67.8
T. P. 526	45 05 15.33 71 27 57.56	153 19 31 51	T. P. 525 T. P. 527	161.7 114.4	T. P. 555	45 05 00.15 71 28 51.54	249 00 54 23	T. P. 554 T. P. 556	67.8 74.3
T. P. 527	45 05 12.18 71 28 00.32	211 51 124 51	T. P. 526 T. P. 528	114.4 74.0	T. P. 556	45 04 58.75 71 28 54.30	234 23 330 18	T. P. 555 T. P. 557	74.3 49.1
T. P. 528	45 05 13.55 71 28 03.10	304 51 40 51 116 23	T. P. 527 T. P. 529 Ref. Mon. 511–13	74.0 46.0 70.2	T. P. 557	45 04 57.37 71 28 53.19	150 18 292 49	T. P. 556 T. P. 558	49.1 76.6

BOUNDARY TURNING POINTS AND REFERENCE MONUMENTS—HALLS STREAM—Contd.

Station	Latitude and longitude	Azimuth	To station	Distance (meters)	Station	Latitude and longitude	Azimuth	To station	Distance (meters)
	° ′ ″	° ′				° ′ ″	° ′		
T. P. 558	45 04 56.41 / 71 28 49.96	112 49 / 358 43	T. P. 557 / T. P. 559	76.6 / 69.9	T. P. 588	45 04 14.63 / 71 29 24.90	220 08 / 119 57	T. P. 587 / T. P. 589	86.0 / 66.3
T. P. 559	45 04 54.15 / 71 28 49.89	178 43 / 28 00	T. P. 558 / T. P. 560	69.9 / 132.9	T. P. 589	45 04 15.71 / 71 29 27.53	299 57 / 99 09	T. P. 588 / T. P. 590	66.3 / 69.9
T. P. 560	45 04 50.35 / 71 28 52.74	208 00 / 45 52	T. P. 559 / T. P. 561	132.9 / 42.7	T. P. 590	45 04 16.07 / 71 29 30.69	279 09 / 110 40	T. P. 589 / T. P. 591	69.9 / 106.1
T. P. 561	45 04 49.39 / 71 28 54.14	225 52 / 93 49	T. P. 560 / T. P. 562	42.7 / 81.7	T. P. 591	45 04 17.28 / 71 29 35.23	290 40 / 95 15	T. P. 590 / T. P. 592	106.1 / 41.7
T. P. 562	45 04 49.56 / 71 28 57.87	273 49 / 353 30	T. P. 561 / T. P. 563	81.7 / 41.9	T. P. 592	45 04 17.40 / 71 29 37.13	275 15 / 68 55 / 15 19	T. P. 591 / T. P. 593 / Ref. Mon. 511-16	41.7 / 62.7 / 44.8
T. P. 563	45 04 48.21 / 71 28 57.65	173 30 / 20 13	T. P. 562 / T. P. 564	41.9 / 115.9	Ref. Mon. 511-16	45 04 16.00 / 71 29 37.67	69 17 / 195 19	Fall / T. P. 592	662.1 / 44.8
T. P. 564	45 04 44.69 / 71 28 59.48	200 13 / 63 16	T. P. 563 / T. P. 565	115.9 / 44.0	T. P. 593	45 04 16.67 / 71 29 39.80	248 55 / 102 55	T. P. 592 / T. P. 594	62.7 / 48.2
T. P. 565	45 04 44.05 / 71 29 01.28	243 16 / 154 57	T. P. 564 / T. P. 566	44.0 / 61.0	T. P. 594	45 04 17.02 / 71 29 41.94	282 55 / 17 29	T. P. 593 / T. P. 595	48.2 / 85.1
T. P. 566	45 04 45.84 / 71 29 02.46	334 57 / 79 58	T. P. 565 / T. P. 567	61.0 / 119.6	T. P. 595	45 04 14.39 / 71 29 43.11	197 29 / 294 32	T. P. 594 / T. P. 596	85.1 / 59.9
T. P. 567	45 04 45.17 / 71 29 07.84	259 58 / 87 05	T. P. 566 / T. P. 568	119.6 / 78.3	T. P. 596	45 04 13.59 / 71 29 40.62	114 32 / 8 41	T. P. 595 / T. P. 597	59.9 / 52.0
T. P. 568	45 04 45.04 / 71 29 11.42	267 05 / 66 00	T. P. 567 / T. P. 569	78.3 / 115.5	T. P. 597	45 04 11.93 / 71 29 40.98	188 41 / 49 04	T. P. 596 / T. P. 598	52.0 / 37.2
T. P. 569	45 04 43.52 / 71 29 16.24	246 00 / 327 31	T. P. 568 / T. P. 570	115.5 / 70.1	T. P. 598	45 04 11.14 / 71 29 42.26	229 04 / 76 08	T. P. 597 / T. P. 599	37.2 / 46.2
T. P. 570	45 04 41.60 / 71 29 14.52	147 31 / 359 29	T. P. 569 / T. P. 571	70.1 / 47.3	T. P. 599	45 04 10.78 / 71 29 44.31	256 08 / 24 03	T. P. 598 / T. P. 600	46.2 / 28.7
T. P. 571	45 04 40.07 / 71 29 14.50	179 29 / 45 50	T. P. 570 / T. P. 572	47.3 / 34.2	T. P. 600	45 04 09.93 / 71 29 44.85	204 03 / 10 22	T. P. 599 / T. P. 601	28.7 / 36.5
T. P. 572	45 04 39.29 / 71 29 15.63	225 50 / 5 18 / 137 35	T. P. 571 / T. P. 573 / Ref. Mon. 511-15	34.2 / 81.4 / 18.3	T. P. 601	45 04 08.77 / 71 29 45.15	190 22 / 55 20	T. P. 600 / T. P. 602	36.5 / 33.3
Ref. Mon. 511-15	45 04 39.73 / 71 29 16.19	263 57 / 317 35	Cone / T. P. 572	735.1 / 18.3	T. P. 602	45 04 08.16 / 71 29 46.40	235 20 / 159 19	T. P. 601 / T. P. 603	33.3 / 55.3
T. P. 573	45 04 36.67 / 71 29 15.97	185 18 / 297 18	T. P. 572 / T. P. 574	81.4 / 80.2	T. P. 603	45 04 09.83 / 71 29 47.29	339 19 / 149 32	T. P. 602 / T. P. 604	55.3 / 89.9
T. P. 574	45 04 35.48 / 71 29 12.71	117 18 / 3 00	T. P. 573 / T. P. 575	80.2 / 89.6	T. P. 604	45 04 12.34 / 71 29 49.37	329 32 / 124 59	T. P. 603 / T. P. 605	89.9 / 56.9
T. P. 575	45 04 32.58 / 71 29 12.93	183 00 / 33 47	T. P. 574 / T. P. 576	89.6 / 50.5	T. P. 605	45 04 13.40 / 71 29 51.50	304 59 / 111 02	T. P. 604 / T. P. 606	56.9 / 50.6
T. P. 576	45 04 31.22 / 71 29 14.21	213 47 / 62 23	T. P. 575 / T. P. 577	50.5 / 76.5	T. P. 606	45 04 13.99 / 71 29 53.66	291 02 / 42 16	T. P. 605 / T. P. 607	50.6 / 41.7
T. P. 577	45 04 30.07 / 71 29 17.31	242 23 / 38 26	T. P. 576 / T. P. 578	76.5 / 99.4	T. P. 607	45 04 12.99 / 71 29 54.94	222 16 / 3 36	T. P. 606 / T. P. 608	41.7 / 113.5
T. P. 578	45 04 27.55 / 71 29 20.14	218 26 / 91 49	T. P. 577 / T. P. 579	99.4 / 49.3	T. P. 608	45 04 09.32 / 71 29 55.27	183 36 / 337 42	T. P. 607 / T. P. 609	113.5 / 39.6
T. P. 579	45 04 27.60 / 71 29 22.39	271 49 / 20 54	T. P. 578 / T. P. 580	49.3 / 63.1	T. P. 609	45 04 08.13 / 71 29 54.58	157 42 / 304 31	T. P. 608 / T. P. 610	39.6 / 31.3
T. P. 580	45 04 25.69 / 71 29 23.42	200 54 / 1 16	T. P. 579 / T. P. 581	63.1 / 75.9	T. P. 610	45 04 07.55 / 71 29 53.40	124 31 / 333 09	T. P. 609 / T. P. 611	31.3 / 51.6
T. P. 581	45 04 23.23 / 71 29 23.49	181 16 / 348 57	T. P. 580 / T. P. 582	75.9 / 79.1	T. P. 611	45 04 06.06 / 71 29 52.34	153 09 / 45 51	T. P. 610 / T. P. 612	51.6 / 43.2
T. P. 582	45 04 20.71 / 71 29 22.80	168 57 / 308 38	T. P. 581 / T. P. 583	79.1 / 88.6	T. P. 612	45 04 05.08 / 71 29 53.76	225 51 / 9 05	T. P. 611 / T. P. 613	43.2 / 21.6
T. P. 583	45 04 18.92 / 71 29 19.64	128 38 / 305 15	T. P. 582 / T. P. 584	88.6 / 43.3	T. P. 613	45 04 04.39 / 71 29 53.92	189 05 / 302 42	T. P. 612 / T. P. 614	21.6 / 30.3
T. P. 584	45 04 18.11 / 71 29 18.02	125 15 / 355 32	T. P. 583 / T. P. 585	43.3 / 27.3	T. P. 614	45 04 03.86 / 71 29 52.75	122 42 / 7 56	T. P. 613 / T. P. 615	30.3 / 99.9
T. P. 585	45 04 17.23 / 71 29 17.92	175 32 / 61 30	T. P. 584 / T. P. 586	27.3 / 58.3	T. P. 615	45 04 00.66 / 71 29 53.38	187 56 / 340 39	T. P. 614 / T. P. 616	99.9 / 98.0
T. P. 586	45 04 16.33 / 71 29 20.26	241 30 / 106 13	T. P. 585 / T. P. 587	58.3 / 47.9	T. P. 616	45 03 57.66 / 71 29 51.90	160 39 / 312 36 / 168 40	T. P. 615 / T. P. 617 / Ref. Mon. 512	98.0 / 61.4 / 96.0
T. P. 587	45 04 16.76 / 71 29 22.37	286 13 / 40 08	T. P. 586 / T. P. 588	47.9 / 86.0	Ref. Mon. 512	45 04 00.71 / 71 29 52.76	129 26 / 348 40	Fall / T. P. 616	374.4 / 96.0

BOUNDARY TURNING POINTS AND REFERENCE MONUMENTS—HALLS STREAM—Contd.

Station	Latitude and longitude	Azimuth	To station	Distance (meters)	Station	Latitude and longitude	Azimuth	To station	Distance (meters)
	° ′ ″	° ′				° ′ ″	° ′		
T. P. 617	45 03 56.31	132 36	T. P. 616	61.4	T. P. 649	45 03 22.37	129 22	T. P. 648	31.3
	71 29 49.84	320 04	T. P. 618	117.1		71 29 52.34	346 22	T. P. 650	38.2
T. P. 618	45 03 53.40	140 04	T. P. 617	117.1	T. P. 650	45 03 21.17	166 22	T. P. 649	38.2
	71 29 46.40	25 44	T. P. 619	113.3		71 29 51.93	32 35	T. P. 651	89.2
							356 56	Ref. Mon. 512–1	40.9
T. P. 619	45 03 50.09	205 44	T. P. 618	113.3	Ref. Mon. 512–1	45 03 19.85	168 20	Fall	1,520.7
	71 29 48.65	5 04	T. P. 620	94.2		71 29 51.83	176 56	T. P. 650	40.9
T. P. 620	45 03 47.05	185 04	T. P. 619	94.2	T. P. 651	45 03 18.74	212 35	T. P. 650	89.2
	71 29 49.03	22 45	T. P. 621	213.4		71 29 54.12	12 48	T. P. 652	74.7
T. P. 621	45 03 40.68	202 45	T. P. 620	213.4	T. P. 652	45 03 16.38	192 48	T. P. 651	74.7
	71 29 52.80	318 42	T. P. 622	68.6		71 29 54.88	39 18	T. P. 653	68.9
T. P. 622	45 03 39.01	138 42	T. P. 621	68.6	T. P. 653	45 03 14.65	219 18	T. P. 652	68.9
	71 29 50.73	14 23	T. P. 623	73.4		71 29 56.87	95 08	T. P. 654	48.1
T. P. 623	45 03 36.71	194 23	T. P. 622	73.4	T. P. 654	45 03 14.79	275 08	T. P. 653	48.1
	71 29 51.56	54 47	T. P. 624	84.3		71 29 59.06	93 24	T. P. 655	79.9
T. P. 624	45 03 35.13	234 47	T. P. 623	84.3	T. P. 655	45 03 14.94	273 24	T. P. 654	79.9
	71 29 54.71	32 41	T. P. 625	83.6		71 30 02.70	26 43	T. P. 656	34.8
T. P. 625	45 03 32.85	212 41	T. P. 624	83.6	T. P. 656	45 03 13.93	206 43	T. P. 655	34.8
	71 29 56.77	12 34	T. P. 626	53.7		71 30 03.42	313 36	T. P. 657	148.8
T. P. 626	45 03 31.15	192 34	T. P. 625	53.7	T. P. 657	45 03 10.61	133 36	T. P. 656	148.8
	71 29 57.30	59 03	T. P. 627	46.3		71 29 58.50	45 45	T. P. 658	61.8
T. P. 627	45 03 30.38	239 03	T. P. 626	46.3	T. P. 658	45 03 09.21	225 45	T. P. 657	61.8
	71 29 59.12	119 06	T. P. 628	43.6		71 30 00.52	71 15	T. P. 659	79.6
T. P. 628	45 03 31.07	299 06	T. P. 627	43.6	T. P. 659	45 03 08.38	251 15	T. P. 658	79.6
	71 30 00.86	139 49	T. P. 629	40.9		71 30 03.96	117 48	T. P. 660	70.5
T. P. 629	45 03 32.08	319 49	T. P. 628	40.9	T. P. 660	45 03 09.45	297 48	T. P. 659	70.5
	71 30 02.06	116 09	T. P. 630	79.7		71 30 06.81	49 36	T. P. 661	49.9
T. P. 630	45 03 33.22	296 09	T. P. 629	79.7	T. P. 661	45 03 08.41	229 36	T. P. 660	49.9
	71 30 05.33	29 36	T. P. 631	53.8		71 30 08.55	103 22	T. P. 662	142.4
T. P. 631	45 03 31.70	209 36	T. P. 630	53.8	T. P. 662	45 03 09.48	283 22	T. P. 661	142.4
	71 30 06.55	356 23	T. P. 632	113.0		71 30 14.88	72 51	T. P. 663	66.7
T. P. 632	45 03 28.05	176 23	T. P. 631	113.0	T. P. 663	45 03 08.84	252 51	T. P. 662	66.7
	71 30 06.22	316 05	T. P. 633	28.3		71 30 17.79	24 53	T. P. 664	150.5
T. P. 633	45 03 27.39	136 05	T. P. 632	28.3	T. P. 664	45 03 04.42	204 53	T. P. 663	150.5
	71 30 05.32	264 00	T. P. 634	31.2		71 30 20.68	7 07	T. P. 665	181.2
T. P. 634	45 03 27.50	84 00	T. P. 633	31.2	T. P. 665	45 02 58.60	187 07	T. P. 664	181.2
	71 30 03.90	240 53	T. P. 635	48.5		71 30 21.71	351 51	T. P. 666	67.9
T. P. 635	45 03 28.26	60 53	T. P. 634	48.5	T. P. 666	45 02 56.42	171 51	T. P. 665	67.9
	71 30 01.96	291 23	T. P. 636	22.7		71 30 21.27	60 23	T. P. 667	99.3
T. P. 636	45 03 27.99	111 23	T. P. 635	22.7	T. P. 667	45 02 54.83	240 23	T. P. 666	99.3
	71 30 01.00	309 05	T. P. 637	48.7		71 30 25.21	6 47	T. P. 668	103.8
T. P. 637	45 03 26.99	129 05	T. P. 636	48.7	T. P. 668	45 02 51.49	186 47	T. P. 667	103.8
	71 29 59.27	277 46	T. P. 638	46.0		71 30 25.77	288 13	T. P. 669	165.2
T. P. 638	45 03 26.79	97 46	T. P. 637	46.0	T. P. 669	45 02 49.82	108 13	T. P. 668	165.2
	71 29 57.19	244 44	T. P. 639	68.7		71 30 18.60	233 24	T. P. 670	61.3
T. P. 639	45 03 27.74	64 44	T. P. 638	68.7	T. P. 670	45 02 51.00	53 24	T. P. 669	61.3
	71 29 54.35	301 44	T. P. 640	29.4		71 30 16.35	132 04	T. P. 671	80.6
T. P. 640	45 03 27.24	121 44	T. P. 639	29.4	T. P. 671	45 02 52.75	312 04	T. P. 670	80.6
	71 29 53.21	2 34	T. P. 641	25.6		71 30 19.08	244 41	T. P. 672	61.9
T. P. 641	45 03 26.41	182 34	T. P. 640	25.6	T. P. 672	45 02 53.61	64 41	T. P. 671	61.9
	71 29 53.26	43 41	T. P. 642	47.7		71 30 16.53	273 02	T. P. 673	69.1
							245 25	Ref. Mon. 512–2	75.9
T. P. 642	45 03 25.29	223 41	T. P. 641	47.7	Ref. Mon. 512–2	45 02 54.63	65 25	T. P. 672	75.9
	71 29 54.77	92 42	T. P. 643	44.2		71 30 13.38	137 54	Shift	896.4
T. P. 643	45 03 25.36	272 42	T. P. 642	44.2	T. P. 673	45 02 53.49	93 02	T. P. 672	69.1
	71 29 56.79	29 07	T. P. 644	32.4		71 30 13.38	329 59	T. P. 674	65.6
T. P. 644	45 03 24.44	209 07	T. P. 643	32.4	T. P. 674	45 02 51.65	149 59	T. P. 673	65.6
	71 29 57.51	39 35	T. P. 645	40.3		71 30 11.88	11 26	T. P. 675	56.9
T. P. 645	45 03 23.43	219 35	T. P. 644	40.3	T. P. 675	45 02 49.84	191 26	T. P. 674	56.9
	71 29 58.68	338 22	T. P. 646	22.3		71 30 12.40	48 31	T. P. 676	171.0
T. P. 646	45 03 22.76	158 22	T. P. 645	22.3	T. P. 676	45 02 46.17	228 31	T. P. 675	171.0
	71 29 58.30	294 27	T. P. 647	67.3		71 30 18.25	311 27	T. P. 677	146.7
T. P. 647	45 03 21.86	114 27	T. P. 646	67.3	T. P. 677	45 02 43.02	131 27	T. P. 676	146.7
	71 29 55.52	231 51	T. P. 648	57.5		71 30 13.23	225 51	T. P. 678	144.1
T. P. 648	45 03 23.01	51 51	T. P. 647	57.5					
	71 29 53.45	309 22	T. P. 649	31.3					

BOUNDARY TURNING POINTS AND REFERENCE MONUMENTS—HALLS STREAM—Contd.

Station	Latitude and longitude	Azimuth	To station	Distance (meters)
	° ′ ″	° ′		
T. P. 678	45 02 46.27 / 71 30 08.51	45 51 / 335 24	T. P. 677 / T. P. 679	144.1 / 124.8
T. P. 679	45 02 42.60 / 71 30 06.13	155 24 / 285 49	T. P. 678 / T. P. 680	124.8 / 86.8
T. P. 680	45 02 41.84 / 71 30 02.31	105 49 / 290 53	T. P. 679 / T. P. 681	86.8 / 62.4
T. P. 681	45 02 41.12 / 71 29 59.65	110 53 / 277 38	T. P. 680 / T. P. 682	62.4 / 95.7
T. P. 682	45 02 40.71 / 71 29 55.32	97 38 / 263 05	T. P. 681 / T. P. 683	95.7 / 105.1
T. P. 683	45 02 41.12 / 71 29 50.55	83 05 / 245 34	T. P. 682 / T. P. 684	105.1 / 70.5
T. P. 684	45 02 42.06 / 71 29 47.62	65 34 / 222 59	T. P. 683 / T. P. 685	70.5 / 54.3
T. P. 685	45 02 43.35 / 71 29 45.93	42 59 / 279 06	T. P. 684 / T. P. 686	54.3 / 43.5
T. P. 686	45 02 43.13 / 71 29 43.97	99 06 / 245 57	T. P. 685 / T. P. 687	43.5 / 147.5
T. P. 687	45 02 45.07 / 71 29 37.80	65 57 / 309 15	T. P. 686 / T. P. 688	147.5 / 106.2
T. P. 688	45 02 42.90 / 71 29 34.04	129 15 / 335 38 / 137 22	T. P. 687 / T. P. 689 / Ref. Mon. 512-3	106.2 / 244.1 / 65.7
Ref. Mon. 512-3	45 02 44.46 / 71 29 36.07	317 22 / 347 28	T. P. 688 / Pasture	65.7 / 1,376.0
T. P. 689	45 02 35.70 / 71 29 29.44	155 38 / 357 21	T. P. 688 / T. P. 690	244.1 / 59.0
T. P. 690	45 02 33.79 / 71 29 29.32	177 21 / 12 55	T. P. 689 / T. P. 691	59.0 / 96.4
T. P. 691	45 02 30.74 / 71 29 30.30	192 55 / 358 52	T. P. 690 / T. P. 692	96.4 / 81.2
T. P. 692	45 02 28.11 / 71 29 30.23	178 52 / 28 00	T. P. 691 / T. P. 693	81.2 / 118.3
T. P. 693	45 02 24.73 / 71 29 32.77	208 00 / 12 35	T. P. 692 / T. P. 694	118.3 / 97.7
T. P. 694	45 02 21.64 / 71 29 33.74	192 35 / 346 55	T. P. 693 / T. P. 695	97.7 / 82.5
T. P. 695	45 02 19.04 / 71 29 32.89	166 55 / 22 04	T. P. 694 / T. P. 696	82.5 / 78.3
T. P. 696	45 02 16.69 / 71 29 34.23	202 04 / 359 14	T. P. 695 / T. P. 697	78.3 / 195.7
T. P. 697	45 02 10.35 / 71 29 34.11	179 14 / 20 09	T. P. 696 / T. P. 698	195.7 / 194.6
T. P. 698	45 02 04.43 / 71 29 37.17	200 09 / 329 12	T. P. 697 / T. P. 699	194.6 / 81.4
T. P. 699	45 02 02.17 / 71 29 35.27	149 12 / 356 24	T. P. 698 / T. P. 700	81.4 / 34.0
T. P. 700	45 02 01.07 / 71 29 35.17	176 24 / 43 07	T. P. 699 / T. P. 701	34.0 / 48.8
T. P. 701	45 01 59.92 / 71 29 36.70	223 07 / 72 19	T. P. 700 / T. P. 702	48.8 / 52.0
T. P. 702	45 01 59.41 / 71 29 38.96	252 19 / 88 37	T. P. 701 / T. P. 703	52.0 / 95.5
T. P. 703	45 01 59.33 / 71 29 43.32	268 37 / 25 24	T. P. 702 / T. P. 704	95.5 / 25.4
T. P. 704	45 01 58.59 / 71 29 43.81	205 24 / 304 35 / 118 51	T. P. 703 / T. P. 705 / Ref. Mon. 512-4	25.4 / 121.4 / 381.0
Ref. Mon. 512-4	45 02 04.54 / 71 29 59.06	277 52 / 298 51	Pasture / T. P. 704	809.5 / 381.0
T. P. 705	45 01 56.36 / 71 29 39.24	124 35 / 341 36	T. P. 704 / T. P. 706	121.4 / 28.8
T. P. 706	45 01 55.48 / 71 29 38.82	161 36 / 39 23	T. P. 705 / T. P. 707	28.8 / 72.0
T. P. 707	45 01 53.68 / 71 29 40.91	219 23 / 77 29	T. P. 706 / T. P. 708	72.0 / 67.5
T. P. 708	45 01 53.21 / 71 29 43.92	257 29 / 115 24	T. P. 707 / T. P. 709	67.5 / 48.1
T. P. 709	45 01 53.88 / 71 29 45.91	295 24 / 154 32	T. P. 708 / T. P. 710	48.1 / 33.3
T. P. 710	45 01 54.85 / 71 29 46.57	334 32 / 80 21	T. P. 709 / T. P. 711	33.3 / 44.5
T. P. 711	45 01 54.60 / 71 29 48.58	260 21 / 32 23	T. P. 710 / T. P. 712	44.5 / 98.7
T. P. 712	45 01 51.90 / 71 29 50.99	212 23 / 4 25	T. P. 711 / T. P. 713	98.7 / 84.4
T. P. 713	45 01 49.17 / 71 29 51.29	184 25 / 66 40	T. P. 712 / T. P. 714	84.4 / 61.8
T. P. 714	45 01 48.38 / 71 29 53.89	246 40 / 358 27	T. P. 713 / T. P. 715	61.8 / 68.7
T. P. 715	45 01 46.16 / 71 29 53.81	178 27 / 332 26	T. P. 714 / T. P. 716	68.7 / 96.4
T. P. 716	45 01 43.39 / 71 29 51.77	152 26 / 39 16	T. P. 715 / T. P. 717	96.4 / 26.7
T. P. 717	45 01 42.72 / 71 29 52.54	219 16 / 65 49	T. P. 716 / T. P. 718	26.7 / 44.7
T. P. 718	45 01 42.13 / 71 29 54.40	245 49 / 91 53	T. P. 717 / T. P. 719	44.7 / 62.7
T. P. 719	45 01 42.20 / 71 29 57.26	271 53 / 329 00	T. P. 718 / T. P. 720	62.7 / 93.5
T. P. 720	45 01 39.60 / 71 29 55.06	149 00 / 351 17	T. P. 719 / T. P. 721	93.5 / 89.0
T. P. 721	45 01 36.75 / 71 29 54.44	171 17 / 12 02	T. P. 720 / T. P. 722	89.0 / 28.0
T. P. 722	45 01 35.86 / 71 29 54.71	192 02 / 88 48	T. P. 721 / T. P. 723	28.0 / 93.4
T. P. 723	45 01 35.79 / 71 29 58.98	268 48 / 120 37	T. P. 722 / T. P. 724	93.4 / 39.6
T. P. 724	45 01 36.44 / 71 30 00.54	300 37 / 54 52	T. P. 723 / T. P. 725	39.6 / 35.0
T. P. 725	45 01 35.79 / 71 30 01.85	234 52 / 16 01	T. P. 724 / T. P. 726	35.0 / 51.7
T. P. 726	45 01 34.18 / 71 30 02.50	196 01 / 302 20	T. P. 725 / T. P. 727	51.7 / 50.7
T. P. 727	45 01 33.30 / 71 30 00.54	122 20 / 328 25	T. P. 726 / T. P. 728	50.7 / 48.4
T. P. 728	45 01 31.96 / 71 29 59.38	148 25 / 9 05	T. P. 727 / T. P. 729	48.4 / 101.6
T. P. 729	45 01 28.71 / 71 30 00.11	189 05 / 275 46	T. P. 728 / T. P. 730	101.6 / 62.4
T. P. 730	45 01 28.51 / 71 29 57.27	95 46 / 291 10	T. P. 729 / T. P. 731	62.4 / 85.0
T. P. 731	45 01 27.52 / 71 29 53.65	111 10 / 327 18	T. P. 730 / T. P. 732	85.0 / 82.9
T. P. 732	45 01 25.26 / 71 29 51.61	147 18 / 30 31	T. P. 731 / T. P. 733	82.9 / 41.4
T. P. 733	45 01 24.10 / 71 29 52.57	210 31 / 66 18	T. P. 732 / T. P. 734	41.4 / 47.3
T. P. 734	45 01 23.48 / 71 29 54.55	246 18 / 98 59	T. P. 733 / T. P. 735	47.3 / 55.5
T. P. 735	45 01 23.76 / 71 29 57.05	278 59 / 118 01	T. P. 734 / T. P. 736	55.5 / 43.7
T. P. 736	45 01 24.42 / 71 29 58.81	298 01 / 116 19	T. P. 735 / T. P. 737	43.7 / 57.0
T. P. 737	45 01 25.24 / 71 30 01.14	296 19 / 67 51	T. P. 736 / T. P. 738	57.0 / 33.4
T. P. 738	45 01 24.84 / 71 30 02.55	247 51 / 345 35	T. P. 737 / T. P. 739	33.4 / 38.9

BOUNDARY TURNING POINTS AND REFERENCE MONUMENTS—HALLS STREAM—Contd.

Station	Latitude and longitude	Azimuth	To station	Distance (meters)
	° ′ ″	° ′		
T. P. 739	45 01 23.62 / 71 30 02.11	165 35 / 354 11	T. P. 738 / T. P. 740	38.9 / 70.2
T. P. 740	45 01 21.36 / 71 30 01.79	174 11 / 306 20	T. P. 739 / T. P. 741	70.2 / 31.1
T. P. 741	45 01 20.76 / 71 30 00.65	126 20 / 13 16 / 75 17	T. P. 740 / T. P. 742 / Ref. Mon. 512-5	31.1 / 60.8 / 23.8
Ref. Mon. 512-5	45 01 20.57 / 71 30 01.70	49 48 / 255 17	Rock / T. P. 741	83.0 / 23.8
T. P. 742	45 01 18.84 / 71 30 01.28	193 16 / 359 45	T. P. 741 / T. P. 743	60.8 / 70.3
T. P. 743	45 01 16.57 / 71 30 01.27	179 45 / 40 46	T. P. 742 / T. P. 744	70.3 / 65.0
T. P. 744	45 01 14.97 / 71 30 03.21	220 46 / 344 07	T. P. 743 / T. P. 745	65.0 / 76.1
T. P. 745	45 01 12.60 / 71 30 02.26	164 07 / 278 54	T. P. 744 / T. P 746	76.1 / 34.6
T. P. 746	45 01 12.43 / 71 30 00.70	98 54 / 235 04	T. P. 745 / T. P. 747	34.6 / 58.6
T. P. 747	45 01 13.51 / 71 29 58.50	55 04 / 287 37	T. P. 746 / T. P. 748	58.6 / 39.0
T. P. 748	45 01 13.13 / 71 29 56.80	107 37 / 51 59	T. P. 747 / T. P. 749	39.0 / 121.7
T. P. 749	45 01 10.70 / 71 30 01.18	231 59 / 109 51	T. P. 748 / T. P. 750	121.7 / 75.3
T. P. 750	45 01 11.53 / 71 30 04.42	289 51 / 17 37	T. P. 749 / T. P. 751	75.3 / 51.7
T. P. 751	45 01 09.94 / 71 30 05.13	197 37 / 344 44	T. P. 750 / T. P. 752	51.7 / 40.8
T. P. 752	45 01 08.66 / 71 30 04.64	164 44 / 278 36	T. P. 751 / T. P. 753	40.8 / 42.8
T. P. 753	45 01 08.45 / 71 30 02.71	98 36 / 249 47	T. P. 752 / T. P. 754	42.8 / 53.0

Station	Latitude and longitude	Azimuth	To station	Distance (meters)
	° ′ ″	° ′		
T. P. 754	45 01 09.05 / 71 30 00.43	69 47 / 349 06	T. P. 753 / T. P. 755	53.0 / 87.8
T. P. 755	45 01 06.26 / 71 29 59.68	169 06 / 38 06	T. P. 754 / T. P. 756	87.8 / 97.0
T. P. 756	45 01 03.78 / 71 30 02.41	218 06 / 109 16	T. P. 755 / T. P. 757	97.0 / 88.0
T. P. 757	45 01 04.72 / 71 30 06.20	289 16 / 22 34	T. P. 756 / T. P. 758	88.0 / 46.5
T. P. 758	45 01 03.33 / 71 30 07.02	202 34 / 328 37 / 92 07	T. P. 757 / T. P. 759 / Ref. Mon. 512-6	46.5 / 69.0 / 131.4
Ref. Mon. 512-6	45 01 03.49 / 71 30 13.01	272 07 / 350 53	T. P. 758 / Mon. 518	131.4 / 464.1
T. P. 759	45 01 01.43 / 71 30 05.38	148 37 / 343 04	T. P. 758 / T. P. 760	69.0 / 63.6
T. P. 760	45 00 59.46 / 71 30 04.53	163 04 / 4 42	T. P. 759 / T. P. 761	63.6 / 56.5
T. P. 761	45 00 57.64 / 71 30 04.74	184 42 / 344 12	T. P. 760 / T. P. 762	56.5 / 33.6
T. P. 762	45 00 56.59 / 71 30 04.33	164 12 / 286 07	T. P. 761 / T. P. 763	33.6 / 79.9
T. P. 763	45 00 55.87 / 71 30 00.82	106 07 / 350 10	T. P. 762 / T. P. 764	79.9 / 64.1
T. P. 764	45 00 53.82 / 71 30 00.32	170 10 / 45 34	T. P. 763 / T. P. 765	64.1 / 82.5
T. P. 765	45 00 51.95 / 71 30 03.01	225 34 / 1 46	T. P. 764 / T. P. 766	82.5 / 74.0
T. P. 766	45 00 49.56 / 71 30 03.11	181 46 / 64 23	T. P. 765 / T. P. 767	74.0 / 61.9
T. P. 767	45 00 48.69 / 71 30 05.66	244 23 / 269 09 / 89 09	T. P. 766 / Ref. Mon. 517 / Mon. 518	61.9 / 104.7 / 87.5
Ref. Mon. 517	45 00 48.74 / 71 30 00.88	89 09 / 89 09	Mon. 518 / T. P. 767	192.2 / 104.7

GEOGRAPHIC POSITIONS OF MONUMENTS MARKING THE INTERNATIONAL BOUNDARY FROM HALLS STREAM TO THE ST. LAWRENCE RIVER

Station	Latitude and longitude	Azimuth	To station	Distance (meters)	Station	Latitude and longitude	Azimuth	To station	Distance (meters)
	° ′ ″	° ′ ″				° ′ ″	° ′ ″		
Mon. 518	45 00 48.65 / 71 30 09.65	269 09 11 / 89 09 11	T. P. 767 / Mon. 519	87.5 / 254.51	Mon. 531–B	45 00 41.31 / 71 43 01.65	270 17 23 / 90 17 23	Mon. 531–A / Mon. 532	139.24 / 569.85
Mon. 519	45 00 48.53 / 71 30 21.28	269 09 03 / 89 08 58	Mon. 518 / Mon. 519–A	254.51 / 10.25	Mon. 532	45 00 41.40 / 71 43 27.68	270 17 05 / 89 46 58	Mon. 531–B / Mon. 533	569.85 / 2,387.71
Mon. 519–A	45 00 48.53 / 71 30 21.75	269 08 58 / 89 08 58	Mon. 519 / Mon. 519–A2	10.25 / 23.30	Mon. 533	45 00 41.09 / 71 45 16.71	269 45 41 / 88 46 07	Mon. 532 / Mon. 534	2,387.71 / 2,061.87
Mon. 519–A2	45 00 48.52 / 71 30 22.81	269 08 57 / 89 08 57	Mon. 519–A / Mon. 519–A3	23.30 / 39.70	Mon. 534	45 00 39.65 / 71 46 50.85	268 45 00 / 88 25 16	Mon. 533 / Mon. 534–A	2,061.87 / 802.04
Mon. 519–A3	45 00 48.50 / 71 30 24.62	269 08 56 / 89 08 56	Mon. 519–A2 / Mon. 519–A4	39.70 / 11.84	Mon. 534–A	45 00 38.93 / 71 47 27.46	268 24 50 / 88 24 50	Mon. 534 / Mon. 534–B	802.04 / 81.03
Mon. 519–A4	45 00 48.49 / 71 30 25.16	269 08 55 / 89 08 55	Mon. 519–A3 / Mon. 520	11.84 / 744.15	Mon. 534–B	45 00 38.86 / 71 47 31.15	268 24 47 / 88 24 47	Mon. 534–A / Mon. 535	81.03 / 91.33
Mon. 520	45 00 48.13 / 71 30 59.14	269 08 31 / 88 40 00	Mon. 519–A4 / Mon. 520–A	744.15 / 253.73	Mon. 535	45 00 38.78 / 71 47 35.32	268 24 44 / 88 24 44	Mon. 534–B / Mon. 535–A	91.33 / 79.04
Mon. 520–A	45 00 47.94 / 71 31 10.73	268 39 52 / 88 39 52	Mon. 520 / Mon. 521	253.73 / 622.09	Mon. 535–A	45 00 38.71 / 71 47 38.93	268 24 42 / 88 24 42	Mon. 535 / Mon. 535–B	79.04 / 99.53
Mon. 521	45 00 47.47 / 71 31 39.13	268 39 32 / 88 56 07	Mon. 520–A / Mon. 521–A	622.09 / 934.14	Mon. 535–B	45 00 38.62 / 71 47 43.47	268 24 39 / 88 24 39	Mon. 535–A / Mon. 535–C	99.53 / 229.66
Mon. 521–A	45 00 46.91 / 71 32 21.79	268 55 37 / 88 55 37	Mon. 521 / Mon. 522	934.14 / 1,448.82	Mon. 535–C	45 00 38.41 / 71 47 53.96	268 24 32 / 88 24 32	Mon. 535–B / Mon. 535–D	229.66 / 66.65
Mon. 522	45 00 46.03 / 71 33 27.94	268 54 50 / 88 54 50	Mon. 521–A / Mon. 522–A	1,448.82 / 206.27	Mon. 535–D	45 00 38.35 / 71 47 57.00	268 24 30 / 88 24 30	Mon. 535–C / Mon. 535–E	66.65 / 53.86
Mon. 522–A	45 00 45.90 / 71 33 37.36	268 54 43 / 88 54 43	Mon. 522 / Mon. 522–A2	206.27 / 28.52	Mon. 535–E	45 00 38.30 / 7t 47 59.46	268 24 28 / 88 24 28	Mon. 535–D / Mon. 535–F	53.86 / 174.09
Mon. 522–A2	45 00 45.88 / 71 33 38.66	268 54 42 / 88 54 42	Mon. 522–A / Mon. 522–A3	28.52 / 63.81	Mon. 535–F	45 00 38.14 / 71 48 07.40	268 24 22 / 88 24 22	Mon. 535–E / Mon. 536	174.09 / 271.23
Mon. 522–A3	45 00 45.84 / 71 33 41.57	268 54 40 / 88 54 40	Mon. 522–A2 / Mon. 523	63.81 / 907.42	Mon. 536	45 00 37.90 / 71 48 19.79	268 24 13 / 87 36 36	Mon. 535–F / Mon. 537	271.23 / 1,836.52
Mon. 523	45 00 45.28 / 71 34 23.01	268 54 11 / 90 36 25	Mon. 522–A3 / Mon. 523–A	907.42 / 826.45	Mon. 537	45 00 35.41 / 71 49 43.58	267 35 37 / 87 35 37	Mon. 536 / Mon. 538	1,836.52 / 62.87
Mon. 523–A	45 00 45.56 / 71 35 00.75	270 35 58 / 90 35 58	Mon. 523 / Mon. 524	826.45 / 350.29	Mon. 538	45 00 35.32 / 71 49 46.44	267 35 35 / 87 56 39	Mon. 537 / Mon. 538–A	62.87 / 1,416.50
Mon. 524	45 00 45.68 / 71 35 16.74	270 35 47 / 90 20 50	Mon. 523–A / Mon. 525	350.29 / 801.55	Mon. 538–A	45 00 33.67 / 71 50 51.09	267 55 53 / 87 55 53	Mon. 538 / Mon. 538–B	1,416.50 / 3,225.74
Mon. 525	45 00 45.84 / 71 35 53.35	270 20 24 / 90 20 24	Mon. 524 / Mon. 525–A	801.55 / 534.79	Mon. 538–B	45 00 29.87 / 71 53 18.29	267 54 09 / 87 54 09	Mon. 538–A / Mon. 539	3,225.74 / 1,339.52
Mon. 525–A	45 00 45.94 / 71 36 17.77	270 20 07 / 90 20 07	Mon. 525 / Mon. 526	534.79 / 651.56	Mon. 539	45 00 28.28 / 71 54 19.42	267 53 26 / 88 39 31	Mon. 538–B / Mon. 539–A	1,339.52 / 501.70
Mon. 526	45 00 46.06 / 71 36 47.52	270 19 46 / 88 58 01	Mon. 525–A / Site of Mon. 527	651.56 / 2,121.16	Mon. 539–A	45 00 27.90 / 71 54 42.32	268 39 15 / 88 39 15	Mon. 539 / Mon. 540	501.70 / 217.99
Site of Mon. 527 [1]	45 00 44.81 / 71 38 24.38	268 56 53 / 88 15 27	Mon. 526 / Mon. 527–A	2,121.16 / 392.24	Mon. 540	45 00 27.74 / 71 54 52.27	268 39 08 / 92 31 01	Mon. 539–A / Mon. 540–A	217.99 / 543.99
Mon. 527–A	45 00 44.42 / 71 38 42.28	268 15 14 / 88 15 14	Site of Mon. 527 / Mon. 527–A2	392.24 / 714.48	Mon. 540–A	45 00 28.51 / 71 55 17.08	272 30 43 / 92 30 43	Mon. 540 / Mon. 541	543.99 / 666.96
Mon. 527–A2	45 00 43.71 / 71 39 14.89	268 14 51 / 88 14 51	Mon. 527–A / Mon. 528	714.48 / 586.43	Mon. 541	45 00 29.45 / 71 55 47.51	272 30 22 / 91 17 22	Mon. 540–A / Mon. 542	666.96 / 1,295.31
Mon. 528	45 00 43.13 / 71 39 41.66	268 14 32 / 87 06 27	Mon. 527–A2 / Mon. 529	586.43 / 450.05	Mon. 542	45 00 30.39 / 71 56 46.64	271 16 40 / 88 28 00	Mon. 541 / Mon. 543	1,295.31 / 740.09
Mon. 529	45 00 42.39 / 71 40 02.18	267 06 12 / 88 56 43	Mon. 528 / Mon. 530	450.05 / 2,370.78	Mon. 543	45 00 29.75 / 71 57 20.43	268 27 36 / 88 25 07	Mon. 542 / Mon. 544	740.09 / 934.85
Mon. 530	45 00 40.96 / 71 41 50.43	268 55 27 / 90 26 35	Mon. 529 / Mon. 531	2,370.78 / 1,031.85	Mon. 544	45 00 28.91 / 71 58 03.10	268 24 37 / 88 24 37	Mon. 543 / Mon. 545	934.85 / 3,159.90
Mon. 531	45 00 41.22 / 71 42 37.55	270 26 02 / 90 17 41	Mon. 530 / Mon. 531–A	1,031.85 / 388.61	Mon. 545	45 00 26.05 / 72 00 27.33	268 22 55 / 88 20 40	Mon. 544 / Mon. 545–A	3,159.90 / 220.28
Mon. 531–A	45 00 41.29 / 71 42 55.30	270 17 28 / 90 17 28	Mon. 531 / Mon. 531–B	388.61 / 139.24	Mon. 545–A	45 00 25.84 / 72 00 37.39	268 20 33 / 88 20 33	Mon. 545 / Mon. 546	220.28 / 562.40

[1] Position not re-marked. Point is now in Wallis Pond.

BOUNDARY MONUMENTS—HALLS STREAM TO THE ST. LAWRENCE—Continued

Station	Latitude and longitude	Azimuth	To station	Distance (meters)	Station	Latitude and longitude	Azimuth	To station	Distance (meters)
	° ′ ″	° ′ ″				° ′ ″	° ′ ″		
Mon. 546	45 00 25.32 / 72 01 03.06	268 20 14 / 87 57 36	Mon. 545-A / Mon. 546-A	562.40 / 483.43	Mon. 561	45 00 21.55 / 72 08 47.39	270 48 14 / 91 43 22	Mon. 560-A / Mon. 562	200.50 / 402.41
Mon. 546-A	45 00 24.76 / 72 01 25.12	267 57 20 / 87 57 20	Mon. 546 / Mon. 547	483.43 / 143.56	Mon. 562	45 00 21.94 / 72 09 05.75	271 43 09 / 89 20 13	Mon. 561 / Mon. 563	402.41 / 1,371.78
Mon. 547	45 00 24.59 / 72 01 31.67	267 57 16 / 88 27 38	Mon. 546-A / Mon. 548	143.56 / 563.07	Mon. 563	45 00 21.42 / 72 10 08.39	269 19 29 / 89 19 29	Mon. 562 / Mon. 563-A	1,371.78 / 178.67
Mon. 548	45 00 24.10 / 72 01 57.37	268 27 20 / 88 32 52	Mon. 547 / Mon. 548-A	563.07 / 628.21	Mon. 563-A	45 00 21.35 / 72 10 16.54	269 19 23 / 89 19 23	Mon. 563 / Mon. 564	178.67 / 181.08
Mon. 548-A	45 00 23.58 / 72 02 26.04	268 32 32 / 88 32 32	Mon. 548 / Mon. 548-B	628.21 / 303.10	Mon. 564	45 00 21.28 / 72 10 24.81	269 19 17 / 88 50 11	Mon. 563-A / Mon. 564-A	181.08 / 56.71
Mon. 548-B	45 00 23.33 / 72 02 39.88	268 32 22 / 88 32 22	Mon. 548-A / Mon. 549	303.10 / 820.59	Mon. 564-A	45 00 21.25 / 72 10 27.40	268 50 09 / 88 50 09	Mon. 564 / Mon. 565	56.71 / 601.44
Mon. 549	45 00 22.66 / 72 03 17.34	268 31 55 / 89 04 49	Mon. 548-B / Mon. 549-A	820.59 / 489.89	Mon. 565	45 00 20.85 / 72 10 54.86	268 49 50 / 88 49 50	Mon. 564-A / Mon. 565-A	601.44 / 122.05
Mon. 549-A	45 00 22.40 / 72 03 39.70	269 04 33 / 89 04 33	Mon. 549 / Mon. 550	489.89 / 139.05	Mon. 565-A	45 00 20.77 / 72 11 00.43	268 49 46 / 88 49 46	Mon. 565 / Mon. 565-B	122.05 / 146.54
Mon. 550	45 00 22.33 / 72 03 46.05	269 04 29 / 89 06 33	Mon. 549-A / Mon. 551	139.05 / 489.03	Mon. 565-B	45 00 20.67 / 72 11 07.12	268 49 41 / 88 49 41	Mon. 565-A / Mon. 566	146.54 / 938.78
Mon. 551	45 00 22.08 / 72 04 08.38	269 06 17 / 89 06 17	Mon. 550 / Mon. 551-A	489.03 / 593.21	Mon. 566	45 00 20.05 / 72 11 49.98	268 49 11 / 88 49 32	Mon. 565-B / Mon. 567	938.78 / 658.39
Mon. 551-A	45 00 21.78 / 72 04 35.46	269 05 58 / 89 05 58	Mon. 551 / Mon. 551-B	593.21 / 1,329.24	Mon. 567	45 00 19.61 / 72 12 20.03	268 49 11 / 88 49 11	Mon. 566 / Mon. 568	658.39 / 207.27
Mon. 551-B	45 00 21.10 / 72 05 36.15	269 05 15 / 89 05 15	Mon. 551-A / Mon. 552	1,329.24 / 191.97	Mon. 568	45 00 19.47 / 72 12 29.50	268 49 04 / 88 49 04	Mon. 567 / Mon. 569	207.27 / 172.84
Mon. 552	45 00 21.00 / 72 05 44.92	269 05 09 / 89 05 09	Mon. 551-B / Mon. 552-A	191.97 / 49.30	Mon. 569	45 00 19.36 / 72 12 37.39	268 48 59 / 88 27 03	Mon. 568 / Mon. 570	172.84 / 61.92
Mon. 552-A	45 00 20.98 / 72 05 47.17	269 05 07 / 89 05 07	Mon. 552 / Mon. 553	49.30 / 166.36	Mon. 570	45 00 19.30 / 72 12 40.21	268 27 01 / 88 27 01	Mon. 569 / Mon. 571	61.92 / 1,643.21
Mon. 553	45 00 20.89 / 72 05 54.76	269 05 02 / 89 05 02	Mon. 552-A / Mon. 554	166.36 / 101.36	Mon. 571	45 00 17.86 / 72 13 55.22	268 26 08 / 88 26 16	Mon. 570 / Mon. 572	1,643.21 / 1,906.39
Mon. 554	45 00 20.84 / 72 05 59.39	269 04 59 / 89 04 59	Mon. 553 / Mon. 554-A	101.36 / 52.68	Mon. 572	45 00 16.17 / 72 15 22.23	268 25 15 / 88 46 43	Mon. 571 / Mon. 572-A	1,906.39 / 95.92
Mon. 554-A	45 00 20.81 / 72 06 01.80	269 04 57 / 89 09 13	Mon. 554 / Mon. 555	52.68 / 490.86	Mon. 572-A	45 00 16.10 / 72 15 26.61	268 46 40 / 88 46 40	Mon. 572 / Mon. 573	95.92 / 132.06
Mon. 555	45 00 20.58 / 72 06 24.21	269 08 57 / 89 31 46	Mon. 554-A / Mon. 555-A	490.86 / 172.63	Mon. 573	45 00 16.01 / 72 15 32.64	268 46 36 / 88 46 36	Mon. 572-A / Mon. 573-A	132.06 / 187.36
Mon. 555-A	45 00 20.53 / 72 06 32.09	269 31 40 / 89 31 40	Mon. 555 / Mon. 555-B	172.63 / 160.01	Mon. 573-A	45 00 15.88 / 72 15 41.19	268 46 30 / 88 46 30	Mon. 573 / Mon. 573-B	187.36 / 372.83
Mon. 555-B	45 00 20.49 / 72 06 39.40	269 31 35 / 89 31 35	Mon. 555-A / Mon. 555-C	160.01 / 9.82	Mon. 573-B	45 00 15.62 / 72 15 58.21	268 46 18 / 88 46 18	Mon. 573-A / Mon. 574	372.83 / 360.81
Mon. 555-C [2]	45 00 20.48 / 72 06 39.84	269 31 35 / 89 31 35	Mon. 555-B / Site of Mon. 556	9.82 / 1.43	Mon. 574	45 00 15.37 / 72 16 14.68	268 46 06 / 90 11 14	Mon. 573-B / Mon. 574-A	360 81 / 337.44
Site of Mon. 556 [3]	45 00 20.48 / 72 06 39.91	269 31 35 / 90 31 28	Mon. 555-C / Mon. 556-A	1.43 / 451.12	Mon. 574-A	45 00 15.40 / 72 16 30.09	270 11 03 / 90 11 03	Mon. 574 / Mon. 575	337.44 / 506.14
Mon. 556-A	45 00 20.62 / 72 07 00.51	270 31 13 / 90 31 13	Site of Mon. 556 / Mon. 557	451.12 / 446.49	Mon. 575	45 00 15.45 / 72 1 53.20	270 10 47 / 90 50 54	Mon. 574-A / Mon. 575-A	506.14 / 186.49
Mon. 557	45 00 20.75 / 72 07 20.89	270 30 59 / 90 30 59	Mon. 556-A / Mon. 557-A	446.49 / 285.48	Mon. 575-A	45 00 15.54 / 72 17 01.72	270 50 48 / 90 50 48	Mon. 575 / Mon. 576	186.49 / 793.94
Mon. 557-A	45 00 20.83 / 72 07 33.93	270 30 50 / 90 30 50	Mon. 557 / Mon. 558	285.48 / 112.32	Mon. 576	45 00 15.92 / 72 17 37.96	270 50 22 / 87 59 55	Mon. 575-A / Mon. 577	793.94 / 882.17
Mon. 558	45 00 20.86 / 72 07 39.06	270 30 46 / 90 49 02	Mon. 557-A / Mon. 558-A	112.32 / 364.30	Mon. 577	45 00 14.92 / 72 18 18.22	267 59 26 / 86 51 52	Mon. 576 / Mon. 578	882.17 / 586.20
Mon. 558-A	45 00 21.03 / 72 07 55.69	270 48 50 / 90 48 50	Mon. 558 / Mon. 559	364.30 / 239.35	Mon. 578	45 00 13.88 / 72 18 44.94	266 51 33 / 92 05 30	Mon. 577 / Mon. 579	586.20 / 181.58
Mon. 559	45 00 21.14 / 72 08 06.62	270 48 42 / 90 48 42	Mon. 558-A / Mon. 559-A	239.35 / 567.90	Mon. 579	45 00 14.09 / 72 18 53.23	272 05 24 / 95 55 03	Mon. 578 / Mon. 580	181.58 / 344.38
Mon. 559-A	45 00 21.40 / 72 08 32.55	270 48 24 / 90 48 24	Mon. 559 / Mon. 560	567.90 / 26.72	Mon. 580	45 00 15.24 / 72 19 08.87	275 54 52 / 94 42 15	Mon. 579 / Mon. 581	344.38 / 1,218.92
Mon. 560	45 00 21.41 / 72 08 33.77	270 48 23 / 90 48 23	Mon. 559-A / Mon. 560-A	26.72 / 97.81	Mon. 581	45 00 18.48 / 72 20 04.34	274 41 36 / 92 41 44	Mon. 580 / Mon. 581-A	1,218.92 / 751.00
Mon. 560-A	45 00 21.46 / 72 08 38.23	270 48 20 / 90 48 20	Mon. 560 / Mon. 561	97.81 / 200.50	Mon. 581-A	45 00 19.62 / 72 20 38.59	272 41 20 / 92 41 20	Mon. 581 / Mon. 581-B	751.00 / 369.72

[2] Undermined and destroyed by river.   [3] Position not re-marked. Point is now in Tomifobia River.

BOUNDARY MONUMENTS—HALLS STREAM TO THE ST. LAWRENCE—Continued

Station	Latitude and longitude	Azimuth	To station	Distance (meters)	Station	Latitude and longitude	Azimuth	To station	Distance (meters)
Mon. 581-B	45 00 20.19 / 72 20 55.45	272 41 08 / 92 41 08	Mon. 581-A / Mon. 582	369.72 / 1,612.02	Mon. 597	45 00 47.44 / 72 36 17.36	276 20 21 / 94 11 38	Mon. 596-B / Mon. 597-A	1,157.27 / 431.14
Mon. 582	45 00 22.63 / 72 22 08.98	272 40 16 / 91 14 20	Mon. 581-B / Mon. 582-A	1,612.02 / 368.19	Mon. 597-A	45 00 48.46 / 72 36 37.00	274 11 24 / 94 11 24	Mon. 597 / Mon. 597-B	431.14 / 271.81
Mon. 582-A	45 00 22.88 / 72 22 25.78	271 14 08 / 91 14 08	Mon. 582 / Mon. 583	368.19 / 128.72	Mon. 597-B	45 00 49.10 / 72 36 49.38	274 11 15 / 94 11 15	Mon. 597-A / Mon. 598	271.81 / 462.87
Mon. 583	45 00 22.98 / 72 22 31.66	271 14 04 / 91 14 04	Mon. 582-A / Mon. 584	128.72 / 323.89	Mon. 598	45 00 50.20 / 72 37 10.46	274 11 00 / 94 11 00	Mon. 597-B / Mon. 598-A	462.87 / 641.01
Mon. 584	45 00 23.20 / 72 22 46.45	271 13 54 / 88 58 14	Mon. 583 / Mon. 584-A	323.89 / 408.53	Mon. 598-A	45 00 51.71 / 72 37 39.65	274 10 40 / 94 10 40	Mon. 598 / Mon. 599	641.01 / 593.65
Mon. 584-A	45 00 22.96 / 72 23 05.10	268 58 01 / 88 58 01	Mon. 584 / Mon. 585	408.53 / 298.16	Mon. 599	45 00 53.11 / 72 38 06.69	274 10 21 / 91 07 37	Mon. 598-A / Mon. 599-A	593.65 / 1,568.70
Mon. 585	45 00 22.79 / 72 23 18.71	268 57 51 / 92 59 43	Mon. 584-A / Mon. 586	298.16 / 467.92	Mon. 599-A	45 00 54.10 / 72 39 18.32	271 06 46 / 91 06 46	Mon. 599 / Mon. 600	1,568.70 / 620.56
Mon. 586	45 00 23.58 / 72 23 40.05	272 59 28 / 92 59 28	Mon. 585 / Mon. 587	467.92 / 1,319.11	Mon. 600	45 00 54.49 / 72 39 46.66	271 06 26 / 91 06 26	Mon. 599-A / Mon. 601	620.56 / 80.40
Mon. 587	45 00 25.80 / 72 24 40.20	272 58 45 / 92 58 45	Mon. 586 / Mon. 587-A	1,319.11 / 200.62	Mon. 601	45 00 54.54 / 72 39 50.33	271 06 23 / 91 06 23	Mon. 600 / Mon. 601-A	80.40 / 791.01
Mon. 587-A	45 00 26.14 / 72 24 49.35	272 58 39 / 92 58 39	Mon. 587 / Mon. 588	200.62 / 234.30	Mon. 601-A	45 00 55.04 / 72 40 26.44	271 05 58 / 91 05 58	Mon. 601 / Mon. 602	791.01 / 93.43
Mon. 588	45 00 26.54 / 72 25 00.03	272 58 31 / 92 58 31	Mon. 587-A / Mon. 588-A	234.30 / 341.04	Mon. 602	45 00 55.10 / 72 40 30.71	271 05 55 / 91 05 55	Mon. 601-A / Mon. 603	93.43 / 733.37
Mon. 588-A	45 00 27.11 / 72 25 15.58	272 58 20 / 92 58 20	Mon. 588 / Mon. 588-B	341.04 / 1,191.75	Mon. 603	45 00 55.55 / 72 41 04.19	271 05 31 / 91 05 31	Mon. 602 / Mon. 603-A	733.37 / 837.09
Mon. 588-B	45 00 29.10 / 72 26 09.93	272 57 42 / 92 57 42	Mon. 588-A / Mon. 589	1,191.75 / 506.86	Mon. 603-A	45 00 56.06 / 72 41 42.42	271 05 05 / 91 05 05	Mon. 603 / Mon. 604	837.09 / 423.98
Mon. 589	45 00 29.95 / 72 26 33.04	272 57 26 / 92 57 26	Mon. 588-B / Mon. 590	506.86 / 667.25	Mon. 604	45 00 56.32 / 72 42 01.78	271 04 51 / 91 04 51	Mon. 603-A / Mon. 605	423.98 / 232.96
Mon. 590	45 00 31.07 / 72 27 03.47	272 57 04 / 90 45 54	Mon. 589 / Mon. 591	667.25 / 2,253.82	Mon. 605	45 00 56.46 / 72 42 12.41	271 04 43 / 90 33 36	Mon. 604 / Mon. 605-A	232.96 / 1,189.98
Mon. 591	45 00 32.03 / 72 28 46.38	270 44 41 / 88 37 48	Mon. 590 / Mon. 591-A	2,253.82 / 401.35	Mon. 605-A	45 00 56.84 / 72 43 06.76	270 32 58 / 90 32 58	Mon. 605 / Mon. 605-B	1,189.98 / 747.16
Mon. 591-A	45 00 31.72 / 72 29 04.70	268 37 35 / 88 37 35	Mon. 591 / Mon. 591-B	401.35 / 226.89	Mon. 605-B	45 00 57.07 / 72 43 40.88	270 32 34 / 90 32 34	Mon. 605-A / Mon. 606	747.16 / 504.14
Mon. 591-B	45 00 31.54 / 72 29 15.06	268 37 28 / 88 37 28	Mon. 591-A / Mon. 592	226.89 / 108.87	Mon. 606	45 00 57.22 / 72 44 03.90	270 32 17 / 88 49 26	Mon. 605-B / Mon. 606-A	504.14 / 844.97
Mon. 592	45 00 31.46 / 72 29 20.03	268 37 24 / 88 18 14	Mon. 591-B / Mon. 592-A	108.87 / 1,146.35	Mon. 606-A	45 00 56.66 / 72 44 42.48	268 48 59 / 88 48 59	Mon. 606 / Mon. 607	844.97 / 280.15
Mon. 592-A	45 00 30.35 / 72 30 12.36	268 17 37 / 88 17 37	Mon. 592 / Mon. 593	1,146.35 / 2,209.28	Mon. 607	45 00 56.47 / 72 44 55.27	268 48 50 / 90 45 37	Mon. 606-A / Mon. 608	280.15 / 1,725.83
Mon. 593	45 00 28.21 / 72 31 53.19	268 16 26 / 90 49 57	Mon. 592-A / Mon. 593-A	2,209.28 / 206.08	Mon. 608	45 00 57.21 / 72 46 14.08	270 44 41 / 90 44 41	Mon. 607 / Mon. 608-A	1,725.83 / 577.54
Mon. 593-A	45 00 28.31 / 72 32 02.60	270 49 50 / 90 49 50	Mon. 593 / Mon. 593-B	206.08 / 425.43	Mon. 608-A	45 00 57.45 / 72 46 40.46	270 44 22 / 90 44 22	Mon. 608 / Mon. 608-B	577.54 / 1,699.52
Mon. 593-B	45 00 28.51 / 72 32 22.02	270 49 37 / 90 49 37	Mon. 593-A / Mon. 594	425.43 / 1,298.42	Mon. 608-B	45 00 58.15 / 72 47 58.07	270 43 27 / 90 43 27	Mon. 608-A / Mon. 608-C	1,699.52 / 142.83
Mon. 594	45 00 29.11 / 72 33 21.31	270 48 55 / 99 41 00	Mon. 593-B / Mon. 594-A	1,298.42 / 1,095.33	Mon. 608-C	45 00 58.21 / 72 48 04.59	270 43 23 / 90 43 23	Mon. 608-B / Mon. 609	142.83 / 84.00
Mon. 594-A	45 00 35.07 / 72 34 10.61	279 40 25 / 99 40 25	Mon. 594 / Mon. 594-B	1,095.33 / 220.54	Mon. 609	45 00 58.24 / 72 48 08.42	270 43 20 / 90 43 20	Mon. 608-C / Mon. 609-A	84.00 / 680.81
Mon. 594-B	45 00 36.28 / 72 34 20.54	279 40 18 / 99 40 18	Mon. 594-A / Mon. 594-C	220.54 / 168.31	Mon. 609-A	45 00 58.52 / 72 48 39.52	270 42 58 / 90 42 58	Mon. 609 / Mon. 610	680.81 / 856.01
Mon. 594-C	45 00 37.19 / 72 34 28.12	279 40 12 / 99 40 12	Mon. 594-B / Mon. 594-D	168.31 / 512.24	Mon. 610	45 00 58.86 / 72 49 18.61	270 42 31 / 91 13 06	Mon. 609-A / Mon. 611	856.01 / 329.23
Mon. 594-D	45 00 39.98 / 72 34 51.18	279 39 56 / 99 39 56	Mon. 594-C / Mon. 595	512.24 / 351.01	Mon. 611	45 00 59.09 / 72 49 33.64	271 12 55 / 91 12 55	Mon. 610 / Mon. 612	329.23 / 734.47
Mon. 595	45 00 41.89 / 72 35 06.98	279 39 44 / 96 21 11	Mon. 594-D / Mon. 596	351.01 / 106.12	Mon. 612	45 00 59.59 / 72 50 07.17	271 12 31 / 91 12 31	Mon. 611 / Mon. 613	734.47 / 590.76
Mon. 596	45 00 42.27 / 72 35 11.80	276 21 08 / 96 21 08	Mon. 595 / Mon. 596-A	106.12 / 22.82	Mon. 613	45 01 00.00 / 72 50 34.15	271 12 12 / 91 12 12	Mon. 612 / Mon. 614	590.76 / 370.68
Mon. 596-A	45 00 42.35 / 72 35 12.83	276 21 07 / 96 21 07	Mon. 596 / Mon. 596-B	22.82 / 264.48	Mon. 614	45 01 00.25 / 72 50 51.07	271 12 00 / 88 34 00	Mon. 613 / Mon. 614-A	370.68 / 242.33
Mon. 596-B	45 00 43.30 / 72 35 24.84	276 20 59 / 96 20 59	Mon. 596-A / Mon. 597	264.48 / 1,157.27	Mon. 614-A	45 01 00.05 / 72 51 02.14	268 33 52 / 88 33 52	Mon. 614 / Mon. 614-B	242.33 / 127.40

BOUNDARY MONUMENTS—HALLS STREAM TO THE ST. LAWRENCE—Continued

Station	Latitude and longitude	Azimuth	To station	Distance (meters)
Mon. 614-B	45 00 59.95 / 72 51 07.97	268 33 48 / 88 33 48	Mon. 614-A / Mon. 614-C	127.40 / 175.76
Mon. 614-C	45 00 59.81 / 72 51 15.99	268 33 42 / 88 33 42	Mon. 614-B / Mon. 614-D	175.76 / 73.99
Mon. 614-D	45 00 59.75 / 72 51 19.37	268 33 40 / 88 33 40	Mon. 614-C / Mon. 615	73.99 / 965.99
Mon. 615	45 00 58.96 / 72 52 03.47	268 33 09 / 85 44 44	Mon. 614-D / Mon. 616	965.99 / 154.75
Mon. 616	45 00 58.59 / 72 52 10.52	265 44 39 / 88 46 57	Mon. 615 / Mon. 616-A	154.75 / 1,572.87
Mon. 616-A	45 00 57.50 / 72 53 22.33	268 46 06 / 88 46 06	Mon. 616 / Mon. 616-B	1,572.87 / 220.57
Mon. 616-B	45 00 57.34 / 72 53 32.40	268 45 59 / 88 45 59	Mon. 616-A / Mon. 616-C	220.57 / 1,062.72
Mon. 616-C	45 00 56.60 / 72 54 20.93	268 45 25 / 88 45 25	Mon. 616-B / Mon. 617	1,062.72 / 82.97
Mon. 617	45 00 56.54 / 72 54 24.72	268 45 22 / 88 45 22	Mon. 616-C / Mon. 618	82.97 / 181.80
Mon. 618	45 00 56.41 / 72 54 33.02	268 45 16 / 88 00 36	Mon. 617 / Mon. 618-A	181.80 / 712.07
Mon. 618-A	45 00 55.61 / 72 55 05.52	268 00 13 / 88 00 13	Mon. 618 / Mon. 618-B	712.07 / 159.46
Mon. 618-B	45 00 55.43 / 72 55 12.79	268 00 08 / 88 00 08	Mon. 618-A / Mon. 619	159.46 / 1,062.24
Mon. 619	45 00 54.23 / 72 56 01.28	267 59 34 / 87 59 34	Mon. 618-B / Mon. 619-A	1,062.24 / 320.68
Mon. 619-A	45 00 53.86 / 72 56 15.91	267 59 24 / 87 59 24	Mon. 619 / Mon. 619-B	320.68 / 432.04
Mon. 619-B	45 00 53.37 / 72 56 35.63	267 59 10 / 87 59 10	Mon. 619-A / Mon. 620	432.04 / 1,904.30
Mon. 620	45 00 51.20 / 72 58 02.54	267 58 08 / 91 44 51	Mon. 619-B / Mon. 620-A	1,904.30 / 534.81
Mon. 620-A	45 00 51.72 / 72 58 26.95	271 44 34 / 91 44 34	Mon. 620 / Mon. 620-B	534.81 / 268.43
Mon. 620-B	45 00 51.99 / 72 58 39.21	271 44 25 / 91 44 25	Mon. 620-A / Mon. 621	268.43 / 69.96
Mon. 621	45 00 52.06 / 72 58 42.40	271 44 23 / 91 44 23	Mon. 620-B / Mon. 621-A	69.96 / 302.80
Mon. 621-A	45 00 52.36 / 72 58 56.22	271 44 13 / 91 44 13	Mon. 621 / Mon. 621-B	302.80 / 1,121.67
Mon. 621-B	45 00 53.45 / 72 59 47.42	271 43 37 / 91 43 37	Mon. 621-A / Mon. 622	1,121.67 / 44.53
Mon. 622	45 00 53.50 / 72 59 49.45	271 43 36 / 91 30 03	Mon. 621-B / Mon. 622-A	44.53 / 1,016.87
Mon. 622-A	45 00 54.36 / 73 00 35.87	271 29 30 / 91 29 30	Mon. 622 / Mon. 623	1,016.87 / 535.47
Mon. 623	45 00 54.81 / 73 01 00.32	271 29 13 / 91 29 13	Mon. 622-A / Mon. 624	535.47 / 244.22
Mon. 624	45 00 55.01 / 73 01 11.47	271 29 05 / 91 29 05	Mon. 623 / Mon. 625	244.22 / 128.82
Mon. 625	45 00 55.12 / 73 01 17.35	271 29 01 / 91 20 15	Mon. 624 / Mon. 625-A	128.82 / 401.02
Mon. 625-A	45 00 55.42 / 73 01 35.66	271 20 02 / 91 20 02	Mon. 625 / Mon. 625-B	401.02 / 795.63
Mon. 625-B	45 00 56.02 / 73 02 11.98	271 19 36 / 91 19 36	Mon. 625-A / Mon. 625-C	795.63 / 444.00
Mon. 625-C	45 00 56.35 / 73 02 32.26	271 19 22 / 91 19 22	Mon. 625-B / Mon. 626	444.00 / 466.57
Mon. 626	45 00 56.70 / 73 02 53.56	271 19 07 / 91 19 07	Mon. 625-C / Mon. 626-A	466.57 / 152.69
Mon. 626-A	45 00 56.81 / 73 03 00.53	271 19 02 / 91 19 02	Mon. 626 / Mon. 627	152.69 / 609.88
Mon. 627	45 00 57.27 / 73 03 28.38	271 18 42 / 91 18 42	Mon. 626-A / Mon. 627-A	609.88 / 177.16
Mon. 627-A	45 00 57.40 / 73 03 36.46	271 18 37 / 91 18 37	Mon. 627 / Mon. 628	177.16 / 278.98
Mon. 628	45 00 57.61 / 73 03 49.20	271 18 28 / 91 18 28	Mon. 627-A / Mon. 629	278.98 / 174.11
Mon. 629	45 00 57.74 / 73 03 57.15	271 18 22 / 87 59 42	Mon. 628 / Mon. 629-A	174.11 / 108.53
Mon. 629-A	45 00 57.61 / 73 04 02.10	267 59 39 / 87 59 39	Mon. 629 / Mon. 629-B	108.53 / 350.98
Mon. 629-B	45 00 57.22 / 73 04 18.12	267 59 27 / 87 59 27	Mon. 629-A / Mon. 629-C	350.98 / 425.57
Mon. 629-C	45 00 56.73 / 73 04 37.55	267 59 14 / 87 59 14	Mon. 629-B / Mon. 629-D	425.57 / 232.65
Mon. 629-D	45 00 56.47 / 73 04 48.16	267 59 06 / 87 59 06	Mon. 629-C / Mon. 629-E	232.65 / 352.60
Mon. 629-E	45 00 56.06 / 73 05 04.26	267 58 55 / 87 58 55	Mon. 629-D / Mon. 630	352.60 / 71.66
Mon. 630	45 00 55.98 / 73 05 07.53	267 58 52 / 87 58 52	Mon. 629-E / Mon. 630-A	71.66 / 30.34
Mon. 630-A	45 00 55.95 / 73 05 08.91	267 58 52 / 87 58 52	Mon. 630 / Mon. 630-B	30.34 / 170.11
Mon. 630-B	45 00 55.76 / 73 05 16.68	267 58 46 / 87 58 46	Mon. 630-A / Mon. 631	170.11 / 221.91
Mon. 631	45 00 55.50 / 73 05 26.80	267 58 39 / 88 31 13	Mon. 630-B / Mon. 632 and 633	221.91 / 8,106.44
Mon. 632 and 633	45 00 48.55 / 73 11 36.89	268 26 51 / 88 26 51	Mon. 631 / Mon. 634	8,106.44 / 1,352.91
Mon. 634	45 00 47.36 / 73 12 38.65	268 26 07 / 88 26 07	Mon. 632 and 633 / Mon. 635	1,352.91 / 164.38
Mon. 635	45 00 47.21 / 73 12 46.15	268 26 02 / 88 26 02	Mon. 634 / Mon. 635-A	164.38 / 26.13
Mon. 635-A	45 00 47.19 / 73 12 47.34	268 26 01 / 88 26 01	Mon. 635 / Mon. 635-B	26.13 / 70.04
Mon. 635-B	45 00 47.13 / 73 12 50.54	268 25 59 / 88 25 59	Mon. 635-A / Mon. 636	70.04 / 255.58
Mon. 636	45 00 46.90 / 73 13 02.21	268 25 50 / 88 25 50	Mon. 635-B / Mon. 637	255.58 / 755.63
Mon. 637	45 00 46.23 / 73 13 36.70	268 25 26 / 88 47 56	Mon. 636 / Mon. 637-A	755.63 / 954.42
Mon. 637-A	45 00 45.58 / 73 14 20.28	268 47 26 / 88 47 26	Mon. 637 / Mon. 637-B	954.42 / 266.12
Mon. 637-B	45 00 45.40 / 73 14 32.43	268 47 17 / 88 47 17	Mon. 637-A / Mon. 638	266.12 / 87.67
Mon. 638	45 00 45.34 / 73 14 36.43	268 47 14 / 88 47 14	Mon. 637-B / Mon. 638-A	87.67 / 78.63
Mon. 638-A	45 00 45.28 / 73 14 40.02	268 47 12 / 88 47 12	Mon. 638 / Mon. 638-B	78.63 / 165.56
Mon. 638-B	45 00 45.17 / 73 14 47.58	268 47 06 / 88 47 06	Mon. 638-A / Mon. 639	165.56 / 311.93
Mon. 639	45 00 44.95 / 73 15 01.82	268 46 56 / 88 46 56	Mon. 638-B / Mon. 639-A	311.93 / 1,592.68
Mon. 639-A	45 00 43.85 / 73 16 14.54	268 46 05 / 88 46 05	Mon. 639 / Mon. 640	1,592.68 / 172.78
Mon. 640	45 00 43.73 / 73 16 22.43	268 45 59 / 88 26 59	Mon. 639-A / Mon. 640-A	172.78 / 553.26
Mon. 640-A	45 00 43.24 / 73 16 47.68	268 26 42 / 88 26 42	Mon. 640 / Mon. 640-B	553.26 / 57.38
Mon. 640-B	45 00 43.20 / 73 16 50.30	268 26 40 / 88 26 40	Mon. 640-A / Mon. 641	57.38 / 46.58
Mon. 641	45 00 43.15 / 73 16 52.43	268 26 38 / 88 26 38	Mon. 640-B / Mon. 641-A	46.58 / 118.31
Mon. 641-A	45 00 43.05 / 73 16 57.83	268 26 34 / 88 26 34	Mon. 641 / Mon. 641-B	118.31 / 481.10
Mon. 641-B	45 00 42.63 / 73 17 19.79	268 26 19 / 88 26 19	Mon. 641-A / Mon. 641-C	481.10 / 409.92

BOUNDARY MONUMENTS—HALLS STREAM TO THE ST. LAWRENCE—Continued

Station	Latitude and longitude	Azimuth	To station	Distance (meters)	Station	Latitude and longitude	Azimuth	To station	Distance (meters)
	° ′ ″	° ′ ″				° ′ ″	° ′ ″		
Mon. 641–C	45 00 42.26 73 17 38.50	268 26 06 88 26 06	Mon. 641–B Mon. 642	409.92 203.61	Mon. 661	45 00 24.04 73 31 57.73	267 27 26 87 28 22	Mon. 660 Mon. 662	1,181.14 797.93
Mon. 642	45 00 42.08 73 17 47.80	268 25 59 88 25 59	Mon. 641–C Mon. 642–A	203.61 558.97	Mon. 662	45 00 22.90 73 32 34.13	267 27 56 87 26 38	Mon. 661 Mon. 663	797.93 800.03
Mon. 642–A	45 00 41.59 73 18 13.31	268 25 41 88 25 41	Mon. 642 Mon. 642–B	558.97 135.91	Mon. 663	45 00 21.74 73 33 10.63	267 26 12 87 24 49	Mon. 662 Mon. 663–A	800.03 604.24
Mon. 642–B	45 00 41.47 73 18 19.52	268 25 37 88 25 37	Mon. 642–A Mon. 643	135.91 238.23	Mon. 663–A	45 00 20.86 73 33 38.19	267 24 29 87 24 27	Mon. 663 Mon. 664	604.24 299.67
Mon. 643	45 00 41.26 73 18 30.39	268 25 29 88 25 29	Mon. 642–B Mon. 643–A	238.23 709.38	Mon. 664	45 00 20.42 73 33 51.86	267 24 18 87 25 38	Mon. 663–A Mon. 665	299.67 686.67
Mon. 643–A	45 00 40.62 73 19 02.78	268 25 06 88 25 06	Mon. 643 Mon. 643–B	709.38 264.05	Mon. 665	45 00 19.42 73 34 23.18	267 25 16 87 43 35	Mon. 664 Mon. 665–A	686.67 593.24
Mon. 643–B	45 00 40.39 73 19 14.83	268 24 58 88 24 58	Mon. 643–A Mon. 643–C	264.05 441.30	Mon. 665–A	45 00 18.66 73 34 50.25	267 43 16 87 43 07	Mon. 665 Mon. 666	593.24 580.26
Mon. 643–C	45 00 39.99 73 19 34.97	268 24 43 88 24 43	Mon. 643–B Mon. 643–D	441.30 222.17	Mon. 666	45 00 17.91 73 35 16.72	267 42 48 87 43 45	Mon. 665–A Mon. 667	580.26 657.72
Mon. 643–D	45 00 39.79 73 19 45.11	268 24 36 88 24 36	Mon. 643–C Mon. 644	222.17 501.25	Mon. 667	45 00 17.06 73 35 46.73	267 43 24 87 45 24	Mon. 666 Mon. 668	657.72 577.32
Mon. 644	45 00 39.34 73 20 08.00	268 24 20 88 43 29	Mon. 643–D Site of Mon. 645	501.25 1,287.26	Mon. 668	45 00 16.33 73 36 13.07	267 45 06 87 37 57	Mon. 667 Mon. 669	577.32 373.04
Site of Mon. 645⁴	45 00 38.41 73 21 06.76	268 42 47 88 59 21	Mon. 644 Mon. 645–A	1,287.26 132.32	Mon. 669	45 00 15.83 73 36 30.09	267 37 45 87 29 48	Mon. 668 Mon. 670	373.04 870.92
Mon. 645–A	45 00 38.33 73 21 12.81	268 59 17 88 59 17	Site of Mon. 645 Mon. 646	132.32 396.50	Mon. 670	45 00 14.60 73 37 09.82	267 29 20 87 28 56	Mon. 669 Mon. 671	870.92 994.86
Mon. 646	45 00 38.10 73 21 30.91	268 59 04 88 58 36	Mon. 645–A Mon. 647	396.50 1,039.21	Mon. 671	45 00 13.18 73 37 55.20	267 28 24 87 27 42	Mon. 670 Mon. 672	994.86 944.98
Mon. 647	45 00 37.50 73 22 18.36	268 58 02 89 01 01	Mon. 646 Mon. 648	1,039.21 406.02	Mon. 672	45 00 11.82 73 38 38.31	267 27 11 87 28 50	Mon. 671 Mon. 673	944.98 534.11
Mon. 648	45 00 37.27 73 22 36.90	269 00 48 88 58 32	Mon. 647 Mon. 649	406.02 1,161.63	Mon. 673	45 00 11.06 73 39 02.67	267 28 33 89 27 20	Mon. 672 Mon. 674	534.11 144.30
Mon. 649	45 00 36.60 73 23 29.94	268 57 54 88 33 47	Mon. 648 Mon. 650	1,161.63 732.44	Mon. 674	45 00 11.02 73 39 09.26	269 27 15 89 22 21	Mon. 673 Mon. 674–A	144.30 634.64
Mon. 650	45 00 36.00 73 24 03.37	268 33 23 88 31 32	Mon. 649 Mon. 650–A	732.44 613.27	Mon. 674–A	45 00 10.79 73 39 38.23	269 22 01 89 22 22	Mon. 674 Mon. 675	634.64 556.62
Mon. 650–A	45 00 35.49 73 24 31.37	268 31 13 88 31 25	Mon. 650 Mon. 651	613.27 484.50	Mon. 675	45 00 10.59 73 40 03.64	269 22 04 90 05 25	Mon. 674–A Mon. 676	556.62 642.20
Mon. 651	45 00 35.09 73 24 53.48	268 31 10 88 33 24	Mon. 650–A Mon. 651–A	484.50 283.04	Mon. 676	45 00 10.62 73 40 32.97	270 05 04 90 47 17	Mon. 675 Mon. 676–A	642.20 487.79
Mon. 651–A	45 00 34.86 73 25 06.40	268 33 15 88 30 20	Mon. 651 Mon. 652	283.04 785.74	Mon. 676–A	45 00 10.84 73 40 55.24	270 47 01 90 46 53	Mon. 676 Mon. 677	487.79 846.86
Mon. 652	45 00 34.19 73 25 42.27	268 29 55 88 10 03	Mon. 651–A Mon. 652–A	785.74 809.17	Mon. 677	45 00 11.21 73 41 33.90	270 46 26 90 45 04	Mon. 676–A Mon. 678	846.86 1,042.05
Mon. 652–A	45 00 33.35 73 26 19.20	268 09 36 88 11 57	Mon. 652 Mon. 653	809.17 282.72	Mon. 678	45 00 11.65 73 42 21.48	270 44 30 89 57 18	Mon. 677 Mon. 678–A	1,042.05 883.88
Mon. 653	45 00 33.06 73 26 32.11	268 11 48 88 09 08	Mon. 652–A Mon. 654	282.72 874.85	Mon. 678–A	45 00 11.63 73 43 01.83	269 56 49 89 56 12	Mon. 678 Mon. 679	883.88 116.97
Mon. 654	45 00 32.15 73 27 12.04	268 08 40 88 09 40	Mon. 653 Mon. 655	874.85 594.35	Mon. 679	45 00 11.62 73 43 07.17	269 56 08 89 57 59	Mon. 678–A Mon. 679–A	116.97 391.08
Mon. 655	45 00 31.53 73 27 39.16	268 09 20 88 08 36	Mon. 654 Mon. 656	594.35 905.46	Mon. 679–A	45 00 11.61 73 43 25.03	269 57 46 89 57 54	Mon. 679 Mon. 680	391.08 489.27
Mon. 656	45 00 30.58 73 28 20.49	268 08 07 87 47 15	Mon. 655 Mon. 657	905.46 789.63	Mon. 680	45 00 11.60 73 43 47.37	269 57 38 89 56 36	Mon. 679–A Mon. 681	489.27 1,311.83
Mon. 657	45 00 29.59 73 28 56.52	267 46 49 87 46 06	Mon. 656 Mon. 657–A	789.63 234.07	Mon. 681	45 00 11.56 73 44 47.27	269 55 53 89 55 51	Mon. 680 Mon. 682	1,311.83 827.61
Mon. 657–A	45 00 29.29 73 29 07.20	267 45 58 87 45 40	Mon. 657 Mon. 658	234.07 571.42	Mon. 682	45 00 11.52 73 45 25.05	269 55 24 89 26 58	Mon. 681 Mon. 683	827.61 868.53
Mon. 658	45 00 28.57 73 29 33.27	267 45 21 87 28 51	Mon. 657–A Mon. 659	571.42 1,112.41	Mon. 683	45 00 11.25 73 46 04.71	269 26 30 89 26 04	Mon. 682 Mon. 684	868.53 561.10
Mon. 659	45 00 26.98 73 30 24.02	267 28 15 87 28 56	Mon. 658 Mon. 660	1,112.41 873.24	Mon. 684	45 00 11.07 73 46 30.33	269 25 46 89 25 19	Mon. 683 Mon. 685	561.10 711.06
Mon. 660	45 00 25.74 73 31 03.85	267 28 28 87 28 04	Mon. 659 Mon. 661	873.24 1,181.14	Mon. 685	45 00 10.83 73 47 02.79	269 24 56 88 52 49	Mon. 684 Mon. 686	711.06 731.10

⁴Monument destroyed by floating ice.

BOUNDARY MONUMENTS—HALLS STREAM TO THE ST. LAWRENCE—Continued

Station	Latitude and longitude	Azimuth	To station	Distance (meters)	Station	Latitude and longitude	Azimuth	To station	Distance (meters)
	° ′ ″	° ′ ″				° ′ ″	° ′ ″		
Mon. 686	45 00 10.37	268 52 26	Mon. 685	731.10	Mon. 716	44 59 34.04	266 52 56	Mon. 715	970.38
	73 47 36.17	88 52 18	Mon. 687	698.95		74 06 38.91	86 52 13	Mon. 717	967.73
Mon. 687	45 00 09.92	268 51 55	Mon. 686	698.95	Mon. 717	44 59 32.32	266 51 42	Mon. 716	967.73
	73 48 08.07	88 50 40	Mon. 688	235.10		74 07 23.02	87 23 44	Mon. 718	955.70
Mon. 688	45 00 09.77	268 50 33	Mon. 687	235.10	Mon. 718	44 59 30.92	267 23 13	Mon. 717	955.70
	73 48 18.81	88 51 38	Mon. 689	1,478.64		74 08 06.60	87 24 00	Mon. 719	966.54
Mon. 689	45 00 08.81	268 50 51	Mon. 688	1,478.64	Mon. 719	44 59 29.49	267 23 29	Mon. 718	966.54
	73 49 26.31	88 50 23	Mon. 690	1,413.43		74 08 50.68	87 20 25	Mon. 720	253.28
Mon. 690	45 00 07.88	268 49 38	Mon. 689	1,413.43	Mon. 720	44 59 29.11	267 20 16	Mon. 719	253.28
	73 50 30.83	87 46 01	Mon. 691	680.06		74 09 02.23	91 24 57	Mon. 721	686.44
Mon. 691	45 00 07.02	267 45 39	Mon. 690	680.06	Mon. 721	44 59 29.66	271 24 35	Mon. 720	686.44
	73 51 01.86	87 46 14	Mon. 692	930.84		74 09 33.56	91 24 48	Mon. 722	582.15
Mon. 692	45 00 05.84	267 45 44	Mon. 691	930.84	Mon. 722	44 59 30.12	271 24 30	Mon. 721	582.15
	73 51 44.32	87 44 45	Mon. 693	848.01		74 10 00.12	90 57 00	Mon. 722-A	677.66
Mon. 693	45 00 04.76	267 44 18	Mon. 692	848.01	Mon. 722-A	44 59 30.49	270 56 38	Mon. 722	677.66
	73 52 23.01	87 45 15	Mon. 694	804.34		74 10 31.05	90 56 37	Mon. 723	487.76
Mon. 694	45 00 03.74	267 44 49	Mon. 693	804.34	Mon. 723	44 59 30.75	270 56 21	Mon. 722-A	487.76
	73 52 59.71	87 08 00	Mon. 695	806.63		74 10 53.32	90 41 04	Mon. 724	949.88
Mon. 695	45 00 02.43	267 07 34	Mon. 694	806.63	Mon. 724	44 59 31.11	270 40 34	Mon. 723	949.88
	73 53 36.49	87 06 45	Mon. 695-A	511.62		74 11 36.68	90 40 21	Mon. 725	944.88
Mon. 695-A	45 00 01.60	267 06 29	Mon. 695	511.62	Mon. 725	44 59 31.47	270 39 50	Mon. 724	944.88
	73 53 59.82	87 07 25	Mon. 696	258.73		74 12 19.81	90 18 55	Mon. 726	1,143.07
Mon. 696	45 00 01.17	267 07 17	Mon. 695-A	258.73	Mon. 726	44 59 31.67	270 18 18	Mon. 725	1,143.07
	73 54 11.62	87 07 04	Mon. 697	803.70		74 13 11.99	90 18 04	Mon. 726-A	669.79
Mon. 697	44 59 59.86	267 06 38	Mon. 696	803.70	Mon. 726-A	44 59 31.78	270 17 43	Mon. 726	669.79
	73 54 48.26	87 05 36	Mon. 698	676.94		74 13 42.57	90 17 43	Mon. 727	480.40
Mon. 698	44 59 58.75	267 05 14	Mon. 697	676.94	Mon. 727	44 59 31.86	270 17 27	Mon. 726-A	480.40
	73 55 19.13	87 05 42	Mon. 699	834.88		74 14 04.50	90 16 52	Mon. 727-A	619.63
Mon. 699	44 59 57.38	267 05 16	Mon. 698	834.88	Mon. 727-A	44 59 31.96	270 16 32	Mon. 727	619.63
	73 55 57.20	87 05 59	Mon. 699-A	570.60		74 14 32.78	90 19 25	Mon. 728	518.65
Mon. 699-A	44 59 56.44	267 05 41	Mon. 699	570.60	Mon. 728	44 59 32.06	270 19 08	Mon. 727-A	518.65
	73 56 23.22	87 05 33	Mon. 700	174.45		74 14 56.46	89 52 47	Mon. 729	1,130.48
Mon. 700	44 59 56.16	267 05 28	Mon. 699-A	174.45	Mon. 729	44 59 31.98	269 52 10	Mon. 728	1,130.48
	73 56 31.17	86 49 20	Mon. 701	839.18		74 15 48.06	89 51 08	Mon. 730	1,125.72
Mon. 701	44 59 54.65	266 48 54	Mon. 700	839.18	Mon. 730	44 59 31.88	269 50 32	Mon. 729	1,125.72
	73 57 09.43	86 48 50	Mon. 702	856.31		74 16 39.46	89 50 25	Mon. 731	1,239.03
Mon. 702	44 59 53.10	266 48 23	Mon. 701	856.31	Mon. 731	44 59 31.76	269 49 45	Mon. 730	1,239.03
	73 57 48.46	86 59 33	Mon. 703	696.50		74 17 36.02	89 50 49	Mon. 732	992.05
Mon. 703	44 59 51.92	266 59 11	Mon. 702	696.50	Mon. 732	44 59 31.67	269 50 17	Mon. 731	992.05
	73 58 20.22	86 59 58	Mon. 704-705	430.19		74 18 21.30	89 49 38	Mon. 735	231.76
Mon. 704-705	44 59 51.19	266 59 44	Mon. 703	430.19	Mon. 735	44 59 31.65	269 49 30	Mon. 732	231.76
	73 58 39.83	86 59 38	Mon. 706	1,197.02		74 18 31.88	89 48 44	Mon. 736	244.63
Mon. 706	44 59 49.15	266 59 00	Mon. 704-705	1,197.02	Mon. 736	44 59 31.62	269 48 36	Mon. 735	244.63
	73 59 34.40	87 09 44	Mon. 706-A	981.66		74 18 43.05	89 14 49	Mon. 737	1,209.33
Mon. 706-A	44 59 47.57	267 09 12	Mon. 706	981.66	Mon. 737	44 59 31.11	269 14 10	Mon. 736	1,209.33
	74 00 19.17	87 07 44	Mon. 707	211.32		74 19 38.25	90 44 10	Mon. 738	764.51
Mon. 707	44 59 47.23	267 07 37	Mon. 706-A	211.32	Mon. 738	44 59 31.42	270 43 45	Mon. 737	764.51
	74 00 28.80	87 09 26	Mon. 708	1,214.11		74 20 13.15	94 08 44	Mon. 739	1,187.82
Mon. 708	44 59 45.28	267 08 47	Mon. 707	1,214.11	Mon. 739	44 59 34.20	274 08 06	Mon. 738	1,187.82
	74 01 24.16	87 07 54	Mon. 709	1,089.55		74 21 07.24	93 32 33	Mon. 740	736.11
Mon. 709	44 59 43.51	267 07 19	Mon. 708	1,089.55	Mon. 740	44 59 35.67	273 32 09	Mon. 739	736.11
	74 02 13.84	87 07 44	Mon. 710	713.71		74 21 40.78	93 33 25	Mon. 741	729.16
Mon. 710	44 59 42.35	267 07 21	Mon. 709	713.71	Mon. 741	44 59 37.14	273 33 02	Mon. 740	729.16
	74 02 46.38	87 15 12	Mon. 711	110.63		74 22 14.00	93 18 56	Mon. 742	818.21
Mon. 711	44 59 42.18	267 15 09	Mon. 710	110.63	Mon. 742	44 59 38.67	273 18 29	Mon. 741	818.21
	74 02 51.43	87 17 04	Mon. 712	1,020.15		74 22 51.29	93 18 14	Mon. 743	804.44
Mon. 712	44 59 40.61	267 16 32	Mon. 711	1,020.15	Mon. 743	44 59 40.17	273 17 48	Mon. 742	804.44
	74 03 37.95	87 14 55	Mon. 713	1,011.89		74 23 27.95	93 17 57	Mon. 744	804.58
Mon. 713	44 59 39.03	267 14 22	Mon. 712	1,011.89	Mon. 744	44 59 41.66	273 17 31	Mon. 743	804.58
	74 04 24.09	87 14 44	Mon. 714	1,016.83		74 24 04.62	93 17 35	Mon. 745	839.47
Mon. 714	44 59 37.45	267 14 11	Mon. 713	1,016.83	Mon. 745	44 59 43.22	273 17 08	Mon. 744	839.47
	74 05 10.46	86 54 05	Mon. 715	970.14		74 24 42.88	93 24 28	Mon. 746	906.66
Mon. 715	44 59 35.75	266 53 34	Mon. 714	970.14	Mon. 746	44 59 44.97	273 23 59	Mon. 745	906.66
	74 05 54.68	86 53 28	Mon. 716	970.38		74 25 24.20	93 23 35	Mon. 747	1,313.15

BOUNDARY MONUMENTS—HALLS STREAM TO THE ST. LAWRENCE—Continued

Station	Latitude and longitude	Azimuth	To station	Distance (meters)	Station	Latitude and longitude	Azimuth	To station	Distance (meters)
	° ′ ″	° ′ ″				° ′ ″	° ′ ″		
Mon. 747	44 59 47.48 / 74 26 24.05	273 22 53 / 92 40 06	Mon. 746 / Mon. 748	1,313.15 / 761.18	Mon. 761	44 59 56.46 / 74 34 05.90	271 07 59 / 91 07 48	Mon. 760 / Mon. 762	722.67 / 616.49
Mon. 748	44 59 48.63 / 74 26 58.76	272 39 42 / 92 39 30	Mon. 747 / Mon. 749	761.18 / 571.04	Mon. 762	44 59 56.86 / 74 34 34.04	271 07 28 / 90 38 26	Mon. 761 / Mon. 763	616.49 / 778.95
Mon. 749	44 59 49.48 / 74 27 24.80	272 39 12 / 91 44 25	Mon. 748 / Mon. 750	571.04 / 704.89	Mon. 763	44 59 57.14 / 74 35 09.60	270 38 00 / 90 37 44	Mon. 762 / Mon. 764	778.95 / 771.90
Mon. 750	44 59 50.18 / 74 27 56.97	271 44 02 / 91 29 19	Mon. 749 / Mon. 751	704.89 / 1,110.23	Mon. 764	44 59 57.41 / 74 35 44.84	270 37 19 / 90 37 22	Mon. 763 / Mon. 765	771.90 / 759.07
Mon. 751	44 59 51.11 / 74 28 47.64	271 28 44 / 91 29 22	Mon. 750 / Mon. 751-A	1,110.23 / 520.93	Mon. 765	44 59 57.67 / 74 36 19.49	270 36 58 / 90 28 10	Mon. 764 / Mon. 766	759.07 / 605.58
Mon. 751-A	44 59 51.55 / 74 29 11.42	271 29 06 / 91 28 43	Mon. 751 / Mon. 752	520.93 / 563.50	Mon. 766	44 59 57.83 / 74 36 47.14	270 27 51 / 90 26 24	Mon. 765 / Mon. 767	605.58 / 609.39
Mon. 752	44 59 52.02 / 74 29 37.13	271 28 24 / 91 29 43	Mon. 751-A / Mon. 753	563.50 / 631.94	Mon. 767	44 59 57.98 / 74 37 14.96	270 26 04 / 90 26 22	Mon. 766 / Mon. 768	609.39 / 627.87
Mon. 753	44 59 52.55 / 74 30 05.98	271 29 22 / 91 27 17	Mon. 752 / Mon. 754	631.94 / 527.41	Mon. 768	44 59 58.14 / 74 37 43.63	270 26 02 / 90 00 50	Mon. 767 / Mon. 769	627.87 / 436.99
Mon. 754	44 59 52.98 / 74 30 30.05	271 27 00 / 91 32 08	Mon. 753 / Mon. 755	527.41 / 94.12	Mon. 769	44 59 58.14 / 74 38 03.58	270 00 36 / 90 00 05	Mon. 768 / Mon. 770	436.99 / 244.98
Mon. 755	44 59 53.06 / 74 30 34.34	271 32 05 / 91 26 33	Mon. 754 / Mon. 756	94.12 / 811.58	Mon. 770	44 59 58.14 / 74 38 14.77	269 59 57 / 90 00 24	Mon. 769 / Mon. 771	244.98 / 777.33
Mon. 756	44 59 53.72 / 74 31 11.38	271 26 07 / 91 26 14	Mon. 755 / Mon. 757	811.58 / 827.42	Mon. 771	44 59 58.15 / 74 38 50.26	269 59 58 / 89 59 32	Mon. 770 / Mon. 772	777.33 / 396.68
Mon. 757	44 59 54.39 / 74 31 49.15	271 25 47 / 91 24 50	Mon. 756 / Mon. 758	827.42 / 890.89	Mon. 772	44 59 58.14 / 74 39 08.37	269 59 20 / 90 00 19	Mon. 771 / Mon. 773	396.68 / 548.84
Mon. 758	44 59 55.10 / 74 32 29.81	271 24 22 / 91 09 06	Mon. 757 / Mon. 759	890.89 / 703.97	Mon. 773	44 59 58.14 / 74 39 33.43	270 00 02 / 89 57 56	Mon. 772 / Mon. 774	548.84 / 156.06
Mon. 759	44 59 55.56 / 74 33 01.94	271 08 43 / 91 08 36	Mon. 758 / Mon. 760	703.97 / 678.39	Mon. 774	44 59 58.14 / 74 39 40.55	269 57 50 / 89 57 50	Mon. 773 / Terminus	156.06 / 32.49
Mon. 760	44 59 56.00 / 74 33 32.91	271 08 14 / 91 08 23	Mon. 759 / Mon. 761	678.39 / 722.67	Terminus	44 59 58.14 / 74 39 42.04	269 57 50	Mon. 774	32.49

We certify that the foregoing is a true description and definition of the international boundary line between the United States and Canada from the source of the St. Croix River to the St. Lawrence River, as reestablished, surveyed, and monumented, and as marked by us on the quadruplicate set of accurate modern maps, which accompany this report, in accordance with Article III of the treaty between the United States and Great Britain, signed at Washington April 11, 1908.

E. Lester Jones

United States Commissioner.

Ottawa, Canada,
August 15, 1924

J. J. McArthur

His Britannic Majesty's Commissioner.

CONCLUSION

The boundary from the source of the St. Croix River to the St. Lawrence River, as reestablished and as described in the foregoing report and as shown on the 61 maps accompanying the report, is marked throughout by durable monuments, the geographic positions of which have been determined on the North American datum and fixed for all time.

Experience has shown, however, that the monuments, no matter how carefully constructed, deteriorate in time and that the vista along the line through timbered areas becomes filled with new growth. The commissioners have, therefore, made a joint recommendation to their respective Governments that provision be made for future periodic inspection and repair of the monuments and for reopening the boundary vista so as to maintain the demarcation of the line in its present state of effectiveness. If this is done an extensive survey of the boundary should never again be necessary.

Monuments are often damaged by falling trees

The commissioners wish to record that throughout the progress of the work of carrying out the provisions of the treaty of 1908 they have had the close cooperation and assistance of the other bureaus and departments of the two Governments. They refer, particularly, to the assistance given by the Geodetic Survey of Canada and by the United States Coast and Geodetic Survey and to the excellent work done by the United States Geological Survey in the printing of the boundary maps. They wish to acknowledge the many courtesies of the customs and immigration officials of both countries which materially facilitated the free movements of the surveyors in the execution of the field work.

Their thanks are due to the Williams-Webb Co., Inc., Washington, D.C., who engraved the boundary maps.

This report would not be complete without recording, also, the commissioners' appreciation of the efficient and conscientious service of those who

267

have been engaged upon the work both in the field and in the office. They are especially indebted to Mr. James H. Van Wagenen, engineer to the United States section of the commission, and to Mr. J. D. Craig, D. L. S., engineer to the Canadian section of the commission, who have had general charge of the completion of the field work and the preparation of the final report and maps; to the chiefs of field parties and their assistants; to Messrs. R. L. Ross and G. L. Rainboth, D. L. S., of the United States and Canadian sections of the commission, respectively, who have had supervision of the preparation of the boundary maps; and to Mr. R. N. Ashmun, of the United States section, and Mr. J. A. Pounder, D. L. S., of the Canadian section, who have had charge of all the computations.

It is with regret that the commissioners have to record the loss of several members of the commission and staff by death during the course of the work. Mr. G. C. Rain-

Monument on New York-Quebec line, which had been heaved by frost since 1902

both, D. L. S., died in 1910; His Britannic Majesty's commissioner, Dr. W. F. King, in 1916; Mr. Thomas Fawcett, D. T. S., in 1920; the United States commissioner, Mr. E. C. Barnard, in 1921; Mr. W. C. Guerin, in 1921; and Mr. G. L. Rainboth, D. L. S., in 1923.

It is most gratifying to record that the reestablishment of the international boundary from the source of the St. Croix River to the St. Lawrence River and the preparation of the maps and the report in accordance with Article III of the treaty of 1908 have been accomplished in a spirit of hearty cooperation and to state that the cordial relations which existed between the former commissioners have been continued by their successors.

E. LESTER JONES,
United States Commissioner.
J. J. McARTHUR,
His Britannic Majesty's Commissioner.

APPENDIX I

HISTORICAL SKETCH OF THE GENESIS OF THE INTERNATIONAL BOUNDARY FROM THE SOURCE OF THE ST. CROIX RIVER TO THE ST. LAWRENCE RIVER

Although this portion of the boundary was settled by the treaty signed at Washington August 9, 1842, the explorations and settlements, claims and disputes dating back almost to the earliest discoveries on the continent of America, as well as decisions made previous to 1842 about other parts of the international boundary, influenced the decision reached by the framers of the treaty. This historical sketch is presented in order to show to some extent how and why the several sections of this boundary have been adopted as such.

In 1493, after Columbus returned from his first voyage and reported the existence of islands and a continent far to the west, Pope Alexander VI issued a bull defining a line of separation of the spheres of influence of the Kingdoms of Spain and Portugal. The following year these two countries agreed by treaty upon a different line, somewhere near the present meridian 60°. All territories east of this line were to belong to Portugal, while those west of it were to fall within the Spanish sphere. This partition was not recognized, however, by England or France and soon disappeared.

In 1497 John Cabot, under a patent from the King of England, set sail for the west and landed on Cape Breton Island; on the return journey he explored the south coast of Newfoundland. The following year he again crossed the Atlantic and resumed his explorations, and took possession in the name of the King of England of all the coast as far south as latitude 36°, thus establishing a claim on the ground of first discovery.

In 1524 a French expedition under Verrazano, sailing in search of a legendary passage to India, explored the coast from latitude 34° north to Newfoundland. The King of France, still bent upon the discovery of the "Strait of Anian," reported by Marco Polo, sent out Jacques Cartier, who explored the Gulf of St. Lawrence in 1534, and who, during the following year, ascended the river of that name.

In 1583, by which time any titles or claims of Spain and Portugal had disappeared, the English took formal possession of Newfoundland and the coast as far south as Cabot's discoveries had extended. King James I granted to the London Company in 1606 the right to form settlements 100 miles square in the territory between parallels 34° and 41°, and to the Plymouth Company the right to form similar settlements in the territory between parallel 38° and parallel 45°. This last-named parallel forms part of our boundary of the present day.

In the meantime, France also claimed territory about the St. Lawrence, basing her claim on Cartier's voyages of 1534 and 1535; and Henry IV of France gave a charter to De Monts in 1603 for the seacoast and territory of America lying between parallels 40° and 46°, under the name "Acadia." It will be noted that the territory granted in 1606 by the charter of the Plymouth Company over-lapped this area which had been granted by France three years before, and it was not long before trouble arose between the two countries.

De Monts, who had Champlain with him as geographer, sailed for Acadia in 1604. He built a fort on an island near the mouth of the St. Croix River, later abandoning it in favor of Port Royal, or Annapolis, as it is now called. Port Royal was captured and destroyed by the English in 1613, although they did not formally lay claim to Acadia, which, at that time, included the present Provinces of Nova Scotia and New Brunswick and a part of the State of Maine.

However, King James I of England in 1620 gave a charter to the Council for New England, granting them territory from parallel 40° to parallel 48°, and this grant was not only for the coast region but for the interior of the continent to the Pacific Ocean.

The following year, 1621, a grant was made which has had a great effect on the international boundary as it exists to-day. This was a grant of Nova Scotia given by King James to Sir William Alexander. The part of his charter which describes this grant reads as follows: [1]

"* * * do give, grant and convey to the aforesaid Sir William Alexander, his heirs or assigns, hereditarily, all and single, the lands of the Continent and islands situated and lying in America, within the head or promontory commonly called Cape of Sable, lying near the forty-third degree of north latitude or thereabouts; from this Cape, stretching along the shores of the sea, westward to the roadstead of St. Mary, commonly called St. Mary's Bay, and thence northward by a straight line, crossing the entrance, or mouth, of that great roadstead which runs towards the eastern part of the land between the countries of the Suriqui and Etchimine, commonly called Suriquois and Etchimines, to the river generally known by the name St. Croix, and to the remotest springs, or source, from the western side of the same, which empty into the first mentioned river; thence by an imaginary straight line, which is conceived to extend through the land, or run northward to the nearest bay, river, or stream emptying into the great river of Canada; and going from that eastward along the low shores of the same river of Canada to the river, harbor, port, or shore, commonly known and called by the name Gathepe or Gaspie, and thence south-southeast to the isles called Bacalaos or Cape Breton, leaving the said isles on the right, and the mouth of the said great river of Canada, or large bay, and the territory of Newfoundland, with the islands belonging to the same lands on the left; thence to the headland, or point of Cape Breton aforesaid, lying near latitude forty-five degrees or thereabouts; and from the said point of Cape Breton toward the south and west to the above mentioned Cape Sable, where the boundary began; including and containing within the said coasts and their circumference, from sea to sea, all lands of the continent with the rivers, falls, bays, shores, islands, or seas, lying near or within six leagues on any side of the same on the west, north or east sides of the same coasts and bounds and on the south-southeast (where Cape Breton lies) and on the south side of the same (where Cape Sable is) all seas and islands southward within forty leagues of said seashore, thereby including the large island commonly called Isle de Sable or Sablon, lying towards Carban, in common speech south-southeast about thirty leagues from the said Cape Breton seaward and being in latitude forty-four degrees or thereabouts * * *

"* * * And if any questions or doubts shall arise on the meaning and construction of any clause in our present charter, all these shall be taken and explained in their amplest form and in favor of the said Sir William Alexander and his aforesaids."

On the best map of the time, Champlain's map of 1612, two features are very prominently marked: the St. Croix River flowing into the "Baye Francoise" or Bay of Fundy; and a large unnamed river (which does not exist), north of the St. Croix, flowing into the St. Lawrence River. As the heads of these two rivers, as shown on the map, are very close to each other, it was probably considered that

[1] Sir John Bourinot. "Builders of Nova Scotia."

they, being natural features easily identified, would make a better boundary for the grant to Alexander than an artificial line, the location of which was unknown.

This grant encroached on territory previously granted to the Council for New England and, also, included the south shore of the St. Lawrence River, which was of course claimed by France. The council, however, waived its right to lands covered by the grant and, also, in 1628 gave a grant to the governor and company of Massachusetts Bay.

War which broke out between England and France in 1627 resulted in the capture by the English of Quebec and Port Royal, which latter place the French had reoccupied after its destruction by the English in 1613.

The convention of Susa, agreed to in 1629, provided that France was to regain her American possessions, and this agreement was formally ratified by the treaty of St. Germain in 1632, by which England agreed to restore to France all the places occupied by her in New France, Acadia, and Canada. France assumed that under the convention all Acadia would be hers, and acting on this assumption gave grants of land therein and proceeded to take possession of the forts and trading posts.

Some time later, in 1638, in consequence of a dispute between La Tour and Charnisay, two lieutenants of France, regarding their respective territories, the King of France granted to the latter as his territory the present Province of New Brunswick and part of the present State of Maine, described as the coast of the Etchimins; and to the former the present Province of Nova Scotia, designated as Acadia. Thus territory under the name Acadia was confined to the peninsula, instead of to the entire territory as formerly. Ten years later, Charnisay was made governor of Acadia by letters patent, and in these documents Acadia is described as extending from the shore of the St. Lawrence River to Virginia.

The contradiction between the descriptions of Acadia in these two cases shows how a name was sometimes applied to one tract of country and sometimes to a quite different one; and thus boundary disputes easily arose over the interpretation of treaties in which such names occurred.

Some French documents of a few years later refer to Acadia as including the mainland to the Penobscot River, as well as the peninsula. In the documents describing a grant made by Sir William Alexander in 1630 within his own territories, Acadia is referred to as if it formed only a part of the peninsula.

It has already been noted that after the convention of Susa, France occupied the forts and trading posts of Acadia and evidently considered the entire country to have been restored to her by the treaty of St. Germain. Nevertheless King Charles of England directed Alexander to continue with his scheme of colonization, claiming that he had never meant to relinquish the entire country. The Council for New England, therefore, gave patent in 1635 to Lord William Alexander, to whose father Nova Scotia had been granted, for lands to be known as the County of Canada, extending along the coast from the Pemaquid River to the St. Croix River, and north to the St. Lawrence River. This territory and an addition to it were transferred to the father on the death of his son.

In 1654 an English expedition under orders from Cromwell seized all the French posts between the Penobscot River and Canso. The next year the treaty of Westminster provided that commissioners should be appointed to decide which country should retain the three forts, Penobscot, St. John, and Port Royal, but whether these commissioners ever made any report is uncertain. At any rate, Cromwell, in 1656, assumed England to be entitled to all Acadia and, ignoring any rights of Alexander, gave to Temple, Crowne, and La Tour a grant comprising rather more than Alexander's Nova Scotia and County of Canada together.

In the document conferring this grant, Acadia is referred to as a part only of the peninsula, and is differentiated from Nova Scotia; and this document was later made use of by the French in the English-French boundary disputes.

In 1663, King Charles II of England, ignoring any rights of France to the territory in question under the treaty of St. Germain, or of Temple, Crowne, and La Tour under the grant from Cromwell, gave a grant to his brother, the Duke of York, comprising practically the same territory as Alexander's County of Canada. This grant later became known as the territory of Sagadahock.

While England thus laid claim to part of the south bank of the St. Lawrence River, as being included in her territories known as Acadia, Nova Scotia, or County of Canada, France was in actual possession and seems to have regarded it as part of New France and not of Acadia, even when her title to the latter was undisputed. Commissions to governors of Quebec of that period place under their jurisdiction the south bank of the St. Lawrence to a depth of 10 leagues.

War broke out again between England and France, and the treaty of Breda in 1667, which brought the dispute to a close, provided that Acadia should be restored to France. The next year, King Charles ceded all Acadia to the King of France, and in particular the forts of Penobscot, St. John, Port Royal, La Havre, and Cape Sable. He also sent orders to Temple, who had bought out the rights of Crowne and La Tour, to surrender Acadia, including these forts to the French; and, after some delay and objection, this was done. In spite of this transfer of Acadia, which included territory to the Penobscot River, King Charles, in 1674, confirmed the grant of Sagadahock to the Duke of York.

In the meantime, the French gave seignorial grants, some of which were in the present State of Maine, and most of these grants were described as being in Acadia.

A treaty of neutrality in 1686, between England and France, confirmed the right of each country to places in America which were then in their actual possession. While this treaty would seem to confirm the title of France to territory as far as the Penobscot River, England later maintained that it wiped out earlier rights, replacing them by one based on occupation.

Notwithstanding these treaties, England continued to claim Sagadahock, and trouble arising in consequence of the attempts of the English to occupy it, they seized Port Royal again in 1690. The next year a new charter was granted to Massachusetts, in which Nova Scotia, or Acadia, and Sagadahock were annexed to that Province.

The war was brought to a close in 1697 by the treaty of Ryswick. By this treaty, all the possessions which the French held before the war were to be restored to them, and commissioners were to be appointed to decide on the boundary.

Massachusetts claimed Sagadahock under her recent charter; the French claimed that Acadia extended to the Kennebec River; and the commissioners were apparently going to make the St. Georges River, between the Kennebec and the Penobscot, the boundary; but before anything was definitely settled, war broke out again in 1702. It was brought to a close in 1713 by the treaty of Utrecht, by which Acadia was ceded to England.

Part of the treaty which describes the territory to be transferred reads:

"* * * Nova Scotia, otherwise called Acadia, in its entirety, conformably to its ancient limits as also the town of Port Royal now called Annapolis Royal and generally of all depending upon the said lands and islands of this country, * * * ."

This treaty only paved the way for a series of boundary disputes.

The French, previous to the treaty of Utrecht, had claimed that Acadia extended to the Kennebec River, or at least to the Penobscot, but now they claimed that the Acadia of the treaty was limited to a part of the peninsula, and continued to occupy the mainland. No real efforts appear to have been made to settle the question until 1748, when the treaty of Aix-la-Chappelle provided that commissioners should be appointed to determine the boundaries of Acadia.

The English commissioners claimed that the Nova Scotia, or Acadia, of the treaty of Utrecht was the Acadia of the period immediately preceding, and that it included the mainland to the Kennebec River, and they were able to cite many French documents, grants, and charters in support of this claim. They also pointed out that in the treaty of Utrecht the words "Nova Scotia" and "Acadia" were names used to refer to the same territory, and that the French previous to and during the preliminary negotiations preceding the treaty considered Acadia as including the mainland as far as the Kennebec; and they contended that this should decide what was meant by the name "Acadia" or "Nova Scotia" in the treaty.

They also contended that the territory called Acadia or Nova Scotia extended to the St. Lawrence River, citing in support the grant of Nova Scotia to Alexander and the subsequent extension of his territory to the Kennebec River.

The French commissioners took advantage of the words "Acadia within its ancient limits," mentioned in the treaty, and maintained that the territory lately called "Acadia" by them or by the English was not the Acadia of the treaty; that the Acadia of the treaty was an ancient Acadia which included only a part of the peninsula. They pointed out that a part of the peninsula had been called Acadia from the earliest times, but that the remainder of the territory claimed by England as Acadia had in those times been called by many names, New France, Canada, Norumbegue, Etchimins, Baye Francoise, Acadia, Grand Baye of St. Lawrence, and Gaspesie, and quoted several documents to show that New France and Acadia were distinct places.

With regard to the English contention that in the treaty of Utrecht, "Nova Scotia" and "Acadia" were synonymous, the French commissioners maintained that what the English had in the past called "Nova Scotia" was a matter of indifference to them, as France had never had a colony called "Nova Scotia" and could not cede what she never had; and that, as the territory always had legally belonged to France, previous to the treaty of Utrecht, the name Nova Scotia was of no real significance, but was invented by the English to sustain claims to the country.

They also stated that the English commissioners "confound, throughout their memoir, the ideal Nova Scotia of 1621 with the Nova Scotia of the treaty of Utrecht, and both of them with Acadia without distinction of ancient limits in order to extend thereby their pretensions to everything, in whatsoever period, which can be designated by the name of Nova Scotia or Acadia."

They quoted many documents to prove that the south bank of the St. Lawrence River had always been part of Canada, and not of Acadia, and that the governors of Canada had always exercised jurisdiction over it.

The commissioners, after debating the questions for over four years, were unable to agree on any boundary, though it is probable that England was willing to abandon her claim to the south bank of the St. Lawrence. Nothing was done, however. War broke out again, and the dispute was finally settled by the treaty of Paris in 1763, by which Canada and Acadia were ceded to England.

In the meantime, in 1719, Nova Scotia had been created a separate Province; and while France and England were disputing as to whether the mainland had been ceded to England by the treaty of Utrecht, Nova Scotia and Massachusetts had a boundary dispute of their own over the division between them of this same territory, and this latter dispute had its effect on the boundary claims of later times.

Massachusetts continued to claim Sagadahock, annexed to her in 1691, but Nova Scotia maintained that her territories included all the old Acadia and, therefore, to the St. Georges River. The commissions to the governors of Nova Scotia between 1719 and 1763 do not give any boundaries for the province, but simply call it Nova Scotia, or Acadia.

The Nova Scotia authorities went so far as to have land surveys made west of the St. Croix River and continued to claim this territory until 1762, when Massachusetts proposed that they should come to an agreement about the boundary. However, Nova Scotia considered that such a question should be settled by the Crown. The governors of the two provinces than agreed to make no further grants of land in the disputed territory until the boundary was fixed, which was not done until after the treaty of Paris.

Article IV of the treaty of Paris of 1763, by which France gave up all claim to Canada and Acadia, reads as follows:

"His Most Christian Majesty renounces all pretensions which he has heretofore formed, or might form, to Nova Scotia or Acadia, in all its parts, and guarantees the whole of it, and with all its dependencies, to the King of Great Britain: moreover his Most Christian Majesty cedes and guarantees to His said Britannic Majesty, in full right, Canada, with all its dependencies, as well as the island of Cape Breton, and all the other islands and coasts in the Gulf and River St. Lawrence and in general, everything that depends on the said countries, lands, islands and coasts, with the sovereignty, property, possession and all rights acquired by treaty or otherwise which the said Most Christian King and the Crown of France have had till now over the said countries, lands, islands, places, coasts, and their inhabitants, so that the most Christian King cedes and makes over the whole to the said King and to the Crown of Great Britain, and that in the most ample manner and form, without restriction and without any liberty to depart from the said cession and guaranty under any pretence, or to disturb Great Britain in the possessions above mentioned *   *   *"

Now that France was no longer in possession of Canada, England, although she had in her boundary disputes with France maintained that the Provinces of Massachusetts and Nova Scotia extended to the St. Lawrence, was no longer desirous that they should do so. In 1763 a royal proclamation creating the new Province of Quebec included all the south bank of the St. Lawrence in that province.

In the royal proclamation, the southern boundary of the new province is described as follows:

" * * * from whence the said line crossing the river St. Lawrence and the Lake Champlain, in 45° of North Latitude, passes along the Highlands which divide the rivers that empty themselves into the said river St. Lawrence from those which fall into the sea; and also along the north coast of the Baye des Chaleurs * * *"

A portion of this boundary was soon afterwards determined, and has remained the boundary until the present day.

After some correspondence between the governors of the provinces of New York and Quebec it was decided that a determination of the forty-fifth parallel, where it intersects Lake Champlain, should be made. Observations for latitude were made in 1766 at several places on the shores of Lake Champlain near Windmill Point, and a point was agreed upon as being on the forty-fifth parallel.

It was subsequently agreed that the line should extend eastward as far as the Connecticut River, and in the years 1771 to 1774 the line was surveyed from the St. Lawrence River to the Connecticut River by John Collins, for Quebec, and Thomas Valentine, for New York.

The southern boundary of Quebec became the northern boundary of Massachusetts and Nova Scotia. The commission to Montague Wilmot in 1763, as governor of Nova Scotia, reads in part:

"To the northward our said province shall be bounded by the southern boundary of our Province of Quebec, as far as the western extremity of the Baye des Chaleurs, to the eastward by the said Bay and the gulf of St. Lawrence to the Cape or Promontory called Cape Breton in the Island of that name including that Island, the Island of St. John's, and all other Islands within six leagues of the coast, to the southward by the Atlantic Ocean from the said Cape to Cape Sable including all other islands within forty leagues of the coast, with all the rights, members and appurtenances whatever thereunto belonging and to the westward, although our said province hath anciently extended and doth of right extend as far as the River Pentagoet or Penobscot, it shall be bounded by a line drawn from Cape Sable across the entrance of the Bay of Fundy to the mouth of the river St. Croix, by the said river to its source and by a line drawn due north from thence to the southern boundary of our Colony of Quebec."

In 1764 Massachusetts was offered the territory up to the St. Croix River and a line drawn due north from its source, if she would waive her claim to any portion of the south bank of the St. Lawrence River, which the Crown, as had been shown in the royal proclamation, wished to include in the new Province of Quebec.

Apparently Massachusetts agreed informally to this, for the right of Quebec to the south bank of the St. Lawrence River was not disputed, nor was that of Massachusetts to the territory up to the St. Croix River; and all commissions to governors of Nova Scotia, subsequent to 1763, made the St. Croix River and a north line from its source the western boundary, without mentioning that that province of right extended to the Penobscot River.

The Quebec act of 1774 described the southern boundary of the province in terms almost identical with those of the royal proclamation. It reads in part as follows:

"That all the territories, Islands and Countries in North America, belonging to the Crown of Great Britain, bounded on the south by a line from the Bay of Chaleurs, along the Highlands, which divide the Rivers that empty themselves into the River St. Lawrence from those which fall into the sea, to a point in forty-five degrees of northern latitude, on the eastern bank of the River Connecticut, keeping the same latitude directly west through the Lake Champlain, until in the same latitude it meets the River St. Lawrence, from thence up the eastern bank of the said river to the Lake Ontario."

In the descriptions of the southern boundary of Quebec in this act and in the royal proclamation is seen reappearing the northern boundary, parallel 45°, of the old grant to the Plymouth Company. The descriptions are somewhat indefinite in that they do not define just where the Highlands are; they also leave one undefined gap between the Highlands and the part of the boundary formed by the forty-fifth parallel, in one case, and the Connecticut River, in the other, and another undefined gap between the Highlands and Chaleur Bay; and they neglect altogether the fact that the Restigouche River flows into neither the St. Lawrence River nor the sea, but into Chaleur Bay, and fail to state whether the Highlands just east of that bay are to be found north or south of the Restigouche.

Some of the maps of the time show the southern boundary of Quebec along the sources of the tributaries of the St. Lawrence River as far as the head of the Restigouche, and thence along that river to the head of Chaleur Bay. On others, the boundary passes around the northern source of the Restigouche and follows a land line to the head of Chaleur Bay.

Most of these maps also show that a line drawn due north from the source of the St. Croix would reach a watershed separating rivers flowing into the River St. Lawrence from those flowing into the Atlantic Ocean, or rather into the Bay of Fundy, while modern maps show that that line does not reach such a St. Lawrence-Atlantic watershed on account of the intervention of the Restigouche River.

While, as we have seen, the St. Croix River was decided upon as the boundary between Massachusetts and Nova Scotia, its location was left undetermined. In 1764, Governor Bernard, of Massachusetts, sent two surveyors, Mitchel and Jones, to survey Passamaquoddy Bay, and to determine and survey the St. Croix River and a pond at its head.

Mitchel identified the Magaguadavic as the St. Croix, on the sworn testimony of three Indians of the locality to that effect. He made a survey of this river to Second Falls and also of Lake Utopia and of Passamaquoddy Bay. A copy of the map made by Mitchel as a result of this survey, annotated by Governor Bernard, as well as some correspondence of the latter with Governor Wilmot, show that Bernard did not accept Mitchel's idea based on the testimony of the Indians that the river they pointed out, the present Magaguadavic, was the St. Croix.

Testimony taken some years later seems to show that both the present Magaguadavic and St. Croix, and even the Cobscook, were known prior to that time to some of the inhabitants of the district as the St. Croix. Bernard at the time decided that the present Digdeguash was the St. Croix, calling the present St. Croix the

Passamaquoddy and identifying it with a river called Riviere des Etchemins by Champlain. As aforesaid, he communicated his views on the subject to Governor Wilmot, of Nova Scotia.

In 1765 Governor Wilmot sent the surveyor general of Nova Scotia, Charles Morris, to survey Passamaquoddy Bay. On the strength of the testimony of Indians and by a comparison of his surveys with Champlain's description of the St. Croix, which had been furnished by Governor Bernard, Morris decided that the Cobscook was the only river that could be the St. Croix. However, no actual decision as to what river was the St. Croix was made by responsible authorities previous to the Revolutionary War.

The War of the American Revolution was brought to a close by a treaty signed at Paris in 1783. Part of Article II of this treaty is as follows:

"And that all disputes which might arise in future, on the subject of the boundaries of the said United States may be prevented, it is hereby agreed and declared, that the following are and shall be their boundaries, viz: From the northwest angle of Nova Scotia, viz: that angle which is formed by a line drawn due north from the source of the Saint Croix River to the Highlands; along the said Highlands which divide those rivers that empty themselves into the river St. Lawrence from those which fall into the Atlantic Ocean, to the northwesternmost head of Connecticut River; thence down along the middle of that river, to the forty-fifth degree of north latitude; from thence, by a line due west on said latitude until it strikes the river Iroquois or Cataraquy; * * * East by a line to be drawn along the middle of the river St. Croix from its mouth in the Bay of Fundy to its source, and from its source directly north to the aforesaid Highlands, which divide the rivers that fall into the Atlantic Ocean from those which fall into the river St. Lawrence; comprehending all islands within twenty leagues of any part of the shores of the United States, and lying between lines to be drawn due east from the points where the aforesaid boundaries between Nova Scotia on the one part and East Florida on the other, shall respectively touch the Bay of Fundy and the Atlantic Ocean; excepting such islands as now are, or heretofore have been, within the limits of the said province of Nova Scotia."

With regard to the portion of the boundary at present under discussion, the United States negotiators of the treaty, under instructions from their Government, tried to secure the St. John River from mouth to source as a boundary, but to this the English negotiators would not agree. The English, on their part, attempted to secure as boundary, first the Piscatqua River, then the Kennebec, and then the Penobscot, but the American negotiators would not agree to any of those rivers as the boundary.

Finally all agreed that the former boundary between Massachusetts and Nova Scotia, the St. Croix River, should continue to be the new boundary. This was held to be in agreement with the old boundary of Sir William Alexander's Nova Scotia of 1621 and with the boundary of Massachusetts Bay under the charter of 1691.

It will be noted that the wording of the description of this portion of the boundary agrees closely with the wording of the description of the western boundary of the Province of Nova Scotia as given in the commission to Wilmot in 1763 and subsequent commissions, and with the wording of the descriptions of the southern boundary of the Province of Quebec as given in the royal proclamation of 1763 and in the Quebec act of 1774.

In spite of the hope of the negotiators of the treaty of 1783, that future boundary disputes might be avoided, and the care taken in describing the boundaries to that end, disputes did arise because the location of the boundary as defined by the treaty was unknown and undetermined. Also, it was not realized at that time that the topography of the country was not then known with sufficient accuracy to insure that when an attempt should be made to trace out the boundary as defined by the treaty, it would fit the topography.

With regard to the portion of the boundary between the Atlantic coast and the St. Lawrence River, the treaty failed to define or make clear:

1. What islands were formerly within the limits of Nova Scotia.

2. What river was the River St. Croix.

3. Where was the location (even on a map) of the northwest angle of Nova Scotia.

4. Where was the location of the Highlands between the northwest angle of Nova Scotia and the northwesternmost head of the Connecticut River.

5. What stream was to be regarded as the northwesternmost head of the Connecticut River.

6. Whether the determination of the forty-fifth parallel, made by Valentine and Collins for the Provinces of New York and Quebec, was to be accepted as the boundary, or whether a new determination was to be made.

A dispute about what river was the St. Croix arose very soon after the treaty of 1783, for royalist refugees settled near St. Andrews, and the State of Massachusetts claimed that they were on United States territory.

The Nova Scotia authorities maintained that the present St. Croix, known locally at that time as the Scoodic, was the St. Croix of the treaty and of earlier periods; they had apparently abandoned the opinion held a few years before that the Cobscook was Champlain's St. Croix.

Massachusetts, in 1784, appointed a committee to investigate the question. This committee visited Passamaquoddy Bay and made inquiries in that district; they also secured the evidence of John Jay, one of the negotiators of the treaty of 1783, and of Mitchel, who had formerly, as we have seen, identified the Magaguadavic with the St. Croix. As a result of this investigation, the committee made a report in which it was admitted that Mitchell's map of 1755 used by the negotiators of the treaty was somewhat inaccurate, yet they claimed on the evidence they had obtained that the Magaguadavic was the St. Croix of the treaty of 1783.

The Governor of Massachusetts wrote to the Governor of Nova Scotia informing him of the report of this committee, and suggested that he recall those British subjects who had settled west of the Magaguadavic.

The Province of New Brunswick had been created in 1784, and this letter was forwarded to its governor. In his reply to the Governor of Massachusetts he claimed that the Scoodic was the St. Croix of the treaty of 1783; which opinion, he had been informed, would be maintained by the Government of Great Britain.

Other suggestions and proposals with regard to this question were made in the next few years, but nothing definite was done until 1794, when, after lengthy negotiations, a treaty commonly known as Jay's treaty was signed, providing for a commission to determine the St. Croix River.

The treaty reads in part as follows:

"Whereas doubts have arisen what river was truly intended under the name of the River St. Croix, mentioned in the said treaty of peace, and forming a part of the boundary therein

described; that question shall be referred to the final decision of commissioners to be appointed in the following manner, viz: * * * The said commissioners shall, by a declaration, under their hands and seals, decide what river is the river St. Croix intended by the treaty. The said declaration shall contain a description of the said river, and shall particularize the latitude and longitude of its mouth and of its source * * * And both parties agree to consider such decision as final and conclusive, so that the same shall never hereafter be called into question, or made the subject of dispute or difference between them."

The United States commissioner was David Howell, of Rhode Island; the British commissioner, Thomas Barclay, of Annapolis. Each Government was represented by an agent; the United States by James Sullivan, of Massachusetts, and Great Britain by Ward Chipman, solicitor general of New Brunswick. The first meeting of the commission took place at Halifax in 1796, when the agents were advised to have surveys made of the rivers claimed by them to be the St. Croix. Also, at this meeting the two commissioners agreed upon a third commissioner, Egbert Benson, of New York.

The full commission met shortly afterwards in St. Andrews, when the agents filed their claims for their respective Governments, Sullivan claiming the Maga-guadavic as the St. Croix—Chipman, the Scoodic. The commissioners visited both rivers, and the respective agents attempted to identify the Isle St. Croix described by Champlain. The testimony of Indians and white settlers as to what river had been known as the St. Croix was also secured. The commission then adjourned until the surveys could be completed.

They met again at Boston in 1797, when the agents presented their respective arguments. Sullivan, the United States agent, claimed that the decision as to what river was the St. Croix of the treaty should not of necessity depend upon the identification of a river with the historic St. Croix. He maintained that the Nova Scotia of 1783, owned by England and mentioned in the treaty, had no connection with the Nova Scotia granted to Alexander in 1621, since all territory east of Massachusetts had been granted to Massachusetts Bay in 1691, and that that territory was first limited by the treaty of 1783. As a deduction from this, he claimed that the St. Croix of the treaty was not the St. Croix described by Champlain, but a new St. Croix brought into existence by the treaty.

He stated that inasmuch as the negotiators of the treaty had made use of Mitchell's map of 1755, the river to be identified was the St. Croix River of that map, which was shown thereon as being the easternmost of those rivers flowing into Passamaquoddy Bay. He claimed that when the United States negotiators of the treaty of 1783 abandoned their claim to the St. John River as the boundary they insisted upon the St. Croix River, the first river shown on Mitchell's map west of the St. John, and that that river, the St. Croix of Mitchell's map, was the river to be determined, and he maintained that this was the Magaguadavic.

Chipman, the British agent, maintained on his part that the St. Croix of the treaty of 1783 was the historic St. Croix described by Champlain and mentioned as the boundary of Nova Scotia in the charter granting that Province to Sir William Alexander in 1621. He, of course, identified the Scoodic as the St. Croix.

Subsequent to the hearing of these arguments the commission obtained the evidence of John Jay and John Adams, two of the negotiators of the treaty of 1783. They testified that the St. Croix, which the negotiators of the treaty intended to make the boundary, was the St. Croix which was the former boundary of Massachusetts Bay. They stated that this was supposed to be the St. Croix marked on Mitchell's map, but that no attention had been paid to the fact that the map might be inaccurate.

In the meantime a copy of the edition of 1613 of Champlain's Voyages had been obtained from Europe, permitting the commission to have a fuller description of the St. Croix River and Isle St. Croix according to Champlain than they had had hitherto.

Chipman, the British agent, had excavations made on Bone, or Dochet, Island, a short distance up the Scoodic from its mouth, and remains of an ancient settlement were found. This island was also surveyed, and a map of it was found to correspond closely with Champlain's descriptions of Isle St. Croix. Chipman claimed that this and the relics found upon the island identified it as Isle St. Croix and that, therefore, the Scoodic was the St. Croix River.

As the surveys were still unfinished, the commission adjourned until June, 1798, when they again adjourned for the same reason until September of that year.

They then heard anew the arguments of the agents and gave their decision. This was to the effect that the river intended under the name of the River St. Croix in the treaty of peace of 1783, forming a part of the boundary therein described, had its mouth in Passamaquoddy Bay at Joes Point, in north latitude 45° 05′ 05″ and in longitude 67° 12′ 30″ west.

They decided that the boundary should follow the northern or Chiputneticook Branch to its source, which point was marked by the commission's surveyors.

A map of the river had been compiled from surveys made by order of the commission and various earlier surveys, and a copy, upon which the river was shown, was annexed to the report.

Although the commissioners did not submit any report showing their reasons for their decisions on various points, these are known from other sources, such as correspondence and a report made by Commissioner Benson to the President of the United States.

The commissioners rejected the claim that the river intended by the treaty of 1783 to be the St. Croix must be the St. Croix of Mitchell's map, and decided that it was the historic St. Croix described by Champlain, the boundary of Alexander's grant of 1621 and of Massachusetts Bay in 1691. They decided that Dochet or Bone Island was the only island which agreed with Champlain's maps and descriptions of Isle St. Croix; that the finding of the relics verified this, and that, therefore, the Scoodic River, in which Dochet Island is, was the St. Croix.

In spite of the wishes of the United States agent that the mouth of the river should be fixed among the islands of Passamaquoddy Bay, the commissioners held that that bay was part of the Bay of Fundy and that to define the boundary among its islands exceeded their authority. For that reason, and in agreement with Champlain, they fixed the mouth of the river at Joes Point. On some other points they were not all in agreement, and their final verdict was, in part at any rate, in the nature of a compromise.

After the commissioners had decided that the St. Croix of the treaty of 1783 was the St. Croix of Champlain and of Alexander's grant, the British agent claimed that the words in Alexander's charter, "to the remotest springs or source from the western side of the same which empty into the first mentioned river," would indicate the most western source of the Scoodic branch. The United States agent claimed that they meant the most remote spring entering from the western side, or the most western source of the Chiputneticook.

The British agent claimed that a due north line from that point would not reach such highlands as are described in the treaty, while one from the source of the western branch of the Scoodic would, but on this point he was in error, as a modern map will show. The United States agent claimed that this point was irrelevant, and his contention was sustained by the commission.

The British commissioner, Barclay, gave the opinion that the western branch to its extreme source should be the boundary in accordance with the treaty. Benson concurred in this, but not to the extreme source; only to the outlet of the lake from which it flowed. Howell, the United States commissioner, thought that the Chiputneticook branch should be chosen and that the principle suggested by Benson should be applied to it.

Barclay and Benson finally agreed to the outlet of the easternmost of the Scoodic Lakes as the source of the St. Croix, with Howell dissenting. A line north from this point would have inclosed in New Brunswick some United States grants lying between the two branches and would have inclosed in the United States the Grand Falls of the St. John River and a British military post at Presque Isle. The United States agent proposed, and the British agent, with the consent of the British Ambassador, Mr. Liston, agreed, that the extreme source of the Chiputneticook should instead be chosen, whereupon this alteration was agreed to by all the commissioners and their decision accordingly rendered.

Referring to the part of Article II of the treaty of 1783, quoted on page 295, it seems probable that the intention of the negotiators of the treaty of 1783 was to make the new boundary between the territory of the United States and of Nova Scotia the same as the former boundary between the former Colony of Massachusetts Bay and Province of Nova Scotia. This is borne out by the testimony and correspondence of the negotiators of both countries and also by the instructions from Congress to the United States negotiators, who were told to try to secure the St. John River from mouth to source as boundary, and if they could not obtain that, to insist on the old boundary between Massachusetts Bay and Nova Scotia becoming the new boundary, and to allow no portion of the original 13 States to be left in the possession of Great Britain.

It should be noted that the wording of the treaty of 1783 closely follows the wording of the royal proclamation of 1763 creating the Province of Quebec, of the Quebec act of 1774, and of the commission to Governor Wilmot, of Nova Scotia, in 1763, all of which have already been quoted.

As has been previously stated, most of the maps of the period 1763 to 1782 show the southern boundary of the Province of Quebec as running along the southern edge of the St. Lawrence River watershed and finally reaching Chaleur Bay. These maps show the northern boundaries of the Provinces of Massachusetts Bay and Nova Scotia coincident with the southern boundary of Quebec.

In 1784 the Province of New Brunswick was created, and in the commission to its first governor, Thomas Carleton, its western and northern boundaries are thus described:

"Our Province of New Brunswick, bounded on the Westward by the Mouth of the River St. Croix, by the said River to its source and by a line drawn due north from thence to the Southern Boundary of our Province of Quebec, to the Northward, by the said Boundary as far as the Western Extremity of the Bay des Chaleurs."

The attention of British officials was first drawn to the question of the location of the international boundary about 1785 on account of an interprovincial boundary dispute between the Provinces of Quebec and New Brunswick, for, as already pointed out, the southern boundary of Quebec constituted the northern boundary of both New Brunswick and Massachusetts. Even previous to this, in 1783, General Haldimand, at Quebec, wrote Governor Parr, at Halifax, regarding a proposed settlement of Acadians in Quebec in which he stated that he planned to grant them lands near Grand Falls on the St. John River, evidently believing that the boundary between Quebec and what was then Nova Scotia lay south of Grand Falls.

In 1785 the authorities of New Brunswick disputed a claim on the part of Quebec to the district about Lake Temiscouata and the Madawaska River. New Brunswick, in 1787, assumed jurisdiction over the Madawaska district without the boundary dispute having been settled, but Quebec continued to exercise occasional authority there.

Lord Dorchester, governor of Quebec, wrote to the governor of New Brunswick in 1787, claiming that the boundary between Quebec and New Brunswick and New England was a range of hills near Grand Falls on the St. John River. Somewhat later he suggested that the surveyors general of the two Provinces should meet and settle the question of the interprovincial boundary.

At this meeting the surveyor general of New Brunswick maintained that the southern boundary of Quebec was north of Lake Temiscouata, while the surveyor general of Quebec claimed that it was south of Grand Falls; but no agreement was reached.

Lord Dorchester wrote again to the governor of New Brunswick about this question, urging the acceptance of an interprovincial boundary extending from the head of Chaleur Bay to the Great Falls of the River St. John, on account of the effect this would have on deciding the location of the international boundary.

He claimed that the words of the Quebec act in describing the southern boundary of that Province should be interpreted as the highest range of hills running westward from Chaleur Bay; that rivers might run through this range in opposite directions, some to the St. Lawrence and others to the Atlantic Ocean; but that the actual sources of these rivers could not and should not define the boundary.

Further correspondence shows that, up to 1792, when Great Britain was asked to settle the interprovincial boundary question, opinion in Quebec and New Brunswick was divided upon the subject. No settlement, however, was made at the time.

This question of the interprovincial boundary has been discussed at some length, because the southern boundary of Quebec had been held to be the northern boundary of Massachusetts.

In the United States attention apparently had not yet been drawn to the question of their northeastern boundary. This was first officially discussed between representatives of the two countries at the hearings of the St. Croix commission.

The British agent, Chipman, to support his claim for the western or Scoodic branch, instead of the Chiputneticook or north branch of the St. Croix, stated that a due north line from the source of the former would reach such highlands as are described in the treaty of 1783 and that one from the latter would not.

On this point he was in error, as has been previously pointed out, for both of these lines would cross the headwaters of the Restigouche River, which flows into neither the St. Lawrence River nor the Atlantic Ocean, but into Chaleur Bay. It was generally supposed at that time, however, that a line due north from the source of the Scoodic would not intersect the Restigouche.

The United States agent, Sullivan, in opposing the British claim to the Scoodic, maintained that it would be difficult or impossible to decide on the actual position of the northwest angle of Nova Scotia, on the ground.

Sullivan later communicated his opinion of the difficulty in locating the northwest angle of Nova Scotia to Madison, Secretary of State, and suggested that if no highlands just south of the St. Lawrence were found to exist, as had been reported to be the case, it would be advisable to appoint a commission to fix its position—an arbitrary one if necessary. Madison apparently agreed with these ideas and instructed the United States minister to Great Britain to commence negotiations regarding the determination of this part of the boundary in accordance with them.

As a result, in 1803, a convention providing for a commission to run the line north from the source of the St. Croix, and to determine the northwest angle of Nova Scotia, was agreed to. This convention, however, was never ratified, nor was a similar one in 1807, and nothing further was done until after the War of 1812.

Correspondence of officials and other well-informed persons of New Brunswick of the period between 1796, when the St. Croix commission met, and the outbreak of the War of 1812, would indicate that they generally believed that this north line would cross the St. John River, thus throwing into the United States part of the route of land communication between New Brunswick and Quebec. This route by the St. John and Madawaska Valleys was very important as a military road, and in winter was the only route open through British territory.

In 1814, the House of Assembly of New Brunswick passed the following resolution:

"*Resolved*, That the Council be requested to appoint a committee to meet a committee of this House, for the purpose of preparing an humble petition to His Royal Highness, the Prince Regent, praying that when a negotiation for peace shall take place between Great Britain and the United States of America, His Royal Highness will be graciously pleased to direct such measures to be adopted as he may think proper to alter the boundaries between those States and this Province, so as that the important line of communication between this and the neighboring Province of Lower Canada, by the River St. John, may not be interrupted."

The British negotiators of the treaty of Ghent, which brought the war to a close, attempted to secure the consent of the United States negotiators to some such arrangement, on the ground that the territory involved was small in area and that it was quite probable that it already in reality belonged to Great Britain. The United States negotiators refused, however, claiming that these proposals would mean a cession of United States territory and that to agree to this would exceed their authority.

By Article V of the treaty of Ghent it was provided that since the northwest angle of Nova Scotia had not been determined nor any portion of the international boundary between the source of the River St. Croix and the St. Lawrence River surveyed or marked, two commissioners should be appointed to determine this portion of the boundary in conformity with the provisions of the treaty of 1783; that they should cause the boundary to be surveyed and marked; and that they should have a map made of the boundary to which they should annex a declaration, certifying it to be a true map.

Both parties agreed to consider such maps and declaration as finally and conclusively fixing the boundary. In case the commissioners should differ, or decline or fail to act, reference of the case was to be made to a friendly sovereign or State.

The commissioners appointed under this article were Thomas Barclay, for Great Britain, and Cornelius Van Ness, for the United States. The British agents were Ward Chipman and Ward Chipman, jr., and the United States agent was William C. Bradley. Barclay and Chipman had served on the St. Croix commission and were also to serve on the Passamaquoddy Islands commission.

The commissioners met first at St. Andrews in September, 1816, and, after being sworn, adjourned until the following June when they met in Boston, at which time various surveys were decided upon.

During this and the succeeding three seasons a large number of surveys were made. These included surveys of the line north from the source of the St. Croix; of parts of the Rivers St. John, Allagash, Aroostook, Penobscot, Ouelle, Connecticut, and others; of the district about Mars Hill, the Temiscouata Portage and the Metgermette Portage; and of several ranges of highlands.

Besides these surveys, Dr. J. C. Tiarks, a British astronomer, made a new determination of latitude near the point where the old line of Valentine and Collins intersected the Connecticut River. The negotiators of the treaty of Ghent were apparently unaware that this line had ever been run, although that fact was well known both in Quebec and Vermont, as was also the fact of the departure of the line from the forty-fifth parallel of latitude.

Observations made by Doctor Tiarks and Mr. F. R. Hassler, first Superintendent of the United States Coast and Geodetic Survey, revealed the fact that the old determination of the forty-fifth parallel, made in 1766 near Lake Champlain, was in error by about three-fourths mile, being about that much too far north. As important fortifications had been erected by the United States north of the true forty-fifth parallel, this discovery was not made public at the time, but was reported to the commission only.

The surveyors appointed to run the line due north from the source of the St. Croix were Colonel Bouchette, for Great Britain, and John Johnson, for the United States, together with several assistants. They had two main tasks; one to mark the boundary north of the St. Croix River, the other to run an "exploring line" until it should reach the highlands of the treaty of 1783, thus locating the northwest angle of Nova Scotia.

For this latter purpose, a party under the personal direction of Colonel Bouchette and Mr. Johnson went ahead with the exploring line, while their assistants proceeded more deliberately to survey and mark the true line, which they were to cut out through the woods to a width of 16 feet. The latter party had reached the Meduxnekeag River by the end of the season.

In the meantime, the former party had run their exploring line close by Mars Hill and, crossing the St. John River a little above Grand Falls, by the end of the season had reached the watershed between the St. John and the Restigouche. This exploring line was continued the following year by Mr. Johnson, for the United States, and Mr. Odell, for Great Britain, until in September it reached a tributary of the Metis River, which flows into the St. Lawrence River.

The survey of this exploring line has been described at some length, because in 1842 that portion of it between the source of the St. Croix River and the St. John River was adopted as the boundary.

The commissioners had met, in the meantime, at several different times and places, but adjournments were necessary on account of the noncompletion of the many surveys. They finally met in New York, in the summer of 1821, when the arguments of the agents were heard.

Chipman, the agent for Great Britain, claimed that the boundary should be a line run due north from the source of the St. Croix River to Mars Hill; thence westerly along a range of highlands to near the head of the Chaudiere River; thence along the range at the sources of that river, to that branch of the Connecticut River on which are three small lakes, north of the forty-fifth parallel; thence down the Connecticut River to a point on the forty-fifth parallel as determined by Doctor Tiarks; and thence along that parallel to the St. Lawrence River.

He maintained that the words of the treaty of 1783 describing the northwest angle of Nova Scotia do not fit any locality exactly, since nowhere on a line, due north from the source of the St. Croix, is there a watershed separating rivers which flow into the St. Lawrence River from those which flow into the Atlantic Ocean, but only watersheds separating River St. Lawrence tributaries from rivers flowing into Chaleur Bay, and rivers flowing into Chaleur Bay from tributaries of the St. John River flowing into the Bay of Fundy.

He emphasized the argument that since the St. John River flows into the Bay of Fundy, and since the treaty of 1783 makes a distinction between the Bay of Fundy and the Atlantic Ocean, therefore, as the highlands of the treaty must be found somewhere, they are to be sought for west of the St. John River. He claimed that they were to be found in the range that runs from the sources of the Connecticut to the western sources of the St. John; that one branch of this range ran eastward from the latter point toward Mars Hill, whence it continued in a northerly direction to Chaleur Bay; that the other branch of this range, which forms the St. Lawrence watershed east and north of those sources of the St. John, and on which the United States agent claimed the northwest angle of Nova Scotia was situated, had not those characteristics of highlands required by the treaty, but were, on the contrary, according to the surveyors' reports, swampy and flat. He quoted Sullivan and Madison in support of the idea that the highlands of the treaty must be a mountainous ridge or range of hills and not a mere watershed. He maintained that the branch of the highlands on which Mars Hill lay had the necessary characteristics and that it was there that the northwest angle of Nova Scotia should be located.

For an additional argument that the North Line should not cross the St. John, assuming that it was impossible to find any location for the northwest angle that literally satisfied the terms of the treaty, he resorted to what he claimed was the intention of the treaty, which, as set forth in the preamble, was to be the mutual advantage and convenience of the two countries. He pointed out the great inconvenience to Great Britain of the line as proposed by the United States agent, in that the only direct winter communication between two British provinces would be cut.

He also drew attention to the fact that the United States negotiators of the treaty, under instructions from Congress, had attempted to secure the St. John River as boundary, but were unsuccessful, and claimed that it was unreasonable to suppose that when the British negotiators had refused to yield to making that river the boundary they would have consented to a boundary which would not only cross it, thereby leaving its upper valley entirely in the United States, but would also yield to that country a portion of the headwaters of the Restigouche.

He claimed that the territory in dispute had been actually occupied and governed by Great Britain, and that Massachusetts had attempted only recently to do so.

With regard to the head of the Connecticut River, he stated that the Connecticut branch, on which are three small lakes, had the distinctive name Connecticut above where Halls Stream, Indian Stream, and Perry Stream join it, and that it was the northwest branch of this Connecticut branch that should be the boundary.

The agent for the United States, Bradley, claimed, on his part, that the boundary should be a line run due north from the source of the St. Croix River to a point on the St. Lawrence River watershed; thence southwesterly along that watershed or range of highlands to the sources of the Connecticut River; thence down the branch of that river known as Halls Stream to the formerly determined forty-fifth parallel; and thence west along that line to the St. Lawrence River.

The United States agent based his claim that the northwest angle of Nova Scotia should be on the St. Lawrence watershed upon the descriptions of the southern boundary of the Province of Quebec, as given in the royal proclamation of 1763 and the Quebec act of 1774; also, upon the boundaries of Nova Scotia as described in the commissions to governors of the Province between 1763 and 1782 as well as upon the instructions by Congress to the negotiators of the treaty of 1783, that if they could not obtain the St. John River from mouth to source as boundary they were to demand the old boundary between Massachusetts Bay and Nova Scotia.

He maintained that the descriptions of the southern boundary of Quebec in the royal proclamation and the Quebec act place it along the highlands just south of the St. Lawrence; that all maps and records of the time agreed in placing it there; and that the boundary between Nova Scotia and Massachusetts was a line drawn due north from the source of the St. Croix to those highlands.

In regard to the objection that the location claimed by him for the northwest angle of Nova Scotia was not situated on a watershed separating rivers that flow into the St. Lawrence River from those which flow into the Atlantic Ocean, he maintained that the treaty of 1783 took note of only two classes of rivers, those flowing into the St. Lawrence and those flowing into the Atlantic Ocean. Therefore, the Restigouche River should be considered as one flowing into the Atlantic Ocean. In connection with this point he drew attention to the fact that the negotiators of the treaty made use of Mitchell's map of 1755, and that on that map the headwaters of the Restigouche lie much farther to the east than they actually are and do not intervene between the tributaries of the St. Lawrence and the St. John. Therefore, he claimed the intention of the negotiators of the treaty was to place the northwest angle of Nova Scotia where he claimed it to be, on the watershed just south of the St. Lawrence, for on that map that watershed does separate rivers flowing into the St. Lawrence River from those flowing into the Atlantic Ocean.

In regard to the claim of the British agent that the St. John River did not flow into the Atlantic Ocean but into the Bay of Fundy, he pointed out that the royal proclamation and the Quebec act, from which the wording of the treaty was apparently copied, use the word "sea" where the latter uses "Atlantic Ocean." However, he maintained they evidently refer to the same thing, since the term "sea" was as applicable to the Bay of Fundy as to the Atlantic Ocean.

He maintained that it was the intention of the treaty to provide for the survey of only such portions of the boundary as had not previously been surveyed. He, therefore, declared that the old line of the forty-fifth parallel should remain as the boundary, and if this opinion were not sustained he would have to claim for the United States the forty-fifth parallel of geocentric latitude, which would be several miles farther north.

He claimed Halls Stream as the northwesternmost stream of the four rivers, Halls Stream, Indian Stream, Perry Stream, and Connecticut River, which are the four principal sources of the Connecticut north of the forty-fifth parallel.

After the claims, arguments, and replies of the agents had been heard and considered the commissioners delivered their opinions to each other in notes, which are as follows:

Barclay to Van Ness.

NEW YORK, *4th October, 1821*

The arguments of the agents under the 5th Article of the Treaty of Ghent on the points in controversy having closed, Mr. Barclay, one of the Commissioners, to whom the decision of the said points is referred, hereby states to Mr. Van Ness, the other Commissioner:

1. That on the question as to the Northwest angle of Nova Scotia he is of opinion that the point ought to be established at or near the mountain or hill called Mars Hill distant about

forty miles on a due north line from the source of the river St. Croix and about thirty-seven miles south of the river St. John.

2. That on the question as to the northwesternmost head of Connecticut River, he is of opinion that it is situate at the northwesternmost stream which empties into the third lake of Connecticut River, north of the 45th degree of north latitude.

3. He is of opinion that the point established by Dr. J. C. Tiarks, His Majesty's Astronomer, on geographical principles to be the 45th degree of north latitude, on Connecticut River, is the point which ought to be established by the Commissioners, as the said 45th degree of north latitude on the said River.

4. That the mode or principles on which the parallel of the said 45th degree of Latitude ought to be run, surveyed and marked, should be according to ordinary geographical principles.

Thos. Barclay

Van Ness to Barclay.

New York, *October 4th, 1821*

The arguments of the agents under the 5th article of the Treaty of Ghent on the points in controversy having closed, Mr. Van Ness, one of the Commissioners to whom the decision of the said points is referred, hereby states to Col. Barclay, the other Commissioner, that on the question as to the northwest angle of Nova Scotia, he is of opinion that that point ought to be fixed at a place about one hundred and forty-four miles due north from the source of the River St. Croix, and about sixty-six miles north of the River St. John and that on the question as to the northwesternmost head of Connecticut River he is of opinion that that point ought to be established at the head of the west branch of Indian Stream; and that these opinions he will report to the two Governments agreeably to the provisions of the said treaty.

As to the questions which have been made by the Agents relative to the Boundary from Connecticut River to the River St. Lawrence or Iroquois, Mr. Van Ness will inform Col. Barclay by the first day of November next, whether he shall consider it necessary to report any opinion on that subject, and if so, he will state to the Col. that opinion.

C. P. Van Ness

Burlington, *Nov. 10, 1821*

The Hon'ble Thos. Barclay

Dear Sir: Yours of the 22nd of October has been duly received.

I have concluded that it will not be necessary for me to report any opinion on the questions which have been made relative to the Boundary Line from Connecticut River to the River Iroquois.

I intended to have made this communication sooner, but have been unavoidably prevented from doing it before.

I am, very respectfully your obedient servant,

C P. Van Ness

With regard to the points about the forty-fifth parallel, it is worthy of note that Mr. Van Ness did not support the claim of the United States agent that the boundary from the Connecticut to the St. Lawrence should be the forty-fifth parallel of geocentric latitude, nor was this view ever adopted by the United States Government.

With regard to the northwesternmost head of the Connecticut River, Mr. Van Ness chose Indian Stream rather than Halls Stream because Halls Stream empties into the Connecticut River south of the old line determined as parallel 45°.

After the commissioners had submitted to each other their opinions, and failed to agree, they prepared reports for the two Governments, in accordance with the terms of the treaty of Ghent, upon their reasons for their decisions on the various points.

The treaty of Ghent had provided that, in case the commissioners should be unable to come to an agreement, the question should be referred to some friendly sovereign or State; and after somewhat lengthy negotiations, a convention was agreed to in 1827 and ratified in 1828, under which the King of the Netherlands was chosen as arbitrator.

This convention also provided that in view of the great number and complication of all the documents bearing on the case, these should be replaced by new and separate statements of the respective cases of each country and that these statements were to be submitted by each to the other and each was to have the right to a statement in reply. It was also agreed that the only official maps were to be the Mitchell map of 1755 as used by the negotiators of the treaty of 1783 and map "A" as accepted by the commissioners under Article V of the treaty of Ghent to show the claims of the two countries.

The United States statement, prepared by Albert Gallatin, with the aid of Wm. C. Preble, is entitled, "Statement on the Part of the United States of the Case Referred in Pursuance of the Convention of the 29th of September 1827, Between the Said States and Great Britain to His Majesty, the King of the Netherlands for His Decision Thereon, Printed but not Published. Washington. Printed at the Office of the United States Telegraph, 1829." It is a comparatively short statement of the case for the United States.

A similar statement of the British case, prepared by Henry U. Addington and William Huskisson, with the aid of Ward Chipman, jr., of New Brunswick, is entitled "First Statement on the Part of Great Britain, According to the Provisions of the Convention Concluded Between Great Britain and the United States on the 29th Sept. 1827 for Regulating the Reference to Arbitration of the Disputed Points of Boundary under the Fifth Article of the Treaty of Ghent."

Dr. Ganong says of these two statements:

"Indeed for a summary of the two sides of the discussion, freed as largely as possible of controversial matter, nothing equals these two presentations giving the matured positions of both parties."

To this British statement, the United States replied in a lengthy "Definitive statement." It answers in detail the British claims, but only two new arguments are introduced: One, based on a claim that the instructions to the negotiators of the treaty of 1783, referring to the source of the St. John, meant the source of the Madawaska; and the other calling attention to the New Brunswick claim for the St. Lawrence watershed as her northern boundary in the interprovincial boundary dispute between that Province and Quebec. It prints many treaties and other documents in full as appendices.

The reply of the British to the United States statement was shorter, with little new argument; but it claimed that an interprovincial dispute could have no bearing on an international question.

These statements, together with a copy of Mitchell's map of 1755 and one of map "A" used by the commissioners appointed under Article V of the treaty of Ghent, were submitted to the King of the Netherlands in 1830.

The decision of the King of the Netherlands was given a few months later. In this decision, after summarizing the evidence submitted by both sides regarding the northwest angle of Nova Scotia, he maintained that it had not been proved that the boundaries established by the treaty of 1783 were identical with the ancient boundaries, when all the disputed territory was a British possession.   Continuing he said:

"That, in view of what precedes, the arguments adduced on either side, and the documents exhibited in support of them, can not be considered as sufficiently preponderating to determine a preference in favor of either one of the two lines respectively claimed by the High Interested Parties, as the boundaries of their possessions, from the source of the river St. Croix to the Northwesternmost head of the Connecticut river; and that the nature of the difference and the vague and not sufficiently determinate stipulations of the Treaty of 1783, do not permit us to award either of those lines to one of the said Parties, without violating the principles of law and equity with regard to the other:

"That, as has already been said, the question resolves itself into the selection of ground dividing the rivers that empty themselves into the river St. Lawrence from those that fall into the Atlantic Ocean; that the High Interested Parties are agreed with regard to the course of the streams delineated by common accord on Map A and affording the only basis of a decision;

"And that, therefore, the circumstances upon which such decision depends could not be further elucidated by means of fresh topographical investigation, nor by the production of additional documents:"

The King then advised that a conventional boundary should be agreed to and adopted.   This boundary was to start at the source of the St. Croix River and to run due north to the middle of the St. John River; thence along the middle of the channel of the St. John River to the mouth of the St. Francis River; thence along the middle of the channel of that river to the source of its southwesternmost branch; thence due west until the watershed of the St. Lawrence River was reached; thence along that watershed to the northwesternmost source of the Connecticut River (which he decided to be the Connecticut branch, the most easterly of the four main head branches); thence along the Connecticut River to the astronomical parallel of 45°, as recently determined; and thence along that parallel, and not along the old line of Valentine and Collins, to the St. Lawrence River.   However, he recommended that the United States be left in possession of territory within a circle of 1 kilometer radius from their fortifications at Rouses Point.

The United States minister at The Hague at once protested against this award, on the ground that the King, in recommending the adoption of a new line of boundary rather than in deciding on which of the two lines claimed by the United States and Great Britain was in accordance with the terms of the treaty of 1783, had exceeded the authority delegated to him by the two parties.

The Government of Great Britain was willing to accept the award, and the United States might have agreed to it, had it not been for the vigorous opposition of the States of Massachusetts and Maine.   The latter had been made a separate State in 1820, while the former retained an interest in certain of the public lands.

The United States Senate rejected the award, and at the same time instructed the President to renew negotiations with the British Government for the settlement of the boundary question.

These negotiations began at once and lasted 10 years, during which time many proposals and counterproposals were made.   In the meantime, Maine was offered 1,000,000 acres of land for territory north and east of the St. Francis.   In 1833, Mr. Livingston, Secretary of State, proposed to Great Britain that another effort be made to locate the boundary in accordance with the terms of the treaty of 1783, and, if unsuccessful, a boundary more convenient to both parties than the one of the treaty of 1783 or of the award might be adopted.

The British Government asked for further particulars as to what this proposal meant.   Mr. Livingston, in reply, suggested having an attempt made to determine the boundary according to the treaty of 1783 by a commission of European experts, with an umpire nominated by some friendly sovereign; and if it should be found, after more accurate surveys, that the due-north line from the source of the St. Croix did not reach such highlands as were described in the treaty, a direct line, whatever its direction, from the head of the St. Croix to such highlands should be adopted, and in no case would this line deviate to the east from the due-north line.

The British Government replied that it believed such a line would run nearly due west from the source of the St. Croix to near the source of the Chaudiere, and that the United States would never agree to such a line.

Great Britain formally withdrew the offer to accept the award of the King of the Netherlands and proposed making the St. John River, from its intersection with the north line to its source, the boundary.   The United States rejected this proposal, but offered to try to get the State of Maine to accept the St. John River from mouth to source as boundary.   This offer the British minister at once declined.

In 1837 the President of the United States informed Congress that the only result of the long negotiations and arbitrations was a belief on the part of the British Government that it was impossible to ascertain the true boundary according to the treaty of 1783, and therefore a conventional line should be adopted.

The next year the Legislature of the State of Maine voted against accepting a conventional line, demanded that the line be established in accordance with the treaty of 1783, refused to consent to the appointment of an arbitrator, urged Congress to pass a law providing for the survey of the boundary either alone or in conjunction with Great Britain, and stated that if this last were not done it would be the duty of the governor of the State to appoint a commission for that purpose.

Congress did not comply with this request and the Governor of the State of Maine appointed a commission consisting of Messrs. John G. Deane, M. O. Norton, and J. Irish.

Apparently this commission did no other work than follow the north line to its termination on the St. Lawrence watershed.   They did not survey any line as the northern boundary of the State.   They made a report to the Governor of Maine, with a map of the disputed territory, locating the northwest angle near the St. Lawrence River.

In the meantime, from 1820, there had been considerable friction between the people of New Brunswick and of Maine.   In that year the United States assumed jurisdiction over the Madawaska settlement by including the settlers there in its official census.   Soon after, New Brunswick assumed rights to the territory claimed by Great Britain, including the Aroostook Valley.   After correspondence between the two governors, an agreement was reached that no exercise of authority before the dispute was settled was to affect the decision; but in spite of this agreement this friction continued and grew worse, resulting finally in 1838 in what was known as the Aroostook war.

In 1839, General Winfield Scott succeeded in getting the Provincial and State authorities to agree that, pending a settlement, New Brunswick was to be in control of the Madawaska district, and Maine of the Aroostook Valley, and that armed forces would be withdrawn. Both sides agreed not to build roads, grant land, or allow timber to be cut in the disputed territory until a settlement of the boundary should be made, but, in spite of this agreement, more or less friction continued until the boundary was finally settled in 1842.

Similar troubles over the question of jurisdiction on Indian Stream took place in 1836, but they did not cause such a widespread or dangerous state of feeling as did those on the Maine-New Brunswick frontier.

In 1838 the United States proposed the formation of a new commission, to which Great Britain finally agreed; and after the formation of this had been agreed to, negotiations as to its constitution occupied two years.

During these negotiations the British Government, for the purpose of securing additional and more accurate information about the disputed territory, had surveys made of it by two engineers, Colonel Mudge and Mr. Featherstonhaugh. They were instructed in particular to determine which of the three following lines present continuous highlands:

First. The line claimed by the British commissioners from the source of the Chaudiere to Mars Hill.

Second. The line from the source of the Chaudiere to the point at which a line drawn from that source to the western extremity of Chaleur Bay intercepts the true north line.

Third. The line claimed by the United States from the source of the Chaudiere to the point at which they claimed the due north line should end.

The surveys were made during the summer of 1839, and a report was presented and published in 1840.

The engineers reported finding an "axis of maximum elevation" in the general location indicated in the second item of their instructions. They reported that no highlands existed at the northwest angle of Nova Scotia claimed by the United States. The elevation at that point they declared to be only 400 feet. (It was later shown to be about 1,300 feet.)

In the report they reviewed the entire boundary question, and insisted that the highlands of the treaty of 1783 must be a continuous mountain range and could not consist even in part of a flat watershed. They stated that the "axis of maximum elevation" on a line between the source of the Chaudiere and Chaleur Bay answered these requirements, but recommended that the boundary should be on another range of highlands, namely, on a northwesterly line from the source of the St. Croix, or rather from the source of the Scoodic, to the source of the Chaudiere, claiming that a proper translation of the charter of 1621 to Alexander supported this pretension. Their views were not formally adopted by the British Government.

The State of Maine appointed a joint committee of the senate and house of representatives, which made a report on March 30, 1841, setting forth the case for the State of Maine, in reply to this report of Messrs. Mudge and Featherstonhaugh.

In 1840 Congress authorized the appointment of a commission, consisting of Messrs. Renwick and Talcott and Major Graham, to make surveys in the disputed territory. Surveys were made of the north line and of the rivers and mountain ranges in the disputed territory. No complete report was ever made, but three interim reports heavily discounted that of Mudge and Featherstonhaugh as to the "axis of maximum elevation."

One survey of particular importance was that of a due-north line from the source of the St. Croix River which was run very accurately by Major Graham and was continued nearly to Grand River. He found that the exploring line of Bouchette and Johnson deviated first to the east and then to the west until, when the St. John River was reached, the exploring line was nearly half a mile west of the true north line.

In 1841 Daniel Webster, Secretary of State, proposed to the British Government that an attempt be made to settle the boundary question, as well as some others, by direct negotiation rather than by the commission agreed to in 1838, the constitution of which was still under discussion. This the British Government agreed to, and appointed as their minister plenipotentiary Lord Ashburton, who arrived in Washington in April, 1842, and negotiations began at once.

Various proposals and counterproposals were made in consultation and confirmed formally by notes. Lord Ashburton proposed as the boundary the exploring north line; the St. John River, from where the north line reached it to its source, but with a deflection to the south of it to include in British territory all the Madawaska settlement; the Highlands, from the source of the Chaudiere to Halls Stream, formerly agreed on by both countries; Halls Stream and the "old line" of the forty-fifth parallel, with certain rights of navigation on the St. John River through New Brunswick.

Mr. Webster replied, refusing this offer, and suggested that if Lord Ashburton would agree to cede all or part of the territory east of the St. Croix River and the north line extending to the St. John River, it might be arranged to accept a line south of the St. John River and west of the north line; otherwise, he refused to let Great Britain retain any territory south of the St. John River above the north line.

If Lord Ashburton could not agree to the above cession, Mr. Webster proposed, on the advice of representatives of the States of Maine and Massachusetts, that the boundary should be the exploring north line; the St. John River from where that line reaches it to 3 miles above the Madawaska River; thence a straight line to the outlet of Long Lake; thence westerly to the head of Lake Pohenagamook, and continuing in the same line to the highlands formerly claimed as boundary by the United States.

If Lord Ashburton was willing to agree to either of the above proposals, and in addition to concede the right of navigation on the St. John River, Mr. Webster was willing to discuss the remainder of the boundary.

Lord Ashburton refused even to consider the first offer, as his instructions did not permit him to cede any territory east of the St. Croix River and north line, or Grand Manan Island or any of the islands of Passamaquoddy Bay.

He declined the second offer, as it gave Great Britain much less territory north of the St. John than she would have obtained under the award of the King of the Netherlands, to say nothing of the award in her favor on the forty-fifth parallel and at the source of the Connecticut, besides granting the valuable right to navigation on the St. John River.

The two plenipotentiaries then apparently abandoned written communications and met in private, coming to an agreement on an avowedly conventional boundary as described in the treaty of 1842, but just how or why the exact terms were decided upon can only be surmised. The treaty, which was signed in Washington on August 9, 1842, finally settled this portion of the boundary.

BIBLIOGRAPHY

While many works have been consulted in preparing this historical sketch, "A Monograph of the Evolution of the Boundaries of the Province of New Brunswick," by Dr. W. F. Ganong, and "International Arbitrations to Which the United States Has Been a Party," by Prof. J. B. Moore, have been of particular assistance. The following is a complete list of the works which have been consulted:

AMERICAN STATE PAPERS. Foreign Relations I–VI, Washington, 1789–1828.

BLUE-BOOK, 1838. Correspondence relating to the boundary between the British possessions in North America and the United States of America under the treaty of 1783. London, 1838.

BLUE-BOOK, 1840. Report of Featherstonhaugh and Mudge.

BOURINOT, Sir JOHN. Builders of Nova Scotia; Transactions of the Royal Society of Canada.

BRITISH AND FOREIGN STATE PAPERS.

GALLATIN, ALBERT. The Rights of the United States of America to the Northeastern Boundary Claimed by Them. New York, 1840.

GANONG, W. F. Monograph of the Evolution of the Boundaries of the Province of New Brunswick; Proceedings and Transactions of the Royal Society of Canada, 1901, second series, Volume VII.

MEMORIALS OF THE ENGLISH AND FRENCH COMMISSARIES CONCERNING THE LIMITS OF NOVA SCOTIA OR ACADIA. London, 1755.

MALLOY, W. M. Treaties, Conventions, International Acts, Protocols, and Agreements between the United States of America and other Powers.

MOORE, J. B. International Arbitrations to which the United States has been a Party.

MURDOCH, B. A History of Nova Scotia or Acadie. Halifax, N. S., 1865–1867.

NEW YORK COLONIAL DOCUMENTS.

SLAFTER, E. F. Sir William Alexander and American Colonization. Boston, Prince Society, 1873.

WHITE, JAMES. Boundary Disputes and Treaties.

APPENDIX II

NEGOTIATIONS, TREATIES, AND CONVENTIONS PERTAINING TO THE BOUNDARY, AND REPORTS OF BOUNDARY COMMISSIONS PREVIOUS TO THE TREATY OF 1908 [1]

The first definition of the international boundary from the source of the St. Croix River to the St. Lawrence River appears in the provisional articles of peace, concluded November 30, 1782, between the United States and Great Britain. This description of the boundary was repeated in the definitive treaty of peace of 1783 as Article II, the full text of which is here reprinted:

DEFINITIVE TREATY OF PEACE

(Concluded at Paris September 3, 1783; ratified by the Congress of the United States January 14, 1784; ratified by Great Britain April 9, 1784)

*　　*　　*　　*　　*　　*　　*　　*　　*

ARTICLE II

And that all disputes which might arise in future, on the subject of the boundaries of the said United States may be prevented, it is hereby agreed and declared, that the following are, and shall be their boundaries, viz: From the northwest angle of Nova Scotia, viz. that angle which is formed by a line drawn due north from the source of Saint Croix River to the Highlands; along the said Highlands which divide those rivers that empty themselves into the river St. Lawrence, from those which fall into the Atlantic Ocean, to the northwesternmost head of Connecticut River; thence down along the middle of that river, to the forty-fifth degree of north latitude; from thence, by a line due west on said latitude, until it strikes the river Iroquois or Cataraquy; thence along the middle of said river into Lake Ontario, through the middle of said lake until it strikes the communication by water between that lake and Lake Erie; thence along the middle of said communication into Lake Erie, through the middle of said lake until it arrives at the water communication between that lake and Lake Huron; thence along the middle of said water communication into the Lake Huron; thence through the middle of said lake to the water communication between that lake and Lake Superior; thence through Lake Superior northward of the Isles Royal and Phelipeaux, to the Long Lake; thence through the middle of said Long Lake, and the water communication between it and the Lake of the Woods, to the said Lake of the Woods; thence through the said lake to the most northwestern point thereof, and from thence on a due west course to the river Mississippi; thence by a line to be drawn along the middle of the said river Mississippi until it shall intersect the northernmost part of the thirty-first degree of north latitude. South, by a line to be drawn due east from the determination of the line last mentioned, in the latitude of thirty-one degrees north of the Equator, to the middle of the river Apalachicola or Catahouche; thence along the middle thereof to its junction with the Flint River; thence strait to the head of St. Mary's River; and thence down along the middle of St. Mary's River to the Atlantic Ocean. East, by a line to be drawn along the middle of the river St. Croix, from its mouth in the Bay of Fundy to its source, and from its source directly north to the aforesaid Highlands, which divide the rivers that fall into the Atlantic Ocean from those which fall into the river St. Lawrence; comprehending all islands within twenty leagues of any part of the shores of the United States, and lying between lines to be drawn due east from the points where the aforesaid boundaries between Nova Scotia on the one part, and East Florida on the other, shall respectively touch the Bay of Fundy and the Atlantic Ocean; excepting such islands as now are, or heretofore have been, within the limits of the said province of Nova Scotia.

---

[1] The text of the treaties and conventions has been taken from "Treaties, Conventions, International Acts, Protocols, and Agreements between the United States of America and other Powers," Vol. I, by W. M. Malloy. This differs from other published texts only in unimportant details of punctuation, capitalization, division into paragraphs, and order of precedence.

The only official record of the intentions of the negotiators of the treaty of 1783 as to the actual location of the boundary is contained in the text of the treaty, for the negotiators did not attach to the treaty a copy of the map used by them in arriving at their agreements. They failed to realize that, owing to the imperfect knowledge of the topography of the country at that time, the identification of places named in the treaty might be disputed. Disputes soon occurred, the first over the identification of the St. Croix River. Much discussion followed, but no successful steps in the settlement of this difference of opinion were taken until, in the negotiation of the treaty of 1794, an article was included providing for a joint commission to decide this question.

The text of this article follows:

TREATY OF AMITY, COMMERCE, AND NAVIGATION

(Concluded November 19, 1794; ratifications exchanged October 28, 1795)

*   *   *   *   *   *   *   *   *

ARTICLE V

Whereas doubts have arisen what river was truly intended under the name of the river St. Croix, mentioned in the said treaty of peace, and forming a part of the boundary therein described; that question shall be referred to the final decision of commissioners to be appointed in the following manner, viz:

One commissioner shall be named by His Majesty, and one by the President of the United States, by and with the advice and consent of the Senate thereof, and the said two commissioners shall agree on the choice of a third; or if they can not so agree, they shall each propose one person, and of the two names so proposed, one shall be drawn by lot in the presence of the two original Commissioners. And the three Commissioners so appointed shall be sworn, impartially to examine and decide the said question, according to such evidence as shall respectively be laid before them on the part of the British Government and of the United States. The said Commissioners shall meet at Halifax, and shall have power to adjourn to such other place or places as they shall think fit. They shall have power to appoint a Secretary, and to employ such surveyors or other persons as they shall judge necessary. The said Commissioners shall, by a declaration, under their hands and seals, decide what river is the river St. Croix, intended by the treaty. The said declaration shall contain a description of the said river, and shall particularize the latitude and longitude of its mouth and of its source. Duplicates of this declaration, and of the statements of their accounts, and of the journal of their proceedings, shall be delivered by them to the agent of His Majesty, and to the agent of the United States, who may be respectively appointed and authorized to manage the business on behalf of the respective Governments. And both parties agree to consider such decision as final and conclusive, so as that the same shall never thereafter be called into question, or made the subject of dispute or difference between them.

The commission authorized by Article V of the treaty of 1794 was organized October 4, 1796, and under its direction surveys were made of Passamaquoddy Bay and the rivers entering into the dispute. Much evidence was considered, but before a decision was handed down the commissioners asked for modifications of their instructions. These were negotiated and made a part of the treaty of 1794 by the acceptance by both Governments of the following explanatory article:

EXPLANATORY ARTICLE (1798) TO THE TREATY OF NOVEMBER 19, 1794, RELEASING THE COMMISSIONERS UNDER THE FIFTH ARTICLE FROM PARTICULARIZING THE LATITUDE AND LONGITUDE OF THE RIVER ST. CROIX

(Concluded March 15, 1798)

Whereas by the twenty-eighth article of the treaty of amity, commerce, and navigation between His Britannic Majesty and the United States, signed at London on the nineteenth day of November, one thousand seven hundred and ninety-four, it was agreed that the contracting parties would, from time to time, readily treat of and concerning such further articles as might be proposed; that they would sincerely endeavour so to form such articles as that they might conduce to mutual convenience and tend to promote mutual satisfaction and friendship; and that such articles, after having been duly ratified, should be added to and make a part of that treaty: And whereas difficulties have arisen with respect to the execution of so much of the fifth article of the said treaty as requires that the Commissioners appointed under the same should in their description particularize the latitude and longitude of the source of the river which may be found to be the one truly intended in the treaty of peace between His Britannic Majesty and the United States, under the name of the river St. Croix, by reason whereof it is expedient that the said Commissioners should be released from the obligation of conforming to the provisions of the said article in this respect. The undersigned being respectively named by His Britannic Majesty and the United States of America their Plenipotentiaries for the purpose of treating of and concluding such articles as may be proper to be added to the said treaty, in conformity to the above-mentioned stipulation, and having communicated to each other their respective full powers, have agreed and concluded, and do hereby declare in the name of His Britannic Majesty and of the United States of America, that the Commissioners appointed under the fifth article of the above-mentioned treaty shall not be obliged to particularize, in their description, the latitude and longitude of the source of the river which may be found to be the one truly intended in the aforesaid treaty of peace under the name of the river St. Croix, but they shall be at liberty to describe the said river, in such other manner as they may judge expedient, which description shall be considered as a complete execution of the duty required of the said Commissioners in this respect by the article aforesaid. And to the end that no uncertainty may hereafter exist on this subject, it is further agreed, That as soon as may be after the decision of the said Commissioners, measures shall be concerted between the Government of the United States and His Britannic Majesty's Governors or Lieutenant Governors in America, in order to erect and keep in repair a suitable monument at the place ascertained and described to be the source of the said river St. Croix, which measures shall immediately thereupon, and as often afterwards as may be requisite, be duly executed on both sides with punctuality and good faith.

This explanatory article, when the same shall have been ratified by His Majesty and by the President of the United States, by and with the advice and consent of their Senate, and the respective ratifications mutually exchanged, shall be added to and make a part of the treaty of amity, commerce, and navigation between His Majesty and the United States, signed at London on the nineteenth day of November, one thousand seven hundred and ninety-four, and shall be permanently binding upon His Majesty and the United States.

In witness whereof we, the said undersigned Plenipotentiaries of His Britannic Majesty and the United States of America, have signed this present article, and have caused to be affixed thereto the seal of our arms.

Done at London this fifteenth day of March, one thousand seven hundred and ninety-eight.

[SEAL.]   GRENVILLE.
[SEAL.]   RUFUS KING.

The commissioners gave their decision on October 25, 1798, which was as follows:

DECLARATION OF THE COMMISSIONERS UNDER THE FIFTH ARTICLE OF THE TREATY OF 1794

" Declaration of the Commissioners under the Fifth Article of the Treaty of 1794, between the United States and Great Britain, respecting the true River St. Croix, by Thomas Barclay, David Howell and Egbert Benson, Commissioners appointed in pursuance of the 5th Article of the Treaty of Amity, Commerce, and Navigation, between His Britannic Majesty and the United States of America, finally to decide the question, 'What River was truly intended under the name of the River Saint Croix mentioned in the treaty of Peace between His Majesty and the United States, and forming a part of the boundary therein described.'

"We, the said Commissioners, having been sworn 'impartially to examine and decide the said question, according to such evidence as should respectively be laid before us, on the part of the British Government, and of the United States,' and having heard the evidence which hath been laid before us, by the Agent of His Majesty, and the Agent of the United States, respectively appointed and authorized to manage the business on behalf of the respective Governments, have decided, and hereby do decide, the River, hereinafter particularly described and mentioned, to be the River truly intended under the name of the River Saint Croix, in the said Treaty of Peace, and forming a part of the boundary therein described; that is to say, the mouth of the said river is in Passamaquoddy Bay, at a point of land called Joe's Point,[2] about one mile northward from the northern part of Saint Andrew's Island, and in the latitude of forty-five degrees five minutes and five seconds north, and in the longitude of sixty-seven degrees twelve minutes and thirty seconds west, from the Royal Observatory at Greenwich, in Great Britain, and three degrees fifty-four minutes and fifteen seconds east from Harvard College, in the University of Cambridge, in the State of Massachusetts, and the course of the said river up from its said mouth, is northerly to a point of land called the Devil's Head, then turning the said point, is westerly to where it divides into two streams, the one coming from the westward, and the other coming from the northward, having the Indian name of Chiputnaticook or Chibuitcook, as the same may be variously spelt, then up the said stream, so coming from the northward to its source, which is at a stake near a Yellow Birch Tree, hooped with iron, and marked S. T. and J. H. 1797, by Samuel Titcomb and John Harris, the Surveyors employed to survey the above mentioned stream, coming from the northward. And the said River is designated on the Map hereunto annexed, and hereby referred to as farther descriptive of it, by the letters A B C D E F G H I K and L, the letter A being at its said mouth, and the letter L being at its said source; and the course and distance of the said source from the Island, at the confluence of the above-mentioned two streams, is, as laid down on the said map, north five degrees and about fifteen minutes west, by the magnet, about forty-eight miles and one quarter.

"In testimony whereof, we have hereunto set our hands and seals, at Providence, in the State of Rhode Island, the twenty-fifth day of October, in the year one thousand seven hundred and ninety-eight.

"(L. S.)	Thomas Barclay,
"(L. S.)	David Howell,
"(L. S.)	Egbert Benson.

"Witness, Ed. Winslow,
   "*Secretary to the Commissioners.*"

A convention "to ascertain and determine the said northwest angle of Nova Scotia * * *" was negotiated in 1803, but was never ratified. A similar unsuccessful attempt to effect a settlement was made in 1807. Under the provisions of Article V of the treaty of Ghent, an attempt was made to settle the boundary dispute by the creation of a commission which was organized September 23, 1816. Their investigation of the dispute was thorough, but they were unable to reach an agreement, and accordingly they submitted separate reports, exchanged notes expressing their respective opinions, and brought their final session to a close on April 13, 1822.

The text of Articles IV and V of the treaty of Ghent follows:

Treaty of Peace and Amity (Treaty of Ghent)

(Concluded at Ghent December 24, 1814; ratifications exchanged February 17, 1815)

*　　*　　*　　*　　*　　*　　*　　*　　*

ARTICLE IV

Whereas it was stipulated by the second article in the treaty of peace of one thousand seven hundred and eighty-three, between His Britannic Majesty and the United States of America, that the boundary of the United States should comprehend all islands within twenty leagues of any part of the shores of the United States, and lying between lines to be drawn due east from the points where the aforesaid boundaries, between Nova Scotia on the one part, and East Florida on the other, shall respectively touch the Bay of Fundy and the Atlantic Ocean, excepting such islands as now are, or heretofore have been, within the limits of Nova Scotia; and whereas the several islands in the Bay of Passamaquoddy, which is part of the Bay of Fundy, and the Island of Grand Menan, in the said Bay of Fundy, are claimed by the United States as being comprehended within their aforesaid boundaries, which said islands are claimed as belonging

---

[2] This is "Ive's Point" in some of the copies of the award, but in the original it is properly given as Joe's Point.

to His Britannic Majesty, as having been, at the time of and previous to the aforesaid treaty of one thousand seven hundred and eighty-three, within the limits of the Province of Nova Scotia; In order, therefore, finally to decide upon these claims, it is agreed that they shall be referred to two Commissioners to be appointed in the following manner, viz: One Commissioner shall be appointed by His Britannic Majesty, and one by the President of the United States, by and with the advice and consent of the Senate thereof; and the said two Commissioners so appointed shall be sworn impartially to examine and decide upon the said claims according to such evidence as shall be laid before them on the part of His Britannic Majesty and of the United States respectively. The said Commissioners shall meet at St. Andrews, in the Province of New Brunswick, and shall have power to adjourn to such other place or places as they shall think fit. The said Commissioners shall, by a declaration or report under their hands and seals, decide to which of the two contracting parties the several islands aforesaid do respectively belong, in conformity with the true intent of the said treaty of peace of one thousand seven hundred and eighty-three. And if the said Commissioners shall agree in their decision, both parties shall consider such decision as final and conclusive. It is further agreed that, in event of the two Commissioners differing upon all or any of the matters so referred to them, or in the event of both or either of the said Commissioners refusing, or declining, or wilfully omitting to act as such, they shall make, jointly or separately, a report or reports, as well to the Government of His Britannic Majesty as to that of the United States, stating in detail the points on which they differ, and the grounds upon which their respective opinions have been formed, or the grounds upon which they, or either of them, have so refused, declined, or omitted to act. And His Britannic Majesty and the Government of the United States hereby agree to refer the report or reports of the said Commissioners to some friendly sovereign or State, to be then named for that purpose, and who shall be requested to decide on the differences which may be stated in the said report or reports, or upon the report of one Commissioner, together with the grounds upon which the other Commissioner shall have refused, declined or omitted to act, as the case may be. And if the Commissioner so refusing, declining or omitting to act, shall also wilfully omit to state the grounds upon which he has so done, in such manner that the said statement may be referred to such friendly sovereign or State, together with the report of such other Commissioner, then such sovereign or State shall decide *ex parte* upon the said report alone. And His Britannic Majesty and the Government of the United States engage to consider the decision of such friendly sovereign or State to be final and conclusive on all the matters so referred.

ARTICLE V

Whereas neither that point of the highlands lying due north from the source of the river St. Croix, and designated in the former treaty of peace between the two Powers as the northwest angle of Nova Scotia, nor the northwesternmost head of Connecticut River has yet been ascertained; and whereas that part of the boundary line between the dominions of the two Powers which extends from the source of the river St. Croix directly north to the abovementioned northwest angle of Nova Scotia, thence along the said highlands which divide those rivers that empty themselves into the river St. Lawrence from those which fall into the Atlantic Ocean to the northwesternmost head of Connecticut River, thence down along the middle of that river to the forty-fifth degree of north latitude; thence by a line due west on said latitude until it strikes the river Iroquois or Cataraquy, has not yet been surveyed; it is agreed that for these several purposes two Commissioners shall be appointed, sworn and authorized to act exactly in the manner directed with respect to those mentioned in the next preceding article, unless otherwise specified in the present article. The said Commissioners shall meet at St. Andrews, in the Province of New Brunswick, and shall have power to adjourn to such other place or places as they shall think fit. The said Commissioners shall have power to ascertain and determine the points above mentioned, in conformity with the provisions of the said treaty of peace of one thousand seven hundred and eighty-three, and shall cause the boundary aforesaid, from the source of the river St. Croix to the river Iroquois or Cataraquy, to be surveyed and marked according to the said provisions. The said Commissioners shall make a map of the said boundary, and annex to it a declaration under their hands and seals, certifying it to be the true map of the said boundary and particularizing the latitude and longitude of the northwest angle of Nova Scotia, of the northwesternmost head of Connecticut River, and of such other points of the said boundary, as they may deem proper. And both parties agree to consider such map and declaration as finally and conclusively fixing the said boundary. And in the event of the said two Commissioners differing, or both or either of them refusing, declining, or wilfully omitting to act, such reports, declarations or statements shall be made by them, or either of them, and such reference to a friendly sovereign or State shall be made in all respects as in the latter part of the fourth article is contained, and in as full a manner as if the same was herein repeated.

The treaty of Ghent provided that, if the commissioners acting under Article V could not agree, the boundary question should be submitted to "some friendly sovereign or State, to be then named for that purpose, and who shall be requested to decide on the differences."

After some years of delay, boundary disputes again brought the matter to the attention of the two Governments, with the result that a convention was concluded September 29, 1827, the text of which follows:

CONVENTION PROVIDING FOR THE SUBMISSION TO ARBITRATION OF THE DISPUTE CONCERNING THE NORTHEASTERN BOUNDARY

(Concluded September 29, 1827; ratifications exchanged April 2, 1828)

ARTICLES

I. Reference of difficulties.	V. Delivery of statement.
II. Statement of respective cases.	VI. Procedure.
III. Evidence.	VII. Decision.
IV. Maps.	VIII. Ratification.

Whereas it is provided by the fifth article of the treaty of Ghent, that, in case the Commissioners appointed under that article, for the settlement of the boundary line therein described, should not be able to agree upon such boundary line, the report or reports of those Commissioners, stating the points on which they had differed, should be submitted to some friendly Sovereign or State, and that the decision given by such Sovereign or State, on such points of difference, should be considered by the contracting parties as final and conclusive; That case having now arisen, and it having, therefore, become expedient to proceed to and regulate the reference as above described, the United States of America and His Majesty the King of the United Kingdom of Great Britain and Ireland have, for that purpose, named their Plenipotentiaries, that is to say:

The President of the United States has appointed Albert Gallatin, their Envoy Extraordinary and Minister Plenipotentiary at the Court of His Britannick Majesty; and His said Majesty, on his part, has appointed the Right Honourable Charles Grant, a member of Parliament, a member of His said Majesty's Most Honourable Privy Council, and President of the Committee of the Privy Council for Affairs of Trade and Foreign Plantations, and Henry Unwin Addington, Esquire;

Who after having exchanged their respective full powers, found to be in due and proper form, have agreed to and concluded the following articles:

ARTICLE I

It is agreed that the points of difference which have arisen in the settlement of the boundary between the American and British dominions, as described in the 5th article of the treaty of Ghent, shall be referred, as therein provided, to some friendly Sovereign or State, who shall be invited to investigate, and make a decision upon, such points of difference.

The two contracting Powers engage to proceed in concert, to the choice of such friendly Sovereign or State, as soon as the ratifications of this convention shall have been exchanged, and to use their best endeavours to obtain a decision, if practicable, within two years after the Arbiter shall have signified his consent to act as such.

ARTICLE II

The reports and documents, thereunto annexed, of the Commissioners appointed to carry into execution the 5th article of the treaty of Ghent, being so voluminous and complicated as to render it improbable that any Sovereign or State should be willing or able to undertake the office of investigating and arbitrating upon them, it is hereby agreed to substitute, for those reports, new and separate statements of the respective cases, severally drawn up by each of the contracting parties, in such form and terms as each may think fit.

The said statements, when prepared, shall be mutually communicated to each other by the contracting parties, that is to say, by the United States to His Britannick Majesty's Minister or Chargé d'Affaires at Washington, and by Great Britain to the Minister or Chargé d'Affaires of the United States at London, within fifteen months after the exchange of the ratifications of the present convention.

After such communication shall have taken place, each party shall have the power of drawing up a second and definitive statement, if it thinks fit so to do, in reply to the statement of the other party, so communicated, which definitive statements shall also be mutually communicated, in the same manner as aforesaid, to each other, by the contracting parties, within twenty-one months after the exchange of ratifications of the present convention.

ARTICLE III

Each of the contracting parties shall, within nine months after the exchange of ratifications of this convention, communicate to the other, in the same manner as aforesaid, all the evidence intended to be brought in support of its claim, beyond that which is contained in the reports of the Commissioners, or papers thereunto annexed, and other written documents laid before the Commission, under the 5th article of the treaty of Ghent.

Each of the contracting parties shall be bound, on the application of the other party, made within six months after the exchange of the ratifications of this convention, to give authentic copies of such individually specified acts of a public nature, relating to the territory in question, intended to be laid as evidence before the Arbiter, as have been issued under the authority, or are in the exclusive possession, of each party.

No maps, surveys, or topographical evidence of any description, shall be adduced by either party, beyond that which is hereinafter stipulated, nor shall any fresh evidence of any description be adduced or adverted to, by either party, other than that mutually communicated or applied for as aforesaid.

Each party shall have full power to incorporate in, or annex to, either its first or second statement, any portion of the reports of the Commissioners, or papers thereunto annexed, and other written documents laid before the Commission under the 5th article of the treaty of Ghent, or of the other evidence mutually communicated or applied for as above provided, which it may think fit.

ARTICLE IV

The map called Mitchell's map, by which the framers of the treaty of 1783 are acknowledged to have regulated their joint and official proceedings, and the map A, which has been agreed on by the contracting parties, as a delineation of the water-courses, and of the boundary lines in reference to the said water-courses, as contended for by each party respectively, and which has accordingly been signed by the above-named Plenipotentiaries, at the same time with this convention, shall be annexed to the statements of the contracting parties, and be the only maps that shall be considered as evidence, mutually acknowledged by the contracting parties, of the topography of the country.

It shall, however, be lawful for either party to annex to its respective first statement, for the purposes of general illustration, any of the maps, surveys, or topographical delineations, which were filed by the Commissioners under the 5th article of the treaty of Ghent, any engraved map heretofore published, and also a transcript of the above-mentioned map A, or of a section thereof, in which transcript each party may lay down the highlands, or other features of the country, as it shall think fit; the water courses and the boundary lines, as claimed by each party, remaining as laid down in the said map A.

But this transcript, as well as all the other maps, surveys, or topographical delineations, other than the map A, and Mitchell's map, intended to be thus annexed, by either party, to the respective statements, shall be communicated to the other party, in the same manner as aforesaid, within nine months after the exchange of the ratifications of this convention, and shall be subject to such objections and observations as the other contracting party may deem it expedient to make thereto, and shall annex to his first statement, either in the margin of such transcript, map or maps, or otherwise.

ARTICLE V

All the statements, papers, maps, and documents, above mentioned, and which shall have been mutually communicated as aforesaid, shall without any addition, subtraction, or alteration, whatsoever, be jointly and simultaneously delivered in to the arbitrating Sovereign or State within two years after the exchange of ratifications of this convention, unless the Arbiter should not, within that time, have consented to act as such; in which case all the said statements, papers, maps, and documents shall be laid before him within six months after the time when he shall have consented so to act. No other statements, papers, maps, or documents shall ever be laid before the Arbiter, except as hereinafter provided.

ARTICLE VI

In order to facilitate the attainment of a just and sound decision on the part of the Arbiter, it is agreed that, in case the said Arbiter should desire further elucidation or evidence in regard to any specific point contained in any of the said statements submitted to him, the requisition for such elucidation or evidence shall be simultaneously made to both parties, who shall thereupon be permitted to bring further evidence, if required and to make, each, a written reply to the specific questions submitted by the said Arbiter, but no further; and such evidence and replies shall be immediately communicated by each party to the other.

And in case the Arbiter should find the topographical evidence, laid as aforesaid before him, insufficient for the purposes of a sound and just decision, he shall have the power of ordering additional surveys to be made of any portions of the disputed boundary line or territory, as he may think fit; which surveys shall be made at the joint expense of the contracting parties, and be considered as conclusive by them.

ARTICLE VII

The decision of the Arbiter, when given, shall be taken as final and conclusive; and it shall be carried, without reserve, into immediate effect, by Commissioners appointed for that purpose by the contracting parties.

ARTICLE VIII

This convention shall be ratified, and the ratifications shall be exchanged in nine months from the date hereof, or sooner if possible.

In witness whereof, we, the respective Plenipotentiaries, have signed the same, and have affixed thereto the seals of our arms.

Done at London the twenty-ninth day of September, in the year of our Lord one thousand eight hundred and twenty-seven.

[SEAL.]   ALBERT GALLATIN.
[SEAL.]   CHA. GRANT.
[SEAL.]   HENRY UNWIN ADDINGTON.

On January 10, 1831, the King of the Netherlands, who had been agreed upon as arbitrator, submitted an award, which, although not accepted by either Government, had some influence upon the final settlement of the boundary dispute, and for this reason the text of the award is here reprinted.

AWARD OF THE KING OF THE NETHERLANDS (TRANSLATION)

"William, by the Grace of God, King of the Netherlands, Prince of Orange-Nassau, Grand Duke of Luxembourg, etc. etc. etc.

"Having accepted the functions of Arbitrator conferred upon us by the note of the Chargé d' Affaires of the United States of America, and by that of the Ambassador Extraordinary and Plenipotentiary of Great Britain, to our Minister of Foreign Affairs, under date of the 12th January, 1829, agreeably to the 5th Article of the Treaty of Ghent, of the 24th December, 1814, and to the 1st Article of the Convention concluded between those Powers, at London, on the 29th of September, 1827, in the difference which has arisen between them on the subject of the boundaries of their respective possessions:

"Animated by a sincere desire to respond, by a scrupulous and impartial decision, to the confidence they have exhibited in us, and thus to give them a new proof of the high value we attach to it:

"Having, to that end, duly examined and maturely weighed the contents of the First Statement, as well as those of the Definitive Statement of the said difference, which the Envoy Extraordinary and Minister Plenipotentiary of the United States of America, and the Ambassador Extraordinary and Plenipotentiary of His Britannic Majesty, respectively delivered to us on the 1st of April of the year 1830, with all the documents thereto annexed in support of them:

" Desirous of fulfilling, at this time, the obligations we contracted in accepting the functions of Arbitrator in the aforesaid difference, by laying before the two High interested Parties the result of our examination, and our opinion on the three points into which, by common accord, the contestation is divided:

"Considering that the three points above mentioned ought to be decided according to the Treaties, Acts and Conventions concluded between the two Powers; that is to say, the

Treaty of Peace of 1783, the Treaty of Friendship, Commerce and Navigation of 1794, the Declaration relative to the river St. Croix of 1798, the Treaty of Peace signed at Ghent in 1814, the Convention of the 29th September, 1827; and Mitchell's Map and the Map A referred to in that Convention:

"WE DECLARE, THAT,

"As to the first point, to wit, the question, what is the place designated in the Treaties as the Northwest Angle of Nova Scotia, and what are the Highlands dividing the Rivers that empty themselves into the River St. Lawrence from those which fall into the Atlantic Ocean, along which is to be drawn the line of boundary from that angle to the Northwesternmost head of Connecticut River:

"CONSIDERING:

"That the High Interested Parties respectively claim that line of boundary at the south and at the north of the river St. John; and have each indicated upon the Map A the line which they claim:

"CONSIDERING:

"That, according to the examples given, the term Highlands applies not only to a hilly or elevated country, but also to land which, without being hilly, divides waters flowing in different directions; and therefore that the more or less hilly and elevated character of the country through which are drawn the two lines respectively claimed, at the north and at the south of the river St. John, cannot form the basis of a choice between them;

"That the text of the 2nd Article of the Treaty of 1783 recites, in part, the words previously used in the Proclamation of 1763 and in the Quebec Act of 1774 to indicate the southern boundaries of the Government of Quebec, from Lake Champlain, 'in forty-five degrees of North latitude, along the highlands which divide the rivers that empty themselves into the river St. Lawrence, from those which fall into the Sea, and also along the North Coast of the Bay des Chaleurs;'

"That in 1763, 1765, 1773, and 1782, it was established that Nova Scotia should be bounded at the north, as far as the western extremity of the Bay des Chaleurs, by the southern boundary of the Province of Quebec; that this delimitation is again found, with respect to the Province of Quebec, in the Commission of the Governor General of Quebec of 1786, wherein the language of the proclamation of 1763, and of the Quebec Act of 1774, has been used, as also in the Commissions of 1786, and others of subsequent dates of the Governors of New Brunswick, with respect to the last mentioned Province, as well as in a great number of maps anterior and posterior to the Treaty of 1783; and that the 1st Article of the said Treaty specifies, by name, the States whose independence is acknowledged;

"But that this specification does not imply the entire coincidence of the boundaries between the two Powers, as settled by the succeeding Article, with the ancient delimitation of the British Provinces, whose preservation is not mentioned in the Treaty of 1783, and which, owing to its continual changes, and the uncertainty which continued to exist respecting it, created from time to time differences between the Provincial authorities;

"That there results from the line drawn under the Treaty of 1783, through the great Lakes, west of the river St. Lawrence, a departure from the ancient Provincial charters, with regard to those boundaries;

"That one would vainly attempt to explain why, if the intention was to retain the ancient Provincial boundary, Mitchell's Map, published in 1755, and consequently anterior to the Proclamation of 1763, and to the Quebec Act of 1774, was precisely the one used in the negotiation of 1783;

"That Great Britain proposed, at first, the river Piscataqua as the eastern boundary of the United States; and did not subsequently agree to the proposition to cause the boundary of Maine, or Massachusetts Bay, to be ascertained at a later period;

"That the Treaty of Ghent stipulated for a new examination on the spot, which could not be applicable to an historical or administrative boundary;

"And that, therefore, the ancient delimitation of the British Provinces, does not, either, afford the basis of a decision;

"That the longitude of the northwest angle of Nova Scotia, which ought to coincide with that of the source of the St. Croix river, was determined only by the Declaration of 1798, which indicated that river;

"That the Treaty of Friendship, Commerce, and Navigation of 1794, alludes to the doubt which had arisen with respect to the river St. Croix; and that the first instructions of the Congress, at the time of the negotiations, which resulted in the Treaty of 1783, locate the said angle at the source of the river St. John.

104709—25†——21

"That the latitude of that angle is upon the banks of the St. Lawrence, according to Mitchell's Map, which is acknowledged to have regulated the joint and official labors of the negotiators of the Treaty of 1783; whereas, agreeably to the delimitation of the Government of Quebec, it is to be looked for in the highlands which divide the rivers that empty themselves into the river St. Lawrence, from those which fall into the sea;

"That the nature of the ground east of the before mentioned angle not having been indicated by the Treaty of 1783, no argument can be drawn from it to locate that angle at one place in preference to another;

"That, moreover, if it were deemed proper to place it nearer the source of the River St. Croix, and look for it, for instance, at Mars Hill, it would be so much the more possible that the boundary of New Brunswick, drawn thence northeastwardly, would give to that province several Northwest angles, situated farther north and east, according to their greater remoteness from Mars Hill since the number of degrees of the angle referred to in the Treaty is not mentioned;

"That, consequently, the Northwest angle of Nova Scotia, here alluded to, having been unknown in 1783, and the Treaty of Ghent having again declared it to be unascertained, the mention of that historical angle in the Treaty of 1783 is to be considered as an evasion of the question (*petition de principe*), affording no basis for a decision; whereas, if considered as a topographical point, having reference to the definition, viz: 'that angle which is formed by a line drawn due north from the source of the St. Croix River to the Highlands,' it forms simply the extremity of the line 'along the said Highlands, which divide those rivers that empty themselves into the river St. Lawrence, from those which fall into the Atlantic Ocean,' an extremity which a reference to the Northwest angle of Nova Scotia does not contribute to ascertain, and which still remaining itself to be found, can not lead to the discovery of the line which it is to terminate;

"Lastly, that the arguments deduced from the rights of sovereignty exercised over the Fief of Madawaska. and over the Madawaska Settlement—even admitting that such exercise were sufficiently proved—cannot decide the question, for the reason that those two settlements embrace only a portion of the territory in dispute, and that the High Interested Parties have acknowledged the country lying between the lines respectively claimed by them, as constituting a subject of contestation, and that therefore possession cannot be considered as derogating from the right; and that if the ancient delimitation of the Provinces adduced in support of the line claimed at the north of the river St. John, and especially that which is mentioned in the Proclamation of 1763, and in the Quebec Act of 1774, be set aside, there would be no ground for admitting, in support of the line claimed at the south of the river St. John, the arguments tending to prove that that part of the territory in dispute belongs to Canada or to New Brunswick:

"CONSIDERING:

"That the question, divested of the inconclusive arguments drawn from the nature, more or less hilly, of the ground,—from the ancient delimitation of the Provinces,—from the Northwest angle of Nova Scotia, and from the actual possession, resolves itself, in the end, into these questions: What is the line drawn due north from the source of the river St. Croix, and what is the ground, no matter whether hilly and elevated or not, which, from that line to the Northwesternmost head of Connecticut river, divides the rivers that empty themselves into the river St. Lawrence from those which fall into the Atlantic Ocean; That the High Interested Parties only agree upon the fact that the boundary sought for must be determined by such a line, and by such ground; that they further agree, in view of the Declaration of 1798, as to the answer to be given to the first question, with the exception of the latitude at which the line drawn due north from the source of the St. Croix river is to terminate; that said latitude coincides with the extremity of the ground which, from that line to the Northwesternmost source of Connecticut river, divides the rivers which empty themselves into the river St. Lawrence from those which fall into the Atlantic Ocean; and that, therefore, it only remains to ascertain that ground;

"That on entering upon this operation, it is discovered, on the one hand:

"First, that if, by adopting the line claimed to the north of the river St. John, Great Britain cannot be considered as obtaining a territory of less value than if she had accepted in 1783 the river St. John as her frontier, yet, that, taking into view the situation of the country lying between the rivers St. John and St. Croix in the vicinity of the sea, and the possession of both banks of the river St. John in the lower part of its course, this compensation would nevertheless be destroyed by the interruption of the communication between Lower Canada and New Brunswick, especially between Quebec and Fredericton; and that one would vainly seek to discover what motive could have determined the Court of London to consent to such an interruption:

"That if, in the second place, in contradistinction to the rivers that empty themselves into the river St. Lawrence, it had been possible, agreeably to the language ordinarily used in geography, to comprehend the rivers falling into the Bays of Fundy and des Chaleurs with those emptying themselves directly into the Atlantic Ocean, in the generic denomination of rivers falling into the Atlantic Ocean, yet it would be hazardous to include in that category the rivers St. John and Restigouche, which the line claimed at the north of the river St. John divides immediately from rivers emptying themselves into the river St. Lawrence, not with other rivers falling into the Atlantic Ocean, but alone; and thus to apply, in interpreting the delimitation established by a Treaty, where each word must have a meaning, to two strictly special cases, and where no mention is made of the genus, a generic expression which would ascribe to them a broader meaning, or which, if extended to the Schoodiac Lakes, the Penobscot and the Kennebec, which empty themselves directly into the Atlantic Ocean, would establish the principle that the Treaty of 1783 meant highlands which divide, as well mediately as immediately, the rivers that empty themselves into the river St. Lawrence from those which fall into the Atlantic Ocean—a principle equally realized by both lines:

"Thirdly: That the line claimed at the north of the river St. John does not divide, immediately, the rivers that empty themselves into the river St. Lawrence from the rivers St. John and Restigouche, but only Rivers that empty themselves into the St. John and Restigouche, with the exception of the last part of said line, near the sources of the river St. John; and that hence in order to reach the Atlantic Ocean, the rivers divided by that line from those that empty themselves into the river St. Lawrence, each need two intermediate channels, to wit: some, the river St. John and the Bay of Fundy; and the others, the river Restigouche and the Bay des Chaleurs:

"And on the other hand,

"That it cannot be sufficiently explained how, if the high Contracting Parties intended in 1783 to establish the boundary at the south of the river St. John, that river, to which the territory in dispute is in a great measure indebted for its distinctive character, has been neutralized and set aside:

"That the verb 'divide' appears to require the contiguity of the objects to be 'divided:'

"That the said boundary forms at its western extremity, only, the immediate separation between the river Mettjarmette, and the Northwesternmost head of the Penobscot, and divides, mediately, only the rivers that empty themselves into the river St. Lawrence from the waters of the Kennebec, Penobscot, and Schoodiac Lakes; while the boundary claimed at the north of the river St. John divides, immediately, the waters of the rivers Restigouche and St. John, and mediately the Schoodiac Lakes and the waters of the rivers Penobscot and Kennebec, from the rivers that empty themselves into the river St. Lawrence, to wit: the rivers Beaver, Metis, Rimousky, Trois Pistoles, Green, Du Loup, Kamouraska, Ouelle, Bras St. Nicholas, Du Sud, La Famine and Chaudière:

"That even setting aside the rivers Restigouche and St. John, for the reason that they could not be considered as falling into the Atlantic Ocean, the northern line would still be as near to the Schoodiac Lakes, and to the waters of the Penobscot and of the Kennebec, as the southern line would be to the rivers Beaver, Metis, Rimousky, and others that empty themselves into the river St. Lawrence; and would, as well as the other, form a mediate separation between these and the rivers falling into the Atlantic Ocean:

"That the prior intersection of the southern boundary by a line drawn due north from the source of the St. Croix river, could only secure to it an accessory advantage over the other, in case both the one and the other boundary should combine, in the same degree, the qualities required by the Treaties:

"And that the fate assigned by that of 1783 to the Connecticut, and even to the St. Lawrence, precludes the supposition that the two Powers could have intended to surrender the whole course of each river from its source to its mouth to the share of either the one or the other:

"CONSIDERING:

"That, in view of what precedes, the arguments adduced on either side, and the documents exhibited in support of them, cannot be considered as sufficiently preponderating to determine a preference in favor of either one of the two lines respectively claimed by the High Interested Parties, as the boundaries of their possessions, from the source of the river St. Croix to the Northwesternmost head of the Connecticut river; and that the nature of the difference and the vague and not sufficiently determinate stipulations of the Treaty of 1783, do not permit us to award either of those lines to one of the said Parties, without violating the principles of law and equity with regard to the other:

"CONSIDERING:

"That, as has already been said, the question resolves itself into the selection of ground dividing the rivers that empty themselves into the river St. Lawrence from those that fall into the Atlantic Ocean; that the High Interested Parties are agreed with regard to the course of the streams delineated by common accord on the Map A and affording the only basis of a decision;

"And that, therefore, the circumstances upon which such decision depends could not be further elucidated by means of fresh topographical investigation, nor by the production of additional documents:

"WE ARE OF OPINION:

"That it will be suitable (*il conviendra*) to adopt, as the boundary of the two States, a line drawn due north from the source of the river St. Croix to the point where it intersects the middle of the *thalweg* of the river St. John; thence, the middle of the *thalweg* of that river, ascending it, to the point where the river St. Francis empties itself into the river St. John; thence, the middle of the *thalweg* of the river St. Francis, ascending it, to the source of its south-westernmost branch, which source we indicate on the Map A by the letter X, authenticated by the signature of our Minister of Foreign Affairs; thence, a line drawn due west, to the point where it unites with the line claimed by the United States of America, and delineated on the Map A; thence, by said line to the point at which, according to said map, it coincides with that claimed by Great Britain; and thence, the line traced on the map by the two Powers, to the northwesternmost source of Connecticut River.

"As regards the second point, to wit: the question, which is the Northwesternmost head of Connecticut River:

"CONSIDERING:

"That, in order to solve this question, it is necessary to choose between Connecticut-lake River, Perry's Stream, Indian Stream and Hall's Stream:

"CONSIDERING:

"That, according to the usage adopted in geography, the source and the bed of a river are denoted by the name of the river which is attached to such source and to such bed, and by their greater relative importance, as compared to that of other waters communicating with said river:

"CONSIDERING:

"That an official letter of 1772 already mentions the name of Hall's Brook, and that, in an official letter of subsequent date, in the same year, Hall's Brook is represented as a small river falling into the Connecticut;

"That the river in which Connecticut Lake is situated appears more considerable than either Hall's, Indian or Perry's Stream; that Connecticut Lake and the two Lakes situated northward of it, seem to assign to it a greater volume of water than to the other three rivers; and that by admitting it to be the bed of the Connecticut, the course of that river is extended farther than it would be if a preference were given to either of the other three rivers;

"Lastly, that the Map A having been recognized by the Convention of 1827 as indicating the courses of streams, the authority of that map would likewise seem to extend to their appellation, since in case of dispute such name of river or lake, respecting which the parties were not agreed, might have been omitted; that said map mentions Connecticut Lake, and that the name of Connecticut Lake implies the applicability of the name of Connecticut to the river which flows through the said lake:

"WE ARE OF OPINION:

"That the stream situated farthest to the northwest among those which fall into the northernmost of the three Lakes, the last of which bears the name of Connecticut Lake, must be considered as the northwesternmost head of Connecticut river.

"And as to the third point, to wit: the question, What is the boundary to be traced from the river Connecticut, along the parallel of the 45th degree of north latitude, to the river St. Lawrence, named in the Treaties Iroquois or Cataraquy:

"CONSIDERING:

"That the High Interested Parties differ in opinion as to the question—Whether the Treaties require a fresh survey of the whole line of boundary from the river Connecticut to the river St. Lawrence, named in the Treaties Iroquois or Cataraquy, or simply the completion of the ancient provincial surveys:

"CONSIDERING:

"That the fifth article of the Treaty of Ghent of 1814 does not stipulate that such portion of the boundaries as may not have hitherto been surveyed, shall be surveyed; but declares that the boundaries have not been, and establishes that they shall be, surveyed:

"That, in effect, such survey ought, in the relations between the two Powers, to be considered as not having been made from the Connecticut to the river St. Lawrence, named in the Treaties Iroquois or Cataraquy, since the ancient survey was found to be incorrect, and had been ordered, not by a common accord of the two Powers, but by the ancient provincial authorities:

"That in determining the latitude of places it is customary to follow the principle of the observed latitude;

"And that the Government of the United States of America has erected certain fortifications at the place called Rouse's Point, under the impression that the ground formed part of their territory—an impression sufficiently authorized by the circumstance that the line had, until then, been reputed to correspond with the 45th degree of north latitude:
"WE ARE OF OPINION:
"That it will be suitable to proceed to fresh operations to measure the observed latitude in order to mark out the boundary from the river Connecticut along the parallel of the 45th degree of north latitude to the river St. Lawrence, named in the Treaties Iroquois or Cataraquy, in such manner however that, in all cases, at the place called Rouse's Point, the territory of the United States of America shall extend to the fort erected at that place, and shall include said fort and its Kilometrical radius (*rayon Kilometrique.*)
"Thus done and given under our Royal Seal, at the Hague, this tenth day of January, in the year of our Lord one thousand eight hundred and thirty-one, and of our Reign the eighteenth.

"WILLIAM.

"VERSTOLK VAN SOELEN,
"*The Minister of Foreign Affairs.*"

The disputes which followed, the attempts to adjust the differences of the two countries, the negotiations, and, finally, the conclusion of the convention of 1842 (the Webster-Ashburton treaty) are discussed at some length in Appendix I of this report, and in greater detail in Moore's History and Digest of International Arbitrations, Volume I, pages 138–157.

The following is the text of the Webster-Ashburton treaty:

WEBSTER-ASHBURTON TREATY

(Concluded August 9, 1842; ratifications exchanged October 13, 1842)

Whereas certain portions of the line of boundary between the United States of America and the British dominions of North America, described in the second article of the treaty of peace of 1783, have not yet been ascertained and determined, notwithstanding the repeated attempts which have been heretofore made for that purpose; and whereas it is now thought to be for the interest of both parties, that, avoiding further discussion of their respective rights, arising in this respect under the said treaty, they should agree on a conventional line in said portions of the said boundary, such as may be convenient to both parties, with such equivalents and compensations as are deemed just and reasonable, and whereas, by the treaty concluded at Ghent on the 24th day of December, 1814, between the United States and His Britannic Majesty, an article was agreed to and inserted of the following tenor, vizt: "Art. 10. Whereas the traffic in slaves is irreconcilable with the principles of humanity and justice; and whereas both His Majesty and the United States are desirous of continuing their efforts to promote its entire abolition, it is hereby agreed that both the contracting parties shall use their best endeavors to accomplish so desirable an object;" and whereas, notwithstanding the laws which have at various times been passed by the two Governments, and the efforts made to suppress it, that criminal traffic is still prosecuted and carried on; and whereas the United States of America and Her Majesty the Queen of the United Kingdom of Great Britain and Ireland are determined that, so far as may be in their power, it shall be effectually abolished; and whereas it is found expedient, for the better administration of justice and the prevention of crime within the territories and jurisdiction of the two parties respectively, that persons committing the crimes hereinafter enumerated, and being fugitives from justice, should, under certain circumstances, be reciprocally delivered up: The United States of America and Her Britannic Majesty, having resolved to treat on these several subjects, have for that purpose appointed their respective Plenipotentiaries to negotiate and conclude a treaty, that is to say:

The President of the United States has on his part, furnished with full powers Daniel Webster, Secretary of State of the United States, and Her Majesty the Queen of the United Kingdom of Great Britain and Ireland has, on Her part, appointed the Right Honorable Alexander Lord Ashburton, a peer of the said United Kingdom, a member of Her Majesty's Most Honorable Privy Council, and Her Majesty's Minister Plenipotentiary on a special mission to the United States;

Who, after a reciprocal communication of their respective full powers, have agreed to and signed the following articles:

ARTICLE I

It is hereby agreed and declared that the line of boundary shall be as follows: Beginning at the monument at the source of the river St. Croix as designated and agreed to by the Commissioners under the fifth article of the treaty of 1794, between the Governments of the United States and Great Britain; thence, north, following the exploring line run and marked by the surveyors of the two Governments in the years 1817 and 1818, under the fifth article of the treaty of Ghent, to its intersection with the river St. John, and to the middle of the channel thereof; thence, up the middle of the main channel of the said river St. John to the mouth of the river St. Francis; thence, up the middle of the channel of the said river St. Francis, and of the lakes through which it flows, to the outlet of the Lake Pohenagamook; thence, southwesterly, in a straight line, to a point on the northwest branch of the river St. John, which point shall be ten miles distant from the main branch of the St. John, in a straight line, and in the nearest direction; but if the said point shall be found to be less than seven miles from the nearest point of the summit or crest of the highlands that divide those rivers which empty themselves into the river Saint Lawrence from those which fall into the river Saint John, then the said point shall be made to recede down the said northwest branch of the river St. John, to a point seven miles in a straight line from the said summit or crest; thence, in a straight line, in a course about south, eight degrees west, to the point where the parallel of latitude of 46° 25′ north intersects the southwest branch of the St. John's; thence, southerly, by the said branch, to the source thereof in the highlands at the Metjarmette portage; thence, down along the said highlands which divide the waters which empty themselves into the river Saint Lawrence from those which fall into the Atlantic Ocean, to the head of Hall's Stream; thence, down the middle of said stream, till the line thus run intersects the old line of boundary surveyed and marked by Valentine and Collins, previously to the year 1774, as the 45th degree of north latitude, and which has been known and understood to be the line of actual division between the States of New York and Vermont on one side, and the British province of Canada on the other; and from said point of intersection, west, along the said dividing line, as heretofore known and understood, to the Iroquois or St. Lawrence River.

ARTICLE III

In order to promote the interests and encourage the industry of all the inhabitants of the countries watered by the river St. John and its tributaries, whether living within the State of Maine or the province of New Brunswick, it is agreed that, where, by the provisions of the present treaty, the river St. John is declared to be the line of boundary, the navigation of the said river shall be free and open to both parties, and shall in no way be obstructed by either; that all the produce of the forest, in logs, lumber, timber, boards, staves, or shingles, or of agriculture, not being manufactured, grown on any of those parts of the State of Maine watered by the river St. John, or by its tributaries, of which fact reasonable evidence shall, if required, be produced, shall have free access into and through the said river and its said tributaries, having their source within the State of Maine, to and from the sea-port at the mouth of the said river St. John's, and to and round the falls of the said river, either by boats, rafts, or other conveyance; that when within the province of New Brunswick, the said produce shall be dealt with as if it were the produce of the said province; that, in like manner, the inhabitants of the territory of the upper St. John, determined by this treaty to belong to Her Britannic Majesty, shall have free access to and through the river, for their produce, in those parts where the said river runs wholly through the State of Maine; Provided, always, that this agreement shall give no right to either party to interfere with any regulations not inconsistent with the terms of this treaty which the governments, respectively, of Maine or of New Brunswick may make respecting the navigation of the said river, where both banks thereof shall belong to the same party.

ARTICLE VI

It is furthermore understood and agreed that, for the purpose of running and tracing those parts of the line between the source of the St. Croix and the St. Lawrence River which will require to be run and ascertained, and for marking the residue of said line by proper monuments on the land, two Commissioners shall be appointed, one by the President of the United States, by and with the advice and consent of the Senate thereof, and one by Her Britannic Majesty; and the said Commissioners shall meet at Bangor, in the State of Maine, on the first day of May next, or as soon thereafter as may be, and shall proceed to mark the line above described from the source of the St. Croix to the river St. John; and shall trace on proper maps the dividing-line along said river and along the river St. Francis to the outlet of the Lake Pohenagamook; and from the outlet of the said lake they shall ascertain, fix, and mark, by proper and durable monuments on the land, the line described in the first article of this treaty; and the said Commissioners shall make to each of their respective Governments, a joint report or declaration, under their hands and seals, designating such line of boundary, and shall accompany such report or declaration with maps, certified by them to be true maps of the new boundary.

ARTICLE XII

The present treaty shall be duly ratified, and the mutual exchange of ratifications shall take place in London, within six months from the date hereof, or earlier if possible.

In faith whereof we, the respective Plenipotentiaries, have signed this treaty and have hereunto affixed our seals.

Done in duplicate at Washington, the ninth day of August, anno Domini one thousand eight hundred and forty-two.

[SEAL.]   DANL. WEBSTER.
[SEAL.]   ASHBURTON.

The work of surveying and marking the boundary from the source of the St. Croix River to the St. Lawrence River under the treaty of 1842 is treated in detail in Appendix III. The text of the joint report of the commissioners appointed to carry out the treaty provisions which apply to the boundary demarcation is here reprinted.

REPORT OF THE JOINT COMMISSION OF BOUNDARY APPOINTED UNDER THE TREATY OF WASHINGTON OF AUGUST 9, 1842

The undersigned, commissioners appointed under the treaty of Washington to trace and mark the boundary, as directed by that treaty, between the British possessions in North America and the United States—that is to say, James Bucknall Bucknall Estcourt, lieutenant-colonel in the British army, appointed commissioner by Her Britannic Majesty, and Albert Smith, appointed commissioner by the President of the United States—having accomplished the duty assigned to them, do now, in accordance with the directions of the said treaty, submit the following report and accompanying maps, jointly signed, to their respective Governments.

In obedience to the terms of the treaty, the undersigned met at Bangor, in the State of Maine, on the 1st day of May, 1843, where they produced and verified the authority under which they each were respectively to act. They then adjourned, because the weather was not sufficiently open for taking the field, to the 1st of the following month (June), and agreed to meet again at that time at Houlton.

Accordingly, they did meet at that place, and began their operations.

It may be desirable to state at the outset that for the sake of convenience the whole line of boundary marked by the undersigned has been divided in the mention made of the different portions into the following grand divisions, viz:

"North Line," from the source of the St. Croix to the intersection of the St. John.

"River St. John," from the intersection of the North Line to the mouth of the St. Francis.

"River St. Francis," from its mouth to the outlet of Lake Pohenagamook.

"Southwest Line," from the outlet of Lake Pohenagamook to the Northwest Branch of the St. John.

"South Line," from the Northwest Branch to the parallel of latitude 46° 25' on the Southwest Branch.

"Southwest Branch," from the parallel 46° 25' to its source.

"Highlands," from the source of the Southwest Branch of the St. John to the source of Halls Stream.

"Halls Stream," from its source to the intersection of the line of Valentine and Collins.

"West Line," from Halls Stream to the St. Lawrence near St. Regis, along the line of Valentine and Collins.

To return to the narration of operations:

The exploring line of Colonel Bouchette and Mr. Johnson, as directed by the treaty, was traced from the monument at the source of the St. Croix to the intersection of the St. John.

The monument found at the source of the St. Croix, as described in the report of Colonel Bouchette and Mr. Johnson, and the course of their exploring line, was traced by blazes or marks upon the trees.

An old line, cut out by the assistant surveyors of Colonel Bouchette and Mr. Johnson, was also found, which terminated about half a mile north of the South Branch of the Meduxnikeag, where, by records to which the undersigned referred, they ascertained that it had been abandoned because of its deviation from the exploring line of Colonel Bouchette and Mr. Johnson.

After the exploration and re-marking of the North Line it was cut out 30 feet wide. The same was afterwards done in all parts where the boundary passed through woodland. After thus opening the North Line it was surveyed, and iron posts were erected at intervals to mark it.

The general bearing of the line was rather to the west of the meridian of the monument at the source of the St. Croix. The precise line laid down by the undersigned was determined by successive courses, of which each was made to be as long as was convenient, provided it did not pass out of the opening of 30 feet.

At each angle of deflection an iron monument was erected, and placed anglewise with the line. Other monuments were erected at the crossing of roads, rivers, and at every mile, commencing from the source of the St. Croix. Those which were not intended to mark angles of deflection were placed square with the line.

At the intersection of the St. John by the North Line the river is deep, and broad. The boundary runs up the middle of the channel of the river, as indicated by the maps, dividing the islands as follows:

No. 1.	Ryan's Island	United States.
No. 2.	King's Island	United States.
No. 3.	Les Trois Isles	United States.
No. 4.	La Septieme Isle	United States.
No. 5.	Quissibis	Great Britain.
No. 6.	La Grand Isle	United States.
No. 7.	Thibideau's Islands	United States.
No. 8.	Madawaska Islands	Great Britain.
No. 9.	Joseph Michaud's three islands	United States.
No. 10.	Pine Island	Great Britain.
No. 11.	{ Baker's, Turtle, Dagle's, Fourth, Fifth } Islands	Great Britain.
No. 12.	Kennedy's Island	Great Britain.
No. 13.	{ Crock's, Cranberry, Gooseberry } Islands	Great Britain.
No. 14.	Savage's Island	United States.
No. 15.	Wheelock's Island	United States.
No. 16.	Caton's Island	United States.
No. 17.	Honeywell's Island	United States.
No. 18.	Savage and Johnson's Island	United States.
No. 19.	Grew's Island	United States.
No. 20.	Kendall's Island	Great Britain.

The islands were distributed to Great Britain or to the United States, as they were found to be on the right or left of the deep channel. There was but one doubtful case, La Septieme Isle, and that was apportioned to the United States because the majority of the owners were ascertained to reside on the United States side of the river.

Monuments were erected upon the islands, marking them for Great Britain or the United States, as the case may have been.

After leaving the St. John the boundary enters the St. Francis, dividing the islands at the mouth of that river in the manner shown on the maps. It then runs up the St. Francis, through the middle of the lakes upon it, to the outlet of Lake Pohenagamook, the third large lake from the mouth of the river. At the outlet a large monument has been erected.

In order to determine the point on the Northwest Branch to which the treaty directed that a straight line should be run from the outlet of Lake Pohenagamook, a survey of that stream was made, and also of the main St. John in the neighborhood of the mouth of the Northwest Branch, and a line was cut between the St. John and the point on the Northwest Branch, ascertained by the survey to be 10 miles in the nearest direction from it, and the distance was afterwards verified by chaining.

It was ascertained also, in accordance with the provisions of the treaty, by a triangulation of the country toward the highlands dividing the waters of the St. Lawrence and of the St. John, that more than 7 miles intervened between the point selected on the Northwest Branch and the crest of the dividing ridge. A large iron monument was afterwards erected on the point thus selected, and the space around was cleared and sown with grass seed. It is a short distance below the outlet of Lake Ishaganalshegeck.

The outlet of Lake Pohenagamook and the point on the Northwest Branch designated by the treaty having been thus ascertained and marked, in the spring of 1844 a straight line was run between them. Along that line, which passes entirely through forest, monuments were erected at every mile, at the crossings of the principal streams and rivers, and at the tops of those hills where a transit instrument had been set up to test the straightness of the line.

As soon as the parallel of latitude 46° 25′ had been determined on the Southwest Branch, in the early part of the summer of 1844, a straight line was drawn from the boundary point on the Northwest Branch to a large monument erected on the left bank of the Southwest Branch where it is intersected by the parallel of latitude 46° 25′. The line so drawn crosses the Southwest Branch once before it reaches the parallel of latitude 46° 25′, and at about a half mile distance from that parallel. There also a large monument has been set up on the left bank.

From the intersection of the parallel 46° 25′ the boundary ascends the Southwest Branch, passes through a lake near its head, and so up a small stream which falls into the lake from the west to the source of that stream, which has been selected as the source of the Southwest Branch.

On the Southwest Branch there are two principal forks, at each of which two monuments have been erected, one on each bank of the river immediately above the forks and upon the branch established as the boundary. The maps point out their positions. At the mouth of the small stream selected as the source of the Southwest Branch a monument has been erected upon a delta formed by two small outlets. Above those outlets three other monuments have been placed at intervals upon the same stream.

Upon the crest of the dividing ridge, very close to the source of the Southwest Branch, a large monument has been erected. It is the first point in the Highlands,[3] and from it the boundary runs along the crest in a southerly direction, passing near to the southeastern shore of the Portage Lake, and so on to a large monument erected on a small eminence on the east side of the Kennebec road. Thence it passes through a dwelling house called Tachereau's, which was standing there at the time the line was run; so, by a tortuous course, it runs to the top of Sandy Stream Mountain; thence, inclining to the southwest, it runs over Hog Back the First, as shown on the maps; thence toward Hog Back the Second, which it leaves on the north side. Further on, at the head of Leech Lake, there is a stream which divides its waters and flows both into Canada and into the United States. The boundary has been made to run up that stream a short distance from the fork where the waters divide to a second fork; thence between the streams which unite to form that fork, and then to ascend again the dividing ridge. A monument has been erected at the fork first mentioned, where the waters divide.

As the boundary approaches the valley of Spider River it bends to the southeast, and, by a wide circuit over high and steep hills, it turns the head of Spider River; thence it bends to the northwest until it approaches within about 4 miles of Lake Megantic; thence it turns again south, having the valley of Arnolds River on the right and of Dead River on the left. It leaves Gosford Mountain in Canada, threads its way over very high ground between the head of Arnolds River and the tributaries of the Magalloway; inclines then to the north, so to the west, over very rocky, mountainous, and difficult country, leaving Gipps Peak in the United States, and turns by a sharp angle at Saddle Back to the south. After that it again inclines to the west, and then to the south, and again to the west, and passes the head of the Connecticut. About 3 miles and a half east of the head of the Connecticut there is a division of waters similar to that described near Leech Lake. The boundary runs down a stream from near its source to the fork where it divides, and then again follows the dividing ridge. The spot is noted on the map.

After the boundary has passed the head of the Connecticut it runs to the northwest, descending into very low, swampy ground between the heads of Indian Stream and the tributaries of the St. Francis. Thus it passes on, bending again to the south of west, over a high hill, to the source of Halls Stream.

Iron monuments have been erected at intervals along the Highlands from the source of the Southwest Branch of the St. John to the source of Halls Stream, the position of each of which is shown upon the maps.

---

[3] The Highlands is considered by the present commission as beginning at Little St. John Lake at monument 314.

From the source of Halls Stream the boundary descends that river, dividing the islands, which are, however, merely unimportant alluvial deposits, in the manner indicated by the maps until it reaches the intersection of that stream by the line formerly run by Valentine and Collins as the forty-fifth degree of north latitude.

At that point a large monument has been erected on the right and a small one on the left bank of the stream. Monuments have also been erected along the bank of this stream, as indicated on the maps.

The line of Valentine and Collins was explored and found by the blazes still remaining in the original forest.

Upon cutting into those blazes it was seen that deep seated in the tree there was a scar, the surface of the original blaze, slightly decayed, and upon counting the rings (which indicate each year's growth of the tree) it was found that the blazes dated back to 1772, 1773, and 1774. The line of Valentine and Collins was run in 1771, 1772, 1773, and 1774. The coincidence of the dates of the blazes with those of the above line, confirmed by the testimony of the people of the country, satisfied the undersigned that the line they had found was that mentioned in the treaty. Along this portion of the boundary, which is known as the forty-fifth degree of Valentine and Collins, and which extends from Halls Stream to St. Regis, there are several interruptions to the blazes in those parts where clearings have been made, and there the authentic marks of the precise situation of the old line have been lost. In those cases the undersigned have drawn the boundary line straight from the original blazes on the one side of a clearing to the original blazes on the other side of the same clearing.

It cannot be positively stated that the line as it has been traced through those clearings precisely coincides with the old line, but the undersigned believe that it does not differ materially from it; nor have they had the means of determining a nearer or a surer approximation.

Along this line, at every point of deflection, an iron monument has been erected; also at the crossing of rivers, lakes, and roads. Those which mark deflections are placed, as on the "North Line," anglewise with the line; all the others are placed square with it. The maps show the position of each.

On the eastern shore of Lake Memphremagog an astronomical station was established, and on a large flat rock of granite, which happened to lie between the astronomical station and the boundary, was cut the following inscription:

```
                CAPT. ROBINSON
 B              AST. STATION
 R              422 FEET NORTH        C
 I                                    O
 T   MERIDIAN  ———<>———  LINE         M
 I                                    M
 S              BOUNDARY LINE         I
 H              595 FEET SOUTH        S
 B              AUGUST 1845           S
 O                                    I
 U                                    O
 N                                    N
 D
 A
 R
 Y
```

A mark was cut upon the stone, as indicated by the dot upon the meridian line above, from which these measurements were made.

At Rouses Point a monument of wrought stone was set up at the intersection of the boundary by the meridian of the transit instrument used there by Major Graham, and an inscription was cut upon it stating the latitude and longitude, the names of the observer and his assistant, the names of the commissioners, and the territories divided.

To mark the position of the instruments used at the following astronomical stations along the west line, two monuments within a few feet of each other have been erected at each station, and they have been placed on the boundary line due north or south of the instrument, as the case may have been.

The stations are: Lake Memphremagog, Richford, John McCoy's, Trout River.

The boundary along the West Line, though very far from being a straight line, is generally about half a mile north of the true parallel of latitude 45° from Halls Stream to Rouses Point. At about 28 miles west of Rouses Point it, however, crosses that parallel to the south until it reaches Chateaugay River, where it bends northward, and crossing the parallel again about 4 miles east of St. Regis, it strikes the St. Lawrence 151 feet north of 45°. At that point a large monument has been erected on the bank of the St. Lawrence. Two large monuments have also been erected, one on either side of the river Richelieu near Rouses Point.

No marks of the old line were to be found about St. Regis. It was therefore agreed to run a line due west from the last blaze which should be found in the woods on the east side of St. Regis. That blaze occurred about 1 mile east of the St. Regis River.

The maps, which exhibit the boundary on a scale of 4 inches to 1 statute mile, consist of 62 consecutive sheets of antiquarian paper as constructed by the British and of 61 as constructed by the American commission. A general map has also been constructed on a scale of 8 miles to 1 inch by the British and of 10 miles to 1 inch by the American commission, upon which the before-mentioned sheets are represented.

The following portions of the boundary have been laid down by the British commission, on detached maps, on a scale of 12 inches to 1 mile, which have been signed by both commissioners:

Grand Falls of the St. John, including the intersection of that river by the North Line; islands of the St. John; the outlet of Lake Pohenagamook; the turning point of the boundary on the Northwest Branch of the St. John; the intersection of the Southwest Branch by the parallel of latitude 46° 25'; the source of the Southwest Branch; the source of Halls Stream; the intersection of Halls Stream by the West Line; Rouses Point; St. Regis; Derby.

But similar maps have not been prepared by the American commission, because during the interval between the finishing of the maps of the British commission and those of the American it was thought that the maps already constructed upon a scale of 4 inches to 1 mile represented the boundary with sufficient clearness and accuracy.

The astronomical observations were begun at the Grand Falls early in June, 1843, and were carried up the St. John River to the Northwest Branch by a chain of stations, which, together with the results obtained, are tabulated in the appendix accompanying this report.

From the valley of the St. John an astronomical connection was made with Quebec, and thence to Montreal, and so to Rouses Point. From Rouses Point a connection was obtained with Cambridge University, near Boston.

The astronomical stations on the West Line were: Intersection of Halls Stream by the West Line, Lake Memphremagog, Richford, Rouses Point, John McCoy's, Trout River, St. Regis.

Latitude was also obtained at an astronomical station established for the purpose at the head of the Connecticut.

Volumes containing the astronomical observations of both commissions are herewith submitted. From them it will be observed that the results for absolute longitude obtained by the British and American astronomers do not agree. It being a difference in no way affecting the survey of the boundary line, the undersigned do not feel called upon to attempt to reconcile it. The data upon which those results are based may be seen in the volumes of observations accompanying this report.

In the appendix will be found, in a tabular form, the following:

An abstract of the survey of the boundary along the North Line; an abstract of the survey of the boundary along the Southwest Line; an abstract of the survey of the boundary along the South Line; an abstract of the survey of the boundary along the Highlands; an abstract of the survey of the boundary along the West Line; the position of the monuments erected on the Southwest Branch of the St. John and on Halls Stream; the distribution of the islands of the St. John and the monuments on them; the guide lines and offsets run by each commission for the survey of the Highlands; the azimuths of verification for the survey of the Highlands; the latitudes and longitudes obtained from the astronomical observations; the comparative longitudes obtained, and the methods used for the purpose.

Upon comparing the maps of the two commissions it will be seen that the American commission numbers two monuments more than the British. Those are to be found, one on the "Fourth Island," in the river St. John, and the other on the Highlands between the source of the Southwest Branch of the river St. John and the Kennebec road.

On the maps of the British commission representing the "West Line" the name of the town of "Derby" has been improperly placed north of the line instead of south of it. Also, on the same maps the direction of Salmon River, near the western extremity of the "West Line," has been incorrectly laid down from the boundary line northward. A direction has been given to it northeasterly instead of northwesterly.

The above two corrections the British commissioner is authorized to make on his maps after his return to England.

To avoid unnecessary delay in making their joint report, the undersigned have attached their signatures to the maps, although the lettering of some of the astronomical stations upon the maps of the American commission, as well as the alterations before mentioned in the maps of the British commission, are yet to be made; but in the maps of both the boundary has been laid down accurately and definitively, and the undersigned engage that it shall not be altered in any respect.

In conclusion the undersigned have the honor to report that the line of boundary described in the foregoing statement has been run, marked, and surveyed, and the accompanying maps faithfully constructed from that survey.

The undersigned take leave to add that the most perfect harmony has subsisted between the two commissions from first to last, and that no differences have arisen between the undersigned in the execution of the duties intrusted to them.

Signed and sealed in duplicate, at the city of Washington, this 28th day of June, A. D. 1847.

J. B. BUCKNALL ESTCOURT, (SEAL.)
Lieutenant-Colonel, Her Britannic Majesty's Commissioner.
ALBERT SMITH (SEAL.)
United States Commissioner.

NOTE.—The astronomical computations of the American commission not being completed, and it being unnecessary to defer the signing of the report on that account, the American commissioner engages to transmit them, with any other papers or tables not yet finished, as soon as they shall be so, to the British commissioner, through the American minister resident in London, to whom, upon delivery of the documents, the British commissioner will give a receipt, to be transmitted to the American commissioner.

J. B. BUCKNALL ESTCOURT,
Lieutenant-Colonel, H. B. M. Commissioner of Boundary.
ALBERT SMITH,
United States Commissioner.

CORRESPONDENCE RESULTING IN JOINT AND CONCURRENT ACTION REGARDING THE NEW YORK-QUEBEC AND VERMONT-QUEBEC BOUNDARIES

The correspondence between officials of the United States and Canada which resulted in the surveying and monumenting of the New York-Quebec and Vermont-Quebec boundaries and which eventually led up to the treaty of 1908, is here reproduced as furnishing the best means of understanding these negotiations.

STATE OF NEW YORK,
OFFICE OF THE STATE ENGINEER AND SURVEYOR,
Albany, March 2, 1900.

Hon. E. DEVILLE,
Surveyor-General, Dept. of Interior,
Topographic Survey Branch, Ottawa, Canada.

From May 15 to June 30, 1899, we held some correspondence in relation to the examination of the monuments marking the boundary line between Canada and the state of New York. Our law stipulates that the State Engineer and Surveyor shall make an examination of the state boundary monuments once in three years. The time has arrived when the monuments between Canada and the state of New York, by the terms of our statute, should be examined.

It would please me very much if a representative of your government could take up this matter at the same time, so that each party will know of any defective monuments, and also know of any repairs to monuments that ought to be made.

I shall be very glad if you will take this subject up with the proper parties, and let me know at an early date what the possibilities are of co-operation by your department with ours in this examination.

EDWARD A. BOND,
State Engineer and Surveyor.

EXTRACT FROM A REPORT OF THE COMMITTEE OF THE HONOURABLE THE PRIVY COUNCIL, APPROVED BY HIS EXCELLENCY ON THE 26TH OF MAY 1900

On a report dated 12th May, 1900, from the Acting Minister of the Interior, stating that he has received a communication from the State Engineer and Surveyor of the state of New York, stating that he is required under their law to make every three years an examination of the monuments marking the boundary of his state, and that the time for the periodical examination is at hand, and asking the co-operation of the Government of Canada so far as regards that portion of the state boundary which coincides with the boundary of the Dominion.

The Minister observes with regard to this proposition that it looks to a mere examination of the monuments, and not the repair or replacing of those broken or lost. This last should be out of the power of the state of New York or of Canada, either separately or jointly without an international agreement with the United States. Without power to replace, the examination would appear to be of little service to the Dominion. For this reason, he (the Minister) is unable to recommend compliance with the State Engineer's request.

The Minister would, however, call attention to the general question of which this is a part, namely, the examination, and where necessary, the remarking of the whole of the southern boundary of Canada, wherever it has been surveyed by the various commissions appointed for that purpose. The portions of the boundary line which have been so marked are:

From the St. Croix to the St. Lawrence river, separating the provinces of New Brunswick and Quebec from the states of Maine, New Hampshire, Vermont and New York; this line was surveyed under the Ashburton Treaty of 1842, and marked with cast-iron monuments.

From the Lake of the Woods to the Rocky Mountains (49th parallel), separating Manitoba and the North-west Territories from the states of Minnesota, North Dakota and Montana; surveyed 1872 to 1874 and marked, in part with iron monuments, in part with earth or stone mounds.

From the Rocky Mountains to the Straits of Georgia (49th parallel) separating British Columbia from the states of Montana, Idaho and Washington; surveyed 1859 to 1861, and marked with mounds and iron posts.

As regards all these portions of the line many complaints have been made from time to time of the disappearance of monuments, and the consequent difficulty of determining the exact position of the boundary, while the British Columbia portion of the line was, in November, 1892, the subject of a formal request by the Lieutenant-Governor in Council for not only a re-establishment of lost posts, but also for an additional or supplementary survey, on the ground that the demarcation by the Commissioners was not sufficiently complete for modern require-ments.

Again, the boundary line between Ontario and Minnesota, between Lake Superior and Lake of the Woods, has been designated by the Commissioners under the Treaty of Ghent, and by the Ashburton Treaty, by description and maps only, and the line (which in general follows the water communication) has never been marked where it crosses the portages.

The Minister submits that while this question was one of those before the Joint High Commission, it is yet essentially different from the other questions before that Commission, as it involves no cession of territory or relinquishment of rights on either side, but is a matter purely of business arrangement to the mutual advantage of both countries.

The Minister, therefore, recommends that Your Excellency be moved to inform Her Majesty's Government of the desire of the Government of Canada to join with the United States in an examination of their common boundary for the purpose of re-establishing lost monuments and of placing such supplementary monuments as may appear necessary to meet modern requirements.

The committee advise that Your Excellency be moved to transmit a certified copy of this Minute to the Right Honourable the Secretary of State for the Colonies.

All which is respectfully submitted for Your Excellency's approval.

JOHN J. McGEE,
Clerk of the Privy Council

STATE OF NEW YORK,
OFFICE OF THE STATE ENGINEER AND SURVEYOR,
Albany, October 23, 1900.

Hon. JOHN HAY,
Secretary of State, Washington, D. C.

By the laws of the state of New York, it devolves on the State Engineer and Surveyor to once in three years examine all of the boundary monuments of the state, and report to the legislature their condition, and in connection with this work I have had the boundary monu-ments between Canada and the state of New York examined this past summer.

Of a total of 130 monuments I find only 37 in perfect condition. I find four are missing; 13 are broken, or have pieces broken off; 8 have fallen down; 5 have cracked; 39 have been heaved by action of the frost; 24 lean; that is, are not plumb. Of these, some of them are firm and others loose.

I would be glad if you would tell me what is best to be done to induce the Canada govern-ment to join, either with the government of the United States or with our state, to have these monuments replaced and put in proper and first-class condition.

If your department will take it up with the Canadians, I shall be very glad; but, if not, and they will assent to joining my department in adjusting this matter, we will gladly attend to it.

If I have not addressed the right department, I would appreciate it very much if you would have this letter referred to the proper parties.

EDWARD A. BOND,
State Engineer and Surveyor.

DEPARTMENT OF STATE,
Washington, October 29, 1900.

EDWARD A. BOND, Esquire,
State Engineer and Surveyor,
Albany, New York.

I have to acknowledge the receipt of your letter of the 23rd instant in relation to the condition of the boundary monuments between the state of New York and the Dominion of Canada.

I have submitted the matter to the British ambassador, with a view to ascertain whether the Canadian government will be willing to join in the replacing and repair of the monuments. As a new survey is not involved but simply the repair of existing monuments, it would not seem to require any new convention, but merely provision on both sides for the joint performance of the work.

JOHN HAY.

EXTRACT FROM A REPORT OF THE COMMITTEE OF THE HONOURABLE THE PRIVY COUNCIL, APPROVED
BY HIS EXCELLENCY ON THE 5TH JANUARY, 1901

The Committee of the Privy Council have had under consideration a copy of a despatch hereto attached, dated 1st November, 1900, from Her Majesty's Ambassador at Washington, transmitting a copy of a note from the Secretary of State of the United States, inquiring whether the government of Canada is willing to join in having the monuments upon the boundary line between Canada and the state of New York put in proper and first-class condition.

The Minister of the Interior, to whom the matter was referred, observes that Your Excellency's government has already, by Minute dated 26th May, 1900, expressed its willingness and desire to join with the government of the United States in the examination and repair of monuments upon the boundary between Canada and the United States.

The Minister further states that the occasion for the above mentioned Minute was an invitation on the part of the authorities of the state of New York to the government of Canada to join with them in an examination of the northern boundary of their state, where it abuts upon the province of Quebec. This proposal Your Excellency's advisers declined to accede to, for the reason that the mere examination of the monuments would not serve any very practical end, unless provision were made for the restoration of lost or broken monuments, a matter which could not be dealt with except with the consent and co-operation of the government of the United States.

The Minister further states that this objection is not set aside by the note of the United States Secretary of State. Although the note indicates the agreement of the United States as regards only a small part of the work proposed by Your Excellency's government, and a more extended agreement would be more satisfactory, he is of the opinion that concurrence in the limited proposal is in the public interest.

The Minister further observes that it appears that of 130 monuments originally placed on the New York boundary, 37 are now in first-class condition, whereas in 1890 an examination of this line by an officer of the Department of the Interior showed 51. The rapid deterioration of the monuments thus apparently not only calls for early action towards their restoration, but also indicates the probable condition of the monuments on the prolongation eastward of this line, north of the states of Vermont, New Hampshire and Maine, and suggests the advisability of action there also.

The committee, on the recommendation of the Minister of the Interior, advise that Your Excellency be moved to inform Her Majesty's Ambassador at Washington that the government of Canada is willing to join with the government of the United States in the examination and restoration where necessary of the monuments along the line between the province of Quebec and the state of New York, but desires to suggest that the scope of the proposed joint operations be enlarged so as to cover the whole of the boundary line, which was marked under the Webster-Ashburton Treaty, from the St. Lawrence to the St. Croix river.

All which is respectfully submitted for Your Excellency's approval.

JOHN J. McGEE,
Clerk of the Privy Council.

EXTRACT FROM A REPORT OF THE COMMITTEE OF THE HONOURABLE THE PRIVY COUNCIL, APPROVED
BY HIS EXCELLENCY ON THE 16TH AUGUST, 1901

The Committee of the Privy Council have had under consideration a despatch, hereto attached, dated July 17, 1901 from His Majesty's Chargé d'Affaires at Washington, transmitting a copy of a note from the Secretary of State of the United States having reference to the condition of the monuments on the boundary between Canada and the state of New York, and suggesting that in view of the simplicity of the task of executing the necessary repairs, these would be carried out by the direct co-operation of the Department of the Interior of Canada with that of the Engineer of the state of New York, without awaiting the conclusion of any future agreement between His Majesty's government and the United States government for the more effective demarcation of the frontier.

The Minister of the Interior, to whom the said despatch was referred, submits that the proposed co-operation with the state of New York, with the concurrence of the government of the United States, is quite in accord with the views expressed by His Excellency's advisers in the Minutes of the Council of the 26th May, 1900, and 5th January, 1901, although the scope of the proposed operations is restricted to the limits of the state of New York, and, as set forth in these Minutes, an inquiry into the conditions of the whole land boundary between the United States and Canada is to be desired.

The Committee advise that His Excellency be moved to inform His Majesty's Chargé d'Affaires at Washington of the concurrence of the government of Canada with the proposal of the Secretary of State of the United States, it being understood that the agreement to the proposed co-operation is without prejudice to any further agreement between the two governments for the more effective demarcation of the existing treaty boundary in that quarter, and that, while each government shall pay the expenses of its Commissioner and surveyors, the actual cost of repairs shall be equally divided.

All which is respectfully submitted for His Excellency's approval.

JOHN J. McGEE,
Clerk of the Privy Council.

BRITISH EMBASSY,
Newport, R. I., July 17, 1901.

HIS EXCELLENCY,
THE EARL OF MINTO, G. C. M. G.

With reference to Lord Pauncefote's despatch, No. 3, of January 12 last, I have the honour to transmit to Your Excellency herewith a copy of a further note from the United States government, drawing attention to the danger of the obliteration of the boundary between Canada and the state of New York through the dilapidation of the monuments, and suggesting that, in view of the simplicity of the task of executing the necessary repairs, it should be carried out by the direct co-operation of the Department of the Interior of Canada with that of the Engineer of the state of New York, without awaiting the conclusion of any further agreement between His Majesty's government and the United States government for the more effective demarcation of the frontier, such as that which, it is hoped, may result from the survey suggested by the latter last January and communicated to Your Excellency in Lord Pauncefote's despatch No. 13.

I should be grateful if Your Excellency would be good enough to inform me what answer I should return to the proposal of the United States government.

GERARD LOWTHER.

DEPARTMENT OF STATE,
Washington, July 15, 1901.

Mr. GERARD A. LOWTHER.

I have the honour to inform you that the department is in receipt of a letter from the Governor of New York, dated the 14th ultimo, in which he says that the State Engineer has called his attention to correspondence that the latter has had with the Department of the Interior of the Dominion of Canada in relation to replacing and repairing the monuments that mark the boundary line between the state of New York and the Dominion of Canada. The State Engineer informs the Governor that the monuments are in such a fragile and broken condition that unless they are replaced very soon by more permanent ones the boundary line may be lost.

The Governor requests that the matter may be brought to the attention of the British Ambassador, with a view to having early action taken to repair and replace the dilapidated monuments.

In this connection I beg to recall to your attention the proposal contained in the department's note to Lord Pauncefote of October 29, 1900.

While the department still adheres to the view expressed in its note of January 29, 1901, in which it is gratified to see that the Government of the Dominion of Canada shares, that a general survey of the whole land and water boundary between the two countries, with a view to replacing lost monuments and erecting new ones, as well as determining by buoys or ranges, or both, the water boundaries in the narrow lake channels, is most desirable, the question presented on the New York boundary is of so simple a nature that it is conceived that no difficulty will be found in carrying out, forthwith, the suggestion of the Governor of the state. There is no question of settling any dispute arising from the total disappearance of old monuments or the insufficient marking of the line by the treaty Commissioners. It is merely a matter of repairing existing line marks, as to the situation of which no question or doubt can arise.

It is not thought that an international convention would be necessary to provide for painting iron monuments, cementing the defective masonry of stone monuments, restoring inscriptions obliterated by exposure to the elements, or, in short, executing all such mere repairs as may be needful to enable the line marks to subserve the purpose for which they were set up. All this can be done by the joint action of the appropriate agents of the Engineer's Department of the state of New York and of the Department of the Interior of Canada, without prejudice to any future agreement between the two governments for the more effective demarcation—if need be—of the existing treaty boundary in that quarter.

It is hoped that an early and favourable consideration may be given to this proposal.

JOHN HAY

BRITISH EMBASSY,
Washington, January 12, 1901.

HIS EXCELLENCY,
THE EARL OF MINTO, G. C. M. G.,
The Governor General.

I have the honour to acknowledge the receipt of Your Excellency's despatch, No. 6, of the 9th instant, inclosing a copy of an approved Minute of the Privy Council for Canada, intimating the willingness of the Canadian government to join with the government of the United States in the examination and restoration, where necessary, of the monuments along the line between the province of Quebec and the state of New York, but suggesting the extension of the proposed joint operations so as to include the whole of the boundary line marked under the Webster-Ashburton Treaty, from the St. Lawrence to the St. Croix river.

I have forwarded the Minute to the United States government, with the request that I may be informed of their views on the suggestion therein contained for communication to Your Excellency.

PAUNCEFOTE.

DEPARTMENT OF STATE,
Washington, August 30, 1901.

HIS EXCELLENCY
THE GOVERNOR OF NEW YORK,
Albany.

Referring to your letter of the 23rd ultimo, I have now the honour to inform you that on the 25th instant the British Chargé d'Affairs *ad interim* advised me that the Privy Council of Canada concurred in your proposal that the restoration of defective monuments marking the boundary between New York and Canada be proceeded with under the joint direction of the state engineer of New York and the Canadian Department of the Interior, without awaiting the conclusion of a more formal agreement between this government and that of Great Britain.

The Canadian government wishes it to be understood, however, that this agreement is without prejudice to any further measures which may be taken for the demarcation of the boundary between the two countries, and that, while each government shall pay the expenses of its Commissioner and surveyors, the actual cost of restoring the monuments shall be equally divided.

I would now request you to put the state engineer of New York in direct communication with the Canadian Department of the Interior.

ALVEY A. ADEE,
Acting Secretary.

STATE OF NEW YORK,
OFFICE OF THE STATE ENGINEER AND SURVEYOR,
Albany, September 4, 1901.

Examination and Repair of Boundary Line Monuments.

Hon. E. DEVILLE,
Surveyor-General, Department of the Interior,
Ottawa, Canada.

You will doubtless recall some correspondence which we had recently with relation to the examination and repair of monuments marking the boundary line between the Dominion of Canada and the State of New York.

During the present year the matter has been the subject of correspondence between the Governor of this state, the Secretary of State at Washington and the representatives of your government, and I am now in receipt of a letter under date of August 30, 1901, from Hon. Alvey A. Adee, Acting Secretary of State (a copy of which is herewith inclosed) transmitted to me by Governor Odell.

In accordance with the suggestion contained in the letter above mentioned, I have the honour to call your attention to this matter, hoping that arrangements can be perfected so that the examination and repair of these monuments can be made at as early a date as possible, especially in view of the fact that the season in which outdoor work can be conducted is now rapidly drawing to a close.

My understanding is that each government shall pay the expenses of its engineers, while the actual cost of restoring the monuments shall be equally divided between the two governments.

In 1900 an agreement was entered into between the State of New York and the State of Pennsylvania for the examination and repair of monuments between the two states on similar terms, and in view of the fact I take the liberty of inclosing herewith a copy of that agreement, as I believe with such modifications as might be made necessary in paragraph 2 the general form of the agreement would cover the work contemplated in reference to the boundary line monuments between Canada and New York. I offer this merely as a suggestion, however, and will be glad to arrange the matter in such way as you desire either by formal agreement or by exchange of letters.

Awaiting your reply,

EDWARD A. BOND,
State Engineer and Surveyor.

EXTRACT FROM A REPORT OF THE COMMITTEE OF THE HONOURABLE THE PRIVY COUNCIL, AP-
PROVED BY HIS EXCELLENCY ON THE 28TH SEPTEMBER, 1901

On a report dated 17th September, 1901, from the Minister of the Interior, submitting with reference to the proposal that the government of Canada should join with that of the state of New York in an examination of their common boundary, with a view to the restoration of destroyed or damaged monuments, that a communication has recently been received from the State Engineer and Surveyor of the State of New York, proposing that a formal working agreement as to the details of the work and a division of the expenses be entered into between the governments of Canada and the state of New York, or by officials designated by those governments; he submits, as a convenient form of agreement, the agreement entered into for a like purpose in the year 1900 between the states of New York and Pennsylvania.

The Minister, seeing no objection to an agreement of the character proposed, recommends that Mr. W. F. King, the Chief Astronomer of the Department of the Interior, who is familiar with this question, be appointed commissioner to act with the officer who may be delegated by the State of New York, with authority to enter into an agreement of the character above mentioned, and to make arrangements for the commencement of field operations before autumn is too far advanced.

The committee submit the same for His Excellency's approval.

JOHN J. McGEE,
Clerk of the Privy Council.

BRITISH EMBASSY,
Newport, R. I., September 2, 1901.

HIS EXCELLENCY,
> THE EARL OF MINTO, G. C. M. G.,
>> *The Governor General.*

With reference to Your Excellency's despatch, No. 70, of the 20th ultimo, I have the honour to transmit herewith a copy of a note I have received from the United States government.

Mr. Adee states that he has made known to the government of New York the assent of Your Excellency's government to the proposal that the restoration of the monuments on the boundary between New York and Canada be undertaken without awaiting the conclusion of a formal agreement between the governments of Great Britain and the United States, and Mr. Adee adds that he has asked the Governor to put the Engineer of the state in communication with the Canadian Department of the Interior.

GERARD LOWTHER.

DEPARTMENT OF STATE,
Washington, August 30, 1901.

Mr. GERARD LOWTHER.

I have the honour to acknowledge with gratification the receipt of your note, No. 232, of the 25th instant, informing me of the assent of the Canadian government to the proposal of the Governor of New York that the restoration of the monuments on the boundary between New York and Canada be undertaken without awaiting the conclusion of a formal agreement between this government and that of Great Britain.

I have made this known to the Governor of New York, and have asked him to put the Engineer of the state in communication with the Canadian Department of the Interior.

ALVEY A. ADEE,
Acting Secretary.

These negotiations resulted in re-marking the New York-Quebec boundary and determining the geographic positions of the monuments by means of an accurate tape traverse. This work is briefly described in this report under "Field operations, season of 1902," and in detail in the annual report for 1904 of the chief astronomer and boundary commissioner, Department of the Interior, Dominion of Canada, and also in the annual report of the New York State engineer and surveyor for 1902.

The next important step toward the re-marking of the remainder of this portion of the boundary was the joint preliminary examination of the line made in 1905 by representatives of the two Governments. Their report showed the necessity for the resurvey and remonumenting of this portion of the boundary, from the source of the St. Croix River to the Richelieu River, at which point the remonumenting of 1902 had been terminated. The Governments had agreed that where the work to be done involved no disputed question as to the source or location of the line, but required only the restoration of the original monuments and the erection of new ones in order to render more effective the boundary as already surveyed and marked, it was not necessary to enter into a formal convention for that purpose, and that an informal arrangement making provision on both sides for the joint performance of the work was all that was required, and these principles were considered applicable to the Vermont-Quebec boundary. Accordingly, appropriations were made by both Governments for this portion of the work. By an exchange of notes between the Department of State and the British Embassy, it was agreed and arranged that a commission should be appointed to carry out the work and that each Government should bear the expense of its own commissioner and of his surveyor and assistants, and that the two Governments should bear equally the cost of the monuments, their transportation, and erection.

EXTRACT FROM A REPORT OF THE COMMITTEE OF THE PRIVY COUNCIL, APPROVED BY THE GOVERNOR GENERAL ON THE 21ST MAY, 1906

The Committee of the Privy Council have had under consideration a despatch, dated 8th January, 1906, from His Majesty's Ambassador at Washington transmitting copy of a note which he has received from the Secretary of State of the United States relative to the more perfect demarcation of the easterly portion of the International boundary line between the United States and Canada.

The Minister of the Interior to whom the despatch was referred observes that the proposal to more perfectly mark the line between Vermont and Quebec, as well as the suggested extension of the work as far as the St. Croix River, is conformable to the view expressed by the Government of Canada in the Minute of Council of the 8th May, 1900, in which the desirability of the re-marking of those portions of the boundary line which had been surveyed and marked in former years, but on which the monuments had fallen largely into disrepair, was pointed out. The boundary line referred to in that Minute, West of Lake Superior, has since been referred to a joint Commission, which is at present engaged in its re-survey and re-marking. The portion eastward, from the St. Lawrence River as far as the Richelieu River, was re-marked under agreement with the State of New York, concurred in by the Government of the United States in 1902 and 1903.

The Minister further observes that of the parts of the Southern Boundary of Canada referred to in the Minute of Council of the 8th May, 1900, there remains, therefore, only the eastern section, from the Richelieu River to the St. Croix. This was marked by a joint Commission about the years 1843 and 1846, in pursuance of the Treaty of Washington of 1842. An examination made last year of the monuments along this line showed that many were in bad repair or altogether missing, and that urgent need exists for a renewal of the marks.

The Minister recommends therefore that the Government of Canada join with that of the United States in this re-survey and renewal of monuments, on an understanding that each Government shall pay the expenses of its Commissioner and his surveyors and assistants, but that the cost of the monuments, with their transport and erection, be shared equally by the two Governments.

The Committee advise that His Excellency be moved to inform, accordingly, the Right Honourable the Secretary of State for the Colonies and His Majesty's Ambassador at Washington.

All which is respectfully submitted for approval.

JOHN J. McGEE,
Clerk of the Privy Council.

To the Honourable,
THE MINISTER OF THE INTERIOR.

On July 10, 1906, Mr. O. H. Tittmann, Superintendent of the United States Coast and Geodetic Survey, was designated as commissioner to represent the United States with respect to the re-marking and mapping of the entire line from the Richelieu River eastward to the waters of the St. Croix River, but in view of the limitation of the work to be carried on under the appropriation referred to, the supervision of the demarcation of the line between the Richelieu River and Halls Stream was the immediate duty assigned to him, and he was authorized " to arrange the details and to carry out the work and to sign the final report and maps, as commissioner for the United States, jointly with the British commissioner."

Mr. W. F. King having been designated as commissioner on the part of Great Britain, the work authorized was thereupon jointly undertaken by him and Mr. Tittmann.

APPENDIX III

ORIGINAL SURVEY AND DEMARCATION OF THE BOUNDARY UNDER THE TREATY OF 1842

In accordance with the provisions of the treaty of Washington, 1842, two commissioners were appointed to survey and mark the boundary from the source of the St. Croix River to the St. Lawrence River, Albert Smith, for the United States, and Lieut. Col. J. B. B. Estcourt, for Great Britain. The United States commissioner's assistants were Major Graham, head of the scientific corps of the United States, Captain Johnson, Lieutenants Whipple, Thom, Emory, Lee, Warner, Raynolds, and Meade of the United States topographical engineers, and Mr. Lally, Mr. A. W. Longfellow, and Mr. S. Longfellow, jr. The British commissioner's assistants were Captains Broughton and Robinson, and Lieutenant Pipon, of the Royal Engineers, and Mr. Featherstonhaugh, Mr. Wilkinson, and Mr. Scott, besides a number of noncommissioned officers of the Royal Sappers and Miners.

The first meeting of the commissioners took place on May 1, 1843, at Bangor, Me. They then agreed to commence the work at the source of the St. Croix; but, on account of the lateness of the season, they decided to postpone field operations until the 1st of June, on which date they agreed to meet again at Houlton, Me. At their first meeting they agreed that the surveys should be controlled by latitudes, longitudes, and azimuths determined from astronomical observations made at stations on or near the boundary.

For the sake of clearness and continuity, an account of the astronomical work of the two commissions will be given first, without reference to the surveying operations which were carried on at the same time, and which will be presented separately.

Astronomical Observations

The commissioners' plans for the astronomical work, for the eastern division of the boundary, extending from the source of the St. Croix to the head of Halls Stream, included the establishment of a chain of astronomical stations along the St. John River, and stations at the ends of the Southwest and South Lines. Among the more important of these stations were those at Grand Falls, the mouth of the Madawaska, the mouth of the Big Black, the forks of the St. John (the junction of the northwest and southwest branches), the outlet of Lake Pohenagamook, English Lake, and the intersection of parallel 46° 25′ with the Southwest Branch of the St. John River. In every case the difference of longitude between two stations was determined by the interchange of chronometers, though lunar observations also were made at many of the stations.

The position of the point 10 miles up the Northwest Branch of the St. John from the forks (defined by the treaty as being the point of intersection of two of the lines of the boundary) was determined by measuring the length and azimuth of a straight line connecting this point with the astronomical station at the forks

322

of the St. John River. This boundary point was also connected by triangulation with the astronomical station "Lake Hill," and the difference of longitude between "Lake Hill" and Quebec was determined by simultaneous observations on signals consisting of flashes of gunpowder.

At several points on the Highlands boundary, astronomical observations were made to determine latitude and azimuth to control the guide lines of the survey in this region.

The astronomical stations of the western division (Halls Stream and the West Line) included Rouses Point, the principal station, the longitude of which was determined by interchange of chronometers with Quebec, Montreal, Albany, and Cambridge, and independently by lunar observations. The other stations in the western division were St. Regis, N. Y., Richford, Vt., and Lake Memphremagog, all of which were directly connected with Rouses Point by observations of gunpowder flashes; and Canaan Corner, which was connected with Lake Memphremagog by interchange of chronometers. Observations for latitude were made at two other points in the western division, at Trout River and John McCoy's on the boundary west of the Richelieu River.

It will be noted that the completion of this program resulted in a chain of astronomical positions, distributed along the boundary, whose longitudes depended on those of Quebec and Cambridge as well as on lunar observations made at many of the stations.

It might be interpolated here that at this time the longitude of Cambridge had been determined by observations of four solar eclipses, a transit of Mercury, and a transit of Venus, by observations of 66 moon culminations with corresponding observations at Greenwich, England, by interchange of 12 chronometers belonging to the Governments of the United States and Great Britain, and from a large number of occultations to which corresponding occultations or meridian observations had been made in England. The longitude of Quebec was determined by a very large number of lunar observations taken there, and combined with values determined from lunar observations taken at some of the other astronomical stations.

Major Graham, the chief astronomer of the United States commission, had been engaged on surveys along the eastern part of the boundary a few years before the survey under the treaty of 1842 was begun. In 1841 and 1842 he had run a due-north line from the source of the St. Croix to a point north of the St. John, and at Houlton he had made many lunar observations for longitude. Other stations at which he had made observations in 1841 and 1842 were the source of the St. Croix River, Grand Falls, Grand River, Green River, Madawaska, Fort Kent, St. Francis, and Allagash, along the St. John River, five places along the St. Francis River, and the Kennebec Road on the Highlands boundary.

As Major Graham had determined the positions of so many stations in the eastern section, the new work in this region was performed chiefly by the British observers, Captain Robinson and Lieutenant Pipon, who, during the preceding winter, had taken a special course of instruction in astronomy at Greenwich Observatory, England, under the personal supervision of Professor Airy, at that time astronomer royal.

The new astronomical work on the St. John River was not commenced until July, 1843, as it was impossible to get boats up the river until the spring floods had subsided. About the end of June, 1843, the British commission reached Grand Falls, where Captain Robinson remained to make observations, while Lieutenant Pipon proceeded up the river to the mouth of the Madawaska. Their chronometers were interchanged several times by carrying them between stations in bateaux or canoes. Captain Robinson then moved by boat to the mouth of the St. Francis, leaving Lieutenant Pipon at Madawaska. The observing program was repeated, and Lieutenant Pipon ascended the St. Francis, passing Captain Robinson, and occupied a station at the outlet of Lake Pohenagamook. After completing the observing at this station, he came down the St. Francis and, passing Robinson again, went up the St. John to the mouth of the Big Black. Robinson then passed him in turn and went to the forks of the St. John.

In November, before the observing program and interchange of chronometers between these last two stations could be completed, the freezing of the river put a stop to operations. But by January 10 of the following year, 1844, the ice was sufficiently strong to permit the use of carioles drawn by horses to carry the chronometers, and the work was resumed and continued until observations on the Northwest Branch were completed at the boundary point 10 miles from the forks, which point had been determined and agreed upon during the preceding summer by survey parties of the commission. Captain Robinson and Lieutenant Pipon carried out their observing program only with much difficulty, as the extreme cold seriously affected the rates of the chronometers and sometimes stopped them; besides it made the men unwilling to undertake the transportation of the chronometers between stations. When this part of the astronomical work had been completed Captain Robinson and Lieutenant Pipon went out to Quebec early in February, where they remained for a month.

Captain Robinson returned early in March to the boundary point at the end of the 10-mile line on the Northwest Branch to supervise the running of the boundary between that point and the outlet of Lake Pohenagamook, known as the Southwest Line. Lieutenant Pipon had gone from Quebec to Riviere du Loup and from there to Lake Pohenagamook, to work along the same line toward Captain Robinson. Having finished the preliminary line from Lake Pohenagamook to the Northwest Branch in a satisfactory manner, in April both left the woods to be gone until the end of the spring "break-up." Both officers then returned; and Captain Robinson made observations at the Northwest Branch while Lieutenant Pipon determined by trial the intersection of parallel 46° 25′ with the Southwest Branch of the St. John River. The difference of longitude between that point and the Northwest Branch was determined by interchange of chronometers.

Major Graham determined the intersection of the Southwest Branch of the St. John River with parallel 46° 25′, and the combined results of his and Lieutenant Pipon's observations were adopted. He also made independent observations for longitude.

As it was desired to connect the station on the Northwest Branch astronomically with Quebec, Lieutenant Pipon, having finished his work on the Southwest Branch, proceeded to Quebec, where he occupied a station on the Plains of Abraham. Captain Robinson moved his instruments from the Northwest Branch to a near-by hill, called Lake Hill, which was connected with the Northwest Branch by triangulation.

About 20 miles from Lake Hill, in the direction of Quebec, a range of hills could be seen, and it was rightly supposed that these would be visible from Quebec. To the highest of these, Captain Robinson sent Sergeant McGuckin, of the Royal Sappers and Miners, with a party of laborers and the necessary camp outfit. From the Lake Hill station a heliostat was kept reflecting in the direction of this hill to enable Sergeant McGuckin on his arrival there to be sure he was on the one chosen.

When he had reached the hill and found, on climbing a tree, that he could see back to Lake Hill and forward in the direction of Quebec, he had his party cut down the timber on top of the hill, leaving one tall tree standing in the center of the clearing. The limbs and branches were cut off this tree and near its top was fastened a small pulley, through which was run an endless rope with a conical tin cup attached. A charge of gunpowder, weighing from one-fourth to one-half pound, was wrapped in paper and put in the cup with a piece of touch paper, which was lighted, and the cup was quickly hoisted to the top of the tree where the charge exploded. The cup was then hauled down again and the operation was repeated.

Sergeant McGuckin had orders to fire these charges every 10 minutes between 8 and 10 o'clock in the evening. He was informed by signals from Lake Hill when Lieutenant Pipon at Quebec was ready to observe. At the beginning and end of each evening's program two rockets were fired, which were found to be more difficult to observe than the bursting charges. Transit observations for time were made on the same evenings as those on which the flashes were observed, this program being carried out on six nights in the last week in September, 1844.

Captain Robinson and Lieutenant Pipon attempted also to find the difference in longitude between Lake Hill and Quebec by interchange of chronometers, but as the trip took over four days on very rough roads, they abandoned the attempt. Captain Robinson then left Lake Hill for Montreal, but arrived at that station too late in the season to begin the determination of its longitude, which involved the interchange of chronometers with Quebec via steamers on the St. Lawrence. Captain Robinson returned to England in December, 1844, taking with him the chronometers and such instruments as needed repairs.

In the meantime, a substantial observatory had been built at Quebec, and Lieutenant Pipon spent the winter there, making observations for absolute longitude by lunar transits and moon culminating stars.

Captain Robinson returned from England in time to commence observations at St. Helen Island, opposite Montreal, at the opening of navigation on the St. Lawrence River. The difference in longitude between this point and Quebec was obtained by four interchanges of chronometers.

Lieutenant Pipon then moved from Quebec to St. Regis, where the West Line ends at the St. Lawrence River, and set up a station there. Chronometers were again exchanged with St. Helen Island, being carried by steamer and coach to

Cornwall and thence to St. Regis by canoe. In the meantime several interchanges of chronometers were made between Captain Robinson, at St. Helen Island, and Major Graham, who was carrying out an extensive observing program at Rouses Point.

St. Regis and Rouses Point were also connected directly, on the suggestion of Lieutenant Pipon, by observations of flashes fired on Lyon Mountain, N. Y. These observations were made by Lieutenant Pipon at St. Regis and Major Graham at Rouses Point, and gave a difference in longitude agreeing very closely with that obtained by the transportation of chronometers via St. Helen Island.

Lieutenant Pipon also made observations for latitude at a station called John McCoy's, on the boundary 4 miles from Russeltown, Quebec, and at another station near the boundary village of Trout River.

In the meantime Captain Robinson had left St. Helen Island and gone to Lake Memphremagog. The difference in longitude between this station and Rouses Point was determined by observations of flashes fired on Jay Peak. These flashes were observed by Captain Robinson at Lake Memphremagog and Major Graham at Rouses Point; some of them were also observed at an astronomical station at Richford by Lieutenant Thom, with whom Captain Robinson made an additional set of observations.

As an experiment, differences in longitude between Rouses Point and Lake Memphremagog and between Richford and Lake Memphremagog were obtained by interchange of chronometers, but only one round trip between each pair of stations was made. The results agreed quite closely with those obtained by observations of flashes. When this work was completed the British officers went to Washington, to assist in revising the computations.

In December of that year, 1845, Major Graham made observations at the intersection of the West Line with Halls Stream, near Canaan Corner, while Lieutenant Whipple occupied the station at Lake Memphremagog. The difference in longitude was obtained by transportation of chronometers, but observations were also made at both places for absolute longitude. At a station on the Highlands near the source of Halls Stream, Lieutenant Emory observed a latitude.

The British observers were assisted in every possible way by Professor Airy, astronomer royal at Greenwich Observatory, who not only gave them special training, but advised them as to the methods and instruments to be used, and finally revised all their computations. Professor Airy also supplied Major Graham with considerable astronomical data obtained not only at Greenwich but at other European observatories. The instruments used by the British commission were two 30-inch transits, a 20-inch transit, a 15-inch altitude and azimuth instrument, a 12-inch altitude and azimuth instrument, besides numerous smaller theodolites, reflecting circles, sextants, compasses, barometers, and chronometers.

Major Graham's observations were taken mostly with two transits, whose focal lengths of telescope were 43 and 46 inches and aperture $2\frac{3}{4}$ inches, whereas Lieutenant Whipple used a 30-inch transit. The last two of these instruments, as well as many of those used by the British commission, were made by the firm of Troughton & Simms, London, England.

SURVEYING THE BOUNDARY

For purposes of reference it will be convenient to retain the names of the nine subdivisions of this portion of the international boundary which were used by the commission of 1842. In the order in which they were surveyed, they are as follows:

1. The North Line, from the source of the St. Croix to the St. John River.
2. The St. John River.
3. The St. Francis River.
4. The Southwest Line.
5. The South Line.
6. The Southwest Branch of the St. John River.
7. The Highlands.
8. Halls Stream.
9. The West Line, or forty-fifth parallel of Valentine and Collins.

THE NORTH LINE

Surveying operations were begun in June, 1843, at the source of the St. Croix River, at the wooden post set in 1817, which point had been first marked in 1797 by the commission appointed under the treaty of 1794 to determine and describe the true St. Croix River.

As the treaty of 1842 provided that the "exploring line" of Colonel Bouchette and Mr. Johnson, run in 1817–18, was to be adopted as the boundary, it had first to be relocated. This was done with difficulty by a joint party from the two commissions, who retraced and reblazed the old line. Afterwards it was cleared to a width of 30 feet by a United States party working from the Presque Isle River to the source of the St. Croix and by a British party working northward from the Presque Isle River to the St. John. After the vista was opened, the line was surveyed by a joint party under Mr. Wilkinson and Mr. Lally. Courses of convenient lengths were laid down, but each one was required to fall within the 30-foot strip. At 1-mile intervals, and at each angle of deflection, as well as at the crossings of roads and rivers, a cast-iron post was subsequently set. This work was completed by December, 1843, except for the setting of a few monuments, which were set the following spring by Mr. Wilkinson and by an officer representing the United States.

THE ST. JOHN RIVER

The St. John River also was surveyed during the summer of 1843, by two joint parties. One party, directed by Captain Broughton and Lieutenant Thom, for the British and United States commissions, respectively, surveyed the river between Grand Falls and Madawaska; another, with Mr. Featherstonhaugh and Lieutenant Lee in similar capacities, surveyed down the river from the mouth of the St. Francis to the Madawaska. Apparently the method employed was a chained traverse run along each bank, with connecting lines to points on the islands, which were also surveyed. Monuments were placed on these islands the following year by Mr. Wilkinson and an officer representing the United States. Soundings were taken in the river near the islands to determine on which side the deeper channel, and consequently the boundary, lay. The surveys were finished, and charts prepared from them were completed at Grand Falls by October 12; and on that and the following day, Mr. Smith and Lieutenant Colonel Estcourt decided the nationality of the islands.

THE ST. FRANCIS RIVER

As the treaty provided that the boundary should follow the St. Francis River from its mouth to the outlet of Lake Pohenagamook, it was necessary to select a point which should be considered the outlet of that lake. This was done on August 15, 1843, by Lieutenant Colonel Estcourt and Captain Johnson; and though the outlet of the lake is well defined, a stake was set at the adopted point as a mark for the surveyors. The river was surveyed in September and October by a joint party, Lieutenant Thom representing the United States commission and Sergeant McGuckin the British, but no monuments were set.

THE SOUTHWEST LINE

The treaty provided that this line was to connect the outlet of Lake Pohenaga-mook with a point on the Northwest Branch of the St. John River, which should be 10 miles in the nearest direction from the main branch of the St. John. The exact point to be considered the outlet of Lake Pohenagamook, as already mentioned, was chosen by Lieutenant Colonel Estcourt and Captain Johnson, and the treaty point on the Northwest Branch was also determined in the summer of 1843.

This work was done chiefly by the United States commission, their parties working under Captain Johnson and Lieutenant Meade. After the Northwest Branch had been surveyed, a trial line was cut and measured, starting at a point just below the junction of the Northwest and Southwest Branches, which was the nearest point on the main stream to the point to be determined, and ending at its intersection with the Northwest Branch. This proved to be nearly 11 miles in length, so a second trial line was cut, which was found by the United States party to be 10 miles and 10 feet in length, and later, by the British measurement, 10 miles and 363 feet. In the meantime, Mr. Featherstonhaugh, for the British commission, determined by triangulation that the approximate position of the treaty point on the Northwest Branch was about 12 miles from the St. Lawrence watershed. Lieutenant Colonel Estcourt's instructions from the British Government were that as long as this distance was at least 7 miles it was quite unimportant whether the point on the Northwest Branch was exactly 10 miles from the forks; and since these instructions were satisfied in both particulars, the intersection of the second trial line with the Northwest Branch was accepted as the treaty point, without any further attempt being made to find a point exactly 10 miles from the forks.

It had been agreed by Mr. Smith and Lieutenant Colonel Estcourt, at a conference held in Washington after most of the field operations of the season of 1843 were finished, that the British commission should be responsible for the opening of the Southwest and South Lines during the winter and spring of 1844, and that the United States commission should cut the line on the Highlands from the Kennebec Road to the source of Halls Stream. The British commission was to be responsible also for that portion of the Highlands east of the Kennebec Road, and it was agreed that the boundary along the Highlands was to be cut during the summer of 1844.

As previously mentioned in the description of the astronomical work, the two ends of this Southwest Line were connected by a chain of astronomical stations, which made it possible to compute the azimuth of the line joining these two points. This part of the astronomical work was completed by the end of January, 1844. The cutting of the line was commenced from both ends in March, 1844, by two British parties, one, under Captain Robinson, working eastward from the treaty point on the Northwest Branch, and the other, under Lieutenant Pipon, working westward from the outlet of Lake Pohenagamook. After Captain Robinson's party had cut 4 miles, their line passed over the shoulder of a very high hill, to which Captain Robinson moved his transit, and from this point he commanded a view of about 40 miles in the direction of the line so that it was not necessary for him to move his instruments again. The chopping party under Mr. Scott ran the line by compass, but they obtained a correction to this line on the top of each hill at night by using a birch-bark torch as a mark and flashes of gun powder for signals. Lieutenant Pipon's party was not so fortunate, and his transit had to be set up at several points on the line.

The two parties came abreast of each other after five weeks of work which was performed under trying and difficult conditions, due to the melting of the snow. The perpendicular distance between the ends of the two lines was 341 feet, which corresponds to an error in the determination of the difference of longitude between the two ends of the line of less than one-half second of time. After the two parties met, each retraced its way, offsetting a signal to the true line on the top of each hill they had passed.

On account of the spring "break-up," work was necessarily suspended until June, when the line as marked by the signals at the end of the offsets was opened out to a width of 30 feet, an 8-foot strip in the center being cut close to the ground. Parties of the British commission, under Mr. Wilkinson, then tested the alignment throughout, using a transit instrument. Lieutenant Thom inspected the line and made a separate survey of it for the United States commission during the same season, 1844.

THE SOUTH LINE

The treaty of Washington defined this part of the international boundary as the straight line extending from the treaty point on the Northwest Branch of the St. John (the end of the Southwest Line) to the intersection of parallel 46° 25′ with the Southwest Branch of the St. John. This latter point was determined by Lieutenant Pipon, of the British commission, in June, 1844, and the determination was later verified by Major Graham of the United States commission. The difference in longitude between the two points was determined by the transportation of chronometers. After the azimuth of the line joining the two points had been computed, work was commenced at both ends, and when the two lines came abreast of each other they were 576 feet apart. Offsets were made from these preliminary lines and the true line was cut out to a width of 30 feet with an 8-foot clear strip. This line, which was cut by the British commission alone, with parties under Mr. Wilkinson and Mr. Scott, was finished in September, 1844, and was examined and surveyed for the United States commission in 1844 by Corporal O'Donnel.

THE SOUTHWEST BRANCH OF THE ST. JOHN RIVER

This portion of the boundary was surveyed in the winter of 1844–45 by Mr. Lally, of the United States commission. The survey consisted of a traverse chained on the ice and controlled by a scheme of long guide lines from which offsets were measured to the river. This work was subsequently examined and verified by Mr. Wilkinson for the British commission.

THE HIGHLANDS

As has already been mentioned, the commissioners had agreed that the United States commission should undertake the cutting of the vista along the Highlands west of the Kennebec Road, while the British commission should be responsible for the part of the Highlands east of that road. The two commissioners agreed to meet at the Kennebec Road on the Highlands, on June 1, 1844. Mr. Smith, the United States commissioner, however, was delayed by Congress not voting funds in time and did not arrive until July 28. In the meantime, Lieutenant Colonel Estcourt had received instructions from the British Government that in case the United States commissioner should not be in a position to push the work rapidly, he had authority to undertake as much of it as he could and to arrange with the United States commissioner about subsequent repayment.

Lieutenant Colonel Estcourt was also instructed that the British Government considered it unnecessary that the boundary in the Highlands should run around the heads of all the small streams, and that a separation of the main valleys was all that was essential. This advice, however, was not followed, possibly due to the objection of Mr. Smith, and the boundary was made to follow the divide between even the smallest streams.

Lieutenant Colonel Estcourt, on the nonarrival of Mr. Smith in June, had made arrangements by which he could quickly secure large numbers of men and quantities of provisions. When Mr. Smith finally arrived, they agreed, in view of the lateness of the season and of Lieutenant Colonel Estcourt's preparedness, that the British commission should undertake the cutting of the line along the Highlands west of the Kennebec Road, while the United States commission should undertake the section east of the Kennebec Road. As this meant that the British commission would have cut a much greater part of the boundary vista than the United States commission, Mr. Smith agreed to accept the entire responsibility for the cutting out of the West Line. They agreed further that the line along the Highlands, as cut by each commission, was to be regarded as exploratory until verified through surveys made later by the other commission.

By the time these plans had been formulated, work had already been commenced at the Kennebec Road. Setting out from the height of land at that point, guide lines were cut through the woods, as nearly as could be estimated in the general direction of the dividing ridge. From these guide lines, offsets at intervals of about one-half mile were run across the dividing ridge into the drainage basin on the other side. Starting near the head of a stream flowing, for instance, into the St. Lawrence, these offsets were made to cross the ridge and were prolonged until they encountered water flowing in the opposite direction or toward the Atlantic.

The highest point on this line would be, as a rule, on the dividing ridge. In this way, a series of summits was obtained, which, with the connecting line following the divide, constituted the boundary. The direction of the guide lines was changed whenever it was thought necessary, and the bearings of the guide lines and offsets were observed and their lengths were measured, thus controlling the traverse of the boundary itself. Incidentally, bearings of high, conspicuous hills were observed as the work progressed, so that their positions could be shown on the boundary maps.

In order to connect the before mentioned summits, a novel method was employed. A man was stationed at one summit with instructions to blow a horn at intervals of a few minutes. This enabled a party at the next summit to form a clear idea of his direction and, following the highest ground in all its windings, they traversed the ridge between the two summits, blazing the trees as they went, after which the line was cleared out to a width of 30 feet. The work on the guide lines was kept well in advance of the other survey operations in order to enable a number of parties to work simultaneously on the boundary itself.

A large number of men, at one time as many as 500, were employed in the several parties of the British commission engaged in this work. About one-fourth of the men were required to pack in supplies on their backs. The parties engaged in opening the vista found that 10 men would clear about one-fourth mile of boundary per day.

A joint party from each commission determined the chain of summits from the Kennebec Road to the source of the Southwest Branch of the St. John River. The boundary was cleared by a party of the United States commission and was later surveyed separately by Messrs. Lally and Wilkinson for the United States and British commissions, respectively.

The British parties, under Captain Broughton and Mr. Featherstonhaugh, cut the guide lines and determined the summits west of the Kennebec Road, Captain Broughton working from the Kennebec Road to Arnold River, and Mr. Featherstonhaugh between Arnold River and the source of Halls Stream. Mr. Featherstonhaugh assisted also in the determination of the line between the Kennebec Road and the source of the Southwest Branch.

The cutting of much of the boundary vista west of the Kennebec Road was done by parties under Mr. Wilkinson and Mr. Scott, who, after finishing the work on the Southwest and South Lines, brought their men through the woods to the Kennebec Road. Wilkinson's party cut from the Kennebec Road to a point 20 miles west, while Scott's party of 140 men cut from that point to Arnold River, a distance of 70 miles, after which he and Captain Broughton went out to the Kennebec Road and thence to Quebec. In the meantime, Mr. Featherstonhaugh was cutting the boundary vista as well as the guide lines west from Arnold River. As the season was getting late, Lieutenant Colonel Estcourt sent orders to Mr. Scott to bring his party to the source of Halls Stream, and with this additional large force the cutting of the line was completed late in November.

The following summer, 1845, Mr. Wilkinson surveyed the boundary for the British commission from the outlet of Lake Pohenagamook to Arnold River, in the

Highlands. From available records it would appear that from that point westward the boundary had been surveyed the previous fall by Captain Broughton and Mr. Featherstonhaugh.

A separate system of guide lines, with offsets to the boundary summits, was established for the United States commission in 1845, and surveys of the boundary through the Highlands were also made by Mr. Lally and Lieutenant Emory.

HALLS STREAM

Halls Stream was surveyed by running a guide line in a northerly direction from the intersection of the stream with the West Line, or forty-fifth parallel of Valentine and Collins. Offsets from this guide line were run to intersect the stream, and a chained traverse was also run along the stream itself, this survey being made by a joint party, Mr. Featherstonhaugh and Mr. A. W. Longfellow representing the respective commissions.

THE WEST LINE

The treaty of Washington provided that the old Valentine and Collins line, approximately following the forty-fifth parallel, should remain the boundary. This line appears to have been merely a compass line, as the resurvey in the summer of 1845 disclosed the fact that it diverged greatly, though not consistently, from the parallel it was supposed to follow. It was found that it could be traced, though with difficulty, by following the old blazes; and when it had been reopened to a width of 30 feet, points were selected in the cleared area and were joined by straight lines. At one of these points the deflection angle was found to be nearly 9°. The exploration was done by the United States commission and verified by the British. The clearing of the line was performed entirely by the United States commission.

Lieutenant Colonel Estcourt, the British commissioner, in his report states that each commission made an independent survey of the line, which appears to be rather a remarkable statement in view of the fact that, though the deflection angles were measured to seconds, there was no discrepancy whatever in the results obtained by the observations of the two commissions. Observations for latitude and longitude were also made at various points along the line by both British and United States observers.

The line was terminated on the bank of the St. Lawrence at the monument set by Andrew Ellicott in 1817 to mark his determination of the forty-fifth parallel. This point was accepted in 1818 by the commissioners, acting under Articles V and VI of the treaty of Ghent, after an independent determination of the latitude had been made by astronomers representing the United States and British commissioners.

Four years after the survey of the Vermont-Quebec boundary under the treaty of 1842, complaints were made that monument 560, in the village of Beebe Plain, had been moved from its original position. This report was investigated, and the monument was restored to its proper place by a commission consisting of Lieutenant Colonels Graham and Ord, representing the United States and Great Britain, respectively. At the same time, this commission set several square, flat-topped granite posts with an east-and-west groove cut in their top surfaces as additional boundary monuments in that vicinity and also reset four of the other cast-iron monuments near Derby Line, Vt., and Rock Island, Quebec, which had been slightly displaced.

The report of Lieutenant Colonels Graham and Ord, made to the Secretary of State of the United States and to the Governor General of Canada, gives in detail the surveying operations and manner of setting of the several additional boundary marks.

In 1851 the West Line was resurveyed for the United States by Lieutenant Thom.

INCIDENTAL SURVEYS

In addition to surveys of the boundary itself, surveys were made of various rivers and lakes near-by, during which the topography was mapped. As already mentioned, a United States party surveyed the Northwest Branch of the St. John River and the St. John itself near the forks in the summer of 1843. During February, March, and April of 1844, British parties surveyed various tributaries and branches of the St. John on the ice. This work was continued by both commissions along the line, although the United States commission devoted more attention to it than did the British. Unfortunately, just before the maps of the United States commission, showing all the topography, were about to be deposited with the Department of State they were destroyed by fire; and although copies had already been sent to England, these did not show all the topography that had been surveyed.

MARKING THE BOUNDARY

Two sizes of hollow cast-iron monuments were designed for boundary marks and approved by the commissioners, and these were cast at Boston. The smaller of these monuments was 6 feet long, 6 inches square at the bottom, tapering to 4 inches square at the top. The larger ones were in three sections, with a total length of 10 feet, 15 inches square at the bottom, tapering to 5 inches square at the top. A total of 773 of these monuments were used to mark the boundary from the source of the St. Croix River to the St. Lawrence. Wooden posts were set at two additional points and were replaced by iron monuments in 1916.

The larger monuments, of which only 13 were used, were set at the following points:

The source of the St. Croix.

The intersection of the River St. John with the North Line.

The outlet of Lake Pohenagamook.

The boundary point on the Northwest Branch.

On the left bank of the Southwest Branch at its first intersection with the South Line.

On the left bank of the Southwest Branch at its intersection with the parallel of 46° 25′.

At the first point on the Highlands near the source of the Southwest Branch.

On the east side of the Kennebec Road.

Near the source of Halls Stream.

On the right bank of Halls Stream at its intersection with the West Line.

The intersection of the Richelieu River with the West Line, on the right bank.

The intersection of the Richelieu River with the West Line, on the left bank.

The intersection of the River St. Lawrence with the West Line near St. Regis.

On the North Line, as has already been mentioned, a monument was set at the end of each mile, at the end of each course, and at points where the line was crossed by roads or rivers. The monuments at the ends of courses were set diagonally to the line; all others were set square. Most of these monuments on this line were set, by a joint party under Mr. Wilkinson and Mr. Lally, in the fall of 1843. The remainder, and those on the islands of the St. John, were set the succeeding spring by Mr. Wilkinson and by an officer representing the United States.

No monuments were set along the St. Francis River. The Southwest and South Lines were marked by monuments set at intervals of 1 mile, at points where rivers or lakes intersect the line, and on every prominent elevation crossed by the boundary. These monuments were hauled to the boundary during the winter of 1844–45 on horse-drawn sleighs, and were set in the spring by a British party under Mr. Wilkinson.

The Southwest Branch of the St. John was marked by two small monuments at each of its two forks, and a monument was also placed at the small lake at the head of the Southwest Branch. Three more were placed along the small stream which flows into that lake from near the point selected as the first point on the Highlands, where one of the large monuments was set. All this work was done by a British party.

Along the Highlands the monuments had to be hauled to their sites on toboggans during the winter of 1844–45. A British party of 80 men started into the woods at Halls Stream and, after undergoing great hardships and exposure, finally came out on the Kennebec Road, having deposited the monuments at intervals as they progressed. The monuments between the Kennebec Road and the source of the Southwest Branch of the St. John were hauled in during the same winter by a United States party. The monuments between the source of the Southwest Branch and Arnold River were erected the following summer by a British party under Mr. Scott; the remainder of the monuments along the Highlands were erected by two United States surveying parties, who also set the monuments along Halls Stream. Many of the monuments along the Highlands were set in the swampy dips or saddles of the ridge, from which streams run in opposite directions, one toward the St. Lawrence and the other toward the Atlantic.

The West Line was marked in 1845, mostly by United States parties, who used methods previously employed on the North Line.

Transportation of Supplies

On account of the sparsely settled condition of the greater part of the country through which this portion of the boundary passes, the problem of the transportation of supplies was a difficult and serious one, especially as the number of men employed was frequently very large, the British commission alone, in 1844, employing about 500 at one time. No railroads approached the boundary, except at Lake Champlain, and few roads, except along part of the St. John Valley and the West Line.

The commissioners at their first meeting, on May 1, 1843, at Bangor, had agreed that it was inadvisable to commence field operations before the first of June. In the meantime, however, the officers of the British commission had reached Fredericton and were making preparations for work. Tents were secured from Boston, provisions from St. John, men were hired at Fredericton, and 18 boats were ordered to be built at Woodstock.

Grand Falls was made the principal supply depot for the summer of 1843, and to that point the supplies of the British commission were taken by boat from Fredericton as soon as the spring floods had somewhat subsided. To supply the parties working along the North Line was comparatively easy, as the St. John River runs nearly parallel and comparatively close to that line. Several roads from the river crossed the boundary, and the United States military roads touched the line near Houlton and Fort Fairfield.

Supplies for the use of the parties working on the St. John were taken up in boats. A subsidiary depot was established at the mouth of the St. Francis, on which stream canoes only could be used; but fortunately only small quantities of provisions were required for the small parties engaged in surveying it.

The United States parties engaged in cutting the 10-mile line from the forks of the St. John to the Northwest Branch had established their principal depot at Seven Islands, to which place the supplies were brought up the St. John in boats. In August, 1843, Lieutenant Colonel Estcourt paid a visit to these parties. It took him a week to go by water from the mouth of the St. Francis to Seven Islands, on account of the rapids and shoals; and with this experience in mind, he decided that transportation on the river would be too slow and expensive for the large quantities of supplies which would be required in that region during the winter and following summer. Similar objections applied to the transportation of any considerable quantities up the St. Francis. Having come to this conclusion, Lieutenant Colonel Estcourt, after reaching the Northwest Branch, set off with a couple of men through the woods toward the St. Lawrence, and in two or three days reached the village of St. Thomas, now called Montmagny.

As he expected the cutting of the North Line to be completed by the end of August, he sent orders for the chopping party on that work to come to St. Thomas via the St. John River and Temiscouata Portage to take up road construction. This party, under Mr. Scott, arrived about the middle of September and immediately began work on a road from that point to Lake Ishaeganalshegeck (now called English Lake) on the Northwest Branch of the St. John.

This road, as soon as completed, was used for the transportation of provisions, chiefly salt pork and sea biscuits, and during the winter of 1843–44 large quantities of supplies were hauled in and stored in a camp built at English Lake. Subsidiary depots were also established during the winter on the other side of this lake and also at the forks of the St. John and at the mouth of the Big Black, and were supplied from the main depot at English Lake. Another depot was also established at the outlet of Lake Pohenagamook, to which point the stores were hauled over a road from the Temiscouata Portage.

The Kennebec Road was also used in the spring of 1844 as a provision road and, as soon as it was agreed that the British commission should undertake to cut out the line along the Highlands during the summer and fall of that year, principal provision depots were established on the Kennebec Road and at Lake Megantic. When the work approached the head of Halls Stream a road was cut from that point to meet the survey parties, and thereafter provisions reached them over this new road.

The supplies had to be carried on men's backs from the provision depots to the working parties; and, as the distances were often long, sometimes as much as 40 miles, and the trails and the weather very bad, many men would make only one trip. Along Halls Stream and the West Line, however, the roads were sufficiently numerous to make the transportation problem comparatively simple.

At the conclusion of the field work, maps of the boundary were prepared and signed by the commissioners. In addition, volumes containing all the astronomical observations of both commissions and appendices containing abstracts of the surveys of the various portions of the boundary were prepared and submitted to the two governments.

A joint report on the work of the commission (reprinted in full in Appendix II) was signed on June 28, 1847, by Lieutenant Colonel Estcourt and Mr. Smith.

APPENDIX IV

ELEVATIONS AND DESCRIPTIONS OF BENCH MARKS

Under this heading are given the elevations and descriptions of all permanent primary level bench marks of the international boundary survey along and adjacent to the boundary, together with similar bench marks of the surveys made by other bureaus, which were used for vertical control of the topographic surveys along the boundary.

The bench marks of the Geodetic Survey of Canada consist, except where otherwise specified, of a "copper bolt, three-quarters of an inch in diameter and four inches long, stamped on the end with the letters 'G. S. C., B. M.' and the number of the bench mark," set usually in the masonry of bridges or buildings.

THE NORTH LINE

	Elevation (feet)
Initial monument, at the source of the St. Croix River; bronze disk set in the north side of the top of the concrete base, 6 inches from the cast-iron post	540. 39
Monument 82, near; top of bowlder 38 feet north of Canadian Pacific Railway, Presque Isle-Andover branch, 54 feet east of international boundary line	373. 48
Monument 14–A, in north face of; 5 miles west of Debec, New Brunswick, on Houlton branch of Canadian Pacific Railway; Geodetic Survey of Canada B. M. No. 22–B	530. 20
Monument 82, in south face of concrete base of; 4¾ miles west of Aroostook, New Brunswick, on Aroostook branch of Canadian Pacific Railway; Geodetic Survey of Canada B. M. No. 42–B	373. 06

THE ST. JOHN AND ST. FRANCIS RIVERS

	Elevation (feet)
Siegas, New Brunswick; in easterly concrete footing under Canadian Pacific Railway water tank; Geodetic Survey of Canada B. M. No. 51–B	451. 83
Siegas, New Brunswick, 2 miles northwest of; opposite a point on Canadian Pacific Railway at mileage 38.9 from Aroostook, New Brunswick; in northwest face of coping on northeast end of concrete arch culvert under Canadian National Railway; Geodetic Survey of Canada B. M. No. 52–B	439. 20
Ste. Anne de Madawaska, New Brunswick, 2 miles northwest of; in southwest concrete wall of culvert under Canadian National Railway, opposite a point on Canadian Pacific Railway at second telegraph pole northwest of milepost 43 from Aroostook, New Brunswick; Geodetic Survey of Canada B. M. No. 53–B	459. 92
Green River, New Brunswick, railway station, three-fourths mile southeast of; in southeast face of concrete wall behind northwest abutment of Canadian Pacific Railway bridge over Green River; Geodetic Survey of Canada B. M. No. 54–B	457. 01
St. Basil, New Brunswick, 2½ miles southeast of; in northeast concrete wall of culvert under Canadian National Railway opposite a point on Canadian Pacific Railway at eighth telegraph pole northwest of milepost 50 from Aroostook, New Brunswick; Geodetic Survey of Canada B. M. No. 55–B	478. 17
Edmundston, New Brunswick; in northeast concrete wing wall of subway under Canadian National Railway, 300 feet west of bridge over Madawaska River; Geodetic Survey of Canada B. M. No. 59–B	461. 82
Edmundston, New Brunswick; in face of rock cut at north side of railway track, 140 feet west of west wall of Canadian Pacific station house; Geodetic Survey of Canada B. M. No. 60–B	482. 94
Baker Brook, New Brunswick, one-fourth mile west of; in east face—north side of track—of concrete retaining wall behind east abutment of plate-girder bridge on Canadian National Railway; Geodetic Survey of Canada B. M. No. 264–B	514. 40

Monument 178, in north face of concrete base of; 10 feet south of south line of Canadian National Railway right of way and one-half mile west of Estcourt, Quebec, on west bank of the St. Francis River; Geodetic Survey of Canada B. M. No. 277–B_____ | Elevation (feet) | 685. 58

THE KENNEBEC ROAD—VICINITY OF JACKMAN, ME., TO THE BOUNDARY

Jackman, Me., 7.3 miles north of; at intersection of Heald Pond Road with Canada (Kennebec) Road; top of large rock opposite schoolhouse; bronze disk stamped "Me. 1922"; United States Geological Survey P. B. M_____ 1, 516. 54

Jackman, Me., 10.2 miles north of; 450 feet south of summit of hill, 10 feet east of road, 60 feet west of logging railroad, on flat top rock; bronze disk marked "U. S. & C. B. Survey B. M.," cemented in rock_____ 2, 083. 87

Jackman, Me., 13.4 miles north of; across road from northwest corner of grain field, 125 feet southeast of branch road, 30 feet northeast of center of road, on large rock 6 by 12 feet; bronze disk marked "U. S. & C. B. Survey B. M.," cemented in rock_____ 1, 778. 84

Monument 351–B, in top of; on east side of old Canada (Kennebec) Road opposite line house; about 16.7 miles north of Jackman, Me.; bronze disk_____ 2, 075. 71

Monument 351; top of iron post_____ 2, 101. 47

Monument 351–A; bronze disk in top of concrete monument_____ 2, 088. 54

Monument 352; top of iron post_____ 2, 068. 14

THE HIGHLANDS BOUNDARY, CANADIAN PACIFIC RAILWAY CROSSING TO THE HEAD OF HALLS STREAM

Monument 402, 89 feet west of; about 160 feet east of Boundary Siding station house; in concrete bench-mark pier, 2 feet north of south line of Canadian Pacific Railway right of way; Geodetic Survey of Canada B. M. No. 24–A–2_____ 1, 849. 48

Monument 402, in base of; bronze disk marked "U. S. & C. B. Survey B. M. 1851"_____ 1, 851. 37

Megantic, Quebec; about 550 feet east of railway station, in second course of stonework below top, in south face of retaining wall behind west abutment of Canadian Pacific Railway bridge over Chaudiere River; Geodetic Survey of Canada B. M. No. 22–A_____ 1, 310. 07

Three Lakes Wharf, 30 feet above red waiting room, on large rock; bronze disk marked "U. S. & C. B. Survey B. M."_____ 1, 311. 53

Monument 403, in base of; bronze disk marked "U. S. & C. B. Survey B. M. 2600"_____ 2, 599. 58

Monument 404, in base of; bronze disk marked "U. S. & C. B. Survey B. M. 2072"_____ 2, 071. 70

Monument 405, in base of; bronze disk marked "U. S. & C. B. Survey B. M. 2913"_____ 2, 913. 38

Monument 406, in base of; bronze disk marked "U. S. & C. B. Survey B. M. 2244"_____ 2, 243. 96

Monument 407, in base of; bronze disk marked "U. S. & C. B. Survey B. M. 2805"_____ 2, 804. 68

Monument 408, in base of; bronze disk marked "U. S. & C. B. Survey B. M. 2458"_____ 2, 458. 47

Monument 409, in base of; bronze disk marked "U. S. & C. B. Survey B. M. 2342"_____ 2, 341. 81

Monument 410, in base of; bronze disk marked "U. S. & C. B. Survey B. M. 3319"_____ 3, 319. 30

Monument 411, in base of; bronze disk marked "U. S. & C. B. Survey B. M. 3581"_____ 3, 582. 02

Monument 412, in base of; bronze disk marked "U. S. & C. B. Survey B. M. 3351"_____ 3, 350. 91

Monument 413, in base of; bronze disk marked "U. S. & C. B. Survey B. M. 2993"_____ 2, 993. 15

Monument 414, in base of; bronze disk marked "U. S. & C. B. Survey B. M. 3541"_____ 3, 541. 11

Monument 415, in base of; bronze disk marked "U. S. & C. B. Survey B. M. 2932"_____ 2, 932. 29

Monument 416, in base of; bronze disk marked "U. S. & C. B. Survey B. M. 2342"_____ 2, 341. 76

Monument 417, in base of; bronze disk marked "U. S. & C. B. Survey B. M. 3324"_____ 3, 324. 87

Monument 418, in base of; bronze disk marked "U. S. & C. B. Survey B. M. 3033"_____ 3, 033. 31

Monument 419, in base of; bronze disk marked "U. S. & C. B. Survey B. M. 1707"_____ 1, 707. 69

	Elevation (feet)
Monument 420, in base of; bronze disk marked "U. S. & C. B. Survey B. M. 1510"_____	1, 511. 29
Monument 421, in base of; bronze disk marked "U. S. & C. B. Survey B. M. 1704"_____	1, 704. 42
Monument 422, in base of; bronze disk marked "U. S. & C. B. Survey B. M. 1565"_____	1, 564. 68
Monument 423, in base of; bronze disk marked "U. S. & C. B. Survey B. M. 1479"_____	1, 478. 77
Spider River, 200 feet from; 2 miles northeast of Louise Mountain and 3 miles above Spider Lake; in large rock in front of Bolduc's foreman's cabin; bronze disk marked "U. S. & C. B. Survey B. M."__	1, 366. 96
Monument 424, in base of; bronze disk marked "U. S. & C. B. Survey B. M. 1611"_____	1, 611. 35
Monument 425, in base of; bronze disk marked "U. S. & C. B. Survey B. M. 2470"_____	2, 470. 38
Monument 426, in base of; bronze disk marked "U. S. & C. B. Survey B. M. 2047"_____	2, 047. 20
Monument 427, in base of; bronze disk marked "U. S. & C. B. Survey B. M. 1961"_____	1, 961. 34
Monument 428, in base of; bronze disk marked "U. S. & C. B. Survey B. M. 2185"_____	2, 185. 70
Monument 429, in base of; bronze disk marked "U. S. & C. B. Survey B. M."_____	1, 542. 34
Monument 430, in base of; bronze disk marked "U. S. & C. B. Survey B. M."_____	1, 407. 27
Monument 431, 100 feet northeast of; bronze disk in large rock, disk marked "U. S. & C. B. Survey B. M."_____	1, 534. 70
Monument 431, in base of; bronze disk marked "U. S. & C. B. Survey B. M. 1533"_____	1, 533. 34
Woburn, Quebec, about 1,200 feet west of; in rock abutment of bridge; bronze disk marked "U. S. & C. B. Survey B. M."_____	1, 465. 48
Monument 432, in base of; bronze disk marked "U. S. & C. B. Survey B. M. 1847"_____	1, 846. 92
Monument 433, in base of; bronze disk marked "U. S. & C. B. Survey B. M. 2393"_____	2, 393. 48
Monument 434, in base of; bronze disk marked "U. S. & C. B. Survey B. M."_____	2, 275. 81
Monument 435, in base of; bronze disk marked "U. S. & C. B. Survey B. M. 2763"_____	2, 763. 90
Monument 436, in base of; bronze disk marked "U. S. & C. B. Survey B. M. 2867"_____	2, 867. 82
Monument 437, in base of; bronze disk marked "U. S. & C. B. Survey B. M. 2997"_____	2, 998. 43
Monument 438, in base of; bronze disk marked "U. S. & C. B. Survey B. M. 2531"_____	2, 531. 99
Monument 439, in base of; bronze disk marked "U. S. & C. B. Survey B. M. 3151"_____	3, 152. 87
Monument 440, in base of; bronze disk marked "U. S. & C. B. Survey B. M. 2833"_____	2, 835. 75
Monument 441, in base of; bronze disk marked "U. S. & C. B. Survey B. M. 3291"_____	3, 293. 22
Monument 442, in base of; bronze disk marked "U. S. & C. B. Survey B. M. 3232"_____	3, 234. 27
Monument 443, in base of; bronze disk marked "U. S. & C. B. Survey B. M. 3791"_____	3, 793. 93
Monument 444, in base of; bronze disk marked "U. S. & C. B. Survey B. M. 3351"_____	3, 353. 38
Monument 445, in base of; bronze disk marked "U. S. & C. B. Survey B. M. 3724"_____	3, 726. 85
Monument 446, in base of; bronze disk marked "U. S. & C. B. Survey B. M. 3556"_____	3, 558. 60
Monument 447, in base of; bronze disk marked "U. S. & C. B. Survey B. M. 3532"_____	3, 534. 43
Monument 448, in base of; bronze disk marked "U. S. & C. B. Survey B. M. 2877"_____	2, 879. 89
Monument 449, in base of; bronze disk marked "U. S. & C. B. Survey B. M. 2932"_____	2, 935. 35
Monument 450, in base of; bronze disk marked "U. S. & C. B. Survey B. M. 3524"_____	3, 526. 54
Monument 451, in base of; bronze disk marked "U. S. & C. B. Survey B. M. 3099"_____	3, 102. 41
Monument 452, in base of; bronze disk marked "U. S. & C. B. Survey B. M. 2478"_____	2, 481. 43
Monument 453, in base of; bronze disk marked "U. S. & C. B. Survey B. M. 2622"_____	2, 625. 15

	Elevation (feet)
Monument 454, in base of; bronze disk marked "U. S. & C. B. Survey B. M. 2801"_____	2,803.73
Monument 455, in base of; bronze disk marked "U. S. & C. B. Survey B. M. 3009"_____	3,011.76
Monument 456, in base of; bronze disk marked "U. S. & C. B. Survey B. M. 2636"_____	2,638.89
Monument 457, in base of; bronze disk marked "U. S. & C. B. Survey B. M. 2560"_____	2,562.89
Monument 458, in base of; bronze disk marked "U. S. & C. B. Survey B. M. 2572"_____	2,575.59
Monument 459, in base of; bronze disk marked "U. S. & C. B. Survey B. M. 2356"_____	2,359.36
Monument 460, in base of; bronze disk marked "U. S. & C. B. Survey B. M."_____	2,254.74
Monument 461, in base of; bronze disk marked "U. S. & C. B. Survey B. M. 2349"_____	2,352.12
Monument 462, in base of; bronze disk marked "U. S. & C. B. Survey B. M. 2409"_____	2,412.60
Monument 463, in base of; bronze disk marked "U. S. & C. B. Survey B. M. 2551"_____	2,554.00
Monument 464, in base of; bronze disk marked "U. S. & C. B. Survey B. M. 2574"_____	2,577.85
Monument 465, in base of; bronze disk marked "U. S. & C. B. Survey B. M. 2140"_____	2,139.62
Monument 466, in base of; bronze disk marked "U. S. & C. B. Survey B. M. 2588"_____	2,588.70
Monument 467, in base of; bronze disk marked "U. S. & C. B. Survey B. M. 2672"_____	2,672.07
Monument 468, in base of; bronze disk marked "U. S. & C. B. Survey B. M. 2488"_____	2,487.84
Monument 469, in base of; bronze disk marked "U. S. & C. B. Survey B. M. 2274"_____	2,274.44
Monument 470, in base of; bronze disk marked "U. S. & C. B. Survey B. M. 3192"_____	3,191.89
Monument 471, in base of; bronze disk marked "U. S. & C. B. Survey B. M. 2211"_____	2,211.45
Monument 472, in base of; bronze disk marked "U. S. & C. B. Survey B. M. 2266"_____	2,266.20
Monument 473, in base of; bronze disk marked "U. S. & C. B. Survey B. M. 2359"_____	2,359.69
Monument 474, in base of; bronze disk marked "U. S. & C. B. Survey B. M. 2259"_____	2,260.08
Monument 475, in base of; bronze disk marked "U. S. & C. B. Survey B. M. 2589"_____	2,589.56
Monument 476, in base of; bronze disk marked "U. S. & C. B. Survey B. M."_____	2,521.63
Monument 477, in base of; bronze disk marked "U. S. & C. B. Survey B. M."_____	2,340.02
Chartierville, Quebec, 225 feet west of cross roads in; south side of road to Sawyerville, Quebec; bronze disk set in concrete culvert retaining wall_____	1,681.90
Monument 478, in base of; bronze disk marked "U. S. & C. B. Survey B. M."_____	2,511.04
Monument 479, in base of; bronze disk marked "U. S. & C. B. Survey B. M."_____	3,177.88
Monument 480, in base of; bronze disk marked "U. S. & C. B. Survey B. M."_____	2,932.88
Monument 481, in base of; bronze disk marked "U. S. & C. B. Survey B. M."_____	2,836.06
Monument 482, in base of; bronze disk marked "U. S. & C. B. Survey B. M."_____	2,911.84
Monument 483, in base of; bronze disk marked "U. S. & C. B. Survey B. M."_____	2,406.88
Monument 484, in base of; bronze disk marked "U. S. & C. B. Survey B. M."_____	2,359.50
Monument 485, in base of; bronze disk marked "U. S. & C. B. Survey B. M."_____	2,406.63
Monument 486, in base of; bronze disk marked "U. S. & C. B. Survey B. M."_____	2,302.58
Monument 487, in base of; bronze disk marked "U. S. & C. B. Survey B. M."_____	2,036.22
Monument 488, in base of; bronze disk marked "U. S. & C. B. Survey B. M."_____	2,037.60
Monument 489, in base of; bronze disk marked "U. S. & C. B. Survey B. M."_____	2,261.20
Monument 490, in base of; bronze disk marked "U. S. & C. B. Survey B. M."_____	2,040.18

	Elevation (feet)
Monument 491, in base of; bronze disk marked "U. S. & C. B. Survey B. M."_____	2, 025. 58
Monument 492, in base of; bronze disk marked "U. S. & C. B. Survey B. M."_____	1, 830. 77
Monument 493, in base of; bronze disk marked "U. S. & C. B. Survey B. M."_____	2, 032. 69
Monument 494, in base of; bronze disk marked "U. S. & C. B. Survey B. M."_____	1, 778. 01
Monument 495, in base of; bronze disk marked "U. S. & C. B. Survey B. M."_____	1, 903. 43
Monument 496, in base of; bronze disk marked "U. S. & C. B. Survey B. M."_____	1, 932. 02
Monument 497, in base of; bronze disk marked "U. S. & C. B. Survey B. M."_____	2, 020. 86
Monument 498, in base of; bronze disk marked "U. S. & C. B. Survey B. M."_____	1, 761. 82
Monument 499, in base of; bronze disk marked "U. S. & C. B. Survey B. M."_____	1, 668. 25
Monument 500, in base of; bronze disk marked "U. S. & C. B. Survey B. M."_____	1, 585. 23
Monument 501, in base of; bronze disk marked "U. S. & C. B. Survey B. M."_____	2, 013. 30
Monument 502, in base of; bronze disk marked "U. S. & C. B. Survey B. M."_____	1, 801. 86
Monument 503, in base of; bronze disk marked "U. S. & C. B. Survey B. M."_____	1, 915. 96
Monument 504, in base of; bronze disk marked "U. S. & C. B. Survey B. M."_____	1, 959. 41
Monument 505, in base of; bronze disk marked "U. S. & C. B. Survey B. M."_____	1, 938. 32
Monument 506, in base of; bronze disk marked "U. S. & C. B. Survey B. M."_____	1, 914. 34
Monument 507, in base of; bronze disk marked "U. S. & C. B. Survey B. M."_____	1, 907. 44

St. Isidore, Quebec, 2 miles south of; in east face of large bowlder, 20 feet east of Maine Central Railroad track, 160 feet south of a wooden culvert, and 780 feet south of milepost 33 from Lime Ridge; Geodetic Survey of Canada B. M. No. 554–B_____ 1, 355. 88

St. Malo, Quebec, one-half mile south of; 720 feet north of milepost 36 from Lime Ridge, in concrete bench-mark pier, 4 feet west of east line of Maine Central Railroad right of way; Geodetic Survey of Canada B. M. No. 555–B_____ 1, 542. 87

Malvina, Quebec, 3 miles south of; in second course of stonework above bridge seat, in east end of south face of retaining wall behind north abutment of Maine Central Railroad bridge over Halls Stream; Geodetic Survey of Canada B. M. No. 556–B_____ 1, 356. 69

The Vermont–Quebec Line

Monument 519–A, in east side of base; one-half mile north of Beecher Falls, Vt., and one-fourth mile south of Comin Mills, Quebec, railway station; in the dooryard of Chouinard's line house, immediately west of the Maine Central Railroad; Geodetic Survey of Canada B. M. No. 562–B__ [1] 1, 102. 63

Norton Mills, Vt., railway station, 400 feet north of; in second course of stonework below top, in southeast face of southeast curved retaining wall of Grand Trunk Railway bridge at international boundary; Geodetic Survey of Canada B. M. No. 23_____ [1] 1, 247. 75

Norton Mills, Vt., railway station, 400 feet north of; in second course of stonework above ground in east end of south face of north abutment of Grand Trunk Railway bridge at international boundary; Geodetic Survey of Canada B. M. No. 24_____ [1] 1, 213. 47

Stanstead, Quebec, railway station, 45 feet east of water tank at; in east end of north face of capstone on north end of old stone culvert under Boston & Maine Railroad; Geodetic Survey of Canada B. M. No. 34_____ [1] 1, 006. 88

Beebe Junction, Quebec, 1¾ miles north of; in first course below capstone, in east face of south abutment of rough stone culvert under Boston & Maine Railroad, and 150 feet south of rock cut on curve; Geodetic Survey of Canada B. M. No. 32–A_____ [1] 705. 24

East Richford, Vt.; in base of international boundary monument 596; United States Coast and Geodetic Survey B. M. No. G–2, 1922_____ [2] 510. 6

[1] Adjusted elevations published in 1913, 1916, and 1917.
[2] Preliminary elevation, subject to correction by final adjustment.

	Elevation (feet)
Abercorn, Quebec, 1 mile south of; in the east face of concrete culvert under Canadian Pacific Railway, 250 feet north of a diagonal highway crossing, at mileage 25.8 from Enlaugra, Quebec; Geodetic Survey of Canada B. M. No. 55 _____	[1] 492. 53
St. Armand, Quebec, 1¼ miles south of; in small granite bowlder 20 feet west of Central Vermont Railway track, 190 feet south of international boundary monument 627–A; Geodetic Survey of Canada B. M. No. 70 _____	[1] 108. 16
Monument 627–A, in base of; United States Coast and Geodetic Survey B. M. No. O–1, 1922 _____	[2] 114. 5

The New York–Quebec Line

	Elevation (feet)
Rouses Point, N. Y., on the water table on the north side of Chapman Block building, 20.6 feet west of the northeast corner, on the west side of Lake Street and on the south side of Chapman Street, 1.6 feet above the ground; United States Coast and Geodetic Survey bench mark consisting of a cross and circle _____	107. 95
Monument 647; in south side of concrete base of; bronze disk marked "U. S. & C. B. Survey B. M. 114" _____	113. 66
Monument 648; in south side of concrete base of; bronze disk marked "U. S. & C. B. Survey B. M. 124" _____	123. 88
Monument 650; in south side of concrete base of; bronze disk marked "U. S. & C. B. Survey B. M. 205" _____	204. 59
Monument 651–A; in south side of concrete base of; bronze disk marked "U. S. & C. B. Survey B. M. 266" _____	265. 62
Monument 653; in south side of concrete base of; bronze disk marked "U. S. & C. B. Survey B. M. 184" _____	184. 29
Monument 654; in south side of concrete base of; bronze disk marked "U. S. & C. B. Survey B. M. 213" _____	212. 98
Monument 657–A; in south side of concrete base of; bronze disk marked "U. S. & C. B. Survey B. M. 173" _____	173. 38
Monument 660; in south side of concrete base of; bronze disk marked "U. S. & C. B. Survey B. M. 265" _____	264. 94
Monument 661; in south side of concrete base of; bronze disk marked "U. S. & C. B. Survey B. M. 354" _____	354. 36
Monument 665–A; in south side of concrete base of; bronze disk marked "U. S. & C. B. Survey B. M. 292" _____	291. 67
Monument 668; in south side of concrete base of; bronze disk marked "U. S. & C. B. Survey B. M. 321" _____	321. 23
Monument 674; in south side of concrete base of; bronze disk marked "U. S. & C. B. Survey B. M. 295" _____	294. 55
Monument 676–A; in south side of concrete base of; bronze disk marked "U. S. & C. B. Survey B. M. 335" _____	334. 44
Monument 679–A; in south side of concrete base of; bronze disk marked "U. S. & C. B. Survey B. M. 516" _____	515. 85
Monument 682; in south side of concrete base of; bronze disk marked "U. S. & C. B. Survey B. M. 757" _____	756. 76
Monument 688; in south side of concrete base of; bronze disk marked "U. S. & C. B. Survey B. M. 935" _____	934. 62
Monument 692; in south side of concrete base of; bronze disk marked "U. S. & C. B. Survey B. M. 1094" _____	1, 093. 82

[1] Adjusted elevations published in 1913, 1916, and 1917.
[2] Preliminary elevation, subject to correction by final adjustment.

	Elevation (feet)
Monument 695–A; in south side of concrete base of; bronze disk marked "U. S. & C. B. Survey B. M. 1027"_ _	1, 026. 73
Monument 699–A; in south side of concrete base of; bronze disk marked "U. S. & C. B. Survey B. M. 873"_ _	873. 27
Monument 703; in south side of concrete base of; bronze disk marked "U. S. & C. B. Survey B. M. 747"_ _	746. 83
Monument 706–A; in south side of concrete base of; bronze disk marked "U. S. & C. B. Survey B. M. 645"_ _	644. 35
Monument 711; in south side of concrete base of; bronze disk marked "U. S. & C. B. Survey B. M. 531"_ _	531. 07
Monument 714; in south side of concrete base of; bronze disk marked "U. S. & C. B. Survey B. M. 468"_ _	467. 99
Monument 719; in south side of concrete base of; bronze disk marked "U. S. & C. B. Survey B. M. 390"_ _	389. 90
Thayers Corners, N. Y., 5.06 miles north of; 0.21 mile west of turn in road; in George Marsh's barnyard, 50 feet south of barn, in granite bowlder; United States Geological Survey bronze bench mark disk stamped "393"_ _	392. 52
Monument 721; in south side of concrete base of; bronze disk marked "U. S. & C. B. Survey B. M. 371"_ _	371. 17
Monument 722–A; in south side of concrete base of; bronze disk marked "U. S. & C. B. Survey B. M. 331"_ _	330. 97
Thayers Corners, N. Y., 8.07 miles northwest of; opposite Luke Fee's farmhouse, 3,400 feet south by east of monument 726; 35 feet south of road, in sandstone bowlder; United States Geological Survey bronze bench mark stamped "309"_ _	308. 60
Monument 726–A; in south side of concrete base of; bronze disk marked "U. S. & C. B. Survey B. M. 288"_ _	287. 93
Monument 727–A; in south side of concrete base of; bronze disk marked "U. S. & C. B. Survey B.M. 266"_ _	266. 18
Monument 735; in south side of concrete base of; bronze disk marked "U. S. & C. B. Survey B. M. 224"_ _	223. 28
Monument 735; in east side of concrete base of; United States Geological Survey Trout River bench mark; bronze disk stamped "N. Y. 224"_ _	223. 18
Monument 742; in south side of concrete base of; bronze disk marked "U. S. & C. B. Survey B. M. 195"_ _	194. 34
Monument 746; in south side of concrete base of; bronze disk marked "U. S. & C. B. Survey B. M. 199"_ _	198. 84
Monument 748; in south side of concrete base of; bronze disk marked "U. S. & C. B. Survey B. M. 208"_ _	207. 75
Monument 751–A; in south side of concrete base of; bronze disk marked "U. S. & C. B. Survey B. M. 169"_ _	168. 52
Monument 752; in south side of concrete base of; bronze disk marked "U. S. & C. B. Survey B. M. 189"_ _	189. 10
Monument 754; in south side of concrete base of; bronze disk marked "U. S. & C. B. Survey B. M. 161"_ _	160. 50
Monument 755; in south side of concrete base of; bronze disk marked "U. S. & C. B. Survey B. M. 160"_ _	159. 40
Monument 760; in south side of concrete base of; bronze disk marked "U. S. & C. B. Survey B. M. 163"_ _	163. 04

Monument 766; in south side of concrete base of; bronze disk marked "U. S. & C. B. Survey B. M. 163"_____ Elevation (feet) 162. 77

Monument 770; in south side of concrete base of; bronze disk marked "U. S. & C. B. Survey B. M. 159"_____ 158. 81

Hogansburg, N. Y.; in foundation wall of St. Patrick's Church; ¼-inch bolt (Deep Waterways P. B. M. "B.")_____ 178. 26

Monument 771; in south side of concrete base of; bronze disk marked "U. S. & C. B. Survey B. M. 167"_____ 166. 37

Monument 773; in south side of concrete base of; bronze disk marked "U. S. & C. B. Survey B. M. 188"_____ 188. 10

APPENDIX V

GEOGRAPHIC POSITIONS AND DESCRIPTIONS OF TRIANGULATION AND TRAVERSE STATIONS

EXPLANATION OF TABLES

These tables consist of the triangulation stations and traverse stations used in determining the positions of the boundary monuments, reference monuments, and turning points. The latitude and longitude of each station are given on North American datum (see p. 138). Along with the latitude and longitude of each station, the azimuths and distances are given of lines from that station to other stations of the triangulation. No azimuths or distances are repeated, and for a given line the azimuth and distance will be found opposite the position of the last mentioned of the two stations involved.

The azimuths are reckoned clockwise from the south (see p. 138).

The distances are all reduced to sea level (see p. 138).

To facilitate the use of the tables, a column is given of the logarithms of the distances. It should be noted that the logarithm is derived from the computations and that the distances given are derived from the corresponding logarithms.

The latitudes and longitudes of the stations in the schemes used for the principal control are given to thousandths of seconds, and to hundredths of seconds in the other schemes. In the columns giving azimuths, distances, and logarithms of distances, the accuracy is indicated to a certain extent by the number of decimal places given.

These tables may be conveniently consulted by using as finders the sketches accompanying the report, published under separate cover, and the index to geographic positions beginning on page 485.

The following abbreviations have been used throughout the tables: "Mon." for monument; "Ref." for reference; and "ecc." for eccentric station.

GEOGRAPHIC POSITIONS OF TRIANGULATION STATIONS, SOURCE OF THE ST. CROIX RIVER TO LAKE POHENAGAMOOK

Station	Latitude and longitude	Azimuth	Back azimuth	To station	Distance (meters)	Logarithm
	° ′ ″	° ′ ″	° ′ ″			
MAJOR SCHEME						
Spring Hill (U. S. C. & G. S.)	45 54 31. 207 67 50 48. 366					
Kennedy (U. S. C. & G. S.)	45 56 15. 695 67 43 29. 399	71 12 41. 4	251 07 26. 0	Spring Hill_____	9, 993. 9	3. 999734
Pole Hill (U. S. C. & G. S.)	45 57 18. 400 67 46 59. 789	293 06 44. 3	113 09 15. 5	Kennedy_____	4, 927. 8	3. 692654
Union_____	46 04 50. 355 67 46 11. 196	4 17 19. 6 17 21 25. 2 347 37 39. 0	184 16 44. 5 197 18 05. 8 167 39 35. 4	Pole Hill_____ Spring Hill_____ Kennedy_____	13, 993. 4 20, 025. 3 16, 267. 1	4. 145922 4. 301578 4. 211310
Linneus_____	46 01 57. 375 67 58 09. 161	250 50 23. 5 299 02 05. 2 300 48 35. 5 325 23 32. 8	70 59 00. 5 119 12 37. 9 120 56 36. 9 145 28 49. 7	Union_____ Kennedy_____ Pole Hill_____ Spring Hill_____	16, 331. 5 21, 676. 3 16, 784. 0 16, 728. 0	4. 213027 4. 335985 4. 224896 4. 223444

345

SOURCE OF ST. CROIX RIVER TO LAKE POHENAGAMOOK—Continued

Station	Latitude and longitude	Azimuth	Back azimuth	To station	Distance (meters)	Logarithm
	° ′ ″	° ′ ″	° ′ ″			
MAJOR SCHEME—con.						
Ludlow	46 09 09. 147	6 41 57. 3	186 41 04. 8	Linneus	13, 422. 7	4. 127840
	67 56 56. 349	299 54 40. 1	120 02 25. 1	Union	15, 992. 6	4. 203918
Richmond	46 08 12. 266	4 58 07. 0	184 57 48. 8	Union	6, 257. 7	3. 796412
	67 45 45. 973	54 08 09. 5	233 59 14. 1	Linneus	19, 721. 7	4. 294945
		97 01 35. 8	276 53 32. 4	Ludlow	14, 494. 5	4. 161202
Littleton	46 13 09. 919	36 10 09. 9	216 07 07. 2	Ludlow	9, 205. 9	3. 964068
	67 52 43. 165	315 43 21. 4	135 48 22. 4	Richmond	12, 827. 2	4. 108131
Wakefield	46 13 27. 758	19 18 31. 6	199 16 36. 9	Richmond	10, 320. 8	4. 013712
	67 43 06. 988	65 54 19. 5	245 44 21. 0	Ludlow	19, 495. 9	4. 289943
		87 30 13. 9	267 23 17. 9	Littleton	12, 361. 0	4. 092052
Monticello	46 20 34. 271	5 52 32. 0	185 51 44. 4	Littleton	13, 792. 4	4. 139640
	67 51 37. 291	320 16 17. 3	140 22 26. 1	Wakefield	17, 110. 7	4. 233268
Wilmot	46 21 38. 849	5 16 15. 6	185 15 28. 4	Wakefield	15, 227. 5	4. 182630
	67 42 01. 715	41 12 38. 1	221 04 54. 4	Littleton	20, 867. 7	4. 319475
		80 51 16. 1	260 44 19. 6	Monticello	12, 467. 1	4. 095767
Blaine	46 28 22. 838	303 03 06. 4	123 13 54. 5	Wilmot	22, 816. 6	4. 358251
	67 56 56. 300	334 44 58. 0	154 48 49. 1	Monticello	15, 992. 4	4. 203913
Wicklow	46 29 32. 793	3 20 01. 3	183 19 32. 4	Wilmot	14, 659. 0	4. 166104
	67 41 21. 842	38 23 08. 9	218 15 43. 1	Monticello	21, 195. 4	4. 326242
		83 54 32. 8	263 43 15. 1	Blaine	20, 049. 0	4. 302093
Mars Hill	46 31 16. 599	62 36 54. 9	242 31 03. 3	Blaine	11, 645. 6	4. 066163
	67 48 51. 604	288 26 14. 2	108 31 40. 5	Wicklow	10, 110. 9	4. 004788
		333 49 56. 1	153 54 53. 2	Wilmot	19, 869. 7	4. 298192
Andover	46 37 44. 632	12 02 12. 5	192 00 45. 5	Mars Hill	12, 250. 6	4. 088158
	67 46 51. 749	36 39 08. 8	216 31 49. 9	Blaine	21, 605. 5	4. 334564
		335 08 13. 7	155 12 13. 3	Wicklow	16, 734. 0	4. 223600
Presque Isle	46 37 44. 987	269 58 09. 8	90 06 47. 9	Andover	15, 160. 2	4. 180706
	67 58 44. 397	313 28 24. 4	133 35 35. 0	Mars Hill	17, 411. 7	4. 240841
		352 25 55. 2	172 27 13. 7	Blaine	17, 510. 2	4. 243292
Caribou	46 47 16. 161	8 28 08. 3	188 26 38. 2	Presque Isle	17, 831. 3	4. 251182
	67 56 40. 953	324 35 48. 8	144 42 57. 7	Andover	21, 635. 8	4. 335173
Aroostook	46 47 08. 384	0 36 10. 8	180 36 04. 5	Andover	17, 409. 1	4. 240777
	67 46 43. 137	41 26 32. 9	221 17 47. 9	Presque Isle	23, 182. 0	4. 365151
		91 08 43. 7	271 01 28. 0	Caribou	12, 682. 7	4. 103211
Limestone	46 54 34. 240	20 51 07. 5	200 48 10. 3	Caribou	14. 473. 6	4. 160576
	67 52 38. 061	331 19 16. 8	151 23 35. 8	Aroostook	15, 687. 7	4. 195560
Woodland	46 54 42. 667	270 49 57. 9	90 59 22. 5	Limestone	16, 363. 8	4. 213885
	68 05 31. 210	300 17 46. 6	120 31 29. 6	Aroostook	27, 713. 0	4. 442684
		320 46 25. 5	140 52 52. 3	Caribou	17, 785. 3	4. 250062
Connor	47 01 46. 467	33 57 06. 1	213 52 01. 9	Woodland	15, 769. 2	4. 197809
	67 58 35. 041	330 28 51. 0	150 33 12. 0	Limestone	15, 333. 0	4. 185626
Caswell	47 01 52. 686	17 05 15. 1	197 02 51. 3	Limestone	14, 163. 2	4. 151161
	67 49 21. 416	57 09 53. 2	236 58 04. 2	Woodland	24, 425. 1	4. 387837
		89 06 54. 4	269 00 09. 3	Connor	11, 691. 5	4. 067872
Van Buren	47 08 16. 885	308 01 21. 7	128 10 07. 2	Caswell	19, 230. 0	4. 283980
	68 01 18. 859	343 59 24. 7	164 01 24. 7	Connor	12, 542. 0	4. 098366
St. Leonard	47 12 20. 246	20 03 55. 4	199 59 47. 4	Connor	20, 832. 1	4. 318733
	67 52 56. 558	54 39 32. 2	234 33 23. 8	Van Buren	12, 976. 1	4. 113145
		346 48 24. 2	166 51 01. 9	Caswell	19, 903. 5	4. 298929
Grand Isle	47 12 50. 674	272 51 22. 7	93 01 59. 7	St. Leonard	18, 290. 9	4. 262236
	68 07 24. 569	317 38 05. 5	137 42 33. 7	Van Buren	11, 436. 5	4. 058294

SOURCE OF ST. CROIX RIVER TO LAKE POHENAGAMOOK—Continued

Station	Latitude and longitude	Azimuth	Back azimuth	To station	Distance (meters)	Logarithm
	° ′ ″	° ′ ″	° ′ ″			
MAJOR SCHEME—con.						
Ste. Anne	47 16 16. 423	5 54 17. 7	185 53 24. 3	Van Buren	14, 887. 8	4. 172830
	68 00 06. 178	55 28 20. 1	235 22 58. 2	Grand Isle	11, 197. 4	4. 049116
		308 51 53. 6	128 57 09. 0	St. Leonard	11, 612. 5	4. 064926
Van Buren south base.	47 11 43. 981	169 54 41. 4	349 53 49. 1	Ste. Anne	8, 545. 9	3. 931757
	67 58 54. 962	261 31 08. 0	81 35 30. 9	St. Leonard	7, 626. 4	3. 882319
Van Buren north base.	47 13 50. 106	209 44 44. 0	29 46 14. 2	Ste. Anne	5, 204. 9	3. 716413
	68 02 09. 032	283 22 12. 3	103 28 57. 7	St. Leonard	11, 951. 3	4. 077416
		313 37 28. 0	133 39 50. 4	Van Buren south base.	5, 643. 49	3. 751548
Green River	47 22 56. 680	321 23 05. 7	141 28 50. 8	Ste. Anne	15, 809. 3	4. 198913
	68 07 55. 554	331 16 29. 5	151 23 07. 5	Van Buren south base.	23, 677. 3	4. 374333
		336 38 13. 2	156 42 28. 7	Van Buren north base.	18, 382. 1	4. 264395
		358 00 16. 9	178 00 39. 7	Grand Isle	18, 726. 2	4. 272449
Madawaska	47 17 52. 081	231 54 03. 8	52 01 04. 9	Green River	15, 265. 3	4. 183706
	68 17 28. 253	277 34 35. 0	97 47 20. 6	Ste. Anne	22, 097. 4	4. 344342
		306 11 29. 5	126 18 52. 8	Grand Isle	15, 740. 3	4. 197013
Edmund	47 23 36. 120	273 18 32. 6	93 30 30. 1	Green River	20, 485. 3	4. 311443
	68 24 10. 531	321 28 58. 4	141 33 54. 3	Madawaska	13, 571. 6	4. 132632
St. Hilaire	47 20 12. 942	190 51 49. 6	10 52 31. 8	Edmund	6, 389. 3	3. 805454
	68 25 07. 953	256 45 24. 6	76 58 04. 0	Green River	22, 247. 3	4. 347277
		294 12 30. 4	114 18 08. 3	Madawaska	10, 589. 3	4. 024868
Second	47 20 40. 765	83 41 55. 1	263 37 24. 2	St. Hilaire	7, 782. 4	3. 891111
	68 18 59. 500	129 43 08. 2	309 39 19. 4	Edmund	8, 480. 2	3. 928406
		253 09 57. 1	73 18 05. 3	Green River	14, 550. 5	4. 162878
First	47 21 54. 460	61 09 12. 7	241 05 53. 5	St. Hilaire	6, 492. 5	3. 812412
	68 20 37. 073	263 03 50. 8	83 13 10. 9	Green River	16, 091. 4	4. 206594
		318 00 37. 3	138 01 49. 1	Second	3, 061. 5	3. 485939
Edmundston astronomic.	47 22 07. 185	75 07 26. 8	255 06 35. 0	First	1, 530. 1	3. 184715
	68 19 26. 597	347 58 09. 1	167 58 29. 0	Second	2, 728. 8	3. 435971
Baker	47 21 38. 867	248 09 59. 8	68 15 17. 5	Edmund	9, 755. 2	3. 989237
	68 31 22. 326	288 37 17. 5	108 41 52. 9	St. Hilaire	8, 293. 8	3. 918755
Kent	47 16 00. 188	169 16 55. 1	349 15 45. 7	Baker	10, 645. 3	4. 027156
	68 29 47. 983	216 58 32. 7	37 01 58. 5	St. Hilaire	9, 774. 2	3. 990083
		257 23 34. 4	77 32 37. 8	Madawaska	15, 925. 4	4. 202089
Ledges	47 13 27. 964	222 05 28. 9	42 13 28. 9	Baker	20, 450. 9	4. 310712
	68 42 15. 590	253 16 37. 9	73 25 46. 8	Kent	16, 410. 1	4. 215112
Long	47 20 37. 804	264 42 24. 4	84 54 31. 6	Baker	20, 837. 6	4. 318847
	68 47 51. 084	290 32 11. 9	110 45 27. 9	Kent	24, 314. 0	4. 385857
		331 59 30. 2	152 03 36. 7	Ledges	15, 030. 6	4. 176976
Center	47 15 09. 819	203 01 53. 3	23 04 24. 0	Long	11, 007. 9	4. 041706
	68 51 16. 249	285 24 23. 8	105 31 00. 7	Ledges	11, 798. 8	4. 071836
St. Francis	47 10 07. 931	183 53 55. 5	3 54 17. 7	Center	9, 344. 5	3. 970557
	68 51 46. 465	194 15 03. 4	14 17 56. 2	Long	20, 071. 5	4. 302580
		242 44 09. 0	62 51 07. 8	Ledges	13, 511. 5	4. 130705
Canadian Glazier	47 16 39. 408	239 27 38. 2	59 34 55. 9	Long	14, 514. 9	4. 161815
	68 57 46. 635	288 35 24. 6	108 40 11. 4	Center	8, 660. 7	3. 937553
		327 53 02. 6	147 57 27. 0	St. Francis	14, 268. 1	4. 154366
U. S. Glazier	47 13 31. 296	232 58 03. 5	53 02 32. 7	Canadian Glazier	9, 654. 1	3. 984710
	69 03 53. 318	292 14 35. 0	112 23 28. 3	St. Francis	16, 538. 6	4. 218500

SOURCE OF ST. CROIX RIVER TO LAKE POHENAGAMOOK—Continued

Station	Latitude and longitude	Azimuth	Back azimuth	To station	Distance (meters)	Logarithm
	° ′ ″	° ′ ″	° ′ ″			
MAJOR SCHEME—con.						
Canadian Beau_____	47 20 17. 713	13 07 33. 3	193 05 51. 1	U. S. Glazier_____	12, 887. 0	4. 110153
	69 01 34. 214	267 51 34. 2	88 01 39. 4	Long_____	17, 290. 6	4. 237811
		324 38 14. 3	144 41 01. 5	Canadian Glazier__	8, 264. 6	3. 917222
U. S. Beau_____	47 21 29. 511	285 43 03. 6	105 47 39. 0	Canadian Beau____	8, 165. 7	3. 911993
	69 07 48. 631	305 15 39. 1	125 23 01. 6	Canadian Glazier__	15, 495. 4	4. 190203
		341 27 56. 4	161 30 49. 3	U. S. Glazier_____	15, 574. 1	4. 192402
Blue River_____	47 25 09. 790	47 42 57. 9	227 38 35. 7	U. S. Beau_____	10, 104. 1	4. 004497
	69 01 52. 427	357 34 22. 1	177 34 35. 5	Canadian Beau____	9, 028. 2	3. 955602
Estcourt_____	47 29 14. 438	295 16 26. 2	115 25 47. 1	Blue River_____	17, 645. 7	4. 246640
	69 14 33. 667	315 19 46. 7	135 29 20. 6	Canadian Beau____	23, 275. 8	4. 366904
		329 21 51. 4	149 26 49. 7	U. S. Beau_____	16, 680. 3	4. 222205
Frontier (Mon. 189) (Geodetic Survey of Canada).	47 22 40. 457 69 18 33. 699	202 26 11. 2 257 30 33. 7 279 07 45. 6	22 29 08. 0 77 42 50. 8 99 15 40. 2	Estcourt_____ Blue River_____ U. S. Beau_____	13, 166. 1 21, 496. 9 13, 710. 8	4. 119458 4. 332375 4. 137064
Parke (Geodetic Survey of Canada).	47 34 37. 493 69 22 59. 976	313 14 25. 7 345 50 26. 7	133 20 39. 3 165 53 43. 0	Estcourt_____ Frontier (Mon.189)	14, 549. 8 22, 835. 5	4. 162858 4. 358611
Chabot_____	47 29 11. 298	186 35 07. 8	6 35 48. 8	Parke_____	10, 141. 1	4. 006085
	69 23 55. 628	269 28 13. 4	89 35 07. 7	Estcourt_____	11, 764. 8	4. 070586
		330 45 54. 0	150 49 51. 1	Frontier (Mon.189)	13, 827. 8	4. 140753
POINTS SUPPLEMENTARY TO MAJOR SCHEME						
Mon. 1 (initial monument).	45 56 37. 001 67 46 54. 713	175 06 42. 4 278 26 22. 0	355 06 38. 7 98 28 49. 5	Pole Hill_____ Kennedy_____	1, 282. 8 4, 471. 4	3. 108175 3. 650440
Westford_____	46 02 16. 502	4 07 42. 2	184 07 07. 6	Spring Hill_____	14, 403. 2	4. 158460
	67 50 00. 258	322 54 08. 1	142 58 49. 3	Kennedy_____	13, 959. 5	4. 144870
		337 06 16. 0	157 08 25. 8	Pole Hill_____	9, 989. 8	3. 999556
Mon. 10–B_____	46 03 05. 013	0 40 45. 9	180 40 41. 6	Pole Hill_____	10, 702. 5	4. 029486
	67 46 53. 895	69 31 23. 3	249 29 09. 1	Westford_____	4, 277. 8	3. 631218
		340 46 47. 8	160 49 14. 9	Kennedy_____	13, 382. 1	4. 126524
Mon. 16_____	46 06 45. 899	108 57 52. 4	288 50 38. 6	Ludlow_____	13, 651. 4	4. 135177
	67 46 54. 719	147 48 17. 5	327 44 06. 1	Littleton_____	14, 016. 8	4. 146650
Mon. 24–B_____	46 13 01. 046	92 08 39. 7	272 04 29. 1	Littleton_____	7, 442. 5	3. 871718
	67 46 56. 164	260 26 43. 2	80 29 28. 6	Wakefield_____	4, 980. 6	3. 697282
		350 24 31. 7	170 25 22. 3	Richmond_____	9, 042. 6	3. 956295
		359 50 48. 1	179 50 49. 1	Mon. 16_____	11, 583. 1	4. 063825
Porter_____	46 19 20. 899	21 07 31. 1	201 05 01. 9	Littleton_____	12, 278. 2	4. 089135
	67 49 16. 700	127 00 28. 3	306 58 46. 6	Monticello_____	3, 764. 9	3. 575759
		323 58 58. 1	144 03 25. 3	Wakefield_____	13, 474. 4	4. 129511
Lunnon_____	46 17 24. 243	40 46 13. 2	220 42 25. 1	Littleton_____	10, 363. 8	4. 015521
	67 47 27. 396	137 41 05. 7	317 38 05. 0	Monticello_____	7, 938. 1	3. 899715
		147 00 46. 3	326 59 27. 3	Porter_____	4, 294. 8	3. 632946
Mon. 26_____	46 13 10. 774	165 16 16. 9	345 14 35. 4	Porter_____	11, 817. 3	4. 072518
	67 46 56. 259	263 53 07. 0	83 55 52. 6	Wakefield_____	4, 941. 7	3. 693874
Mon. 35–A_____	46 18 33. 376	15 42 34. 0	195 42 13. 7	Lunnon_____	2, 217. 4	3. 345849
	67 46 59. 348	116 32 53. 3	296 31 14. 0	Porter_____	3, 284. 7	3. 516494
Mon. 44_____	46 25 05. 235	34 48 54. 0	214 45 37. 1	Monticello_____	10, 187. 4	4. 008064
	67 47 05. 310	115 52 19. 0	295 45 10. 6	Blaine_____	14, 012. 7	4. 146522
		168 49 25. 5	348 48 08. 4	Mars Hill_____	11, 689. 0	4. 067777
Mon. 53_____	46 30 19. 975	73 53 17. 4	253 46 13. 2	Blaine_____	12, 987. 1	4. 113511
	67 47 11. 465	129 19 44. 4	309 18 31. 8	Mars Hill_____	2, 759. 4	3. 440818

SOURCE OF ST. CROIX RIVER TO LAKE POHENAGAMOOK—Continued

Station	Latitude and longitude	Azimuth	Back azimuth	To station	Distance (meters)	Loga- rithm
POINTS SUPPLE- MENTARY TO MAJOR SCHEME—contd.	° ′ ″	° ′ ″	° ′ ″			
Easton	46 40 27. 327	204 19 26. 7	24 22 38. 9	Aroostook	13, 593. 6	4. 133336
	67 51 07. 104	312 44 58. 8	132 48 04. 4	Andover	7, 397. 5	3. 869085
Watson	46 46 01. 283	256 26 07. 4	76 31 03. 3	Aroostook	8, 860. 8	3. 947474
	67 53 29. 218	331 07 15. 5	151 12 04. 7	Andover	17, 507. 4	4. 243221
		343 40 20. 6	163 42 04. 1	Easton	10, 744. 9	4. 031201
Mon. 64	46 36 56. 829	143 26 24. 9	323 23 40. 0	Easton	8, 094. 6	3. 908194
	67 47 20. 261	202 20 17. 0	22 20 37. 7	Andover	1, 595. 9	3. 202999
Mon. 72–A	46 42 21. 917	53 28 24. 7	233 25 41. 3	Easton	5, 941. 8	3. 773918
	67 47 22. 467	131 03 32. 0	310 59 05. 0	Watson	10, 320. 6	4. 013703
		355 38 08. 2	175 38 30. 5	Andover	8, 587. 1	3. 933847
Mon. 81–B	46 47 33. 365	69 50 00. 9	249 45 35. 5	Watson	8, 233. 5	3. 915583
	67 47 24. 983	310 59 24. 0	130 59 54. 5	Aroostook	1, 175. 9	3. 070380
Falls	46 52 11. 925	5 32 06. 5	185 31 35. 3	Aroostook	9, 417. 1	3. 973917
	67 46 00. 315	117 36 01. 9	297 31 11. 5	Limestone	9, 498. 4	3. 977649
		166 40 50. 2	346 38 23. 3	Caswell	18, 431. 4	4. 265559
Mon. 92	46 52 16. 412	274 26 24. 3	94 27 25. 6	Falls	1, 786. 2	3. 251935
	67 47 24. 403	354 44 32. 0	174 45 02. 1	Aroostook	9, 551. 9	3. 980091
Mon. 103	46 58 49. 980	39 58 16. 9	219 54 28. 4	Limestone	10, 300. 2	4. 012844
	67 47 25. 398	156 31 55. 5	336 30 30. 7	Caswell	6, 151. 4	3. 788974
Grand	47 06 03. 159	1 21 06. 5	181 21 00. 2	Caswell	7, 737. 0	3. 888574
	67 49 12. 774	105 10 22. 6	285 01 30. 5	Van Buren	15, 853. 3	4. 200121
Hamlin	47 06 21. 082	112 14 43. 5	292 09 38. 8	Van Buren	9, 463. 4	3. 976045
	67 54 23. 205	189 20 11. 7	9 21 15. 1	St. Leonard	11, 240. 7	4. 050793
		274 48 05. 7	94 51 53. 1	Grand	6, 569. 3	3. 817517
Cyr	47 06 54. 433	40 36 27. 5	220 31 44. 9	Connor	12, 519. 7	4. 097594
	67 52 09. 129	69 59 41. 8	249 58 03. 6	Hamlin	3, 008. 6	3. 478362
		102 26 58. 7	282 20 15. 8	Van Buren	11, 863. 3	4. 074205
		339 11 21. 4	159 13 24. 2	Caswell	9, 967. 5	3. 998588
Ref. Mon. S–2	47 04 09. 923	133 39 42. 9	313 36 37. 9	Cyr	7, 361. 9	3. 866988
	67 47 56. 506	155 18 08. 6	335 17 12. 8	Grand	3, 849. 2	3. 585367
Ref. Mon. S–6	47 04 51. 704	113 24 52. 5	293 21 10. 8	Hamlin	6, 954. 3	3. 842256
	67 49 20. 548	136 50 55. 3	316 48 51. 8	Cyr	5, 196. 5	3. 715708
		184 14 55. 4	4 15 01. 1	Grand	2, 212. 7	3. 344923
Ref. Mon. S–17	47 07 19. 368	26 33 41. 0	206 33 09. 7	Hamlin	2, 012. 2	3. 303681
	67 53 40. 532	291 46 26. 1	111 47 33. 0	Cyr	2, 075. 0	3. 317012
Bruno	47 09 45. 084	64 38 25. 9	244 35 06. 2	Van Buren	6, 353. 0	3. 802981
	67 56 46. 430	312 01 04. 3	132 04 27. 6	Cyr	7, 868. 8	3. 895908
Ref. Mon. C–22	47 09 31. 984	107 22 32. 4	287 21 47. 4	Bruno	1, 355. 2	3. 131993
	67 55 45. 028	316 53 55. 2	136 56 33. 5	Cyr	6, 661. 2	3. 823552
Ref. Mon. S–32	47 11 57. 723	54 01 30. 0	234 01 09. 6	Van Buren south base.	722. 4	2. 858795
	67 58 27. 188	165 24 08. 0	345 22 55. 3	Ste. Anne	8, 256. 0	3. 916771
		264 15 30. 5	84 19 33. 0	St. Leonard	6, 993. 5	3. 844697
Ref. Mon. S–42	47 15 26. 598	166 10 45. 1	346 08 45. 2	Green River	14, 315. 1	4. 155795
	68 05 12. 526	256 31 54. 1	76 35 39. 1	Ste. Anne	6, 621. 6	3. 820963
Ref. Mon. C–47	47 19 53. 122	112 18 22. 6	292 08 31. 7	Edmund	18, 207. 7	4. 260256
	68 10 47. 297	212 25 51. 3	32 27 57. 6	Green River	6, 717. 5	3. 827208
Ref. Mon. C–54	47 21 33. 492	34 42 20. 9	214 41 41. 4	Second	1, 980. 6	3. 296796
	68 18 05. 778	74 21 44. 6	254 16 34. 2	St. Hilaire	9, 203. 9	3. 963970
		101 32 38. 2	281 30 46. 9	First	3, 240. 1	3. 510565

SOURCE OF ST. CROIX RIVER TO LAKE POHENAGAMOOK—Continued

Station	Latitude and longitude	Azimuth	Back azimuth	To station	Distance (meters)	Logarithm
POINTS SUPPLEMENTARY TO MAJOR SCHEME—contd.	° ′ ″	° ′ ″	° ′ ″			
Edmundston bench mark.	47 22 02. 632 68 19 18. 482	81 18 26. 2 351 02 38. 0	261 17 28. 4 171 02 52. 0	First Second	1, 668. 2 2, 559. 4	3. 222257 3. 408146
Brook	47 17 27. 342 68 30 09. 184	168 49 22. 1 231 01 11. 4 267 11 11. 5 350 35 50. 5	348 48 28. 3 51 04 52. 8 87 20 30. 6 170 36 06. 1	Baker St. Hilaire Madawaska Kent	7, 918. 1 8, 135. 3 16, 006. 1 2, 728. 1	3. 898620 3. 910373 4. 204286 3. 435863
Ref. Mon. S–69	47 16 57. 189 68 22 29. 619	95 33 16. 7 151 11 57. 0	275 27 38. 9 331 10 00. 6	Brook St. Hilaire	9, 702. 1 6, 899. 8	3. 986865 3. 838834
Clair	47 15 51. 977 68 38 53. 629	43 42 09. 1 128 04 25. 9 221 27 27. 5 268 40 40. 7	223 39 40. 8 307 57 50. 9 41 32 59. 2 88 47 21. 5	Ledges Long Baker Kent	6, 149. 7 14, 331. 4 14, 304. 4 11, 473. 6	3. 788857 4. 156288 4. 155470 4. 059700
Fort	47 13 11. 365 68 37 18. 355	94 42 58. 8 158 00 42. 0 241 07 28. 3	274 39 20. 7 337 59 32. 1 61 12 59. 0	Ledges Clair Kent	6, 274. 6 5, 349. 5 10, 812. 0	3. 797589 3. 728311 4. 033904
Baker Brook bench mark.	47 18 06. 550 68 30 47. 612	67 54 31. 7 173 39 37. 8 326 18 01. 0	247 48 34. 7 353 39 12. 3 146 18 29. 3	Clair Baker Brook	11, 027. 0 6, 597. 3 1, 455. 3	4. 042458 3. 819363 3. 162959
Ref. Mon. S–78	47 17 39. 484 68 30 57. 620	71 41 22. 3 175 59 18. 5	251 35 32. 6 355 59 00. 3	Clair Baker	10, 540. 8 7, 410. 9	4. 022873 3. 869871
Ref. Mon. S–87	47 16 03. 164 68 35 36. 125	22 04 12. 7 85 15 49. 5	202 02 57. 6 265 13 24. 5	Fort Clair	5, 724. 6 4, 166. 3	3. 757743 3. 619753
Ref. Mon. S–96	47 13 52. 417 68 40 30. 218	208 48 23. 8 287 25 00. 2	28 49 34. 7 107 27 21. 0	Clair Fort	4, 214. 1 4, 230. 9	3. 624704 3. 626430
Ref. Mon. C–92	47 14 57. 124 68 43 24. 401	49 50 41. 9 292 56 54. 5 332 15 50. 9	229 44 33. 5 113 01 23. 1 152 16 41. 4	St. Francis Fort Ledges	13, 834. 6 8, 363. 7 3, 110. 7	4. 140966 3. 922398 3. 492853
Ref. Mon. C–99	47 12 46. 841 68 49 32. 873	29 49 47. 8 262 05 48. 6	209 48 09. 8 82 11 09. 5	St. Francis Ledges	5, 656. 2 9, 288. 1	3. 752521 3. 967927
Ref. Mon. C–105	47 11 18. 158 68 52 49. 901	253 13 17. 0 328 21 50. 8	73 21 02. 4 148 22 37. 3	Ledges St. Francis	13, 938. 5 2, 547. 1	4. 144215 3. 406045
Twin	47 13 01. 750 69 02 07. 502	112 17 44. 8 155 28 03. 4 182 58 16. 8	292 16 27. 2 335 23 52. 8 2 58 41. 3	U. S. Glazier U. S. Beau Canadian Beau	2, 406. 1 17, 241. 6 13, 481. 7	3. 381312 4. 236577 4. 129743
Ref. Mon. S–122	47 14 17. 556 69 01 50. 712	8 34 53. 8 61 01 47. 4	188 34 41. 4 241 00 17. 4	Twin U. S. Glazier	2, 367. 5 2, 948. 3	3. 374295 3. 469579
Ref. Mon. S–135	47 20 36. 417 69 03 40. 138	194 58 17. 5 282 18 46. 4	14 59 36. 8 102 20 19. 0	Blue River Canadian Beau	8, 739. 6 2, 705. 8	3. 941493 3. 432302
Dave	47 26 15. 590 69 05 36. 909	17 22 30. 3 67 53 11. 1 116 13 13. 8 293 20 17. 9	197 20 53. 3 247 43 39. 2 296 06 38. 2 113 23 03. 2	U. S. Beau Frontier (Mon. 189) Estcourt Blue River	9, 256. 7 17, 589. 2 12, 525. 6 5, 124. 8	3. 966455 4. 245247 4. 097798 3. 709674
Ref. Mon. C–139	47 23 59. 575 69 02 11. 959	134 22 36. 0 190 41 33. 0	314 20 05. 1 10 41 47. 4	Dave Blue River	6, 008. 4 2, 206. 8	3. 778759 3. 343754
Ref. Mon. C–162	47 25 54. 096 69 05 53. 095	119 37 32. 4 207 03 48. 2 285 09 09. 0	299 31 08. 7 27 04 00. 1 105 12 06. 2	Estcourt Dave Blue River	12, 536. 8 745. 4 5, 226. 5	4. 098185 2. 872413 3. 718207
Ref. Mon. C–176	47 27 47. 005 69 13 18. 826	34 54 53. 1 149 52 41. 6	214 51 01. 3 329 51 46. 5	Frontier (Mon.189) Estcourt	11, 540. 7 3, 122. 0	4. 062231 3. 494435

SOURCE OF ST. CROIX RIVER TO LAKE POHENAGAMOOK—Continued

Station	Latitude and longitude	Azimuth	Back azimuth	To station	Distance (meters)	Logarithm
MINOR SCHEME, ST. JOHN AND ST. FRANCIS RIVERS	° ′ ″	° ′ ″	° ′ ″			
S–1	47 03 58. 03 67 47 27. 16					
C–1	47 04 05. 75 67 47 21. 52	26 32 04	206 32 00	S–1	266. 4	2. 425567
Ref. Mon. S–2	47 04 09. 92 67 47 56. 51	279 54 06 300 40 09	99 54 32 120 40 31	C–1 S–1	749. 4 720. 0	2. 874721 2. 857311
C–2	47 04 18. 27 67 47 52. 50	18 10 01 300 36 05 319 27 08	198 09 58 120 36 28 139 27 27	Ref. Mon. S–2 C–1 S–1	271. 2 759. 4 822. 5	2. 433366 2. 880496 2. 915128
Ref. Mon. C–3	47 04 24. 86 67 48 13. 27	294 55 09 322 31 09	114 55 24 142 31 21	C–2 Ref. Mon. S–2	483. 3 581. 4	2. 684247 2. 764481
Ref. Mon. S–3	47 04 17. 38 67 48 21. 09	215 31 02 267 23 24 293 55 55	35 31 08 87 23 45 113 56 13	Ref. Mon. C–3 C–2 Ref. Mon. S–2	284. 0 603. 9 567. 6	2. 453275 2. 780995 2. 754016
Ref. Mon. S–4	47 04 31. 34 67 48 46. 33	286 00 10 308 59 50	106 00 34 129 00 08	Ref. Mon. C–3 Ref. Mon. S–3	725. 6 685. 2	2. 860692 2. 835817
C–4	47 04 37. 49 67 48 39. 30	38 02 20 305 22 17 328 15 37	218 02 15 125 22 36 148 15 50	Ref. Mon. S–4 Ref. Mon. C–3 Ref. Mon. S–3	240. 9 673. 3 730. 1	2. 381806 2. 828222 2. 863386
Ref. Mon. S–5	47 04 42. 29 67 48 58. 42	290 11 03 322 57 52	110 11 17 142 58 01	C–4 Ref. Mon. S–4	429. 9 423. 5	2. 633361 2. 626845
C–5	47 04 54. 23 67 48 55. 21	10 24 04 327 00 06 345 09 11	190 24 02 147 00 18 165 09 18	Ref. Mon. S–5 C–4 Ref. Mon. S–4	374. 9 616. 6 731. 3	2. 573969 2. 789991 2. 864072
Ref. Mon. S–6	47 04 51. 70 67 49 20. 55	261 41 06 301 54 43	81 41 25 121 55 00	C–5 Ref. Mon. S–5	540. 1 549. 9	2. 732490 2. 740279
C–6 (Grand Falls east base).	47 05 11. 95 67 49 26. 09	310 01 21 349 24 14	130 01 44 169 24 18	C–5 Ref. Mon. S–6	850. 6 636. 0	2. 929728 2. 803443
Ref. Mon. S–7	47 05 02. 04 67 49 44. 34	231 31 08 283 05 10 302 26 25	51 31 21 103 05 46 122 26 42	C–6 C–5 Ref. Mon. S–6	491. 8 1, 064. 1 594. 8	2. 691823 3. 026972 2. 774391
C–7 (Grand Falls west base).	47 05 23. 34 67 50 13. 02	289 33 46 317 24 04	109 34 20 137 24 25	C–6 Ref. Mon. S–7	1, 050. 53 893. 7	3. 021407 2. 951182
Ref. Mon. S–8	47 05 09. 61 67 50 31. 84	223 06 36 267 00 49 283 08 01	43 06 50 87 01 37 103 08 36	C–7 C–6 Ref. Mon. S–7	580. 8 1, 388. 7 1, 028. 8	2. 764060 3. 142623 3. 012332
C–8	47 05 43. 32 67 51 03. 80	299 56 14 327 04 21	119 56 51 147 04 44	C–7 Ref. Mon. S–8	1, 235. 9 1, 240. 1	3. 091970 3. 093438
Ref. Mon. S–9	47 05 23. 88 67 51 16. 02	203 14 41 270 42 48 295 18 26	23 14 50 90 43 34 115 18 58	C–8 C–7 Ref. Mon. S–8	653. 2 1, 328. 9 1, 030. 8	2. 815038 3. 123486 3. 013184
Ref. Mon. S–10	47 05 46. 98 67 51 53. 35	276 10 51 312 10 34	96 11 28 132 11 02	C–8 Ref. Mon. S–9	1, 051. 2 1, 062. 5	3. 021698 3. 026335
C–9	47 06 01. 98 67 51 45. 51	19 40 03 303 13 24 332 08 04	199 39 58 123 13 55 152 08 27	Ref. Mon. S–10 C–8 Ref. Mon. S–9	491. 6 1, 051. 5 1, 330. 6	2. 691626 3. 021826 3. 124058
C–10	47 06 05. 06 67 52 00. 86	286 21 31 344 09 01	106 21 42 164 09 06	C–9 Ref. Mon. S–10	337. 5 580. 1	2. 528300 2. 763473

SOURCE OF ST. CROIX RIVER TO LAKE POHENAGAMOOK—Continued

Station	Latitude and longitude	Azimuth	Back azimuth	To station	Distance (meters)	Logarithm
MINOR SCHEME, ST. JOHN AND ST. FRANCIS RIVERS—continued	° ′ ″	° ′ ″	° ′ ″			
Ref. Mon. S–11	47 05 56. 69	234 41 56	54 42 09	C–10	447. 2	2. 650498
	67 52 18. 17	256 39 25	76 39 49	C–9	707. 9	2. 849998
		299 47 02	119 47 20	Ref. Mon. S–10	603. 1	2. 780384
Ref. Mon. C–11	47 06 12. 94	284 24 18	104 24 51	C–10	979. 0	2. 990775
	67 52 45. 83	310 43 05	130 43 25	Ref. Mon. S–11	769. 5	2. 886235
Ref. Mon. S–12	47 06 03. 41	221 00 00	41 00 09	Ref. Mon. C–11	390. 1	2. 591133
	67 52 57. 97	267 34 50	87 35 32	C–10	1, 205. 2	3. 081055
		283 53 41	103 54 10	Ref. Mon. S–11	864. 5	2. 936757
Ref. Mon. S–13	47 06 10. 02	260 25 11	80 25 30	Ref. Mon. C–11	543. 2	2. 734921
	67 53 11. 23	306 06 23	126 06 33	Ref. Mon. S–12	346. 2	2. 539302
C–12	47 06 17. 58	13 58 11	193 58 08	Ref. Mon. S–12	450. 9	2. 654044
	67 52 52. 80	58 59 34	238 59 21	Ref. Mon. S–13	453. 3	2. 656377
		314 13 36	134 13 42	Ref. Mon. C–11	205. 2	2. 312243
C–13	47 06 27. 83	16 25 57	196 25 52	Ref. Mon. S–13	573. 3	2. 758419
	67 53 03. 54	324 25 29	144 25 37	C–12	389. 0	2. 589962
Ref. Mon. S–14	47 06 17. 22	233 57 17	53 57 33	C–13	556. 6	2. 745516
	67 53 24. 88	269 03 32	89 03 56	C–12	676. 4	2. 830231
		307 41 43	127 41 54	Ref. Mon. S–13	363. 8	2. 560857
Ref. Mon. S–15	47 06 33. 76	290 52 28	110 52 45	C–13	514. 0	2. 710981
	67 53 26. 32	356 36 27	176 36 28	Ref. Mon. S–14	511. 6	2. 708890
C–14	47 06 37. 79	20 19 24	200 19 16	Ref. Mon. S–14	677. 5	2. 830886
	67 53 13. 72	64 51 25	244 51 16	Ref. Mon. S–15	293. 3	2. 467368
		325 06 00	145 06 08	C–13	375. 3	2. 574390
C–15	47 06 55. 47	17 58 02	197 57 55	Ref. Mon. S–15	704. 8	2. 848049
	67 53 16. 00	354 57 33	174 57 35	C–14	547. 9	2. 738689
Ref. Mon. S–16	47 06 57. 83	283 42 30	103 42 40	C–15	307. 7	2. 488128
	67 53 30. 18	330 42 22	150 42 34	C–14	709. 4	2. 850890
		353 44 17	173 44 20	Ref. Mon. S–15	747. 8	2. 873783
C–16	47 07 22. 13	19 14 04	199 13 55	Ref. Mon. S–16	794. 7	2. 900182
	67 53 17. 77	357 25 00	177 25 01	C–15	824. 1	2. 915965
Ref. Mon. S–17	47 07 19. 37	259 56 03	79 56 20	C–16	487. 3	2. 687823
	67 53 40. 53	324 59 14	144 59 32	C–15	901. 1	2. 954794
		341 50 45	161 50 53	Ref. Mon. S–16	700. 0	2. 845095
Ref. Mon. C–17	47 07 56. 27	331 32 08	151 32 28	C–16	1, 199. 3	3. 078939
	67 53 44. 89	355 23 41	175 23 44	Ref. Mon. S–17	1, 143. 2	3. 058130
Ref. Mon. S–18	47 07 50. 31	235 14 42	55 14 51	Ref. Mon. C–17	322. 7	2. 508814
	67 53 57. 47	316 07 33	136 08 02	C–16	1, 207. 4	3. 081841
		339 30 55	159 31 07	Ref. Mon. S–17	1, 020. 1	3. 008626
Ref. Mon. S–19	47 08 04. 87	292 32 39	112 33 01	Ref. Mon. C–17	692. 4	2. 840375
	67 54 15. 23	320 12 23	140 12 36	Ref. Mon. S–18	585. 0	2. 767127
C–18	47 08 15. 41	44 20 28	224 20 17	Ref. Mon. S–19	455. 2	2. 658158
	67 54 00. 14	331 27 51	151 28 02	Ref. Mon. C–17	672. 8	2. 827859
		355 50 57	175 50 59	Ref. Mon. S–18	777. 0	2. 890441
Ref. Mon. S–20	47 08 31. 53	306 47 14	126 47 37	C–18	831. 4	2. 919786
	67 54 31. 73	337 06 22	157 06 34	Ref. Mon. S–19	893. 8	2. 951249
C–19	47 08 31. 48	1 13 25	181 13 24	Ref. Mon. S–19	822. 2	2. 914973
	67 54 14. 40	90 13 27	270 13 14	Ref. Mon. S–20	365. 2	2. 562561
		328 48 37	148 48 47	C–18	580. 4	2. 763691

SOURCE OF ST. CROIX RIVER TO LAKE POHENAGAMOOK—Continued

Station	Latitude and longitude	Azimuth	Back azimuth	To station	Distance (meters)	Logarithm
MINOR SCHEME, ST. JOHN AND ST. FRANCIS RIVERS—continued	° ′ ″	° ′ ″	° ′ ″			
C–20	47 08 58. 80	328 00 48	148 01 07	C–19	994. 7	2. 997690
	67 54 39. 40	349 08 00	169 08 06	Ref. Mon. S–20	857. 7	2. 933313
Ref. Mon. S–21	47 08 51. 61	233 51 26	53 51 37	C–20	376. 9	2. 576227
	67 54 53. 85	306 46 31	126 47 01	C–19	1, 037. 9	3. 016142
		323 03 50	143 04 07	Ref. Mon. S–20	775. 6	2. 889660
C–21	47 09 17. 24	302 35 36	122 36 07	C–20	1, 056. 7	3. 023940
	67 55 21. 66	323 29 23	143 29 43	Ref. Mon. S–21	984. 8	2. 993344
Ref. Mon. S–22	47 09 09. 60	235 16 07	55 16 19	C–21	413. 8	2. 616828
	67 55 37. 80	285 09 37	105 10 20	C–20	1, 274. 8	3. 105430
		300 58 02	120 58 34	Ref. Mon. S–21	1, 080. 0	3. 033428
Ref. Mon. S–23	47 09 22. 75	283 52 17	103 52 41	C–21	710. 1	2. 851325
	67 55 54. 38	319 17 42	139 17 54	Ref. Mon. S–22	535. 6	2. 728853
Ref. Mon. C–22	47 09 31. 98	34 39 19	214 39 12	Ref. Mon. S–23	346. 6	2. 539815
	67 55 45. 03	312 46 03	132 46 20	C–21	670. 6	2. 826476
		347 34 48	167 34 53	Ref. Mon. S–22	707. 7	2. 849856
Ref. Mon. S–24	47 09 45. 34	300 08 05	120 08 30	Ref. Mon. C–22	821. 6	2. 914676
	67 56 18. 76	323 38 31	143 38 49	Ref. Mon. S–23	866. 2	2. 937640
C–23	47 09 52. 01	57 57 27	237 57 15	Ref. Mon. S–24	388. 2	2. 589016
	67 56 03. 14	328 19 47	148 20 00	Ref. Mon. C–22	726. 7	2. 861345
		348 27 42	168 27 48	Ref. Mon. S–23	922. 2	2. 964834
S–25	47 10 01. 66	302 24 45	122 25 02	C–23	555. 9	2. 745031
	67 56 25. 42	344 26 27	164 26 32	Ref. Mon. S–24	523. 1	2. 718609
C–24	47 10 08. 08	10 53 06	190 53 01	Ref. Mon. S–24	715. 0	2. 854310
	67 56 12. 35	54 15 11	234 15 01	S–25	339. 2	2. 530487
		338 38 43	158 38 50	C–23	532. 8	2. 726540
C–25	47 10 34. 84	335 05 28	155 05 42	C–24	911. 1	2. 959560
	67 56 30. 57	353 57 32	173 57 36	S–25	1, 030. 3	3. 012945
Ref. Mon. S–26	47 10 13. 22	182 50 47	2 50 48	C–25	668. 5	2. 825089
	67 56 32. 15	290 50 12	110 50 27	C–24	446. 1	2. 649438
		338 21 16	158 21 21	S–25	384. 0	2. 584280
Ref. Mon. S–27	47 10 25. 40	232 13 54	52 14 07	C–25	475. 6	2. 677223
	67 56 48. 42	317 40 28	137 40 40	Ref. Mon. S–26	509. 1	2. 706787
		326 32 55	146 33 12	S–25	878. 8	2. 943902
Ref. Mon. S–28	47 10 34. 63	269 17 31	89 17 49	C–25	520. 3	2. 716240
	67 56 55. 28	333 08 00	153 08 06	Ref. Mon. S–27	319. 3	2. 504234
Ref. Mon. C–26	47 10 43. 58	18 45 06	198 45 01	Ref. Mon. S–27	592. 7	2. 772861
	67 56 39. 38	50 27 38	230 27 27	Ref. Mon. S–28	434. 2	2. 637677
		325 31 26	145 31 33	C–25	327. 5	2. 515256
C–27	47 10 55. 48	7 35 34	187 35 32	Ref. Mon. S–28	649. 7	2. 812739
	67 56 51. 20	325 53 30	145 53 39	Ref. Mon. C–26	444. 0	2. 647381
Ref. Mon. S–29	47 10 50. 93	249 19 00	69 19 13	C–27	397. 8	2. 599683
	67 57 08. 88	290 04 55	110 05 17	Ref. Mon. C–26	661. 4	2. 820455
		330 22 22	150 22 33	Ref. Mon. S–28	579. 3	2. 762882
Ref. Mon. S–30	47 11 05. 40	295 07 18	115 07 41	C–27	721. 4	2. 858200
	67 57 22. 22	327 49 53	147 50 03	Ref. Mon. S–29	527. 8	2. 722503
C–28	47 11 15. 02	17 45 03	197 44 55	Ref. Mon. S–29	781. 1	2. 892687
	67 56 57. 56	60 13 17	240 12 59	Ref. Mon. S–30	598. 1	2. 776771
		347 28 27	167 28 32	C–27	618. 1	2. 791055

SOURCE OF ST. CROIX RIVER TO LAKE POHENAGAMOOK—Continued

Station	Latitude and longitude	Azimuth	Back azimuth	To station	Distance (meters)	Loga-rithm
MINOR SCHEME, ST. JOHN AND ST. FRANCIS RIVERS—continued	° ′ ″	° ′ ″	° ′ ″			
Keegan, Me., water tower.	47 11 16. 51 67 57 17. 36	16 36 02 276 17 49	196 35 59 96 18 04	Ref. Mon. S–30___ C–28_____	358. 0 419. 3	2. 553881 2. 622574
Ref. Mon. C–29_____	47 11 49. 94 67 57 13. 55	4 27 00 342 40 13	184 26 57 162 40 25	Keegan water tower. C–28_____	1, 035. 4 1, 129. 6	3. 015129 3. 052928
S–31_____	47 11 32. 13 67 57 42. 04	227 28 26 312 52 18 333 10 53	47 28 47 132 52 36 153 11 08	Ref. Mon. C–29___ Keegan water tower. Ref. Mon. S–30___	813. 8 708. 9 924. 8	2. 910512 2. 850556 2. 966064
Tripod_____	47 11 46. 11 67 57 41. 70	0 56 58 258 42 20	180 56 58 78 42 41	S–31_____ Ref. Mon. C–29___	431. 8 604. 3	2. 635252 2. 781245
Ref. Mon. S–32_____	47 11 57. 72 67 58 27. 19	278 48 23 290 31 50 309 44 36	98 49 17 110 32 23 129 45 09	Ref. Mon. C–29___ Tripod_____ S–31_____	1, 568. 6 1, 022. 5 1, 236. 1	3. 195513 3. 009658 3. 092056
Ref. Mon. C–30_____	47 12 19. 94 67 58 09. 28	28 46 27 308 17 48 330 56 15	208 46 14 128 18 29 150 56 35	Ref. Mon. S–32___ Ref. Mon. C–29___ Tripod_____	782. 9 1, 494. 9 1, 195. 4	2. 893699 3. 174624 3. 077507
C–31_____	47 12 29. 14 67 58 36. 10	296 43 04 349 03 41	116 43 24 169 03 48	Ref. Mon. C–30___ Ref. Mon. S–32___	631. 8 988. 3	2. 800554 2. 994867
Ref. Mon. S–33_____	47 12 10. 54 67 58 45. 78	199 32 22 249 17 32 315 19 31	19 32 29 69 17 59 135 19 45	C–31_____ Ref. Mon. C–30___ Ref. Mon. S–32___	609. 5 821. 2 556. 7	2. 784978 2. 914463 2. 745630
S–34_____	47 12 25. 78 67 59 12. 00	262 09 43 310 26 47	82 10 09 130 27 06	C–31_____ Ref. Mon. S–33___	762. 7 725. 1	2. 882380 2. 860405
Ref. Mon. C–32_____	47 12 36. 07 67 59 03. 71	28 46 24 290 13 19 334 26 04	208 46 18 110 13 39 154 26 17	S–34_____ C–31_____ Ref. Mon. S–33___	362. 8 619. 2 874. 0	2. 559675 2. 791797 2. 941514
Ref. Mon. C–33_____	47 12 47. 32 67 59 31. 08	301 05 20 328 53 52	121 05 40 148 54 06	Ref. Mon. C–32___ S–34_____	672. 6 777. 0	2. 827761 2. 890445
Ref. Mon. S–35_____	47 12 30. 54 67 59 35. 17	189 26 05 255 31 45 286 47 48	9 26 08 75 32 08 106 48 05	Ref. Mon. C–33___ Ref. Mon. C–32___ S–34_____	525. 3 683. 8 509. 2	2. 720394 2. 834931 2. 706920
Ref. Mon. S–36_____	47 12 52. 74 68 00 07. 19	282 24 40 315 29 09	102 25 06 135 29 32	Ref. Mon. C–33___ Ref. Mon. S–35___	778. 1 961. 2	2. 891057 2. 982825
C–34_____	47 13 04. 16 67 59 50. 29	45 14 39 322 07 55 342 57 30	225 14 27 142 08 09 162 57 41	Ref. Mon. S–36___ Ref. Mon. C–33___ Ref. Mon. S–35___	500. 8 658. 6 1, 085. 8	2. 699706 2. 818630 3. 035743
Ref. Mon. S–37_____	47 13 15. 28 68 00 27. 42	293 43 41 328 33 30	113 44 08 148 33 45	C–34_____ Ref. Mon. S–36___	853. 3 815. 8	2. 931112 2. 911610
C–35 (Ste. Anne east base).	47 13 33. 62 68 00 14. 34	25 54 00 330 55 23 353 12 26	205 53 51 150 55 41 173 12 32	Ref. Mon. S–37___ C–34_____ Ref. Mon. S–36___	629. 9 1, 041. 3 1, 271. 6	2. 799263 3. 017559 3. 104359
Ref. Mon. S–38_____	47 14 02. 91 68 01 22. 63	302 10 59 321 41 52	122 11 49 141 42 33	C–35_____ Ref. Mon. S–37___	1, 697. 5 1, 874. 2	3. 229807 3. 272825
C–36 (Ste. Anne west base).	47 14 08. 56 68 00 52. 98	74 22 24 323 00 04 341 54 00	254 22 02 143 00 32 161 54 19	Ref. Mon. S–38___ C–35_____ Ref. Mon. S–37___	647. 7 1, 350. 71 1, 731. 1	2. 811347 3. 130562 3. 238311
Ref. Mon. C–37_____	47 14 43. 21 68 01 42. 97	315 29 31 341 01 17	135 30 08 161 01 32	C–36_____ Ref. Mon. S–38___	1, 500. 2 1, 316. 0	3. 176156 3. 119254

SOURCE OF ST. CROIX RIVER TO LAKE POHENAGAMOOK—Continued

Station	Latitude and longitude	Azimuth	Back azimuth	To station	Distance (meters)	Loga- rithm
	° ′ ″	° ′ ″	° ′ ″			
MINOR SCHEME, ST. JOHN AND ST. FRANCIS RIVERS— continued						
Ref. Mon. S–39	47 14 32.75	242 59 02	62 59 24	Ref. Mon. C–37	711.1	2.851950
	68 02 13.10	293 53 52	113 54 51	C–36	1,843.3	3.265607
		310 57 15	130 57 52	Ref. Mon. S–38	1,405.7	3.147898
C–38	47 15 05.66	301 52 49	121 53 28	Ref. Mon. C–37	1,312.7	3.118176
	68 02 35.98	334 39 54	154 40 11	Ref. Mon. S–39	1,124.5	3.050978
Ref. Mon. S–40	47 14 55.46	241 09 16	61 09 36	C–38	653.0	2.814923
	68 03 03.18	282 38 10	102 39 09	Ref. Mon. C–37	1,728.6	3.237704
		303 39 22	123 39 59	Ref. Mon. S–39	1,265.4	3.102229
Ref. Mon. S–41	47 15 14.41	281 21 12	101 21 59	C–38	1,371.2	3.137106
	68 03 39.91	307 08 28	127 08 55	Ref. Mon. S–40	969.0	2.986320
Ref. Mon. C–39	47 15 27.52	32 50 00	212 49 51	Ref. Mon. S–41	482.1	2.683098
	68 03 27.48	301 56 08	121 56 46	C–38	1,276.2	3.105904
		332 42 02	152 42 20	Ref. Mon. S–40	1,114.2	3.046980
C–40	47 15 46.26	295 27 16	115 27 58	Ref. Mon. C–39	1,345.8	3.128974
	68 04 25.27	315 52 37	135 53 10	Ref. Mon. S–41	1,370.1	3.136748
Ref. Mon. S–42	47 15 26.60	238 33 59	58 34 34	C–40	1,164.3	3.066048
	68 05 12.53	269 14 55	89 16 12	Ref. Mon. C–39	2,208.8	3.344161
		280 55 59	100 57 07	Ref. Mon. S–41	1,983.4	3.297414
Ref. Mon. S–43	47 16 41.26	299 50 40	119 52 24	C–40	3,411.7	3.532973
	68 06 46.03	319 32 29	139 33 38	Ref. Mon. S–42	3,029.8	3.481420
Ref. Mon. C–41	47 16 51.12	73 22 39	253 22 03	Ref. Mon. S–43	1,064.1	3.026981
	68 05 57.52	315 55 18	135 56 26	C–40	2,787.8	3.445266
		340 04 37	160 05 10	Ref. Mon. S–42	2,776.2	3.443455
C–42	47 17 22.71	302 08 10	122 09 04	Ref. Mon. C–41	1,833.8	3.263351
	68 07 11.41	337 23 02	157 23 20	Ref. Mon. S–43	1,386.8	3.142002
Ref. Mon. S–44	47 17 01.85	219 34 36	39 34 55	C–42	836.0	2.922227
	68 07 36.76	279 00 57	99 02 10	Ref. Mon. C–41	2,111.7	3.324625
		300 48 26	120 49 03	Ref. Mon. S–43	1,241.2	3.093839
Ref. Mon. S–45	47 17 41.49	286 17 50	106 18 59	C–42	2,064.9	3.314904
	68 08 45.73	310 10 45	130 11 35	Ref. Mon. S–44	1,897.1	3.278095
Ref. Mon. C–43	47 18 03.56	30 06 52	210 06 38	Ref. Mon. S–45	788.0	2.896518
	68 08 26.91	308 28 57	128 29 52	C–42	2,026.8	3.306807
		331 03 13	151 03 49	Ref. Mon. S–44	2,177.8	3.338013
Ref. Mon. S–46	47 18 12.60	281 53 43	101 54 30	Ref. Mon. C–43	1,354.4	3.131753
	68 09 30.00	315 55 55	135 56 28	Ref. Mon. S–45	1,337.3	3.126241
Ref. Mon. C–44	47 18 52.22	30 30 08	210 29 43	Ref. Mon. S–46	1,419.9	3.152265
	68 08 55.69	338 05 03	158 05 25	Ref. Mon. C–43	1,619.8	3.209466
		354 31 37	174 31 44	Ref. Mon. S–45	2,194.4	3.341322
Ref. Mon. S–47	47 19 01.10	281 28 19	101 29 06	Ref. Mon. C–44	1,377.7	3.139158
	68 09 59.98	337 11 34	157 11 56	Ref. Mon. S–46	1,624.6	3.210751
Ref. Mon. C–45	47 19 22.97	14 51 00	194 50 40	Ref. Mon. S–46	2,248.0	3.351799
	68 09 02.57	60 44 54	240 44 12	Ref. Mon. S–47	1,381.8	3.140443
		351 20 39	171 20 44	Ref. Mon. C–44	960.4	2.982467
C–46	47 19 51.67	296 18 40	116 19 43	Ref. Mon. C–45	1,999.0	3.300820
	68 10 27.90	339 24 50	159 25 11	Ref. Mon. S–47	1,668.2	3.222237
Ref. Mon. S–48	47 19 27.99	196 36 17	16 36 24	C–46	763.0	2.882509
	68 10 38.29	274 24 19	94 25 29	Ref. Mon. C–45	2,016.0	3.304481
		315 54 17	135 54 45	Ref. Mon. S–47	1,156.3	3.063081

SOURCE OF ST. CROIX RIVER TO LAKE POHENAGAMOOK—Continued

Station	Latitude and longitude	Azimuth	Back azimuth	To station	Distance (meters)	Logarithm
MINOR SCHEME, ST. JOHN AND ST. FRANCIS RIVERS—continued	° ′ ″	° ′ ″	° ′ ″			
Ref. Mon. C–47	47 19 53. 12 68 10 47. 30	276 18 00 346 18 14	96 18 14 166 18 21	C–46 Ref. Mon. S–48	409. 6 798. 8	2. 612383 2. 902453
Ref. Mon. S–49	47 19 38. 91 68 10 55. 08	200 24 32 235 21 57 313 43 19	20 24 37 55 22 16 133 43 31	Ref. Mon. C–47 C–46 Ref. Mon. S–48	468. 4 693. 4 487. 7	2. 670615 2. 840954 2. 688197
Ref. Mon. S–50	47 20 05. 96 68 12 03. 94	283 50 16 300 01 03	103 51 12 120 01 54	Ref. Mon. C–47 Ref. Mon. S–49	1, 657. 3 1, 670. 0	3. 219400 3. 222704
Ref. Mon. C–48	47 20 13. 87 68 11 42. 22	61 49 19 299 03 28 317 29 07	241 49 03 119 04 08 137 29 42	Ref. Mon. S–50 Ref. Mon. C–47 Ref. Mon. S–49	517. 3 1, 319. 3 1, 464. 9	2. 713701 3. 120335 3. 165807
Ref. Mon. C–49	47 20 35. 38 68 12 16. 44	312 45 12 343 52 50	132 45 37 163 52 59	Ref. Mon. C–48 Ref. Mon. S–50	978. 5 945. 7	2. 990559 2. 975770
Ref. Mon. S–51	47 20 18. 18 68 12 33. 58	214 05 25 277 01 12 301 12 54	34 05 38 97 01 50 121 13 16	Ref. Mon. C–49 Ref. Mon. C–48 Ref. Mon. S–50	641. 7 1, 086. 4 727. 7	2. 807336 3. 035971 2. 861923
Ref. Mon. S–52	47 20 43. 61 68 13 54. 82	277 00 20 294 43 22	97 01 33 114 44 22	Ref. Mon. C–49 Ref. Mon. S–51	2, 080. 6 1, 877. 7	3. 318196 3. 273624
Ref. Mon. C–50	47 21 04. 36 68 13 27. 36	41 58 29 301 00 18 321 37 51	221 58 09 121 01 11 141 38 31	Ref. Mon. S–52 Ref. Mon. C–49 Ref. Mon. S–51	861. 8 1, 736. 9 1, 819. 0	2. 935413 3. 239763 3. 259842
C–51	47 21 37. 64 68 14 34. 21	306 13 15 333 38 22	126 14 04 153 38 51	Ref. Mon. C–50 Ref. Mon. S–52	1, 739. 1 1, 862. 1	3. 240337 3. 270011
Ref. Mon. S–53	47 21 02. 35 68 14 59. 29	205 46 07 268 08 45 293 08 43	25 46 25 88 09 52 113 09 30	C–51 Ref. Mon. C–50 Ref. Mon. S–52	1, 210. 4 1, 930. 3 1, 471. 6	3. 082914 3. 285634 3. 167791
Ref. Mon. C–52	47 21 32. 17 68 15 26. 85	261 17 24 327 51 39	81 18 02 147 51 59	C–51 Ref. Mon. S–53	1, 117. 5 1, 087. 5	3. 048239 3. 036417
Ref. Mon. S–54	47 20 52. 09 68 16 16. 12	219 52 37 236 39 23 258 52 46	39 53 13 56 40 37 78 53 42	Ref. Mon. C–52 C–51 Ref. Mon. S–53	1, 612. 8 2, 560. 0 1, 643. 6	3. 207590 3. 408244 3. 215793
Ref. Mon. C–53	47 21 38. 68 68 16 49. 59	276 36 01 333 58 29	96 37 02 153 58 54	Ref. Mon. C–52 Ref. Mon. S–54	1, 748. 0 1, 601. 1	3. 242545 3. 204426
Ref. Mon. S–55	47 20 57. 38 68 17 22. 40	208 21 25 246 05 43 276 41 24	28 21 49 66 07 08 96 42 13	Ref. Mon. C–53 Ref. Mon. C–52 Ref. Mon. S–54	1, 449. 4 2, 652. 4 1, 400. 7	3. 161202 3. 423640 3. 146333
Ref. Mon. C–54	47 21 33. 49 68 18 05. 78	264 16 10 320 46 16	84 17 06 140 46 48	Ref. Mon. C–53 Ref. Mon. S–55	1, 606. 7 1, 439. 7	3. 205943 3. 158259
Ref. Mon. S–56	47 21 05. 35 68 18 22. 34	201 48 02 242 07 23 281 04 16	21 48 14 62 08 31 101 05 00	Ref. Mon. C–54 Ref. Mon. C–53 Ref. Mon. S–55	935. 9 2, 201. 8 1, 282. 0	2. 971232 3. 342773 3. 107876
Ref. Mon. S–57	47 21 11. 52 68 19 31. 83	249 23 41 277 25 40	69 24 44 97 26 31	Ref. Mon. C–54 Ref. Mon. S–56	1, 929. 2 1, 470. 7	3. 285369 3. 167534
Ref. Mon. C–55	47 21 43. 91 68 19 06. 33	28 08 47 284 11 55 322 12 24	208 08 28 104 12 39 142 12 56	Ref. Mon. S–57 Ref. Mon. C–54 Ref. Mon. S–56	1, 134. 4 1, 310. 7 1, 506. 6	3. 054769 3. 117510 3. 177986
C–56	47 21 42. 19 68 19 44. 35	266 12 19 344 29 54	86 12 47 164 30 03	Ref. Mon. C–55 Ref. Mon. S–57	799. 5 983. 2	2. 902828 2. 992634

SOURCE OF ST. CROIX RIVER TO LAKE POHENAGAMOOK—Continued

Station	Latitude and longitude	Azimuth	Back azimuth	To station	Distance (meters)	Logarithm
MINOR SCHEME, ST. JOHN AND ST. FRANCIS RIVERS—continued	° ′ ″	° ′ ″	° ′ ″			
Ref. Mon. S–58	47 21 13. 06	199 52 51	19 53 03	C–56	956. 7	2. 980793
	68 19 59. 85	229 41 38	49 42 18	Ref. Mon. C–55	1, 472. 7	3. 168128
		274 38 05	94 38 26	Ref. Mon. S–57	590. 1	2. 770932
Ref. Mon. S–59	47 21 14. 82	236 28 56	56 29 41	C–56	1, 531. 3	3. 185064
	68 20 45. 19	273 15 34	93 16 07	Ref. Mon. S–58	953. 0	2. 979098
C–57	47 21 39. 76	267 08 20	87 09 13	C–56	1, 512. 1	3. 179581
	68 20 56. 32	304 49 19	124 50 00	Ref. Mon. S–58	1, 443. 5	3. 159428
		343 07 43	163 07 51	Ref. Mon. S–59	804. 8	2. 905686
C–58	47 21 35. 16	248 04 01	68 04 13	C–57	380. 5	2. 580334
	68 21 13. 13	316 57 19	136 57 39	Ref. Mon. S–59	859. 3	2. 934165
Ref. Mon. S–60	47 21 12. 21	175 29 05	355 29 03	C–58	710. 7	2. 851665
	68 21 10. 47	199 14 52	19 15 02	C–57	900. 9	2. 954694
		261 22 50	81 23 08	Ref. Mon. S–59	536. 7	2. 729705
Ref. Mon. S–61	47 20 57. 21	223 06 58	43 07 36	C–58	1, 605. 4	3. 205595
	68 22 05. 42	248 06 27	68 07 07	Ref. Mon. S–60	1, 243. 0	3. 094473
Ref. Mon. C–59	47 21 21. 02	252 42 11	72 43 00	C–58	1, 468. 8	3. 166977
	68 22 19. 96	280 33 11	100 34 02	Ref. Mon. S–60	1, 483. 6	3. 171327
		337 27 26	157 27 37	Ref. Mon. S–61	796. 1	2. 900960
Ref. Mon. C–60	47 20 40. 49	216 17 15	36 17 47	Ref. Mon. C–59	1, 552. 8	3. 191103
	68 23 03. 75	247 07 49	67 08 32	Ref. Mon. S–61	1, 328. 7	3. 123441
Ref. Mon. S–62	47 20 34. 19	102 39 13	282 38 43	Ref. Mon. C–60	888. 3	2. 948544
	68 22 22. 46	182 04 40	2 04 42	Ref. Mon. C–59	1, 447. 0	3. 160471
		206 42 41	26 42 54	Ref. Mon. S–61	795. 7	2. 900759
Ref. Mon. S–63	47 20 05. 52	153 23 01	333 22 42	Ref. Mon. C–60	1, 208. 2	3. 082149
	68 22 37. 97	200 10 26	20 10 37	Ref. Mon. S–62	943. 5	2. 974760
Ref. Mon. C–61 (Edmundston north base).	47 20 03. 56	181 19 26	1 19 27	Ref. Mon. C–60	1, 140. 8	3. 057210
	68 23 05. 01	223 21 01	43 21 32	Ref. Mon. S–62	1, 301. 0	3. 114277
		263 55 53	83 56 13	Ref. Mon. S–63	571. 0	2. 756610
Ref. Mon. C–62 (Edmundston south base).	47 19 46. 79	189 19 37	9 19 40	Ref. Mon. C–61	524. 99	2. 720147
	68 23 09. 06	228 27 34	48 27 57	Ref. Mon. S–63	872. 2	2. 940629
Ref. Mon. S–64	47 19 38. 53	121 22 24	301 22 09	Ref. Mon. C–62	489. 6	2. 689870
	68 22 49. 15	156 41 51	336 41 39	Ref. Mon. C–61	841. 6	2. 925104
		195 44 23	15 44 31	Ref. Mon. S–63	865. 7	2. 937387
Ref. Mon. C–63	47 19 28. 93	198 44 06	18 44 12	Ref. Mon. C–62	582. 4	2. 765199
	68 23 17. 97	243 53 05	63 53 26	Ref. Mon. S–64	673. 9	2. 828610
Ref. Mon. S–65	47 19 23. 42	104 09 49	284 09 25	Ref. Mon. C–63	695. 5	2. 842288
	68 22 45. 86	145 58 31	325 58 13	Ref. Mon. C–62	870. 7	2. 939891
		171 34 07	351 34 04	Ref. Mon. S–64	471. 9	2. 673809
Ref. Mon. S–66	47 18 35. 10	154 03 57	334 03 29	Ref. Mon. C–63	1, 848. 6	3. 266850
	68 22 39. 47	174 51 49	354 51 45	Ref. Mon. S–65	1, 498. 3	3. 175597
Ref. Mon. C–64	47 18 51. 56	190 09 40	10 09 47	Ref. Mon. C–63	1, 172. 4	3. 069080
	68 23 27. 82	221 50 49	41 51 20	Ref. Mon. S–65	1, 320. 9	3. 120856
		296 35 17	116 35 52	Ref. Mon. S–66	1, 135. 7	3. 055261
Ref. Mon. C–65	47 18 43. 31	193 14 09	13 14 12	Ref. Mon. C–64	261. 7	2. 417741
	68 23 30. 67	283 16 00	103 16 38	Ref. Mon. S–66	1, 105. 0	3. 043361
Ref. Mon. S–67	47 18 26. 72	117 41 21	297 40 47	Ref. Mon. C–65	1, 103. 0	3. 042574
	68 22 44. 17	129 55 37	309 55 06	Ref. Mon. C–64	1, 195. 4	3. 077523
		200 53 36	20 53 40	Ref. Mon. S–66	277. 0	2. 442466

SOURCE OF ST. CROIX RIVER TO LAKE POHENAGAMOOK—Continued

Station	Latitude and longitude	Azimuth	Back azimuth	To station	Distance (meters)	Logarithm
	° ′ ″	° ′ ″	° ′ ″			
MINOR SCHEME, ST. JOHN AND ST. FRANCIS RIVERS—continued						
Ref. Mon. S–68	47 17 59. 95	136 26 18	316 25 34	Ref. Mon. C–65	1, 848. 3	3. 266778
	68 22 30. 03	160 14 06	340 13 56	Ref. Mon. S–67	878. 5	2. 943758
Ref. Mon. C–66	47 17 46. 28	197 08 46	17 09 05	Ref. Mon. C–65	1, 843. 3	3. 265607
	68 23 56. 55	230 35 28	50 36 21	Ref. Mon. S–67	1, 967. 6	3. 293939
		256 54 55	76 55 58	Ref. Mon. S–68	1, 866. 0	3. 270920
Ref. Mon. S–69	47 16 57. 19	129 41 55	309 40 51	Ref. Mon. C–66	2, 373. 8	3. 375435
	68 22 29. 62	179 44 36	359 44 35	Ref. Mon. S–68	1, 938. 1	3. 287386
Ref. Mon. S–70	47 16 35. 69	169 45 44	349 45 30	Ref. Mon. C–66	2, 215. 2	3. 345410
	68 23 37. 81	208 41 12	28 42 01	Ref. Mon. S–68	2, 966. 3	3. 472221
		245 08 07	65 08 57	Ref. Mon. S–69	1, 579. 5	3. 198510
Ref. Mon. S–71	47 16 54. 51	207 06 11	27 06 39	Ref. Mon. C–66	1, 796. 0	3. 254304
	68 24 35. 49	295 36 25	115 37 07	Ref. Mon. S–70	1, 344. 4	3. 128544
Ref. Mon. C–67	47 17 27. 52	236 57 29	56 58 00	Ref. Mon. C–66	1, 062. 6	3. 026381
	68 24 38. 94	321 14 23	141 15 08	Ref. Mon. S–70	2, 052. 4	3. 312270
		355 55 44	175 55 47	Ref. Mon. S–71	1, 022. 0	3. 009434
Ref. Mon. C–68	47 17 26. 54	269 07 35	89 08 44	Ref. Mon. C–67	1, 996. 4	3. 300245
	68 26 13. 94	295 32 45	115 33 57	Ref. Mon. S–71	2, 293. 2	3. 360449
Ref. Mon. S–72	47 16 40. 52	170 13 36	350 13 28	Ref. Mon. C–68	1, 442. 3	3. 159063
	68 26 02. 29	230 20 35	50 21 36	Ref. Mon. C–67	2, 274. 8	3. 356943
		256 39 54	76 40 58	Ref. Mon. S–71	1, 874. 7	3. 272937
Ref. Mon. S–73	47 17 00. 08	243 53 06	63 54 04	Ref. Mon. C–68	1, 857. 1	3. 268841
	68 27 33. 30	287 31 13	107 32 19	Ref. Mon. S–72	2, 005. 9	3. 302304
Ref. Mon. C–69	47 17 45. 82	1 35 05	181 35 04	Ref. Mon. S–73	1, 413. 0	3. 150129
	68 27 31. 44	290 04 12	110 05 09	Ref. Mon. C–68	1, 733. 7	3. 238986
		317 05 54	137 06 59	Ref. Mon. S–72	2, 752. 5	3. 439730
Ref. Mon. S–74	47 17 27. 82	242 24 50	62 25 27	Ref. Mon. C–69	1, 200. 3	3. 079285
	68 28 22. 08	309 53 07	129 53 43	Ref. Mon. S–73	1, 335. 8	3. 125746
Ref. Mon. C–70	47 18 01. 17	11 19 19	191 19 12	Ref. Mon. S–74	1, 050. 2	3. 021288
	68 28 12. 26	298 55 41	118 56 11	Ref. Mon. C–69	979. 9	2. 991198
		336 32 13	156 32 42	Ref. Mon. S–73	2, 056. 5	3. 313120
Ref. Mon. C–71	47 18 19. 49	294 50 02	114 50 45	Ref. Mon. C–70	1, 347. 0	3. 129371
	68 29 10. 45	327 30 01	147 30 37	Ref. Mon. S–74	1, 891. 8	3. 276886
Ref. Mon. S–75	47 17 27. 82	182 13 43	2 13 45	Ref. Mon. C–71	1, 597. 0	3. 203311
	68 29 13. 41	231 16 25	51 17 10	Ref. Mon. C–70	1, 646. 6	3. 216580
		269 59 12	89 59 50	Ref. Mon. S–74	1, 078. 6	3. 032860
Ref. Mon. S–76	47 17 36. 70	220 38 52	40 39 32	Ref. Mon. C–71	1, 742. 0	3. 241053
	68 30 04. 47	284 19 51	104 20 29	Ref. Mon. S–75	1, 107. 4	3. 044310
Ref. Mon. C–72	47 18 14. 14	262 51 57	82 52 43	Ref. Mon. C–71	1, 331. 5	3. 124332
	68 30 13. 34	318 38 20	138 39 04	Ref. Mon. S–75	1, 905. 9	3. 280093
		350 50 29	170 50 35	Ref. Mon. S–76	1, 171. 3	3. 068677
Ref. Mon. S–77	47 17 39. 78	200 20 26	20 20 40	Ref. Mon. C–72	1, 131. 7	3. 053726
	68 30 32. 07	234 25 12	54 26 12	Ref. Mon. C–71	2, 108. 1	3. 323890
		279 19 44	99 20 04	Ref. Mon. S–76	587. 7	2. 769127
Ref. Mon. S–78	47 17 39. 48	220 59 26	40 59 59	Ref. Mon. C–72	1, 418. 0	3. 151676
	68 30 57. 62	269 01 14	89 01 33	Ref. Mon. S–77	536. 9	2. 729908
Ref. Mon. C–73	47 18 00. 12	250 58 17	70 59 01	Ref. Mon. C–72	1, 328. 4	3. 123324
	68 31 13. 12	306 03 34	126 04 04	Ref. Mon. S–77	1, 067. 0	3. 028168
		332 55 35	152 55 46	Ref. Mon. S–78	715. 7	2. 854729

SOURCE OF ST. CROIX RIVER TO LAKE POHENAGAMOOK—Continued

Station	Latitude and longitude	Azimuth	Back azimuth	To station	Distance (meters)	Loga- rithm
MINOR SCHEME, ST. JOHN AND ST. FRANCIS RIVERS— continued	° ′ ″	° ′ ″	° ′ ″			
Ref. Mon. C–74	47 17 46. 97	234 56 27	54 56 48	Ref. Mon. C–73	707. 3	2. 849627
	68 31 40. 68	284 19 03	104 19 35	Ref. Mon. S–78	933. 8	2. 970257
Ref. Mon. S–79	47 17 35. 41	127 41 58	307 41 42	Ref. Mon. C–74	583. 5	2. 766050
	68 31 18. 71	188 44 30	8 44 35	Ref. Mon. C–73	772. 1	2. 887653
		254 08 46	74 09 02	Ref. Mon. S–78	460. 6	2. 663336
Ref. Mon. S–80	47 17 22. 29	177 25 18	357 25 17	Ref. Mon. C–74	762. 9	2. 882478
	68 31 39. 05	204 59 34	24 59 54	Ref. Mon. C–73	1, 289. 2	3. 110310
		226 31 00	46 31 15	Ref. Mon. S–79	589. 0	2. 770151
Ref. Mon. C–75	47 17 27. 77	238 13 54	58 14 28	Ref. Mon. C–74	1, 126. 0	3. 051549
	68 32 26. 25	279 41 14	99 41 49	Ref. Mon. S–80	1, 006. 1	3. 002651
Ref. Mon. S–81	47 16 56. 89	172 00 34	352 00 29	Ref. Mon. C–75	963. 0	2. 983615
	68 32 19. 88	208 02 07	28 02 36	Ref. Mon. C–74	1, 752. 0	3. 243541
		227 33 59	47 34 29	Ref. Mon. S–80	1, 162. 4	3. 065350
Ref. Mon. C–76	47 17 18. 56	239 11 51	59 12 07	Ref. Mon. C–75	555. 8	2. 744957
	68 32 48. 97	317 34 29	137 34 50	Ref. Mon. S–81	906. 3	2. 957260
Ref. Mon. S–82	47 16 46. 35	201 05 29	21 05 42	Ref. Mon. C–76	1, 066. 0	3. 027740
	68 33 07. 22	213 56 37	33 57 06	Ref. Mon. C–75	1, 542. 0	3. 188082
		251 52 48	71 53 22	Ref. Mon. S–81	1, 047. 0	3. 019928
Ref. Mon. S–83	47 16 51. 08	236 44 23	56 45 09	Ref. Mon. C–76	1, 547. 6	3. 189665
	68 33 50. 56	279 05 51	99 06 24	Ref. Mon. S–82	922. 3	2. 964859
Ref. Mon. C–77	47 17 18. 23	23 13 42	203 13 29	Ref. Mon. S–83	912. 5	2. 960250
	68 33 33. 43	269 22 42	89 23 15	Ref. Mon. C–76	934. 3	2. 970491
		330 46 29	150 46 49	Ref. Mon. S–82	1, 128. 0	3. 052324
Ref. Mon. C–78	47 17 24. 41	280 10 35	100 11 12	Ref. Mon. C–77	1, 080. 4	3. 033582
	68 34 24. 04	325 38 54	145 39 18	Ref. Mon. S–83	1, 247. 0	3. 095868
Ref. Mon. S–84	47 16 51. 32	169 46 12	349 46 06	Ref. Mon. C–78	1, 038. 6	3. 016444
	68 34 15. 26	226 36 01	46 36 32	Ref. Mon. C–77	1, 209. 7	3. 082676
		270 49 22	90 49 40	Ref. Mon. S–83	519. 2	2. 715349
Ref. Mon. S–85	47 16 47. 72	202 38 18	22 38 35	Ref. Mon. C–78	1, 227. 9	3. 089147
	68 34 46. 53	260 23 49	80 24 12	Ref. Mon. S–84	666. 5	2. 823817
Ref. Mon. C–79	47 17 08. 61	249 29 15	69 30 01	Ref. Mon. C–78	1, 393. 5	3. 144098
	68 35 26. 15	289 42 38	109 43 30	Ref. Mon. S–84	1, 582. 6	3. 199358
		307 45 49	127 46 18	Ref. Mon. S–85	1, 053. 3	3. 022541
Ref. Mon. C–80	47 16 41. 30	221 20 10	41 20 36	Ref. Mon. C–79	1, 123. 2	3. 050439
	68 36 01. 45	262 49 07	82 50 02	Ref. Mon. S–85	1, 587. 0	3. 200578
Ref. Mon. S–86	47 16 26. 19	112 43 47	292 43 08	Ref. Mon. C–80	1, 208. 0	3. 082062
	68 35 08. 44	164 08 17	344 08 04	Ref. Mon. C–79	1, 361. 8	3. 134105
		214 42 13	34 42 29	Ref. Mon. S–85	808. 7	2. 907789
Ref. Mon. S–87	47 16 03. 16	155 41 03	335 40 44	Ref. Mon. C–80	1, 292. 5	3. 111427
	68 35 36. 12	219 17 44	39 18 04	Ref. Mon. S–86	919. 0	2. 963310
Ref. Mon. C–81	47 16 29. 38	232 02 50	52 03 06	Ref. Mon. C–80	598. 9	2. 777370
	68 36 23. 92	273 32 18	93 33 13	Ref. Mon. S–86	1, 589. 6	3. 201284
		308 51 23	128 51 58	Ref. Mon. S–87	1, 290. 1	3. 110639
Ref. Mon. C–82	47 15 15. 49	177 49 27	357 49 24	Ref. Mon. C–81	2, 283. 3	3. 358567
	68 36 19. 79	211 56 38	31 57 10	Ref. Mon. S–87	1, 735. 0	3. 239298
Ref. Mon. S–89	47 14 48. 33	121 40 37	301 39 50	Ref. Mon. C–82	1, 597. 8	3. 203517
	68 35 15. 13	155 08 26	335 07 36	Ref. Mon. C–81	3, 439. 4	3. 536485
		169 11 10	349 10 55	Ref. Mon. S–87	2, 352. 9	3. 371598

SOURCE OF ST. CROIX RIVER TO LAKE POHENAGAMOOK—Continued

Station	Latitude and longitude	Azimuth	Back azimuth	To station	Distance (meters)	Logarithm
MINOR SCHEME, ST. JOHN AND ST. FRANCIS RIVERS—continued	° ′ ″	° ′ ″	° ′ ″			
Ref. Mon. S–88	47 15 36. 63	63 26 17	243 25 32	Ref. Mon. C–82	1, 459. 7	3. 164260
	68 35 17. 70	139 29 20	319 28 32	Ref. Mon. C–81	2, 142. 6	3. 330937
		357 55 18	177 55 20	Ref. Mon. S–89	1, 492. 7	3. 173983
S–90	47 14 40. 76	180 33 37	0 33 37	Ref. Mon. C–82	1, 072. 7	3. 030486
	68 36 20. 29	217 19 42	37 20 27	Ref. Mon. S–88	2, 170. 2	3. 336498
		260 18 46	80 19 33	Ref. Mon. S–89	1, 390. 3	3. 143093
Ref. Mon. C–83	47 14 58. 33	220 06 57	40 07 13	Ref. Mon. C–82	693. 3	2. 840931
	68 36 41. 04	279 41 14	99 42 17	Ref. Mon. S–89	1, 832. 9	3. 263130
		321 11 20	141 11 36	S–90	696. 2	2. 842709
Ref. Mon. C–84	47 14 55. 44	263 07 33	83 07 58	Ref. Mon. C–83	745. 0	2. 872133
	68 37 16. 21	291 04 38	111 05 19	S–90	1, 260. 3	3. 100477
Clair east base	47 14 55. 20	90 33 20	270 32 53	Ref. Mon. C–84	780. 0	2. 892104
	68 36 39. 12	157 19 44	337 19 42	Ref. Mon. C–83	104. 7	2. 020035
Clair west base	47 14 48. 81	152 09 17	332 09 13	Ref. Mon. C–84	231. 7	2. 364848
	68 37 11. 07	245 01 59	65 02 20	Ref. Mon. C–83	696. 5	2. 842914
		253 37 40	73 38 03	Clair east base	700. 17	2. 845202
Ref. Mon. S–91	47 14 20. 68	158 45 16	338 45 02	Ref. Mon. C–84	1, 151. 7	3. 061329
	68 36 56. 36	195 29 42	15 29 53	Ref. Mon. C–83	1, 206. 4	3. 081477
		230 44 19	50 44 46	S–90	979. 8	2. 991142
Ref. Mon. S–92	47 14 17. 49	207 39 12	27 39 34	Ref. Mon. C–84	1, 323. 2	3. 121639
	68 37 45. 41	264 31 54	84 32 30	Ref. Mon. S–91	1, 036. 4	3. 015516
Ref. Mon. C–85	47 14 41. 63	235 43 54	55 44 16	Ref. Mon. C–84	757. 4	2. 879295
	68 37 45. 97	301 47 54	121 48 30	Ref. Mon. S–91	1, 227. 7	3. 089076
		359 05 54	179 05 54	Ref. Mon. S–92	745. 7	2. 872587
Ref. Mon. C–86	47 14 39. 34	264 07 04	84 07 28	Ref. Mon. C–85	691. 8	2. 839952
	68 38 18. 69	313 57 02	133 57 26	Ref. Mon. S–92	972. 2	2. 987761
Ref. Mon. S–93	47 14 16. 52	163 54 32	343 54 25	Ref. Mon. C–86	733. 4	2. 865351
	68 38 09. 03	212 00 41	32 00 58	Ref. Mon. C–85	914. 6	2. 961246
		266 33 13	86 33 30	Ref. Mon. S–92	497. 5	2. 696821
Ref. Mon. S–94	47 14 17. 56	222 02 30	42 02 51	Ref. Mon. C–86	905. 6	2. 956953
	68 38 47. 53	272 16 06	92 16 34	Ref. Mon. S–93	810. 5	2. 908746
Ref. Mon. C–87	47 14 42. 79	277 58 35	97 59 01	Ref. Mon. C–86	767. 7	2. 885178
	68 38 54. 84	310 05 25	130 05 58	Ref. Mon. S–93	1, 259. 6	3. 100235
		348 50 03	168 50 08	Ref. Mon. S–94	794. 2	2. 899903
Ref. Mon. C–88	47 14 43. 60	271 30 15	91 30 48	Ref. Mon. C–87	947. 7	2. 976660
	68 39 39. 89	306 07 52	126 08 30	Ref. Mon. S–94	1, 363. 5	3. 134656
Ref. Mon. S–95	47 14 10. 86	160 55 33	340 55 21	Ref. Mon. C–88	1, 069. 8	3. 029302
	68 39 23. 26	211 13 20	31 13 41	Ref. Mon. C–87	1, 153. 1	3. 061886
		254 36 00	74 36 26	Ref. Mon. S–94	779. 6	2. 891875
Ref. Mon. S–96	47 13 52. 42	213 48 28	33 49 05	Ref. Mon. C–88	1, 902. 4	3. 279294
	68 40 30. 22	247 58 31	67 59 20	Ref. Mon. S–95	1, 519. 2	3. 181616
Ref. Mon. C–89	47 14 36. 80	17 00 12	196 59 57	Ref. Mon. S–96	1, 433. 4	3. 156356
	68 40 10. 29	251 49 37	71 49 59	Ref. Mon. C–88	673. 0	2. 828031
		309 00 05	129 00 39	Ref. Mon. S–95	1, 272. 9	3. 104800
Ref. Mon. C–90	47 14 56. 18	289 20 18	109 21 18	Ref. Mon. C–89	1, 806. 7	3. 256893
	68 41 31. 35	326 51 05	146 51 50	Ref. Mon. S–96	2, 351. 9	3. 371414
Ref. Mon. S–97	47 14 17. 69	202 40 55	22 41 13	Ref. Mon. C–90	1, 288. 6	3. 110123
	68 41 54. 98	254 58 46	75 00 04	Ref. Mon. C–89	2, 279. 6	3. 357867
		293 37 40	113 38 43	Ref. Mon. S–96	1, 946. 3	3. 289205

SOURCE OF ST. CROIX RIVER TO LAKE POHENAGAMOOK—Continued

Station	Latitude and longitude	Azimuth	Back azimuth	To station	Distance (meters)	Logarithm
	° ′ ″	° ′ ″	° ′ ″			
MINOR SCHEME, ST. JOHN AND ST. FRANCIS RIVERS—continued						
Ref. Mon. C–91____	47 14 53. 41	264 11 48	84 12 18	Ref. Mon. C–90___	848. 8	2. 928822
	68 42 11. 51	342 30 31	162 30 43	Ref. Mon. S–97___	1, 156. 6	3. 063196
Ref. Mon. S–98_____	47 14 20. 04	220 36 02	40 36 33	Ref. Mon. C–91___	1, 357. 3	3. 132679
	68 42 53. 51	237 07 44	57 08 45	Ref. Mon. C–90___	2, 057. 1	3. 313264
		273 22 20	93 23 03	Ref. Mon. S–97___	1, 233. 3	3. 091053
Ref. Mon. C–92_____	47 14 57. 12	274 16 27	94 17 21	Ref. Mon. C–91___	1, 537. 1	3. 186709
	68 43 24. 40	302 55 09	122 56 15	Ref. Mon. S–97___	2, 240. 5	3. 350349
		330 26 06	150 26 29	Ref. Mon. S–98___	1, 316. 6	3. 119469
Ref. Mon. C–93_____	47 14 51. 68	248 01 54	68 02 08	Ref. Mon. C–92___	449. 6	2. 652866
	68 43 44. 23	312 29 07	132 29 44	Ref. Mon. S–98___	1, 446. 5	3. 160317
Ref. Mon. S–99_____	47 14 08. 73	161 32 00	341 31 45	Ref. Mon. C–93___	1, 398. 4	3. 145625
	68 43 23. 17	179 00 21	359 00 20	Ref. Mon. C–92___	1, 494. 8	3. 174576
		240 44 50	60 45 12	Ref. Mon. S–98___	714. 9	2. 854229
Ref. Mon. S–100____	47 13 27. 16	207 23 04	27 23 51	Ref. Mon. C–93___	2, 939. 7	3. 468301
	68 44 48. 53	234 25 47	54 26 49	Ref. Mon. S–99___	2, 207. 4	3. 343873
Ref. Mon. C–94_____	47 14 31. 74	247 39 59	67 40 51	Ref. Mon. C–93___	1, 621. 2	3. 209831
	68 44 55. 54	290 04 42	110 05 49	Ref. Mon. S–99___	2, 068. 7	3. 315691
		355 46 12	175 46 17	Ref. Mon. S–100__	1, 999. 7	3. 300965
Ref. Mon. C–95_____	47 13 50. 34	221 52 01	41 52 41	Ref. Mon. C–94___	1, 716. 9	3. 234753
	68 45 50. 02	298 56 55	118 57 40	Ref. Mon. S–100__	1, 478. 5	3. 169823
Ref. Mon. S–101____	47 13 20. 01	146 22 53	326 22 31	Ref. Mon. C–95___	1, 124. 8	3. 051074
	68 45 20. 42	193 17 27	13 17 45	Ref. Mon. C–94___	2, 276. 1	3. 357191
		251 46 37	71 47 00	Ref. Mon. S–100__	706. 4	2. 849030
Ref. Mon. S–102____	47 13 13. 76	185 31 10	5 31 14	Ref. Mon. C–95___	1, 134. 9	3. 054944
	68 45 55. 21	255 13 44	75 14 10	Ref. Mon. S–101__	757. 0	2. 879124
Ref. Mon. C–96_____	47 13 46. 61	264 20 15	84 20 56	Ref. Mon. C–95___	1, 167. 5	3. 067245
	68 46 45. 25	294 42 34	114 43 37	Ref. Mon. S–101__	1, 964. 7	3. 293296
		313 56 10	133 56 47	Ref. Mon. S–102__	1, 462. 0	3. 164953
Ref. Mon. C–97_____	47 13 22. 36	220 55 02	40 55 25	Ref. Mon. C–96___	991. 0	2. 996097
	68 47 16. 11	278 51 48	98 52 48	Ref. Mon. S–102__	1, 722. 6	3. 236187
Ref. Mon. S–103____	47 13 02. 54	172 38 59	352 38 56	Ref. Mon. C–97___	617. 4	2. 790598
	68 47 12. 35	202 43 30	22 43 50	Ref. Mon. C–96___	1, 475. 8	3. 169035
		257 56 04	77 57 01	Ref. Mon. S–102__	1, 659. 7	3. 220031
Ref. Mon. S–104____	47 12 44. 04	217 53 03	37 53 35	Ref. Mon. C–97___	1, 499. 7	3. 176007
	68 47 59. 88	240 15 41	60 16 16	Ref. Mon. S–103__	1, 151. 7	3. 061340
Ref. Mon. C–98_____	47 13 06. 48	249 10 12	69 10 57	Ref. Mon. C–97 __	1, 380. 4	3. 139990
	68 48 17. 43	275 04 15	95 05 03	Ref. Mon. S–103__	1, 374. 7	3. 138192
		331 56 35	151 56 48	Ref. Mon. S–104__	785. 1	2. 894941
Ref. Mon. C–99_____	47 12 46. 84	249 05 19	69 06 14	Ref. Mon. C–98___	1, 699. 4	3. 230304
	68 49 32. 87	272 31 19	92 32 27	Ref. Mon. S–104__	1, 958. 9	3. 292004
Ref. Mon S–105____	47 12 20. 60	137 50 33	317 50 07	Ref. Mon. C–99___	1, 093. 0	3. 038633
	68 48 58. 01	211 04 55	31 05 24	Ref. Mon. C–98___	1, 654. 1	3. 218567
		239 23 17	59 23 59	Ref. Mon. S–104__	1, 421. 4	3. 152729
Ref. Mon. S–106____	47 12 00. 97	193 09 03	13 09 14	Ref. Mon. C–99___	1, 454. 6	3. 162758
	68 49 48. 60	240 20 17	60 20 54	Ref. Mon. S–105__	1, 225. 3	3. 088232
Ref. Mon. C–100____	47 12 25. 76	222 36 40	42 37 01	Ref. Mon. C–99___	884. 8	2. 946820
	68 50 01. 34	276 48 05	96 48 52	Ref. Mon. S–105__	1, 342. 2	3. 127828
		340 41 42	160 41 52	Ref. Mon. S–106__	811. 0	2. 909006

SOURCE OF ST. CROIX RIVER TO LAKE POHENAGAMOOK—Continued

Station	Latitude and longitude	Azimuth	Back azimuth	To station	Distance (meters)	Logarithm
MINOR SCHEME, ST. JOHN AND ST. FRANCIS RIVERS—continued	° ′ ″	° ′ ″	° ′ ″			
Ref. Mon. C–101	47 12 10. 38	243 07 07	63 07 39	Ref. Mon. C–100	1, 050. 1	3. 021238
	68 50 45. 84	283 33 24	103 34 06	Ref. Mon. S–106	1, 239. 4	3. 093212
Ref. Mon. S–107	47 11 51. 29	150 31 23	330 31 11	Ref. Mon. C–101	677. 4	2. 830838
	68 50 30. 01	209 32 43	29 33 03	Ref. Mon. C–100	1, 223. 6	3. 087624
		251 03 28	71 03 58	Ref. Mon. S–106	921. 4	2. 964460
Ref. Mon. S–108	47 11 36. 56	195 27 11	15 27 21	Ref. Mon. C–101	1, 083. 7	3. 034902
	68 50 59. 56	233 49 47	53 50 09	Ref. Mon. S–107	770. 7	2. 886867
Ref. Mon. C–102	47 11 51. 91	231 42 13	51 42 38	Ref. Mon. C–101	920. 7	2. 964118
	68 51 20. 18	271 02 02	91 02 39	Ref. Mon. S–107	1, 056. 2	3. 023739
		317 31 29	137 31 44	Ref. Mon. S–108	642. 6	2. 807922
Ref. Mon. C–103	47 11 41. 10	237 32 18	57 32 37	Ref. Mon. C–102	621. 9	2. 793723
	68 51 45. 10	278 18 52	98 19 26	Ref. Mon. S–108	968. 9	2. 986265
Ref. Mon. S–109	47 11 21. 94	144 49 06	324 48 51	Ref. Mon. C–103	724. 2	2. 859834
	68 51 25. 28	186 37 32	6 37 36	Ref. Mon. C–102	931. 9	2. 969351
		230 09 46	50 10 05	Ref. Mon. S–108	705. 1	2. 848260
Ref. Mon. C–104	47 11 34. 26	233 40 39	53 40 49	Ref. Mon. C–103	356. 9	2. 552593
	68 51 58. 77	298 21 14	118 21 39	Ref. Mon. S–109	801. 0	2. 903626
Ref. Mon. S–110	47 11 05. 60	184 39 38	4 39 41	Ref. Mon. C–104	888. 0	2. 948410
	68 52 02. 20	198 09 48	18 10 01	Ref. Mon. C–103	1, 154. 0	3. 062202
		236 59 52	57 00 20	Ref. Mon. S–109	926. 6	2. 966869
Ref. Mon. C–105	47 11 18. 16	245 12 26	65 13 04	Ref. Mon. C–104	1, 185. 7	3. 073972
	68 52 49. 90	291 06 53	111 07 28	Ref. Mon. S–110	1, 076. 7	3. 032092
Ref. Mon. S–111	47 10 52. 92	138 21 33	318 21 09	Ref. Mon. C–105	1, 043. 0	3. 018292
	68 52 16. 98	196 43 05	16 43 19	Ref. Mon. C–104	1, 332. 9	3. 124796
		218 29 31	38 29 42	Ref. Mon. S–110	500. 2	2. 699130
Ref. Mon. S–112	47 10 34. 59	177 58 28	357 58 26	Ref. Mon. C–105	1, 346. 3	3. 129152
	68 52 47. 64	228 45 06	48 45 28	Ref. Mon. S–111	858. 6	2. 933787
Ref. Mon. C–106	47 10 59. 66	229 14 37	49 15 00	Ref. Mon. C–105	875. 3	2. 942143
	68 53 21. 39	278 42 55	98 43 42	Ref. Mon. S–111	1, 372. 1	3. 137378
		317 26 29	137 26 54	Ref. Mon. S–112	1, 050. 9	3. 021556
Ref. Mon. S–113	47 10 03. 57	190 09 00	10 09 10	Ref. Mon. C–106	1, 759. 7	3. 245435
	68 53 36. 12	226 49 02	46 49 37	Ref. Mon. S–112	1, 400. 1	3. 146153
Ref. Mon. S–114	47 10 33. 86	234 23 37	54 24 15	Ref. Mon. C–106	1, 368. 3	3. 136182
	68 54 14. 23	269 17 11	89 18 14	Ref. Mon. S–112	1, 823. 5	3. 260911
		319 22 24	139 22 52	Ref. Mon. S–113	1, 232. 6	3. 090839
St. Francis east base	47 10 35. 44	87 31 13	267 30 34	Ref. Mon. S–114	1, 126. 2	3. 051633
	68 53 20. 80	179 02 15	359 02 14	Ref. Mon. C–106	747. 8	2. 873793
St. Francis west base	47 10 19. 71	156 01 11	336 01 04	Ref. Mon. S–114	478. 2	2. 679646
	68 54 05. 00	216 39 37	36 40 08	Ref. Mon. C–106	1, 537. 7	3. 186885
		242 26 12	62 26 44	St. Francis east base	1, 049. 99	3. 021186
S–115	47 10 38. 26	273 14 57	93 16 06	Ref. Mon. S–112	1, 995. 6	3. 300083
	68 54 22. 26	317 47 38	137 48 12	Ref. Mon. S–113	1, 446. 4	3. 160287
C–108	47 11 39. 27	4 23 47	184 23 42	S–115	1, 889. 6	3. 276359
	68 54 15. 38	317 13 40	137 14 44	Ref. Mon. S–112	2, 720. 7	3. 434680
		344 22 13	164 22 42	Ref. Mon. S–113	3, 068. 9	3. 486981
S–116	47 11 24. 96	254 46 29	74 47 26	C–108	1, 683. 1	3. 226105
	68 55 32. 53	314 15 42	134 16 34	S–115	2, 066. 1	3. 315159

SOURCE OF ST. CROIX RIVER TO LAKE POHENAGAMOOK—Continued

Station	Latitude and longitude	Azimuth	Back azimuth	To station	Distance (meters)	Loga- rithm
MINOR SCHEME, ST. JOHN AND ST. FRANCIS RIVERS— continued	° ′ ″	° ′ ″	° ′ ″			
C-109	47 11 48. 39 68 54 40. 82	56 23 39 297 44 55 349 46 15	236 23 01 117 45 14 169 46 29	S-116 C-108 S-115	1, 307. 1 605. 1 2, 200. 7	3. 116292 2. 781809 3. 342562
S-117	47 11 32. 83 68 56 00. 08	253 55 12 292 43 01	73 56 10 112 43 21	C-109 S-116	1, 736. 3 628. 7	3. 239624 2. 798477
C-110	47 12 23. 17 68 55 21. 56	7 19 04 27 32 39 321 23 08	187 18 56 207 32 11 141 23 38	S-116 S-117 C-109	1, 812. 2 1, 753. 3 1, 374. 3	3. 258199 3. 243844 3. 138082
C-111	47 12 51. 06 68 57 11. 03	290 29 16 328 16 09	110 30 36 148 17 01	C-110 S-117	2, 459. 5 2, 840. 2	3. 390842 3. 453350
S-118	47 12 23. 11 68 58 37. 14	244 31 20 269 57 19 295 08 37	64 32 23 89 59 42 115 10 32	C-111 C-110 S-117	2, 007. 0 4, 116. 0 3, 652. 4	3. 302554 3. 614478 3. 562581
S-119	47 12 50. 00 68 59 30. 70	269 20 45 306 22 06	89 22 27 126 22 45	C-111 S-118	2, 939. 2 1, 399. 9	3. 468222 3. 146112
C-112	47 13 45. 80 68 58 39. 24	32 08 36 312 19 18 359 00 22	212 07 58 132 20 22 179 00 23	S-119 C-111 S-118	2, 035. 2 2, 510. 4 2, 554. 0	3. 308612 3. 399747 3. 407218
C-113	47 14 20. 71 69 00 13. 60	298 29 46 342 08 09	118 30 55 162 08 40	C-112 S-119	2, 258. 7 2, 943. 2	3. 353866 3. 468815
S-120	47 13 28. 45 69 00 48. 49	204 26 53 258 50 11 305 57 03	24 27 19 78 51 46 125 58 00	C-113 C-112 S-119	1, 772. 9 2, 771. 4 2, 022. 1	3. 248693 3. 442704 3. 305812
Ref. Mon. S-122	47 14 17. 56 69 01 50. 71	267 15 45 319 11 54	87 16 56 139 12 39	C-113 S-120	2, 044. 8 2, 003. 3	3. 310651 3. 301751
C-114	47 14 27. 78 69 02 03. 20	275 24 07 319 22 25 320 14 27	95 25 27 139 23 19 140 14 36	C-113 S-120 Ref. Mon. S-122	2, 315. 4 2, 414. 0 410. 7	3. 364630 3. 382734 2. 613534
Ref. Mon. S-123	47 14 29. 31 69 02 09. 44	276 12 36 289 46 37 312 39 21 317 49 00	96 14 01 109 46 42 132 39 35 137 49 59	C-113 C-114 Ref. Mon. S-122 S-120	2, 450. 7 139. 4 535. 6 2, 536. 1	3. 38929 2. 14430 2. 72881 3. 40417
Ref. Mon. C-114	47 14 37. 68 69 02 13. 38	325 00 51 342 14 45	145 00 59 162 14 48	C-114 Ref. Mon. S-123	373. 2 271. 5	2. 57196 2. 43382
S-123	47 14 44. 88 69 02 46. 37	287 45 12 301 45 17	107 45 36 121 45 44	Ref. Mon. C-114 Ref. Mon. S-123	728. 6 913. 5	2. 86251 2. 96071
C-116	47 14 47. 64 69 02 24. 60	79 26 03 322 29 21 330 36 28	259 25 47 142 29 29 150 36 39	S-123 Ref. Mon. C-114 Ref. Mon. S-123	465. 7 387. 8 649. 9	2. 66809 2. 58861 2. 81282
C-117	47 14 58. 69 69 02 36. 89	25 03 24 322 50 49	205 03 17 142 50 58	S-123 C-116	470. 7 427. 9	2. 67278 2. 63132
S-124	47 14 58. 56 69 02 45. 52	2 24 34 268 46 59 307 27 45	182 24 33 88 47 05 127 28 00	S-123 C-117 C-116	423. 0 181. 6 554. 3	2. 62630 2. 25914 2. 74376
C-118	47 15 05. 48 69 02 47. 46	313 20 04 349 12 07	133 20 12 169 12 09	C-117 S-124	305. 6 217. 5	2. 48521 2. 33737
S-125	47 15 05. 05 69 02 49. 13	249 17 52 307 21 30 339 16 20	69 17 53 127 21 39 159 16 23	C-118 C-117 S-124	37. 5 323. 8 214. 2	1. 57400 2. 51030 2. 33085

SOURCE OF ST. CROIX RIVER TO LAKE POHENAGAMOOK—Continued

Station	Latitude and longitude	Azimuth	Back azimuth	To station	Distance (meters)	Logarithm
MINOR SCHEME, ST. JOHN AND ST. FRANCIS RIVERS—continued	° ′ ″	° ′ ″	° ′ ″			
S-126	47 15 11. 85	308 56 27	128 56 35	C-118	313. 1	2. 49569
	69 02 59. 04	315 13 05	135 13 12	S-125	295. 9	2. 47119
Ref. Mon. C-115	47 15 26. 05	336 57 08	156 57 17	C-118	690. 5	2. 83914
	69 03 00. 32	340 03 54	160 04 02	S-125	690. 0	2. 83882
		356 30 19	176 30 20	S-126	439. 4	2. 64284
S-127	47 15 20. 45	239 49 13	59 49 23	Ref. Mon. C-115	344. 2	2. 53683
	69 03 14. 47	309 18 12	129 18 23	S-126	419. 2	2. 62240
Ref. Mon. S-125	47 15 36. 68	20 39 59	200 39 53	S-127	535. 8	2. 72900
	69 03 05. 48	341 42 59	161 43 03	Ref. Mon. C-115	345. 7	2. 53875
		349 59 49	169 59 55	S-126	778. 7	2. 89136
C-120	47 15 30. 08	3 53 56	183 53 56	Ref. Mon. C-115	124. 6	2. 09536
	69 02 59. 91	150 10 55	330 10 51	Ref. Mon. S-125	235. 2	2. 37135
C-121	47 15 36. 77	85 33 18	265 33 17	Ref. Mon. S-125	35. 4	1. 54922
	69 03 03. 80	338 27 30	158 27 33	C-120	222. 3	2. 34692
		347 32 20	167 32 23	Ref. Mon. C-115	339. 0	2. 53022
S-129	47 15 42. 40	7 52 58	187 52 57	Ref. Mon. S-125	178. 3	2. 25127
	69 03 04. 31	356 25 47	176 25 47	C-121	174. 3	2. 24119
C-122	47 15 43. 26	21 02 21	201 02 18	C-121	214. 6	2. 33165
	69 03 00. 13	28 57 30	208 57 26	Ref. Mon. S-125	232. 1	2. 36560
		73 17 33	253 17 30	S-129	91. 8	1. 96269
S-130	47 15 45. 86	13 11 06	193 11 05	C-122	82. 6	1. 91690
	69 02 59. 24	44 59 05	224 59 01	S-129	151. 0	2. 17892
C-123	47 15 45. 14	38 18 38	218 18 36	C-122	74. 1	1. 86964
	69 02 57. 95	57 43 41	237 43 36	S-129	158. 3	2. 19937
		129 27 11	309 27 10	S-130	35. 1	1. 54496
C-124	47 15 49. 29	54 20 32	234 20 26	C-123	219. 7	2. 34190
	69 02 49. 46	62 46 15	242 46 08	S-130	231. 2	2. 36407
C-125	47 15 52. 65	13 08 14	193 08 12	C-123	238. 2	2. 37703
	69 02 55. 37	21 10 20	201 10 17	S-130	224. 9	2. 35201
		309 52 42	129 52 46	C-124	162. 1	2. 20973
S-131	47 15 53. 44	280 49 18	100 49 23	C-125	129. 3	2. 11159
	69 03 01. 41	348 55 57	168 55 59	S-130	238. 4	2. 37738
S-132	47 15 59. 52	7 19 14	187 19 12	S-130	425. 2	2. 62857
	69 02 56. 66	28 01 58	208 01 54	S-131	212. 7	2. 32768
		352 43 37	172 43 38	C-125	213. 7	2. 32982
C-126	47 15 54. 17	80 19 22	260 19 17	S-131	134. 7	2. 12922
	69 02 55. 10	168 45 49	348 45 48	S-132	168. 3	2. 22608
C-127	47 15 58. 16	24 44 53	204 44 51	C-126	135. 7	2. 13256
	69 02 52. 40	52 25 11	232 25 04	S-131	239. 2	2. 37871
		115 01 56	295 01 53	S-132	98. 9	1. 99514
S-133	47 16 02. 95	24 41 12	204 41 10	S-132	116. 8	2. 06730
	69 02 54. 34	344 34 10	164 34 11	C-127	153. 5	2. 18600
C-128	47 16 03. 64	5 00 46	185 00 45	C-127	170. 0	2. 23035
	69 02 51. 69	39 19 52	219 19 48	S-132	164. 8	2. 21695
		68 59 42	248 59 40	S-133	59. 6	1. 77557
S-134	47 16 07. 53	326 52 34	146 52 37	C-128	143. 2	2. 15583
	69 02 55. 41	350 55 52	170 55 53	S-133	143. 1	2. 15554

SOURCE OF ST. CROIX RIVER TO LAKE POHENAGAMOOK—Continued

Station	Latitude and longitude	Azimuth	Back azimuth	To station	Distance (meters)	Logarithm
	° ′ ″	° ′ ″	° ′ ″			
MINOR SCHEME, ST. JOHN AND ST. FRANCIS RIVERS—continued						
C–129	47 16 07. 77	0 25 44	180 25 44	S–133	148. 7	2. 17222
	69 02 54. 29	72 39 39	252 39 38	S–134	24. 8	1. 39427
		336 47 42	156 47 44	C–128	138. 5	2. 14142
C–130	47 16 10. 23	333 58 48	153 58 49	C–129	84. 6	1. 92751
	69 02 56. 05	350 50 06	170 50 06	S–134	84. 5	1. 92694
S–135 (Rapids south base).	47 16 10. 47	286 34 17	106 34 18	C–130	25. 7	1. 40946
	69 02 57. 22	323 28 57	143 28 59	C–129	103. 7	2. 01593
		337 14 42	157 14 43	S–134	98. 4	1. 99308
S–136 (Rapids north base).	47 16 14. 90	18 24 56	198 24 54	C–130	152. 2	2. 18235
	69 02 53. 76	27 56 08	207 56 05	S–135	155. 14	2. 19072
Ref. Mon. C–117	47 16 15. 22	29 03 10	209 03 07	C–130	176. 3	2. 24627
	69 02 51. 98	36 54 02	216 53 58	S–135	183. 6	2. 26382
		75 27 21	255 27 20	S–136	38. 8	1. 58868
S–137	47 16 18. 01	5 33 05	185 33 05	Ref. Mon. C–117	86. 6	1. 93750
	69 02 51. 58	25 34 48	205 34 47	S–136	106. 4	2. 02676
C–132	47 16 18. 44	17 39 06	197 39 05	Ref. Mon. C–117	104. 4	2. 01888
	69 02 50. 47	32 21 07	212 21 05	S–136	129. 3	2. 11174
		60 12 28	240 12 27	S–137	26. 8	1. 42878
C–133	47 16 24. 28	332 11 06	152 11 09	C–132	203. 7	2. 30903
	69 02 54. 99	339 39 09	159 39 11	S–137	206. 4	2. 31470
S–138	47 16 24. 63	289 21 55	109 21 56	C–133	32. 6	1. 51291
	69 02 56. 46	326 37 43	146 37 47	C–132	228. 7	2. 35924
		333 21 30	153 21 33	S–137	228. 6	2. 35905
C–134	47 16 28. 05	12 04 06	192 04 05	S–138	108. 0	2. 03352
	69 02 55. 38	355 59 50	175 59 50	C–133	116. 7	2. 06716
S–139	47 16 28. 26	0 41 03	180 41 03	S–138	112. 2	2. 05015
	69 02 56. 39	287 14 37	107 14 38	C–134	22. 2	1. 34723
		346 33 49	166 33 50	C–133	126. 5	2. 10208
C–135	47 16 33. 71	18 43 32	198 43 30	C–134	184. 8	2. 26675
	69 02 52. 56	25 33 55	205 33 52	S–139	186. 7	2. 27120
Ref. Mon. S–127	47 16 29. 84	222 09 19	42 09 23	C–135	161. 2	2. 20735
	69 02 57. 71	318 39 47	138 39 49	C–134	74. 0	1. 86905
Ref. Mon. C–119	47 16 34. 39	280 21 04	100 21 08	C–135	116. 4	2. 06601
	69 02 58. 01	344 16 12	164 16 14	C–134	203. 6	2. 30873
		357 25 00	177 25 00	Ref. Mon. S–127	140. 6	2. 14786
S–143	47 16 27. 52	215 08 26	35 08 31	Ref. Mon. C–119	259. 5	2. 41406
	69 03 05. 11	245 15 18	65 15 23	Ref. Mon. S–127	171. 4	2. 23405
S–144	47 16 33. 91	0 34 56	180 34 56	S–143	197. 3	2. 29521
	69 03 05. 02	264 14 55	84 15 00	Ref. Mon. C–119	148. 1	2. 17049
		309 15 18	129 15 23	Ref. Mon. S–127	198. 5	2. 29766
S–141	47 16 25. 93	115 50 15	295 50 11	S–143	112. 8	2. 05245
	69 03 00. 28	158 00 32	338 00 29	S–144	265. 8	2. 42463
S–142	47 16 32. 36	6 21 26	186 21 25	S–141	199. 8	2. 30055
	69 02 59. 23	39 37 27	219 37 23	S–143	193. 9	2. 28764
		111 30 41	291 30 37	S–144	130. 8	2. 11654
C–138	47 16 38. 12	34 23 07	214 23 04	S–144	157. 7	2. 19777
	69 03 00. 78	349 37 12	169 37 13	S–142	181. 0	2. 25778

SOURCE OF ST. CROIX RIVER TO LAKE POHENAGAMOOK—Continued

Station	Latitude and longitude	Azimuth	Back azimuth	To station	Distance (meters)	Logarithm
MINOR SCHEME, ST. JOHN AND ST. FRANCIS RIVERS—continued	° ′ ″	° ′ ″	° ′ ″			
S–145	47 16 37. 63	9 32 51	189 32 50	S–144	116. 5	2. 06639
	69 03 04. 10	257 40 59	77 41 01	C–138	71. 4	1. 85349
		327 51 13	147 51 16	S–142	192. 3	2. 28408
C–139	47 16 42. 84	8 51 59	188 51 58	S–145	163. 0	2. 21216
	69 03 02. 90	342 59 35	162 59 36	C–138	152. 5	2. 18324
Ref. Mon. S–128	47 16 43. 01	272 06 33	92 06 38	C–139	139. 7	2. 14517
	69 03 09. 55	309 20 09	129 20 15	C–138	238. 2	2. 37686
		325 26 18	145 26 22	S–145	201. 8	2. 30492
S–147 (Cross Lake south base).	47 16 47. 39	21 59 17	201 59 15	Ref. Mon. S–128	145. 7	2. 16353
	69 03 06. 95	328 46 27	148 46 30	C–139	164. 0	2. 21492
C–140	47 16 47. 83	37 27 43	217 27 39	Ref. Mon. S–128	187. 6	2. 27322
	69 03 04. 12	76 58 10	256 58 08	S–147	61. 1	1. 78612
		350 36 08	170 36 09	C–139	156. 1	. 19352
S–148 (Cross Lake north base).	47 16 50. 94	7 44 14	187 44 13	S–147	110. 65	2. 04396
	69 03 06. 24	335 01 50	155 01 51	C–140	105. 7	2. 02428
Ref. Mon. C–120	47 16 50. 19	32 58 12	212 58 10	S–147	103. 4	2. 01444
	69 03 04. 27	118 58 57	298 58 56	S–148	47. 3	1. 67472
		357 25 41	177 25 41	C–140	73. 0	1. 86349
S–149	47 16 57. 27	0 01 10	180 01 10	Ref. Mon. C–120	218. 6	2. 33972
	69 03 04. 27	11 57 13	191 57 12	S–148	200. 1	2. 30117
C–142	47 16 56. 48	32 33 22	212 33 18	Ref. Mon. C–120	230. 4	2. 36245
	69 02 58. 38	43 59 25	223 59 20	S–148	238. 1	2. 37667
		101 09 57	281 09 53	S–149	126. 3	2. 10136
Ref. Mon. S–129	47 17 01. 14	19 11 35	199 11 34	S–149	126. 3	2. 10136
	69 03 02. 30	330 10 46	150 10 49	C–142	165. 7	2. 21921
C–143	47 17 03. 72	29 34 56	209 34 52	S–149	229. 0	2. 35982
	69 02 58. 89	41 50 40	221 50 37	Ref. Mon. S–129	107. 2	2. 03028
		357 13 21	177 13 21	C–142	223. 9	2. 34998
S–151	47 17 08. 74	315 44 31	135 44 36	C–143	216. 2	2. 33482
	69 03 06. 07	341 19 17	161 19 20	Ref. Mon. S–129	247. 8	2. 39403
C–144	47 17 11. 96	7 02 21	187 02 20	C–143	256. 4	2. 40891
	69 02 57. 40	17 06 53	197 06 49	Ref. Mon. S–129	349. 8	2. 54386
		61 20 31	241 20 25	S–151	207. 7	2. 31752
S–152	47 17 17. 40	6 43 00	186 42 59	S–151	269. 3	2. 43020
	69 03 04. 57	318 03 19	138 03 24	C–144	225. 6	2. 35334
Ref. Mon. C–121	47 17 19. 30	21 11 29	201 11 25	S–151	350. 0	2. 54402
	69 03 00. 05	58 12 58	238 12 55	S–152	111. 8	2. 04832
		346 10 28	166 10 30	C–144	233. 4	2. 36816
S–153	47 17 20. 78	7 08 39	187 08 39	S–152	105. 5	2. 02322
	69 03 03. 95	299 13 09	119 13 12	Ref. Mon. C–121	93. 8	1. 97232
		333 11 37	153 11 42	C–144	305. 3	2. 48469
C–146	47 17 28. 48	6 05 21	186 05 20	S–153	239. 1	2. 37862
	69 03 02. 74	348 43 39	168 43 41	Ref. Mon. C–121	289. 1	2. 46112
S–154	47 17 27. 30	242 27 36	62 27 38	C–146	78. 9	1. 89715
	69 03 06. 07	332 53 22	152 53 26	Ref. Mon. C–121	277. 6	2. 44339
		347 30 14	167 30 15	S–153	206. 2	2. 31422
Ref. Mon. C–122	47 17 36. 73	335 10 14	155 10 18	C–146	280. 6	2. 44806
	69 03 08. 35	350 40 00	170 40 02	S–154	295. 0	2. 46988

SOURCE OF ST. CROIX RIVER TO LAKE POHENAGAMOOK—Continued

Station	Latitude and longitude	Azimuth	Back azimuth	To station	Distance (meters)	Logarithm
MINOR SCHEME, ST. JOHN AND ST. FRANCIS RIVERS—continued	° ′ ″	° ′ ″	° ′ ″			
S-155	47 17 34. 67	245 11 38	65 11 43	Ref. Mon. C-122	151. 5	2. 18038
	69 03 14. 89	306 48 34	126 48 43	C-146	318. 9	2. 50368
		320 50 09	140 50 16	S-154	293. 5	2. 46763
S-156	47 17 40. 48	8 28 06	188 28 05	S-155	181. 5	2. 25894
	69 03 13. 62	316 18 59	136 19 03	Ref. Mon. C-122	160. 4	2. 20519
Ref. Mon. C-123	47 17 40. 73	29 19 51	209 19 47	S-155	214. 7	2. 33186
	69 03 09. 89	84 26 10	264 26 07	S-156	78. 8	1. 89660
		345 20 35	165 20 36	Ref. Mon. C-122	127. 8	2. 10651
Ref. Mon. C-124	47 17 44. 38	28 58 27	208 58 25	S-156	137. 4	2. 13791
	69 03 10. 45	353 57 59	173 58 00	Ref. Mon. C-123	113. 2	2. 05372
S-157	47 17 44. 00	1 13 15	181 13 15	S-156	108. 7	2. 03606
	69 03 13. 51	259 48 18	79 48 20	Ref. Mon. C-124	65. 3	1. 81466
		322 59 25	142 59 28	Ref. Mon. C-123	126. 5	2. 10198
S-158	47 17 47. 51	318 06 51	138 06 54	Ref. Mon. C-124	130. 2	2. 11460
	69 03 14. 59	348 11 02	168 11 03	S-157	110. 8	2. 04465
C-150	47 17 48. 60	12 55 34	192 55 33	S-157	145. 6	2. 16323
	69 03 11. 96	58 48 51	238 48 49	S-158	64. 6	1. 81026
		346 21 10	166 21 11	Ref. Mon. C-124	134. 2	2. 12766
C-151	47 17 51. 99	16 52 06	196 52 04	S-158	144. 4	2. 15958
	69 03 12. 60	352 43 40	172 43 40	C-150	105. 6	2. 02362
Ref. Mon. S-130	47 17 52. 11	273 07 49	93 07 52	C-151	70. 6	1. 84854
	69 03 15. 95	322 20 12	142 20 15	C-150	137. 2	2. 13728
		348 38 07	168 38 08	S-158	144. 9	2. 16103
Ref. Mon. S-131	47 17 57. 29	7 58 29	187 58 29	C-151	165. 4	2. 21852
	69 03 11. 50	30 16 57	210 16 54	Ref. Mon. S-130	185. 2	2. 26768
C-152	47 17 53. 90	55 52 55	235 52 53	C-151	105. 1	2. 02179
	69 03 08. 45	70 42 40	250 42 35	Ref. Mon. S-130	166. 9	2. 22237
		148 33 11	328 33 09	Ref. Mon. S-131	122. 9	2. 08943
Ref. Mon. C-125	47 18 01. 83	25 35 52	205 35 48	C-152	271. 8	2. 43418
	69 03 02. 87	33 55 07	213 55 01	C-151	366. 4	2. 56396
		52 18 19	232 18 13	Ref. Mon. S-131	229. 4	2. 36056
S-161	47 18 04. 65	295 26 55	115 27 02	Ref. Mon. C-125	202. 5	2. 30641
	69 03 11. 57	348 51 09	168 51 12	C-152	338. 5	2. 52954
		359 39 42	179 39 43	Ref. Mon. S-131	227. 3	2. 35656
C-154	47 18 13. 99	4 34 21	184 34 20	Ref. Mon. C-125	376. 7	2. 57600
	69 03 01. 44	22 18 03	202 17 57	Ref. Mon. S-131	557. 5	2. 74621
		36 25 24	216 25 17	S-161	358. 5	2. 55452
Ref. Mon. S-133	47 18 21. 63	306 36 26	126 36 37	C-154	395. 4	2. 59709
	69 03 16. 55	334 49 04	154 49 14	Ref. Mon. C-125	675. 5	2. 82964
		348 43 08	168 43 12	S-161	534. 6	2. 72806
Ref. Mon. S-132	47 18 15. 26	140 27 05	320 26 59	Ref. Mon. S-133	255. 1	2. 40665
	69 03 08. 82	284 10 21	104 10 26	C-154	159. 9	2. 20384
C-155	47 18 22. 68	26 43 20	206 43 15	C-154	300. 3	2. 47756
	69 02 55. 01	51 42 03	231 41 53	Ref. Mon. S-132	369. 6	2. 56774
		85 54 20	265 54 04	Ref. Mon. S-133	453. 6	2. 65669
S-164	47 18 48. 17	310 13 33	130 14 06	C-155	1, 218. 9	3. 08598
	69 03 39. 31	329 44 23	149 44 40	Ref. Mon. S-133	948. 9	2. 97724

SOURCE OF ST. CROIX RIVER TO LAKE POHENAGAMOOK—Continued

Station	Latitude and longitude	Azimuth	Back azimuth	To station	Distance (meters)	Loga-rithm
MINOR SCHEME, ST. JOHN AND ST. FRANCIS RIVERS—continued	° ′ ″	° ′ ″	° ′ ″			
C–156	47 18 56. 26	16 38 08	196 37 57	Ref. Mon. S–133	1, 116. 2	3. 04775
	69 03 01. 34	72 36 40	252 36 12	S–164	835. 9	2. 92213
		352 41 50	172 41 55	C–155	1, 045. 6	3. 01936
S–165	47 19 17. 48	2 43 30	182 43 28	S–164	906. 1	2. 95717
	69 03 37. 26	310 58 03	130 58 29	C–156	999. 3	2. 99969
C–157	47 19 14. 20	43 46 30	223 46 03	S–164	1, 113. 1	3. 04652
	69 03 02. 65	97 56 14	277 55 49	S–165	733. 9	2. 86564
		357 08 56	177 08 57	C–156	554. 6	2. 74398
S–166	47 19 40. 19	6 34 48	186 34 45	S–165	706. 0	2. 84879
	69 03 33. 41	321 10 13	141 10 35	C–157	1, 030. 3	3. 01295
C–158	47 19 33. 73	2 12 41	182 12 40	C–157	603. 6	2. 78076
	69 03 01. 54	56 13 11	236 12 45	S–165	902. 5	2. 95546
		106 36 02	286 35 39	S–166	698. 3	2. 84404
S–167 (Ecc. Ref. Mon. S–135).	47 20 36. 83	338 14 30	158 14 57	C–158	2, 098. 3	3. 32186
	69 03 38. 58	356 26 51	176 26 55	S–166	1, 752. 8	3. 24372
C–159	47 20 18. 24	5 41 57	185 41 52	C–158	1, 381. 5	3. 14035
	69 02 55. 01	34 27 27	214 26 59	S–166	1, 425. 2	3. 15388
		122 07 14	302 06 42	S–167	1, 080. 0	3. 03343
S–168	47 21 39. 29	0 05 21	180 05 21	S–167	1, 928. 9	3. 28530
	69 03 38. 44	339 59 02	159 59 34	C–159	2, 663. 9	3. 42551
C–160	47 21 41. 43	0 36 46	180 36 45	C–159	2, 569. 3	3. 40982
	69 02 53. 70	25 16 52	205 16 19	S–167	2, 206. 2	3. 34365
		85 58 32	265 57 59	S–168	941. 2	2. 97368
C–161	47 21 53. 66	62 50 52	242 50 22	S–168	972. 2	2. 98775
	69 02 57. 22	348 56 17	168 56 20	C–160	384. 7	2. 58517
S–169	47 22 01. 05	283 38 55	103 39 28	C–161	967. 4	2. 98559
	69 03 42. 02	300 51 34	120 52 10	C–160	1, 181. 1	3. 07230
		353 37 37	173 37 40	S–168	676. 2	2. 83010
Ref. Mon. C–130	47 22 27. 47	2 27 21	182 27 19	C–161	1, 045. 2	3. 01918
	69 02 55. 08	50 21 45	230 21 10	S–169	1, 278. 8	3. 10680
Ref. Mon. S–137–A	47 22 36. 50	22 58 00	202 57 44	S–169	1, 189. 0	3. 07520
	69 03 19. 90	298 10 26	118 10 45	Ref. Mon. C–130	590. 7	2. 77140
		340 12 40	160 12 57	C–161	1, 406. 2	3. 14804
C–163 (Beau Lake south base).	47 22 40. 89	16 19 17	196 19 13	Ref. Mon. C–130	431. 8	2. 63529
	69 02 49. 30	78 05 23	258 05 00	Ref. Mon. S–137–A	656. 2	2. 81704
Ref. Mon. C–131 (Beau Lake north base).	47 22 46. 05	56 44 27	236 44 11	Ref. Mon. S–137–A	537. 5	2. 73038
	69 02 58. 48	309 35 51	129 35 58	C–163	249. 97	2. 39789
		352 55 05	172 55 08	Ref. Mon. C–130	578. 1	2. 76204
Ref. Mon. C–133	47 22 52. 71	32 27 53	212 27 45	C–163	432. 8	2. 63625
	69 02 38. 22	64 09 29	244 09 14	Ref. Mon. C–131	472. 1	2. 67405
Ref. Mon. C–132	47 22 57. 80	0 02 13	180 02 13	C–163	522. 2	2. 71782
	69 02 49. 28	28 00 09	208 00 02	Ref. Mon. C–131	411. 0	2. 61379
		304 05 54	124 06 02	Ref. Mon. C–133	280. 1	2. 44732
Ref. Mon. C–134	47 23 07. 79	37 30 30	217 30 17	Ref. Mon. C–133	586. 9	2. 76860
	69 02 21. 19	62 21 53	242 21 32	Ref. Mon. C–132	665. 2	2. 82295
S–173	47 23 11. 78	10 05 14	190 05 10	Ref. Mon. C–133	598. 0	2. 77668
	69 02 33. 23	37 57 04	217 56 52	Ref. Mon. C–132	547. 4	2. 73834
		295 58 51	115 59 00	Ref. Mon. C–134	281. 0	2. 44874

SOURCE OF ST. CROIX RIVER TO LAKE POHENAGAMOOK—Continued

Station	Latitude and longitude	Azimuth	Back azimuth	To station	Distance (meters)	Loga- rithm
MINOR SCHEME, ST. JOHN AND ST. FRANCIS RIVERS— continued	° ′ ″	° ′ ″	° ′ ″			
C–166	47 23 28. 40	6 42 40	186 42 38	S–173	516. 9	2. 71340
	69 02 30. 35	343 11 42	163 11 49	Ref. Mon. C–134	664. 8	2. 82272
Ref. Mon. C–135	47 23 29. 11	274 49 11	94 49 21	C–166	262. 1	2. 41852
	69 02 42. 80	325 26 48	145 27 05	Ref. Mon. C–134	799. 5	2. 90282
		339 26 17	159 26 25	S–173	571. 8	2. 75724
C–167 (azimuth sta- tion).	47 23 35. 80	41 55 44	221 55 37	Ref. Mon. C–135	277. 6	2. 44341
	69 02 33. 96	341 40 17	161 40 20	C–166	240. 8	2. 38161
Ref. Mon. C–136	47 23 37. 91	4 17 13	184 17 12	Ref. Mon. C–135	272. 4	2. 43524
	69 02 41. 83	291 31 32	111 31 38	C–167	177. 5	2. 24920
		320 38 44	140 38 53	C–166	379. 8	2. 57957
C–168	47 23 40. 15	51 58 08	231 58 02	C–167	218. 1	2. 33872
	69 02 25. 76	78 23 08	258 22 56	Ref. Mon. C–136	344. 0	2. 53653
Ref. Mon. C–137	47 23 43. 88	12 15 34	192 15 32	C–167	255. 2	2. 40695
	69 02 31. 37	49 57 39	229 57 31	Ref. Mon. C–136	286. 5	2. 45707
		314 21 42	134 21 46	C–168	164. 5	2. 21620
C–169	47 23 43. 52	60 32 01	240 31 55	C–168	211. 4	2. 32507
	69 02 16. 99	92 05 52	272 05 42	Ref. Mon. C–137	301. 9	2. 47980
Ref. Mon. S–138	47 23 46. 66	22 21 19	202 21 16	C–168	217. 5	2. 33754
	69 02 21. 82	66 43 50	246 43 43	Ref. Mon. C–137	218. 1	2. 33865
		313 49 09	133 49 12	C–169	140. 4	2. 14734
Ref. Mon. C–138	47 23 49. 45	35 48 38	215 48 33	C–169	225. 8	2. 35379
	69 02 10. 69	69 47 23	249 47 15	Ref. Mon. S–138	248. 7	2. 39576
S–178	47 23 51. 38	30 22 31	210 22 28	Ref. Mon. S–138	168. 7	2. 22705
	69 02 17. 75	291 54 37	111 54 42	Ref. Mon. C–138	159. 7	2. 20322
		356 13 40	176 13 40	C–169	243. 3	2. 38606
C–171	47 23 58. 10	25 18 13	205 18 09	Ref. Mon. C–138	295. 7	2. 47078
	69 02 04. 67	52 53 16	232 53 07	S–178	344. 2	2. 53684
Ref. Mon. C–139	47 23 59. 58	25 38 53	205 38 49	S–178	280. 8	2. 44845
	69 02 11. 96	286 33 17	106 33 22	C–171	159. 6	2. 20290
		355 08 32	175 08 33	Ref. Mon. C–138	313. 9	2. 49676
C–172	47 24 01. 76	59 28 15	239 28 11	Ref. Mon. C–139	132. 8	2. 12305
	69 02 06. 51	341 07 52	161 07 53	C–171	119. 3	2. 07669
Ref. Mon. C–141	47 24 07. 83	8 58 04	188 58 03	C–172	189. 8	2. 27837
	69 02 05. 10	29 26 56	209 26 51	Ref. Mon. C–139	292. 8	2. 46654
S–180	47 24 06. 33	264 48 22	84 48 40	Ref. Mon. C–141	512. 2	2. 70944
	69 02 29. 42	299 40 07	119 40 20	Ref. Mon. C–139	421. 4	2. 62471
Ref. Mon. C–140	47 24 12. 00	37 59 13	217 59 08	S–180	222. 2	2. 34675
	69 02 22. 90	289 01 51	109 02 04	Ref. Mon. C–141	394. 9	2. 59651
		329 07 41	149 07 49	Ref. Mon. C–139	447. 1	2. 65038
Ref. Mon. S–139	47 24 09. 55	254 35 04	74 35 14	Ref. Mon. C–140	284. 8	2. 45453
	69 02 35. 99	305 48 55	125 49 00	S–180	169. 9	2. 23025
Ref. Mon. S–140	47 24 16. 15	0 38 27	180 38 27	Ref. Mon. S–139	203. 8	2. 30910
	69 02 35. 88	295 11 08	115 11 18	Ref. Mon. C–140	300. 9	2. 47838
		335 54 58	155 55 03	S–180	332. 1	2. 52124
C–173	47 24 06. 15	37 34 18	217 34 11	C–171	313. 5	2. 49617
	69 01 55. 55	59 27 29	239 27 21	C–172	266. 7	2. 42605
		104 33 35	284 33 28	Ref. Mon. C–141	206. 8	2. 31545

SOURCE OF ST. CROIX RIVER TO LAKE POHENAGAMOOK—Continued

Station	Latitude and longitude	Azimuth	Back azimuth	To station	Distance (meters)	Loga- rithm
MINOR SCHEME, ST. JOHN AND ST. FRANCIS RIVERS— continued	° ′ ″	° ′ ″	° ′ ″			
Ref. Mon. S–141____	47 24 11. 85	48 34 23	228 34 18	Ref. Mon. C–141__	187. 5	2. 27299
	69 01 58. 39	341 18 58	161 19 00	C–173_____	185. 8	2. 26911
C–174_____	47 24 10. 64	9 43 31	189 43 30	C–173_____	140. 6	2. 14808
	69 01 54. 42	68 50 40	248 50 32	Ref. Mon. C–141__	240. 0	2. 38030
		114 11 50	294 11 47	Ref. Mon. S–141__	91. 3	1. 96049
Ref. Mon. C–142____	47 24 16. 81	2 36 41	182 36 41	Ref. Mon. S–141__	153. 4	2. 18579
	69 01 58. 06	338 11 23	158 11 26	C–174_____	205. 3	2. 31249
S–186_____	47 24 16. 22	260 49 01	80 49 05	Ref. Mon. C–142__	113. 9	2. 05634
	69 02 03. 42	312 25 48	132 25 55	C–174_____	255. 6	2. 40763
		322 01 47	142 01 51	Ref. Mon. S–141__	171. 3	2. 23381
Ref. Mon. S–142____	47 24 23. 62	13 01 56	193 01 54	S–186_____	234. 5	2. 37008
	69 02 00. 90	344 11 38	164 11 40	Ref. Mon. C–142__	218. 5	2. 33949
C–176_____	47 24 23. 95	8 52 38	188 52 37	Ref. Mon. C–142__	223. 1	2. 34847
	69 01 56. 42	31 36 27	211 36 22	S–186_____	280. 1	2. 44737
		83 49 47	263 49 44	Ref. Mon. S–142__	94. 5	1. 97539
Ref. Mon. C–143____	47 24 33. 05	15 15 39	195 15 36	Ref. Mon. S–142__	301. 9	2. 47981
	69 01 57. 11	357 02 55	177 02 55	C–176_____	281. 4	2. 44938
C–177 (Quebec south base).	47 24 33. 52	15 56 29	195 56 26	C–176_____	307. 6	2. 48800
	69 01 52. 38	30 15 07	210 15 01	Ref. Mon. S–142__	354. 2	2. 54921
		81 32 28	261 32 25	Ref. Mon. C–143__	100. 1	2. 00026
S–190_____	47 24 36. 41	310 09 24	130 09 28	C–177_____	138. 3	2. 14089
	69 01 57. 43	356 17 10	176 17 11	Ref. Mon. C–143__	104. 1	2. 01762
C–178 (Quebec north base).	47 24 38. 15	18 47 05	198 47 04	Ref. Mon. C–143__	166. 6	2. 22158
	69 01 54. 55	48 18 54	228 18 52	S–190_____	80. 8	1. 90768
		342 24 21	162 24 23	C–177_____	149. 99	2. 17605
S–192_____	47 24 45. 57	313 39 38	133 39 46	C–178_____	331. 9	2. 52100
	69 02 06. 00	327 34 21	147 34 27	S–190_____	335. 2	2. 52526
C–179_____	47 24 47. 08	75 21 06	255 21 00	S–192_____	183. 3	2. 26319
	69 01 57. 54	347 10 11	167 10 13	C–178_____	282. 6	2. 45110
		359 35 18	179 35 18	S–190_____	329. 3	2. 51756
Ref. Mon. C–145____	47 24 48. 25	280 17 26	100 17 33	C–179_____	203. 4	2. 30834
	69 02 07. 09	344 36 17	164 36 18	S–192_____	85. 8	1. 93336
C–180_____	47 24 53. 01	26 39 02	206 38 58	S–192_____	256. 9	2. 40983
	69 02 00. 50	43 12 22	223 12 17	Ref. Mon. C–145__	201. 6	2. 30449
		341 16 54	161 16 56	C–179_____	193. 5	2. 28672
Ref. Mon. C–146____	47 24 56. 06	300 38 30	120 38 36	C–180_____	184. 7	2. 26644
	69 02 08. 08	355 02 56	175 02 57	Ref. Mon. C–145__	242. 0	2. 38378
Ref. Mon. S–144____	47 24 52. 06	217 26 14	37 26 17	Ref. Mon. C–146__	155. 3	2. 19130
	69 02 12. 59	263 25 12	83 25 21	C–180_____	255. 0	2. 40656
		315 35 30	135 35 34	Ref. Mon. C–145__	164. 8	2. 21696
C–182_____	47 24 59. 11	285 50 36	105 50 47	Ref. Mon. C–146__	345. 0	2. 53782
	69 02 23. 92	312 29 32	132 29 41	Ref. Mon. S–144__	322. 0	2. 50792
S–195_____	47 24 54. 38	219 21 33	39 21 38	C–182_____	188. 8	2. 27591
	69 02 29. 63	263 27 39	83 27 55	Ref. Mon. C–146__	454. 6	2. 65759
		281 20 01	101 20 14	Ref. Mon. S–144__	364. 3	2. 56144
Ref. Mon. S–145____	47 25 05. 27	323 47 56	143 48 00	C–182_____	235. 9	2. 37273
	69 02 30. 56	356 39 40	176 39 40	S–195_____	336. 9	2. 52747

SOURCE OF ST. CROIX RIVER TO LAKE POHENAGAMOOK—Continued

Station	Latitude and longitude	Azimuth	Back azimuth	To station	Distance (meters)	Logarithm
MINOR SCHEME, ST. JOHN AND ST. FRANCIS RIVERS— continued	° ′ ″	° ′ ″	° ′ ″			
C–183	47 25 07. 86	0 34 26	180 34 26	C–182	270. 4	2. 43204
	69 02 23. 79	16 23 05	196 23 00	S–195	434. 0	2. 63746
		60 35 43	240 35 38	Ref. Mon. S–145	163. 0	2. 21228
S–197	47 25 11. 47	21 13 18	201 13 16	Ref. Mon. S–145	205. 2	2. 31221
	69 02 27. 02	328 39 40	148 39 43	C–183	130. 3	2. 11480
C–184	47 25 12. 02	12 54 43	192 54 42	C–183	131. 5	2. 11899
	69 02 22. 38	39 27 39	219 27 33	Ref. Mon. S–145	269. 7	2. 43091
		80 06 24	260 06 20	S–197	98. 6	1. 99387
S–198	47 25 14. 60	305 44 03	125 44 07	C–184	136. 9	2. 13649
	69 02 27. 69	351 46 13	171 46 13	S–197	97. 9	1. 99087
Ref. Mon. C–147	47 25 15. 87	32 09 11	212 09 08	S–197	160. 5	2. 20559
	69 02 22. 94	68 35 00	248 34 57	S–198	106. 8	2. 02869
		354 23 11	174 23 12	C–184	119. 6	2. 07756
Ref. Mon. C–148	47 25 21. 93	16 56 31	196 56 29	S–198	236. 4	2. 37361
	69 02 24. 40	350 43 15	170 43 16	Ref. Mon. C–147	189. 6	2. 27782
S–199	47 25 21. 93	270 00 23	90 00 28	Ref. Mon. C–148	147. 7	2. 16952
	69 02 31. 45	316 22 50	136 22 56	Ref. Mon. C–147	258. 5	2. 41244
		340 46 23	160 46 26	S–198	239. 5	2. 37930
C–187	47 25 27. 75	12 55 43	192 55 42	S–199	184. 4	2. 26584
	69 02 29. 48	329 21 41	149 21 45	Ref. Mon. C–148	208. 9	2. 32003
Ref. Mon. C–149	47 25 27. 36	261 54 30	81 54 32	C–187	84. 0	1. 92440
	69 02 33. 45	311 31 25	131 31 31	Ref. Mon. C–148	253. 3	2. 40370
		345 58 56	165 58 57	S–199	173. 1	2. 23826
S–201	47 25 30. 99	315 48 03	135 48 06	C–187	139. 6	2. 14496
	69 02 34. 12	352 47 39	172 47 40	Ref. Mon. C–149	112. 8	2. 05237
C–188	47 25 31. 72	23 47 03	203 47 01	Ref. Mon. C–149	146. 9	2. 16688
	69 02 30. 62	72 59 01	252 58 58	S–201	76. 7	1. 88498
		348 56 12	168 56 12	C–187	124. 9	2. 09648
S–202	47 25 37. 43	321 50 14	141 50 19	C–188	224. 4	2. 35100
	69 02 37. 24	341 49 46	161 49 48	S–201	209. 3	2. 32082
Ref. Mon. C–150	47 25 38. 96	38 27 33	218 27 32	S–202	60. 6	1. 78241
	69 02 35. 44	335 43 32	155 43 36	C–188	245. 6	2. 39021
		353 36 33	173 36 34	S–201	247. 9	2. 39423
S–203 (Blue River east base).	47 25 42. 04	308 43 53	128 43 57	Ref. Mon. C–150	151. 8	2. 18139
	69 02 41. 09	330 26 52	150 26 55	S–202	163. 8	2. 21419
C–190	47 25 42. 67	1 36 57	181 36 57	S–202	161. 8	2. 20907
	69 02 37. 02	77 14 33	257 14 30	S–203	87. 5	1. 94194
		343 50 34	163 50 35	Ref. Mon. C–150	119. 0	2. 07564
C–191	47 25 45. 66	23 12 10	203 12 08	S–203	121. 6	2. 08495
	69 02 38. 81	337 57 54	157 57 55	C–190	99. 7	1. 99884
C–192	47 25 45. 74	271 23 31	91 23 34	C–191	97. 6	1. 98928
	69 02 43. 46	305 05 31	125 05 36	C–190	164. 9	2. 21730
		336 30 07	156 30 09	S–203	124. 5	2. 09503
Ref. Mon. C–151 (Blue River west base and azimuth station).	47 25 41. 12	214 22 58	34 23 01	C–192	172. 8	2. 23756
	69 02 48. 12	259 03 09	79 03 14	S–203	149. 94	2. 17592

SOURCE OF ST. CROIX RIVER TO LAKE POHENAGAMOOK—Continued

Station	Latitude and longitude	Azimuth	Back azimuth	To station	Distance (meters)	Loga- rithm
MINOR SCHEME, ST. JOHN AND ST. FRANCIS RIVERS— continued	° ′ ″	° ′ ″	° ′ ″			
C–193	47 25 45. 25	264 10 39	84 10 44	C–192	147. 3	2. 16834
	69 02 50. 46	296 49 02	116 49 09	S–203	219. 9	2. 34215
		339 00 05	159 00 07	Ref. Mon. C–151	136. 7	2. 13592
C–194	47 25 39. 47	227 49 56	47 50 03	C–193	265. 9	2. 42467
	69 02 59. 86	258 19 54	78 20 03	Ref. Mon. C–151	251. 3	2. 40012
S–205	47 25 37. 88	126 55 09	306 55 07	C–194	81. 9	1. 91334
	69 02 56. 73	210 01 23	30 01 28	C–193	263. 0	2. 41990
		241 01 10	61 01 17	Ref. Mon. C–151	206. 4	2. 31477
S–211	47 25 35. 21	226 19 53	46 19 58	C–194	190. 7	2. 28029
	69 03 06. 44	247 56 02	67 56 09	S–205	219. 5	2. 34141
C–195	47 25 38. 08	7 39 55	187 39 54	S–211	89. 3	1. 95067
	69 03 05. 87	251 04 52	71 04 56	C–194	133. 2	2. 12455
		271 47 51	91 47 57	S–205	191. 6	2. 28240
S–206	47 25 30. 46	117 28 12	297 28 02	S–211	317. 8	2. 50212
	69 02 52. 99	161 04 27	341 04 24	S–205	242. 1	2. 38403
S–210	47 25 31. 20	170 11 20	350 11 19	S–211	125. 7	2. 09944
	69 03 05. 42	221 24 38	41 24 43	S–205	275. 1	2. 43954
		274 58 32	94 58 40	S–206	261. 5	2. 41749
Ref. Mon. S–146	47 25 20. 16	170 16 45	350 16 43	S–210	346. 0	2. 53902
	69 03 02. 63	212 24 49	32 24 56	S–206	377. 1	2. 57640
S–208	47 25 19. 61	227 40 26	47 40 39	S–206	498. 0	2. 69727
	69 03 10. 55	264 08 26	84 08 32	Ref. Mon. S–146	167. 0	2. 22269
Ref. Mon. S–147	47 25 26. 77	16 40 23	196 40 21	S–208	230. 9	2. 36342
	69 03 07. 39	196 51 06	16 51 08	S–210	143. 0	2. 15529
		333 55 53	153 55 57	Ref. Mon. S–146	227. 3	2. 35653
S–212	47 25 38. 44	275 24 32	95 24 37	C–195	121. 0	2. 08293
	69 03 11. 62	312 36 15	132 36 19	S–211	147. 5	2. 16891
C–196	47 25 39. 43	59 25 49	239 25 47	S–212	59. 9	1. 77764
	69 03 09. 16	301 17 56	121 17 59	C–195	80. 6	1. 90653
		336 23 01	156 23 03	S–211	142. 3	2. 15312
C–197	47 25 43. 42	326 27 35	146 27 38	C–196	147. 9	2. 16997
	69 03 13. 06	348 55 01	168 55 02	S–212	156. 7	2. 19500
Ref. Mon. S–149	47 25 42. 49	242 05 45	62 05 47	C–197	61. 3	1. 78767
	69 03 15. 64	304 49 47	124 49 52	C–196	165. 6	2. 21901
		326 00 33	146 00 36	S–212	150. 8	2. 17847
S–214	47 25 44. 15	280 27 31	100 27 35	C–197	122. 9	2. 08942
	69 03 18. 82	307 26 16	127 26 18	Ref. Mon. S–149	83. 9	1. 92378
Ref. Mon. C–153	47 25 46. 22	12 15 05	192 15 04	S–214	65. 5	1. 81636
	69 03 18. 16	308 55 07	128 55 10	C–197	137. 4	2. 13804
		335 22 42	155 22 43	Ref. Mon. S–149	126. 5	2. 10221
S–215	47 25 46. 74	276 39 28	96 39 33	Ref. Mon. C–153	139. 0	2. 14312
	69 03 24. 75	302 50 06	122 50 10	S–214	147. 8	2. 16970
Ref. Mon. C–154	47 25 48. 84	17 57 20	197 57 19	S–215	68. 2	1. 83356
	69 03 23. 75	304 39 54	124 39 59	Ref. Mon. C–153	142. 4	2. 15336
		324 33 47	144 33 51	S–214	178. 0	2. 25032
S–216	47 25 52. 24	323 09 24	143 09 26	Ref. Mon. C–154	131. 3	2. 11831
	69 03 27. 50	341 14 15	161 14 17	S–215	179. 5	2. 25399

SOURCE OF ST. CROIX RIVER TO LAKE POHENAGAMOOK—Continued

Station	Latitude and longitude	Azimuth	Back azimuth	To station	Distance (meters)	Logarithm
MINOR SCHEME, ST. JOHN AND ST. FRANCIS RIVERS—continued	° ′ ″	° ′ ″	° ′ ″			
Ref. Mon. S–150	47 25 54. 04	42 54 16	222 54 14	S–216	75. 8	1. 87970
	69 03 25. 04	350 24 44	170 24 44	Ref. Mon. C–154	162. 9	2. 21189
		358 26 45	178 26 45	S–215	225. 5	2. 35323
S–217	47 25 55. 14	285 25 00	105 25 04	Ref. Mon. S–150	127. 9	2. 10687
	69 03 30. 92	321 18 47	141 18 50	S–216	114. 7	2. 05955
Ref. Mon. C–155	47 25 56. 59	39 22 44	219 22 42	S–217	57. 9	1. 76286
	69 03 29. 17	312 18 28	132 18 32	Ref. Mon. S–150	117. 0	2. 06830
		345 24 58	165 25 00	S–216	138. 8	2. 14231
Ref. Mon. C–156	47 25 57. 93	285 10 00	105 10 06	Ref. Mon. C–155	157. 7	2. 19782
	69 03 36. 43	306 41 31	126 41 35	S–217	144. 0	2. 15831
S–218	47 25 55. 36	185 41 28	5 41 28	Ref. Mon. C–156	79. 7	1. 90127
	69 03 36. 81	256 38 35	76 38 41	Ref. Mon. C–155	164. 6	2. 21631
		273 08 11	93 08 15	S–217	123. 5	2. 09181
S–219	47 25 56. 65	256 10 10	76 10 16	Ref. Mon. C–156	165. 2	2. 21788
	69 03 44. 08	284 37 40	104 37 46	S–218	157. 6	2. 19748
Ref. Mon. C–157	47 25 59. 77	7 28 02	187 28 02	S–219	97. 3	1. 98802
	69 03 43. 48	291 05 27	111 05 32	Ref. Mon. C–156	158. 3	2. 19956
		314 15 28	134 15 33	S–218	195. 2	2. 29054
C–206	47 25 58. 84	262 39 45	82 39 53	Ref. Mon. C–157	225. 7	2. 35344
	69 03 54. 16	287 45 35	107 45 42	S–219	221. 7	2. 34583
C–205	47 26 03. 76	26 14 59	206 14 56	C–206	169. 5	2. 22924
	69 03 50. 58	309 37 29	129 37 34	Ref. Mon. C–157	193. 2	2. 28606
		328 12 14	148 12 18	S–219	258. 5	2. 41241
Ref. Mon. C–158	47 25 51. 67	152 40 25	332 40 21	C–206	249. 4	2. 39681
	69 03 48. 70	212 08 41	32 08 44	S–219	181. 7	2. 25946
C–208	47 25 51. 86	212 13 46	32 13 51	C–206	254. 7	2. 40603
	69 04 00. 64	271 23 14	91 23 23	Ref. Mon. C–158	250. 4	2. 39861
S–220	47 25 50. 24	98 14 16	278 14 03	C–208	351. 2	2. 54560
	69 03 44. 06	114 27 14	294 27 10	Ref. Mon. C–158	106. 9	2. 02893
		141 27 11	321 27 03	C–206	339. 8	2. 53125
		179 49 39	359 49 39	S–219	198. 1	2. 29695
S–221	47 25 49. 72	114 14 22	294 14 16	C–208	161. 5	2. 20809
	69 03 53. 62	239 42 16	59 42 19	Ref. Mon. C–158	119. 4	2. 07693
		265 26 26	85 26 33	S–220	201. 0	2. 30323
Ref. Mon. S–151	47 25 47. 26	183 13 57	3 13 57	C–208	142. 6	2. 15402
	69 04 01. 03	243 54 17	63 54 22	S–221	172. 9	2. 23780
C–209	47 25 49. 26	236 51 29	56 51 33	C–208	147. 2	2. 16798
	69 04 06. 53	266 59 39	86 59 49	S–221	270. 9	2. 43278
		298 13 25	118 13 29	Ref. Mon. S–151	130. 8	2. 11656
Ref. Mon. C–159 (Kelly Rapids east base).	47 25 41. 21	199 58 19	19 58 22	C–209	264. 3	2. 42216
	69 04 10. 83	227 45 52	47 45 59	Ref. Mon. S–151	277. 6	2. 44340
S–223	47 25 40. 19	107 00 41	287 00 38	Ref. Mon. C–159	108. 4	2. 03520
	69 04 05. 89	177 15 37	357 15 37	C–209	280. 5	2. 44791
		205 00 21	25 00 25	Ref. Mon. S–151	240. 9	2. 38182
Ref. Mon. S–152	47 25 34. 74	214 36 55	34 37 00	Ref. Mon. C–159	242. 9	2. 38534
	69 04 17. 42	235 10 12	55 10 20	S–223	294. 4	2. 46893
C–211 (Kelly Rapids west base).	47 25 39. 58	255 25 19	75 25 26	Ref. Mon. C–159	200. 01	2 30105
	69 04 20. 07	266 24 57	86 25 07	S–223	297. 9	2. 47400
		339 35 49	159 35 51	Ref. Mon. S–152	159. 5	2. 20284

SOURCE OF ST. CROIX RIVER TO LAKE POHENAGAMOOK—Continued

Station	Latitude and longitude	Azimuth	Back azimuth	To station	Distance (meters)	Loga-rithm
MINOR SCHEME, ST. JOHN AND ST. FRANCIS RIVERS— continued	° ′ ″	° ′ ″	° ′ ″			
Ref. Mon. S–153____	47 25 32. 33	234 32 37	54 32 48	C–211_____	386. 4	2. 58707
	69 04 35. 09	258 36 22	78 36 35	Ref. Mon. S–152__	377. 8	2. 57731
Ref. Mon. C–160___	47 25 39. 48	269 33 36	89 33 51	C–211_____	414. 7	2. 61769
	69 04 39. 85	287 17 05	107 17 22	Ref. Mon. S–152__	492. 5	2. 69242
		335 40 44	155 40 48	Ref. Mon. S–153__	242. 5	2. 38472
C–213_____	47 25 35. 80	232 52 18	52 52 23	Ref. Mon. C–160__	188. 5	2. 27526
	69 04 47. 02	293 12 00	113 12 09	Ref. Mon. S–153__	272. 2	2. 43483
S–226_____	47 25 29. 37	157 15 59	337 15 56	C–213_____	215. 4	2. 33321
	69 04 43. 05	192 06 40	12 06 42	Ref. Mon. C–160__	319. 5	2. 50451
		241 17 16	61 17 22	Ref. Mon. S–153__	190. 3	2. 27948
C–214_____	47 25 29. 14	233 52 23	53 52 33	C–213_____	348. 8	2. 54252
	69 05 00. 46	268 54 19	88 54 32	S–226_____	365. 0	2. 56230
S–227_____	47 25 24. 69	173 36 48	353 36 47	C–214_____	138. 2	2. 14065
	69 04 59. 73	217 49 37	37 49 46	C–213_____	434. 3	2. 63774
		247 33 40	67 33 52	S–226_____	378. 2	2. 57772
S–228_____	47 25 28. 92	268 47 02	88 47 13	C–214_____	318. 8	2. 50352
	69 05 15. 67	291 21 09	111 21 21	S–227_____	358. 7	2. 55478
Ref. Mon. C–161____	47 25 33. 09	290 08 52	110 09 03	C–214_____	354. 4	2. 54946
	69 05 16. 34	306 42 01	126 42 13	S–227_____	434. 1	2. 63762
		353 48 59	173 48 59	S–228_____	129. 6	2. 11254
S–229_____	47 25 32. 99	269 33 23	89 33 38	Ref. Mon. C–161__	420. 2	2. 62348
	69 05 36. 39	286 07 51	106 08 06	S–228_____	452. 0	2. 65511
C–216_____	47 25 39. 11	12 05 43	192 05 41	S–229_____	193. 3	2. 28623
	69 05 34. 46	296 04 07	116 04 20	Ref. Mon. C–161__	422. 7	2. 62604
		308 37 42	128 37 55	S–228_____	503. 9	2. 70237
S–230_____	47 25 36. 08	250 07 32	70 07 41	C–216_____	274. 8	2. 43907
	69 05 46. 79	293 40 37	113 40 45	S–229_____	238. 0	2. 37659
C–217_____	47 25 41. 44	282 07 28	102 07 40	C–216_____	342. 0	2. 53401
	69 05 50. 41	311 35 34	131 35 44	S–229_____	392. 9	2. 59432
		335 20 01	155 20 04	S–230_____	181. 9	2. 25974
Ref. Mon. S–155____	47 25 36. 06	210 04 49	30 04 52	C–217_____	191. 8	2. 28295
	69 05 55. 00	269 41 12	89 45 18	S–230_____	172. 1	2. 23567
S–232_____	47 25 41. 51	271 21 38	91 21 41	C–217_____	96. 5	1. 98445
	69 05 55. 01	314 11 29	134 11 35	S–230_____	240. 4	2. 38089
		359 53 51	179 53 51	Ref. Mon. S–155__	168. 3	2. 22608
S–233_____	47 25 48. 70	328 56 50	148 56 54	C–217_____	261. 8	2. 41791
	69 05 56. 85	350 08 33	170 08 34	S–232_____	225. 3	2. 35273
C–218_____	47 25 49. 95	18 02 52	198 02 49	S–232_____	274. 3	2. 43817
	69 05 50. 96	72 33 32	252 33 28	S–233_____	129. 5	2. 11223
		357 30 00	177 30 00	C–217_____	263. 3	2. 42048
Ref. Mon. C–162____	47 25 54. 10	25 15 44	205 15 41	S–233_____	184. 4	2. 26580
	69 05 53. 10	340 41 35	160 41 36	C–218_____	135. 6	2. 13225
C–220_____	47 25 54. 34	272 28 17	92 28 23	Ref. Mon. C–162__	175. 7	2. 24469
	69 06 01. 47	301 35 53	121 36 00	C–218_____	258. 7	2. 41278
		330 57 37	150 57 40	S–233_____	199. 4	2. 29979
S–234_____	47 25 47. 17	220 44 47	40 44 54	C–220_____	292. 5	2. 46606
	69 06 10. 58	260 40 51	80 41 01	S–233_____	291. 5	2. 46471

SOURCE OF ST. CROIX RIVER TO LAKE POHENAGAMOOK—Continued

Station	Latitude and longitude	Azimuth	Back azimuth	To station	Distance (meters)	Loga- rithm
MINOR SCHEME, ST. JOHN AND ST. FRANCIS RIVERS— continued	° ′ ″	° ′ ″	° ′ ″			
C–221	47 25 52. 39	259 01 17	79 01 28	C–220	316. 6	2. 50048
	69 06 16. 30	285 38 02	105 38 16	S–233	423. 3	2. 62661
		323 22 21	143 22 25	S–234	201. 0	2. 30312
Ref. Mon. C–163	47 25 47. 39	231 38 53	51 39 00	C–221	248. 8	2. 39590
	69 06 25. 61	271 15 05	91 15 16	S–234	315. 1	2. 49847
S–235	47 25 39. 73	151 35 17	331 35 13	Ref. Mon. C–163	269. 1	2. 42991
	69 06 19. 50	189 44 08	9 44 11	C–221	396. 8	2. 59856
		219 08 14	39 08 21	S–234	296. 3	2. 47169
Ref. Mon. S–156	47 25 38. 86	204 37 36	24 37 41	Ref. Mon. C–163	289. 8	2. 46205
	69 06 31. 37	263 52 03	83 52 12	S–235	250. 2	2. 39834
S–237	47 25 47. 14	266 22 33	86 22 38	Ref. Mon. C–163	122. 3	2. 08756
	69 06 31. 43	312 28 00	132 28 09	S–235	339. 1	2. 53032
		359 41 53	179 41 53	Ref. Mon. S–156	255. 7	2. 40770
S–238	47 25 58. 56	336 28 13	156 28 18	Ref. Mon. C–163	376. 1	2. 57534
	69 06 32. 77	355 26 54	175 26 55	S–237	353. 7	2. 54864
C–223	47 25 59. 35	17 16 29	197 16 24	S–237	394. 6	2. 59619
	69 06 25. 84	80 31 39	260 31 34	S–238	147. 3	2. 16806
		359 14 18	179 14 18	Ref. Mon. C–163	369. 1	2. 56718
Ref. Mon. C–164	47 26 13. 49	335 10 59	155 11 06	C–223	481. 1	2. 68226
	69 06 35. 48	352 59 16	172 59 18	S–238	464. 4	2. 66690
Ref. Mon. S–157	47 26 08. 42	236 45 28	56 45 36	Ref. Mon. C–164	285. 4	2. 45544
	69 06 46. 87	302 27 21	122 27 36	C–223	522. 2	2. 71785
		315 52 04	135 52 14	S–238	424. 2	2. 62761
S–240	47 26 17. 02	286 00 51	106 01 05	Ref. Mon. C–164	395. 0	2. 59657
	69 06 53. 60	332 01 39	152 01 45	Ref. Mon. S–157	300. 5	2. 47788
C–225	47 26 21. 75	26 32 32	206 32 29	S–240	163. 5	2. 21365
	69 06 50. 11	309 47 07	129 47 18	Ref. Mon. C–164	398. 9	2. 60090
		350 38 21	170 38 24	Ref. Mon. S–157	417. 3	2. 62044
C–226	47 26 23. 31	279 59 20	99 59 30	C–225	276. 4	2. 44152
	69 07 03. 10	314 17 30	134 17 37	S–240	278. 2	2. 44433
S–241	47 26 19. 50	203 44 14	23 44 16	C–226	128. 5	2. 10907
	69 07 05. 57	257 51 04	77 51 16	C–225	331. 4	2. 52031
		286 58 31	106 58 40	S–240	262. 3	2. 41880
S–242	47 26 26. 08	290 40 09	110 40 17	C–226	242. 9	2. 38535
	69 07 13. 94	319 12 51	139 12 57	S–241	268. 6	2. 42916
C–227	47 26 28. 12	55 06 52	235 06 49	S–242	109. 9	2. 04092
	69 07 09. 64	317 18 07	137 18 12	C–226	202. 2	2. 30568
		342 13 38	162 13 41	S–241	279. 6	2. 44652
S–243	47 26 31. 47	297 17 51	117 17 58	C–227	225. 8	2. 35368
	69 07 19. 22	326 24 44	146 24 48	S–242	199. 7	2. 30047
Ref. Mon. C–165	47 26 32. 66	58 44 19	238 44 17	S–243	70. 8	1. 84982
	69 07 16. 33	315 01 33	135 01 38	C–227	198. 3	2. 29728
		346 10 08	166 10 10	S–242	209. 2	2. 32052
C–229	47 26 35. 91	312 30 55	132 30 59	Ref. Mon. C–165	148. 6	2. 17189
	69 07 21. 55	340 19 53	160 19 55	S–243	145. 6	2. 16319
C–230	47 26 35. 10	250 25 46	70 25 48	C–229	74. 6	1. 87280
	69 07 24. 91	292 45 04	112 45 10	Ref. Mon. C–165	195. 0	2. 28996
		313 13 19	133 13 23	S–243	163. 7	2. 21412

SOURCE OF ST. CROIX RIVER TO LAKE POHENAGAMOOK—Continued

Station	Latitude and longitude	Azimuth	Back azimuth	To station	Distance (meters)	Logarithm
MINOR SCHEME, ST. JOHN AND ST. FRANCIS RIVERS— continued	° ′ ″	° ′ ″	° ′ ″			
C–231	47 26 28. 63	198 17 28	18 17 31	C–230	210. 6	2. 32345
	69 07 28. 06	244 39 04	64 39 11	S–243	205. 2	2. 31208
C–232	47 26 31. 74	223 25 52	43 25 56	C–230	143. 0	2. 15526
	69 07 29. 60	272 10 56	92 11 04	S–243	217. 8	2. 33798
		341 28 48	161 28 49	C–231	101. 4	2. 00593
Ref. Mon. S–158	47 26 26. 66	192 29 24	12 29 25	C–232	160. 8	2. 20636
	69 07 31. 26	227 43 31	47 43 33	C–231	90. 5	1. 95677
S–245	47 26 30. 72	244 25 49	64 25 51	C–232	73. 0	1. 86358
	69 07 32. 75	303 22 02	123 22 05	C–231	117. 5	2. 06986
		346 04 39	166 04 40	Ref. Mon. S–158	129. 3	2. 11157
S–246	47 26 34. 65	296 31 54	116 32 01	C–232	200. 9	2. 30300
	69 07 38. 18	316 48 19	136 48 24	S–245	166. 3	2. 22101
C–233	47 26 36. 60	43 36 50	223 36 48	S–246	83. 2	1. 91989
	69 07 35. 44	320 46 44	140 46 49	C–232	193. 6	2. 28681
		342 42 26	162 42 29	S–245	190. 1	2. 27891
S–247	47 26 37. 86	280 51 59	100 52 06	C–233	207. 2	2. 31640
	69 07 45. 15	304 11 20	124 11 25	S–246	176. 7	2. 24714
C–234	47 26 40. 22	4 07 45	184 07 45	S–247	73. 2	1. 86440
	69 07 44. 90	299 28 47	119 28 54	C–233	227. 7	2. 35736
		320 43 35	140 43 40	S–246	222. 5	2. 34737
S–248	47 26 39. 00	257 37 22	77 37 28	C–234	176. 2	2. 24598
	69 07 53. 12	281 55 24	101 55 30	S–247	170. 5	2. 23173
Ref. Mon. C–166	47 26 41. 39	12 50 41	192 50 41	S–248	75. 7	1. 87929
	69 07 52. 31	283 04 49	103 04 55	C–234	159. 4	2. 20247
		306 01 22	126 01 28	S–247	185. 5	2. 26823
C–236	47 26 41. 10	267 11 23	87 11 29	Ref. Mon. C–166	181. 2	2. 25809
	69 08 00. 95	291 35 36	111 35 42	S–248	176. 5	2. 24676
S–249	47 26 38. 77	172 42 18	352 42 18	C–236	72. 8	1. 86189
	69 08 00. 51	244 43 55	64 44 01	Ref. Mon. C–166	189. 9	2. 27849
		267 20 01	87 20 07	S–248	155. 0	2. 19047
S–250	47 26 39. 88	252 42 15	72 42 19	C–236	126. 8	2. 10304
	69 08 06. 73	284 49 24	104 49 28	S–249	134. 8	2. 12959
C–237	47 26 41. 60	23 34 47	203 34 46	S–250	57. 8	1. 76217
	69 08 05. 62	278 53 20	98 53 23	C–236	99. 1	1. 99607
		309 13 49	129 13 52	S–249	138. 3	2. 14091
S–251	47 26 43. 47	296 23 51	116 23 55	C–237	129. 6	2. 11253
	69 08 11. 16	319 57 51	139 57 54	S–250	144. 5	2. 15978
C–238	47 26 44. 86	29 33 08	209 33 07	S–251	49. 3	1. 69321
	69 08 10. 00	317 37 16	137 37 19	C–237	136. 1	2. 13384
		335 55 33	155 55 35	S–250	168. 2	2. 22573
S–252	47 26 44. 45	265 20 31	85 20 37	C–238	155. 8	2. 19262
	69 08 17. 41	283 00 48	103 00 52	S–251	134. 4	2. 12847
C–239	47 26 45. 90	24 30 40	204 30 39	S–252	49. 3	1. 69256
	69 08 16. 44	283 25 04	103 25 09	C–238	138. 7	2. 14192
		304 11 34	124 11 38	S–251	133. 6	2. 12590
C–240	47 26 48. 40	309 21 25	129 21 29	C–239	122. 0	2. 08653
	69 08 20. 94	328 49 53	148 49 56	S–252	142. 8	2. 15486

SOURCE OF ST. CROIX RIVER TO LAKE POHENAGAMOOK—Continued

Station	Latitude and longitude	Azimuth	Back azimuth	To station	Distance (meters)	Logarithm
MINOR SCHEME, ST. JOHN AND ST. FRANCIS RIVERS—continued	° ′ ″	° ′ ″	° ′ ″			
S–253	47 26 46. 97	242 10 31	62 10 34	C–240	94. 9	1. 97704
	69 08 24. 95	280 31 34	100 31 41	C–239	181. 3	2. 25841
		296 17 09	116 17 15	S–252	176. 0	2. 24556
Ref. Mon. C–167	47 26 50. 15	29 14 49	209 14 47	S–253	112. 4	2. 05095
	69 08 22. 32	331 44 12	151 44 13	C–240	61. 1	1. 78624
C–242	47 26 47. 72	231 24 17	51 24 20	Ref. Mon. C–167	120. 3	2. 08024
	69 08 26. 81	260 13 04	80 13 09	C–240	124. 8	2. 09614
		300 33 35	120 33 37	S–253	45. 4	1. 65689
C–243	47 26 44. 47	196 07 01	16 07 02	C–242	104. 4	2. 01875
	69 08 28. 20	221 23 18	41 23 21	S–253	102. 9	2. 01261
S–254	47 26 44. 20	98 12 23	278 12 21	C–243	58. 0	1. 76379
	69 08 25. 45	165 18 38	345 18 37	C–242	112. 3	2. 05024
		187 04 23	7 04 24	S–253	86. 2	1. 93539
C–244	47 26 40. 23	182 25 54	2 25 54	C–243	131. 0	2. 11743
	69 08 28. 46	207 11 37	27 11 39	S–254	137. 9	2. 13952
S–255	47 26 39. 48	105 52 11	285 52 08	C–244	84. 4	1. 92648
	69 08 24. 59	153 50 29	333 50 26	C–243	171. 6	2. 23450
		172 53 01	352 53 00	S–254	146. 9	2. 16691
S–256	47 26 37. 98	139 10 11	319 10 09	C–244	91. 7	1. 96251
	69 08 25. 60	204 37 38	24 37 39	S–255	51. 0	1. 70720
Ref. Mon. S–159	47 26 38. 34	218 48 40	38 48 42	C–244	74. 8	1. 87403
	69 08 30. 70	254 37 42	74 37 47	S–255	132. 9	2. 12338
		275 55 55	95 55 59	S–256	107. 4	2. 03119
S–258	47 26 41. 65	288 57 46	108 57 51	C–244	135. 0	2. 13027
	69 08 34. 56	321 40 26	141 40 29	Ref. Mon. S–159	130. 2	2. 11471
C–245	47 26 42. 68	59 14 10	239 14 08	S–258	62. 3	1. 79469
	69 08 32. 00	315 37 50	135 37 53	C–244	106. 0	2. 02514
		348 31 44	168 31 45	Ref. Mon. S–159	136. 8	2. 13602
S–259	47 26 47. 02	321 22 10	141 22 14	C–245	171. 3	2. 23388
	69 08 37. 10	342 08 12	162 08 14	S–258	174. 1	2. 24088
C–246	47 26 47. 99	60 18 46	240 18 44	S–259	60. 5	1. 78210
	69 08 34. 59	341 38 32	161 38 34	C–245	172. 6	2. 23711
		359 45 44	179 45 44	S–258	195. 7	2. 29165
C–247	47 26 52. 44	317 28 27	137 28 32	C–246	186. 5	2. 27066
	69 08 40. 61	336 18 44	156 18 47	S–259	182. 8	2. 26205
S–260	47 26 50. 80	228 08 23	48 08 25	C–247	75. 8	1. 87971
	69 08 43. 31	295 26 52	115 26 59	C–246	202. 1	2. 30562
		311 58 01	131 58 06	S–259	174. 7	2. 24236
S–261	47 26 54. 41	291 57 25	111 57 30	C–247	162. 9	2. 21197
	69 08 47. 82	319 40 36	139 40 39	S–260	146. 3	2. 16511
Ref. Mon. C–168	47 26 55. 94	44 03 55	224 03 54	S–261	65. 8	1. 81830
	69 08 45. 64	315 46 18	135 46 22	C–247	151. 0	2. 17899
		342 53 37	162 53 39	S–260	166. 1	2. 22048
S–262	47 26 56. 08	271 40 43	91 40 48	Ref. Mon. C–168	149. 8	2. 17562
	69 08 52. 79	296 25 21	116 25 25	S–261	116. 1	2. 06496
C–249	47 26 58. 38	11 54 14	191 54 13	S–262	72. 4	1. 85970
	69 08 52. 08	299 09 25	119 09 29	Ref. Mon. C–168	154. 4	2. 18866
		323 58 56	143 58 59	S–261	151. 5	2. 18033

SOURCE OF ST. CROIX RIVER TO LAKE POHENAGAMOOK—Continued

Station	Latitude and longitude	Azimuth	Back azimuth	To station	Distance (meters)	Logarithm
MINOR SCHEME, ST. JOHN AND ST. FRANCIS RIVERS— continued	° ′ ″	° ′ ″	° ′ ″			
C–250	47 26 56. 48	243 16 01	63 16 05	C–249	130. 5	2. 11550
	69 08 57. 64	276 49 11	96 49 14	S–262	102. 3	2. 00993
Ref. Mon. S–160	47 26 54. 61	178 39 16	358 39 16	C–250	57. 8	1. 76161
	69 08 57. 57	224 41 12	44 41 16	C–249	163. 8	2. 21422
		245 32 26	65 32 29	S–262	110. 1	2. 04185
S–264	47 26 54. 70	244 19 30	64 19 34	C–250	126. 7	2. 10283
	69 09 03. 09	271 24 29	91 24 33	Ref. Mon. S–160	115. 6	2. 06295
C–251	47 26 56. 39	13 49 37	193 49 37	S–264	53. 8	1. 73068
	69 09 02. 48	268 29 22	88 29 26	C–250	101. 4	2. 00598
		298 11 57	118 12 01	Ref. Mon. S–160	116. 5	2. 06647
C–252	47 26 58. 09	296 56 53	116 56 56	C–251	115. 7	2. 06325
	69 09 07. 40	319 13 20	139 13 23	S–264	138. 2	2. 14051
S–265	47 26 56. 48	213 27 41	33 27 42	C–252	59. 5	1. 77428
	69 09 08. 96	271 11 05	91 11 09	C–251	135. 9	2. 13333
		294 05 55	114 05 59	S–264	134. 8	2. 12969
S–266	47 26 59. 91	295 23 13	115 23 18	C–252	131. 2	2. 11803
	69 09 13. 06	320 59 21	140 59 25	S–265	136. 3	2. 13435
C–253	47 27 01. 21	45 14 29	225 14 27	S–266	56. 9	1. 75523
	69 09 11. 13	320 57 16	140 57 19	C–252	124. 0	2. 09358
		342 44 17	162 44 19	S–265	152. 8	2. 18422
C–254	47 27 03. 46	297 30 46	117 30 51	C–253	151. 0	2. 17892
	69 09 17. 52	319 35 32	139 35 35	S–266	144. 2	2. 15904
S–267	47 27 01. 58	206 25 43	26 25 44	C–254	65. 0	1. 81262
	69 09 18. 90	274 04 01	94 04 07	C–253	163. 2	2. 21279
		292 52 47	112 52 51	S–266	132. 9	2. 12338
S–268	47 27 04. 33	280 35 40	100 35 45	C–254	145. 8	2. 16390
	69 09 24. 36	306 35 41	126 35 45	S–267	142. 6	2. 15397
Ref. Mon. C–169	47 27 06. 14	28 36 28	208 36 27	S–268	63. 7	1. 80431
	69 09 22. 90	306 15 21	126 15 25	C–254	139. 9	2. 14595
		329 13 18	149 13 21	S–267	164. 0	2. 21493
S–269	47 27 05. 23	253 53 12	73 53 16	Ref. Mon. C–169	101. 5	2. 00663
	69 09 27. 56	292 29 53	112 29 55	S–268	72. 6	1. 86070
C–256	47 27 07. 12	8 27 46	188 27 45	S–269	58. 9	1. 77020
	69 09 27. 15	288 42 10	108 42 13	Ref. Mon. C–169	93. 8	1. 97237
		325 50 45	145 50 47	S–268	104. 0	2. 01689
C–257	47 27 06. 28	243 34 37	63 34 39	C–256	58. 2	1. 76479
	69 09 29. 64	306 42 12	126 42 13	S–269	54. 2	1. 73380
C–258	47 27 03. 68	194 01 35	14 01 36	C–257	82. 7	1. 91731
	69 09 30. 59	233 00 17	53 00 19	S–269	79. 5	1. 90019
S–270	47 27 02. 94	115 32 07	295 32 06	C–258	53. 1	1. 72527
	69 09 28. 30	164 51 31	344 51 31	C–257	106. 8	2. 02859
		192 23 28	12 23 29	S–269	72. 4	1. 85977
C–259	47 26 59. 34	196 52 53	16 52 55	C–258	140. 1	2. 14630
	69 09 32. 53	218 34 02	38 34 05	S–270	142. 1	2. 15267
S–271	47 26 58. 45	114 16 44	294 16 42	C–259	66. 8	1. 82483
	69 09 29. 63	172 51 40	352 51 40	C–258	162. 8	2. 21153
		191 18 19	11 18 20	S–270	141. 3	2. 15025
C–260	47 26 55. 88	215 51 24	35 51 27	C–259	131. 8	2. 11989
	69 09 36. 22	240 07 11	60 07 16	S–271	159. 3	2. 20213

SOURCE OF ST. CROIX RIVER TO LAKE POHENAGAMOOK—Continued

Station	Latitude and longitude	Azimuth	Back azimuth	To station	Distance (meters)	Logarithm
MINOR SCHEME, ST. JOHN AND ST. FRANCIS RIVERS—continued	° ′ ″	° ′ ″	° ′ ″			
Ref. Mon. S–161____	47 26 53. 94	141 56 00	321 55 59	C–260_____	76. 3	1. 88252
	69 09 33. 97	190 14 32	10 14 34	C–259_____	169. 6	2. 22939
		213 08 56	33 09 00	S–271_____	166. 5	2. 22146
C–261_____	47 26 53. 11	232 42 27	52 42 31	C–260_____	141. 3	2. 15027
	69 09 41. 59	260 53 33	80 53 38	Ref. Mon. S–161__	161. 5	2. 20824
S–273_____	47 26 50. 56	162 11 23	342 11 23	C–261_____	82. 8	1. 91781
	69 09 40. 38	207 55 10	27 55 14	C–260_____	186. 1	2. 26972
		232 07 31	52 07 36	Ref. Mon. S–161__	170. 0	2. 23041
S–274_____	47 26 50. 13	233 59 06	53 59 11	C–261_____	156. 8	2. 19538
	69 09 47. 64	264 57 42	84 57 47	S–273_____	152. 7	2. 18397
Nigger Brook east base.	47 26 47. 08	121 08 52	301 08 47	S–274_____	181. 8	2. 25954
	69 09 40. 22	178 10 42	358 10 42	S–273_____	107. 5	2. 03137
Nigger Brook west base.	47 26 46. 09	198 35 16	18 35 18	S–274_____	131. 6	2. 11937
	69 09 49. 64	234 33 15	54 33 22	S–273_____	238. 3	2. 37708
		261 09 08	81 09 15	Nigger Brook east base.	199. 91	2. 30084
C–262_____	47 26 53. 34	31 17 57	211 17 55	S–274_____	116. 2	2. 06537
	69 09 44. 76	276 07 05	96 07 08	C–261_____	66. 8	1. 82499
		313 06 50	133 06 53	S–273_____	125. 7	2. 09936
Ref. Mon. S–162____	47 26 59. 90	307 42 10	127 42 19	C–262_____	331. 0	2. 51983
	69 09 57. 26	326 16 01	146 16 08	S–274_____	362. 9	2. 55973
C–263 _____	47 27 01. 33	76 16 33	256 16 27	Ref. Mon. S–162__	186. 4	2. 27034
	69 09 48. 62	341 51 07	161 51 10	C–262_____	259. 6	2. 41424
		356 36 58	176 36 59	S–274_____	346. 6	2. 53980
S–276_____	47 27 03. 02	284 27 52	104 27 59	C–263_____	209. 1	2. 32039
	69 09 58. 28	347 27 30	167 27 31	Ref. Mon. S–162__	98. 8	1. 99480
C–264_____	47 27 05. 92	17 35 36	197 35 34	Ref. Mon. S–162__	195. 0	2. 28999
	69 09 54. 44	41 57 36	221 57 33	S–276_____	120. 2	2. 08002
		319 14 17	139 14 21	C–263_____	187. 0	2. 27185
S–277_____	47 27 05. 36	262 08 55	82 08 59	C–264_____	126. 7	2. 10290
	69 10 00. 44	327 56 11	147 56 12	S–276_____	85. 1	1. 92979
S–278_____	47 27 06. 02	271 02 59	91 03 05	C–264_____	178. 9	2. 25260
	69 10 02. 98	291 07 01	111 07 03	S–277_____	57. 2	1. 75705
		313 15 52	133 15 55	S–276_____	135. 2	2. 13109
C–265___ _____	47 27 08. 66	294 19 38	114 19 45	C–264_____	205. 5	2. 31287
	69 10 03. 38	328 48 50	148 48 53	S–277_____	119. 2	2. 07630
		354 05 58	174 05 59	S–278_____	81. 8	1. 91288
Ref. Mon. S–163____	47 27 08. 62	269 25 57	89 26 01	C–265_____	122. 4	2. 08793
	69 10 09. 23	301 29 51	121 29 56	S–278_____	153. 5	2. 18599
Ref. Mon. C–170____	47 27 10. 58	33 30 14	213 30 13	Ref. Mon. S–163__	72. 8	1. 86211
	69 10 07. 31	305 52 33	125 52 36	C–265_____	101. 5	2. 00651
		327 14 08	147 14 12	S–278_____	167. 5	2. 22410
S–280_____	47 27 10. 71	271 47 20	91 47 24	Ref. Mon. C–170__	127. 6	2. 10583
	69 10 13. 40	306 31 16	126 31 19	Ref. Mon. S–163__	108. 7	2. 03620
C–267_____	47 27 13. 40	302 53 37	122 53 42	Ref. Mon. C–170__	160. 1	2. 20445
	69 10 13. 73	327 26 43	147 26 47	Ref. Mon. S–163__	175. 2	2. 24350
		355 14 01	175 14 02	S–280_____	83. 3	1. 92046
S–281_____	47 27 11. 96	254 19 51	74 19 56	C–267_____	165. 0	2. 21747
	69 10 21. 31	283 02 45	103 02 51	S–280_____	170. 2	2. 23090

SOURCE OF ST. CROIX RIVER TO LAKE POHENAGAMOOK—Continued

Station	Latitude and longitude	Azimuth	Back azimuth	To station	Distance (meters)	Logarithm
	° ′ ″	° ′ ″	° ′ ″			
MINOR SCHEME, ST. JOHN AND ST. FRANCIS RIVERS—continued						
C–268	47 27 13. 88	274 56 44	94 56 50	C–267	172. 6	2. 23698
	69 10 21. 94	298 41 01	118 41 08	S–280	203. 9	2. 30936
		347 35 50	167 35 51	S–281	60. 9	1. 78434
S–282	47 27 13. 24	250 39 20	70 39 22	C–268	59. 5	1. 77480
	69 10 24. 62	299 50 10	119 50 13	S–281	79. 8	1. 90218
S–283	47 27 15. 57	300 01 39	120 01 42	C–268	104. 0	2. 01686
	69 10 26. 24	334 45 21	154 45 22	S–282	79. 3	1. 89939
C–269	47 27 17. 15	9 04 34	189 04 33	C–268	102. 1	2. 00919
	69 10 21. 17	30 56 36	210 56 33	S–282	140. 6	2. 14796
		65 17 16	245 17 12	S–283	116. 8	2. 06750
S–284	47 27 20. 34	311 58 29	131 58 33	C–269	147. 3	2. 16831
	69 10 26. 40	358 40 15	178 40 15	S–283	147. 4	2. 16855
C–270	47 27 20. 88	23 13 00	203 12 58	S–283	178. 5	2. 25168
	69 10 22. 88	77 15 35	257 15 33	S–284	75. 7	1. 87884
		342 45 57	162 45 59	C–269	120. 6	2. 08150
C–271	47 27 22. 25	3 07 56	183 07 56	S–284	59. 2	1. 77203
	69 10 26. 24	300 59 40	120 59 42	C–270	82. 3	1. 91546
C–272	47 27 22. 12	267 59 03	87 59 07	C–271	117. 5	2. 07008
	69 10 31. 85	295 41 23	115 41 27	S–284	126. 7	2. 10289
S–285	47 27 19. 41	209 00 58	29 01 00	C–272	95. 5	1. 98008
	69 10 34. 06	241 50 25	61 50 31	C–271	185. 8	2. 26894
		259 54 06	79 54 12	S–284	163. 1	2. 21236
S–286	47 27 23. 77	296 23 54	116 23 58	C–272	115. 0	2. 06062
	69 10 36. 77	337 10 44	157 10 46	S–285	146. 1	2. 16461
S–287	47 27 22. 69	249 08 00	69 08 03	S–286	93. 8	1. 97212
	69 10 40. 95	275 18 33	95 18 40	C–272	191. 4	2. 28204
		305 03 20	125 03 25	S–285	176. 3	2. 24618
C–273	47 27 24. 93	46 01 22	226 01 20	S–287	99. 6	1. 99827
	69 10 37. 53	335 57 10	155 57 10	S–286	39. 2	1. 59280
C–274	47 27 24. 00	250 02 54	70 02 57	C–273	84. 1	1. 92497
	69 10 41. 30	274 14 30	94 14 33	S–286	95. 3	1. 97910
		349 37 16	169 37 16	S–287	41. 1	1. 61412
S–288	47 27 25. 88	305 00 59	125 01 02	C–274	101. 4	2. 00597
	69 10 45. 27	317 28 46	137 28 49	S–287	133. 8	2. 12652
S–289	47 27 23. 84	228 38 42	48 38 44	S–288	95. 5	1. 98008
	69 10 48. 69	268 10 22	88 10 27	C–274	154. 8	2. 18980
		282 21 21	102 21 26	S–287	166. 0	2. 22007
C–275	47 27 27. 73	15 02 31	195 02 31	S–289	124. 5	2. 09520
	69 10 47. 15	325 25 09	145 25 10	S–288	69. 4	1. 84131
C–276	47 27 24. 43	213 53 59	33 54 01	C–275	123. 1	2. 09014
	69 10 50. 42	247 22 43	67 22 46	S–288	117. 0	2. 06829
		296 28 53	116 28 54	S–289	40. 6	1. 60836
S–290	47 27 21. 83	207 28 48	27 28 49	C–276	90. 5	1. 95655
	69 10 52. 42	231 28 09	51 28 11	S–289	99. 8	1. 99917
C–277	47 27 23. 14	234 26 19	54 26 21	C–276	68. 0	1. 83280
	69 10 53. 07	256 48 58	76 49 01	S–289	94. 2	1. 97388
		341 31 05	161 31 06	S–290	42. 9	1. 63258

SOURCE OF ST. CROIX RIVER TO LAKE POHENAGAMOOK—Continued

Station	Latitude and longitude	Azimuth	Back azimuth	To station	Distance (meters)	Logarithm
MINOR SCHEME, ST. JOHN AND ST. FRANCIS RIVERS—continued	° ′ ″	° ′ ″	° ′ ″			
S–291	47 27 21. 50	242 38 17	62 38 20	C–277	110. 6	2. 04377
	69 10 57. 76	264 49 15	84 49 19	S–290	112. 3	2. 05035
C–278	47 27 22. 78	263 28 54	83 28 57	C–277	99. 9	1. 99957
	69 10 57. 81	284 34 53	104 34 57	S–290	116. 6	2. 06675
		358 30 54	178 30 54	S–291	39. 5	1. 59668
C–279	47 27 23. 43	281 35 46	101 35 49	C–278	99. 5	1. 99800
	69 11 02. 46	301 07 39	121 07 42	S–291	115. 1	2. 06109
S–292	47 27 21. 41	197 31 47	17 31 48	C–279	65. 4	1. 81558
	69 11 03. 40	250 07 53	70 07 57	C–278	124. 6	2. 09561
		268 36 49	88 36 53	S–291	118. 3	2. 07286
S–293	47 27 21. 97	243 01 28	63 01 31	C–279	98. 8	1. 99492
	69 11 06. 67	284 22 41	104 22 43	S–292	70. 6	1. 84878
C–280	47 27 23. 56	271 51 13	91 51 17	C–279	123. 1	2. 09023
	69 11 08. 33	302 42 13	122 42 16	S–292	122. 8	2. 08918
		324 24 12	144 24 13	S–293	60. 0	1. 77840
C–281	47 27 20. 89	228 26 33	48 26 36	C–280	124. 2	2. 09405
	69 11 12. 77	255 17 35	75 17 39	S–293	132. 2	2. 12122
S–294	47 27 18. 80	143 02 19	323 02 17	C–281	80. 6	1. 90622
	69 11 10. 46	196 51 31	16 51 32	C–280	153. 4	2. 18569
		219 02 11	39 02 13	S–293	126. 1	2. 10070
S–295	47 27 18. 61	232 57 23	52 57 26	C–281	116. 7	2. 06722
	69 11 17. 22	267 35 49	87 35 54	S–294	141. 8	2. 15154
C–282	47 27 19. 90	254 05 50	74 05 54	C–281	110. 9	2. 04504
	69 11 17. 86	282 21 28	102 21 34	S–294	158. 8	2. 20089
		341 19 06	161 19 07	S–295	42. 2	1. 62484
C–283	47 27 17. 48	239 01 24	59 01 28	C–282	145. 7	2. 16353
	69 11 23. 83	255 47 07	75 47 12	S–295	142. 8	2. 15478
S–296	47 27 16. 11	136 36 48	316 36 47	C–283	57. 9	1. 76244
	69 11 21. 93	216 02 43	36 02 46	C–282	144. 8	2. 16069
		231 59 38	51 59 42	S–295	125. 3	2. 09778
S–297	47 27 12. 58	192 31 39	12 31 40	C–283	154. 9	2. 19012
	69 11 25. 43	213 53 45	33 53 47	S–296	131. 5	2. 11904
C–284	47 27 16. 32	253 07 40	73 07 44	C–283	123. 3	2. 09086
	69 11 29. 46	272 16 42	92 16 47	S–296	157. 8	2. 19822
		323 50 40	143 50 43	S–297	143. 0	2. 15532
S–298	47 27 12. 54	178 09 47	358 09 47	C–284	116. 8	2. 06745
	69 11 29. 28	269 05 11	89 05 14	S–297	80. 6	1. 90650
S–299	47 27 15. 50	227 32 36	47 32 37	C–284	37. 5	1. 57397
	69 11 30. 78	308 49 22	128 49 26	S–297	143. 8	2. 15774
		341 02 30	161 02 31	S–298	96. 7	1. 98532
C–285	47 27 18. 91	315 07 04	135 07 07	C–284	113. 0	2. 05295
	69 11 33. 26	333 42 27	153 42 29	S–299	117. 5	2. 07008
S–300	47 27 17. 79	221 57 08	41 57 09	C–285	46. 4	1. 66693
	69 11 34. 75	292 20 00	112 20 04	C–284	119. 7	2. 07826
		310 26 08	130 26 11	S–299	109. 2	2. 03814
C–286	47 27 20. 65	294 39 25	114 39 29	C–285	129. 0	2. 11045
	69 11 38. 86	315 43 06	135 43 09	S–300	123. 4	2. 09130

SOURCE OF ST. CROIX RIVER TO LAKE POHENAGAMOOK—Continued

Station	Latitude and longitude	Azimuth	Back azimuth	To station	Distance (meters)	Loga- rithm
MINOR SCHEME, ST. JOHN AND ST. FRANCIS RIVERS— continued	° ′ ″	° ′ ″	° ′ ″			
S–301	47 27 19. 29 69 11 39. 77	204 34 09 274 59 24 293 48 01	24 34 09 94 59 28 113 48 04	C–286 C–285 S–300	46. 1 136. 9 115. 1	1. 66337 2. 13632 2. 06105
Ref. Mon. C–173	47 27 21. 08 69 11 45. 09	275 44 17 296 16 22	95 44 21 116 16 26	C–286 S–301	131. 3 124. 3	2. 11815 2. 09446
S–302	47 27 19. 55 69 11 45. 42	188 08 15 256 04 54 273 48 11	8 08 15 76 04 58 93 48 15	Ref. Mon. C–173 C–286 S–301	47. 6 141. 5 118. 5	1. 67798 2. 15078 2. 07357
C–288	47 27 20. 40 69 11 50. 17	258 54 41 284 47 57	78 54 45 104 48 01	Ref. Mon. C–173 S–302	108. 4 103. 0	2. 03495 2. 01297
S–303	47 27 18. 99 69 11 49. 63	165 18 18 235 49 31 258 54 33	345 18 17 55 49 34 78 54 36	C–288 Ref. Mon. C–173 S–302	45. 1 114. 7 89. 9	1. 65396 2. 05968 1. 95355
C–289	47 27 18. 76 69 11 56. 43	248 56 21 267 13 42	68 56 25 87 13 47	C–288 S–303	140. 5 142. 8	2. 14782 2. 15460
S–304	47 27 17. 07 69 11 55. 05	151 03 39 224 48 06 242 26 31	331 03 38 44 48 09 62 26 35	C–289 C–288 S–303	59. 9 145. 0 128. 2	1. 77720 2. 16142 2. 10777
S–305	47 27 14. 73 69 12 00. 22	212 28 12 236 17 43	32 28 14 56 17 46	C–289 S–304	147. 7 130. 1	2. 16936 2. 11440
Ref. Mon. C–174	47 27 16. 79 69 12 02. 14	242 54 32 266 38 33 327 41 50	62 54 36 86 38 38 147 41 52	C–289 S–304 S–305	134. 2 148. 7 75. 1	2. 12763 2. 17222 1. 87585
C–291	47 27 15. 41 69 12 05. 59	239 37 37 280 36 21	59 37 39 100 36 25	Ref. Mon. C–174 S–305	83. 9 114. 5	1. 92386 2. 05885
S–306	47 27 12. 81 69 12 04. 29	161 17 20 200 11 44 235 11 57	341 17 19 20 11 45 55 12 00	C–291 Ref. Mon. C–174 S–305	84. 9 130. 9 103. 9	1. 92875 2. 11681 2. 01668
C–292	47 27 09. 82 69 12 16. 04	231 41 27 249 24 07	51 41 35 69 24 16	C–291 S–306	278. 8 262. 8	2. 44533 2. 41965
S–307	47 27 06. 84 69 12 13. 47	149 39 05 211 56 41 226 12 48	329 39 03 31 56 47 46 12 55	C–292 C–291 S–306	106. 4 311. 9 266. 3	2. 02695 2. 49402 2. 42539
C–293	47 27 07. 87 69 12 19. 64	231 27 15 283 47 08	51 27 17 103 47 12	C–292 S–307	96. 5 133. 0	1. 98441 2. 12401
Ref. Mon. S–166	47 27 06. 41 69 12 19. 58	178 35 38 215 13 49 264 00 21	358 35 38 35 13 51 84 00 25	C–293 C–292 S–307	45. 2 128. 9 128. 8	1. 65484 2. 11017 2. 10995
S–309	47 27 07. 57 69 12 22. 53	261 17 59 300 11 38	81 18 01 120 11 40	C–293 Ref. Mon. S–166	61. 3 71. 4	1. 78726 1. 85343
S–310	47 27 12. 58 69 12 21. 16	10 31 57 347 39 23	190 31 56 167 39 24	S–309 C–293	157. 3 148. 8	2. 19672 2. 17266
C–294	47 27 12. 01 69 12 18. 56	10 00 50 31 13 47 107 51 20	190 00 49 211 13 44 287 51 18	C–293 S–309 S–310	129. 8 160. 4 57. 1	2. 11339 2. 20510 1. 75695
C–295	47 27 14. 58 69 12 19. 90	22 55 02 340 27 54	202 55 01 160 27 55	S–310 C–294	67. 3 84. 3	1. 82776 1. 92596

SOURCE OF ST. CROIX RIVER TO LAKE POHENAGAMOOK—Continued

Station	Latitude and longitude	Azimuth	Back azimuth	To station	Distance (meters)	Logarithm
MINOR SCHEME, ST. JOHN AND ST. FRANCIS RIVERS—continued	° ′ ″	° ′ ″	° ′ ″			
S–311	47 27 14. 46 69 12 25. 95	268 14 33 300 01 52	88 14 37 120 01 55	C–295 S–310	126. 7 116. 0	2. 10277 2. 06455
C–296	47 27 16. 01 69 12 25. 50	11 08 32 290 39 21 319 23 35	191 08 32 110 39 25 139 23 38	S–311 C–295 S–310	49. 0 125. 2 139. 8	1. 69004 2. 09768 2. 14547
C–297	47 27 19. 81 69 12 32. 93	307 00 29 318 31 35	127 00 34 138 31 40	C–296 S–311	194. 9 220. 7	2. 28982 2. 34384
S–312	47 27 17. 03 69 12 37. 25	226 30 34 277 17 55 288 35 17	46 30 37 97 18 03 108 35 25	C–297 C–296 S–311	124. 7 248. 1 249. 6	2. 09573 2. 39461 2. 39732
Ref. Mon. C–175	47 27 25. 32 69 12 42. 98	308 56 04 334 51 43	128 56 11 154 51 47	C–297 S–312	270. 6 282. 6	2. 43235 2. 45122
S–313	47 27 17. 69 69 12 44. 89	189 38 13 255 21 32 277 14 59	9 38 14 75 21 40 97 15 04	Ref. Mon. C–175 C–297 S–312	238. 9 258. 9 161. 3	2. 37816 2. 41312 2. 20774
Ref. Mon. S–167	47 27 21. 60 69 13 03. 45	255 00 33 287 14 06	75 00 48 107 14 20	Ref. Mon. C–175 S–313	444. 0 407. 2	2. 64739 2. 60982
C–299	47 27 33. 56 69 12 59. 35	13 05 14 135 30 41 306 34 59 328 16 12	193 05 11 315 30 27 126 35 11 148 16 23	Ref. Mon. S–167 Ref. Mon. C–176 Ref. Mon. C–175 S–313	379. 3 582. 0 427. 2 576. 2	2. 57896 2. 76490 2. 63060 2. 76058
S–315 (Boundary Lake east base).	47 27 23. 35 69 13 17. 26	177 26 15 229 56 23 280 34 04	357 26 14 49 56 36 100 34 14	Ref. Mon. C–176 C–299 Ref. Mon. S–167	731. 3 490. 2 294. 3	2. 86412 2. 69034 2. 46877
C–300	47 27 40. 87 69 13 15. 78	3 17 21 161 24 14 303 14 56 336 32 30	183 17 20 341 24 12 123 15 08 156 32 39	S–315 Ref. Mon. C–176 C–299 Ref. Mon. S–167	541. 9 200. 0 411. 4 648. 6	2. 73394 2. 30108 2. 61428 2. 81198
S–316 (Boundary Lake west base).	47 27 30. 06 69 13 30. 73	205 28 09 223 09 47 260 38 24 306 17 41	25 28 18 43 09 58 80 38 47 126 17 51	Ref. Mon. C–176 C–300 C–299 S–315	579. 8 457. 7 666. 1 349. 96	2. 76328 2. 66061 2. 82352 2. 54402
Mon. 178	47 27 34. 80 69 13 31. 39	214 54 43 240 10 42 273 15 26 320 05 26 354 38 21	34 54 52 60 10 53 93 15 49 140 05 36 174 38 21	Ref. Mon. C–176 C–300 C–299 S–315 S–316	459. 7 376. 8 672. 0 461. 1 147. 2	2. 66244 2. 57607 2. 82739 2. 66376 2. 16777
Mon. 181	47 27 13. 78 69 13 53. 02	214 54 27 222 52 37 241 27 58 248 27 27	34 54 52 42 52 53 61 28 37 68 27 53	Ref. Mon. C–176 S–316 C–299 S–315	1, 251. 4 686. 1 1, 279. 4 805. 2	3. 09740 2. 83638 3. 10702 2. 90588
REFERENCE MONUMENTS DETERMINED FROM MINOR SCHEME, ST. JOHN AND ST. FRANCIS RIVERS						
Mon. 117	47 03 57. 98 67 47 27. 12					
Ref. Mon. C–1	47 04 05. 58 67 47 20. 43	31 02 09 99 59 36	211 02 04 279 59 10	Mon. 117 Ref. Mon. S–2	273. 9 772. 9	2. 43764 2. 88813

SOURCE OF ST. CROIX RIVER TO LAKE POHENAGAMOOK—Continued

Station	Latitude and longitude	Azimuth	Back azimuth	To station	Distance (meters)	Logarithm
REFERENCE MONUMENTS DETERMINED FROM MINOR SCHEME, ST. JOHN AND ST. FRANCIS RIVERS—con.	° ′ ″	° ′ ″	° ′ ″			
Ref. Mon. S–1	47 04 00. 26	236 04 21	56 04 30	Ref. Mon. C–1	294. 6	2. 46929
	67 47 32. 02	304 14 00	124 14 04	Mon. 117	124. 9	2. 09655
Ref. Mon. C–2	47 04 18. 19	19 02 48	199 02 45	Ref. Mon. S–2	270. 0	2. 43138
	67 47 52. 33	87 38 48	267 38 27	Ref. Mon. S–3	607. 4	2. 78346
Ref. Mon. C–4	47 04 38. 10	39 34 48	219 34 42	Ref. Mon. S–4	270. 8	2. 43262
	67 48 38. 15	106 50 02	286 49 47	Ref. Mon. S–5	446. 7	2. 65003
Ref. Mon. C–5	47 04 54. 33	10 02 09	190 02 07	Ref. Mon. S–5	377. 6	2. 57708
	67 48 55. 30	81 20 15	261 19 56	Ref. Mon. S–6	538. 7	2. 73136
		102 57 49	282 56 31	Ref. Mon. S–7	1, 061. 5	3. 02593
Ref. Mon. C–6	47 05 08. 82	59 58 06	239 57 53	Ref. Mon. S–7	418. 8	2. 62200
	67 49 27. 16	345 13 38	165 13 43	Ref. Mon. S–6	546. 8	2. 73781
Ref. Mon. C–7	47 05 18. 75	199 33 44	19 33 46	C–7	150. 32	2. 17702
	67 50 15. 41					
Ref. Mon. C–8	47 05 39. 03	53 30 38	233 29 16	Ref. Mon. S–9	786. 4	2. 89565
	67 50 46. 05	99 50 20	279 48 35	Ref. Mon. S–10	1, 440. 5	3. 15851
		341 45 39	161 44 49	Ref. Mon. S–8	956. 7	2. 98079
Ref. Mon. 119	47 05 34. 68	34 58 26	214 58 18	Ref. Mon. S–9	407. 0	2. 60963
	67 51 04. 96	251 24 33	71 24 47	Ref. Mon. C–8	420. 9	2. 62415
Ref. Mon. C–9	47 06 01. 94	19 17 55	199 17 49	Ref. Mon. S–10	489. 4	2. 68964
	67 51 45. 68	331 58 17	151 58 39	Ref. Mon. S–9	1, 331. 4	3. 12432
Ref. Mon. C–10	47 06 05. 16	48 53 34	228 53 24	Ref. Mon. S–11	397. 8	2. 59966
	67 52 03. 96	321 34 15	141 34 50	Ref. Mon. S–9	1, 627. 2	3. 21144
Ref. Mon. C–12	47 06 19. 58	5 42 28	185 42 26	Ref. Mon. S–12	501. 8	2. 70052
	67 52 55. 60	48 08 28	228 08 16	Ref. Mon. S–13	442. 5	2. 64593
Ref. Mon. C–13	47 06 30. 62	103 03 55	283 03 40	Ref. Mon. S–15	429. 2	2. 63270
	67 53 06. 49	347 55 51	167 55 57	Ref. Mon. S–12	859. 1	2. 93403
Ref. Mon. C–14	47 06 37. 73	65 17 16	245 17 07	Ref. Mon. S–15	293. 3	2. 46725
	67 53 13. 68	150 43 46	330 43 34	Ref. Mon. S–16	711. 6	2. 85223
Ref. Mon. C–15	47 06 54. 77	107 11 48	287 11 37	Ref. Mon. S–16	320. 0	2. 50511
	67 53 15. 68	145 25 17	325 24 59	Ref. Mon. S–17	922. 8	2. 96510
Ref. Mon. C–16	47 07 22. 18	19 18 20	199 18 11	Ref. Mon. S–16	796. 7	2. 90131
	67 53 17. 69	79 47 08	259 46 51	Ref. Mon. S–17	489. 2	2. 68949
		136 01 32	316 01 03	Ref. Mon. S–18	1, 207. 3	3. 08183
Ref. Mon. 120	47 07 31. 93	25 26 07	205 26 01	Ref. Mon. S–17	429. 4	2. 63288
	67 53 31. 78	136 22 04	316 21 45	Ref. Mon. S–18	784. 5	2. 89459
Ref. Mon. C–18	47 08 14. 95	45 48 35	225 48 24	Ref. Mon. S–19	446. 6	2. 64991
	67 54 00. 04	127 29 01	307 28 38	Ref. Mon. S–20	841. 6	2. 92511
Ref. Mon. C–19	47 08 31. 47	90 18 30	270 18 17	Ref. Mon. S–20	366. 4	2. 56396
	67 54 14. 34	126 46 07	306 45 38	Ref. Mon. S–21	1, 039. 1	3. 01667
Ref. Mon. C–20	47 09 00. 12	45 57 08	225 56 58	Ref. Mon. S–21	377. 9	2. 57740
	67 54 40. 96	347 34 41	167 34 48	Ref. Mon. S–20	903. 9	2. 95612
Ref. Mon. C–21	47 09 23. 09	37 09 10	217 08 59	Ref. Mon. S–22	522. 6	2. 71821
	67 55 22. 82	89 05 42	269 05 19	Ref. Mon. S–23	665. 0	2. 82282
		120 24 46	300 24 30	Ref. Mon. C–22	542. 4	2. 73435

SOURCE OF ST. CROIX RIVER TO LAKE POHENAGAMOOK—Continued

Station	Latitude and longitude	Azimuth	Back azimuth	To station	Distance (meters)	Loga-rithm
REFERENCE MONU-MENTS DETER-MINED FROM MINOR SCHEME, ST. JOHN AND ST. FRAN-CIS RIVERS—con.	° ′ ″	° ′ ″	° ′ ″			
Ref. Mon. C–23_____	47 09 52. 96	60 20 13	240 19 59	Ref. Mon. S–24___	475. 4	2. 67710
	67 55 59. 14	353 51 39	173 51 43	Ref. Mon. S–23___	938. 3	2. 97235
Van Buren highway bridge Boundary Point.	47 09 35. 37	3 04 07	183 04 06	Ref. Mon. S–23___	390. 2	2. 59134
	67 55 53. 39	300 41 34	120 41 40	Ref. Mon. C–22___	204. 9	2. 31151
Ref. Mon. S–25_____	47 10 01. 60	295 48 14	115 48 33	Ref. Mon. C–23___	612. 9	2. 78742
	67 56 25. 34	344 33 28	164 33 33	Ref. Mon. S–24___	521. 0	2. 71680
Ref. Mon. C–24_____	47 10 17. 24	69 07 02	249 06 51	Ref. Mon. S–26___	348. 0	2. 54160
	67 56 16. 71	149 36 09	329 35 52	Ref. Mon. C–26___	943. 3	2. 97466
Ref. Mon. C–25_____	47 10 37. 94	118 36 14	298 35 48	Ref. Mon. S–29___	838. 2	2. 92335
	67 56 33. 93	146 36 50	326 36 46	Ref. Mon. C–26___	208. 5	2. 31916
Keegan railroad bridge Boundary Point.	47 10 30. 16	131 39 04	311 38 39	Ref. Mon. S–29___	965. 3	2. 98468
	67 56 34. 63	166 24 52	346 24 54	Ref. Mon. C–26___	426. 3	2. 62974
		183 28 53	3 28 54	Ref. Mon. C–25___	240. 7	2. 38153
Ref. Mon. C–27_____	47 10 55. 89	7 05 51	187 06 57	Ref. Mon. S–28___	661. 7	2. 82064
	67 56 51. 39	67 25 12	247 24 59	Ref. Mon. S–29___	398. 8	2. 60079
		114 20 27	294 20 04	Ref. Mon. S–30___	712. 6	2. 85284
Ref. Mon. C–28_____	47 11 15. 13	17 29 20	197 29 12	Ref. Mon. S–29___	783. 6	2. 89407
	67 56 57. 69	59 48 22	239 48 04	Ref. Mon. S–30___	597. 5	2. 77636
Ref. Mon. 123_____	47 12 03. 42	74 47 25	254 47 02	Ref. Mon. S–32___	671. 0	2. 82673
	67 57 56. 43	152 03 19	332 03 09	Ref. Mon. C–30___	577. 5	2. 76155
Ref. Mon. S–31 ecc__	47 11 46. 12	149 46 33	329 46 22	Ref. Mon. 123____	618. 3	2. 79122
	67 57 41. 64	258 43 33	78 43 53	Ref. Mon. C–29___	602. 9	2. 78026
Ref. Mon. S–31_____	47 11 46. 11	258 43 53	78 43 53	Ref. Mon. S–31ecc_	1. 76	0. 2448
	67 57 41. 72					
Ref. Mon. 122_____	47 11 54. 05	34 41 32	214 41 26	Ref. Mon. S–31ecc_	298. 0	2. 47423
	67 57 33. 58	121 01 43	301 01 26	Ref. Mon. 123____	561. 2	2. 74908
		286 46 58	106 47 12	Ref. Mon. C–29___	440. 4	2. 64388
Ref. Mon. 121_____	47 11 42. 52	141 13 29	321 13 19	Ref. Mon. 122____	456. 9	2. 65980
	67 57 19. 99	210 37 17	30 37 22	Ref. Mon. C–29___	266. 1	2. 42505
Ref. Mon. C–31_____	47 12 30. 65	10 37 03	190 36 59	Ref. Mon. S–33___	631. 8	2. 80055
	67 58 40. 26	108 45 00	288 44 43	Ref. Mon. C–32___	521. 2	2. 71697
Ref. Mon. S–34_____	47 12 23. 09	122 52 02	302 51 50	Ref. Mon. S–35___	424. 0	2. 62737
	67 59 18. 25	217 20 58	37 21 09	Ref. Mon. C–32___	504. 4	2. 70274
Ref. Mon. C–34_____	47 13 06. 17	37 27 37	217 27 26	Ref. Mon. S–36___	522. 7	2. 71827
	67 59 52. 08	342 04 32	162 04 44	Ref. Mon. S–35___	1, 156. 5	3. 06315
Ref. Mon. 124_____	47 12 58. 41	43 56 12	223 56 06	Ref. Mon. S–36___	243. 3	2. 38611
	67 59 59. 17	329 35 35	149 35 53	Ref. Mon. S–35___	997. 9	2. 99908
Ref. Mon. C–35____	47 13 32. 80	205 54 00	25 54 00	C–35_____	28. 19	1. 45086
	68 00 14. 93					
Ref. Mon. 126_____	47 13 31. 67	263 44 30	83 44 41	Ref. Mon. C–35___	320. 5	2. 50586
	68 00 30. 07	353 42 21	173 42 23	Ref. Mon. S–37___	509. 4	2. 70702
Ref. Mon. C–36_____	47 14 07. 41	76 34 49	256 34 29	Ref. Mon. S–38___	598. 6	2. 77713
	68 00 54. 95	137 35 12	317 34 37	Ref. Mon. C–37___	1, 497. 5	3. 17536

SOURCE OF ST. CROIX RIVER TO LAKE POHENAGAMOOK—Continued

Station	Latitude and longitude	Azimuth	Back azimuth	To station	Distance (meters)	Logarithm
REFERENCE MONUMENTS DETERMINED FROM MINOR SCHEME, ST. JOHN AND ST.FRANCIS RIVERS—con.	° ′ ″	° ′ ″	° ′ ″			
Ref. Mon. C–38	47 15 05. 79 68 02 35. 13	61 35 34 101 03 37	241 35 13 281 02 49	Ref. Mon. S–40 Ref. Mon. S–41	670. 5 1, 387. 9	2. 82641 3. 14235
Ref. Mon. 128	47 15 14. 83 68 03 14. 22	88 37 33 338 47 11	268 37 14 158 47 19	Ref. Mon. S–41 Ref. Mon. S–40	540. 4 641. 6	2. 73270 2. 80724
Ref. Mon. C–40	47 15 57. 50 68 04 36. 53	38 25 15 116 24 58	218 24 49 296 23 23	Ref. Mon. S–42 Ref. Mon. S–43	1, 217. 9 3, 039. 1	3. 08560 3. 48275
Ref. Mon. 130	47 15 58. 58 68 05 02. 76	11 44 44 121 16 33	191 44 37 301 15 17	Ref. Mon. S–42 Ref. Mon. S–43	1, 008. 7 2, 539. 6	3. 00376 3. 40476
Ref. Mon. C–42	47 17 20. 21 68 07 10. 65	44 03 26 108 12 53	224 03 07 288 11 43	Ref. Mon. S–44 Ref. Mon. S–45	789. 1 2, 103. 1	2. 89713 3. 32287
Ref. Mon. 134	47 17 27. 69 68 07 40. 01	107 09 48 355 06 38	287 09 00 175 06 40	Ref. Mon. S–45 Ref. Mon. S–44	1, 445. 3 800. 8	3. 15996 2. 90350
Ref. Mon. C–46	47 19 49. 01 68 10 35. 60	52 39 10 117 19 59	232 38 56 297 19 50	Ref. Mon. S–49 Ref. Mon. C–47	514. 4 276. 4	2. 71130 2. 44159
Ref. Mon. 134–A	47 21 11. 70 68 15 27. 44	59 21 17 181 08 06	239 20 41 1 08 06	Ref. Mon. S–54 Ref. Mon. C–52	1, 187. 6 632. 3	3. 07467 2. 80093
Ref. Mon. C–51	47 21 37. 45 68 14 33. 57	26 28 07 56 57 05	206 27 48 236 55 50	Ref. Mon. S–53 Ref. Mon. S–54	1, 211. 0 2, 568. 1	3. 08316 3. 40961
Ref. Mon. C–56	47 21 42. 67 68 19 44. 45	351 49 13	171 49 13	C–56	14. 98	1. 17554
Ref. Mon. 136	47 21 24. 01 68 18 20. 67	3 28 28 226 52 43	183 28 27 46 52 54	Ref. Mon. S–56 Ref. Mon. C–54	577. 3 428. 3	2. 76139 2. 63170
Ref. Mon. 138	47 21 28. 76 68 18 11. 52	17 27 06 313 13 36	197 26 58 133 14 12	Ref. Mon. S–56 Ref. Mon. S–55	757. 6 1, 414. 8	2. 87945 3. 15069
Ref. Mon. C–57	47 21 39. 55 68 21 01. 09	13 07 13 336 23 36	193 07 06 156 23 48	Ref. Mon. S–60 Ref. Mon. S–59	866. 9 833. 6	2. 93797 2. 92096
Ref. Mon. C–58	47 21 30. 14 68 21 15. 38	45 55 54 306 44 49 349 27 27	225 55 17 126 45 10 169 27 31	Ref. Mon. S–61 Ref. Mon. S–59 Ref. Mon. S–60	1, 461. 9 790. 8 563. 0	3. 16493 2. 89805 2. 75054
Ref. Mon. 139	47 17 08. 45 68 22 51. 85	43 40 31 306 39 25	223 39 57 126 39 41	Ref. Mon. S–70 Ref. Mon. S–69	1, 398. 7 582. 5	3. 14573 2. 76527
Ref. Mon. 140	47 17 06. 15 68 23 40. 19	280 33 22 356 57 31	100 34 14 176 57 33	Ref. Mon. S–69 Ref. Mon. S–70	1, 508. 6 941. 8	3. 17856 2. 97398
Ref. Mon. 142	47 17 02. 45 68 23 53. 68	177 26 43 275 14 31 338 01 23	357 26 41 95 15 33 158 01 35	Ref. Mon. C–66 Ref. Mon. S–69 Ref. Mon. S–70	1, 355. 0 1, 773. 9 891. 0	3. 13193 3. 24893 2. 94989
Ref. Mon. 141	47 17 09. 20 68 23 48. 18	28 57 51 348 06 09	208 57 47 168 06 17	Ref. Mon. 142 Ref. Mon. S–70	238. 3 1, 057. 5	2. 37715 3. 02428
Ref. Mon. 144	47 17 10. 99 68 27 32. 41	3 11 12 296 24 41	183 11 11 116 25 47	Ref. Mon. S–73 Ref. Mon. S–72	337. 4 2, 114. 8	2. 52809 3. 32527
Ref. Mon. 143	47 17 07. 84 68 27 16. 19	56 19 32 105 55 49	236 19 19 285 55 37	Ref. Mon. S–73 Ref. Mon. 144	432. 2 354. 5	2. 63564 2. 54959
Ref. Mon. 145	47 17 53. 33 68 28 51. 66	30 06 58 71 27 07	210 06 42 251 26 13	Ref. Mon. S–75 Ref. Mon. S–76	910. 6 1, 613. 6	2. 95933 3. 20780

SOURCE OF ST. CROIX RIVER TO LAKE POHENAGAMOOK—Continued

Station	Latitude and longitude	Azimuth	Back azimuth	To station	Distance (meters)	Logarithm
REFERENCE MONUMENTS DETERMINED FROM MINOR SCHEME, ST. JOHN AND ST. FRANCIS RIVERS—con.	° ′ ″	° ′ ″	° ′ ″			
Ref. Mon. 146	47 18 07. 11 68 29 26. 37	40 27 00 221 09 15 347 20 49	220 26 32 41 09 27 167 20 59	Ref. Mon. S–76 Ref. Mon. C–71 Ref. Mon. S–75	1, 233. 9 508. 1 1, 243. 4	3. 09128 2. 70598 3. 09462
Ref. Mon. 147	47 17 46. 17 68 29 02. 41	22 11 17 77 22 11	202 11 09 257 21 25	Ref. Mon. S–75 Ref. Mon. S–76	611. 8 1, 336. 3	2. 78664 3. 12590
Ref. Mon. 149	47 17 51. 98 68 29 59. 68	12 02 53 307 29 33	192 02 49 127 30 07	Ref. Mon. S–76 Ref. Mon. S–75	482. 3 1, 225. 4	2. 68335 3. 08827
Ref. Mon. 151	47 17 56. 98 68 30 18. 50	28 13 31 334 47 46	208 13 21 154 47 56	Ref. Mon. S–77 Ref. Mon. S–76	602. 8 692. 3	2. 78016 2. 84030
Ref. Mon. 151–A	47 17 51. 20 68 30 20. 36	34 54 22 323 18 22	214 54 14 143 18 34	Ref. Mon. S–77 Ref. Mon. S–76	430. 0 558. 7	2. 63350 2. 74714
Ref. Mon. 153	47 17 52. 01 68 30 32. 20	309 03 19 359 34 20	129 03 39 179 34 20	Ref. Mon. S–76 Ref. Mon. S–77	750. 4 377. 6	2. 87529 2. 57698
Ref. Mon. S–90	47 14 41. 01 68 36 18. 14	80 24 43	260 24 41	S–90	45. 80	1. 66086
Ref. Mon. 154	47 14 16. 43 68 39 38. 19	55 52 52 298 42 21	235 52 14 118 42 32	Ref. Mon. S–96 Ref. Mon. S–95	1, 321. 9 358. 1	3, 12120 2. 55402
Ref. Mon. 155	47 14 23. 37 68 40 00. 00	33 37 41 296 33 00	213 37 19 116 33 27	Ref. Mon. S–96 Ref. Mon. S–95	1, 147. 8 863. 9	3. 05986 2. 93645
Ref. Mon. 156	47 14 32. 38 68 43 00. 23	288 17 16 339 38 31	108 18 04 159 38 36	Ref. Mon. S–97 Ref. Mon. S–98	1, 445. 5 406. 5	3. 16003 2. 60903
Ref. Mon. 157	47 14 42. 27 68 43 23. 27	177 01 35 317 38 47	357 01 34 137 39 09	Ref. Mon. C–92 Ref. Mon. S–98	459. 4 928. 9	2. 66217 2. 96798
Ref. Mon. 158	47 14 27. 41 68 43 24. 62	94 00 13 180 17 06	273 59 06 0 17 06	Ref. Mon. C–94 Ref. Mon. C–92	1, 916. 9 917. 6	3. 28261 2. 96266
Ref. Mon. 159	47 14 29. 44 68 43 47. 01	184 52 29 209 05 20	4 52 31 29 05 36	Ref. Mon. C–93 Ref. Mon. C–92	689. 1 978. 2	2. 83826 2. 99041
Ref. Mon. 159–A	47 14 18. 97 68 43 33. 27	102 51 03 167 09 14 267 43 13	282 50 04 347 09 06 87 43 42	Ref. Mon. C–94 Ref. Mon. C–93 Ref. Mon. S–98	1, 774. 6 1, 036. 2 837. 0	3. 24910 3. 01546 2. 92271
Ref. Mon. 159–B	47 14 16. 64 68 43 31. 67	104 49 12 166 16 49	284 48 11 346 16 40	Ref. Mon. C–94 Ref. Mon. C–93	1, 824. 7 1, 114. 1	3. 26119 3. 04693
Ref. Mon. 160	47 14 14. 30 68 44 06. 66	117 39 32 202 13 25	297 38 56 22 13 41	Ref. Mon. C–94 Ref. Mon. C–93	1, 160. 6 1, 247. 2	3. 06468 3. 09593
Ref. Mon. 161	47 14 04. 95 68 44 31. 42	148 29 26 214 30 52	328 29 08 34 31 27	Ref. Mon. C–94 Ref. Mon. C–93	970. 4 1, 751. 5	2. 98696 3. 24342
Ref. Mon. 162	47 13 58. 88 68 44 14. 79	139 48 55 210 30 07	319 48 25 30 30 44	Ref. Mon. C–94 Ref. Mon. C–92	1, 328. 2 2, 087. 7	3. 12327 3. 31967
Ref. Mon. 163	47 13 45. 50 68 44 35. 08	163 13 55 207 37 07	343 13 40 27 37 44	Ref. Mon. C–94 Ref. Mon. C–93	1, 491. 4 2, 306. 7	3. 17358 3. 36299
Ref. Mon. 163–A	47 13 23. 51 68 46 45. 96	51 55 31 285 44 16	231 54 37 105 44 53	Ref. Mon. S–104 Ref. Mon. S–102	1, 976. 1 1, 109. 2	3. 29580 3. 04500
Ref. Mon. 164	47 12 55. 01 68 48 00. 88	135 28 50 356 27 15	315 28 38 176 27 16	Ref. Mon. C–98 Ref. Mon. S–104	496. 7 339. 4	2. 69608 2. 53070

SOURCE OF ST. CROIX RIVER TO LAKE POHENAGAMOOK—Continued

Station	Latitude and longitude	Azimuth	Back azimuth	To station	Distance (meters)	Logarithm
REFERENCE MONUMENTS DETERMINED FROM MINOR SCHEME, ST. JOHN AND ST. FRANCIS RIVERS—con.	° ′ ″	° ′ ″	° ′ ″			
Ref. Mon. 165	47 12 43. 79	181 03 39	1 03 39	Ref. Mon. C–98	700. 8	2. 84558
	68 48 18. 05	268 49 52	88 50 05	Ref. Mon. S–104	382. 3	2. 58245
Ref. Mon. 166	47 12 51. 37	214 34 38	34 34 49	Ref. Mon. C–98	566. 6	2. 75326
	68 48 32. 71	288 08 21	108 08 45	Ref. Mon. S–104	727. 0	2. 86153
Ref. Mon. 167	47 12 49. 65	229 08 18	49 08 39	Ref. Mon. C–98	794. 7	2. 90019
	68 48 45. 99	280 06 13	100 06 47	Ref. Mon. S–104	985. 6	2. 99372
Ref. Mon. 168	47 12 36. 27	210 32 32	30 32 51	Ref. Mon. C–98	1, 083. 2	3. 03471
	68 48 43. 59	255 22 15	75 22 47	Ref. Mon. S–104	950. 6	2. 97801
Ref. Mon. 169	47 12 16. 94	21 14 05	201 13 58	Ref. Mon. S–106	529. 1	2. 72354
	68 49 39. 50	120 38 00	300 37 44	Ref. Mon. C–100	534. 2	2. 72774
Ref. Mon. 170	47 11 08. 66	190 35 20	10 35 22	Ref. Mon. C–105	298. 4	2. 47473
	68 52 52. 50	235 03 16	55 03 55	Ref. Mon. C–104	1, 380. 0	3. 13989
Ref. Mon. 171	47 10 53. 58	15 27 07	195 26 52	Ref. Mon. S–113	1, 602. 2	3. 20472
	68 53 15. 85	148 09 45	328 09 41	Ref. Mon. C–106	221. 1	2. 34465
Ref. Mon. 172	47 10 43. 82	7 50 18	187 50 13	Ref. Mon. S–113	1, 254. 7	3. 09854
	68 53 27. 99	195 51 59	15 52 04	Ref. Mon. C–106	508. 5	2. 70631
		288 32 03	108 32 33	Ref. Mon. S–112	896. 3	2. 95245
Ref. Mon. 173	47 10 54. 76	234 25 03	54 25 10	Ref. Mon. C–106	260. 1	2. 41519
	68 53 31. 44	304 01 25	124 01 57	Ref. Mon. S–112	1, 112. 9	3. 04644
Ref. Mon. 175	47 10 48. 73	247 54 22	67 54 51	Ref. Mon. C–106	897. 4	2. 95297
	68 54 00. 88	339 29 51	159 30 09	Ref. Mon. S–113	1, 489. 0	3. 17290
Ref. Mon. S–115	47 10 44. 89	247 35 24	67 36 02	Ref. Mon. C–106	1, 196. 3	3. 07785
	68 54 13. 92	279 55 26	99 56 29	Ref. Mon. S–112	1, 844. 5	3. 26587
Ref. Mon. C–107	47 11 16. 09	106 31 51	286 31 19	S–116	963. 8	2. 98397
	68 54 48. 64	189 22 14	9 22 20	C–109	1, 011. 2	3. 00482
Ref. Mon. S–116	47 11 15. 77	108 56 39	288 56 10	S–116	875. 2	2. 94209
	68 54 53. 21	194 30 43	14 30 52	C–109	1, 040. 8	3. 01736
		264 07 01	84 07 04	Ref. Mon. C–107	96. 7	1. 98538
Ref. Mon. C–108	47 11 53. 47	2 38 58	182 38 56	S–116	881. 3	2. 94513
	68 55 30. 59	191 42 27	11 42 33	C–110	936. 5	2. 97152
		278 30 33	98 31 09	C–109	1, 059. 4	3. 02506
Ref. Mon. S–117	47 11 48. 57	196 27 18	16 27 29	C–110	1, 114. 1	3. 04691
	68 55 36. 56	219 40 20	39 40 25	Ref. Mon. C–108	196. 7	2. 29377
		270 15 39	90 16 20	C–109	1, 173. 3	3. 06941
Ref. Mon. C–109	47 12 16. 38	93 55 36	273 53 50	S–118	3, 048. 0	3. 48402
	68 56 12. 65	131 05 01	311 04 18	C–111	1, 630. 0	3. 21218
		294 05 00	114 06 07	C–109	2, 117. 3	3. 32578
Ref. Mon. S–118	47 12 11. 30	209 22 15	29 22 18	Ref. Mon. C–109	180. 0	2. 25533
	68 56 16. 84	289 16 50	109 18 00	C–109	2, 141. 4	3. 33070
Ref. Mon. C–110	47 12 20. 10	92 40 14	272 39 04	S–118	2, 005. 3	3. 30218
	68 57 01. 96	168 42 17	348 42 10	C–111	975. 1	2. 98903
		288 13 42	108 15 25	C–109	3, 127. 9	3. 49525
Ref. Mon. S–119	47 12 10. 60	218 02 56	38 03 04	Ref. Mon. C–110	372. 6	2. 57122
	68 57 12. 87	261 58 32	81 59 16	Ref. Mon. C–109	1, 280. 0	3. 10720
		282 04 43	102 06 34	C–109	3, 273. 0	3. 51495

SOURCE OF ST. CROIX RIVER TO LAKE POHENAGAMOOK—Continued

Station	Latitude and longitude	Azimuth	Back azimuth	To station	Distance (meters)	Loga-rithm
REFERENCE MONU-MENTS DETER-MINED FROM MINOR SCHEME, ST. JOHN AND ST. FRAN-CIS RIVERS—con.	° ′ ″	° ′ ″	° ′ ″			
Ref. Mon. C–111____	47 12 50. 10	41 03 35	221 03 10	S–118_____	1, 105. 1	3. 04340
	68 58 02. 65	89 54 50	269 53 46	S–119_____	1, 852. 9	3. 26785
		155 53 29	335 53 03	C–112_____	1, 884. 7	3. 27525
Ref. Mon. S–120____	47 12 43. 13	168 36 34	348 36 21	C–112_____	1, 974. 4	3. 29544
	68 58 20. 71	240 28 14	60 28 27	Ref. Mon. C–111__	436. 8	2. 64024
		260 30 21	80 31 12	C–111_____	1, 486. 4	3. 17215
Ref. Mon. C–112____	47 13 12. 87	60 20 39	240 19 56	S–119_____	1, 427. 6	3. 15462
	68 58 31. 74	134 21 40	314 20 25	C–113_____	2, 996. 7	3. 47664
		171 10 50	351 10 45	C–112_____	1, 029. 0	3. 01243
Ref. Mon. C–113____	47 14 04. 72	14 44 51	194 44 40	S–120_____	1, 158. 2	3. 06378
	69 00 34. 48	103 53 55	283 52 59	Ref. Mon. S–122__	1, 651. 8	3. 21797
		110 54 01	290 52 56	C–114_____	1, 997. 5	3. 30049
Ref. Mon. S–121____	47 13 41. 47	163 33 15	343 33 07	Ref. Mon. C–113__	748. 4	2. 87411
	69 00 24. 41	266 31 57	86 33 14	C–112_____	2, 216. 3	3. 34563
		290 25 31	110 26 53	Ref. Mon. C–112__	2, 529. 5	3. 40303
Ref. Mon. S–124____	47 15 04. 75	235 46 20	55 46 21	S–125_____	16. 47	1. 21673
	69 02 49. 78					
Ref. Mon. C–116____	47 15 44. 37	63 19 28	243 19 24	S–129_____	135. 0	2. 13031
	69 02 58. 58	163 15 32	343 15 31	S–130_____	48. 2	1. 68331
		231 35 34	51 35 40	C–124_____	244. 7	2. 38857
Ref. Mon. S–126____	47 16 03. 26	301 51 02	121 51 03	S–133_____	18. 08	1. 25720
	69 02 55. 07					
Ref. Mon. C–118 ___	47 16 26. 41	33 39 54	213 39 53	S–138_____	66. 2	1. 82060
	69 02 54. 71	148 16 48	328 16 47	S–139_____	67. 2	1. 82740
		164 25 55	344 25 55	C–134_____	52. 5	1. 72015
Ref. Mon. S–134____	47 19 41. 75	329 05 03	149 05 04	S–166_____	56. 20	1. 74972
	69 03 34. 78					
Ref. Mon. C–126____	47 18 56. 42	75 36 16	255 36 15	C–156_____	20. 20	1. 30529
	69 03 00. 40					
Ref. Mon. S–135____	47 20 36. 42	248 33 40	68 33 41	S–167_____	35. 10	1. 54536
	69 03 40. 14					
Ref. Mon. C–127____	47 19 33. 34	129 02 21	309 02 21	C–158_____	18. 79	1. 27404
	69 03 00. 84					
Ref. Mon. S–136____	47 21 39. 14	258 25 02	78 25 03	S–168_____	23. 95	1. 37931
	69 03 39. 56					
Ref. Mon. C–128____	47 20 18. 57	59 39 36	239 39 35	C–159_____	19. 94	1. 29966
	69 02 54. 19					
Ref. Mon. S–137____	47 22 01. 06	270 31 53	90 31 54	S–169_____	28. 25	1. 45102
	69 03 43. 36					
Ref. Mon. C–129____	47 21 53. 69	87 29 21	267 29 20	C–161_____	19. 79	1. 29645
	69 02 56. 27					
Ref. Mon. S–143____	47 24 25. 96	230 57 46	50 57 56	Ref. Mon. C–143__	347. 3	2. 54069
	69 02 09. 97	237 39 36	57 39 49	C–177_____	436. 4	2. 63990
		290 51 04	110 51 11	Ref. Mon. S–142__	203. 7	2. 30889
Ref. Mon. S–148____	47 25 34. 93	184 22 29	4 22 29	S–211_____	8. 57	0. 93298
	69 03 06. 47					

SOURCE OF ST. CROIX RIVER TO LAKE POHENAGAMOOK—Continued

Station	Latitude and longitude	Azimuth	Back azimuth	To station	Distance (meters)	Logarithm
REFERENCE MONU-MENTS DETER-MINED FROM MINOR SCHEME, ST. JOHN AND ST. FRAN-CIS RIVERS—con.	° ′ ″	° ′ ″	° ′ ″			
Ref. Mon. C–144____	47 24 38. 76 69 02 07. 81	190 13 06 273 52 38 288 27 04	10 13 08 93 52 48 108 27 12	S–192_____ C–178_____ S–190_____	213. 7 278. 7 229. 4	2. 32976 2. 44506 2. 36065
Ref. Mon. C–152____	47 25 50. 65 69 03 16. 97	10 20 53 10 57 28 339 49 49	190 20 53 190 57 27 159 49 52	Ref. Mon. C–153__ S–214_____ C–197_____	139. 0 204. 5 237. 7	2. 14307 2. 31071 2. 37595
Ref. Mon. S–154 ___	47 25 28. 41 69 05 15. 59	173 48 58	353 48 58	S–228_____	15. 83	1. 19954
Ref. Mon. S–164____	47 27 20. 85 69 10 57. 73	178 31 00	358 31 00	S–291_____	20. 14	1. 30396
Ref. Mon. S–165____	47 27 11. 77 69 11 24. 56	143 50 43	323 50 42	S–297_____	30. 98	1. 49115
Ref. Mon. C–171____	47 27 30. 88 69 10 45. 90	15 02 31	195 02 30	C–275_____	100. 55	2. 00239
Ref. Mon. C–172____	47 27 24. 04 69 11 08. 84	324 24 09	144 24 09	C–280_____	18. 31	1. 26259
Mon. 179_____	47 27 32. 37 69 13 33. 88	214 54 41 267 05 29 317 18 35	34 54 43 87 05 54 137 18 37	Mon. 178_____ C–299_____ S–316_____	91. 4 724. 2 97. 4	1. 96076 2. 85984 1. 98854
Mon. 180_____	47 27 29. 93 69 13 36. 40	214 54 39 231 58 20 261 46 37	34 54 41 51 58 35 81 47 04	Mon. 179_____ C–300_____ C–299_____	91. 9 548. 1 783. 9	1. 96336 2. 73887 2. 89426
Mon. 180–A_____	47 27 26. 17 69 13 40. 27	34 54 36 214 54 36 255 04 46 280 15 11	214 54 27 34 54 39 75 05 16 100 15 28	Mon. 181_____ Mon. 180_____ C–299_____ S–315_____	466. 8 141. 7 886. 8 489. 6	2. 66909 2. 15140 2. 94784 2. 68987
POINTS SUPPLEMEN-TARY TO MINOR SCHEME, ST. JOHN RIVER						
Chapel of St. Joseph and St. Anthelm, spire, near Ham-lin, Me., 1909.	47 04 12. 98 67 48 25. 30	141 57 17 213 08 53 290 36 22	321 57 02 33 08 56 110 36 24	Ref. Mon. S–4_____ Ref. Mon. S–3____ Ref. Mon. S–1____	720. 1 162. 3 1, 309. 7	2. 85738 2. 21020 3. 11716
St. Leonard, New Brunswick, L'Eglise Church, spire, southeast of village, 1909.	47 08 51. 05 67 54 29. 12	5 12 43 91 54 27 348 23 59	185 12 41 271 54 08 168 24 09	Ref. Mon. S–20___ Ref. Mon. S–21___ Ref. Mon. S–19___	605. 2 521. 3 1, 455. 8	2. 78187 2. 71709 3. 16310
Van Buren, Me., customhouse, flagpole, 1909.	47 09 20. 86 67 56 03. 47	156 55 53 159 51 11 253 02 37	336 55 42 339 50 55 73 02 44	Ref. Mon. S–24___ S–25_____ Ref. Mon. S–23___	821. 7 1, 342. 1 200. 2	2. 91473 3. 12780 2. 30150
Van Buren, Me., Episcopal Church, cross on spire, 1909.	47 09 21. 98 67 55 58. 66	149 35 07 255 16 11	329 34 52 75 16 14	Ref. Mon. S–24___ Ref. Mon. S–23___	836. 4 93. 1	2. 92243 1. 96895
Van Buren, Me., St. Mary's Catholic College, cupola flagpole, 1909.	47 09 39. 39 67 56 33. 67	194 10 57 301 49 20	14 11 03 121 49 49	S–25_____ Ref. Mon. S–23___	709. 5 974. 2	2. 85095 2. 98864

SOURCE OF ST. CROIX RIVER TO LAKE POHENAGAMOOK—Continued

Station	Latitude and longitude	Azimuth	Back azimuth	To station	Distance (meters)	Loga-rithm
POINTS SUPPLEMEN-TARY TO MINOR SCHEME, ST. JOHN RIVER—continued	° ′ ″	° ′ ″	° ′ ″			
Van Buren, Me., nuns' building, cross on red roof, 1909.	47 09 40. 94 67 56 33. 94	195 39 27 303 59 25	15 39 33 123 59 54	S–25_____ Ref. Mon. S–23___	664. 7 1, 004. 9	2. 82262 3. 00213
Van Buren, Me., convent school, base of gilded fig-ure on dome, 1909.	47 09 38. 62 67 56 23. 80	207 04 48 308 20 42	27 04 52 128 21 04	Ref. Mon. S–24___ Ref. Mon. S–23___	233. 0 790. 0	2. 36737 2. 89765
Van Buren, Me., St. Bruno's Cath-olic Church, spire, 1909.	47 09 44. 37 67 56 28. 04	159 42 59 185 54 09 313 16 49	339 42 39 5 54 11 133 17 14	Ref. Mon. S–28___ S–25_____ Ref. Mon. S–23___	1, 654. 6 536. 7 974. 0	3. 21870 2. 72970 2. 98855
Van Buren, Me., fire house, bell clapper, 1909.	47 09 19. 90 67 56 03. 17	157 19 20 244 36 07	337 19 09 64 36 14	Ref. Mon. S–24___ Ref. Mon. S–23___	851. 4 205. 1	2. 93014 2. 31187
Van Buren Lumber Co.'s mill, largest stack, (Me.) 1909.	47 10 21. 49 67 56 35. 49	113 55 37 340 53 32	293 55 27 160 53 39	Ref. Mon. S–27___ S–25_____	297. 8 648. 2	2. 47393 2. 81171
St. Leonard, New Brunswick, build-ing north of vil-lage, flagpole on cupola, 1909.	47 10 04. 19 67 55 38. 31	14 49 25 55 40 11 85 30 38	194 49 13 235 39 41 265 30 03	Ref. Mon. S–23___ Ref. Mon. S–24___ S–25_____	1, 323. 6 1, 031. 8 995. 3	3. 12177 3. 01360 2. 99797
St. Leonard, New Brunswick, large red barn, south peak, northeast of village, 1909.	47 10 41. 20 67 54 15. 54	40 40 53 56 23 54 65 57 20	220 39 41 236 22 24 245 55 45	Ref. Mon. S–23___ Ref. Mon. S–24___ S–25_____	3, 194. 3 3, 116. 1 2, 995. 4	3. 50437 3. 49360 3. 47645
Van Buren, Me., iron cross on bowl-der, 1909.	47 10 34. 91 67 56 55. 14	18 47 38 334 17 36	198 47 37 154 17 41	Ref. Mon. S–28___ Ref. Mon. S–27___	9. 2 325. 8	0. 96477 2. 51300
Van Buren, Me., judges' stand, race track, 1909.	47 10 27. 91 67 56 56. 33	159 36 27 186 04 29	339 36 17 6 04 30	Ref. Mon. S–29___ Ref. Mon. S–28___	758. 4 208. 5	2. 87992 2. 31914
Keegan, Me., St. John Lumber Co.'s mill, largest stack, 1909.	47 11 19. 45 67 57 15. 61	17 47 20 125 07 49 350 51 09	197 47 15 305 07 52 170 51 14	Ref. Mon. S–30___ S–31_____ Ref. Mon. S–29___	455. 6 680. 5 892. 0	2. 65863 2. 83281 2. 95038
Keegan, Me., old schoolhouse, flag-pole, 1909.	47 10 57. 74 67 57 15. 82	150 19 48 325 10 36	330 19 43 145 10 41	Ref. Mon. S–30___ Ref. Mon. S–29___	272. 3 256. 0	2. 43509 2. 40832
Ste. Anne, New Brunswick, church spire, 1909.	47 14 51. 64 68 01 47. 26	42 58 44 94 14 13 341 00 10	222 58 25 274 13 21 161 00 28	Ref. Mon. S–39___ Ref. Mon. S–40___ Ref. Mon. S–38___	797. 3 1, 601. 0 1, 591. 4	2. 90160 3. 20439 3. 20179
Ste. Anne, New Brunswick, butter factory stack, 1909.	47 14 42. 96 68 01 36. 77	101 59 59 346 28 44	281 58 55 166 28 54	Ref. Mon. S–40___ Ref. Mon. S–38___	1, 857. 8 1, 272. 2	3. 26899 3. 10454
Lille, Me., boom house, smoke pipe, southeast of vil-lage, 1909.	47 15 59. 27 68 05 27. 67	128 12 58 342 29 19	308 12 00 162 29 30	Ref. Mon. S–43___ Ref. Mon. S–42___	2, 096. 3 1, 058. 1	3. 32146 3. 02452

SOURCE OF ST. CROIX RIVER TO LAKE POHENAGAMOOK—Continued

Station	Latitude and longitude	Azimuth	Back azimuth	To station	Distance (meters)	Loga- rithm
POINTS SUPPLEMEN- TARY TO MINOR SCHEME, ST. JOHN RIVER—continued	° ′ ″	° ′ ″	° ′ ″			
Lille, Me., school- house flagpole, 1909.	47 16 43. 53 68 06 31. 24	77 18 56 325 08 05	257 18 45 145 09 03	Ref. Mon. S–43___ Ref. Mon. S–42___	318. 7 2, 895. 1	2. 50343 3. 46166
Lille, Me., old church, cross on cupola, 1909.	47 16 44. 37 68 06 35. 54	66 29 49 112 46 25 323 59 18	246 29 41 292 45 26 144 00 19	Ref. Mon. S–43___ Ref. Mon. S–44___ Ref. Mon. S–42___	240. 5 1, 395. 2 2, 968. 7	2. 38114 3. 14464 3. 47256
Lille, Me., new church, northwest cupola, 1909.	47 16 44. 97 68 06 33. 61	66 17 56 111 26 50 324 49 54	246 17 47 291 26 04 144 51 08	Ref. Mon. S–43___ Ref. Mon. S–44___ Ref. Mon. S–42___	285. 1 1, 425. 7 2, 960. 2	2. 45504 3. 15403 3. 47133
Lille, Me., sawmill stack, northwest of village, 1909.	47 17 04. 87 68 07 16. 13	77 52 02 190 12 03 319 03 10	257 51 47 10 12 07 139 03 32	Ref. Mon. S–44___ Ref. Mon. C–42___ Ref. Mon. S–43___	443. 4 560. 0 965. 1	2. 64682 2. 74820 2. 98457
Grand Isle, Me., windmill on barn, center of upright, 1909.	47 18 17. 88 68 09 11. 93	66 46 02 319 34 18 333 54 06	246 45 48 139 35 25 153 54 25	Ref. Mon. S–46___ Ref. Mon. S–44___ Ref. Mon. S–45___	413. 0 3, 084. 3 1, 251. 5	2. 61597 3. 48915 3. 09743
Green River, New Brunswick, hotel, flagpole on cupola, 1909.	47 19 07. 22 68 08 42. 52	1 27 25 30 35 45 83 22 33	181 27 23 210 35 10 263 21 32	Ref. Mon. S–45___ Ref. Mon. S–46___ Ref. Mon. S–47___	2, 648. 6 1, 959. 5 1, 637. 6	3. 42301 3. 29214 3. 21420
Grand Isle, Me., Crawford's saw- mill stack, 1909.	47 18 37. 34 68 09 19. 89	15 31 55 131 04 22 337 24 27	195 31 47 311 03 48 157 24 52	Ref. Mon. S–46___ Ref. Mon. S–47___ Ref. Mon. S–45___	793. 0 1, 116. 7 1, 868. 3	2. 89926 3. 04793 3. 27145
Grand Isle, Me., flagpole on house, 1909.	47 18 30. 51 68 09 23. 37	14 07 56 140 52 04 332 24 50	194 07 51 320 51 33 152 25 18	Ref. Mon. S–46___ Ref. Mon. S–47___ Ref. Mon. S–45___	570. 1 1, 218. 0 1, 707. 9	2. 75596 3. 08566 3. 23247
St. Basil, New Brunswick, flag- pole on brown house with red roof, 1909.	47 21 21. 93 68 13 40. 86	13 54 24 69 49 48 324 20 37	193 54 14 249 48 51 144 21 19	Ref. Mon. S–52___ Ref. Mon. S–53___ Ref. Mon. S–51___	1, 219. 2 1, 753. 6 2, 423. 1	3. 08606 3. 24392 3. 38438
St. Basil, New Brunswick, church spire, 1909.	47 21 24. 09 68 13 56. 42	63 01 51 319 29 21 358 27 42	243 01 05 139 30 14 178 27 43	Ref. Mon. S–53___ Ref. Mon. S–51___ Ref. Mon. S–52___	1, 480. 4 2, 677. 3 1, 250. 6	3. 17039 3. 42769 3. 09711
St. Basil, New Brunswick, con- vent cupola, gild- ed cross, 1909.	47 21 30. 31 68 14 10. 01	50 08 35 317 43 54 347 31 53	230 07 59 137 44 57 167 32 04	Ref. Mon. S–53___ Ref. Mon. S–51___ Ref. Mon. S–52___	1, 347. 2 3, 009. 9 1, 476. 9	3. 12944 3. 47855 3. 16935
St. Basil, New Bruns- wick, flagpole on white house with black roof, west of village, 1909.	47 21 41. 56 68 14 54. 93	4 19 15 48 07 53 324 48 44	184 19 12 228 07 04 144 49 28	Ref. Mon. S–53___ Ref. Mon. S–54___ Ref. Mon. S–52___	1, 214. 3 2, 288. 7 2, 189. 4	3. 08433 3. 35958 3. 34032
St. Basil, New Bruns- wick, flagpole on white house with red roof, west of village, 1909.	47 21 40. 57 68 15 38. 28	27 57 16 58 36 48 325 15 47	207 56 49 238 35 38 145 16 16	Ref. Mon. S–54___ Ref. Mon. S–55___ Ref. Mon. S–53___	1, 694. 7 2, 060. 1 1, 436. 2	3. 22910 3. 40826 3. 15720
St. David, Me., church, cross on cupola, 1909.	47 20 57. 44 68 16 40. 81	89 52 30 121 59 09 287 41 31	269 51 59 301 58 06 107 41 49	Ref. Mon. S–55___ Ref. Mon. C–54___ Ref. Mon. S–54___	872. 9 2, 102. 2 543. 9	2. 94098 3. 32268 2. 73551
St. David, Me., schoolhouse belfry, 1909.	47 20 56. 51 68 16 47. 28	92 04 56 281 47 35	272 04 30 101 47 58	Ref. Mon. S–55___ Ref. Mon. S–54___	737. 6 668. 1	2. 86780 2. 82486

SOURCE OF ST. CROIX RIVER TO LAKE POHENAGAMOOK—Continued

Station	Latitude and longitude	Azimuth	Back azimuth	To station	Distance (meters)	Logarithm
POINTS SUPPLEMENTARY TO MINOR SCHEME, ST. JOHN RIVER—continued	° ′ ″	° ′ ″	° ′ ″			
Madawaska, Me., sawmill stack, 1909.	47 21 17. 12 68 18 13. 79	112 10 56 126 53 19 198 23 00	292 09 48 306 52 41 18 23 06	C–56_____ Ref. Mon. C–55___ Ref. Mon. C–54___	2, 052. 2 1, 378. 5 532. 9	3. 31222 3. 13941 2. 72668
Madawaska, Me., flagpole on yellow store, 1909.	47 21 11. 84 68 18 23. 85	89 36 25 138 00 49 350 59 44	269 35 35 318 00 18 170 59 45	Ref. Mon. S–57___ Ref. Mon. C–55___ Ref. Mon. S–56___	1, 426. 7 1, 332. 4 202. 8	3. 15432 3. 12464 2. 30700
Edmundston, New Brunswick, flagpole on square white cupola, 1909.	47 21 55. 92 68 19 40. 20	313 41 49 352 41 40	133 42 46 172 41 46	Ref. Mon. S–56___ Ref. Mon. S–57___	2, 260. 3 1, 382. 7	3. 35417 3. 14072
Edmundston, New Brunswick, flagpole on pointed green cupola, 1909.	47 21 56. 73 68 19 21. 75	8 36 43 321 50 01	188 36 36 141 50 45	Ref. Mon. S–57___ Ref. Mon. S–56___	1, 412. 2 2, 017. 9	3. 14990 3. 30489
Madawaska, Me., customhouse, flagpole, 1909.	47 21 20. 14 68 19 26. 20	23 56 12 72 48 38 288 48 32	203 56 08 252 48 03 108 49 19	Ref. Mon. S–57___ Ref. Mon. S–58___ Ref. Mon. S–56___	291. 4 739. 4 1, 415. 8	2. 46443 2. 86889 3. 15100
Edmundston, New Brunswick, flagpole on cupola with round windows, 1909.	47 21 52. 20 68 19 55. 51	4 18 56 306 29 22 338 25 04	184 18 42 126 30 30 158 25 21	Ref. Mon. S–58___ Ref. Mon. S–56___ Ref. Mon. S–57___	1, 212. 0 2, 432. 1 1, 351. 0	3. 08352 3. 38599 3. 13067
Edmundston, New Brunswick, flagpole on cupola of brick building, 1909.	47 22 18. 21 68 19 30. 57	0 44 04 16 59 11 327 31 25	180 44 03 196 58 39 147 32 15	Ref. Mon. S–57___ Ref. Mon. S–58___ Ref. Mon. S–56___	2, 059. 8 2, 103. 7 2, 666. 9	3. 31383 3. 32298 3. 42600
Edmundston, New Brunswick, Catholic Church, spire, 1909.	47 21 46. 18 68 19 57. 65	2 35 14 45 50 55 333 08 58	182 35 12 225 50 20 153 09 31	Ref. Mon. S–58___ Ref. Mon. S–59___ Ref. Mon. S–57___	1, 024. 0 1, 390. 5 1, 199. 9	3. 01028 3. 14317 3. 07915
Edmundston, New Brunswick, flagpole on sheet-iron covered cupola, 1909.	47 21 47. 94 68 19 38. 72	22 23 06 352 40 31	202 22 50 172 40 36	Ref. Mon. S–58___ Ref. Mon. S–57___	1, 164. 8 1, 134. 0	3. 06626 3. 05462
Madawaska, Me., flagpole on schoolhouse, 1909.	47 21 23. 86 68 19 54. 89	201 21 03 238 43 20	21 21 11 58 43 56	Ref. Mon. C–56___ Ref. Mon. C–55___	607. 8 1, 192. 4	2. 78378 3. 07641
Edmundston, New Brunswick, sawmill stack, 1909.	47 21 49. 17 68 19 54. 02	6 15 41 338 10 09	186 15 37 158 10 26	Ref. Mon. S–58___ Ref. Mon. S–57___	1, 121. 8 1, 252. 7	3. 04993 3. 09784
Madawaska, Me., chimney on yellow house, 1909.	47 21 17. 38 68 20 24. 09	227 25 11 243 20 15	47 25 40 63 21 12	Ref. Mon. C–56___ Ref. Mon. C–55___	1, 132. 5 1, 825. 8	3. 05403 3. 26145
Upper Frenchville, Me., church spire, 1910.	47 16 46. 88 68 25 38. 27	68 43 22 99 34 47 148 31 56	248 43 04 279 33 23 328 31 30	Ref. Mon. S–72___ Ref. Mon. S–73___ Ref. Mon. C–68___	541. 8 2, 451. 7 1, 436. 0	2. 73387 3. 38946 3. 15715
St. Hilaire, New Brunswick, church spire, 1910.	47 17 16. 24 68 26 31. 92	68 51 05 126 08 37 330 33 29	248 50 20 306 07 53 150 33 50	Ref. Mon. S–73____ Ref. Mon. C–69___ Ref. Mon. S–72___	1, 383. 1 1, 548. 6 1, 266. 9	3. 14086 3. 18995 3. 10274

SOURCE OF ST. CROIX RIVER TO LAKE POHENAGAMOOK—Continued

Station	Latitude and longitude	Azimuth	Back azimuth	To station	Distance (meters)	Logarithm
POINTS SUPPLEMENTARY TO MINOR SCHEME, ST. JOHN RIVER—continued	° ′ ″	° ′ ″	° ′ ″			
Fort Kent, Me., Catholic school, cross, 1910.	47 15 11.44 68 35 31.48	97 01 16 200 25 39 334 16 31	277 00 41 20 25 49 154 16 43	Ref. Mon. C–82___ Ref. Mon. S–88___ Ref. Mon. S–89___	1,023.5 830.1 792.4	3.01010 2.91913 2.89894
Fort Kent, Me., Madawaska Training School, weather vane, 1910.	47 15 00.47 68 35 27.54	61 15 23 112 54 10 190 29 36	241 14 45 292 53 32 10 29 43	S–90_____ Ref. Mon. C–82___ Ref. Mon. S–88___	1,265.3 1,192.8 1,136.0	3.10220 3.07655 3.05536
Fort Kent, Me., Protestant Church, spire, 1910.	47 14 59.02 68 35 22.95	64 56 52 185 25 41 333 29 28	244 56 11 5 25 49 153 29 34	S–90_____ Ref. Mon. S–88___ Ref. Mon. S–89___	1,331.1 1,167.0 368.8	3.12422 3.06707 2.56674
Fort Kent, Me., astronomic pier, 1910.	47 15 00.45 68 35 38.19	55 31 36 201 04 38 307 39 22	235 31 06 21 04 57 127 39 39	S–90_____ Ref. Mon. S–88___ Ref. Mon. S–89___	1,074.1 1,197.7 612.6	3.03105 3.07833 2.78716
Clair, New Brunswick, church spire, 1910.	47 15 15.75 68 36 08.45	12 59 07 238 50 52 307 03 55	192 58 55 58 51 29 127 04 34	S–90_____ Ref. Mon. S–88___ Ref. Mon. S–89___	1,109.1 1,246.6 1,405.1	3.04498 3.09571 3.14771
Ledges, New Brunswick, church spire, 1910.	47 14 31.62 68 42 13.68	117 55 07 183 53 05 229 33 09	297 54 14 3 53 06 49 33 40	Ref. Mon. C–92___ Ref. Mon. C–91___ Ref. Mon. C–90___	1,683.0 674.6 1,169.8	3.22608 2.82905 3.06810
Connor, New Brunswick, Protestant Church, spire, 1910.	47 12 39.96 68 49 23.42	23 45 35 265 53 20 318 10 37	203 45 17 85 54 31 138 10 56	Ref. Mon. S–106__ Ref. Mon. S–104__ Ref. Mon. S–105__	1,315.4 1,762.5 802.0	3.11906 3.24614 2.90416
Connor, New Brunswick, Catholic Church, spire, 1910.	47 12 23.71 68 50 04.58	223 02 41 273 54 40 334 24 39	43 03 04 93 55 29 154 24 51	Ref. Mon. C–99___ Ref. Mon. S–105__ Ref. Mon. S–106__	977.4 1,404.2 778.6	2.99008 3.14744 2.89130
St. Francis, Me., Protestant Church, spire, 1910.	47 10 34.96 68 53 00.86	37 27 17 150 26 51 189 48 35	217 26 52 330 26 36 9 48 43	Ref. Mon. S–113__ Ref. Mon. C–106__ Ref. Mon. C–105__	1,221.3 876.7 1,353.8	3.08682 2.94284 3.13155
St. Francis, Me., Catholic Church, spire, 1910.	47 10 06.94 68 54 07.15	169 49 59 242 58 19 279 03 07	349 49 54 62 59 17 99 03 30	Ref. Mon. S–114__ Ref. Mon. S–112__ Ref. Mon. S–113__	844.7 1,879.5 661.7	2.92671 3.27405 2.82068
St. Francis, Me., upper schoolhouse, west of village, 1910.	47 09 47.27 68 55 23.77	225 30 09 257 28 39	45 31 00 77 29 58	Ref. Mon. S–114__ Ref. Mon. S–113__	2,053.0 2,322.5	3.31239 3.36595

GEOGRAPHIC POSITIONS OF TRIANGULATION AND TRAVERSE STATIONS, LAKE POHENA-GAMOOK TO THE VERMONT-QUEBEC BOUNDARY

Station	Latitude and longitude	Azimuth	Back azimuth	To station	Distance (meters)	Loga-rithm
MAJOR SCHEME TRIANGULATION	° ′ ″	° ′ ″	° ′ ″			
Leverrier (Geodetic Survey of Canada).	46 44 47. 389 69 57 02. 632					
Talon (Geodetic Survey of Canada).	46 44 36. 053 70 06 10. 933	268 13 19. 06	88 19 58. 39	Leverrier	11, 644. 41	4. 0661174
Standon (Geodetic Survey of Canada).	46 36 17. 888 70 29 19. 373	242 19 45. 78 248 53 17. 18	62 36 35. 83 69 16 46. 13	Talon Leverrier	33, 280. 30 44, 068. 97	4. 5221872 4. 6441329
Bonnet	46 32 25. 106 70 20 30. 091	122 34 48. 1 218 54 21. 7 232 24 56. 0	302 28 23. 7 39 04 46. 3 52 41 59. 3	Standon Talon Leverrier	13, 368. 0 29, 040. 1 37, 700. 7	4. 1260676 4. 4629975 4. 5763500
Hardwood Mountain	46 24 47. 425 70 01 23. 551	120 08 04. 3 120 59 39. 1 170 33 48. 6	299 54 13. 0 300 39 23. 4 350 30 19. 9	Bonnet Standon Talon	28, 248. 0 41, 606. 1 37, 209. 5	4. 4509876 4. 6191574 4. 5706539
St. Justine Church, northeast spire.	46 24 38. 226 70 20 56. 231	182 12 45. 1 206 55 02. 1 269 13 56. 1	2 13 04. 1 27 05 45. 1 89 28 05. 5	Bonnet Talon Hardwood Mountain.	14, 427. 0 41, 513. 8 25, 047. 7	4. 1591765 4. 6181922 4. 3987680
Maheux	46 08 57. 112 70 16 17. 156	168 24 33. 0 172 56 00. 7 191 01 26. 4	348 21 11. 3 352 52 57. 7 11 08 45. 7	St. Justine Church, northeast spire. Bonnet Talon	29, 666. 5 43, 809. 9 67, 301. 0	4. 4722660 4. 6415720 4. 8280215
Megantic (Geodetic Survey of Canada).	45 26 51. 567 71 07 15. 050					
Liniere (Geodetic Survey of Canada).	45 49 45. 435 70 22 22. 431	54 14 17. 17	233 42 12. 08	Megantic	72, 109. 93	4. 8579951
Bald	45 45 59. 942 70 12 17. 053	63 56 33. 5 118 05 44. 0 171 11 41. 4 173 05 26. 5 190 59 20. 5	243 17 16. 8 297 58 30. 0 351 05 27. 4 353 02 33. 9 11 07 11. 3	Megantic Liniere St. Justine Church, northeast spire. Maheux Hardwood Mountain.	79, 777. 8 14, 812. 0 72, 442. 3 42, 833. 1 73, 221. 1	4. 901882 4. 170615 4. 859992 4. 631780 4. 864636
Ste. Cecile	45 41 19. 489 70 58 12. 194	23 46 15. 8 251 12 09. 7 261 27 24. 4	203 39 48. 1 71 37 49. 8 82 00 17. 2	Megantic Liniere Bald	29, 267. 0 49, 015. 0 60, 201. 6	4. 466378 4. 690329 4. 779608
Kibby	45 25 07. 803 70 32 41. 646	94 16 14. 6 132 15 11. 0 214 21 13. 8	273 51 37. 4 311 56 58. 4 34 35 48. 7	Megantic Ste. Cecile Bald	45, 182. 9 44, 744. 1 46, 892. 9	4. 654974 4. 650736 4. 671107
Snow	45 17 29. 594 70 42 35. 410	118 27 44. 5 155 21 06. 5 222 21 29. 1	298 10 11. 5 335 09 58. 6 42 28 31. 6	Megantic Ste. Cecile Kibby	36, 575. 3 48, 605. 7 19, 160. 9	4. 563188 4. 686687 4. 282415
Hughey	45 32 59. 993 70 40 56. 305	71 47 56. 6 124 35 48. 5 323 33 48. 9	251 29 10. 6 304 23 28. 3 143 39 41. 7	Megantic Ste. Cecile Kibby	36, 115. 0 27, 230. 2 18, 108. 3	4. 557688 4. 435051 4. 257878
Traverse station 69=H.	45 39 42. 134 70 33 32. 294	95 30 27. 5 357 39 49. 8	275 12 48. 9 177 40 26. 0	Ste. Cecile Kibby	32, 171. 3 27, 015. 3	4. 507468 4. 431610

LAKE POHENAGAMOOK TO THE VERMONT-QUEBEC BOUNDARY—Continued

Station	Latitude and longitude	Azimuth	Back azimuth	To station	Distance (meters)	Loga- rithm
MAJOR SCHEME TRIANGULATION — continued.	° ′ ″	° ′ ″	° ′ ″			
Ken	45 33 08. 612	123 40 20. 3	303 27 47. 1	Ste. Cecile	27, 408. 5	4. 437886
	70 40 38. 055	217 10 16. 2	37 15 20. 4	Traverse station 69=H.	15, 255. 4	4. 183424
		325 04 34. 9	145 10 14. 7	Kibby	18, 093. 6	4. 257524
Mon. 411	45 25 43. 075	20 26 21. 3	200 23 15. 9	Snow	16, 255. 4	4. 210998
	70 38 14. 910	278 30 51. 3	98 34 48. 7	Kibby	7, 326. 7	3. 864908
Moccasin	45 26 07. 605	24 58 25. 6	204 54 22. 4	Snow	17, 636. 5	4. 246412
	70 36 53. 703	66 47 14. 3	246 46 16. 5	Mon. 411	1, 920. 8	3. 283480
		288 35 43. 7	108 38 43. 3	Kibby	5, 782. 2	3. 762093
Bump	45 27 16. 503	311 42 52. 2	131 44 10. 4	Moccasin	3, 195. 8	3. 504585
	70 38 43. 458	347 51 26. 5	167 51 46. 9	Mon. 411	2, 950. 3	3. 469869
Layton	45 28 08. 524	8 47 08. 4	188 46 45. 6	Mon. 411	4, 543. 6	3. 657399
	70 37 42. 987	39 17 29. 8	219 16 46. 6	Bump	2, 074. 9	3. 316996
		343 59 19. 5	163 59 54. 5	Moccasin	3, 883. 6	3. 589230
Merrill	45 28 34. 753	279 52 10. 0	99 54 42. 7	Layton	4, 714. 3	3. 673415
	70 41 16. 792	305 56 04. 7	125 57 54. 2	Bump	4, 114. 8	3. 614353
Van Dyke	45 29 34. 186	21 04 25. 9	201 04 02. 7	Merrill	1, 966. 3	3. 293653
	70 40 44. 241	303 52 31. 8	123 54 41. 3	Layton	4, 742. 4	3. 675999
		328 18 15. 4	148 19 41. 7	Bump	4, 995. 0	3. 698538
Mon. 410	45 26 42. 218	140 30 18. 4	320 28 44. 4	Merrill	4, 503. 0	3. 653498
	70 39 04. 937	203 47 35. 7	23 47 51. 0	Bump	1, 156. 8	3. 063263
		329 13 13. 0	149 13 48. 7	Mon. 411	2, 125. 1	3. 327382
Mon. 405	45 30 11. 991	292 45 01. 7	112 46 33. 0	Van Dyke	3, 016. 5	3. 479499
	70 42 52. 351	325 20 13. 3	145 21 21. 4	Merrill	3, 649. 4	3. 562217
Wait	45 31 43. 580	24 47 54. 6	204 47 11. 7	Mon. 405	3, 114. 6	3. 493408
	70 41 52. 178	339 43 51. 4	159 44 39. 8	Van Dyke	4, 258. 2	3. 629229
Lowell	45 31 51. 570	22 17 18. 5	202 16 21. 3	Van Dyke	4, 583. 6	3. 661208
	70 39 24. 181	85 37 20. 7	265 35 35. 1	Wait	3, 221. 0	3. 507985
		342 17 39. 6	162 18 52. 0	Layton	7, 228. 0	3. 859018
Mon. 425	45 25 52. 765	213 22 27. 7	33 25 20. 9	Mon. 405	9, 585. 9	3. 981632
	70 46 55. 247	235 45 02. 7	55 49 03. 9	Merrill	8, 893. 5	3. 949073
		261 27 32. 1	81 33 07. 2	Mon. 410	10, 335. 5	4. 014333
		271 27 48. 5	91 33 59. 2	Mon. 411	11, 315. 1	4. 053658
		339 58 11. 5	160 01 16. 4	Snow	16, 531. 1	4. 218302
Dome	45 32 09. 237	68 38 55. 0	248 37 48. 4	Wait	2, 174. 7	3. 337394
	70 40 18. 842	152 35 24. 7	332 34 58. 1	Hughey	1, 765. 2	3. 246792
		294 41 26. 2	114 42 05. 2	Lowell	1, 305. 4	3. 115760
Dean	45 32 36. 508	40 01 36. 7	220 00 51. 6	Wait	2, 133. 7	3. 329129
	70 40 48. 941	307 01 18. 9	127 02 19. 4	Lowell	2, 303. 6	3. 362411
		322 11 53. 5	142 12 15. 0	Dome	1, 065. 5	3. 027543
Boundary	45 32 31. 441	18 45 12. 0	198 44 55. 5	Wait	1, 560. 4	3. 193235
	70 41 29. 061	218 52 15. 6	38 52 39. 1	Hughey	1, 132. 3	3. 053946
		259 48 28. 8	79 48 57. 4	Dean	884. 3	2. 946618
		294 13 05. 4	114 13 55. 5	Dome	1, 670. 6	3. 222870
Lowelltown south base.	45 32 14. 587	131 21 33. 8	311 21 14. 4	Boundary	787. 5	2. 896250
	70 41 01. 816	184 52 31. 6	4 52 35. 7	Hughey	1, 406. 9	3. 148270
		202 25 37. 8	22 25 47. 0	Dean	732. 1	2. 864593
		280 02 22. 9	100 02 53. 6	Dome	946. 9	2. 976312
Lowelltown north base.	45 32 28. 931	236 54 03. 4	56 54 15. 2	Dean	428. 4	2. 631852
	70 41 05. 484	300 59 32. 7	121 00 06. 0	Dome	1, 180. 5	3. 072078
		349 48 45. 1	169 48 47. 7	Lowelltown south base	449. 91	2. 653130

LAKE POHENAGAMOOK TO THE VERMONT-QUEBEC BOUNDARY—Continued

Station	Latitude and longitude	Azimuth	Back azimuth	To station	Distance (meters)	Loga- rithm
MAJOR SCHEME TRIANGULATION— continued	° ′ ″	° ′ ″	° ′ ″			
Gosford	45 18 06. 050	204 51 02. 9	24 54 41. 4	Mon. 425	15, 882. 5	4. 200918
	70 52 02. 304	275 09 00. 1	95 15 43. 0	Snow	12, 403. 4	4. 093539
Woburn	45 23 02. 930	242 56 44. 3	63 02 21. 2	Mon. 425	11, 546. 0	4. 062431
	70 54 48. 277	302 44 43. 0	122 53 24. 3	Snow	18, 987. 5	4. 278467
		338 27 57. 9	158 29 56. 0	Gosford	9, 851. 8	3. 993515
Mon. 470	45 20 51. 955	242 08 52. 2	62 13 02. 7	Woburn	8, 664. 7	3. 937752
	71 00 40. 411	294 21 45. 7	114 27 54. 1	Gosford	12, 391. 6	4. 093127
Rump	45 12 13. 770	194 30 53. 7	14 33 08. 9	Mon. 470	16, 525. 8	4. 218163
	71 03 50. 671	210 28 35. 8	30 35 01. 2	Woburn	23, 266. 0	4. 366721
		234 46 57. 5	54 55 20. 6	Gosford	18, 891. 0	4. 276256
Bon Durban	45 17 42. 995	231 34 00. 9	51 38 01. 2	Mon. 470	9, 391. 5	3. 972736
	71 06 18. 345	267 43 48. 8	87 53 57. 2	Gosford	18, 665. 4	4. 271038
		342 24 15. 8	162 26 00. 7	Rump	10, 661. 5	4. 027819
Pros	45 15 13. 210	243 22 05. 7	63 27 06. 8	Bon Durban	10, 330. 7	4. 014129
	71 13 22. 152	293 54 02. 9	114 00 48. 6	Rump	13, 642. 3	4. 134887
Salmon	45 14 37. 775	99 10 00. 3	279 06 18. 8	Pros	6, 889. 7	3. 838203
	71 08 10. 226	203 05 21. 7	23 06 41. 2	Bon Durban	6, 216. 4	3. 793540
		308 06 29. 5	128 09 33. 8	Rump	7, 199. 3	3. 857289
Northwest Knoll	45 18 09. 963	4 05 18. 6	184 05 05. 9	Pros	5, 470. 5	3. 738026
	71 13 04. 265	275 20 15. 0	95 25 03. 5	Bon Durban	8, 883. 4	3. 948581
		315 35 39. 5	135 39 08. 4	Salmon	9, 164. 7	3. 962117
Spect	45 15 07. 193	192 27 07. 7	12 27 48. 3	Northwest Knoll	5, 778. 4	3. 761807
	71 14 01. 454	257 45 58. 6	77 46 26. 5	Pros	876. 9	2. 942958
Bien	45 18 04. 322	268 05 40. 7	88 08 33. 7	Northwest Knoll	5, 305. 1	3. 724693
	71 17 07. 629	317 02 35. 7	137 05 15. 9	Pros	7, 215. 1	3. 858242
		323 24 05. 8	143 26 18. 1	Spect	6, 809. 5	3. 833113
Indian	45 12 03. 301	176 37 26. 4	356 37 05. 0	Bien	11, 164. 5	4. 047840
	71 16 37. 453	210 55 38. 1	30 57 28. 9	Spect	6, 618. 9	3. 820787
Howe	45 15 27. 076	229 21 43. 6	49 24 48. 2	Bien	7, 457. 5	3. 872595
	71 21 27. 369	273 34 05. 0	93 39 21. 8	Spect	9, 742. 7	3. 988678
		314 49 04. 4	134 52 30. 2	Indian	8, 920. 4	3. 950382
Joe	45 14 20. 378	233 44 32. 8	53 46 04. 3	Howe	3, 482. 6	3. 541898
	71 23 36. 161	294 48 45. 8	114 53 43. 0	Indian	10, 068. 1	4. 002948
Eck	45 13 44. 127	149 13 29. 9	329 13 08. 2	Joe	1, 302. 6	3. 114796
	71 23 05. 605	213 58 33. 0	33 59 42. 8	Howe	3, 832. 8	3. 583522
		290 08 24. 4	110 12 59. 9	Indian	9, 023. 5	3. 955375
Hereford (Geodetic Survey of Canada).	45 04 57. 486 71 36 05. 573	222 45 08. 67	43 05 38. 00	Megantic	55, 399. 04	4. 7435022
Metallak	45 09 34. 081	61 19 28. 4	241 11 03. 7	Hereford	17, 754. 7	4. 249313
	71 24 13. 348	185 14 36. 5	5 15 02. 9	Joe	8, 875. 4	3. 948188
		245 07 16. 4	65 12 39. 8	Indian	10, 968. 2	4. 040134
Sightly	45 13 22. 106	37 11 18. 0	217 04 55. 1	Hereford	19, 540. 4	4. 290934
	71 27 05. 547	248 28 58. 4	68 31 27. 1	Joe	4, 909. 1	3. 691003
		262 34 36. 7	82 37 27. 1	Eck	5, 278. 6	3. 722521
		280 00 11. 1	100 07 36. 9	Indian	13, 920. 3	4. 143649
		331 52 49. 7	151 54 51. 9	Metallak	7, 980. 1	3. 902008
Quillette (south base)	45 10 24. 683	48 11 20. 9	228 05 15. 3	Hereford	15, 135. 9	4. 180008
	71 27 29. 752	185 30 26. 7	5 30 43. 9	Sightly	5, 502. 6	3. 740568
		289 59 29. 8	110 01 49. 1	Metallak	4, 564. 9	3. 659429

LAKE POHENAGAMOOK TO THE VERMONT-QUEBEC BOUNDARY—Continued

Station	Latitude and longitude	Azimuth	Back azimuth	To station	Distance (meters)	Loga-rithm
MAJOR SCHEME TRIANGULATION— continued	° ′ ″	° ′ ″	° ′ ″			
Crete (north base)___	45 10 54. 105 71 27 05. 861	29 52 21. 4 180 05 09. 6 303 14 17. 4	209 52 04. 4 0 05 09. 8 123 16 19. 7	Ouillette _____ Sightly_____ Metallak _____	1, 047. 44 4, 568. 9 4, 505. 0	3. 020131 3. 659811 3. 653695
Corbert_____	45 12 00. 174 71 25 53. 052	35 37 02. 5 147 58 59. 7 334 13 25. 4	215 35 53. 9 327 58 08. 3 154 14 36. 2	Ouillette _____ Sightly_____ Metallak _____	3, 625. 8 2, 983. 3 5, 007. 9	3. 559407 3. 474694 3. 699654
Knoll_____	45 10 30. 605 71 25 06. 789	86 39 44. 4 105 36 11. 0 326 13 05. 5	266 38 03. 0 285 34 46. 6 146 13 43. 4	Ouillette _____ Crete_____ Metallak _____	3, 127. 1 2, 699. 2 2, 099. 3	3. 495140 3. 431232 3. 322065
Laperle_____	45 10 16. 436 71 26 41. 979	103 43 04. 4 155 50 57. 5 258 06 27. 0	283 42 30. 5 335 50 40. 6 78 07 34. 5	Ouillette _____ Crete_____ Knoll_____	1, 073. 8 1, 274. 4 2, 124. 1	3. 030934 3. 105315 3. 327179
Hill_____	45 03 24. 222 71 28 51. 664	106 54 55. 7 187 08 58. 4	286 49 48. 5 7 10 13. 6	Hereford _____ Sightly_____	9, 919. 2 18, 602. 0	3. 996478 4. 269560
Hill tablet_____	45 03 24. 186 71 28 52. 243	265 01 45	85 01 45	Hill_____	12. 73	1. 10473
Wheeler_____	45 05 02. 671 71 29 47. 146	88 55 45. 2 338 13 27. 7	268 51 17. 2 158 14 07. 0	Hereford _____ Hill_____	8, 278. 0 3, 272. 5	3. 917928 3. 514881
Lambert_____	45 02 51. 663 71 31 28. 020	122 37 56. 8 196 23 38. 2 208 36 38. 8 253 36 50. 5	302 34 40. 3 16 26 44. 2 28 37 50. 2 73 38 41. 2	Hereford _____ Sightly_____ Wheeler_____ Hill_____	7, 208. 2 20, 289. 5 4, 607. 2 3, 566. 1	3. 857829 4. 307272 3. 663433 3. 552190
Beecher_____	45 00 44. 066 71 29 07. 507	130 34 24. 2 142 01 36. 4 173 48 08. 6	310 29 28. 3 321 59 57. 0 353 47 40. 5	Hereford _____ Lambert_____ Wheeler_____	12, 037. 7 4, 997. 7 8, 030. 1	4. 080545 3. 698768 3. 904722
Beecher tablet_____	45 00 44. 050 71 29 07. 439	108 23 130 34 14. 1	288 23 310 29 18. 2	Beecher_____ Hereford _____	1. 565 12, 039. 2	0. 194514 4. 080597
POINTS SUPPLEMEN-TARY TO MAJOR SCHEME TRIANGU-LATION						
Mon. 269_____	46 44 41. 566 69 56 55. 564	140 09 32. 8	320 09 27. 7	Leverrier_____	234. 2	2. 369565
Mon. 273_____	46 42 07. 619 69 59 28. 624	212 07 49. 6 214 20 49. 2	32 09 35. 9 34 22 40. 6	Leverrier_____ Mon. 269_____	5, 826. 8 5, 758. 76	3. 765431 3. 760329
Mon. 303_____	46 25 48. 267 70 03 15. 559	308 08 09. 9	128 09 31. 0	Hardwood Mtn___	3, 041. 4	3. 483075
Mon. 307_____	46 25 12. 831 70 03 23. 074	188 20 31. 2 287 04 17. 7	8 20 36. 7 107 05 44. 3	Mon. 303_____ Hardwood Mtn___	1, 105. 87 2, 670. 4	3. 043706 3. 426570
Ref. Mon. S–73_____	46 09 31. 183 70 15 03. 088	56 30 27. 4	236 29 33. 9	Maheux_____	1, 906. 0	3. 280121
Ref. Mon. S–74_____	46 09 03. 452 70 14 23. 300	85 25 50. 0 135 05 07. 2	265 24 27. 8 315 04 38. 5	Maheux_____ Ref. Mon. S–73___	2, 451. 2 1, 209. 16	3. 389376 3. 082483
Bear_____	45 30 31. 891 70 39 49. 906	33 31 01. 8 81 12 04. 4 129 50 23. 9 168 12 02. 3	213 30 23. 0 261 09 54. 3 309 48 56. 7 348 11 41. 7	Van Dyke_____ Mon. 405_____ Wait_____ Dome_____	2, 136. 7 4, 008. 0 3, 455. 6 3, 070. 2	3. 329734 3. 602933 3. 538520 3. 487172

LAKE POHENAGAMOOK TO THE VERMONT-QUEBEC BOUNDARY—Continued

Station	Latitude and longitude	Azimuth	Back azimuth	To station	Distance (meters)	Logarithm
POINTS SUPPLEMENTARY TO MAJOR SCHEME TRIANGULATION—contd.	° ′ ″	° ′ ″	° ′ ″			
Saddle	45 22 41. 943	21 26 23. 8	201 24 20. 2	Snow	10, 358. 3	4. 015290
	70 39 41. 659	122 02 15. 7	301 57 06. 9	Mon. 425	11, 118. 5	4. 046046
		198 38 07. 4	18 39 09. 2	Mon. 411	5, 901. 6	3. 770969
		243 43 08. 5	63 48 07. 6	Kibby	10, 184. 9	4. 007955
Mon. 402	45 32 48. 770	12 33 50. 1	192 33 46. 1	Boundary	548. 1	2. 738899
	70 41 23. 566	239 37 56. 0	59 38 15. 5	Hughey	685. 4	2. 835935
		296 44 49. 1	116 45 13. 7	Dean	841. 1	2. 924873
Mon. 403–6	45 31 36. 319	12 00 32. 6	192 00 14. 5	Mon. 405	2, 661. 6	3. 425149
	70 42 26. 843	329 25 12. 2	149 26 25. 4	Van Dyke	4, 379. 2	3. 641397
		344 48 47. 8	164 49 37. 8	Merrill	5, 808. 0	3. 764030
Traverse station A	45 32 48. 875	12 13 30. 3	192 13 26. 3	Boundary	550. 7	2. 740938
	70 41 23. 687	239 58 28. 7	59 58 48. 2	Hughey	686. 0	2. 836346
		296 51 42. 2	116 52 06. 8	Dean	844. 9	2. 926826
Hughey Ridge	45 33 02. 028	42 23 13. 3	222 22 44. 8	Boundary	1, 278. 4	3. 106663
	70 40 49. 339	67 26 08. 9	247 26 03. 9	Hughey	163. 6	2. 213885
Traverse station B	45 33 38. 463	3 39 14. 7	183 39 11. 5	Traverse station A	1, 534. 02	3. 185832
	70 41 19. 181	5 54 56. 1	185 54 48. 9	Boundary	2, 080. 2	3. 318110
		330 04 49. 7	150 05 11. 0	Hughey Ridge	1, 297. 8	3. 113204
Mon. 403	45 31 47. 862	20 37 33. 7	200 36 57. 1	Mon. 405	3, 162. 4	3. 500013
	70 42 01. 038	57 31 48. 7	237 31 30. 2	Mon. 403–6	663. 7	2. 821988
		304 30 25. 9	124 30 32. 2	Wait	233. 3	2. 367985
Mon. 404 ecc	45 31 08. 57	180 17 37	0 17 37	Mon. 403–6	856. 8	2. 932895
	70 42 27. 05	322 32 23	142 33 36	Van Dyke	3, 670. 2	3. 564694
		342 11 06	162 11 57	Merrill	4, 987. 5	3. 697887
Mon. 404	45 31 21. 38	323 21 42	143 23 03	Van Dyke	4, 123. 4	3. 615257
	70 42 37. 56	330 00 03	150 00 11	Mon. 404 ecc	456. 56	2. 659498
Mon. 406 ecc	45 29 16. 43	187 49 32	7 49 40	Mon. 405	1, 731. 5	3. 238416
	70 43 03. 21	259 41 24	79 43 03	Van Dyke	3, 067. 1	3. 486729
		299 05 38	119 06 54	Merrill	2, 645. 2	3. 422459
Mon. 406	45 29 16. 37	100 37 40	280 37 40	Mon. 406 ecc	9. 30	0. 968296
	70 43 02. 79	259 37 40	79 39 19	Van Dyke	3,058. 4	3. 485498
Mon. 407 ecc	45 28 38. 07	171 57 08	351 56 42	Mon. 403–6	5, 557. 8	3. 744906
	70 41 50. 99	179 44 30	359 44 29	Wait	5, 727. 3	3. 757948
		219 54 41	39 55 29	Van Dyke	2, 258. 9	3. 353900
Mon. 407	45 28 38. 72	10 26 11	190 26 11	Mon. 407 ecc	20. 53	1. 312389
	70 41 50. 82	220 10 11	40 10 59	Van Dyke	2, 241. 1	3. 350454
South	45 28 24. 539	185 25 24. 7	5 25 31. 1	Van Dyke	2, 159. 8	3. 334420
	70 40 53. 640	276 47 22. 1	96 49 38. 0	Layton	4, 170. 9	3. 620225
		306 35 12. 9	126 36 45. 7	Bump	3, 522. 9	3. 546897
		323 12 17. 7	143 13 35. 1	Mon. 410	3, 944. 2	3. 595958
Mon. 408 ecc	45 28 00. 32	231 18 26	51 18 56	South	1, 196. 4	3. 077878
	70 41 36. 63	267 07 08	87 09 54	Layton	5, 081. 9	3. 706027
		289 45 22	109 47 25	Bump	3, 998. 1	3. 601859
Mon. 408	45 28 00. 02	137 15 28	317 15 28	Mon. 408 ecc	12. 31	1. 090258
	70 41 36. 25	289 40 28	109 42 31	Bump	3, 987. 2	3. 600672
Mon. 409 ecc	45 27 24. 31	251 43 34	71 45 49	Layton	4, 357. 1	3. 639202
	70 40 53. 45	274 51 58	94 53 30	Bump	2, 834. 7	3. 452510
		298 51 01	118 52 18	Mon. 410	2, 692. 4	3. 430133

LAKE POHENAGAMOOK TO THE VERMONT-QUEBEC BOUNDARY—Continued

Station	Latitude and longitude	Azimuth	Back azimuth	To station	Distance (meters)	Logarithm
POINTS SUPPLEMENTARY TO MAJOR SCHEME TRIANGULATION—contd.	° ′ ″	° ′ ″	° ′ ″			
Mon. 409	45 27 24. 28 70 40 53. 49	218 11 31 274 50 31	38 11 31 94 52 04	Mon. 409 ecc Bump	1. 42 2, 835. 5	0. 153662 3. 452630
Mon. 412 ecc	45 25 20. 75 70 37 40. 12	132 20 20 214 53 27 273 29 45	312 19 55 34 54 00 93 33 17	Mon. 411 Moccasin Kibby	1, 023. 3 1, 763. 6 6, 501. 5	3. 009999 3. 246392 3. 813014
Mon. 412	45 25 21. 51 70 37 42. 50	273 40 22 294 25 22	93 43 56 114 25 24	Kibby Mon. 412 ecc	6, 554. 6 56. 83	3. 816549 1. 754562
Brown	45 24 00. 768 70 37 25. 232	50 39 46. 0 161 07 26. 3 189 55 36. 8 251 25 16. 7	230 38 08. 9 341 06 50. 9 9 55 59. 2 71 28 38. 7	Saddle Mon. 411 Moccasin Kibby	3, 837. 9 3, 338. 0 3, 975. 3 6, 504. 8	3. 584098 3. 523486 3. 599365 3. 813236
Rain	45 24 10. 696 70 35 18. 440	83 40 15. 4 126 38 20. 6 150 09 31. 9 242 38 31. 4	263 38 45. 1 306 36 14. 9 330 08 24. 0 62 40 23. 1	Brown Mon. 411 Moccasin Kibby	2, 774. 6 4, 780. 9 4, 161. 3 3, 838. 4	3. 443200 3. 679507 3. 619232 3. 584147
Le Roy	45 24 57. 256 70 34 28. 348	37 09 39. 8 106 02 42. 3 124 30 53. 3 262 00 01. 1	217 09 04. 1 286 00 00. 9 304 29 09. 7 82 01 17. 1	Rain Mon. 411 Moccasin Kibby	1, 803. 5 5, 124. 8 3, 834. 4 2, 342. 7	3. 256119 3. 709676 3. 583697 3. 369724
Mon. 414 ecc	45 24 09. 00 70 37 18. 95	49 07 45 157 16 28 188 31 26 268 50 38	229 06 03 337 15 48 8 31 44 88 52 04	Saddle Mon. 411 Moccasin Rain	4, 106. 2 3, 148. 8 3, 702. 5 2, 621. 5	3. 613435 3. 498148 3. 568494 3. 418549
Mon. 414	45 24 09. 09 70 37 19. 27	157 22 09 292 34 09	337 21 29 112 34 09	Mon. 411 Mon. 414 ecc	3, 143. 6 7. 39	3. 497423 0. 868527
Back	45 23 11. 214 70 39 43. 803	202 23 58. 8 243 04 36. 4 357 02 40. 2	22 25 02. 1 63 06 15. 1 177 02 41. 7	Mon. 411 Brown Saddle	5, 071. 1 3, 380. 2 904. 9	3. 705106 3. 528947 2. 956587
Mon. 413 ecc	45 24 36. 83 70 38 05. 68	30 29 32 38 55 47 282 29 31 321 41 07	210 28 23 218 54 37 102 31 30 141 41 36	Saddle Back Rain Brown	4, 115. 7 3, 397. 3 3, 725. 4 1, 418. 9	3. 614441 3. 531129 3. 571169 3. 151938
Mon. 413	45 24 37. 24 70 38 05. 66	1 24 23 30 24 23	181 24 23 210 23 15	Mon. 413 ecc Saddle	12. 66 4, 126. 8	1. 102331 3. 615609
Joseph	45 23 18. 634 70 38 19. 772	57 33 31. 1 82 51 55. 5 222 21 38. 9	237 32 32. 8 262 50 55. 7 42 22 17. 8	Saddle Back Brown	2, 111. 2 1, 842. 4 1, 760. 5	3. 324521 3. 265373 3. 245636
Mon. 415 ecc	45 22 56. 95 70 38 14. 78	76 14 18 102 49 12 170 47 09 208 40 31	256 13 16 282 48 09 350 47 06 28 41 07	Saddle Back Joseph Brown	1, 946. 2 1, 986. 2 678. 3 2, 245. 8	3. 289185 3. 298025 2. 831396 3. 351369
Mon. 415	45 22 57. 57 70 38 13. 25	59 59 39 75 55 39	239 59 38 255 54 36	Mon. 415 ecc Saddle	38. 49 1, 983. 2	1. 585348 3. 297361
Mon. 416 ecc	45 22 41. 12 70 38 57. 00	91 30 11 132 22 51 214 57 37	271 29 39 312 22 18 34 58 03	Saddle Back Joseph	972. 1 1, 378. 5 1, 413. 2	2. 987703 3. 139401 3. 150218
Mon. 416	45 22 40. 90 70 38 56. 77	91 53 16 143 09 16	271 52 44 323 09 16	Saddle Mon. 416 ecc	977. 3 8. 37	2. 990026 0. 922570
Mon. 417	45 22 42. 41 70 39 41. 06	42 29 09 230 40 38	222 29 09 50 42 15	Saddle Brown	19. 48 3, 818. 7	1. 289522 3. 581913

LAKE POHENAGAMOOK TO THE VERMONT-QUEBEC BOUNDARY—Continued

Station	Latitude and longitude	Azimuth	Back azimuth	To station	Distance (meters)	Logarithm
POINTS SUPPLEMENTARY TO MAJOR SCHEME TRIANGULATION—contd.	° ′ ″	° ′ ″	° ′ ″			
Mon. 418	45 23 11. 31	277 26 26	97 26 26	Back	22. 65	1. 354992
	70 39 44. 84	355 38 26	175 38 28	Saddle	909. 2	2. 958674
Mon. 419 ecc	45 23 42. 13	260 23 16	80 25 58	Mon. 414	4, 997. 2	3. 698723
	70 41 05. 81	298 08 16	118 09 14	Back	2, 023. 1	3. 306016
		315 25 00	135 26 00	Saddle	2, 608. 3	3. 416363
Mon. 419	45 23 41. 86	121 59 46	301 59 46	Mon. 419 ecc	15. 48	1. 189631
	70 41 05. 20	315 29 46	135 30 46	Saddle	2, 593. 3	3. 413847
Mon. 420 ecc	45 23 37. 31	261 12 24	81 15 52	Mon. 414	6, 439. 0	3. 808817
	70 42 11. 85	284 01 52	104 03 37	Back	3, 319. 7	3. 521105
		297 36 07	117 37 54	Saddle	3, 687. 5	3. 566732
Mon. 420	45 23 36. 98	181 34 26	1 34 26	Mon. 420 ecc	10. 36	1. 015234
	70 42 11. 86	297 27 26	117 29 13	Saddle	3, 683. 0	3. 566198
Mon. 421 ecc	45 23 42. 49	225 08 43	45 11 46	Mon. 410	7, 870. 2	3. 895984
	70 43 21. 66	240 48 15	60 51 54	Mon. 411	7, 638. 7	3. 883019
		264 00 59	84 05 17	Mon. 414	7, 924. 7	3. 898982
		291 18 46	111 21 23	Saddle	5, 138. 1	3. 710800
Mon. 421	45 23 42. 07	136 11 38	316 11 38	Mon. 421 ecc	18. 15	1. 258901
	70 43 21. 08	291 13 38	111 16 14	Saddle	5, 121. 6	3. 709405
Mon. 422 ecc	45 24 25. 73	126 58 51	306 56 54	Mon. 425	4, 468. 6	3. 650168
	70 44 11. 03	237 37 35	57 41 13	Mon. 410	7, 876. 3	3. 896323
		252 49 31	72 53 45	Mon. 411	8, 102. 9	3. 908640
		298 38 36	118 41 48	Saddle	6, 678. 2	3. 824662
Mon. 422	45 24 25. 87	252 52 48	72 57 02	Mon. 411	8, 112. 8	3. 909170
	70 44 11. 57	290 52 48	110 52 48	Mon. 422 ecc	12. 59	1. 100164
Mon. 423 ecc	45 25 17. 34	110 19 26	290 17 49	Mon. 425	3, 150. 7	3. 498404
	70 44 39. 33	250 08 33	70 12 32	Mon. 410	7, 726. 5	3. 887984
		264 31 53	84 36 27	Mon. 411	8, 394. 9	3. 924017
		306 30 33	126 34 05	Saddle	8, 057. 9	3. 906224
Mon. 423	45 25 16. 53	225 49 44	45 49 45	Mon. 423 ecc	35. 79	1. 553762
	70 44 40. 51	264 22 44	84 27 19	Mon. 411	8, 422. 9	3. 925461
Mon. 424 ecc	45 25 36. 82	257 13 27	77 18 20	Mon. 410	9, 159. 4	3. 961865
	70 45 55. 96	268 50 59	88 56 28	Mon. 411	10, 024. 7	4. 001071
		303 30 52	123 35 18	Saddle	9, 768. 0	3. 989807
Mon. 424	45 25 36. 07	244 19 25	64 19 26	Mon. 424 ecc	53. 25	1. 726311
	70 45 58. 17	268 43 25	88 48 55	Mon. 411	10, 073. 2	4. 003167
Mon. 426 ecc	45 25 03. 925	227 44 11. 9	47 45 06. 3	Mon. 425	2, 242. 2	3. 350683
	70 48 11. 585	255 37 13. 8	75 43 43. 3	Mon. 410	12, 264. 1	4. 088636
		332 24 54. 7	152 28 53. 9	Snow	15, 820. 0	4. 199207
Mon. 426	45 25 04. 352	228 15 09. 0	48 16 03. 9	Mon. 425	2, 245. 0	3. 351213
	70 48 12. 300	310 17 09. 0	130 17 09. 5	Mon. 426 ecc	20. 39	1. 309417
Moran	45 17 38. 822	111 23 14. 7	291 22 04. 7	Gosford	2, 306. 0	3. 362854
	70 50 23. 753	196 33 06. 9	16 35 35. 3	Mon. 425	15, 909. 7	4. 201663
		271 33 09. 8	91 38 42. 7	Snow	10, 209. 5	4. 009004
Mon. 427 ecc	45 24 11. 531	6 41 56. 3	186 41 09. 8	Moran	12, 206. 7	4. 086598
	70 49 18. 405	224 52 11. 7	44 53 53. 7	Mon. 425	4, 410. 9	3. 644532
		324 41 55. 5	144 46 42. 2	Snow	15, 196. 6	4. 181746
Mon. 427	45 24 11. 792	225 02 15. 4	45 03 57. 7	Mon. 425	4, 412. 5	3. 644682
	70 49 18. 875	308 14 15. 4	128 14 15. 7	Mon. 427 ecc	13. 01	1. 114244

LAKE POHENAGAMOOK TO THE VERMONT-QUEBEC BOUNDARY—Continued

Station	Latitude and longitude	Azimuth	Back azimuth	To station	Distance (meters)	Loga-rithm
POINTS SUPPLEMEN-TARY TO MAJOR SCHEME TRIANGU-LATION—contd.	° ′ ″	° ′ ″	° ′ ″			
Mon. 428 ecc	45 23 27. 680	6 24 31. 4	186 23 51. 9	Moran	10, 837. 4	4. 034926
	70 49 28. 238	83 46 07. 2	263 42 19. 4	Woburn	7, 004. 1	3. 845350
		216 35 18. 3	36 37 07. 3	Mon. 425	5, 579. 4	3. 746588
		320 50 45. 4	140 55 39. 1	Snow	14, 247. 5	4. 153740
Mon. 428	45 23 29. 561	216 59 35. 4	37 01 24. 5	Mon. 425	5, 536. 3	3. 743217
	70 49 28. 496	354 29 15. 2	174 29 15. 3	Mon. 428 ecc	58. 34	1. 765958
Mine	45 20 40. 475	124 36 26. 9	304 32 58. 3	Woburn	7, 749. 0	3. 889244
	70 49 55. 118	186 27 45. 6	6 28 04. 7	Mon. 428 ecc	5, 194. 9	3. 715580
		202 04 22. 8	22 06 30. 9	Mon. 425	10, 404. 8	4. 017232
Dead	45 21 03. 798	67 03 47. 0	247 02 51. 4	Mine	1, 846. 9	3. 266454
	70 48 36. 990	165 54 41. 3	345 54 04. 8	Mon. 428 ecc	4, 579. 7	3. 660840
Arnold	45 22 04. 024	201 45 34. 1	21 46 07. 8	Mon. 428 ecc	2, 780. 8	3. 444175
	70 50 15. 628	310 53 02. 1	130 54 12. 3	Dead	2, 840. 1	3. 453329
		350 10 41. 4	170 10 56. 0	Mine	2, 617. 6	3. 417910
Mon. 429 ecc	45 23 02. 735	46 36 08. 2	226 35 05. 5	Arnold	2, 637. 7	3. 421220
	70 48 47. 560	131 02 05. 9	311 01 36. 9	Mon. 428 ecc	1, 173. 1	3. 069327
		356 24 50. 9	176 24 58. 4	Dead	3, 679. 0	3. 565729
Mon. 429	45 23 05. 039	45 17 55. 4	225 16 53. 2	Arnold	2, 677. 5	3. 427723
	70 48 48. 178	128 44 06. 9	308 43 38. 4	Mon. 428 ecc	1, 117. 2	3. 048113
		349 18 11. 7	169 18 12. 2	Mon. 429 ecc	72. 4	1. 859591
Mon. 430 ecc	45 22 37. 231	66 55 53. 2	246 54 34. 5	Arnold	2, 615. 1	3. 417495
	70 48 25. 067	138 34 49. 9	318 34 04. 9	Mon. 428 ecc	2, 077. 1	3. 317462
		148 08 22. 6	328 08 06. 6	Mon. 429 ecc	927. 1	2. 967108
Mon. 430	45 22 37. 228	148 38 49. 4	328 38 33. 7	Mon. 429 ecc	922. 1	2. 964783
	70 48 25. 507	269 32 49. 4	89 32 49. 7	Mon. 430 ecc	9. 57	0. 980912
Mon. 431	45 21 54. 394	96 21 08. 2	276 19 40. 7	Arnold	2, 692. 2	3. 430104
	70 48 12. 678	150 17 12. 7	330 16 18. 9	Mon. 428 ecc	3, 316. 1	3. 520632
		160 13 00. 7	340 12 35. 9	Mon. 429 ecc	2, 242. 2	3. 350675
		192 52 58. 8	12 53 54. 0	Mon. 425	7, 549. 2	3. 877900
Stone	45 21 32. 937	115 27 08. 4	295 26 02. 5	Arnold	2, 233. 8	3. 349052
	70 48 42. 943	164 27 21. 6	344 26 49. 4	Mon. 428 ecc	3, 676. 9	3. 565477
Mon. 432 ecc	45 21 31. 337	110 26 34. 4	290 26 30. 0	Stone	141. 5	2. 150680
	70 48 36. 851	115 09 20. 0	295 08 09. 7	Arnold	2, 374. 8	3. 375629
		162 42 48. 0	342 42 11. 4	Mon. 428 ecc	3, 761. 7	3. 575388
		175 16 47. 8	355 16 40. 2	Mon. 429 ecc	2, 831. 2	3. 451977
Mon. 432	45 21 31. 691	106 41 30. 0	286 41 25. 8	Stone	133. 9	2. 126926
	70 48 37. 047	338 42 30. 0	158 42 30. 2	Mon. 432 ecc	11. 74	1. 069782
Mon. 433	45 21 07. 046	63 09 23. 9	243 08 31. 0	Mine	1, 816. 1	3. 259140
	70 48 40. 688	130 24 56. 1	310 23 48. 6	Arnold	2, 713. 7	3. 433559
		166 35 58. 9	346 35 25. 1	Mon. 428 ecc	4, 463. 2	3. 649649
River	45 20 59. 450	70 37 23. 7	250 36 29. 3	Mine	1, 764. 9	3. 246723
	70 48 38. 642	133 22 14. 6	313 21 05. 6	Arnold	2, 903. 5	3. 462918
		194 59 57. 3	14 59 58. 5	Dead	139. 0	2. 142928
White	45 20 58. 035	264 36 59. 6	84 38 01. 4	Dead	1, 899. 5	3. 278648
	70 50 03. 866	268 38 32. 6	88 39 33. 2	River	1, 855. 8	3. 268520
		340 38 27. 4	160 38 33. 6	Mine	574. 6	2. 759341
Seymour	45 19 22. 438	20 29 21. 4	200 28 52. 7	Gosford	2, 517. 4	3. 400951
	70 51 21. 860	146 35 31. 8	326 33 04. 9	Woburn	8, 156. 2	3. 911487
		338 24 14. 2	158 24 55. 5	Moran	3, 440. 1	3. 536574

LAKE POHENAGAMOOK TO THE VERMONT-QUEBEC BOUNDARY—Continued

Station	Latitude and longitude	Azimuth	Back azimuth	To station	Distance (meters)	Loga- rithm
POINTS SUPPLEMEN- TARY TO MAJOR SCHEME TRIANGU- LATION—contd.	° ′ ″	° ′ ″	° ′ ″			
Steep	45 19 40. 656	30 32 50. 0	210 31 37. 6	Moran	4, 366. 9	3. 640169
	70 48 41. 898	56 14 07. 1	236 11 44. 7	Gosford	5, 252. 2	3. 720344
		296 50 21. 6	116 54 42. 2	Snow	8, 950. 4	3. 951841
Mon. 434 ecc	45 20 48. 311	81 04 34. 7	261 03 44. 4	Mine	1, 558. 2	3. 192610
	70 48 44. 414	99 51 14. 4	279 50 17. 9	White	1, 755. 5	3. 244402
		200 04 09. 9	20 04 14. 0	River	366. 1	2. 563630
		358 29 31. 3	178 29 33. 1	Steep	2, 089. 6	3. 320056
Mon. 434	45 20 48. 787	203 53 05. 3	23 53 10. 1	River	360. 0	2. 556340
	70 48 45. 339	306 07 05. 3	126 07 06. 0	Mon. 434 ecc	24. 93	1. 396722
Mon. 435 ecc	45 20 24. 078	40 43 48. 9	220 41 49. 2	Gosford	5, 621. 7	3. 749868
	70 49 13. 942	55 40 25. 2	235 38 54. 2	Seymour	3, 373. 5	3. 528076
		119 27 25. 3	299 26 55. 9	Mine	1, 029. 5	3. 012634
		124 00 40. 3	303 56 42. 3	Woburn	8, 774. 8	3. 943238
Mon. 435	45 20 23. 830	40 53 50. 5	220 51 50. 3	Gosford	5, 625. 7	3. 750178
	70 49 13. 252	117 01 50. 5	297 01 50. 0	Mon. 435 ecc	16. 87	1. 227218
Mon. 436 ecc	45 19 55. 323	22 42 21. 3	202 41 23. 8	Moran	4, 567. 8	3. 659704
	70 49 02. 837	49 13 27. 0	229 11 19. 5	Gosford	5, 163. 4	3. 712936
		71 28 32. 5	251 26 53. 7	Seymour	3, 193. 3	3. 504233
Mon. 436	45 19 54. 808	49 23 03. 1	229 20 55. 5	Gosford	5, 155. 8	3. 712294
	70 49 02. 671	167 11 03. 1	347 11 03. 0	Mon. 436 ecc	16. 30	1. 212188
Mon. 437	45 19 40. 955	69 36 20. 9	249 36 20. 1	Steep	26. 49	1. 423033
	70 48 40. 758	181 50 13. 0	1 50 15. 7	Dead	2, 558. 8	3. 408038
Mon. 438 ecc	45 19 25. 555	35 18 00. 8	215 16 44. 7	Moran	4, 036. 8	3. 606037
	70 48 36. 700	61 17 47. 2	241 15 21. 1	Gosford	5, 107. 2	3. 708179
		88 29 01. 3	268 27 03. 9	Seymour	3, 598. 3	3. 556099
		166 21 08. 7	346 21 05. 0	Steep	479. 7	2. 680987
Mon. 438	45 19 27. 758	61 29 18. 4	241 26 47. 0	Gosford	5, 280. 9	3. 722704
	70 48 29. 318	67 04 18. 4	247 04 13. 1	Mon. 438 ecc	174. 56	2. 241945
Mon. 439 ecc	45 18 42. 470	50 59 42. 7	230 58 23. 6	Moran	3, 121. 2	3. 494318
	70 48 32. 444	76 12 16. 4	256 09 47. 3	Gosford	4, 708. 1	3. 672847
		108 30 18. 6	288 28 18. 2	Seymour	3, 890. 9	3. 590054
		173 27 42. 2	353 27 35. 5	Steep	1, 808. 0	3. 257209
Mon. 439	45 18 42. 492	108 32 24. 4	288 30 24. 3	Seymour	3, 881. 7	3. 589023
	70 48 32. 880	274 04 24. 4	94 04 24. 7	Mon. 439 ecc	9. 52	0. 978774
Mon. 440 ecc	45 18 21. 419	58 30 25. 7	238 29 15. 7	Moran	2, 516. 6	3. 400814
	70 48 45. 272	83 42 44. 2	263 40 24. 2	Gosford	4, 318. 8	3. 635362
		281 11 32. 7	101 15 55. 6	Snow	8, 216. 0	3. 914660
Mon. 440	45 18 21. 769	4 48 03. 5	184 48 03. 5	Mon. 440 ecc	10. 85	1. 035430
	70 48 45. 230	281 16 03. 5	101 20 26. 3	Snow	8, 217. 2	3. 914724
Mon. 441 ecc	45 17 55. 218	73 23 51. 6	253 22 56. 3	Moran	1, 770. 7	3. 248156
	70 49 05. 878	168 08 00. 0	348 07 25. 0	Mine	5, 213. 2	3. 717107
		189 06 52. 0	9 07 09. 1	Steep	3, 296. 6	3. 518071
Mon. 441	45 17 55. 419	189 32 01. 6	9 32 19. 4	Steep	3, 294. 3	3. 517766
	70 49 06. 953	284 48 01. 6	104 48 02. 3	Mon. 441 ecc	24. 24	1. 384533
Mon. 442 ecc	45 17 50. 592	140 48 24. 5	320 47 09. 1	Seymour	3, 659. 0	3. 563366
	70 49 35. 691	144 48 56. 8	324 45 14. 5	Woburn	11, 802. 3	4. 071965
		175 23 21. 7	355 23 07. 9	Mine	5, 261. 6	3. 721117
Mon. 442	45 17 50. 460	144 49 38. 1	324 45 55. 8	Woburn	11, 805. 6	4. 072088
	70 49 35. 691	180 08 38. 1	0 08 38. 1	Mon. 442 ecc	4. 08	0. 610979

LAKE POHENAGAMOOK TO THE VERMONT-QUEBEC BOUNDARY—Continued

Station	Latitude and longitude	Azimuth	Back azimuth	To station	Distance (meters)	Logarithm
POINTS SUPPLEMENTARY TO MAJOR SCHEME TRIANGULATION—contd.	° ′ ″	° ′ ″	° ′ ″			
Boots	45 17 11. 946	202 31 09. 4	22 31 32. 0	Gosford	1, 808. 2	3. 257237
	70 52 34. 090	253 42 10. 8	73 43 43. 4	Moran	2, 959. 0	3. 471138
Dutch	45 16 01. 528	128 53 57. 6	308 52 29. 7	Boots	3, 462. 8	3. 539427
	70 50 30. 430	152 29 43. 5	332 28 38. 2	Gosford	4, 334. 4	3. 636926
		182 46 23. 6	2 46 28. 3	Moran	3, 007. 1	3. 478151
Boggy	45 14 32. 864	198 13 23. 2	18 14 15. 9	Boots	5, 170. 6	3. 713541
	70 53 48. 285	237 35 15. 5	57 37 36. 1	Dutch	5, 109. 3	3. 708363
Mon. 450	45 14 14. 620	96 53 29. 3	276 50 57. 0	Boggy	4, 708. 4	3. 672874
	70 50 13. 962	150 50 54. 5	330 49 14. 9	Boots	6, 269. 1	3. 797206
		173 47 30. 3	353 47 18. 6	Dutch	3, 319. 9	3. 521122
Suptic	45 13 36. 234	123 40 49. 2	303 39 23. 8	Boggy	3, 153. 4	3. 498784
	70 51 47. 968	200 38 54. 8	20 39 49. 9	Dutch	4, 793. 5	3. 680657
		239 58 07. 8	59 59 14. 6	Mon. 450	2, 368. 4	3. 374457
Dennison	45 15 12 320	23 15 25. 4	203 14 43. 9	Suptic	3, 228. 5	3. 508999
	70 50 49. 534	72 39 55. 2	252 37 48. 3	Boggy	4, 084. 0	3. 611091
		195 19 53. 4	15 20 07. 0	Dutch	1, 575. 2	3. 197333
Smith	45 16 51. 626	241 49 34. 2	61 51 54. 2	Gosford	4, 869. 3	3. 687463
	70 55 19. 316	260 06 06. 0	80 08 03. 4	Boots	3, 655. 2	3. 562910
		335 07 56. 1	155 09 00. 8	Boggy	4, 721. 2	3. 674052
Boulder	45 14 54. 458	74 32 29. 8	254 31 11. 4	Boggy	2, 499. 3	3. 397825
	70 51 57. 834	249 40 38. 0	69 41 26. 5	Dennison	1, 588. 2	3. 200907
		298 29 10. 7	118 30 24. 5	Mon. 450	2, 577. 8	3. 411241
		354 54 23. 1	174 54 30. 1	Suptic	2, 424. 4	3. 384608
Mon. 443 ecc	45 17 38. 553	8 31 25. 7	188 31 11. 1	Dutch	3, 028. 7	3. 481261
	70 50 09. 838	91 34 11. 8	271 34 01. 9	Moran	303. 3	2. 481912
		271 33 18. 1	91 38 41. 1	Snow	9, 906. 2	3. 995905
Mon. 443	45 17 38. 112	94 12 02. 9	274 11 53. 2	Moran	299. 3	2. 476156
	70 50 10. 053	198 59 02. 9	18 59 03. 1	Mon. 443 ecc	14. 40	1. 158362
Mon. 444 ecc	45 17 06. 367	92 49 59. 7	272 48 05. 6	Boots	3, 504. 2	3. 544587
	70 49 53. 493	146 39 06. 1	326 38 44. 6	Moran	1, 199. 5	3. 078989
		265 39 41. 0	85 44 52. 4	Snow	9, 573. 8	3. 981083
Mon. 444	45 17 06. 357	93 09 25. 1	273 09 24. 9	Mon. 444 ecc	5. 74	0. 758912
	70 49 53. 230	265 39 25. 1	85 44 36. 3	Snow	9, 568. 1	3. 980825
Mon. 445 ecc	45 16 06. 850	125 40 51. 8	305 39 20. 5	Boots	3, 446. 4	3. 537369
	70 50 25. 634	150 13 01. 9	330 11 53. 2	Gosford	4, 240. 3	3. 627393
		180 49 36. 7	0 49 38. 0	Moran	2, 839. 6	3. 453254
Mon. 445	45 16 06. 881	70 51 43. 5	250 51 43. 4	Mon. 445 ecc	2. 90	0. 462098
	70 50 25. 508	150 10 43. 5	330 09 34. 7	Gosford	4, 240. 8	3. 627448
Mon. 446 ecc	45 15 52. 837	136 49 18. 4	316 48 03. 7	Boots	3, 349. 6	3. 524989
	70 50 48. 918	158 45 18. 6	338 44 26. 5	Gosford	4, 412. 5	3. 644687
		189 30 50. 3	9 31 08. 2	Moran	3, 317. 5	3. 520816
		236 20 57. 3	56 21 10. 5	Dutch	484. 2	2. 685010
Mon. 446	45 15 52. 746	158 45 24. 0	338 44 31. 9	Gosford	4, 415. 5	3. 644983
	70 50 48. 873	160 57 24. 0	340 57 24. 0	Mon. 446 ecc	2. 96	0. 470998
		236 00 34. 1	56 00 47. 2	Dutch	484. 9	2. 685691
Mon. 447 ecc	45 15 17. 191	19 48 21. 9	199 47 45. 3	Suptic	3, 312. 5	3. 520157
	70 50 56. 519	189 16 27. 5	9 16 50. 7	Moran	4, 430. 3	3. 646432
		202 33 52. 2	22 34 10. 7	Dutch	1, 482. 2	3. 170916
		314 37 59. 0	134 38 03. 9	Dennison	214. 0	2. 330500

LAKE POHENAGAMOOK TO THE VERMONT-QUEBEC BOUNDARY—Continued

Station	Latitude and longitude	Azimuth	Back azimuth	To station	Distance (meters)	Logarithm
POINTS SUPPLEMENTARY TO MAJOR SCHEME TRIANGULATION—contd.	° ′ ″	° ′ ″	° ′ ″			
Mon. 447	45 15 17. 093	202 40 47. 5	22 41 06. 2	Dutch	1, 486. 7	3. 172234
	70 50 56. 725	236 10 47. 5	56 10 47. 7	Mon. 447 ecc	5. 41	0. 733197
Mon. 448 ecc	45 14 48. 503	26 23 54. 3	206 23 18. 3	Suptic	2, 490. 6	3. 396308
	70 50 57. 209	82 38 38. 1	262 36 36. 7	Boggy	3, 762. 1	3. 575434
		97 55 20. 3	277 54 37. 3	Boulder	1, 334. 8	3. 125430
Mon. 448	45 14 48. 903	318 11 12. 2	138 11 43. 1	Mon. 450	1, 419. 9	3. 152259
	70 50 57. 363	344 48 12. 2	164 48 12. 3	Mon. 448 ecc	12. 79	1. 106837
Mon. 449 ecc	45 14 27. 085	92 29 08. 9	272 26 54. 1	Boggy	4, 144. 4	3. 617463
	70 50 38. 440	116 01 17. 0	296 00 20. 6	Boulder	1, 926. 7	3. 284817
		170 10 19. 6	350 10 11. 7	Dennison	1, 417. 3	3. 151447
Mon. 449	45 14 26. 984	170 46 02. 0	350 45 54. 6	Dennison	1, 417. 9	3. 151660
	70 50 39. 101	257 46 02. 0	77 46 02. 5	Mon. 449 ecc	14. 74	1. 168615
Mon. 451 ecc	45 13 56. 304	107 49 17. 6	287 47 23. 2	Boggy	3, 691. 0	3. 567141
	70 51 07. 172	148 23 35. 3	328 22 59. 3	Boulder	2, 108. 1	3. 323889
		189 18 27. 7	9 18 40. 2	Dennison	2, 378. 0	3. 376218
		191 42 21. 5	11 42 47. 6	Dutch	3, 948. 0	3. 596376
Mon. 451	45 13 55. 903	148 40 19. 9	328 39 44. 0	Boulder	2, 116. 3	3. 325579
	70 51 07. 378	199 54 19. 9	19 54 20. 0	Mon. 451 ecc	13. 17	1. 119586
Mon. 452 ecc	45 14 03. 363	118 44 45. 4	298 43 51. 4	Boggy	1, 894. 1	3. 277410
	70 52 32. 141	205 22 28. 9	25 22 53. 3	Boulder	1, 745. 8	3. 242000
		226 25 12. 7	46 26 25. 6	Dennison	3, 088. 6	3. 489760
		263 24 35. 2	83 26 13. 4	Mon. 450	3, 034. 0	3. 482017
Mon. 452	45 14 03. 234	107 18 23. 7	287 18 23. 3	Mon. 452 ecc	13. 37	1. 126131
	70 52 31. 556	204 56 23. 7	24 56 47. 7	Boulder	1, 744. 0	3. 241546
Mon. 453 ecc	45 14 05. 314	223 43 38. 3	43 44 25. 5	Boulder	2, 099. 7	3. 322150
	70 53 04. 386	234 51 59. 2	54 53 34. 9	Dennison	3, 595. 6	3. 555777
		265 33 51. 5	85 35 52. 5	Mon. 450	3, 728. 5	3. 571529
		298 17 44. 1	118 18 38. 3	Suptic	1, 893. 4	3. 277238
Mon. 453	45 14 05. 808	265 49 38. 0	85 51 39. 9	Mon. 450	3, 753. 7	3. 574464
	70 53 05. 601	299 53 38. 0	119 53 38. 9	Mon. 453 ecc	30. 57	1. 485324
Mon. 454 ecc	45 14 19. 704	240 20 55. 4	60 21 56. 8	Boulder	2, 169. 2	3. 336306
	70 53 24. 279	244 16 58. 7	64 18 48. 6	Dennison	3, 745. 3	3. 573491
		302 33 32. 4	122 34 40. 8	Suptic	2, 492. 9	3. 396712
Mon. 454	45 14 19. 896	240 33 09. 7	60 34 11. 3	Boulder	2, 170. 9	3. 336632
	70 53 24. 519	318 31 09. 7	138 31 09. 9	Mon. 454 ecc	7. 90	0. 897517
Mon. 455 ecc	45 14 27. 473	155 02 49. 3	335 02 46. 8	Boggy	183. 6	2. 263768
	70 53 44. 734	235 33 27. 8	55 35 45. 8	Dutch	5, 136. 4	3. 710656
		250 03 52. 8	70 05 57. 2	Dennison	4, 063. 9	3. 608943
		250 19 36. 1	70 20 52. 0	Boulder	2, 475. 8	3. 393708
Mon. 455	45 14 27. 195	243 49 05. 3	63 49 05. 9	Mon. 455 ecc	19. 45	1. 289009
	70 53 45. 535	250 02 05. 3	70 04 10. 3	Dennison	4, 083. 2	3. 611005
Louis	45 17 12. 546	79 06 42. 1	259 04 52. 8	Smith	3, 414. 3	3. 533297
	70 52 45. 484	209 39 47. 7	29 40 18. 4	Gosford	1, 900. 9	3. 278963
McLeod	45 17 36. 287	61 17 16. 0	241 15 54. 0	Smith	2, 868. 9	3. 457713
	70 53 23. 871	242 39 13. 0	62 40 11. 0	Gosford	2, 000. 7	3. 301185
		311 13 08. 9	131 13 36. 2	Louis	1, 112. 2	3. 046175
Jule	45 18 11. 107	57 48 45. 3	237 46 38. 3	Smith	4, 604. 0	3. 663131
	70 52 20. 544	114 34 08. 1	294 28 12. 7	Mon. 470	11, 965. 3	4. 077922

LAKE POHENAGAMOOK TO THE VERMONT-QUEBEC BOUNDARY—Continued

Station	Latitude and longitude	Azimuth	Back azimuth	To station	Distance (meters)	Loga- rithm
POINTS SUPPLEMEN- TARY TO MAJOR SCHEME TRIANGU- LATION—contd.	° ′ ″	° ′ ″	° ′ ″			
Nicollet	45 18 48. 550	25 35 10. 3	205 32 00. 4	Rump	13, 509. 4	4. 130635
	70 59 23. 347	156 14 04. 6	336 13 09. 8	Mon. 470	4, 162. 9	3. 619401
		217 17 55. 3	37 21 10. 9	Woburn	9, 875. 7	3. 994567
		277 06 40. 5	97 11 41. 0	Jule	9, 282. 9	3. 967685
		277 43 56. 4	97 49 09. 9	Gosford	9, 697. 3	3. 986651
Bowman	45 17 07. 089	4 59 03. 4	184 58 37. 7	Rump	9, 089. 4	3. 958533
	71 03 14. 487	54 28 02. 8	234 24 32. 7	Salmon	7, 925. 8	3. 899043
		105 28 59. 5	285 26 48. 8	Bon Durban	4, 157. 1	3. 618788
		238 05 50. 5	58 08 34. 8	Nicollet	5, 930. 7	3. 773107
Barker	45 18 21. 618	33 40 45. 5	213 39 55. 5	Bowman	2, 764. 7	3. 441643
	71 02 04. 139	256 37 52. 1	76 39 46. 4	Nicollet	3, 600. 1	3. 556309
Lake	45 17 40. 790	73 28 44. 4	253 26 50. 1	Bowman	3, 655. 3	3. 562918
	71 00 33. 689	122 36 39. 1	302 35 34. 8	Barker	2, 339. 3	3. 369085
		216 13 11. 9	36 14 01. 9	Nicollet	2, 593. 1	3. 413826
Marble	45 19 59. 460	28 24 47. 3	208 23 54. 0	Barker	3, 434. 0	3. 535795
	71 00 49. 137	186 41 10. 0	6 41 16. 2	Mon. 470	1, 631. 7	3. 212652
		286 45 06. 6	106 51 08. 1	Jule	11, 571. 7	4. 063397
		319 30 36. 2	139 31 37. 2	Nicollet	2, 878. 0	3. 459096
		355 30 14. 7	175 30 25. 7	Lake	4, 294. 1	3. 632875
Mon. 456 ecc	45 15 03. 032	149 23 55. 1	329 22 50. 4	Smith	3, 895. 2	3. 590533
	70 53 48. 336	265 46 35. 7	85 48 42. 7	Dennison	3, 909. 5	3. 592126
		276 15 27. 7	96 16 46. 2	Boulder	2, 424. 2	3. 384575
		315 34 22. 5	135 35 48. 0	Suptic	3, 751. 4	3. 574190
Mon. 456	45 15 02. 836	122 25 39. 9	302 25 39. 6	Mon. 456 ecc	11. 28	1. 052232
	70 53 47. 900	265 40 39. 9	85 42 46. 6	Dennison	3, 900. 5	3. 591120
Mon. 457 ecc	45 15 31. 203	190 45 25. 2	10 45 49. 1	McLeod	3, 930. 6	3. 594458
	70 53 57. 538	206 39 05. 2	26 39 56. 4	Louis	3, 500. 7	3. 544155
		258 16 01. 1	78 18 28. 3	Dutch	4, 611. 4	3. 663835
		293 28 40. 6	113 30 05. 7	Boulder	2, 846. 1	3. 454247
Mon. 457	45 15 30. 567	147 03 21. 2	327 03 20. 8	Mon. 457 ecc	23. 39	1. 369049
	70 53 56. 955	190 31 21. 2	10 31 44. 7	McLeod	3, 947. 5	3. 596326
Mon. 458 ecc	45 15 52. 652	201 45 24. 0	21 46 05. 6	McLeod	3, 444. 8	3. 537170
	70 54 22. 470	220 35 27. 9	40 36 36. 8	Louis	3, 248. 4	3. 511674
		266 52 36. 7	86 55 21. 6	Dutch	5, 066. 1	3. 704676
		299 39 14. 4	119 40 57. 2	Boulder	3, 629. 5	3. 559851
Mon. 458	45 15 52. 127	201 49 07. 1	21 49 49. 1	McLeod	3, 463. 8	3. 539554
	70 54 22. 952	212 57 07. 1	32 57 07. 5	Mon. 458 ecc	19. 33	1. 286187
Mon. 459 ecc	45 16 10. 391	209 09 39. 6	29 10 27. 8	McLeod	3, 036. 8	3. 482414
	70 54 31. 778	222 21 39. 0	42 23 25. 2	Gosford	4, 833. 2	3. 684239
		230 21 28. 4	50 22 43. 9	Louis	3, 008. 2	3. 478310
Mon. 459	45 16 10. 222	222 25 57. 1	42 27 43. 7	Gosford	4, 845. 9	3. 685370
	70 54 32. 373	248 05 57. 1	68 05 57. 5	Mon. 459 ecc	13. 98	1. 145600
Mon. 460 ecc	45 16 30. 706	225 04 53. 8	45 06 00. 0	McLeod	2, 867. 7	3. 457536
	70 54 57. 062	232 17 00. 4	52 19 04. 6	Gosford	4, 813. 2	3. 682437
		245 44 24. 5	65 45 58. 0	Louis	3, 145. 2	3. 497652
Mon. 460	45 16 30. 473	207 21 56. 9	27 21 57. 0	Mon. 460 ecc	8. 10	0. 908485
	70 54 57. 233	225 01 56. 9	45 03 03. 2	McLeod	2, 875. 4	3. 458703
Mon. 461 ecc	45 17 17. 604	255 31 17. 9	75 32 30. 8	McLeod	2, 308. 5	3. 363327
	70 55 06. 447	272 53 45. 9	92 55 26. 1	Louis	3, 075. 9	3. 487977
		341 28 06. 1	161 29 01. 7	Boggy	5, 363. 6	3. 729459

LAKE POHENAGAMOOK TO THE VERMONT-QUEBEC BOUNDARY—Continued

Station	Latitude and longitude	Azimuth	Back azimuth	To station	Distance (meters)	Logarithm
POINTS SUPPLEMENTARY TO MAJOR SCHEME TRIANGULATION—contd.	° ′ ″	° ′ ″	° ′ ″			
Mon. 461	45 17 17. 513	106 43 08. 5	286 43 08. 2	Mon. 461 ecc	9. 81	0. 991890
	70 55 06. 016	272 51 08. 5	92 52 48. 4	Louis	3, 066. 4	3. 486629
Mon. 462 ecc	45 17 34. 607	24 54 16. 7	204 53 56. 6	Smith	1, 462. 9	3. 165207
	70 54 51. 051	268 25 38. 4	88 26 40. 3	McLeod	1, 900. 4	3. 278847
		283 57 50. 1	103 59 19. 3	Louis	2, 819. 8	3. 450222
Mon. 462	45 17 35. 218	268 59 51. 6	89 00 53. 6	McLeod	1, 903. 0	3. 279442
	70 54 51. 190	350 51 51. 6	170 51 51. 7	Mon. 462 ecc	19. 11	1. 281261
Mon. 463 ecc	45 18 11. 053	8 31 42. 3	188 31 30. 3	Smith	2, 479. 4	3. 394350
	70 55 02. 445	296 32 31. 3	116 33 41. 3	McLeod	2, 401. 0	3. 380396
		301 10 10. 1	121 11 47. 4	Louis	3, 488. 4	3. 542623
Mon. 463	45 18 10. 773	218 50 21. 9	38 50 22. 1	Mon. 463 ecc	11. 10	1. 045323
	70 55 02. 764	272 06 21. 9	92 08 30. 1	Gosford	3, 934. 4	3. 594879
Mon. 464 ecc	45 18 51. 259	89 06 10. 7	269 03 20. 9	Nicollet	5, 204. 4	3. 716370
	70 55 24. 454	185 47 04. 4	5 47 30. 1	Woburn	7, 809. 3	3. 892614
		287 10 22. 9	107 12 33. 6	Jule	4, 193. 8	3. 622607
Mon. 464	45 18 50. 959	185 56 21. 8	5 56 48. 2	Woburn	7, 820. 8	3. 893252
	70 55 25. 474	247 22 21. 8	67 22 22. 5	Mon. 464 ecc	24. 06	1. 381260
Landon	45 19 01. 550	189 46 55. 3	9 47 37. 3	Woburn	7, 561. 9	3. 878629
	70 55 47. 331	225 05 15. 3	45 09 45. 0	Mon. 428 ecc	11, 644. 5	4. 066119
		289 02 58. 6	109 05 25. 6	Jule	4, 766. 2	3. 678174
Mon. 465 ecc	45 19 09. 974	192 40 48. 7	12 41 41. 6	Woburn	7, 371. 7	3. 867570
	70 56 02. 656	227 08 24. 4	47 13 05. 0	Mon. 428 ecc	11, 704. 7	4. 068362
		307 55 16. 4	127 55 27. 3	Landon	423. 1	2. 626478
Mon. 465	45 19 09. 784	246 04 35. 4	66 04 35. 8	Mon. 465 ecc	14. 43	1. 159176
	70 56 03. 261	306 13 35. 4	126 13 46. 7	Landon	430. 1	2. 633600
Fish	45 20 37. 489	37 57 06. 9	217 56 37. 0	Marble	1, 488. 8	3. 172827
	71 00 07. 090	121 37 29. 5	301 37 05. 8	Mon. 470	851. 9	2. 930377
		344 10 51. 6	164 11 22. 7	Nicollet	3, 495. 4	3. 543495
Mon. 466 ecc	45 20 04. 962	51 49 29. 5	231 47 51. 6	Nicollet	3, 815. 5	3. 581550
	70 57 05. 648	104 16 45. 5	284 14 36. 5	Fish	4, 076. 1	3. 610247
		237 47 56. 8	57 53 22. 2	Mon. 428 ecc	11, 758. 8	4. 070364
Mon. 466	45 20 05. 592	15 13 56. 4	195 13 56. 2	Mon. 466 ecc	20. 15	1. 304232
	70 57 05. 405	237 51 56. 4	57 57 21. 6	Mon. 428 ecc	11, 744. 0	4. 069816
Charlie	45 23 21. 857	13 18 04. 9	193 17 29. 2	Mon. 470	4, 755. 2	3. 677166
	70 59 50. 155	313 42 03. 9	133 47 36. 7	Gosford	14, 099. 4	4. 149201
		356 02 27. 1	176 02 46. 2	Nicollet	8, 457. 6	3. 927246
Mon. 467 ecc	45 20 16. 339	83 07 22. 9	263 05 02. 2	Marble	4, 339. 5	3. 637435
	70 57 31. 288	100 54 37. 9	280 52 47. 1	Fish	3, 454. 5	3. 538379
		152 11 36. 0	332 09 57. 2	Charlie	6, 475. 8	3. 811293
Mon. 467	45 20 16. 297	152 24 15. 1	332 22 37. 2	Charlie	6, 464. 7	3. 810550
	70 57 32. 493	267 11 15. 1	87 11 16. 0	Mon. 467 ecc	26. 28	1. 419625
Mon. 468 ecc	45 19 56. 641	20 40 36. 9	200 40 11. 0	Nicollet	2, 246. 7	3. 351544
	70 58 46. 928	55 41 20. 3	235 39 00. 1	Barker	5, 201. 5	3. 716126
		125 51 22. 3	305 50 25. 3	Fish	2, 153. 3	3. 333101
		167 45 05. 2	347 44 20. 2	Charlie	6, 483. 1	3. 811785
Mon. 468	45 19 56. 832	20 19 42. 7	200 19 17. 2	Nicollet	2, 247. 9	3. 351774
	70 58 47. 496	295 29 42. 7	115 29 43. 1	Mon. 468 ecc	13. 71	1. 137101
Neil	45 20 35. 215	128 36 33. 2	308 36 30. 3	Fish	112. 52	2. 051230
	71 00 03. 051					

104709—25†——28

LAKE POHENAGAMOOK TO THE VERMONT-QUEBEC BOUNDARY—Continued

Station	Latitude and longitude	Azimuth	Back azimuth	To station	Distance (meters)	Loga- rithm
POINTS SUPPLEMEN- TARY TO MAJOR SCHEME TRIANGU- LATION—contd.	° ′ ″	° ′ ″	° ′ ″			
Mon. 469 ecc	45 20 17. 671	43 14 00. 7	223 12 10. 8	Barker	4, 916. 3	3. 691634
	70 59 29. 565	72 01 50. 0	252 00 53. 4	Marble	1, 821. 6	3. 260444
		126 49 50. 2	306 49 23. 5	Fish	1, 020. 7	3. 008888
		230 09 58. 1	50 13 18. 2	Woburn	7, 969. 3	3. 901419
Mon. 469	45 20 17. 792	126 52 57. 0	306 52 33. 6	Neil	896. 2	2. 952422
	70 59 30. 124	286 59 57. 0	106 59 57. 4	Mon. 469 ecc	12. 73	1. 104828
Cookee	45 19 54. 092	34 01 54. 3	214 00 51. 4	Barker	3, 444. 4	3. 537119
	71 00 35. 655	322 05 55. 8	142 06 47. 2	Nicollet	2, 564. 0	3. 408916
		359 24 13. 6	179 24 15. 0	Lake	4, 115. 4	3. 614415
Mon. 471 ecc	45 19 49. 342	40 54 17. 1	220 53 00. 6	Barker	3, 582. 6	3. 554199
	71 00 16. 458	63 42 34. 3	243 38 17. 1	Bon Durban	8, 795. 2	3. 944245
		109 19 52. 3	289 19 38. 7	Cookee	443. 0	2. 646405
		328 20 49. 3	148 21 27. 1	Nicollet	2, 204. 6	3. 343325
Mon. 471	45 19 49. 728	328 29 16. 9	148 29 54. 7	Nicollet	2, 215. 2	3. 345416
	71 00 16. 501	355 29 16. 9	175 29 16. 9	Mon. 471 ecc	11. 95	1. 077368
Hugh	45 18 44. 240	30 16 17. 7	210 15 40. 4	Lake	2, 267. 9	3. 355627
	70 59 41. 223	77 22 16. 1	257 20 34. 5	Barker	3, 190. 7	3. 503890
		147 30 38. 8	327 29 50. 5	Marble	2, 753. 2	3. 439839
Mon. 472 ecc	45 19 01. 338	180 43 54. 9	0 43 55. 6	Marble	1, 794. 5	3. 253934
	71 00 50. 189	289 21 07. 8	109 21 56. 8	Hugh	1, 592. 3	3. 202025
		351 46 20. 8	171 46 32. 5	Lake	2, 512. 5	3. 400098
Mon. 472	45 19 01. 027	180 57 00. 9	0 57 01. 8	Marble	1, 804. 2	3. 256274
	71 00 50. 511	216 07 00. 9	36 07 01. 1	Mon. 472 ecc	11. 88	1. 074670
Campbell	45 18 15. 553	243 21 58. 8	63 25 27. 8	Marble	7, 162. 9	3. 855087
	71 05 43. 179	267 43 52. 6	87 46 28. 3	Barker	4, 775. 7	3. 679034
		303 06 11. 7	123 07 57. 4	Bowman	3, 868. 4	3. 587534
Art	45 20 50. 824	21 12 28. 2	201 11 29. 9	Barker	4, 940. 6	3. 693776
	71 00 42. 101	25 40 55. 2	205 39 07. 0	Bowman	7, 663. 2	3. 884409
		53 51 38. 9	233 48 04. 8	Campbell	8, 122. 2	3. 909673
		358 12 37. 9	178 12 44. 0	Lake	5, 869. 5	3. 768599
Mon. 473 ecc	45 18 53. 835	33 30 37. 9	213 30 16. 4	Barker	1, 192. 8	3. 076577
	71 01 33. 910	197 20 34. 4	17 21 11. 1	Art	3, 783. 7	3. 577920
		205 41 52. 4	25 42 24. 2	Marble	2, 248. 4	3. 351869
		329 48 09. 7	149 48 52. 5	Lake	2, 608. 9	3. 416457
Mon. 473	45 18 54. 887	15 13 28. 8	195 13 28. 5	Mon. 473 ecc	33. 67	1. 527179
	71 01 33. 504	330 19 28. 8	150 20 11. 3	Lake	2, 632. 6	3. 420390
Mon. 474 ecc	45 18 44. 401	221 36 32. 0	41 38 25. 1	Art	5, 221. 1	3. 717766
	71 03 21. 361	235 02 02. 9	55 03 51. 1	Marble	4, 044. 8	3. 606900
		292 40 54. 7	112 41 49. 6	Barker	1, 823. 3	3. 260870
		357 08 42. 1	177 08 47. 0	Bowman	3, 007. 9	3. 478261
Mon. 474	45 18 44. 958	57 05 41. 0	237 05 40. 1	Mon. 474 ecc	31. 68	1. 500730
	71 03 20. 140	293 30 41. 0	113 31 35. 0	Barker	1, 805. 6	3. 256630
Mon. 475 ecc	45 18 19. 770	81 04 34. 5	261 04 07. 5	Campbell	838. 9	2. 923686
	71 05 05. 141	281 28 25. 1	101 31 38. 1	Lake	6, 035. 6	3. 780717
		312 55 46. 9	132 57 05. 6	Bowman	3, 293. 6	3. 517673
		351 48 50. 9	171 49 43. 8	Rump	11, 414. 9	4. 057471
Mon. 475 (Maine- New Hampshire boundary).	45 18 19. 999	66 22 58. 8	246 22 58. 3	Mon. 475 ecc	17. 66	1. 246917
	71 05 04. 399	351 53 58. 8	171 54 51. 2	Rump	11, 419. 6	4. 057650

LAKE POHENAGAMOOK TO THE VERMONT-QUEBEC BOUNDARY—Continued

Station	Latitude and longitude	Azimuth	Back azimuth	To station	Distance (meters)	Loga- rithm
POINTS SUPPLEMEN- TARY TO MAJOR SCHEME TRIANGU- LATION—contd,	° ′ ″	° ′ ″	° ′ ″			
Mon. 476 ecc	45 18 17. 599	82 03 16. 1	262 03 01. 3	Campbell	456. 7	2. 659647
	71 05 22. 417	232 12 05. 5	52 15 24. 7	Art	7, 722. 9	3. 887780
		307 58 20. 8	127 59 51. 7	Bowman	3, 536. 8	3. 548605
Mon. 476	45 18 17. 524	81 54 03. 3	261 53 49. 3	Campbell	431. 7	2. 635207
	71 05 23. 560	264 42 03. 3	84 42 04. 1	Mon. 476 ecc	25. 02	1. 398322
Trumbull	45 16 13. 702	27 09 24. 6	207 08 35. 1	Salmon	3, 328. 1	3. 522194
	71 07 00. 576	114 23 55. 2	294 19 36. 7	Northwest Knoll	8, 700. 7	3. 939554
		198 27 35. 0	18 28 05. 0	Bon Durban	2, 906. 2	3. 463326
		251 29 07. 7	71 31 48. 4	Bowman	5, 196. 2	3. 715688
Peterie	45 16 08. 579	71 32 20. 0	251 29 33. 5	Pros	5, 391. 3	3. 731694
	71 09 27. 632	267 09 39. 6	87 11 24. 1	Trumbull	3, 209. 7	3. 506458
		328 56 25. 0	148 57 20. 0	Salmon	3, 272. 1	3. 514829
Southeast Knoll	45 16 55. 479	32 44 54. 1	212 43 47. 9	Pros	3, 753. 4	3. 574427
	71 11 49. 038	144 31 20. 2	324 30 26. 7	Northwest Knoll	2, 823. 9	3. 450853
		295 08 51. 1	115 10 31. 4	Peterie	3, 405. 4	3. 532168
Bluff	45 17 23. 029	19 54 58. 8	199 54 33. 5	Trumbull	2, 276. 3	3. 357226
	71 06 25. 005	60 00 56. 9	239 58 47. 1	Peterie	4, 596. 4	3. 662417
		83 09 53. 0	263 06 02. 9	Southeast Knoll	7, 112. 8	3. 852040
Round Top	45 17 12. 806	4 37 01. 2	184 36 48. 6	Salmon	4, 801. 6	3. 681382
	71 07 52. 504	260 35 38. 2	80 36 40. 4	Bluff	1, 932. 7	3. 286175
		328 10 58. 1	148 11 35. 0	Trumbull	2, 147. 1	3. 331861
Tallman	45 17 06. 612	17 37 16. 1	197 36 28. 5	Salmon	4, 820. 8	3. 683119
	71 07 03. 312	100 07 04. 6	280 06 29. 6	Round Top	1, 089. 0	3. 037021
		238 44 05. 3	58 44 32. 5	Bluff	976. 6	2. 989715
Birches	45 15 10. 434	222 35 48. 3	42 38 09. 5	Bon Durban	6, 400. 0	3. 806178
	71 09 37. 141	240 12 25. 1	60 14 16. 3	Trumbull	3, 932. 8	3. 594703
		298 00 02. 7	118 01 04. 4	Salmon	2, 146. 9	3. 331807
Nash	45 15 39. 353	73 15 11. 7	253 13 35. 2	Birches	3, 096. 0	3. 490798
	71 07 21. 184	108 08 05. 3	288 06 35. 5	Peterie	2, 900. 6	3. 462493
		111 57 02. 6	291 53 52. 5	Southeast Knoll	6, 294. 1	3. 798935
Mon. 477 ecc	45 17 10. 262	80 04 52. 7	260 04 31. 7	Tallman	653. 8	2. 815477
	71 06 33. 758	92 37 43. 5	272 36 47. 5	Round Top	1, 717. 9	3. 235000
		205 49 29. 0	25 49 35. 2	Bluff	437. 9	2. 641348
Mon. 477	45 17 10. 339	79 35 01. 8	259 34 41. 4	Tallman	636. 2	2. 803595
	71 06 34. 601	277 26 01. 8	97 26 02. 4	Mon. 477 ecc	18. 51	1. 267500
Mon. 478 ecc	45 15 34. 071	111 22 12. 0	291 20 43. 2	Peterie	2, 925. 1	3. 466145
	71 07 22. 676	113 25 49. 4	293 22 40. 3	Southeast Knoll	6, 327. 0	3. 801198
		191 17 11. 5	11 17 12. 5	Nash	166. 3	2. 220837
Mon. 478	45 15 34. 495	19 17 18. 8	199 17 18. 6	Mon. 478 ecc	13. 86	1. 141826
	71 07 22. 466	113 18 18. 8	293 15 09. 5	Southeast Knoll	6, 326. 0	3. 801130
Mon. 482	45 14 24. 085	209 13 27. 3	29 14 26. 0	Peterie	3, 696. 6	3. 567805
	71 10 50. 421	235 56 59. 5	55 59 42. 7	Trumbull	6, 047. 3	3. 781561
		263 05 13. 8	83 07 07. 5	Salmon	3, 519. 4	3. 546465
Mon. 481	45 15 01. 559	50 20 19. 3	230 19 33. 9	Mon. 482	1, 812. 3	3. 258239
	71 09 46. 454	94 23 39. 6	274 21 06. 4	Pros	4, 717. 3	3. 673694
		142 46 51. 8	322 45 24. 8	Southeast Knoll	4, 417. 0	3. 645131
		289 16 28. 3	109 17 36. 6	Salmon	2, 223. 3	3. 346999
Mon. 480	45 14 36. 614	80 53 41. 3	260 52 22. 8	Mon. 482	2, 441. 4	3. 387638
	71 08 59. 897	127 10 59. 7	307 10 26. 6	Mon. 481	1, 274. 3	3. 105276
		142 07 22. 1	322 06 55. 6	Birches	1, 322. 7	3. 121475

LAKE POHENAGAMOOK TO THE VERMONT-QUEBEC BOUNDARY—Continued

Station	Latitude and longitude	Azimuth	Back azimuth	To station	Distance (meters)	Loga- rithm
POINTS SUPPLEMEN- TARY TO MAJOR SCHEME TRIANGU- LATION—contd.	° ′ ″	° ′ ″	° ′ ″			
Mon. 479 ecc	45 14 28.349	128 40 03.4	308 39 21.7	Mon. 481	1,641.1	3.215145
	71 08 47.694	140 18 44.5	320 18 09.4	Birches	1,688.4	3.227482
		164 17 05.9	344 16 37.5	Peterie	3,214.4	3.507106
		250 23 41.7	70 24 08.3	Salmon	867.5	2.938245
Mon. 479	45 14 28.680	60 24 46.8	240 24 46.2	Mon. 479 ecc	20.71	1.316138
	71 08 46.869	302 46 16.8	122 49 47.1	Rump	7,688.1	3.885819
Deer	45 12 24.699	80 22 55.3	260 20 48.8	Indian	3,946.6	3.596223
	71 13 39.173	174 28 04.5	354 27 48.7	Spect	5,039.8	3.702416
		184 04 51.7	4 05 03.8	Pros	5,215.3	3.717282
		271 26 48.8	91 33 46.5	Rump	12,848.1	4.108838
Mon. 483 ecc	45 15 06.695	27 36 15.8	207 34 50.8	Deer	5,642.7	3.751490
	71 11 39.365	176 24 28.7	356 24 21.9	Southeast Knoll	3,364.9	3.526976
		236 21 25.9	56 22 59.4	Peterie	3,449.5	3.537760
Mon. 483	45 15 10.547	25 48 42.2	205 47 21.7	Deer	5,686.7	3.754864
	71 11 45.713	310 39 29.2	130 39 33.7	Mon. 483 ecc	182.49	2.261239
Mon. 484 ecc	45 15 19.065	170 15 51.8	350 15 22.2	Northwest Knoll	5,353.0	3.728595
	71 12 22.717	193 51 12.9	13 51 36.8	Southeast Knoll	3,065.6	3.486517
Mon. 484	45 15 10.423	165 16 22.2	345 16 19.9	Mon. 484 ecc	275.85	2.440673
	71 12 19.501					
Hen	45 17 08.457	120 31 29.9	300 29 54.5	Bien	3,396.8	3.531074
	71 14 53.330	330 48 00.2	150 49 05.0	Pros	4,075.4	3.610166
		343 11 08.6	163 11 45.5	Spect	3,910.6	3.592248
Mon. 485 ecc	45 15 42.530	87 05 12.4	267 00 11.2	Howe	9,254.8	3.966369
	71 14 23.467	166 12 53.9	346 12 32.6	Hen	2,731.3	3.436377
		304 05 36.7	124 06 20.2	Pros	1,614.5	3.208039
		336 14 57.1	156 15 12.7	Spect	1,191.8	3.076213
Mon. 485	45 15 42.474	260 28 50.1	80 28 50.4	Mon. 485 ecc	10.45	1.018950
	71 14 23.939	303 50 20.1	123 51 03.9	Pros	1,622.1	3.210073
Mon. 486 ecc	45 16 05.672	173 18 24.9	353 18 17.4	Hen	1,951.5	3.290376
	71 14 42.894	312 36 21.6	132 37 18.9	Pros	2,392.1	3.378772
		333 24 33.0	153 25 02.4	Spect	2,018.8	3.305091
Mon. 486	45 16 05.786	280 35 45.3	100 35 45.9	Mon. 486 ecc	19.13	1.281828
	71 14 43.756	312 21 52.3	132 22 50.2	Pros	2,408.3	3.381712
Fourth	45 16 46.235	39 09 04.0	219 07 59.2	Howe	3,150.8	3.498422
	71 19 56.133	236 41 54.1	56 43 53.9	Bien	4,392.6	3.642720
		333 35 35.5	153 37 56.6	Indian	9,750.3	3.989019
Nob	45 16 49.891	68 38 40.1	248 35 07.3	Howe	7,011.4	3.845805
	71 16 27.885	88 35 45.2	268 33 17.2	Fourth	4,540.3	3.657083
		159 21 06.6	339 20 38.4	Bien	2,455.6	3.390154
Mon. 487 ecc	45 17 09.263	50 55 01.0	230 54 37.0	Nob	948.6	2.977064
	71 15 54.104	136 41 59.2	316 41 07.0	Bien	2,335.8	3.368436
		271 04 15.1	91 04 58.3	Hen	1,324.7	3.122120
		317 13 44.7	137 15 32.7	Pros	4,879.4	3.688363
Mon. 487	45 17 12.121	4 14 14.3	184 14 14.1	Mon. 487 ecc	88.47	1.946772
	71 15 53.804	47 16 05.3	227 15 41.1	Nob	1,011.3	3.004881
Mon. 488 ecc	45 17 45.482	5 47 12.3	185 47 06.6	Nob	1,725.0	3.236780
	71 16 19.906	119 13 28.9	299 12 55.0	Bien	1,191.4	3.076064
Mon. 488	45 17 47.931	311 28 11.1	131 28 13.9	Mon. 488 ecc	114.17	2.057548
	71 16 23.832					

LAKE POHENAGAMOOK TO THE VERMONT-QUEBEC BOUNDARY—Continued

Station	Latitude and longitude	Azimuth	Back azimuth	To station	Distance (meters)	Logarithm
POINTS SUPPLEMENTARY TO MAJOR SCHEME TRIANGULATION—contd.	° ′ ″	° ′ ″	° ′ ″			
Mon. 489 ecc	45 18 00. 042	134 16 25. 3	314 16 20. 9	Bien	189. 3	2. 277054
	71 17 01. 409	317 07 08. 7	137 09 44. 5	Pros	7, 026. 0	3. 846711
		323 39 45. 6	143 41 53. 5	Spect	6, 622. 6	3. 821031
		341 21 21. 9	161 21 45. 7	Nob	2, 285. 6	3. 358992
Mon. 489	45 17 59. 306	130 32 27. 0	310 32 26. 1	Mon. 489 ecc	34. 97	1. 543733
	71 17 00. 190	133 41 31. 0	313 41 25. 7	Bien	224. 2	2. 350573
Mon. 490 ecc	45 17 49. 558	247 18 51. 7	67 19 27. 2	Bien	1, 182. 0	3. 072627
	71 17 57. 685	308 45 35. 4	128 48 51. 1	Pros	7, 705. 0	3. 886773
		314 12 17. 3	134 15 05. 1	Spect	7, 186. 0	3. 856490
		330 38 02. 4	150 41 05. 9	Deer	11, 504. 5	4. 060867
Mon. 490	45 17 49. 548	247 24 45. 5	67 25 21. 2	Bien	1, 187. 7	3. 074718
	71 17 57. 962	266 58 52. 5	86 58 52. 7	Mon. 490 ecc	6. 06	0. 782186
Mon. 491 ecc	45 17 10. 492	49 23 12. 9	229 21 11. 7	Howe	4, 902. 8	3. 690444
	71 18 36. 676	66 37 22. 8	246 36 26. 4	Fourth	1, 886. 7	3. 275705
		302 21 51. 8	122 25 07. 4	Spect	7, 105. 3	3. 851585
		323 38 25. 5	143 41 56. 8	Deer	10, 951. 5	4. 039472
Mon. 491	45 17 13. 192	338 26 39. 7	158 26 40. 8	Mon. 491 ecc	89. 62	1. 952410
	71 18 38. 187					
Mon. 492 ecc	45 16 54. 551	71 33 48. 3	251 33 23. 2	Fourth	811. 7	2. 909387
	71 19 20. 805	291 46 20. 2	111 50 35. 0	Pros	8, 421. 4	3. 925384
		295 25 30. 1	115 29 17. 0	Spect	7, 710. 7	3. 887093
Mon. 492	45 16 54. 592	71 22 00. 2	251 21 35. 3	Fourth	807. 4	2. 907105
	71 19 21. 030	284 37 10. 2	104 37 10. 4	Mon. 492 ecc	5. 08	0. 705864
Mon. 493 ecc	45 16 32. 249	43 29 51. 3	223 28 49. 1	Howe	2, 773. 2	3. 442979
	71 19 59. 824	190 33 14. 2	10 33 16. 8	Fourth	439. 2	2. 642644
		288 32 26. 0	108 36 40. 6	Spect	8, 242. 5	3. 916061
		331 58 59. 6	152 01 23. 3	Indian	9, 403. 1	3. 973271
Mon. 493	45 16 33. 294	195 02 14. 3	15 02 17. 8	Fourth	413. 7	2. 616636
	71 20 01. 057	320 11 54. 3	140 11 55. 2	Mon. 493 ecc	42. 00	1. 623198
Mon. 494 ecc	45 16 18. 157	27 49 40. 4	207 49 13. 3	Howe	1, 783. 1	3. 251165
	71 20 49. 194	233 08 42. 1	53 09 19. 8	Fourth	1, 445. 4	3. 159976
		325 03 45. 9	145 06 44. 7	Indian	9, 594. 3	3. 982015
Mon. 494	45 16 19. 618	304 29 32. 0	124 29 34. 1	Mon. 494 ecc	79. 62	1. 901022
	71 20 52. 204					
Mon. 495 ecc	45 16 05. 061	241 32 09. 8	61 33 26. 2	Fourth	2, 667. 9	3. 426167
	71 21 43. 740	280 00 17. 3	100 05 45. 7	Spect	10, 236. 4	4. 010149
		302 43 07. 5	122 48 51. 6	Deer	12, 569. 4	4. 099313
		343 04 06. 7	163 04 18. 3	Howe	1, 225. 7	3. 088398
Mon. 495	45 16 05. 722	242 05 34. 1	62 06 51. 2	Fourth	2, 673. 1	3. 427022
	71 21 44. 515	320 22 09. 1	140 22 09. 8	Mon. 495 ecc	26. 48	1. 423000
Mon. 496 ecc	45 15 51. 866	24 23 52. 5	204 22 54. 3	Eck	4, 329. 9	3. 636473
	71 21 43. 619	40 59 57. 9	220 58 38. 0	Joe	3. 741. 6	3. 573059
		335 09 23. 6	155 09 35. 2	Howe	843. 3	2. 926007
Mon. 496	45 15 52. 274	24 07 47. 0	204 06 49. 3	Eck	4, 334. 6	3. 636944
	71 21 44. 378	307 18 59. 0	127 18 59. 5	Mon. 496 ecc	20. 81	1. 318189
Holl's	45 14 49. 873	37 51 07. 3	217 50 16. 0	Eck	2, 570. 2	3. 409971
	71 21 53. 308	67 55 01. 9	247 53 48. 9	Joe	2, 421. 0	3. 383986
Ridge	45 14 04. 115	77 35 48. 2	257 34 17. 0	Eck	2, 869. 9	3. 457860
	71 20 57. 122	98 15 02. 9	278 13 10. 0	Joe	3, 505. 1	3. 544704
		139 03 47. 6	319 03 07. 7	Hollis	1, 870. 1	3. 271861

LAKE POHENAGAMOOK TO THE VERMONT-QUEBEC BOUNDARY—Continued

Station	Latitude and longitude	Azimuth	Back azimuth	To station	Distance (meters)	Loga- rithm
POINTS SUPPLEMEN- TARY TO MAJOR SCHEME TRIANGU- LATION—contd.	° ′ ″	° ′ ″	° ′ ″			
Near	45 14 27. 941	235 05 48. 6	55 06 20. 2	Hollis	1, 183. 4	3. 073133
	71 22 37. 811	288 30 23. 3	108 31 34. 8	Ridge	2, 316. 1	3. 364761
Alec	45 14 48. 267	52 11 00. 1	232 10 33. 8	Near	1, 023. 3	3. 010008
	71 22 00. 747	253 00 20. 8	73 00 26. 1	Hollis	169. 6	2. 229515
		314 28 46. 2	134 29 31. 4	Ridge	1, 945. 1	3. 288952
Tall	45 14 43. 268	20 46 15. 2	200 46 09. 4	Near	506. 0	2. 704179
	71 22 29. 583	255 32 34. 0	75 32 59. 8	Hollis	817. 0	2. 912204
		300 55 37. 6	120 56 43. 3	Ridge	2, 351. 2	3. 371281
Mon. 497 ecc	45 15 06. 453	39 02 43. 5	219 01 36. 4	Eck	3, 272. 0	3. 514807
	71 21 31. 124	43 23 17. 6	223 23 01. 8	Hollis	704. 3	2. 847763
		62 27 55. 3	242 26 26. 5	Joe	3, 075. 6	3. 487930
		338 55 23. 4	158 55 47. 5	Ridge	2, 062. 4	3. 314370
Mon. 497	45 15 06. 741	38 52 05. 9	218 50 59. 0	Eck	3, 275. 2	3. 515239
	71 21 31. 391	326 48 13. 9	146 48 14. 1	Mon. 497 ecc	10. 63	1. 026452
Mon. 498	45 14 52. 229	339 41 08. 6	159 41 09. 5	Hollis	77. 56	1. 889614
	71 21 54. 543					
Mon. 499	45 14 47. 223	256 57 07. 6	76 57 19. 1	Hollis	362. 5	2. 559253
	71 22 09. 499	260 24 40. 5	80 24 46. 7	Alec	193. 6	2. 286848
		310 07 26. 8	130 08 18. 2	Ridge	2, 064. 7	3. 314858
Mon. 500 ecc	45 14 40. 175	1 21 27. 7	181 21 27. 4	Near	377. 8	2. 577245
	71 22 37. 401	240 45 09. 2	60 45 14. 7	Tall	195. 4	2. 290929
		296 57 53. 6	116 59 04. 8	Ridge	2, 454. 2	3. 389911
Mon. 500	45 14 40. 103	242 47 03. 1	62 47 09. 3	Tall	213. 6	2. 329621
	71 22 38. 294	263 29 17. 1	83 29 17. 8	Mon. 500 ecc	19. 60	1. 292167
Mon. 501 ecc	45 14 14. 876	70 09 02. 8	250 06 36. 0	Sightly	4, 793. 0	3. 680609
	71 23 38. 912	199 27 26. 3	19 27 28. 2	Joe	180. 1	2. 255633
		322 33 56. 9	142 34 20. 5	Eck	1, 195. 4	3. 077507
Mon. 501	45 14 14. 875	70 43 32. 2	250 41 00. 7	Sightly	4, 929. 9	3. 692838
	71 23 32. 252	153 20 52. 8	333 20 50. 0	Joe	190. 1	2. 278931
		328 30 55. 2	148 31 14. 1	Eck	1, 113. 1	3. 046516
Mon. 502 ecc	45 14 18. 184	267 18 53. 1	87 19 40. 1	Joe	1, 449. 0	3. 161077
	71 24 42. 523	296 25 56. 1	116 27 04. 8	Eck	2, 361. 1	3. 373117
		355 50 40. 2	175 51 00. 8	Metallak	8, 793. 6	3. 944165
Mon. 502	45 14 25. 787	50 24 15. 6	230 24 06. 4	Mon. 502 ecc	368. 22	2. 566108
	71 24 29. 515	305 05 07. 9	125 06 07. 5	Eck	2, 237. 0	3. 349661
Mon. 503 ecc	45 14 00. 855	21 36 18. 9	201 34 52. 9	Ouillette	7, 177. 1	3. 855949
	71 25 28. 731	256 11 53. 4	76 13 13. 3	Joe	2, 528. 3	3. 402829
		279 22 39. 0	99 24 20. 6	Eck	3, 164. 6	3. 500321
		348 41 38. 1	168 42 31. 5	Metallak	8, 398. 3	3. 924190
Mon. 503	45 14 01. 497	36 35 35. 6	216 35 35. 1	Mon. 503 ecc	24. 70	1. 392609
	71 25 28. 056	348 49 07. 7	168 50 00. 6	Metallak	8, 414. 8	3. 925046
Mon. 504	45 14 20. 803	270 11 25. 2	90 13 23. 5	Joe	3, 635. 2	3. 560527
	71 26 22. 826	284 43 31. 5	104 45 51. 5	Eck	4, 448. 5	3. 648215
		342 16 48. 4	162 18 20. 3	Metallak	9, 291. 5	3. 968087
Mon. 505 ecc	45 14 14. 003	21 41 26. 0	201 41 05. 3	Sightly	1, 724. 2	3. 236580
	71 26 36. 339	281 19 27. 4	101 21 57. 1	Eck	4, 688. 5	3. 671033
		340 07 39. 2	160 09 20. 7	Metallak	9, 187. 7	3. 963209
Mon. 505	45 14 11. 604	21 34 04. 9	201 33 45. 3	Sightly	1, 643. 1	3. 215652
	71 26 37. 863	204 09 51. 8	24 09 52. 9	Mon. 505 ecc	81. 19	1. 909477

LAKE POHENAGAMOOK TO THE VERMONT-QUEBEC BOUNDARY—Continued

Station	Latitude and longitude	Azimuth	Back azimuth	To station	Distance (meters)	Logarithm
POINTS SUPPLEMENTARY TO MAJOR SCHEME TRIANGULATION—contd.	° ′ ″	° ′ ″	° ′ ″			
King	45 09 56. 409	162 45 48. 4	342 44 44. 3	Sightly	6, 648. 9	3. 822752
	71 25 35. 243	210 28 41. 3	30 29 01. 5	Knoll	1, 225. 0	3. 088119
		291 03 59. 6	111 04 57. 7	Metallak	1, 916. 8	3. 282587
Chesham, Quebec, church spire, 1916.	45 23 37. 45	25 21 33	205 17 59	Peterie	15, 331. 0	4. 185570
	71 04 26. 43	38 32 34	218 25 45	Spect	20, 123. 8	4. 303710
		58 15 06	238 06 05	Bien	19, 502. 8	4. 290098
Chartierville, Quebec, church spire, 1916.	45 17 51. 11	16 16 13	196 15 27	Pros	5, 077. 5	3. 705653
	71 12 16. 92	119 26 34	299 26 01	Northwest Knoll	1, 184. 7	3. 073595
		310 36 33	130 38 33	Peterie	4, 861. 0	3. 686723
MINOR SCHEME, SOUTHWEST BRANCH OF ST. JOHN RIVER						
Mon. 308	46 25 02. 489	188 20 29. 6	8 20 31. 2	Mon. 307	322. 76	2. 508881
	70 03 25. 267					
Ref. Mon. 309	46 24 58. 575	188 20 29. 0	8 20 29. 6	Mon. 308	122. 15	2. 086911
	70 03 26. 097					
S–1	46 24 58. 338	96 27 20. 3	276 27 18. 1	Ref. Mon. 309	65. 0	1. 813110
	70 03 23. 071					
S–2	46 24 52. 917	192 49 59. 4	12 50 00. 7	Ref. Mon. 309	179. 2	2. 253323
	70 03 27. 961	211 57 12. 2	31 57 15. 7	S–1	197. 3	2. 295133
C–2	46 24 54. 702	218 23 40. 1	38 23 43. 3	Ref. Mon. 309	152. 6	2. 183503
	70 03 30. 535	234 50 13. 7	54 50 19. 1	S–1	195. 0	2. 289940
		315 05 12. 5	135 05 14. 4	S–2	77. 8	1. 891258
S–3	46 24 51. 962	227 53 55. 6	47 53 58. 8	C–2	126. 2	2. 101017
	70 03 34. 919	258 46 54. 8	78 46 59. 9	S–2	151. 5	2. 180373
C–3	46 24 54. 528	267 44 33. 5	87 44 38. 1	C–2	136. 3	2. 134512
	70 03 36. 912	284 35 26. 4	104 35 32. 9	S–2	197. 5	2. 295646
		331 45 00. 6	151 45 02. 0	S–3	89. 9	1. 953986
C–4	46 24 53. 096	246 25 49. 9	66 25 53. 3	C–3	110. 6	2. 043747
	70 03 41. 659	283 40 09. 9	103 40 14. 8	S–3	148. 1	2. 170679
S–4	46 24 49. 915	162 08 48. 8	342 08 47. 7	C–4	103. 2	2. 013606
	70 03 40. 178	206 05 12. 1	26 05 14. 5	C–3	158. 6	2. 200284
		240 37 52. 4	60 37 56. 2	S–3	128. 9	2. 110170
C–5	46 24 52. 049	257 58 46. 5	77 58 51. 6	C–4	155. 2	2. 190905
	70 03 48. 767	289 45 28. 9	109 45 35. 1	S–4	194. 9	2. 289840
S–5	46 24 49. 219	186 43 31. 0	6 43 31. 4	C–5	88. 0	1. 944383
	70 03 49. 249	233 33 28. 4	53 33 33. 9	C–4	201. 5	2. 304292
		263 40 19. 3	83 40 25. 9	S–4	194. 9	2. 289876
S–6	46 24 49. 248	232 19 03. 9	52 19 07. 7	C–5	141. 5	2. 150635
	70 03 54. 009	270 30 30. 8	90 30 34. 2	S–5	101. 7	2. 007133
C–6	46 24 51. 383	263 38 48. 1	83 38 54. 4	C–5	185. 8	2. 269029
	70 03 57. 413	290 58 04. 4	110 58 10. 3	S–5	186. 7	2. 271180
		312 11 51. 4	132 11 53. 9	S–6	98. 1	1. 991809
C–7	46 24 46. 780	206 28 31. 0	26 28 33. 4	C–6	158. 8	2. 200766
	70 04 00. 727	242 01 35. 2	62 01 40. 1	S–6	162. 5	2. 210753
S–7 (east base)	46 24 45. 117	141 32 21. 6	321 32 20. 2	C–7	65. 6	1. 816891
	70 03 58. 817	188 48 30. 1	8 48 31. 1	C–6	195. 8	2. 291797
		218 49 50. 5	38 49 54. 0	S–6	163. 8	2. 214209

LAKE POHENAGAMOOK TO THE VERMONT-QUEBEC BOUNDARY—Continued

Station	Latitude and longitude	Azimuth	Back azimuth	To station	Distance (meters)	Loga-rithm
MINOR SCHEME, SOUTHWEST BRANCH OF ST. JOHN RIVER—con.	° ′ ″	° ′ ″	° ′ ″			
Ref. Mon. C-8	46 24 45. 615 70 04 06. 197	252 52 26. 1 275 34 08. 9	72 52 30. 1 95 34 14. 3	C-7 S-7	122. 2 158. 4	2. 087201 2. 199661
Ref. Mon. S-8 (west base).	46 24 42. 139 70 04 04. 364	159 57 33. 0 208 27 22. 8 232 11 05. 6	339 57 31. 6 28 27 25. 4 52 11 09. 6	Ref. Mon. C-8 C-7 S-7	114. 2 163. 0 149. 97	2. 057792 2. 212201 2. 175991
S-9	46 24 40. 924 70 04 11. 710	219 06 14. 3 256 32 36. 5	39 06 18. 3 76 32 41. 9	Ref. Mon. C-8 Ref. Mon. S-8	186. 7 161. 3	2. 271068 2. 207673
C-9	46 24 45. 153 70 04 13. 666	264 53 09. 4 295 05 44. 2 342 15 37. 8	84 53 14. 8 115 05 51. 0 162 15 39. 2	Ref. Mon. C-8 Ref. Mon. S-8 S-9	160. 1 219. 4 137. 1	2. 204515 2. 341169 2. 137033
C-10	46 24 41. 725 70 04 26. 190	248 24 39. 0 274 34 18. 4	68 24 48. 1 94 34 28. 9	C-9 S-9	287. 7 310. 3	2. 458896 2. 491719
S-10	46 24 36. 612 70 04 21. 614	148 14 17. 2 212 46 11. 3 237 48 51. 8	328 14 13. 9 32 46 17. 1 57 48 59. 0	C-10 C-9 S-9	185. 7 313. 6 249. 9	2. 268752 2. 496411 2. 397835
C-11	46 24 37. 430 70 04 38. 864	243 53 54. 3 273 55 07. 2	63 54 03. 5 93 55 19. 7	C-10 S-10	301. 4 369. 3	2. 479204 2. 567391
S-11	46 24 31. 079 70 04 38. 820	179 43 19. 3 219 22 15. 7 245 03 47. 1	359 43 19. 3 39 22 24. 9 65 03 59. 6	C-11 C-10 S-10	196. 1 425. 2 405. 3	2. 292510 2. 628636 2. 607753
Ref. Mon. 311	46 24 34. 134 70 04 37. 601	15 25 32. 0 165 09 13. 8	195 25 31. 1 345 09 12. 9	S-11 C-11	97. 9 105. 3	1. 990594 2. 022410
Ref. Mon. 310	46 24 35. 530 70 04 37. 128	13 11 59. 4 147 42 11. 7	193 11 59. 1 327 42 10. 5	Ref. Mon. 311 C-11	44. 3 69. 4	1. 646147 1. 841456
S-12	46 24 34. 442 70 04 55. 789	255 40 49. 9 285 59 11. 5	75 41 02. 1 105 59 23. 7	C-11 S-11	373. 1 377. 0	2. 571802 2. 576379
C-12	46 24 41. 677 70 04 53. 796	10 47 20. 2 292 20 55. 5 315 39 01. 3	190 47 18. 8 112 21 06. 3 135 39 12. 1	S-12 C-11 S-11	227. 4 344. 8 457. 6	2. 356803 2. 537595 2. 660492
Ref. Mon. C-13	46 24 40. 697 70 05 13. 816	265 57 02. 1 296 38 13. 3	85 57 16. 6 116 38 26. 4	C-12 S-12	428. 7 430. 7	2. 632105 2. 634222
S-13	46 24 32. 594 70 05 18. 230	200 38 58. 8 241 44 40. 4 263 12 29. 7	20 39 02. 0 61 44 58. 1 83 12 46. 0	Ref. Mon. C-13 C-12 S-12	267. 4 592. 5 482. 7	2. 427125 2. 772665 2. 683687
C-14	46 24 40. 994 70 05 35. 135	271 08 59. 8 305 41 17. 7	91 09 15. 2 125 41 29. 9	Ref. Mon. C-13 S-13	455. 4 444. 6	2. 658433 2. 647931
Ref. Mon. S-14	46 24 33. 766 70 05 36. 527	187 35 18. 0 246 11 23. 6 275 17 08. 7	7 35 19. 0 66 11 40. 0 95 17 21. 9	C-14 Ref. Mon. C-13 S-13	225. 2 530. 2 392. 5	2. 352490 2. 724448 2. 593814
Ref. Mon. C-16	46 24 34. 301 70 05 52. 130	240 20 34. 4 272 50 05. 2	60 20 46. 7 92 50 16. 5	C-14 Ref. Mon. S-14	417. 7 333. 7	2. 620876 2. 523328
C-15	46 24 41. 179 70 05 49. 006	17 26 32. 8 271 06 01. 7 310 39 09. 3	197 26 30. 5 91 06 11. 7 130 39 18. 3	Ref. Mon. C-16 C-14 Ref. Mon. S-14	222. 6 296. 3 351. 3	2. 347544 2. 471763 2. 545713
S-15	46 24 15. 058 70 05 43. 020	161 51 59. 6 193 29 57. 1	341 51 53. 0 13 30 01. 8	Ref. Mon. C-16 Ref. Mon. S-14	625. 2 594. 1	2. 796042 2. 773845
C-17	46 24 15. 141 70 06 03. 558	202 25 10. 5 225 06 39. 2 270 20 02. 1	22 25 18. 8 45 06 58. 8 90 20 17. 0	Ref. Mon. C-16 Ref. Mon. S-14 S-15	640. 0 814. 9 438. 7	2. 806168 2. 911116 2. 642190

LAKE POHENAGAMOOK TO THE VERMONT-QUEBEC BOUNDARY—Continued

Station	Latitude and longitude	Azimuth	Back azimuth	To station	Distance (meters)	Logarithm
MINOR SCHEME, SOUTHWEST BRANCH OF ST. JOHN RIVER—con.	° ′ ″	° ′ ″	° ′ ″			
Ref. Mon. S–16	46 23 55. 225	165 50 40. 8	345 50 35. 5	C–17	634. 2	2. 802246
	70 05 56. 297	204 50 58. 5	24 51 08. 1	S–15	674. 9	2. 829232
Ref. Mon. C–18	46 23 58. 646	192 23 49. 9	12 23 53. 7	C–17	521. 5	2. 717248
	70 06 08. 799	227 22 36. 0	47 22 54. 7	S–15	748. 4	2. 874122
		291 34 42. 8	111 34 51. 9	Ref. Mon. S–16	287. 2	2. 458210
S–17	46 23 39. 797	180 27 33. 9	0 27 34. 0	Ref. Mon. C–18	582. 0	2. 764956
	70 06 09. 018	209 42 07. 8	29 42 17. 0	Ref. Mon. S–16	548. 5	2. 739140
C–19	46 23 45. 135	208 52 02. 7	28 52 10. 5	Ref. Mon. C–18	476. 4	2. 677982
	70 06 19. 566	237 55 10. 5	57 55 27. 4	Ref. Mon. S–16	586. 7	2. 768400
		306 10 45. 9	126 10 53. 6	S–17	279. 2	2. 445908
Ref. Mon. C–20	46 23 32. 273	228 13 05. 4	48 13 20. 4	C–19	596. 1	2. 775284
	70 06 40. 370	250 52 10. 7	70 52 33. 4	S–17	709. 0	2. 850642
Ref. Mon. S–18	46 23 21. 977	144 39 12. 0	324 39 04. 4	Ref. Mon. C–20	389. 8	2. 590824
	70 06 29. 816	197 01 37. 0	17 01 44. 4	C–19	747. 8	2. 873812
		218 55 18. 5	38 55 33. 6	S–17	707. 3	2. 849586
Ref. Mon. C–22	46 23 21. 914	236 33 08. 8	56 33 25. 2	Ref. Mon. C–20	580. 4	2. 763740
	70 07 03. 037	269 50 18. 1	89 50 42. 1	Ref. Mon. S–18	709. 8	2. 851156
Ref. Mon. C–21	46 23 10. 009	152 31 12. 1	332 31 05. 6	Ref. Mon. C–22	414. 3	2. 617355
	70 06 54. 089	203 05 28. 6	23 05 38. 5	Ref. Mon. C–20	747. 4	2. 873531
		234 31 38. 0	54 31 55. 5	Ref. Mon. S–18	636. 8	2. 804032
S–19	46 22 59. 600	204 24 04. 2	24 24 14. 8	Ref. Mon. C–22	756. 6	2. 878863
	70 07 17. 666	237 27 37. 5	57 27 54. 6	Ref. Mon. C–21	597. 6	2. 776410
C–23	46 23 12. 750	244 24 51. 1	64 25 11. 1	Ref. Mon. C–22	655. 3	2. 816437
	70 07 30. 699	276 10 11. 9	96 10 38. 4	Ref. Mon. C–21	786. 8	2. 895882
		325 33 11. 6	145 33 21. 0	S–19	492. 4	2. 692286
Ref. Mon. S–20	46 22 49. 225	190 45 52. 5	10 45 57. 2	C–23	739. 4	2. 868871
	70 07 37. 162	232 26 28. 9	52 26 43. 0	S–19	525. 5	2. 720603
Ref. Mon. C–24	46 22 58. 128	227 29 06. 1	47 29 22. 8	C–23	668. 1	2. 824863
	70 07 53. 747	266 37 20. 1	86 37 46. 2	S–19	772. 4	2. 887818
		307 47 41. 2	127 47 53. 2	Ref. Mon. S–20	448. 5	2. 651783
C–25	46 22 37. 250	182 43 58. 1	2 43 59. 1	Ref. Mon. C–24	645. 4	2. 809820
	70 07 55. 187	226 10 14. 3	46 10 27. 3	Ref. Mon. S–20	534. 0	2. 727505
S–21	46 22 34. 879	102 57 06. 3	282 56 55. 5	C–25	326. 7	2. 514157
	70 07 40. 289	158 10 04. 8	338 09 55. 0	Ref. Mon. C–24	773. 3	2. 888363
		188 34 42. 6	8 34 44. 8	Ref. Mon. S–20	448. 0	2. 651266
Ref. Mon. C–26	46 22 21. 656	163 58 01. 3	343 57 56. 6	C–25	501. 0	2. 699839
	70 07 48. 712	203 47 36. 3	23 47 42. 4	S–21	446. 2	2. 649553
Ref. Mon. S–22 (north base).	46 22 24. 041	76 00 45. 0	256 00 35. 0	Ref. Mon. C–26	304. 6	2. 483783
	70 07 34. 882	133 13 35. 2	313 13 20. 5	C–25	595. 6	2. 774923
		160 56 58. 8	340 56 54. 9	S–21	354. 0	2. 549059
S–23 (south base)	46 22 13. 120	124 06 26. 6	304 06 13. 4	Ref. Mon. C–26	470. 0	2. 672123
	70 07 30. 504	164 29 26. 8	344 29 23. 6	Ref. Mon. S–22	349. 94	2. 543990
S–24	46 22 09. 742	165 26 59. 1	345 26 55. 9	Ref. Mon. C–26	380. 1	2. 579847
	70 07 44. 245	204 22 59. 2	24 23 06. 0	Ref. Mon. S–22	484. 7	2. 685515
		250 26 45. 3	70 26 55. 3	S–23	311. 7	2. 493715
C–27	46 22 13. 920	247 27 30. 3	67 27 49. 8	Ref. Mon. C–26	623. 2	2. 794616
	70 08 15. 642	280 52 38. 2	100 53 00. 9	S–24	683. 4	2. 834657

LAKE POHENAGAMOOK TO THE VERMONT-QUEBEC BOUNDARY—Continued

Station	Latitude and longitude	Azimuth	Back azimuth	To station	Distance (meters)	Loga- rithm
MINOR SCHEME, SOUTHWEST BRANCH OF ST. JOHN RIVER—con.	° ′ ″	° ′ ″	° ′ ″			
Ref. Mon. S–25	46 22 03. 381	162 22 00. 9	342 21 57. 4	C–27	341. 5	2. 533357
	70 08 10. 802	219 55 03. 3	39 55 19. 3	Ref. Mon. C–26	735. 8	2. 866747
		250 54 34. 3	70 54 53. 5	S–24	600. 7	2. 778650
Ref. Mon. C–28	46 21 57. 795	222 55 00. 7	42 55 16. 4	C–27	679. 9	2. 832438
	70 08 37. 302	253 03 47. 7	73 04 06. 9	Ref. Mon. S–25	592. 1	2. 772404
Ref. Mon. S–26	46 21 49. 283	131 30 27. 3	311 30 17. 2	Ref. Mon. C–28	396. 6	2. 598342
	70 08 23. 408	192 18 33. 3	12 18 38. 9	C–27	778. 6	2. 891324
		211 45 26. 9	31 45 36. 0	Ref. Mon. S–25	511. 9	2. 709217
C–29	46 21 40. 916	215 34 01. 3	35 34 13. 9	Ref. Mon. C–28	640. 7	2. 806658
	70 08 54. 736	248 54 09. 7	68 54 32. 4	Ref. Mon. S–26	717. 8	2. 856007
S–27	46 21 34. 560	119 37 46. 2	299 37 34. 5	C–29	397. 0	2. 598788
	70 08 38. 594	182 12 14. 5	2 12 15. 4	Ref. Mon. C–28	718. 0	2. 856096
		215 31 44. 9	35 31 55. 9	Ref. Mon. S–26	558. 6	2. 747110
Ref. Mon. S–29	46 21 28. 254	204 03 38. 6	24 03 44. 5	C–29	428. 2	2. 631633
	70 09 02. 902	249 27 26. 2	69 27 43. 8	S–27	555. 0	2. 744267
S–28	46 21 22. 378	120 52 24. 9	300 52 14. 6	Ref. Mon. S–29	353. 6	2. 548452
	70 08 48. 708	167 18 46. 2	347 18 41. 8	C–29	586. 7	2. 768433
		209 53 36. 7	29 53 44. 0	S–27	433. 9	2. 637352
Ref. Mon. C–30	46 21 42. 104	275 06 28. 4	95 06 42. 3	C–29	412. 0	2. 614869
	70 09 13. 930	331 07 53. 7	151 08 01. 7	Ref. Mon. S–29	488. 4	2. 688737
S–30	46 21 31. 621	189 15 37. 6	9 15 39. 4	Ref. Mon. C–30	328. 0	2. 515837
	70 09 16. 399	238 12 39. 1	58 12 54. 8	C–29	544. 8	2. 736275
		289 48 51. 2	109 49 01. 0	Ref. Mon. S–29	306. 7	2. 486741
Ref. Mon. C–31	46 21 43. 840	275 04 21. 0	95 04 41. 4	Ref. Mon. C–30	605. 9	2. 782433
	70 09 42. 164	304 24 31. 1	124 24 49. 7	S–30	667. 6	2. 824543
Ref. Mon. S–31	46 21 27. 708	167 34 10. 9	347 34 07. 2	Ref. Mon. C–31	510. 1	2. 707627
	70 09 37. 028	228 00 17. 3	48 00 34. 0	Ref. Mon. C–30	664. 4	2. 822425
		254 40 44. 9	74 40 59. 8	S–30	457. 3	2. 660176
Ref. Mon. C–32	46 21 34. 305	246 01 28. 6	66 01 51. 0	Ref. Mon. C–31	724. 6	2. 860124
	70 10 13. 137	284 46 39. 4	104 47 05. 5	Ref. Mon. S–31	798. 4	2. 902212
Ref. Mon. S–32	46 21 23. 305	159 54 56. 9	339 54 52. 7	Ref. Mon. C–32	361. 6	2. 558266
	70 10 07. 328	220 18 38. 2	40 18 56. 4	Ref. Mon. C–31	831. 5	2. 919877
		258 08 41. 0	78 09 02. 9	Ref. Mon. S–31	661. 9	2. 820796
S–33	46 21 28. 288	211 42 10. 9	31 42 14. 8	Ref. Mon. C–32	218. 4	2. 339176
	70 10 18. 505	302 46 37. 0	122 46 45. 1	Ref. Mon. S–32	284. 2	2. 453623
Ref. Mon. S–34	46 21 16. 880	211 38 28. 8	31 38 36. 1	S–33	413. 8	2. 616758
	70 10 28. 658	246 29 10. 3	66 29 25. 7	Ref. Mon. S–32	497. 3	2. 696631
Ref. Mon. C–33	46 21 24. 060	245 00 17. 4	65 00 40. 4	Ref. Mon. C–32	748. 8	2. 874347
	70 10 44. 881	256 57 38. 0	76 57 57. 1	S–33	578. 8	2. 762551
		271 39 28. 4	91 39 55. 6	Ref. Mon. S–32	803. 2	2. 904827
		302 34 56. 8	122 35 08. 6	Ref. Mon. S–34	411. 6	2. 614526
Ref. Mon. S–35	46 21 04. 649	192 04 04. 3	12 04 08. 6	Ref. Mon. C–33	612. 9	2. 787386
	70 10 50. 875	231 30 41. 3	51 30 57. 4	Ref. Mon. S–34	606. 9	2. 783084
Ref. Mon. C–34	46 21 11. 268	216 16 05. 3	36 16 15. 1	Ref. Mon. C–33	489. 9	2. 690120
	70 10 58. 437	254 46 14. 0	74 46 35. 6	Ref. Mon. S–34	659. 9	2. 819452
		321 38 52. 7	141 38 58. 2	Ref. Mon. S–35	260. 6	2. 415957
S–36	46 20 56. 189	213 45 20. 2	33 45 30. 7	Ref. Mon. C–34	560. 0	2. 748199
	70 11 12. 991	241 04 48. 9	61 05 04. 9	Ref. Mon. S–35	540. 2	2. 732592

LAKE POHENAGAMOOK TO THE VERMONT-QUEBEC BOUNDARY—Continued

Station	Latitude and longitude	Azimuth	Back azimuth	To station	Distance (meters)	Logarithm
MINOR SCHEME, SOUTHWEST BRANCH OF ST. JOHN RIVER—con.	° ′ ″	° ′ ″	° ′ ″			
C–35	46 21 02. 426 70 11 19. 404	238 39 23. 5 263 34 32. 4 324 32 50. 6	58 39 38. 7 83 34 53. 1 144 32 55. 3	Ref. Mon. C–34 Ref. Mon. S–35 S–36	524. 9 613. 9 236. 4	2. 720068 2. 788064 2. 373672
Ref. Mon. S–37	46 20 50. 529 70 11 24. 551	196 40 42. 6 234 44 23. 4	16 40 46. 3 54 44 31. 8	C–35 S–36	383. 5 302. 7	2. 583733 2. 481049
Ref. Mon. C–36	46 20 54. 068 70 11 35. 845	233 42 58. 3 262 21 52. 4 294 20 30. 8	53 43 10. 2 82 22 09. 0 114 20 39. 0	C–35 S–36 Ref. Mon. S–37	436. 1 493. 1 265. 1	2. 639600 2. 692899 2. 423364
S–38	46 20 42. 109 70 11 36. 420	181 54 28. 7 224 18 37. 7	1 54 29. 1 44 18 46. 3	Ref. Mon. C–36 Ref. Mon. S–37	369. 5 363. 3	2. 567560 2. 560311
C–37	46 20 44. 584 70 11 44. 941	213 35 31. 1 247 10 02. 3 292 45 24. 6	33 35 37. 7 67 10 17. 1 112 45 30. 8	Ref. Mon. C–36 Ref. Mon. S–37 S–38	351. 5 473. 1 197. 6	2. 545958 2. 674926 2. 295747
Ref. Mon. C–38	46 20 29. 407 70 11 52. 453	198 55 14. 6 221 09 30. 6	18 55 20. 0 41 09 42. 2	C–37 S–38	495. 4 520. 9	2. 694938 2. 716764
Ref. Mon. S–39	46 20 27. 832 70 11 39. 908	100 16 38. 9 168 14 46. 8 189 36 07. 9	280 16 29. 8 348 14 43. 1 9 36 10. 4	Ref. Mon. C–38 C–37 S–38	272. 7 528. 3 447. 1	2. 435606 2. 722905 2. 650389
S-40	46 20 16. 524 70 11 49. 652	171 26 07. 7 210 49 43. 7	351 26 05. 7 30 49 50. 8	Ref. Mon. C–38 Ref. Mon. S–39	402. 3 406. 6	2. 604514 2. 609164
C–39	46 20 18. 743 70 12 02. 178	212 16 33. 1 239 29 21. 4 284 20 40. 6	32 16 40. 1 59 29 37. 5 104 20 49. 6	Ref. Mon. C–38 Ref. Mon. S–39 S–40	389. 4 552. 8 276. 5	2. 590449 2. 742556 2. 441708
Ref. Mon. S–41	46 20 04. 772 70 12 05. 263	188 41 41. 1 222 36 54. 0	8 41 43. 4 42 37 05. 3	C–39 S–40	436. 4 493. 1	2. 639880 2. 692930
Ref. Mon. C–40	46 20 10. 175 70 12 14. 579	225 04 12. 8 249 48 24. 4 309 56 05. 9	45 04 21. 8 69 48 42. 4 129 56 12. 6	C–39 S–40 Ref. Mon. S–41	374. 6 568. 0 259. 9	2. 573585 2. 754365 2. 414755
S–42	46 19 53. 734 70 12 17. 633	187 19 49. 5 217 49 12. 9	7 19 51. 7 37 49 21. 8	Ref. Mon. C–40 Ref. Mon. S–41	511. 8 431. 5	2. 709122 2. 634944
C–41	46 20 00. 185 70 12 29. 018	225 01 52. 2 254 25 15. 1 309 16 55. 3	45 02 02. 6 74 25 32. 2 129 17 03. 5	Ref. Mon. C–40 Ref. Mon. S–41 S–42	436. 5 527. 4 314. 6	2. 639950 2. 722176 2. 497757
Ref. Mon. C–42	46 19 47. 586 70 12 36. 716	202 56 28. 8 245 03 25. 7	22 56 34. 4 65 03 39. 5	C–41 S–42	422. 4 450. 2	2. 625755 2. 653370
Ref. Mon. S–43	46 19 43. 128 70 12 25. 509	119 51 55. 3 171 53 26. 9 207 13 24. 7	299 51 47. 2 351 53 24. 4 27 13 30. 4	Ref. Mon. C–42 C–41 S–42	276. 4 532. 0 368. 3	2. 441576 2. 725895 2. 566162
C–43	46 19 28. 917 70 12 35. 643	177 43 12. 4 206 17 24. 1	357 43 11. 6 26 17 31. 4	Ref. Mon. C–42 Ref. Mon. S–43	576. 9 489. 4	2. 761094 2. 689679
S–44	46 19 27. 476 70 12 19. 380	97 17 32. 1 149 09 21. 5 164 49 24. 0	277 17 20. 4 329 09 09. 0 344 49 19. 6	C–43 Ref. Mon. C–42 Ref. Mon. S–43	350. 7 723. 2 500. 8	2. 544973 2. 859286 2. 699634
Ref. Mon. S–45	46 19 18. 579 70 12 23. 022	139 46 39. 5 195 50 01. 8	319 46 30. 4 15 50 04. 4	C–43 S–44	418. 1 285. 5	2. 621267 2. 455680
Ref. Mon. C–44	46 19 18. 462 70 12 36. 664	183 52 21. 6 233 01 43. 9 269 17 24. 0	3 52 22. 3 53 01 56. 3 89 17 33. 8	C–43 S–44 Ref. Mon. S–45	323. 6 462. 8 291. 9	2. 509969 2. 665395 2. 465195

LAKE POHENAGAMOOK TO THE VERMONT-QUEBEC BOUNDARY—Continued

Station	Latitude and longitude	Azimuth	Back azimuth	To station	Distance (meters)	Loga- rithm
MINOR SCHEME, SOUTHWEST BRANCH OF ST. JOHN RIVER—con.	° ′ ″	° ′ ″	° ′ ″			
C–45	46 19 10. 719	159 14 25. 6	339 14 22. 6	Ref. Mon. C–44	255. 7	2. 407701
	70 12 32. 428	219 39 47. 1	39 39 53. 9	Ref. Mon. S–45	315. 3	2. 498677
S–46	46 19 13. 005	70 46 40. 0	250 46 33. 2	C–45	214. 4	2. 331163
	70 12 22. 967	119 54 02. 5	299 53 52. 7	Ref. Mon. C–44	338. 0	2. 528957
		179 36 19. 9	359 36 19. 9	Ref. Mon. S–45	172. 1	2. 235819
C–46	46 19 02. 899	159 24 10. 6	339 24 07. 6	C–45	258. 0	2. 411551
	70 12 28. 187	199 41 23. 7	19 41 27. 5	S–46	331. 4	2. 520392
S–47	46 19 06. 443	69 09 08. 1	249 08 58. 4	C–46	307. 4	2. 487758
	70 12 14. 758	109 15 20. 1	289 15 07. 4	C–45	400. 4	2. 602548
		139 05 01. 4	319 04 55. 5	S–46	268. 2	2. 428380
S–48	46 18 57. 582	113 12 18. 9	293 12 06. 0	C–46	416. 7	2. 619815
	70 12 10. 286	160 43 35. 7	340 43 32. 5	S–47	289. 8	2. 462159
C–47	46 18 54. 147	159 16 24. 8	339 16 21. 4	C–46	288. 9	2. 460808
	70 12 23. 407	205 59 05. 3	25 59 11. 6	S–47	422. 4	2. 625681
		249 18 05. 7	69 18 15. 2	S–48	300. 1	2. 477268
Ref. Mon. S–49	46 18 42. 074	139 15 33. 4	319 15 22. 6	C–47	492. 0	2. 691993
	70 12 08. 399	175 10 46. 9	355 10 45. 6	S–48	480. 6	2. 681741
Ref. Mon. C–48	46 18 42. 761	169 21 53. 1	349 21 50. 9	C–47	357. 7	2. 553536
	70 12 20. 322	205 08 06. 0	25 08 13. 3	S–48	505. 5	2. 703724
		274 45 13. 6	94 45 22. 2	Ref. Mon. S–49	256. 0	2. 408233
Ref. Mon. S–50	46 18 34. 281	160 59 00. 7	340 58 57. 7	Ref. Mon. C–48	276. 9	2. 442386
	70 12 16. 105	214 25 15. 6	34 25 21. 2	Ref. Mon. S–49	291. 7	2. 464904
C–49	46 18 33. 542	198 20 37. 5	18 20 40. 7	Ref. Mon. C–48	299. 9	2. 476959
	70 12 24. 733	232 59 32. 1	52 59 43. 9	Ref. Mon. S–49	437. 7	2. 641138
		262 57 07. 7	82 57 13. 9	Ref. Mon. S–50	186. 0	2. 269587
S–51	46 18 22. 527	168 15 12. 1	348 15 09. 7	C–49	347. 4	2. 540825
	70 12 21. 428	197 25 23. 8	17 25 27. 6	Ref. Mon. S–50	380. 4	2. 580238
Ref. Mon. C–50	46 18 23. 492	200 43 52. 5	20 43 56. 5	C–49	331. 8	2. 520860
	70 12 30. 222	222 12 02. 0	42 12 12. 2	Ref. Mon. S–50	449. 7	2. 652920
		279 00 09. 3	99 00 15. 7	S–51	190. 5	2. 279963
C–51 (north base)	46 18 11. 604	175 54 33. 9	355 54 33. 0	Ref. Mon. C–50	368. 0	2. 565852
	70 12 28. 995	205 38 53. 0	25 38 58. 5	S–51	374. 1	2. 573002
S–52	46 18 11. 142	93 29 17. 6	273 29 09. 7	C–51	234. 5	2. 370217
	70 12 18. 056	145 40 41. 9	325 40 33. 1	Ref. Mon. C–50	461. 7	2. 664390
		168 23 57. 1	348 23 54. 7	S–51	358. 8	2. 554908
Ref. Mon. C–52 (south base).	46 18 02. 112	192 15 10. 2	12 15 12. 4	C–51	299. 90	2. 476983
	70 12 31. 969	226 52 53. 1	46 53 03. 2	S–52	407. 9	2. 610570
Ref. Mon. S–53	46 17 57. 540	122 34 21. 6	302 34 14. 1	Ref. Mon. C–52	262. 3	2. 418719
	70 12 21. 643	160 04 59. 2	340 04 53. 9	C–51	461. 9	2. 664535
		190 21 27. 2	10 21 29. 8	S–52	426. 9	2. 630376
S–54	46 17 48. 653	213 00 49. 6	33 00 58. 7	Ref. Mon. C–52	495. 6	2. 695122
	70 12 44. 586	240 48 08. 7	60 48 25. 3	Ref. Mon. S–53	562. 5	2. 750123
Ref. Mon. C–53	46 17 55. 554	245 14 05. 2	65 14 20. 0	Ref. Mon. C–52	483. 4	2. 684344
	70 12 52. 481	264 41 21. 7	84 41 44. 0	Ref. Mon. S–53	662. 8	2. 821411
		321 34 59. 4	141 35 05. 1	S–54	271. 9	2. 434466
C–54	46 17 44. 392	211 03 40. 9	31 03 47. 9	Ref. Mon. C–53	402. 3	2. 604585
	70 13 02. 180	250 44 20. 0	70 44 32. 7	S–54	398. 9	2. 600859

LAKE POHENAGAMOOK TO THE VERMONT-QUEBEC BOUNDARY—Continued

Station	Latitude and longitude	Azimuth	Back azimuth	To station	Distance (meters)	Logarithm
MINOR SCHEME, SOUTHWEST BRANCH OF ST. JOHN RIVER—con.	° ′ ″	° ′ ″	° ′ ″			
S-55	46 17 37. 137 70 12 54. 626	144 10 55. 7 184 37 00. 5 211 08 45. 5	324 10 50. 2 4 37 02. 0 31 08 52. 7	C-54 Ref. Mon. C-53 S-54	276. 3 570. 5 415. 5	2. 441327 2. 756261 2. 618555
Ref. Mon. S-56	46 17 32. 446 70 13 05. 368	190 28 56. 7 237 47 33. 5	10 28 59. 0 57 47 41. 3	C-54 S-55	375. 1 271. 7	2. 574155 2. 434155
C-55	46 17 41. 756 70 13 12. 255	249 19 08. 7 290 42 14. 2 332 51 06. 1	69 19 16. 0 110 42 27. 0 152 51 11. 1	C-54 S-55 Ref. Mon. S-56	230. 5 403. 4 323. 0	2. 362650 2. 605708 2. 509254
Ref. Mon. C-56	46 17 38. 377 70 13 25. 191	249 21 09. 1 293 20 34. 9	69 21 18. 4 113 20 49. 2	C-55 Ref. Mon. S-56	295. 9 462. 1	2. 471123 2. 664753
S-57	46 17 28. 853 70 13 21. 634	165 29 12. 3 206 44 34. 0 252 19 17. 3	345 29 09. 8 26 44 40. 8 72 19 29. 1	Ref. Mon. C-56 C-55 Ref. Mon. S-56	303. 8 446. 1 365. 4	2. 482554 2. 649466 2. 562794
PRECISE TRAVERSE, SOUTHWEST BRANCH OF ST. JOHN RIVER AND THE HIGHLANDS TO THE CANADIAN PACIFIC RAILWAY CROSSING						
Ref. Mon. C-57	46 17 46. 842 70 13 46. 179	300 11 23. 0	120 11 38. 2	Ref. Mon. C-56	519. 73	2. 715778
Substation C-58	46 17 12. 948 70 14 12. 438	208 14 13. 3	28 14 32. 3	Ref. Mon. C-57	1, 187. 92	3. 074789
Ref. Mon. C-58	46 17 10. 133 70 14 04. 883	118 15 08. 8	298 15 03. 3	Substation C-58	183. 61	2. 263894
Ref. Mon. S-58	46 17 07. 217 70 13 57. 058	118 15 29. 3	298 15 23. 6	Ref. Mon. C-58	190. 17	2. 279133
Ref. Mon. C-59	46 16 38. 162 70 14 39. 378	208 13 53. 8	28 14 13. 3	Substation C-58	1, 219. 15	3. 086056
Ref. Mon. S-59	46 16 31. 199 70 14 20. 620	118 09 40. 1	298 09 26. 5	Ref. Mon. C-59	455. 54	2. 658530
Ref. Mon. C-60	46 16 16. 425 70 14 56. 206	208 13 41. 6	28 13 53. 8	Ref. Mon. C-59	761. 76	2. 881818
Ref. Mon. S-60	46 16 10. 781 70 14 41. 102	118 19 02. 9	298 18 52. 0	Ref. Mon. C-60	367. 38	2. 565112
Ref. Mon. C-61	46 15 43. 434 70 15 21. 740	208 13 23. 2	28 13 41. 6	Ref. Mon. C-60	1, 156. 14	3. 063012
Ref. Mon. S-61	46 15 36. 633 70 15 06. 758	123 12 20. 7	303 12 09. 9	Ref. Mon. C-61	383. 47	2. 583736
Ref. Mon. C-62	46 15 20. 988 70 15 26. 420	188 13 44. 4	8 13 47. 8	Ref. Mon. C-61	700. 27	2. 845265
Ref. Mon. S-62	46 15 19. 328 70 15 11. 077	98 52 04. 7	278 51 53. 6	Ref. Mon. C-62	332. 61	2. 521936
Ref. Mon. C-63	46 15 10. 244 70 15 28. 660	188 13 42. 8	8 13 44. 4	Ref. Mon. C-62	335. 18	2. 525273
Ref. Mon. S-63	46 15 08. 335 70 15 06. 463	97 04 11. 1	277 03 55. 1	Ref. Mon. C-63	479. 11	2. 680436

LAKE POHENAGAMOOK TO THE VERMONT-QUEBEC BOUNDARY—Continued

Station	Latitude and longitude	Azimuth	Back azimuth	To station	Distance (meters)	Loga- rithm
PRECISE TRAVERSE, SOUTHWEST BRANCH OF ST. JOHN RIVER AND THE HIGHLANDS TO THE CANADIAN PACIFIC RAILWAY CROSSING—contd.	° ′ ″	° ′ ″	° ′ ″			
Ref. Mon. C–64_____	46 14 54. 823 70 15 31. 874	188 13 40. 5	8 13 42. 8	Ref. Mon. C–63___	481. 10	2. 682240
Ref. Mon. S–64_____	46 14 48. 409 70 15 02. 006	107 12 00. 9	287 11 39. 3	Ref. Mon. C–64___	669. 77	2. 825924
Ref. Mon. C–65_____	46 14 46. 819 70 15 35. 455	197 14 27. 5	17 14 30. 1	Ref. Mon. C–64___	258. 77	2. 412917
Ref. Mon. C–66_____	46 14 16. 953 70 15 48. 815	197 14 32. 4	17 14 42. 1	Ref. Mon. C–65___	965. 56	2. 984777
Ref. Mon. S–65_____	46 14 13. 092 70 15 29. 647	106 11 23. 4	286 11 09. 6	Ref. Mon. C–66___	427. 64	2. 631081
Traverse station 5___	46 14 13. 447 70 15 50. 383	197 14 31. 3	17 14 32. 4	Ref. Mon. C–66___	113. 36	2. 054440
Ref. Mon. C–67_____	46 13 41. 827 70 16 16. 140	209 28 37. 7	29 28 56. 3	Traverse station 5_	1, 121. 52	3. 049806
Ref. Mon. S–66_____	46 13 29. 586 70 15 50. 525	124 33 02. 2	304 32 43. 7	Ref. Mon. C–67___	666. 46	2. 823772
Ref. Mon. C–68_____	46 12 50. 263 70 16 58. 122	209 28 07. 4	29 28 37. 7	Ref. Mon. C–67___	1, 828. 76	3. 262156
Ref. Mon. S–67_____	46 12 33. 524 70 16 18. 731	121 28 25. 2	301 27 56. 8	Ref. Mon. C–68___	990. 01	2. 995641
Ref. Mon. C–69_____	46 12 42. 552 70 17 00. 578	192 28 20. 6	12 28 22. 4	Ref. Mon. C–68___	243. 83	2. 387086
Traverse station 7___	46 12 17. 050 70 17 08. 702	192 28 14. 8	12 28 20. 6	Ref. Mon. C–69___	806. 44	2. 906569
Ref. Mon. C–70_____	46 12 07. 079 70 17 11. 876	192 27 50. 9	12 27 53. 2	Traverse station 7_	315. 30	2. 498718
Ref. Mon. S–68_____	46 11 58. 753 70 16 51. 306	120 14 22. 9	300 14 08. 1	Ref. Mon. C–70___	510. 49	2. 707986
Ref. Mon. S–69_____	46 11 25. 191 70 17 25. 207	192 27 41. 3	12 27 50. 9	Ref. Mon. C–70___	1, 324. 55	3 .122068
Ref. Mon. 313_____	46 11 29. 151 70 17 36. 190	297 26 04. 2	117 26 12. 1	Ref. Mon. S–69___	265. 36	2. 423828
Ref. Mon. 312_____	46 11 29. 437 70 17 35. 324	64 32 49. 8	244 32 49. 2	Ref. Mon. 313____	20. 57	1. 313255
Ref. Mon. C–71_____	46 10 55. 765 70 17 34. 569	192 27 34. 5	12 27 41. 3	Ref. Mon. S–69___	930. 50	2. 968718
Ref. Mon. C–72_____	46 10 27. 927 70 16 58. 456	137 58 44. 0	317 58 18. 0	Ref. Mon. C–71___	1, 157. 04	3. 063347
Ref. Mon. S–70_____	46 10 37. 145 70 16 43. 690	48 03 34. 7	228 03 24. 0	Ref. Mon. C–72___	425. 82	2. 629223
Ref. Mon. C–73_____	46 10 16. 223 70 16 43. 277	137 58 55. 0	317 58 44. 0	Ref. Mon. C–72___	486. 43	2. 687018

LAKE POHENAGAMOOK TO THE VERMONT-QUEBEC BOUNDARY—Continued

Station	Latitude and longitude	Azimuth	Back azimuth	To station	Distance (meters)	Loga-rithm
PRECISE TRAVERSE, SOUTHWEST BRANCH OF ST. JOHN RIVER AND THE HIGHLANDS TO THE CANADIAN PACIFIC RAILWAY CROSSING—contd.	° ′ ″	° ′ ″	° ′ ″			
Ref. Mon. S–71_____	46 10 20. 549 70 16 09. 644	79 30 52. 8	259 30 28. 5	Ref. Mon. C–73___	733. 75	2. 865546
Ref. Mon. S–72_____	46 09 58. 952 70 15 46. 659	143 31 17. 8	323 31 01. 2	Ref. Mon. S–71___	829. 35	2. 918737
Ref. Mon. C–74_____	46 09 53. 986 70 15 56. 461	233 54 05. 9	53 54 13. 0	Ref. Mon. S–72___	260. 27	2. 415418
Ref. Mon. C–75_____	46 09 27. 808 70 15 13. 531	143 32 00. 0	323 31 36. 1	Ref. Mon. S–72___	1, 195. 77	3. 077648
Ref. Mon. S–73_____	46 09 31. 183 70 15 03. 088	65 03 33. 5	245 03 26. 0	Ref. Mon. C–75___	247. 12	2. 392914
Ref. Mon. S–74_____	46 09 03. 452 70 14 23. 300	135 05 07. 2	315 04 38. 5	Ref. Mon. S–73___	1, 209. 16	3. 082483
Ref. Mon. C–76_____	46 08 56. 024 70 14 33. 882	224 43 02. 5	44 43 10. 1	Ref. Mon. S–74___	322. 74	2. 508859
Ref. Mon. S–75_____	46 08 47. 165 70 13 59. 939	135 05 24. 0	315 05 07. 2	Ref. Mon. S–74___	710. 07	2. 851304
Ref. Mon. S–76_____	46 08 13. 064 70 14 19. 348	201 35 01. 7	21 35 15. 7	Ref. Mon. S–75___	1, 132. 31	3. 053967
Ref. Mon. C–77_____	46 08 16. 632 70 14 32. 256	291 40 56. 6	111 41 05. 9	Ref. Mon. S–76___	298. 18	2. 474477
Ref. Mon. S–77_____	46 07 29. 895 70 14 43. 907	201 34 44. 0	21 35 01. 7	Ref. Mon. S–76___	1, 433. 35	3. 156352
Ref. Mon. C–78_____	46 07 33. 732 70 14 57. 873	291 33 20. 9	111 33 31. 0	Ref. Mon. S–77___	322. 39	2. 508376
Ref. Mon. S–78_____	46 07 08. 483 70 14 56. 084	201 34 35. 2	21 34 44. 0	Ref. Mon. S–77___	710. 94	2. 851833
Ref. Mon. C–79_____	46 07 12. 641 70 15 10. 502	292 31 15. 4	112 31 25. 8	Ref. Mon. S–78___	335. 14	2. 525224
Ref. Mon. S–79_____	46 06 35. 275 70 15 14. 963	201 34 19. 2	21 34 32. 8	Ref. Mon. S–78___	1, 102. 56	3. 042401
Ref. Mon. C–80_____	46 06 37. 623 70 15 23. 495	291 34 51. 2	111 34 57. 3	Ref. Mon. S–79___	197. 04	2. 294549
Ref. Mon. C–81_____	46 06 17. 566 70 15 25. 029	201 34 11. 9	21 34 19. 2	Ref. Mon. S–79___	587. 98	2. 769364
Mon. 314 (traverse station).	46 05 59. 000 70 15 28. 073	186 30 20. 0	6 30 22. 2	Ref. Mon. C–81___	576. 97	2. 761151
Substation 315_____	46 05 59. 320 70 16 12. 138	270 35 35. 1	90 36 06. 8	Mon. 314_____	946. 54	2. 976141
Mon. 315_____	46 06 04. 708 70 16 12. 422	357 54 00. 3	177 54 00. 5	Substation 315____	166. 47	2. 221325
Substation 316_____	46 05 59. 470 70 16 33. 081	270 35 20. 0	90 35 35. 1	Substation 315____	449. 87	2. 653090

LAKE POHENAGAMOOK TO THE VERMONT-QUEBEC BOUNDARY—Continued

Station	Latitude and longitude	Azimuth	Back azimuth	To station	Distance (meters)	Logarithm
	° ′ ″	° ′ ″	° ′ ″			
PRECISE TRAVERSE, SOUTHWEST BRANCH OF ST. JOHN RIVER AND THE HIGHLANDS TO THE CANADIAN PACIFIC RAILWAY CROSSING—contd.						
Mon. 316	46 06 05.553 70 16 31.423	10 44 15.4	190 44 14.2	Substation 316	191.15	2.281378
Substation 317	46 05 59.592 70 16 50.238	270 35 07.6	90 35 20.0	Substation 316	368.54	2.566482
Mon. 317	46 06 00.065 70 16 50.998	311 49 04.6	131 49 05.1	Substation 317	21.91	1.340587
Traverse station 18	46 05 59.668 70 17 00.846	270 35 00.0 270 35 00.0	90 36 06.8 90 35 07.6	Mon. 314 Substation 317	1,992.82 227.86	3.299467 2.357666
Mon. 318 (traverse station).	46 05 59.744 70 17 11.536	270 34 59.4	90 35 07.1	Traverse station 18	229.62	2.361010
Traverse station 21	46 05 56.822 70 17 13.195	201 33 20.2	21 33 21.4	Mon. 318	96.99	1.986737
Substation 319	46 05 20.514 70 17 33.805	201 32 53.8	21 33 08.7	Traverse station 21	1,205.31	3.081100
Mon. 319	46 05 19.228 70 17 30.988	123 16 15.5	303 16 13.5	Substation 319	72.38	1.859612
Traverse station 22	46 04 41.481 70 17 55.951	201 32 37.9 201 32 37.9	21 33 08.7 21 32 53.8	Traverse station 21 Substation 319	2,501.00 1,295.69	3.398113 3.112499
Traverse station 23	46 04 21.255 70 18 07.420	201 32 09.5	21 32 17.8	Traverse station 22	671.36	2.826953
Substation 320	46 04 18.218 70 18 09.139	201 30 02.8	21 30 04.0	Traverse station 23	100.78	2.003353
Mon. 320	46 04 15.196 70 18 11.321	206 40 51.6	26 40 53.2	Substation 320	104.43	2.018832
Substation 321	46 03 43.254 70 17 47.549	160 00 04.5	339 59 50.2	Traverse station 23	1,248.60	3.096424
Mon. 321	46 03 39.055 70 17 56.284	235 22 22.1	55 22 28.4	Substation 321	228.16	2.358245
Traverse station 24	46 03 38.718 70 17 45.178	160 00 06.2 160 00 06.2	339 59 50.2 340 00 04.5	Traverse station 23 Substation 321	1,397.66 149.06	3.145402 2.173358
Traverse station 25	46 03 39.265 70 16 59.140	89 01 33.8	269 01 00.6	Traverse station 24	989.71	2.995510
Traverse station 26	46 03 39.409 70 16 46.970	89 01 46.9	269 01 38.1	Traverse station 25	261.62	2.417664
Mon. 322	46 03 35.148 70 16 44.768	160 12 34.8	340 12 33.2	Traverse station 26	139.82	2.145574
Traverse station 27	46 02 55.901 70 17 05.879	196 50 02.7	16 50 16.3	Traverse station 26	1,403.48	3.147207
Mon. 323	46 02 54.632 70 17 06.883	208 50 59.7	28 51 00.4	Traverse station 27	44.73	1.650561
Traverse station 28	46 02 49.440 70 17 16.095	227 45 02.3	47 45 09.6	Traverse station 27	296.71	2.472336

LAKE POHENAGAMOOK TO THE VERMONT-QUEBEC BOUNDARY—Continued

Station	Latitude and longitude	Azimuth	Back azimuth	To station	Distance (meters)	Loga- rithm
PRECISE TRAVERSE, SOUTHWEST BRANCH OF ST. JOHN RIVER AND THE HIGHLANDS TO THE CANADIAN PACIFIC RAILWAY CROSSING—contd.	° ′ ″	° ′ ″	° ′ ″			
Traverse station 29_	46 02 41. 832 70 17 28. 106	227 42 30. 1	47 42 38. 8	Traverse station 28_	349. 10	2. 542955
Traverse station 30_	46 02 26. 117 70 17 52. 980	227 46 59. 3	47 47 17. 2	Traverse station 29_	722. 13	2. 858616
Mon. 324_____	46 02 27. 732 70 17 44. 743	74 16 50. 7	254 16 44. 8	Traverse station 30_	183. 99	2. 264792
Traverse station 31_	46 02 07. 429 70 17 55. 352	185 03 09. 0	5 03 10. 7	Traverse station 30_	579. 24	2. 762856
Traverse station 32_	46 01 54. 500 70 17 56. 988	185 02 13. 3	5 02 14. 5	Traverse station 31_	400. 72	2. 602843
Substation 325_____	46 01 43. 489 70 18 12. 962	225 17 51. 4	45 18 02. 9	Traverse station 32_	483. 33	2. 684244
Mon. 325_____	46 01 39. 796 70 18 07. 124	132 14 43. 1	312 14 38. 9	Substation 325____	169. 61	2. 229451
Traverse station 33_	46 01 12. 775 70 18 57. 505	225 17 19. 3 225 17 19. 3	45 18 02. 9 45 17 51. 4	Traverse station 32_ Substation 325____	1, 831. 36 1, 348. 03	3. 262773 3. 129699
Mon. 326_____	46 01 08. 497 70 19 06. 697	236 15 16. 0	56 15 22. 6	Traverse station 33_	237. 80	2. 376209
Substation 327_____	46 00 50. 266 70 18 29. 864	139 27 11. 1	319 26 51. 2	Traverse station 33_	914. 61	2. 961235
Mon. 327_____	46 00 43. 397 70 18 42. 052	231 01 54. 8	51 02 03. 6	Substation 327____	337. 22	2. 527915
Substation 328_____	46 00 08. 866 70 17 39. 047	139 27 47. 7	319 27 11. 1	Substation 327____	1, 682. 04	3. 225837
Mon. 328_____	45 59 55. 341 70 18 01. 973	229 45 01. 2	49 45 17. 7	Substation 328____	646. 33	2. 810451
Traverse station 34_	45 59 41. 969 70 17 06. 047	139 28 11. 4 139 28 11. 4	319 26 51. 2 319 27 47. 7	Traverse station 33_ Substation 328____	3, 689. 33 1, 092. 69	3. 566948 3. 038495
Mon. 329_____	45 59 43. 745 70 17 04. 477	31 38 11. 6	211 38 10. 5	Traverse station 34_	64. 41	1. 808926
Substation 330_____	45 58 37. 154 70 18 09. 711	214 23 41. 4	34 24 27. 2	Traverse station 34_	2, 425. 35	3. 384775
Mon. 330_____	45 58 47. 367 70 18 32. 760	302 25 57. 9	122 26 14. 5	Substation 330____	587. 88	2. 769291
Traverse station 35_	45 57 52. 350 70 18 53. 690	214 23 09. 8 214 23 09. 8	34 24 27. 2 34 23 41. 4	Traverse station 34_ Substation 330____	4, 101. 68 1, 676. 33	3. 612962 3. 224360
Mon. 331_____	45 57 49. 478 70 18 59. 573	235 00 26. 2	55 00 30. 4	Traverse station 35_	154. 62	2. 189262
Traverse station 36_	45 57 52. 513 70 17 43. 813	89 48 54. 5	269 48 04. 3	Traverse station 35_	1, 504. 60	3. 177422
Mon. 332_____	45 57 47. 182 70 17 45. 637	193 25 18. 7	13 25 20. 0	Traverse station 36_	169. 22	2. 228462

LAKE POHENAGAMOOK TO THE VERMONT-QUEBEC BOUNDARY—Continued

Station	Latitude and longitude	Azimuth	Back azimuth	To station	Distance (meters)	Loga- rithm
PRECISE TRAVERSE, SOUTHWEST BRANCH OF ST. JOHN RIVER AND THE HIGHLANDS TO THE CANADIAN PACIFIC RAILWAY CROSSING—contd.	° ′ ″	° ′ ″	° ′ ″			
Traverse station 37	45 57 52. 659 70 16 36. 142	89 49 48. 0	269 48 59. 3	Traverse station 36	1, 457. 10	3. 163489
Substation 333	45 57 40. 203 70 16 16. 919	132 53 49. 1	312 53 35. 3	Traverse station 37	565. 00	2. 752049
Mon. 333	45 57 44. 420 70 16 10. 452	46 55 28. 5	226 55 23. 9	Substation 333	190. 63	2. 280193
Substation 334	45 57 13. 253 70 15 35. 340	132 54 19. 0	312 53 49. 1	Substation 333	1, 222. 33	3. 087188
Mon. 334	45 57 09. 088 70 15 40. 582	221 16 41. 5	41 16 45. 3	Substation 334	171. 11	2. 233271
Traverse station 38	45 57 07. 330 70 15 26. 205	132 54 25. 6 132 54 25. 6	312 53 35. 3 312 54 19. 0	Traverse station 37 Substation 334	2, 055. 93 268. 60	3. 313008 2, 429108
Substation 335	45 56 49. 399 70 14 58. 557	132 54 56. 3	312 54 36. 4	Traverse station 38	813. 07	2. 910130
Mon. 335	45 56 55. 817 70 14 46. 474	52 43 02. 1	232 42 53. 4	Substation 335	327. 09	2. 514673
Traverse station 39	45 56 38. 360 70 14 41. 540	132 55 08. 5 132 55 08. 5	312 54 36. 4 312 54 56. 3	Traverse station 38 Substation 335	1, 313. 58 500. 50	3. 118455 2. 699406
Traverse station 40	45 56 24. 736 70 14 23. 270	136 54 31. 6	316 54 18. 5	Traverse station 39	576. 05	2. 760459
Mon. 336	45 56 26. 107 70 14 26. 539	301 00 17. 3	121 00 19. 7	Traverse station 40	82. 17	1. 914697
Substation 337	45 56 03. 322 70 14 46. 065	216 36 00. 7	36 36 17. 1	Traverse station 40	823. 57	2. 915702
Mon. 337	45 56 07. 599 70 14 54. 705	305 21 00. 9	125 21 07. 1	Substation 337	228. 22	2. 358362
Substation 338	45 55 45. 471 70 15 05. 062	216 35 47. 1	36 36 00. 7	Substation 337	686. 50	2. 836642
Mon. 338	45 55 51. 183 70 15 16. 475	305 38 50. 8	125 38 59. 0	Substation 338	302. 60	2. 480862
Substation 339	45 55 30. 291 70 15 21. 213	216 35 35. 5	36 35 47. 1	Substation 338	583. 75	2. 766224
Mon. 339	45 55 36. 782 70 15 33. 794	306 28 22. 6	126 28 31. 6	Substation 339	337. 12	2. 527779
Substation 340	45 55 16. 950 70 15 35. 406	216 35 25. 3	36 35 35. 5	Substation 339	513. 02	2. 710141
Mon. 340	45 55 22. 851 70 15 46. 839	306 29 04. 6	126 29 12. 8	Substation 340	306. 42	2. 486312
Traverse station 41	45 55 12. 239 70 15 40. 417	216 35 21. 7 216 35 21. 7	36 36 17. 1 36 35 25. 3	Traverse station 40 Substation 340	2, 788. 00 181. 16	3. 445292 2. 258060
Traverse station 42	45 54 46. 186 70 16 08. 127	216 35 16. 7	36 35 36. 6	Traverse station 41	1, 001. 81	3, 000786

LAKE POHENAGAMOOK TO THE VERMONT-QUEBEC BOUNDARY—Continued

Station	Latitude and longitude	Azimuth	Back azimuth	To station	Distance (meters)	Loga-rithm
PRECISE TRAVERSE, SOUTHWEST BRANCH OF ST. JOHN RIVER AND THE HIGHLANDS TO THE CANADIAN PACIFIC RAILWAY CROSSING—contd.	° ′ ″	° ′ ″	° ′ ″			
Traverse station 43__	45 54 38. 588 70 15 45. 794	115 59 08. 6	295 58 52. 6	Traverse station 42_	535. 45	2. 728718
Substation 341_____	45 54 37. 883 70 15 43. 722	115 59 43. 0	295 59 41. 5	Traverse station 43_	49. 68	1. 696217
Mon. 341_____	45 54 47. 044 70 15 32. 546	40 25 10. 0	220 25 02. 0	Substation 341____	371. 50	2. 569965
Traverse station 44__	45 54 32. 490 70 15 27. 880	115 59 54. 4 115 59 54. 4	295 59 41. 5 295 59 43. 0	Traverse station 43_ Substation 341____	429. 57 379. 88	2. 633029 2. 579648
Substation 342_____	45 54 02. 409 70 15 28. 251	180 29 36. 2	0 29 36. 5	Traverse station 44_	928. 79	2. 967917
Mon. 342_____	45 54 02. 795 70 15 27. 811	38 32 22. 4	218 32 22. 1	Substation 342____	15. 23	1. 182604
Traverse station 45__	45 53 59. 316 70 15 28. 289	180 29 36. 2 180 29 36. 2	0 29 36. 5 0 29 36. 2	Traverse station 44_ Substation 342____	1, 024. 28 95. 50	3, 010420 1. 979990
Traverse station 46__	45 53 38. 640 70 15 43. 700	207 29 36. 4	27 29 47. 5	Traverse station 45_	719. 62	2. 857104
Substation 343_____	45 53 14. 075 70 16 05. 287	211 32 00. 0	31 32 15. 5	Traverse station 46_	889. 86	2. 949320
Mon. 343_____	45 53 09. 106 70 16 05. 750	183 43 32. 6	3 43 32. 9	Substation 343____	153. 74	2. 186798
Traverse station 47__	45 52 37. 239 70 16 37. 644	211 31 36. 8 211 31 36. 8	31 32 15. 5 31 32 00. 0	Traverse station 46_ Substation 343____	2, 224. 15 1, 334. 29	3. 347164 3. 125251
Traverse station 48__	45 52 27. 104 70 16 55. 899	231 31 13. 2	51 31 26. 3	Traverse station 47_	502. 88	2. 701468
Substation 345_____	45 51 59. 999 70 17 44. 204	231 13 22. 5	51 13 57. 2	Traverse station 48_	1, 336. 34	3. 125918
Mon. 345_____	45 51 59. 308 70 17 40. 946	106 53 17. 5	286 53 15. 2	Substation 345____	73. 45	1. 865988
Traverse station 49__	45 51 52. 485 70 17 57. 591	231 13 12. 9 231 13 12. 9	51 13 57. 2 51 13 22. 5	Traverse station 48_ Substation 345____	1, 706. 76 370. 41	3. 232172 2. 568687
Traverse station 50__	45 51 45. 948 70 18 14. 069	240 24 38. 7	60 24 50. 5	Traverse station 49_	408. 73	2. 611439
Traverse station 51__	45 51 02. 521 70 20 00. 925	239 48 21. 8	59 49 38. 5	Traverse station 50_	2, 666. 84	3. 425998
Mon. 346_____	45 51 11. 845 70 20 06. 475	337 24 56. 1	157 25 00. 1	Traverse station 51_	311. 79	2. 493861
Substation 347_____	45 50 45. 803 70 20 52. 247	245 00 16. 5	65 00 53. 3	Traverse station 51_	1, 221. 75	3. 086981
Mon. 347_____	45 50 51. 017 70 20 57. 208	326 22 35. 7	146 22 39. 3	Substation 347____	193. 33	2. 286295
Traverse station 52__	45 50 42. 042 70 21 03. 788	245 00 08. 2 245 00 08. 2	65 00 53. 3 65 00 16. 5	Traverse station 51_ Substation 347____	1, 496. 52 274. 77	3. 175082 2. 438976

LAKE POHENAGAMOOK TO THE VERMONT-QUEBEC BOUNDARY—Continued

Station	Latitude and longitude	Azimuth	Back azimuth	To station	Distance (meters)	Loga-rithm
PRECISE TRAVERSE, SOUTHWEST BRANCH OF ST. JOHN RIVER AND THE HIGHLANDS TO THE CANADIAN PACIFIC RAILWAY CROSSING—contd.	° ′ ″	° ′ ″	° ′ ″			
Traverse station 53__	45 50 21. 953 70 21 24. 260	215 27 32. 7	35 27 47. 4	Traverse station 52_	761. 48	2. 881656
Substation 348_____	45 50 15. 750 70 21 47. 149	248 48 24. 1	68 48 40. 5	Traverse station 53_	529. 78	2. 724098
Mon. 348_____	45 50 08. 940 70 21 45. 096	168 06 01. 3	348 05 59. 8	Substation 348____	214. 88	2. 332188
Traverse station 54__	45 50 09. 647 70 22 09. 666	248 48 07. 9 248 48 07. 9	68 48 40. 5 68 48 24. 1	Traverse station 53_ Substation 348____	1, 051. 00 521. 22	3. 021602 2. 717018
Traverse station 55 (Liniere).	45 49 45. 435 70 22 22. 431	200 13 53. 4	20 14 02. 6	Traverse station 54_	796. 67	2. 901280
Substation 349_____	45 49 16. 872 70 22 54. 820	218 24 15. 9	38 24 39. 1	Traverse station 55_	1, 125. 38	3. 051298
Mon. 349_____	45 49 19. 038 70 23 03. 308	290 02 58. 2	110 03 04. 3	Substation 349____	195. 05	2. 290146
Traverse station 56_	45 48 56. 909 70 23 17. 450	218 23 59. 6 218 23 59. 6	38 24 39. 1 38 24 15. 9	Traverse station 55_ Substation 349____	1, 911. 85 786. 48	3. 281455 2. 895686
Mon. 350_____	45 48 51. 691 70 23 18. 564	188 29 25. 1	8 29 25. 9	Traverse station 56_	162. 88	2. 211864
Traverse station 57_	45 48 43. 281 70 23 32. 882	218 22 18. 6	38 22 29. 7	Traverse station 56_	536. 70	2. 729728
Substation 351_____	45 48 32. 605 70 23 39. 940	204 48 52. 3	24 48 57. 4	Traverse station 57_	363. 13	2. 560063
Mon. 351_____	45 48 33. 120 70 23 45. 846	277 06 41. 5	97 06 45. 7	Substation 351____	128. 51	2. 108943
Substation 353_____	45 48 22. 861 70 23 46. 382	204 48 47. 7	24 48 52. 3	Substation 351____	331. 45	2. 520415
Mon. 353_____	45 48 24. 911 70 23 51. 108	301 48 33. 5	121 48 36. 9	Substation 353____	120. 08	2. 079458
Substation 354_____	45 48 10. 936 70 23 54. 265	204 48 42. 1	24 48 47. 7	Substation 353____	405. 63	2. 608127
Mon. 354_____	45 48 08. 911 70 23 46. 849	111 19 51. 3	291 19 46. 0	Substation 354____	171. 91	2. 235304
Substation 355_____	45 48 02. 148 70 24 00. 074	204 48 37. 9	24 48 42. 1	Substation 354____	298. 92	2. 475559
Mon. 355_____	45 47 58. 362 70 23 46. 656	111 58 10. 2	291 58 00. 6	Substation 355____	312. 45	2. 494781
Traverse station 58_	45 47 45. 789 70 24 10. 885	204 48 30. 2 204 48 30. 2	24 48 57. 4 24 48 37. 9	Traverse station 57_ Substation 355____	1, 955. 54 556. 41	3. 291267 2. 745395
Substation 356_____	45 47 44. 183 70 24 15. 548	243 47 08. 5	63 47 11. 8	Traverse station 58_	112. 25	2. 050202
Mon. 356_____	45 47 46. 600 70 24 13. 647	28 49 43. 7	208 49 42. 3	Substation 356____	85. 16	1. 930256

LAKE POHENAGAMOOK TO THE VERMONT-QUEBEC BOUNDARY—Continued

Station	Latitude and longitude	Azimuth	Back azimuth	To station	Distance (meters)	Loga- rithm
PRECISE TRAVERSE, SOUTHWEST BRANCH OF ST. JOHN RIVER AND THE HIGHLANDS TO THE CANADIAN PACIFIC RAILWAY CROSSING—contd.	° ′ ″	° ′ ″	° ′ ″			
Substation 357_____	45 47 40. 204 70 24 27. 099	243 47 00. 2	63 47 08. 5	Substation 356____	278. 08	2. 444168
Mon. 357_____	45 47 49. 326 70 24 39. 704	315 58 21. 8	135 58 30. 8	Substation 357____	391. 70	2. 592952
Substation 358_____	45 47 34. 710 70 24 43. 048	243 46 48. 8	63 47 00. 2	Substation 357____	383. 97	2. 584293
Mon. 358_____	45 47 43. 711 70 25 03. 258	302 28 50. 6	122 29 05. 1	Substation 358____	517. 45	2. 713871
Traverse station 59__	45 47 30. 452 70 24 55. 405	243 46 39. 9 243 46 39. 9	63 47 11. 8 63 46 48. 8	Traverse station 58_ Substation 358____	1, 071. 81 297. 51	3. 030116 2. 473497
Substation 359_____	45 47 27. 047 70 24 53. 476	158 23 06. 0	338 23 04. 6	Traverse station 59_	113. 08	2. 053393
Mon. 359_____	45 47 26. 939 70 24 54. 581	262 02 44. 8	82 02 45. 6	Substation 359____	24. 10	1. 381929
Substation 360_____	45 47 07. 244 70 24 42. 261	158 23 14. 0	338 23 06. 0	Substation 359____	657. 64	2. 817988
Mon. 360_____	45 47 04. 708 70 24 51. 917	249 25 17. 7	69 25 24. 6	Substation 360____	222. 80	2. 347920
Traverse station 60__	45 46 48. 964 70 24 31. 911	158 23 21. 4 158 23 21. 4	338 23 04. 6 338 23 14. 0	Traverse station 59_ Substation 360____	1, 377. 77 607. 05	3. 139177 2. 783222
Mon. 361_____	45 46 49. 651 70 24 31. 594	17 53 22. 9	197 53 22. 7	Traverse station 60_	22. 30	1. 348385
Substation 362_____	45 46 38. 371 70 24 25. 914	158 23 25. 7	338 23 21. 4	Traverse station 60_	351. 77	2. 546254
Mon. 362_____	45 46 38. 898 70 24 26. 451	324 29 25. 3	144 29 25. 7	Substation 362____	19. 98	1. 300509
Substation 363_____	45 46 31. 297 70 24 21. 910	158 23 28. 6	338 23 25. 7	Substation 362____	234. 90	2. 370883
Mon. 363_____	45 46 24. 425 70 24 29. 462	217 33 28. 6	37 33 34. 0	Substation 363____	267. 65	2. 427572
Substation 364_____	45 46 10. 640 70 24 10. 219	158 23 37. 0	338 23 28. 6	Substation 363____	685. 97	2. 836306
Mon. 364_____	45 46 06. 133 70 24 25. 059	246 32 31. 4	66 32 42. 0	Substation 364____	349. 55	2. 543510
Substation 365_____	45 45 56. 106 70 24 01. 994	158 23 42. 9	338 23 37. 0	Substation 364____	482. 65	2. 683631
Mon. 365_____	45 45 49. 326 70 24 27. 348	249 05 16. 4	69 05 34. 6	Substation 365____	586. 50	2. 768266
Substation 366_____	45 45 37. 146 70 23 51. 267	158 23 50. 6	338 23 42. 9	Substation 365____	629. 58	2. 799054
Mon. 366_____	45 45 30. 981 70 24 09. 997	244 48 47. 0	64 49 00. 4	Substation 366____	447. 29	2. 650591

LAKE POHENAGAMOOK TO THE VERMONT-QUEBEC BOUNDARY—Continued

Station	Latitude and longitude	Azimuth	Back azimuth	To station	Distance (meters)	Loga- rithm
PRECISE TRAVERSE, SOUTHWEST BRANCH OF ST. JOHN RIVER AND THE HIGHLANDS TO THE CANADIAN PACIFIC RAILWAY CROSSING—contd.	° ′ ″	° ′ ″	° ′ ″			
Traverse station 61__	45 45 15. 699	158 23 59. 2	338 23 21. 4	Traverse station 60_	3, 097. 06	3. 490950
	70 23 39. 136	158 23 59. 2	338 23 50. 6	Substation 366_____.	712. 19	2. 852595
Mon. 367_____	45 45 15. 593	257 59 20. 0	77 59 20. 5	Traverse station 61_	15. 73	1. 196640
	70 23 39. 848					
Substation 368_____	45 44 49. 923	170 14 00. 6	350 13 56. 1	Traverse station 61_	807. 51	2. 907148
	70 23 32. 798					
Mon. 368_____	45 44 49. 605	92 40 39. 8	272 40 32. 8	Substation 368____	210. 16	2. 322553
	70 23 23. 086					
Substation 369_____	45 44 24. 755	170 14 05. 0	350 14 00. 6	Substation 368____	788. 46	2. 896780
	70 23 26. 612					
Mon. 369_____	45 44 23. 626	262 46 38. 4	82 46 47. 5	Substation 369____	277. 36	2. 443049
	70 23 39. 340					
Traverse station 62__	45 44 15. 893	170 14 06. 6	350 13 56. 1	Traverse station 61_	1, 873. 57	3. 272671
	70 23 24. 434	170 14 06. 6	350 14 05. 0	Substation 369____	277. 60	2. 443420
Substation 370_____	45 44 11. 104	199 16 18. 9	19 16 20. 6	Traverse station 62_	156. 62	2. 194847
	70 23 26. 825					
Mon. 370_____	45 44 11. 219	348 19 29. 9	168 19 29. 9	Substation 370____	3. 63	0. 559271
	70 23 26. 859					
Substation 371_____	45 44 10. 818	199 16 18. 8	19 16 18. 9	Substation 370____	9. 37	0. 971647
	70 23 26. 968					
Mon. 371_____	45 44 09. 349	96 13 17. 6	276 13 03. 8	Substation 371____	418. 54	2. 621737
	70 23 07. 723					
Substation 373_____	45 43 50. 860	199 16 11._7	19 16 18. 8	Substation 371____	652. 75	2. 814746
	70 23 36. 932					
Substation 372 and 374.	45 43 46. 439	199 16 10. 1	19 16 11. 7	Substation 373____	144. 61	2. 160192
	70 23 39. 139					
Mon. 372_____	45 43 55. 953	61 58 53. 2	241 58 34. 9	Substation 372 and 374.	625. 24	2. 796044
	70 23 13. 612					
Mon. 373_____	45 43 46. 518	114 04 30. 6	294 04 20. 7	Substation 373____	328. 61	2. 516686
	70 23 23. 056					
Mon. 374_____	45 43 45. 249	260 28 14. 1	80 28 21. 3	Substation 372 and 374.	221. 89	2. 346143
	70 23 49. 259					
Traverse station 63__	45 43 10. 296	199 15 57. 2	19 16 20. 6	Traverse station 62_	2, 145. 41	3. 331511
	70 23 57. 176	199 15 57. 2	19 16 10. 1	Substation 372 and 374.	1, 182. 07	3. 072643
Substation 375_____	45 43 09. 043	245 12 56. 6	65 12 59. 4	Traverse station 63_	92. 28	1. 965103
	70 24 01. 050					
Mon. 375_____	45 43 11. 040	301 47 59. 6	121 48 02. 9	Substation 375____	117. 00	2. 068188
	70 24 05. 648					
Substation 376_____	45 42 59. 986	245 12 36. 6	65 12 56. 6	Substation 375____	666. 96	2. 824103
	70 24 29. 047					
Mon. 376_____	45 43 00. 884	338 24 46. 2	158 24 46. 6	Substation 376____	29. 81	1. 474301
	70 24 29. 554					

LAKE POHENAGAMOOK TO THE VERMONT-QUEBEC BOUNDARY—Continued

Station	Latitude and longitude	Azimuth	Back azimuth	To station	Distance (meters)	Loga- rithm
PRECISE TRAVERSE, SOUTHWEST BRANCH OF ST. JOHN RIVER AND THE HIGHLANDS TO THE CANADIAN PACIFIC RAILWAY CROSSING—contd.	° ′ ″	° ′ ″	° ′ ″			
Substation 377_____	45 42 53. 511 70 24 49. 059	245 12 22. 3	65 12 36. 6	Substation 376____	476. 75	2. 678294
Mon. 377_____	45 42 59. 764 70 24 49. 080	359 51 52. 3	179 51 52. 3	Substation 377____	193. 04	2. 285652
Substation 378_____	45 42 53. 297 70 24 49. 720	245 12 21. 8	65 12 22. 3	Substation 377____	15. 74	1. 196977
Mon. 378_____	45 42 55. 120 70 24 51. 896	320 05 51. 5	140 05 53. 1	Substation 378____	73. 36	1. 865445
Substation 380_____	45 42 35. 567 70 25 44. 493	245 11 42. 6	65 12 21. 8	Substation 378____	1, 305. 06	3. 115629
Substation 379_____	45 42 34. 534 70 25 47. 682	245 11 40. 3	65 11 42. 6	Substation 380____	75. 99	1. 880739
Mon. 379_____	45 42 33. 404 70 25 47. 018	157 37 15. 8	337 37 15. 3	Substation 379____	37. 72	1. 576561
Mon. 380_____	45 42 26. 369 70 25 34. 635	143 05 57. 2	323 05 50. 1	Substation 380____	355. 12	2. 550369
Traverse station 64_	45 42 21. 411 70 26 28. 200	245 11 11. 3 245 11 11. 3	65 12 59. 4 65 11 40. 3	Traverse station 63_ Substation 379____	3, 598. 36 965. 58	3. 556105 2. 984790
Mon. 381_____	45 42 19. 047 70 26 29. 245	197 12 27. 8	17 12 28. 5	Traverse station 64_	76. 41	1. 883170
Substation 382_____	45 42 18. 711 70 27 13. 492	265 07 54. 6	85 08 27. 0	Traverse station 64_	983. 30	2. 992688
Mon. 382_____	45 42 23. 411 70 27 17. 076	331 52 59. 1	151 53 01. 7	Substation 382____	164. 53	2. 216233
Substation 383_____	45 42 15. 598 70 28 05. 595	265 07 17. 3	85 07 54. 6	Substation 382____	1, 131. 20	3. 053541
Mon. 383_____	45 42 23. 750 70 27 58. 043	32 59 17. 7	212 59 12. 3	Substation 383____	300. 05	2. 477194
Traverse station 65_	45 42 15. 533 70 28 06. 684	265 07 16. 5 265 07 16. 5	85 08 27. 0 85 07 17. 3	Traverse station 64_ Substation 383____	2, 138. 14 23. 64	3. 330037 1. 373592
Traverse station 66_	45 41 20. 311 70 29 39. 370	229 37 11. 3	49 38 17. 6	Traverse station 65_	2, 632. 09	3. 420301
Mon. 384_____	45 41 19. 897 70 29 40. 595	244 14 32. 9	64 14 33. 8	Traverse station 66_	29. 44	1. 468939
Substation 385_____	45 41 11. 245 70 29 55. 753	231 42 29. 1	51 42 40. 8	Traverse station 66_	451. 68	2. 654831
Mon. 385_____	45 41 09. 161 70 29 49. 720	116 14 22. 1	296 14 17. 8	Substation 385____	145. 54	2. 162997
Traverse station 67_	45 40 47. 129 70 30 39. 323	231 41 57. 9 231 41 57. 9	51 42 40. 8 51 42 29. 1	Traverse station 66_ Substation 385____	1, 653. 10 1, 201. 42	3. 218298 3. 079693
Substation 386_____	45 40 24. 313 70 31 07. 244	220 37 22. 9	40 37 42. 9	Traverse station 67_	928. 11	2. 967601

LAKE POHENAGAMOOK TO THE VERMONT-QUEBEC BOUNDARY—Continued

Station	Latitude and longitude	Azimuth	Back azimuth	To station	Distance (meters)	Loga- rithm
PRECISE TRAVERSE, SOUTHWEST BRANCH OF ST. JOHN RIVER AND THE HIGHLANDS TO THE CANADIAN PACIFIC RAILWAY CROSSING—contd.	° ′ ″	° ′ ″	° ′ ″			
Mon. 386_____	45 40 23. 869 70 31 06. 590	134 05 43. 4	314 05 42. 9	Substation 386____	19. 71	1. 294591
Substation 387_____	45 40 14. 132 70 31 19. 700	220 37 14. 0	40 37 22. 9	Substation 386____	414. 11	2. 617118
Mon. 387_____	45 40 13. 856 70 31 11. 821	92 51 57. 1	272 51 51. 5	Substation 387____	170. 76	2. 232391
Traverse station 68__	45 39 59. 436 70 31 37. 677	220 37 01. 2 220 37 01. 2	40 37 42. 9 40 37 14. 0	Traverse station 67_ Substation 387____	1, 939. 94 597. 71	3. 287788 2. 776492
Substation 388_____	45 39 54. 629 70 32 09. 546	257 51 21. 1	77 51 43. 9	Traverse station 68_	705. 66	2. 848596
Mon. 388_____	45 40 09. 423 70 32 15. 959	343 05 32. 0	163 05 36. 6	Substation 388____	477. 37	2. 678851
Substation 389_____	45 39 48. 604 70 32 49. 465	257 50 52. 5	77 51 21. 1	Substation 388____	883. 96	2. 946433
Mon. 389_____	45 39 58. 253 70 32 51. 937	349 48 58. 2	169 49 00. 0	Substation 389____	302. 66	2. 480957
Substation 390_____	45 39 42. 754 70 33 28. 196	257 50 24. 8	77 50 52. 5	Substation 389____	857. 72	2. 933344
Mon. 390_____	45 39 51. 220 70 33 38. 990	318 12 15. 9	138 12 23. 6	Substation 390____	350. 60	2. 544816
Traverse station 69=H	45 39 42. 134 70 33 32. 294	257 50 21. 9 257 50 21. 9	77 51 43. 9 77 50 24. 8	Traverse station 68_ Substation 390____	2, 538. 09 90. 75	3. 404507 1. 957851
Substation 391_____	45 39 14. 513 70 34 11. 678	224 59 38. 6	45 00 06. 8	Traverse station 69_	1, 205. 91	3. 081316
Mon. 391_____	45 39 12. 752 70 34 04. 899	110 19 42. 6	290 19 37. 8	Substation 391____	156. 52	2. 194578
Substation 392_____	45 39 00. 936 70 34 31. 031	224 59 24. 8	44 59 38. 6	Substation 391____	592. 69	2. 772827
Mon. 392_____	45 38 56. 292 70 34 24. 355	134 45 55. 8	314 45 51. 0	Substation 392____	203. 59	2. 308755
Substation 393_____	45 38 31. 726 70 35 12. 655	224 58 55. 0	44 59 24. 8	Substation 392____	1, 275. 04	3. 105522
Mon. 393_____	45 38 24. 643 70 35 03. 705	138 26 52. 6	318 26 46. 2	Substation 393____	292. 22	2. 465706
Substation 394_____	45 37 54. 400 70 36 05. 818	224 58 17. 0	44 58 55. 0	Substation 393____	1, 629. 04	3. 211933
Mon. 394_____	45 37 44. 146 70 35 54. 289	141 43 59. 4	321 43 51. 2	Substation 394____	403. 23	2. 605550
Traverse station G_	45 37 37. 789 70 36 29. 468	224 58 00. 1 224 58 00. 1	45 00 06. 8 44 58 17. 0	Traverse station 69_ Substation 394____	5, 427. 57 724. 89	3. 734605 2. 860273
Substation 395_____	45 37 19. 410 70 36 59. 282	228 41 49. 3	48 42 10. 6	Traverse station G_	859. 70	2. 934346
Mon. 395_____	45 37 10. 403 70 36 47. 792	138 10 07. 1	318 09 58. 9	Substation 395____	373. 22	2. 571963

LAKE POHENAGAMOOK TO THE VERMONT-QUEBEC BOUNDARY—Continued

Station	Latitude and longitude	Azimuth	Back azimuth	To station	Distance (meters)	Loga-rithm
PRECISE TRAVERSE, SOUTHWEST BRANCH OF ST. JOHN RIVER AND THE HIGHLANDS TO THE CANADIAN PACIFIC RAILWAY CROSSING—contd.	° ′ ″	° ′ ″	° ′ ″			
Traverse station F___	45 36 45. 471	228 41 10. 0	48 42 10. 6	Traverse station G_	2, 447. 00	3. 388634
	70 37 54. 314	228 41 10. 0	48 41 49. 3	Substation 395____	1, 587. 31	3. 200661
Substation 396_____	45 36 43. 372	220 15 27. 6	40 15 29. 4	Traverse station F_	84. 92	1. 929020
	70 37 56. 847					
Mon. 396_____	45 36 36. 984	116 53 59. 1	296 53 46. 3	Substation 396____	435. 96	2. 639450
	70 37 38. 904					
Substation P_____	45 36 27. 692	220 15 14. 1	40 15 27. 6	Substation 396____	634. 32	2. 802309
	70 38 15. 763					
Substation 397_____	45 36 21. 723	220 15 08. 9	40 15 14. 1	Substation P_____	241. 48	2. 382872
	70 38 22. 963					
Substation M_____	45 36 21. 907	225 54 13. 2	45 54 19. 3	Substation P_____	256. 7	2. 409385
	70 38 24. 270	281 21 06. 9	101 21 07. 8	Substation 397____	28. 9	1. 460481
Substation N_____	45 36 23. 163	249 38 09. 5	69 38 21. 9	Substation P_____	401. 9	2. 604110
	70 38 33. 150	281 23 21. 5	101 23 27. 8	Substation M_____	196. 3	2. 292939
Mon. 397_____	45 36 24. 656	281 23 13. 0	101 23 20. 5	Substation N_____	233. 46	2. 368204
	70 38 43. 711					
Traverse station E__	45 35 54. 196	220 14 45. 2	40 15 29. 4	Traverse station F_	2, 074. 17	3. 316843
	70 38 56. 159	220 14 45. 2	40 15 08. 9	Substation 397____	1, 113. 45	3. 046671
Substation 398_____	45 35 39. 113	203 23 04. 6	23 23 11. 2	Traverse station E_	507. 33	2. 705290
	70 39 05. 450					
Mon. 398_____	45 35 41. 107	295 21 50. 3	115 21 54. 6	Substation 398____	143. 72	2. 157517
	70 39 11. 441					
Traverse station D__	45 35 27. 300	203 22 59. 4	23 23 11. 2	Traverse station E_	904. 66	2. 956485
	70 39 12. 725	203 22 59. 4	23 23 04. 6	Substation 398____	397. 33	2. 599154
Substation 399_____	45 34 51. 415	223 19 52. 9	43 20 27. 3	Traverse station D_	1, 523. 20	3. 182757
	70 40 00. 946					
Mon. 399_____	45 34 54. 133	330 23 13. 8	150 23 15. 4	Substation 399____	96. 53	1. 984665
	70 40 03. 146					
Substation 400_____	45 34 07. 596	223 19 10. 8	43 19 52. 9	Substation 399____	1, 859. 64	3. 269429
	70 40 59. 795					
Mon. 400_____	45 34 09. 493	322 25 54. 3	142 25 55. 8	Substation 400____	73. 87	1. 868463
	70 41 01. 872					
Traverse station C__	45 34 02. 572	223 19 06. 0	43 20 27. 3	Traverse station D_	3, 596. 01	3. 555821
	70 41 06. 539	223 19 06. 0	43 19 10. 8	Substation 400____	213. 17	2. 328728
Traverse station B__	45 33 38. 463	200 13 09. 1	20 13 18. 1	Traverse station C_	793. 21	2. 899386
	70 41 19. 181					
Substation 401_____	45 33 30. 161	183 39 14. 2	3 39 14. 7	Traverse station B_	256. 84	2. 409660
	70 41 19. 936					
Mon. 401_____	45 33 30. 858	84 26 28. 5	264 26 21. 2	Substation 401____	222. 03	2. 346411
	70 41 09. 747					
Traverse station A__	45 32 48. 875	183 39 11. 5	3 39 14. 7	Traverse station B_	1, 534. 02	3. 185832
	70 41 23. 687	183 39 11. 5	3 39 14. 2	Substation 401____	1, 277. 16	3. 106245

LAKE POHENAGAMOOK TO THE VERMONT-QUEBEC BOUNDARY—Continued

Station	Latitude and longitude	Azimuth	Back azimuth	To station	Distance (meters)	Loga-rithm
MINOR SCHEME TRIANGULATION, HALLS STREAM	° ′ ″	° ′ ″	° ′ ″			
Ref. Mon. 512–6____	45 01 03. 49 71 30 13. 01	292 41 00	112 41 46	Beecher_____	1, 554. 7	3. 19165
Tank_____	45 00 50. 16 71 30 34. 43	228 43 32 275 38 16	48 43 48 95 39 18	Ref. Mon. 512–6__ Beecher_____	623. 9 1, 554. 7	2. 79510 3. 28164
Lot_____	45 00 47. 87 71 30 04. 71	96 12 56 159 21 15	276 12 35 339 21 09	Tank_____ Ref. Mon. 512–6__	654. 5 515. 5	2. 81592 2. 71220
Chaloux_____	45 00 59. 19 71 29 50. 67	41 20 08 73 47 12 105 11 56	221 19 58 253 46 41 285 11 40	Lot_____ Tank_____ Ref. Mon. 512–6__	465. 4 997. 8 506. 9	2. 66787 2. 99903 2. 70490
Rock_____	45 01 18. 83 71 30 04. 59	21 16 30 36 26 02 310 38 38 333 18 54	201 16 24 216 25 41 130 39 19 153 19 04	Ref. Mon. 512–6__ Tank_____ Beecher_____ Chaloux_____	508. 1 1, 100. 0 1, 647. 5 678. 7	2. 70598 3. 04140 3. 21682 2. 83165
Beecher Falls south base.	45 01 22. 92 71 29 32. 97	27 53 10 55 37 56 79 40 33	207 52 58 235 37 27 259 40 11	Chaloux_____ Ref. Mon. 512–6__ Rock_____	828. 8 1, 062. 2 703. 7	2. 91843 3. 02620 2. 84740
Beecher Falls north base.	45 01 37. 15 71 29 28. 95	11 20 30 54 04 36	191 20 27 234 04 11	Beecher Falls south base. Rock_____	448. 07 963. 7	2. 65135 2. 98396
Van_____	45 01 47. 55 71 30 00. 69	5 30 30 294 47 24 321 24 15	185 30 28 114 47 46 141 24 34	Rock_____ Beecher Falls north base. Beecher Falls south base.	890. 6 765. 4 972. 7	2. 94967 2. 88391 2. 98800
Van reference mark_	45 01 47. 62 71 30 00. 67	10 05	190 05	Van_____	2. 42	0. 38438
Pasture_____	45 02 00. 95 71 29 22. 43	10 59 39 63 42 51	190 59 34 243 42 24	Beecher Falls north base. Van_____	748. 5 934. 2	2. 87418 2. 97044
Ref. Mon. 512–4____	45 02 04. 54 71 29 59. 06	3 53 04 277 51 41 322 03 15	183 53 03 97 52 07 142 03 36	Van_____ Pasture_____ Beecher Falls north base.	525. 8 809. 5 1, 072. 1	2. 72078 2. 90824 3. 03025
Advent_____	45 02 32. 25 71 30 25. 94	232 07 11 304 47 39 325 28 51	52 08 17 124 48 24 145 29 10	Hill_____ Pasture_____ Ref. Mon. 512–4___	2, 613. 5 1, 692. 9 1, 038. 2	3. 41722 3. 22864 3. 01627
Meadow_____	45 02 31. 53 71 29 43. 22	91 22 18 334 15 34	271 21 48 154 15 49	Advent_____ Pasture_____	935. 3 1, 047. 8	2. 97096 3. 02029
Center_____	45 02 12. 71 71 29 54. 16	23 01 53 130 56 49 202 24 53 297 34 31	203 01 49 310 56 26 22 25 01 117 34 54	Ref. Mon. 512–4___ Advent_____ Meadow_____ Pasture_____	273. 9 920. 7 628. 5 783. 8	2. 43763 2. 96410 2. 79830 2. 89420
Bryant_____	45 02 44. 64 71 29 35. 16	23 32 26 71 00 34 348 19 40	203 32 20 250 59 58 168 19 49	Meadow_____ Advent_____ Pasture_____	441. 7 1, 175. 4 1, 377. 3	2. 64510 3. 07019 3. 13902
Shift_____	45 03 16. 17 71 30 40. 84	264 02 57 317 31 59 346 28 20	84 04 15 137 32 40 166 28 30	Hill_____ Meadow_____ Advent_____	2, 401. 8 1, 868. 1 1, 394. 5	3. 38054 3. 27139 3. 14442
Cherry_____	45 02 58. 27 71 29 59. 69	35 33 59 121 32 07 241 42 31 336 24 16	215 33 41 301 31 38 61 43 19 156 24 28	Advent_____ Shift_____ Hill_____ Meadow_____	987. 6 1, 056. 4 1, 690. 4 901. 0	2. 99456 3. 02384 3. 22800 2. 95471

LAKE POHENAGAMOOK TO THE VERMONT-QUEBEC BOUNDARY—Continued

Station	Latitude and longitude	Azimuth	Back azimuth	To station	Distance (meters)	Loga-rithm
MINOR SCHEME TRIANGULATION, HALLS STREAM— continued	° ′ ″	° ′ ″	° ′ ″			
Fall	45 04 08. 41	8 22 18	188 22 04	Advent	3, 000. 5	3. 47720
	71 30 05. 98	193 48 50	13 49 03	Wheeler	1, 724. 8	3. 23674
		309 59 28	130 00 21	Hill	2, 122. 4	3. 32682
		356 21 56	176 22 00	Cherry	2, 169. 6	3. 33638
Pond	45 03 55. 79	12 20 34	192 20 22	Cherry	1, 817. 6	3. 25951
	71 29 41. 94	46 30 08	226 29 26	Shift	1, 776. 8	3. 24965
		126 31 55	306 31 38	Fall	654. 5	2. 81591
		176 50 28	356 50 24	Wheeler	2, 067. 7	3. 31548
		311 32 16	131 32 52	Hill	1, 469. 6	3. 16720
Gendreau	45 05 47. 41	9 45 13	189 44 48	Hill	4, 484. 9	3. 65175
	71 28 16. 94	37 58 42	217 57 25	Fall	3, 876. 3	3. 58842
		55 00 52	234 59 48	Wheeler	2, 408. 0	3. 38166
Gendreau reference mark.	45 05 47. 34	148 30	328 30	Gendreau	2. 56	0. 40778
	71 28 16. 88					
Cone	45 04 42. 24	60 10 05	240 09 06	Fall	2, 098. 4	3. 32189
	71 28 42. 76	114 08 12	294 07 27	Wheeler	1, 542. 9	3. 18835
		195 40 45	15 41 03	Gendreau	2, 089. 5	3. 32005
Caron	45 05 17. 06	52 04 13	232 03 28	Cone	1, 748. 7	3. 24271
	71 27 39. 70	80 57 20	260 55 50	Wheeler	2, 822. 3	3. 45060
		139 00 19	318 59 53	Gendreau	1, 241. 1	3. 09382
Cedar	45 05 54. 41	72 53 11	252 52 48	Gendreau	734. 3	2. 86590
	71 27 44. 84	354 26 01	174 26 04	Caron	1, 158. 3	3. 06382
Cedar reference mark	45 05 54. 33	1 06	181 06	Cedar	2. 41	0. 38164
	71 27 44. 84					
Ledge	45 06 11. 77	6 48 39	186 48 32	Caron	1, 700. 9	3. 23068
	71 27 30. 48	30 21 40	210 21 30	Cedar	621. 3	2. 79328
		53 29 04	233 28 31	Gendreau	1, 264. 0	3. 10174
Old	45 05 57. 10	79 42 56	259 42 42	Cedar	465. 5	2. 66792
	71 27 23. 90	162 21 52	342 21 47	Ledge	475. 3	2. 67695
Barn	45 06 03. 32	55 10 51	235 10 42	Old	336. 4	2. 52690
	71 27 11. 26	69 27 14	249 26 51	Cedar	784. 1	2. 89437
		121 50 00	301 49 47	Ledge	494. 6	2. 69422
Poplar	45 06 16. 37	32 25 05	212 25 02	Ledge	168. 2	2. 22576
	71 27 26. 36	320 40 17	140 40 28	Barn	520. 7	2. 71662
Path	45 06 11. 22	44 50 24	224 50 16	Barn	343. 6	2. 53603
	71 27 00. 18	91 29 29	271 29 07	Ledge	662. 7	2. 82129
		105 32 49	285 32 30	Poplar	594. 0	2. 77378
Stump (south base)	45 06 27. 02	38 41 29	218 41 20	Poplar	421. 3	2. 62461
	71 27 14. 31	327 40 08	147 40 18	Path	577. 6	2. 76160
		354 47 47	174 47 49	Barn	734. 7	2. 86611
Corner	45 06 18. 66	45 02 47	225 02 40	Path	325. 2	2. 51219
	71 26 49. 66	84 58 29	264 58 03	Poplar	805. 5	2. 90607
		115 36 07	295 35 49	Stump	597. 7	2. 77647
House	45 06 40. 56	13 01 22	193 01 17	Corner	693. 8	2. 84126
	71 26 42. 50	59 00 21	238 59 58	Stump	811. 2	2. 90911
Paquette (north base).	45 06 49. 30	28 04 29	208 04 17	Stump	779. 44	2. 89178
	71 26 57. 53	309 24 53	129 25 04	House	425. 2	2. 62860
		349 41 02	169 41 07	Corner	961. 5	2. 98296
Birch	45 06 57. 33	11 07 06	191 07 02	House	527. 7	2. 72239
	71 26 37. 85	60 03 37	240 03 24	Paquette	496. 5	2. 69592

LAKE POHENAGAMOOK TO THE VERMONT-QUEBEC BOUNDARY—Continued

Station	Latitude and longitude	Azimuth	Back azimuth	To station	Distance (meters)	Logarithm
MINOR SCHEME TRIANGULATION, HALLS STREAM— continued	° ′ ″	° ′ ″	° ′ ″			
Road	45 06 46.95	62 30 42	242 30 30	House	427.4	2.63080
	71 26 25.16	95 52 15	275 51 52	Paquette	711.3	2.85206
		139 07 58	319 07 49	Birch	423.9	2.62722
Bank	45 07 02.34	53 08 31	233 08 24	Birch	257.7	2.41105
	71 26 28.42	351 28 47	171 28 49	Road	480.4	2.68159
Hazel	45 07 01.68	39 48 39	219 48 26	Road	591.8	2.77219
	71 26 07.83	92 36 17	272 36 02	Bank	450.5	2.65372
N	45 06 58.66	78 19 04	258 18 57	Birch	202.4	2.30611
	71 26 28.78	184 01 49	4 01 49	Bank	113.9	2.05642
		258 30 23	78 30 38	azel	467.5	2.66976
		347 38 45	167 38 48	Road	370.1	2.56829
Brush	45 07 13.73	25 38 12	205 38 07	Bank	390.2	2.59126
	71 26 20.69	322 55 30	142 55 39	Hazel	466.5	2.66887
Saint	45 07 12.86	62 48 08	242 47 46	Hazel	755.1	2.87803
	71 25 37.10	73 51 34	253 50 57	Bank	1,167.7	3.06734
		91 37 47	271 37 16	Brush	953.2	2.97920
Thicket	45 07 27.38	11 14 58	191 14 55	Brush	429.5	2.63293
	71 26 16.86	297 16 51	117 17 20	Saint	977.8	2.99026
Cyr	45 07 20.93	25 56 00	205 55 56	Saint	277.2	2.44281
	71 25 31.55	78 18 48	258 18 13	Brush	1,096.8	3.04013
		101 21 53	281 21 21	Thicket	1,010.0	3.00433
Shack	45 07 33.19	72 40 07	252 39 48	Thicket	602.2	2.77971
	71 25 50.56	312 19 33	132 19 46	Cyr	561.9	2.74965
Cliff	45 07 29.55	4 36 28	184 36 27	Cyr	266.8	2.42611
	71 25 30.57	86 13 08	266 12 36	Thicket	1,013.9	3.00598
		104 26 25	284 26 10	Shack	451.1	2.65425
Stub	45 07 41.98	14 05 09	194 05 05	Thicket	464.6	2.66710
	71 26 11.69	293 07 13	113 07 42	Cliff	977.0	2.98991
		306 31 11	126 31 39	Cyr	1,091.5	3.03802
Jim	45 07 45.18	42 14 21	222 14 10	Shack	500.0	2.69901
	71 25 35.18	348 13 03	168 13 07	Cliff	493.1	2.69291
Burnt	45 07 46.16	2 57 18	182 57 17	Shack	401.1	2.60320
	71 25 49.61	275 29 11	95 29 21	Jim	316.9	2.50092
		320 56 56	140 57 10	Cliff	660.6	2.81991
White	45 07 52.96	22 48 46	202 48 43	Burnt	227.8	2.35755
	71 25 45.57	316 36 43	136 36 50	Jim	330.6	2.51935
Fir	45 07 53.99	44 34 26	224 34 18	Burnt	339.2	2.53041
	71 25 38.72	78 04 18	258 04 13	White	153.0	2.18474
		344 06 31	164 06 33	Jim	282.7	2.45135
Elm	45 07 58.24	35 58 50	215 58 46	White	201.1	2.30341
	71 25 40.17	346 27 55	166 27 56	Fir	134.9	2.12986
Rotten	45 07 57.41	261 01 48	81 01 53	Elm	164.4	2.21580
	71 25 47.60	298 32 38	118 32 44	Fir	220.7	2.34389
		342 07 49	162 07 50	White	144.1	2.15854
Spruce	45 08 05.10	13 59 12	193 59 10	Rotten	244.6	2.38852
	71 25 44.89	334 00 46	154 00 49	Elm	235.6	2.37213
Brook	45 08 04.44	263 33 05	83 33 11	Spruce	178.9	2.25266
	71 25 53.03	304 17 41	124 17 50	Elm	340.2	2.53168
		331 21 36	151 21 40	Rotten	247.6	2.39372

LAKE POHENAGAMOOK TO THE VERMONT-QUEBEC BOUNDARY—Continued

Station	Latitude and longitude	Azimuth	Back azimuth	To station	Distance (meters)	Loga- rithm
MINOR SCHEME TRIANGULATION, HALLS STREAM— continued	° ′ ″	° ′ ″	° ′ ″			
Hall_____	45 08 10. 90	18 23 07	198 23 05	Brook_____	210. 1	2. 32239
	71 25 49. 99	328 06 49	148 06 53	Spruce_____	211. 1	2. 32454
Bridge_____	45 08 10. 37	262 50 59	82 51 03	Hall_____	133. 0	2. 12386
	71 25 56. 03	303 45 05	123 45 13	Spruce_____	292. 9	2. 46666
		340 13 43	160 13 45	Brook_____	194. 3	2. 28838
Woods_____	45 08 17. 04	5 33 34	185 33 33	Bridge_____	207. 1	2. 31625
	71 25 55. 12	329 27 06	149 27 09	Hall_____	220. 2	2. 34275
Stream_____	45 08 14. 60	236 31 09	56 31 13	Woods_____	136. 9	2. 13643
	71 26 00. 34	296 46 23	116 46 30	Hall_____	253. 2	2. 40354
		324 13 31	144 13 34	Bridge_____	161. 0	2. 20686
Camp_____	45 08 18. 79	283 41 39	103 41 46	Woods_____	227. 3	2. 35655
	71 26 05. 22	320 29 50	140 29 53	Stream_____	167. 6	2. 22432
Pole_____	45 08 22. 13	42 10 05	222 10 02	Camp_____	139. 1	2. 14339
	71 26 00. 95	320 55 22	140 55 26	Woods_____	202. 1	2. 30565
		356 44 33	176 44 33	Stream_____	232. 8	2. 36702
Cut_____	45 08 34. 92	1 31 26	181 31 26	Camp_____	498. 3	2. 69751
	71 26 04. 62	348 31 55	168 31 58	Pole_____	403. 1	2. 60538
Duran_____	45 08 37. 11	284 15 53	104 16 01	Cut_____	273. 9	2. 43755
	71 26 16. 76	323 13 58	143 14 09	Pole_____	577. 4	2. 76144
		335 58 09	155 58 17	Camp_____	619. 3	2. 79190
Leau_____	45 08 46. 64	27 33 02	207 32 57	Duran_____	331. 7	2. 52071
	71 26 09. 74	342 47 08	162 47 11	Cut_____	378. 5	2. 57808
Bird_____	45 08 43. 52	25 21 47	205 21 43	Cut_____	293. 5	2. 46767
	71 25 58. 86	63 10 54	243 10 42	Duran_____	438. 3	2. 64178
		112 03 11	292 03 04	Leau_____	256. 5	2. 40911
Ref. Mon. 511–4____	45 08 53. 99	44 43 00	224 42 53	Leau_____	319. 5	2. 50444
	71 25 59. 45	357 42 14	177 42 14	Bird_____	323. 6	2. 50999
Fence_____	45 08 55. 14	5 22 58	185 22 57	Leau_____	263. 6	2. 42089
	71 26 08. 61	280 01 47	100 01 53	Ref. Mon. 511–4___	203. 2	2. 30783
		329 17 44	149 17 50	Bird_____	417. 2	2. 62034
Blind_____	45 09 07. 63	31 39 39	211 39 30	Ref. Mon. 511–4__	494. 7	2. 69436
	71 25 47. 57	50 00 15	230 00 00	Fence_____	600. 1	2. 77821
Brown_____	45 09 01. 51	56 59 11	236 58 59	Ref. Mon. 511–4__	425. 9	2. 62934
	71 25 43. 10	70 33 35	250 33 17	Fence_____	590. 9	2. 77152
		152 43 08	332 43 05	Blind_____	212. 7	2. 32772
Mink_____	45 09 12. 69	25 47 58	205 47 52	Brown_____	383. 4	2. 58362
	71 25 35. 47	59 25 51	239 25 42	Blind_____	307. 0	2. 48713
Switch_____	45 09 13. 95	9 47 35	189 47 32	Brown_____	389. 6	2. 59067
	71 25 40. 07	40 01 51	220 01 45	Blind_____	254. 6	2. 40584
		291 05 53	111 05 56	Mink_____	107. 8	2. 03262
Valley_____	45 09 19. 40	13 17 12	193 17 10	Mink_____	212. 7	2. 32782
	71 25 33. 23	41 37 12	221 37 07	Switch_____	225. 0	2. 35224
Ref. Mon. 511–3____	45 09 24. 04	14 18 29	194 18 26	Switch_____	321. 6	2. 50731
	71 25 36. 43	333 59 04	153 59 06	Valley_____	159. 6	2. 20292
		356 33 18	176 33 18	Mink_____	351. 1	2. 54538
Lumber_____	45 09 27. 81	19 56 33	199 56 30	Valley_____	276. 3	2. 44134
	71 25 28. 91	54 41 21	234 41 16	Ref. Mon. 511–3__	201. 2	2. 30370

LAKE POHENAGAMOOK TO THE VERMONT-QUEBEC BOUNDARY—Continued

Station	Latitude and longitude	Azimuth	Back azimuth	To station	Distance (meters)	Loga-rithm
MINOR SCHEME TRIANGULATION, HALLS STREAM—continued	° ' ''	° ' ''	° ' ''			
Ref. Mon. 511–2____	45 09 27. 45	17 47 09	197 47 08	Ref. Mon. 511–3__	110. 4	2. 04307
	71 25 34. 89	265 06 26	85 06 30	Lumber_____	131. 0	2. 11712
		351 42 04	171 42 05	Valley_____	251. 2	2. 39996
Ref. Mon. 511–1____	45 09 35. 85	19 14 06	199 14 03	Ref. Mon. 511–2__	274. 7	2. 43889
	71 25 30. 74	350 51 05	170 51 06	Lumber_____	251. 4	2. 40039
Company_____	45 09 35. 66	21 36 00	201 35 57	Lumber_____	260. 7	2. 41620
	71 25 24. 52	41 45 56	221 45 49	Ref. Mon. 511–2__	340. 0	2. 53147
		92 26 25	272 26 21	Ref. Mon. 511–1__	136. 1	2. 13378
Culvert_____	45 09 41. 42	177 34 06	357 34 05	King_____	463. 2	2. 66573
	71 25 34. 34	309 38 01	129 38 08	Company_____	278. 6	2. 44492
		335 25 58	155 26 01	Ref. Mon. 511–1__	189. 0	2. 27648
Alder_____	45 09 45. 72	20 09 43	200 09 40	Ref. Mon. 511–1__	324. 6	2. 51129
	71 25 25. 62	55 07 03	235 06 57	Culvert_____	232. 2	2. 36577
		147 31 04	327 30 57	King_____	391. 2	2. 59237
		355 33 50	175 33 51	Company_____	311. 4	2. 49331
Ref. Mon. 510–26 (Robert's east base).	45 10 13. 38 71 25 14. 48	197 32 16	17 32 22	Knoll_____	557. 6	2. 74630
Robert's west base__	45 10 17. 86	226 13 05	46 13 19	Knoll_____	568. 6	2. 75477
	71 25 25. 59	299 41 28	119 41 36	Ref. Mon. 510–26_	279. 14	2. 44582
Clay_____	45 10 07. 89	23 00 38	203 00 33	King_____	385. 1	2. 58557
	71 25 28. 35	191 05 15	11 05 17	Robert's west base_	313. 7	2. 49650
		240 45 06	60 45 16	Ref. Mon. 510–26_	347. 1	2. 54041
Ref. Mon. 510–27___	45 10 04. 86	53 00 21	233 00 10	King_____	433. 7	2. 63720
	71 25 19. 38	115 30 45	295 30 38	Clay_____	217. 0	2. 33650
		161 20 23	341 20 19	Robert's west base_	423. 6	2. 62692
		202 07 45	22 07 48	Ref. Mon. 510–26_	283. 9	2. 45324
Swamp_____	45 09 56. 89	1 09 17	181 09 17	Alder_____	344. 8	2. 53760
	71 25 25. 31	22 27 30	202 27 24	Culvert_____	516. 7	2. 71325
		86 06 17	266 06 10	King_____	217. 5	2. 33752
		168 55 28	348 55 26	Clay_____	346. 1	2. 53923
		207 43 10	27 43 14	Ref. Mon. 510–27_	278. 1	2. 44424
Ref. Mon. 510–25___	45 10 27. 70	40 21 43	220 21 31	Ref. Mon. 510–26_	579. 8	2. 76329
	71 24 57. 29	63 50 32	243 50 12	Robert's west base_	688. 5	2. 83790
		113 24 53	293 24 46	Knoll_____	226. 1	2. 35424
Ref. Mon. 510–24___	45 10 40. 36	16 43 28	196 43 25	Knoll_____	314. 3	2. 49739
	71 25 02. 65	343 20 09	163 20 13	Ref. Mon. 510–25_	408. 0	2. 61066
Willow_____	45 10 39. 56	22 45 36	202 45 31	Ref. Mon. 510–25_	397. 1	2. 59888
	71 24 50. 25	52 34 25	232 34 13	Knoll_____	454. 7	2. 65771
		95 12 58	275 12 49	Ref. Mon. 510–24_	271. 7	2. 43414
Ref. Mon. 510–23___	45 10 48. 19	16 43 25	196 43 23	Ref. Mon. 510–24_	252. 6	2. 40239
	71 24 59. 32	323 24 29	143 24 36	Willow_____	332. 0	2. 52117
Lower_____	45 10 50. 96	7 13 10	187 13 09	Willow_____	354. 8	2. 55004
	71 24 48. 21	43 55 07	223 54 57	Ref. Mon. 510–24_	454. 4	2. 65745
		70 35 32	250 35 24	Ref. Mon. 510–23_	257. 1	2. 41013
Ref. Mon. 510–22___	45 10 55. 82	297 13 22	117 13 32	Lower_____	327. 9	2. 51578
	71 25 01. 57	348 13 15	168 13 17	Ref. Mon. 510–23_	240. 5	2. 38116
Flat_____	45 10 56. 72	37 58 30	217 58 24	Ref. Mon. 510–23_	334. 1	2. 52387
	71 24 49. 90	83 44 53	263 44 45	Ref. Mon. 510–22_	256. 2	2. 40856
		348 16 26	168 16 28	Lower_____	181. 7	2. 25939

LAKE POHENAGAMOOK TO THE VERMONT-QUEBEC BOUNDARY—Continued

Station	Latitude and longitude	Azimuth	Back azimuth	To station	Distance (meters)	Loga-rithm
MINOR SCHEME TRIANGULATION, HALLS STREAM—continued						
	° ′ ″	° ′ ″	° ′ ″			
Ref. Mon. 510–21___	45 11 06. 79	15 04 53	195 04 50	Ref. Mon. 510–22_	350. 7	2. 54495
	71 24 57. 39	332 15 35	152 15 40	Flat_____	351. 1	2. 54540
Steep_____	45 11 07. 12	16 44 54	196 44 51	Flat_____	335. 1	2. 52522
	71 24 45. 48	45 11 55	225 11 44	Ref. Mon. 510–22_	495. 0	2. 69462
		87 45 21	267 45 13	Ref. Mon. 510–21_	260. 2	2. 41527
Ref. Mon. 510–20___	45 11 14. 47	304 09 43	124 09 54	Steep_____	404. 3	2. 60666
	71 25 00. 80	342 33 28	162 33 31	Ref. Mon. 510–21_	248. 6	2. 39557
Point_____	45 11 18. 74	46 09 50	226 09 38	Steep_____	517. 9	2. 71421
	71 24 28. 37	79 28 08	259 27 45	Ref. Mon. 510–20_	720. 1	2. 85742
Ref. Mon. 510–19___	45 11 26. 87	26 11 02	206 10 52	Steep_____	679. 3	2. 83206
	71 24 31. 75	42 05 08	222 04 50	Ref. Mon. 510–21_	835. 1	2. 92174
		58 54 09	238 53 48	Ref. Mon. 510–20_	740. 7	2. 86962
		343 36 41	163 36 43	Point_____	261. 5	2. 41755
Yard_____	45 11 31. 47	19 34 40	199 34 36	Point_____	417. 1	2. 62019
	71 24 21. 97	56 22 24	236 22 17	Ref. Mon. 510–19_	256. 4	2. 40900
Engine_____	45 11 33. 97	13 52 19	193 52 17	Ref. Mon. 510–19_	225. 8	2. 35381
	71 24 29. 27	295 51 13	115 51 18	Yard_____	177. 1	2. 24825
		357 36 26	177 36 27	Point_____	470. 6	2. 67264
Farm_____	45 11 39. 75	29 10 47	209 10 44	Engine_____	204. 3	2. 31030
	71 24 24. 71	346 50 20	166 50 22	Yard_____	262. 5	2. 41916
Ref. Mon. 510–18 (south base).	45 11 37. 03	28 54 38	208 54 35	Yard_____	196. 1	2. 29241
	71 24 17. 63	44 30 35	224 30 25	Ref. Mon. 510–19_	439. 8	2. 64328
		69 37 33	249 37 25	Engine_____	271. 1	2. 43318
		118 31 12	298 31 07	Farm_____	175. 9	2. 24527
Ash_____	45 11 47. 94	0 02 34	180 02 34	Ref. Mon. 510–18_	337. 1	2. 52770
	71 24 17. 61	31 27 18	211 27 13	Farm_____	296. 7	2. 47226
Ref. Mon. 510–17 (north base).	45 11 46. 84	26 22 48	206 22 43	Ref. Mon. 510–18_	338. 36	2. 52938
	71 24 10. 74	54 17 40	234 17 30	Farm_____	375. 5	2. 57458
		102 44 18	282 44 13	Ash_____	153. 9	2. 18715
Ref. Mon. 510–16___	45 11 54. 25	3 06 39	183 06 39	Ref. Mon. 510–17_	229. 0	2. 35986
	71 24 10. 17	39 50 36	219 50 31	Ash_____	253. 6	2. 40423
Across_____	45 11 58. 39	7 49 25	187 49 24	Ash_____	325. 4	2. 51246
	71 24 15. 59	317 12 01	137 12 05	Ref. Mon. 510–16_	174. 0	2. 24049
		343 27 56	163 28 00	Ref. Mon. 510–17_	371. 7	2. 57020
Ref. Mon. 510–15___	45 12 07. 20	32 36 33	212 36 25	Ref. Mon. 510–16_	474. 4	2. 67611
	71 23 58. 46	53 58 04	233 57 52	Across_____	462. 3	2. 66490
Coat_____	45 12 08. 93	17 16 51	197 16 47	Ref. Mon. 510–16_	474. 6	2. 67637
	71 24 03. 71	38 31 31	218 31 23	Across_____	416. 1	2. 61924
		295 04 03	115 04 07	Ref. Mon. 510–15_	126. 6	2. 10229
Shot_____	45 12 13. 09	7 22 28	187 22 27	Ref. Mon. 510–15_	183. 4	2. 26332
	71 23 57. 38	47 08 18	227 08 13	Coat_____	188. 5	2. 27532
Ref. Mon. 510–14___	45 12 12. 56	42 41 03	222 40 58	Ref. Mon. 510–15_	225. 2	2. 35264
	71 23 51. 46	67 16 43	247 16 34	Coat_____	289. 8	2. 46215
		97 10 52	277 10 48	Shot_____	130. 2	2. 11456
Ref. Mon. 510–13___	45 12 19. 18	30 14 13	210 14 10	Shot_____	217. 7	2. 33776
	71 23 52. 36	354 31 52	174 31 53	Ref. Mon. 510–14_	205. 2	2. 31227
Lost_____	45 12 21. 55	292 04 36	112 04 42	Ref. Mon. 510–13_	195. 2	2. 29037
	71 24 00. 64	324 10 44	144 10 51	Ref. Mon. 510–14_	342. 4	2. 53457
		344 45 12	164 45 15	Shot_____	270. 9	2. 43285

LAKE POHENAGAMOOK TO THE VERMONT-QUEBEC BOUNDARY—Continued

Station	Latitude and longitude	Azimuth	Back azimuth	To station	Distance (meters)	Loga-rithm
MINOR SCHEME TRIANGULATION, HALLS STREAM—continued	° ′ ″	° ′ ″	° ′ ″			
Ref. Mon. 510–12	45 12 28. 22 71 23 56. 33	24 37 18 342 45 24	204 37 15 162 45 27	Lost Ref. Mon. 510–13	226. 2 292. 1	2. 35452 2. 46557
Duke	45 12 27. 04 71 24 06. 57	260 48 09 308 03 47 322 40 17	80 48 16 128 03 57 142 40 21	Ref. Mon. 510–12 Ref. Mon. 510–13 Lost	226. 4 393. 8 213. 1	2. 35484 2. 59531 2. 32862
Ref. Mon. 510–11	45 12 41. 39 71 24 02. 87	10 19 02 340 38 48	190 19 00 160 38 53	Duke Ref. Mon. 510–12	450. 2 431. 1	2. 65337 2. 63454
Slim	45 12 36. 23 71 24 11. 59	230 04 54 306 36 40 338 51 58	50 05 00 126 36 51 158 52 02	Ref. Mon. 510–11 Ref. Mon. 510–12 Duke	248. 1 415. 0 304. 2	2. 39460 2. 61806 2. 48309
Tall	45 12 43. 95 71 24 16. 88	284 29 23 334 09 13	104 29 33 154 09 17	Ref. Mon. 510–11 Slim	315. 7 264. 7	2. 49926 2. 42269
Ref. Mon. 510–10	45 12 46. 35 71 24 07. 86	14 35 25 69 19 27 324 35 11	194 35 23 249 19 21 144 35 15	Slim Tall Ref. Mon. 510–11	322. 8 210. 2 188. 0	2. 50898 2. 32271 2. 27419
Log	45 12 52. 71 71 24 20. 78	304 50 13 342 31 32	124 50 22 162 31 35	Ref. Mon. 510–10 Tall	343. 3 283. 5	2. 53573 2. 45248
Ref. Mon. 510–9	45 12 55. 93 71 24 12. 28	15 11 22 61 49 03 341 57 02	195 11 19 241 48 57 161 57 05	Tall Log Ref. Mon. 510–10	383. 2 210. 5 310. 8	2. 58337 2. 32315 2. 49252
Heavy	45 13 02. 46 71 24 17. 10	14 57 24 332 27 23	194 57 21 152 27 26	Log Ref. Mon. 510–9	311. 5 227. 3	2. 49343 2. 35660
Ground	45 13 03. 23 71 24 36. 14	273 17 16 314 05 29	93 17 30 134 05 40	Heavy Log	416. 3 466. 8	2. 61944 2. 66914
Ref. Mon. 510–8	45 12 58. 88 71 24 26. 76	123 13 02 242 23 07 286 06 54 325 37 55	303 12 55 62 23 14 106 07 04 145 37 59	Ground Heavy Ref. Mon. 510–9 Log	244. 9 237. 9 328. 8 231. 0	2. 38896 2. 37635 2. 51695 2. 36360
Ref. Mon. 510–7	45 12 59. 81 71 24 36. 65	186 00 47 259 10 11 277 32 59	6 00 47 79 10 25 97 33 06	Ground Heavy Ref. Mon. 510–8	106. 1 434. 5 217. 9	2. 02573 2. 63799 2. 33822
Ref. Mon. 510–6	45 13 01. 80 71 24 43. 57	254 45 28 292 06 52	74 45 33 112 06 57	Ground Ref. Mon. 510–7	168. 0 163. 0	2. 22532 2. 21211
Owl	45 13 06. 98 71 24 42. 34	9 35 12 310 35 20 330 44 15	189 35 11 130 35 24 150 44 19	Ref. Mon. 510–6 Ground Ref. Mon. 510–7	162. 2 177. 9 253. 6	2. 20997 2. 25014 2. 40418
Home	45 13 05. 61 71 24 51. 65	258 16 56 303 44 51	78 17 03 123 44 57	Owl Ref. Mon. 510–6	207. 6 212. 0	2. 31716 2. 32625
Ref. Mon. 510–5	45 13 01. 84 71 24 54. 88	211 10 49 239 54 36 270 18 12	31 10 51 59 54 45 90 18 20	Home Owl Ref. Mon. 510–6	136. 1 316. 3 246. 7	2. 13387 2. 50016 2. 39219
Ref. Mon. 510–4	45 13 05. 31 71 25 00. 30	267 06 44 312 06 09	87 06 50 132 06 13	Home Ref. Mon. 510–5	189. 0 159. 5	2. 27652 2. 20269
High	45 13 08. 59 71 24 56. 33	40 29 45 311 59 09 351 21 14	220 29 42 131 59 12 171 21 15	Ref. Mon. 510–4 Home Ref. Mon. 510–5	133. 4 137. 4 210. 8	2. 12518 2. 13807 2. 32381
shade (south base)	45 13 10. 62 71 25 02. 87	293 44 04 341 11 53	113 44 09 161 11 55	High Ref. Mon. 510–4	155. 7 173. 4	2. 19221 2. 23895

LAKE POHENAGAMOOK TO THE VERMONT-QUEBEC BOUNDARY—Continued

Station	Latitude and longitude	Azimuth	Back azimuth	To station	Distance (meters)	Logarithm
MINOR SCHEME TRIANGULATION, HALLS STREAM—continued	° ′ ″	° ′ ″	° ′ ″			
Ridge (Halls Stream)	45 13 12. 96	5 06 21	185 06 20	Ref. Mon. 510-4	237. 2	2. 37503
	71 24 59. 34	46 52 22	226 52 19	Shade	105. 5	2. 02314
		334 04 09	154 04 11	High	149. 9	2. 17566
Ref. Mon. 510-3 (north base).	45 13 16. 79	303 42 08	123 42 14	Ridge	213. 1	2. 32860
	71 25 07. 46	332 12 39	152 12 42	Shade	215. 17	2. 33278
Dry	45 13 19. 62	47 10 53	227 10 50	Ref. Mon. 510-3	128. 7	2. 10942
	71 25 03. 14	338 02 39	158 02 42	Ridge	221. 8	2. 34592
		358 46 27	178 46 27	Shade	277. 9	2. 44383
Block	45 13 25. 41	307 37 21	127 37 28	Dry	292. 6	2. 46633
	71 25 13. 76	332 41 11	152 41 15	Ref. Mon. 510-3	299. 5	2. 47637
Ref. Mon. 510-2	45 13 22. 81	231 14 05	51 14 08	Block	127. 9	2. 10691
	71 25 18. 33	286 33 21	106 33 31	Dry	345. 9	2. 53890
		308 06 23	128 06 30	Ref. Mon. 510-3	301. 4	2. 47914
Gum	45 13 30. 65	308 59 08	128 59 14	Block	257. 4	2. 41053
	71 25 22. 93	337 29 10	157 29 13	Ref. Mon. 510-2	262. 0	2. 41824
Ref. Mon. 510-1	45 13 28. 10	232 21 40	52 21 43	Gum	129. 0	2. 11059
	71 25 27. 61	285 22 48	105 22 57	Block	313. 4	2. 49613
		308 52 28	128 52 34	Ref. Mon. 510-2	260. 1	2. 41507
Sun	45 13 31. 05	273 09 31	93 09 38	Gum	224. 6	2. 35137
	71 25 33. 21	306 44 48	126 44 52	Ref. Mon. 510-1	152. 4	2. 18288
Shine	45 13 26. 61	222 42 00	42 42 04	Sun	186. 7	2. 27125
	71 25 39. 01	250 24 37	70 24 48	Gum	372. 4	2. 57105
		259 30 08	79 30 16	Ref. Mon. 510-1	253. 0	2. 40306
		284 33 07	104 33 21	Ref. Mon. 510-2	466. 2	2. 66853
Labor	45 13 32. 06	276 38 47	96 38 56	Sun	268. 7	2. 42934
	71 25 45. 44	320 11 37	140 11 42	Shine	219. 1	2. 34073
Day	45 13 37. 36	1 08 32	181 08 32	Shine	331. 9	2. 52104
	71 25 38. 71	41 56 20	221 56 15	Labor	219. 8	2. 34205
		328 20 13	148 20 17	Sun	228. 7	2. 35918
Berry	45 13 37. 54	271 01 30	91 01 40	Day	316. 6	2. 50053
	71 25 53. 22	314 55 06	134 55 11	Labor	239. 6	2. 37948
Bunch	45 13 44. 32	303 20 19	123 20 30	Day	391. 2	2. 59240
	71 25 53. 69	334 34 34	154 34 40	Labor	419. 1	2. 62232
		357 11 36	177 11 37	Berry	209. 6	2. 32137
Stop	45 13 45. 92	282 40 38	102 40 45	Bunch	224. 9	2. 35207
	71 26 03. 75	318 23 42	138 23 50	Berry	346. 0	2. 53905
Run	45 13 50. 63	309 23 47	129 23 55	Bunch	306. 6	2. 48663
	71 26 04. 55	328 31 55	148 32 04	Berry	473. 6	2. 67542
		353 07 38	173 07 39	Stop	146. 3	2. 16527
Leaf	45 13 54. 05	286 45 40	106 45 51	Run	366. 6	2. 56416
	71 26 20. 64	304 15 22	124 15 34	Stop	445. 9	2. 64919
Bog	45 13 59. 16	36 51 35	216 51 31	Leaf	197. 0	2. 29451
	71 26 15. 23	318 31 23	138 31 30	Run	351. 5	2. 54593
		328 30 28	148 30 36	Stop	479. 2	2. 68051
Snag	45 13 58. 22	263 54 12	83 54 21	Bog	271. 9	2. 43443
	71 26 27. 62	310 13 58	130 14 03	Leaf	199. 4	2. 29963
Solid	45 14 03. 56	30 50 36	210 50 33	Snag	191. 9	2. 28298
	71 26 23. 11	308 18 03	128 18 09	Bog	219. 2	2. 34081
		349 36 24	169 36 26	Leaf	298. 4	2. 47477

LAKE POHENAGAMOOK TO THE VERMONT-QUEBEC BOUNDARY—Continued

Station	Latitude and longitude	Azimuth	Back azimuth	To station	Distance (meters)	Loga-rithm
MINOR SCHEME TRIANGULATION, HALLS STREAM—continued	° ′ ″	° ′ ″	° ′ ″			
Hub	45 14 05. 94	137 10 08	317 10 03	Mon. 505	238. 5	2. 37745
	71 26 30. 43	294 41 50	114 41 55	Solid	175. 7	2. 24478
		345 34 16	165 34 18	Snag	245. 9	2. 39075
Nail	45 14 03. 36	160 41 03	340 41 00	Mon. 505	269. 5	2. 43062
	71 26 33. 77	222 33 31	42 33 33	Hub	107. 9	2. 03300
		268 30 26	88 30 33	Solid	232. 7	2. 36677
		319 45 54	139 45 58	Snag	207. 8	2. 31773
Still	45 14 05. 53	190 06 15	10 06 16	Mon. 505	190. 3	2. 27950
	71 26 39. 39	266 20 45	86 20 51	Hub	195. 9	2. 29208
		298 39 43	118 39 47	Nail	139. 7	2. 14508
Big	45 14 12. 08	5 42 20	185 42 19	Still	203. 1	2. 30769
	71 26 38. 47	317 14 20	137 14 25	Hub	258. 2	2. 41203
		339 10 21	159 10 24	Nail	287. 9	2. 45922
POINTS SUPPLEMEN-TARY TO MINOR SCHEME, HALLS STREAM						
Ref. Mon. 517	45 00 48. 74	72 09 56	252 09 53	Lot	88. 2	1. 94552
	71 30 00. 88	149 44 06	329 43 57	Ref. Mon. 512–6	527. 2	2. 72198
		214 42 59	34 43 06	Chaloux	392. 3	2. 59364
Mon. 518	45 00 48. 65	170 53 03	350 53 00	Ref. Mon. 512–6	464. 1	2. 66657
	71 30 09. 66	231 56 49	51 57 02	Chaloux	527. 8	2. 72248
		269 08 55	89 09 01	Ref. Mon. 517	192. 2	2. 28381
Mon. 519	45 00 48. 53	201 23 20	21 23 25	Ref. Mon. 512–6	496. 1	2. 69560
	71 30 21. 28	243 50 28	63 50 49	Chaloux	746. 6	2. 87306
		269 08 56	89 09 10	Ref. Mon. 517	446. 7	2. 65005
		269 09 03	89 09 11	Mon. 518	254. 5	2. 40570
Mon. 520	45 00 48. 13	257 09 46	77 10 34	Chaloux	1, 537. 6	3. 18685
	71 30 59. 14	269 08 31	89 09 12	Ref. Mon. 517	1, 276. 0	3. 10584
		270 22 51	90 23 29	Lot	1, 191. 9	3. 07624
Ref. Mon. 512–5	45 01 20. 57	49 47 30	229 47 28	Rock	83. 02	1. 91917
	71 30 01. 70					
Rowell's house chim-ney.	45 01 29. 66	187 20 07	7 20 10	Van	556. 9	2. 74574
	71 30 03. 94	253 11 36	73 12 01	Beecher Falls north base.	800. 2	2. 90319
		287 03 15	107 03 37	Beecher Falls south base.	709. 1	2. 85072
Van Dyke's tenant house chimney.	45 01 52. 53	69 24 40	249 24 27	Van	437. 8	2. 64127
	71 29 41. 97	329 01 43	149 01 52	Beecher Falls north base.	553. 9	2. 74344
		347 50 35	167 50 41	Beecher Falls south base.	935. 2	2. 97092
Van Dyke's house chimney.	45 02 13. 83	6 25 12	186 25 09	Van	816. 5	2. 91195
	71 29 56. 52	331 56 22	151 56 41	Beecher Falls north base.	1, 283. 2	3. 10828
Ref. Mon. 512–3	45 02 44. 46	254 27 27	74 27 28	Bryant	20. 83	1. 31879
	71 29 36. 07					
Old schoolhouse flagpole.	45 02 54. 47	17 40 30	197 40 14	Ref. Mon. 512–4	1, 617. 7	3. 20891
	71 29 36. 62	57 33 57	237 33 22	Advent	1, 278. 9	3. 10682
		349 20 53	169 21 03	Pasture	1, 681. 1	3. 22560
Ref. Mon. 512–2	45 02 54. 63	21 41 52	201 41 43	Advent	743. 4	2. 87123
	71 30 13. 38	137 54 08	317 53 48	Shift	896. 4	2. 95248
		249 23 48	69 23 57	Cherry	320. 0	2. 50514

LAKE POHENAGAMOOK TO THE VERMONT-QUEBEC BOUNDARY—Continued

Station	Latitude and longitude	Azimuth	Back azimuth	To station	Distance (meters)	Loga- rithm
POINTS SUPPLEMEN- TARY TO MINOR SCHEME, HALLS STREAM—contd.	° ′ ″	° ′ ″	° ′ ″			
Azimuth mark	45 02 54. 17	53 36 56	233 36 26	Advent	1, 140. 8	3. 05721
	71 29 43. 98	110 12 03	290 11 52	Cherry	366. 5	2. 56408
		358 38 13	178 38 13	Meadow	699. 3	2. 84467
Ref. Mon. 512–1	45 03 19. 85	168 20 02	348 19 52	Fall	1, 530. 7	3. 18489
	71 29 51. 83	264 08 41	84 09 24	Hill	1, 323. 4	3. 12168
New schoolhouse flagpole.	45 03 46. 67	36 07 16	216 06 57	Ref. Mon. 512–1	1, 024. 8	3. 01063
	71 29 24. 22	60 41 22	240 40 27	Shift	1, 922. 7	3. 28392
		167 56 14	347 55 58	Wheeler	2, 399. 2	3. 38007
		314 12 19	134 12 42	Hill	993. 8	2. 99729
Ref. Mon. 512	45 04 00. 71	129 26 26	309 26 16	Fall	374. 4	2. 57335
	71 29 52. 76	230 03 14	50 04 04	Cone	1, 997. 0	3. 30037
		302 39 11	122 39 19	Pond	281. 2	2. 44905
Ref. Mon. 511–16	45 04 16. 00	69 16 41	249 16 21	Fall	662. 1	2. 82098
	71 29 37. 67	171 48 32	351 48 26	Wheeler	1, 455. 4	3. 16299
		327 48 04	147 48 37	Hill	1, 888. 9	3. 27622
Ref. Mon. 511–15	45 04 39. 73	48 24 34	228 23 59	Fall	1, 456. 3	3. 16325
	71 29 16. 19	263 57 25	83 57 49	Cone	735. 1	2. 86637
		347 02 07	167 02 24	Hill	2, 391. 9	3. 37875
East Hereford, Cath- olic church cross.	45 04 41. 98	218 01 51	38 02 07	Wheeler	810. 7	2. 90888
	71 30 09. 99	269 45 25	89 46 27	Cone	1, 907. 7	3. 28052
		336 42 56	156 43 17	Pond	1, 552. 3	3. 19098
Red barn cupola	45 04 46. 61	9 21 00	189 20 53	Fall	1, 195. 1	3. 07739
	71 29 57. 10	330 37 14	150 38 00	Hill	2, 918. 6	3. 46517
		348 03 32	168 03 42	Pond	1, 603. 5	3. 20506
Ref. Mon. 511–14	45 05 00. 08	18 00 09	198 00 03	Cone	579. 0	2. 76269
	71 28 34. 58	51 25 38	231 24 33	Fall	2, 557. 2	3. 40777
		92 53 49	272 52 58	Wheeler	1, 589. 0	3. 20112
Ref. Mon. 511–13	45 05 14. 56	38 52 52	218 52 26	Cone	1, 281. 6	3. 10776
	71 28 05. 98	80 35 32	260 34 20	Wheeler	2, 242. 7	3. 35076
		262 20 10	82 20 28	Caron	579. 9	2. 76335
Ref. Mon. 511–12	45 05 34. 45	37 29 32	217 28 52	Cone	2, 031. 1	3. 30774
	71 27 46. 25	182 50 54	2 50 55	Cedar	617. 0	2. 79027
		345 04 34	165 04 39	Caron	555. 4	2. 74457
Ref. Mon. 511–11	45 06 00. 80	64 03 58	244 03 44	Cedar	451. 5	2. 65466
	71 27 26. 27	64 20 18	244 20 04	Cedar reference mark.	450. 4	2. 65361
		256 40 07	76 40 17	Barn	337. 3	2. 52796
		335 33 08	155 33 10	Old	125. 6	2. 09902
Ref. Mon. 511–10	45 06 14. 76	31 22 28	211 22 21	Barn	413. 5	2. 61645
	71 27 01. 42	56 30 42	236 30 12	Cedar	1, 138. 5	3. 05633
		56 36 42	236 36 12	Cedar reference mark.	1, 137. 1	3. 05581
		95 13 12	275 12 54	Poplar	547. 5	2. 73841
Ref. Mon. 511–9	45 06 46. 66	100 45 00	280 44 46	Paquette	436. 76	2. 64024
	71 26 37. 90					
Ref. Mon. 511–8	45 07 19. 36	111 32 59	291 32 39	Thicket	673. 6	2. 82838
	71 25 48. 20	143 40 04	323 39 47	Stub	866. 5	2. 93777
		230 46 58	50 47 10	Cliff	497. 1	2. 69648
Ref. Mon. 511–7	45 07 49. 40	138 05 54	318 05 51	White	147. 7	2. 16950
	71 25 41. 06	315 24 50	135 24 54	Jim	183. 0	2. 26248
		339 30 12	159 30 18	Cliff	654. 5	2. 81588

LAKE POHENAGAMOOK TO THE VERMONT-QUEBEC BOUNDARY—Continued

Station	Latitude and longitude	Azimuth	Back azimuth	To station	Distance (meters)	Loga- rithm
POINTS SUPPLEMEN- TARY TO MINOR SCHEME, HALLS STREAM—contd.	° ′ ″	° ′ ″	° ′ ″			
Ref. Mon. 511–6____	45 08 11. 95	45 52 25	225 52 23	Bridge_____	70. 1	1. 84590
	71 25 53. 73	169 06 33	349 06 32	Woods_____	160. 2	2. 20471
		291 34 20	111 34 22	Hall_____	87. 8	1. 94338
Car_____	45 08 29. 24	134 11 31	314 11 23	Duran_____	348. 6	2. 54228
	71 26 05. 32	336 27 36	156 27 39	Pole_____	239. 5	2. 37927
		359 35 58	179 35 58	Camp_____	322. 7	2. 50877
Ref. Mon. 511–5____	45 08 43. 75	1 15 11	181 15 11	Cut_____	272. 6	2. 43549
	71 26 04. 34	52 55 53	232 55 45	Duran_____	340. 1	2. 53164
		127 02 44	307 02 41	Leau_____	147. 8	2. 16970
		273 28 08	93 28 12	Bird_____	120. 0	2. 07916
Ref. Mon. 511_____	45 09 58. 03	65 26 14	245 26 10	King_____	120. 4	2. 08076
	71 25 30. 23	187 40 14	7 40 15	Clay_____	307. 1	2. 48734
		288 10 21	108 10 24	Swamp_____	113. 1	2. 05360
Ref. Mon. 510_____	45 13 37. 70	17 47 09	197 47 07	Labor_____	183. 0	2. 26234
	71 25 42. 88	88 43 28	268 43 21	Berry_____	225. 6	2. 35333
		276 42 09	96 42 12	Day_____	91. 6	1. 96213
Ref. Mon. 509_____	45 13 48. 60	24 45 35	204 45 34	Stop_____	90. 9	1. 95871
	71 26 02. 00	138 25 58	318 25 56	Run_____	83. 8	1. 92315
		306 02 01	126 02 07	Bunch_____	224. 3	2. 35080
Ref. Mon. 508_____	45 13 58. 76	3 06 27	183 06 27	Leaf_____	145. 7	2. 16339
	71 26 20. 28	84 02 45	264 02 40	Snag_____	161. 0	2. 20670
		263 41 57	83 42 01	Bog_____	111. 0	2. 04514
Mon. 507_____	45 14 05. 58	84 49 29	264 49 29	Still_____	15. 7	1. 19628
	71 26 38. 68	266 28 42	86 28 48	Hub_____	180. 2	2. 25579
		302 36 55	122 36 59	Nail_____	126. 9	2. 10351
Mon. 506_____	45 14 08. 21	11 26 08	191 26 08	Still_____	84. 3	1. 92587
	71 26 38. 63	181 39 58	1 39 59	Big_____	119. 5	2. 07738
		291 25 13	111 25 19	Hub_____	192. 1	2. 28347

GEOGRAPHIC POSITIONS OF TRIANGULATION STATIONS ALONG THE VERMONT-QUEBEC AND NEW YORK-QUEBEC BOUNDARIES TO THE ST. LAWRENCE RIVER

Station	Latitude and longitude	Azimuth	Back azimuth	To station	Distance (meters)	Loga-rithm
MAJOR SCHEME	° ′ ″	° ′ ″	° ′ ″			
Stewart	44 59 38. 293	146 59 41. 3	326 56 14. 2	Hereford	11, 753. 4	4. 070165
	71 31 12. 846	233 31 12. 9	53 32 41. 6	Beecher tablet	3, 415. 3	3. 533427
Fino	45 02 33. 832	128 19 38. 6	308 16 37. 0	Hereford	7, 154. 8	3. 854597
	71 31 48. 942	313 46 13. 6	133 48 07. 9	Beecher tablet	4, 897. 5	3. 689975
		351 41 53. 1	171 42 18. 7	Stewart	5, 476. 2	3. 738479
Searchme	45 00 08. 294	173 17 01. 2	353 16 27. 2	Hereford	8, 989. 1	3. 953717
	71 35 17. 505	225 26 40. 2	45 29 07. 7	Fino	6, 405. 9	3. 806579
		262 12 27. 7	82 16 49. 4	Beecher tablet	8, 179. 2	3. 912709
		279 46 51. 7	99 49 44. 7	Stewart	5, 438. 3	3. 735461
Brown	45 04 33. 231	263 54 56. 4	83 58 45. 0	Hereford	7, 101. 4	3. 851346
	71 41 28. 440	315 10 23. 9	135 14 46. 3	Searchme	11, 524. 1	4. 061608
Averill	44 58 04. 540	197 46 29. 6	17 48 34. 0	Brown	12, 601. 5	4. 100423
	71 44 24. 313	220 31 56. 8	40 37 49. 6	Hereford	16, 784. 6	4. 224911
		252 15 32. 3	72 21 58. 8	Searchme	12, 574. 0	4. 099472
Pinnacle	45 01 25. 406	250 11 55. 3	70 20 38. 1	Brown	17, 176. 3	4. 234929
	71 53 47. 262	296 38 25. 6	116 45 03. 6	Averill	13, 802. 2	4. 139947
Duck	44 57 04. 019	209 51 01. 8	29 53 31. 3	Pinnacle	9, 305. 1	3. 968723
	71 57 18. 810	236 13 45. 8	56 24 57. 9	Brown	25, 007. 5	4. 398071
		263 38 36. 5	83 47 43. 7	Averill	17, 077. 9	4. 232434
Fairfax	45 05 00. 530	271 48 34. 0	92 02 06. 8	Brown	25, 122. 5	4. 400062
	72 00 36. 398	306 31 35. 9	126 36 25. 5	Pinnacle	11, 146. 9	4. 047154
		343 35 28. 2	163 37 48. 0	Duck	15, 332. 8	4. 185622
Dufferin	45 03 57. 155	244 55 34. 6	64 57 50. 0	Fairfax	4, 619. 7	3. 664618
	72 03 47. 721	326 13 34. 5	146 18 09. 5	Duck	15, 335. 8	4. 185706
Oats	45 03 57. 720	270 07 24. 1	90 10 55. 7	Dufferin	6, 539. 3	3. 815534
	72 08 46. 629	310 13 30. 5	130 21 36. 9	Duck	19, 747. 9	4. 295521
Derrick	45 03 58. 973	260 10 12. 3	80 16 09. 1	Fairfax	11, 186. 6	4. 048697
	72 09 00. 375	270 26 21. 6	90 30 03. 0	Dufferin	6, 840. 3	3. 835072
		277 19 44. 6	97 19 54. 4	Oats	303. 2	2. 481741
		309 45 02. 7	129 53 18. 9	Duck	20, 003. 2	4. 301099
East Lake	44 58 44. 101	180 19 09. 7	0 19 11. 4	Derrick	9, 720. 2	3. 987675
	72 09 02. 851	182 05 58. 1	2 06 09. 6	Oats	9, 687. 9	3. 986228
		215 29 36. 9	35 33 19. 8	Dufferin	11, 874. 1	4. 074600
		281 15 12. 5	101 23 30. 0	Duck	15, 735. 9	4. 196892
Newport	44 56 55. 590	217 34 35. 1	37 39 59. 4	Oats	16, 452. 0	4. 216219
	72 16 25. 219	250 53 47. 4	70 59 00. 0	East Lake	10, 257. 4	4. 011038
Owl's Head (Geo-detic Survey of Canada).	45 03 45. 412	267 25 55. 5	87 55 32. 1	Hereford	54, 934. 2	4. 739842
	72 17 54. 811	267 53 49. 0	88 00 07. 3	Derrick	11, 699. 8	4. 068180
		268 07 53. 7	88 14 21. 8	Oats	11, 999. 2	4. 079151
		308 33 31. 7	128 39 48. 0	East Lake	14, 905. 4	4. 173343
		351 10 30. 8	171 11 34. 2	Newport	12, 802. 3	4. 107289
Jay	44 55 27. 292	229 19 51. 3	49 29 30. 6	Owl's Head	23, 633. 9	4. 373535
	72 31 34. 145	262 07 23. 2	82 18 05. 3	Newport	20, 115. 3	4. 303527
Round Top	45 04 51. 404	275 51 25. 6	96 01 58. 8	Owl's Head	19, 668. 8	4. 293777
	72 32 49. 112	304 11 18. 3	124 22 54. 3	Newport	26, 074. 8	4. 416221
		354 36 23. 0	174 37 16. 0	Jay	17, 491. 2	4. 242819
Doctor	44 53 02. 795	209 10 07. 8	29 16 42. 6	Round Top	25, 064. 7	4. 399062
	72 42 07. 647	252 08 40. 8	72 16 08. 0	Jay	14, 596. 6	4. 164253

VERMONT-QUEBEC AND NEW YORK-QUEBEC BOUNDARIES—Continued

Station	Latitude and longitude	Azimuth	Back azimuth	To station	Distance (meters)	Loga-rithm
MAJOR SCHEME—con.	° ′ ″	° ′ ″	° ′ ″			
St. Armand (Geo-detic Survey of Canada).	45 02 47. 117 72 44 22. 842	255 44 42. 8 266 52 45. 63 308 48 02. 7 350 39 30. 8	75 52 53. 9 87 11 29. 60 128 57 06. 1 170 41 06. 4	Round Top___ Owl's Head__ Jay_____ Doctor_____	15, 655. 0 34, 795. 44 21, 632. 2 18, 279. 4	4. 194654 4. 5415223 4. 335100 4. 261963
Franklin_____	44 57 52. 153 72 54 56. 708	236 40 33. 8 297 49 46. 1	56 48 02. 1 117 58 49. 3	St. Armand___ Doctor_____	16, 601. 8 19, 085. 7	4. 220154 4. 280709
McDermott_____	45 03 08. 701 72 52 52. 476	15 34 12. 9 273 22 07. 6	195 32 45. 0 93 28 08. 3	Franklin_____ St. Armand___	10, 143. 4 11, 172. 6	4. 006184 4. 048153
Sheldon_____	44 53 44. 191 72 59 01. 616	215 01 52. 3 228 52 48. 7 273 11 15. 3	35 04 44. 4 49 03 09. 0 93 23 10. 2	Franklin_____ St. Armand___ Doctor_____	9, 350. 6 25, 529. 0 22, 287. 6	3. 970840 4. 407033 4. 348064
Saint_____	45 00 03. 650 73 02 45. 123	246 10 42. 7 258 04 52. 5 291 32 05. 4 337 16 43. 4	66 17 42. 0 78 17 52. 3 111 37 36. 5 157 19 21. 3	McDermott___ St. Armand___ Franklin_____ Sheldon_____	14, 176. 3 24, 654. 7 11, 036. 2 12, 697. 2	4. 151564 4. 391900 4. 042820 4. 103707
Blair_____	44 58 48. 129 73 14 25. 093	261 17 10. 6 294 46 14. 4	81 25 25. 5 114 57 06. 7	Saint_____ Sheldon_____	15, 509. 9 22, 316. 4	4. 190608 4. 348625
Alburg_____	44 54 29. 595 73 17 30. 426	206 57 48. 9 241 55 37. 9 273 11 19. 2	26 59 59. 8 62 06 03. 4 93 24 21. 9	Blair_____ Saint_____ Sheldon_____	8, 955. 6 21, 975. 4 24, 367. 5	3. 952094 4. 341937 4. 386811
Mon. 650–A_____	45 00 35. 490 73 24 31. 367	283 57 10. 8 320 42 54. 9	104 04 19. 5 140 47 52. 4	Blair_____ Alburg_____	13, 687. 4 14, 584. 2	4. 136321 4. 163884
Champlain_____	44 57 37. 821 73 27 24. 900	214 42 43. 5 262 41 06. 8 293 57 58. 2	34 44 46. 1 82 50 17. 9 114 04 58. 1	Mon. 650–A__ Blair_____ Alburg_____	6, 673. 4 17, 225. 9 14, 271. 7	3. 824349 4. 236181 4. 154476
Covey Hill (Geo-detic Survey of Canada).	45 01 05. 025 73 47 46. 114	267 27 30. 45	88 12 21. 32	St. Armand___	83, 313. 63	4. 9207161
Huntingdon (Geo-detic Survey of Canada).	45 05 33. 933 74 15 15. 627	282 47 23. 99	103 06 51. 51	Covey Hill____	37, 035. 93	4. 5686233
Bonville (Geodetic Survey of Can-ada).	45 07 33. 156 74 50 06. 446	274 23 52. 43	94 48 33. 68	Huntingdon __	45, 854. 95	4. 6613861
St. Raphael church spire (Geodetic Survey of Can-ada).	45 12 42. 283 74 35 51. 177	63 01 13. 07	242 51 06. 53	Bonville_____	20, 974. 15	4. 3216844
POINTS SUPPLEMEN-TARY TO MAJOR SCHEME						
Mon. 519_____	45 00 48. 528 71 30 21. 279	27 31 10. 8 274 52 41. 6	207 30 34. 3 94 53 33. 8	Stewart_____ Beecher tablet_	2, 444. 6 1, 622. 8	3. 388215 3. 210266
Mon. 523–A_____	45 00 45. 558 71 35 00. 749	231 27 41. 4 270 18 35. 1 292 33 54. 5	51 29 57. 0 90 22 45. 0 112 36 35. 7	Fino_____ Beecher tablet_ Stewart_____	5, 366. 9 7, 736. 8 5, 406. 1	3. 729724 3. 888564 3. 732882
Sup_____	45 01 47. 635 71 48 49. 473	51 55 46. 0 84 01 13. 0 242 02 49. 7 319 49 57. 5	231 49 46. 0 263 57 42. 4 62 08 01. 9 139 53 05. 0	Duck_____ Pinnacle_____ Brown_____ Averill_____	14, 182. 5 6, 555. 3 10, 921. 1 9, 008. 9	4. 151754 3. 816594 4. 038266 3. 954670
Craig's Knoll_____	45 00 24. 924 71 47 47. 972	152 11 57. 1 314 08 45. 4	332 11 13. 6 134 11 09. 4	Sup_____ Averill_____	2, 886. 6 6, 219. 8	3. 460390 3. 793778

VERMONT-QUEBEC AND NEW YORK-QUEBEC BOUNDARIES—Continued

Station	Latitude and longitude	Azimuth	Back azimuth	To station	Distance (meters)	Loga-rithm
POINTS SUPPLEMEN-TARY TO MAJOR SCHEME—contd.	° ′ ″	° ′ ″	° ′ ″			
Mon. 534–A	45 00 38. 930 71 47 27. 455	46 06 16. 0 139 45 15. 4	226 06 01. 5 319 44 17. 4	Craig's Knoll Sup	623. 5 2, 779. 1	2. 794859 3. 443898
Pond	45 00 45. 386 71 55 21. 445	20 37 57. 2 239 03 56. 7 288 57 57. 0	200 36 34. 3 59 05 03. 3 109 05 41. 6	Duck Pinnacle Averill	7, 301. 3 2, 403. 9 15, 227. 5	3. 863400 3. 380921 4. 182630
Mon. 538–B	45 00 29. 875 71 53 18. 291	100 04 48. 0 159 41 42. 5	280 03 20. 9 339 41 22. 0	Pond Pinnacle	2, 739. 1 1, 827. 9	3. 437605 3. 261944
Mon. 539	45 00 28. 282 71 54 19. 416	111 14 51. 1 201 45 41. 5 267 53 26. 2	291 14 07. 2 21 46 04. 2 87 54 09. 4	Pond Pinnacle Mon. 538–B	1, 457. 4 1, 898. 8 1, 339. 5	3. 163566 3. 278472 3. 126949
Mon. 550 ecc	45 00 21. 474 72 03 46. 500	134 22 20. 0 179 46 12. 3	314 18 37. 9 359 46 11. 4	Derrick Dufferin	9, 606. 3 6, 658. 1	3. 982557 3. 823350
Mon. 550	45 00 22. 329 72 03 46. 054	20 17 49	200 17 49	Mon. 550 ecc	28. 13	1. 449218
Mon. 545 ecc	45 00 26. 233 72 00 27. 324	88 05 26. 2 146 03 08. 7	268 03 05. 3 326 00 47. 0	Mon. 550 ecc Dufferin	4, 364. 4 7, 850. 8	3. 639926 3. 894915
Mon. 545	45 00 26. 050 72 00 27. 332	181 41	1 41	Mon. 545 ecc	5. 64	0. 751188
Mon. 551–A	45 00 21. 781 72 04 35. 465	139 10 16. 2 188 55 41. 6	319 07 08. 7 8 56 15. 4	Derrick Dufferin	8, 864. 3 6, 730. 2	3. 947645 3. 828028
Stanstead benchmark	45 01 09. 259 72 05 50. 652	43 13 52. 5 60 40 18. 6 106 59 15. 5	223 11 36. 6 240 32 50. 0 286 50 43. 1	East Lake Newport Owl's Head	6, 148. 2 15, 956. 1 16, 566. 4	3. 788750 4. 202927 4. 219229
Mon. 566	45 00 20. 047 72 11 49. 977	43 43 28. 8 308 57 27. 4	223 40 14. 3 128 59 25. 5	Newport East Lake	8, 729. 7 4, 709. 1	3. 940997 3. 672934
Mon. 567	45 00 19. 609 72 12 20. 034	268 49 11. 1 304 17 50. 1	88 49 32. 4 124 20 09. 5	Mon. 566 East Lake	658. 4 5, 229. 7	2. 818486 3. 718476
Mon. 574	45 00 15. 367 72 16 14. 681	2 08 43. 0 286 32 34. 3	182 08 35. 6 106 37 39. 6	Newport East Lake	6, 157. 3 9, 870. 2	3. 790379 3. 994325
Broo	45 03 12. 192 72 26 50. 752	23 25 14. 8 111 22 25. 7 264 56 57. 8 310 15 17. 1	203 21 54. 4 291 18 12. 0 85 03 17. 2 130 22 39. 5	Jay Round Top Owl's Head Newport	15, 636. 5 8, 416. 8 11, 771. 4 17, 968. 3	4. 194140 3. 925148 4. 070828 4. 254506
Sicard	44 58 30. 927 72 22 17. 524	65 08 11. 8 145 27 25. 7 290 49 46. 0	245 01 38. 6 325 24 12. 5 110 53 55. 1	Jay Broo Newport	13, 454. 5 10, 544. 3 8, 263. 3	4. 128869 4. 023018 3. 917154
Bickford	44 57 17. 713 72 21 34. 554	75 31 23. 6 157 23 03. 3 275 43 13. 8	255 24 20. 0 337 22 32. 9 95 46 52. 5	Jay Sicard Newport	13, 581. 1 2, 448. 4 6, 815. 2	4. 132934 3. 388888 3. 833479
Mon. 581–A	45 00 19. 625 72 20 38. 588	32 52 07. 0 57 55 52. 0 123 12 55. 9	212 50 57. 1 237 48 08. 7 303 08 32. 6	Sicard Jay Broo	3, 994. 6 16, 966. 2 9, 734. 2	3. 601468 4. 229584 3. 988302
Mon. 581	45 00 18. 482 72 20 04. 337	41 19 15. 3 59 19 57. 5 92 41 43. 7	221 17 41. 2 239 11 50. 0 272 41 19. 5	Sicard Jay Mon. 581–A	4, 420. 0 17, 588. 3 751. 0	3. 645421 4. 245225 2. 875616
Mon. 584	45 00 23. 198 72 22 46. 448	134 18 42. 8 225 36 46. 5 272 14 35. 9	314 15 49. 9 45 40 13. 0 92 16 06. 3	Broo Owl's Head Mon. 581–A	7, 471. 1 8, 928. 6 2, 802. 4	3. 873385 3. 950781 3. 447523

VERMONT-QUEBEC AND NEW YORK-QUEBEC BOUNDARIES—Continued

Station	Latitude and longitude	Azimuth	Back azimuth	To station	Distance (meters)	Logarithm
POINTS SUPPLEMENTARY TO MAJOR SCHEME—contd.	° ′ ″	° ′ ″	° ′ ″			
Mon. 588–B	45 00 29. 104	169 56 19. 6	349 55 50. 6	Broo	5, 113. 2	3. 708689
	72 26 09. 930	240 44 21. 8	60 50 12. 1	Owl's Head	12, 416. 9	4. 094013
		297 10 01. 1	117 16 54. 4	Newport	14, 407. 5	4. 158589
Mon. 590	45 00 31. 066	183 12 11. 5	3 12 20. 4	Broo	4, 981. 7	3. 697376
	72 27 03. 473	243 24 06. 2	63 30 34. 4	Owl's Head	13, 424. 8	4. 127908
		272 57 03. 9	92 57 41. 8	Mon. 588–B	1, 174. 1	3. 069710
Lot 5, R 7 (Potton Tp., cadastral No. 768).	45 01 17. 383	51 46 57. 2	231 39 35. 5	Jay	17, 445. 2	4. 241676
	72 21 09. 190	113 24 07. 5	293 15 52. 1	Round Top	16, 680. 6	4. 222212
		222 56 02. 2	42 58 19. 8	Owl's Head	6, 243. 4	3. 795424
Mon. 602	45 00 55. 095	8 18 08. 4	188 17 00. 0	Doctor	14, 733. 7	4. 168312
	72 40 30. 707	124 15 30. 3	304 12 46. 1	St. Armand	6, 146. 6	3. 788636
		310 39 45. 2	130 46 04. 4	Jay	15, 513. 0	4. 190697
Mon. 606 ecc	45 00 56. 973	173 00 07. 5	352 59 54. 0	St. Armand	3, 425. 7	3. 534743
	72 44 03. 771	270 41 26. 4	90 43 57. 1	Mon. 602	4, 665. 7	3. 668918
		301 42 20. 3	121 51 10. 2	Jay	19, 324. 3	4. 286104
Mon. 606	45 00 57. 224	340 06	160 06	Mon. 606 ecc	8. 23	0. 915380
	72 44 03. 899					
Mon. 621–B ecc	45 00 53. 520	245 17 00. 7	65 21 54. 2	McDermott	9, 995. 7	3. 999812
	72 59 47. 415	260 04 46. 9	80 15 41. 0	St. Armand	20, 541. 3	4. 312627
Mon. 621–B	45 00 53. 454	181 27	1 27	Mon. 621–B ecc	2. 04	0. 310091
	72 59 47. 417					
Abercorn benchmark	45 01 15. 814	57 52 55. 3	237 52 22. 4	Mon. 602	1, 202. 8	3. 080196
	72 39 44. 184	114 49 39. 2	294 46 22. 1	St. Armand	6, 719. 4	3. 827333
Mon. 625	45 00 55. 121	50 25 52. 2	230 24 50. 2	Saint	2, 493. 9	3. 396877
	73 01 17. 348	261 03 06. 6	81 15 04. 4	St. Armand	22, 475. 8	4. 351716
		271 25 46. 2	91 26 49. 9	Mon. 621–B ecc	1, 969. 9	3. 294446
		304 04 29. 4	124 08 58. 5	Franklin	10, 071. 4	4. 003088
Mon. 629	45 00 57. 737	271 18 22. 2	91 20 15. 2	Mon. 625	3, 500. 0	3. 544073
	73 03 57. 150	316 37 15. 8	136 38 06. 8	Saint	2, 296. 9	3. 361143
Mon. 632 and 633	45 00 48. 553	44 45 37. 5	224 43 38. 5	Blair	5, 233. 9	3. 718826
	73 11 36. 887	263 59 50. 3	84 19 06. 3	St. Armand	35, 957. 8	4. 555793
		276 44 07. 9	96 50 23. 9	Saint	11, 727. 7	4. 069214
Mon. 634	45 00 47. 359	264 08 47. 0	84 28 46. 7	St. Armand	37, 306. 8	4. 571788
	73 12 38. 648	268 26 07. 2	88 26 50. 9	Mon. 632 and 633	1, 352. 9	3. 131280
		275 52 05. 8	95 59 05. 5	Saint	13, 068. 0	4. 116208
Mon. 641–A ecc	45 00 42. 549	88 47 15. 9	268 41 55. 0	Mon. 650–A	9, 934. 8	3. 997160
	73 16 57. 798	273 35 43. 9	93 45 46. 9	Saint	18, 712. 2	4. 272126
		316 32 40. 6	136 34 28. 5	Blair	4, 864. 6	3. 687043
Mon. 641–A	45 00 43. 050	357 28 55	177 28 55	Mon. 641–A ecc	15. 49	1. 190162
	73 16 57. 829					
Fort	45 00 23. 410	95 23 38. 4	275 21 30. 4	Mon. 650–A	3, 980. 0	3. 599887
	73 21 30. 425	334 15 33. 4	154 18 23. 0	Alburg	12, 122. 9	4. 083606
45th parallel Mon. ecc.	44 59 55. 475	108 40 18. 4	288 38 20. 2	Mon. 650–A	3, 861. 7	3. 586779
	73 21 44. 305	199 25 01. 9	19 25 11. 7	Fort	914. 4	2. 961120
45th parallel Mon.	44 59 55. 489	33 18	213 18	45th parallel Mon. ecc.	0. 51	9. 7058–10
	73 21 44. 292					
Mon. 646	45 00 38. 104	88 50 52. 5	268 48 44. 9	Mon. 650–A	3, 952. 6	3. 596882
	73 21 30. 910	358 39 33. 6	178 39 34. 0	Fort	453. 7	2. 656796

VERMONT-QUEBEC AND NEW YORK-QUEBEC BOUNDARIES—Continued

Station	Latitude and longitude	Azimuth	Back azimuth	To station	Distance (meters)	Logarithm
POINTS SUPPLEMENTARY TO MAJOR SCHEME—contd.	° ′ ″	° ′ ″	° ′ ″			
Mon. 644 ecc	45 00 39. 206	74 53 32. 0	254 52 33. 7	Fort	1, 870. 0	3. 271833
	73 20 07. 990	88 53 10. 8	268 50 04. 5	Mon. 650–A	5, 768. 7	3. 761080
		88 56 04. 2	268 55 05. 5	Mon. 646	1, 816. 1	3. 259147
Mon. 644	45 00 39. 339	358 18	178 18	Mon. 644 ecc	4. 11	0. 614350
	73 20 07. 996					
Mon. 647	45 00 37. 500	88 47 33. 6	268 45 59. 5	Mon. 650–A	2, 913. 3	3. 464391
	73 22 18. 360	268 55 48. 7	88 57 20. 9	Mon. 644 ecc	2, 855. 4	3. 455666
		292 30 06. 5	112 30 40. 4	Fort	1, 136. 3	3. 055490
Havelock	45 00 54. 436	257 19 37. 8	77 20 24. 8	Covey Hill	1, 490. 71	3. 173393
	73 48 52. 538					
Clinton	44 59 50. 800	182 09 49. 3	2 09 51. 7	Havelock	1, 965. 8	3. 293543
	73 48 55. 927	213 42 24. 3	33 43 13. 7	Covey Hill	2, 754. 5	3. 440048
Mooers	44 59 02. 379	138 47 02. 0	318 46 19. 7	Clinton	1, 987. 3	3. 298255
	73 47 56. 146	160 21 21. 6	340 20 41. 7	Havelock	3, 673. 1	3. 565027
		183 19 14. 4	3 19 21. 5	Covey Hill	3, 792. 4	3. 578914
Bolt near line ecc	45 00 09. 368	19 51 35. 1	199 51 28. 4	Clinton	609. 4	2. 784900
	73 48 46. 476	174 32 59. 6	354 32 55. 3	Havelock	1, 397. 6	3. 145375
		217 34 00. 8	37 34 43. 5	Covey Hill	2, 167. 8	3. 336013
Bolt near line	45 00 09. 370	37 34	217 34	Bolt near line ecc	0. 07	8. 8439–10
	73 48 46. 474	217 34 01	37 34 44	Covey Hill	2, 167. 7	3. 335999
Shea	45 00 09. 328	58 21 30. 1	238 19 41. 9	Mooers	3, 937. 8	3. 595255
	73 45 23. 127	83 01 30. 4	262 58 59. 9	Clinton	4, 695. 8	3. 671711
		90 02 08. 5	269 59 44. 7	Bolt near line ecc	4, 453. 6	3. 648716
		118 47 07. 0	298 45 25. 9	Covey Hill	3, 572. 2	3. 552936
Mon. 682	45 00 11. 520	118 08 51	298 07 11	Covey Hill	3, 502. 9	3. 544423
	73 45 25. 054	328 02 49	148 02 50	Shea	79. 73	1. 901627
Mon. 688	45 00 09. 769	88 50 17	268 49 57	Bolt near line	606. 10	2. 782545
	73 48 18. 806					
Dalgliesh	45 05 01. 856	200 48 53. 0	20 49 05. 2	Huntingdon	1, 059. 4	3. 025046
	74 15 32. 842	281 10 14. 6	101 29 54. 2	Covey Hill	37, 198. 6	4. 570527
Fee	44 59 58. 254	144 56 20. 4	324 52 47. 5	Dalgliesh	11, 454. 0	4. 058958
	74 10 31. 993					
Mon. 722–A	44 59 30. 488	178 37 30	358 37 29	Fee	857. 38	2. 933175
	74 10 31. 054					
Leblanc	45 01 44. 790	228 32 33	48 36 16	Dalgliesh	9, 194. 2	3. 963513
	74 20 47. 903	283 38 38	103 45 53	Fee	13, 881. 8	4. 142446
Boulder	44 59 09. 220	159 23 19	339 22 21	Leblanc	5, 131. 1	3. 710212
	74 19 25. 392	205 02 18	25 05 03	Dalgliesh	12, 017. 2	4. 079803
Langevin	45 00 10. 443	193 17 59	13 18 21	Leblanc	2, 992. 8	3. 476074
	74 21 19. 352	307 07 07	127 08 27	Boulder	3, 131. 0	3. 495685
Brady	45 01 00. 093	48 41 47	228 40 51	Langevin	2, 321. 7	3. 365812
	74 19 59. 716	142 36 11	322 35 37	Leblanc	1, 736. 9	3. 239772
Huntingdon southwest base.	45 01 15. 740	19 42 23	199 42 00	Langevin	2, 141. 1	3. 330627
	74 20 46. 388	177 52 57	357 52 56	Leblanc	897. 4	2. 952982
		295 17 36	115 18 09	Brady	1, 130. 3	3. 053191
Huntingdon northeast base.	45 01 28. 617	50 47 45	230 47 29	Huntingdon southwest base.	628. 86	2. 798554
	74 20 24. 131	133 48 52	313 48 35	Leblanc	721. 2	2. 858041
		328 44 09	148 44 26	Brady	1, 030. 1	3. 012869

VERMONT-QUEBEC AND NEW YORK-QUEBEC BOUNDARIES—Continued

Station	Latitude and longitude	Azimuth	Back azimuth	To station	Distance (meters)	Logarithm
POINTS SUPPLEMENTARY TO MAJOR SCHEME—contd.	° ′ ″	° ′ ″	° ′ ″			
Mon. 739 ecc_____	44 59 34. 072	166 56 27	346 56 19	Langevin_____	1, 152. 6	3. 061668
	74 21 07. 461	186 03 24	6 03 38	Leblanc_____	4, 057. 9	3. 608301
		288 55 39	108 56 51	Boulder_____	2, 363. 9	3. 373638
Mon. 739_____	44 59 34. 200	51 29	231 29	Mon. 739 ecc_____	6. 34	0. 801870
	74 21 07. 235					
Godmanchester Township, southwest corner.	44 59 34. 584 74 21 14. 620	275 45 08	95 45 13	Mon. 739 ecc_____	157. 61	2. 197599
Cornwall east church Catholic.	45 01 08. 042	140 58 21. 8	320 53 09. 4	Bonville_____	15, 313. 0	4. 185059
	74 42 45. 237	202 51 15. 0	22 56 08. 4	St. Raphael church spire.	23, 264. 2	4. 366688
		257 01 36. 5	77 21 04. 1	Huntingdon_____	37, 017. 0	4. 568401
St. Regis east base__	44 59 57. 971 74 39 33. 281	117 14 52. 0	297 12 36. 3	Cornwall east church.	4, 727. 5	3. 674634
St. Regis west base__	44 59 22. 925	138 10 56. 1	318 09 22. 3	Cornwall east church.	4, 354. 9	3. 638978
	74 40 32. 620	230 13 22. 4	50 14 04. 3	St. Regis east base_	1, 691. 11	3. 228173
Mon. 1 (I. W. C.) (Int. Bdy. Comm. 1923).	45 00 33. 599 74 40 16. 534	9 10 31. 2 319 15 26. 6	189 10 19. 9 139 15 57. 2	St. Regis west base_ St. Regis east base_	2, 209. 9 1, 451. 5	3. 344380 3. 161827
Mon. 774 (Int. Bdy. Comm. 1923).	44 59 58. 142 74 39 40. 552	144 15 03. 3 271 53 59. 8	324 14 37. 8 91 54 04. 9	Mon. 1 (I. W. C.)_ St. Regis east base_	1, 348. 7 159. 3	3. 129917 2. 202340
Mon. 3 (I. W. C.) (Int. Bdy. Comm. 1923).	45 00 02. 387 74 40 59. 702	131 15 36. 5	311 14 21. 9	Cornwall east church	3, 073. 9	3. 487688
		274 06 38. 8	94 07 39. 9	St. Regis east base_	1, 897. 8	3. 278239
		274 18 53. 2	94 19 49. 2	Mon. 774_____	1, 738. 5	3. 240183
		334 01 55. 9	154 02 15. 1	St. Regis west base_	1, 354. 9	3. 131918
Mon. 4 (I. W. C.) (Int. Bdy. Comm. 1923).	45 00 15. 196 74 42 09. 992	154 41 05. 5	334 40 40. 6	Cornwall east church.	1, 804. 7	3. 256404
		284 23 52. 2	104 24 41. 9	Mon. 3 (I. W. C.)_	1, 589. 4	3. 201244
		307 05 58. 3	127 07 07. 2	St. Regis west base_	2, 674. 4	3. 427231
U. S. L. S. No. 8 ecc_	44 59 30. 817 74 42 43. 445	179 15 05. 6	359 15 04. 3	Cornwall east church.	3, 001. 6	3. 477346
		208 08 14. 6	28 08 38. 2	Mon. 4 (I. W. C.)_	1, 553. 6	3. 191341
		246 46 37. 2	66 47 50. 5	Mon. 3 (I. W. C.)_	2, 472. 6	3. 393147
		274 50 45. 4	94 52 17. 9	St. Regis west base_	2, 876. 2	3. 458822
St. Regis church_____	45 00 10. 629	85 26 20. 6	265 24 38. 0	Mon. 3 (I. W. C.)_	3, 189. 7	3. 503745
	74 38 34. 532	107 37 13. 7	287 36 01. 6	Mon. 1 (I. W. C.)_	2, 343. 7	3. 369902
		107 54 57. 4	287 52 00. 2	Cornwall east church.	5, 769. 0	3. 761102
Cornwall west church Catholic.	45 01 15. 978	145 17 41. 1	325 13 19. 7	Bonville_____	14, 169. 5	4. 151354
	74 43 57. 302	278 49 09. 5	98 50 00. 5	Cornwall east church.	1, 596. 8	3. 203245
		292 35 08. 7	112 38 15. 4	St. Regis east base_	6, 263. 1	3. 796792
		307 52 55. 7	127 55 20. 5	St. Regis west base_	5, 681. 0	3. 754424
U. S. L. S. No. 13 (Int. Bdy. Comm. 1923).	44 59 22. 394 74 40 30. 489	109 21 45	289 21 44	St. Regis west base_	49. 49	1. 694495
U. S. L. S. No. 8 (Int. Bdy. Comm. 1923).	44 59 30. 588 74 42 44. 411	251 32 06	71 32 07	U. S. L. S. No. 8 ecc.	22. 30	1. 348349

DESCRIPTIONS OF TRIANGULATION STATIONS

SOURCE OF THE ST. CROIX RIVER TO LAKE POHENAGAMOOK, MAJOR SCHEME AND POINTS SUPPLE-
MENTARY TO IT

Spring Hill (Maine, Aroostook County; United States Coast and Geodetic Survey, 1889; J. L. Rannie, 1916).—Near the center of Amity Township and west of the Houlton-Baring road, on a large flat-topped hill, known as Spring Hill. The station is about 300 feet south of the highest part of the hill, on the farm owned by Percy Boles.

Station mark: Bronze disk, lettered "U. S. & C. B. Survey" set in a hole drilled in a pear-shaped bowlder, whose top is a little above the surface of the ground. A rough triangle, cut in the rock, surrounds the disk.

Kennedy (New Brunswick, York County; United States Coast and Geodetic Survey, 1889; J. L. Rannie, 1916).—In North Lake Parish, on the summit of a hill about 3 miles east of initial monument of the international boundary.

Station mark: Standard bronze disk of the United States Coast and Geodetic Survey, set in a hole drilled in a bowlder which is $2\frac{1}{2}$ by 3 feet, its highest part projecting about 6 inches above the ground.

Pole Hill (Maine, Aroostook County; United States Coast and Geodetic Survey, 1889; J. L. Rannie, 1916).—In Amity Township, on a low knob known as Pole Hill. It is about 400 feet west of the international boundary and about 4,200 feet north of initial monument at the source of the St. Croix River. The station is on the highest part of the hill on a gray sandstone bowlder, the visible part of which is 6 by 3 feet and 2 feet above the ground.

Station mark: Bronze disk lettered "U. S. & C. B. Survey" set in a hole drilled in the bowlder, and surrounded by a triangle cut in the rock.

Union (New Brunswick, Carleton County; J. L. Rannie, 1916).—In Richmond Parish, on the north half of lot 1 of the sixth tier of lots from the St. John River, on the farm of Alfred T. Henderson. From Green Road station, on the Houlton Branch of the Canadian Pacific Railway, go one-fourth mile south to Mr. Henderson's house and go back (west) along a lane up a hill. One passes a fence corner about one-fourth mile back from the farm buildings just at the final rise at the top of the hill. The station lies about 100 feet southwest of this fence corner in a cultivated field.

Station mark: Standard bolt of the Geodetic Survey of Canada set in an irregular mass of concrete about $1\frac{1}{2}$ feet in diameter and $1\frac{1}{2}$ feet deep, resting on bedrock.

Linneus (Maine, Aroostook County; J. L. Rannie, 1916).—In Linneus Township, on lot 12, range 5, on a farm owned by Henry Howard. The station is in the middle of a stone fence running back (west) from the farm buildings, about 600 feet from the buildings, and about 600 feet east of the highest part of the hill.

Station mark: Bronze disk set in the top of a long bowlder which is firmly set in cement in the middle of a stone fence.

Ludlow (Maine, Aroostook County; J. L. Rannie, 1916).—In Ludlow Township, on lot 2 of range 5, on a farm owned by R. D. Stevenson. The station lies on the easterly slope of a hill about 900 feet east of and 60 feet lower than the top of the hill. It is on a rock outcrop about 50 feet north of the north end of a stone fence which runs back (north) from the farm buildings and it is about one-fourth mile from these buildings.

Station mark: Bronze disk cemented in the rock outcrop.

Richmond (New Brunswick, Carleton County; J. L. Rannie, 1916).—In Richmond Parish, on Parks Hill on the farm of Charles Parks, in the fifth tier of the township. The hill is the highest in this vicinity and is a rounded, cultivated knoll. The station is on the east side of the stone rubble foundation of a fence which runs north and south.

Station mark: Standard bolt of the Geodetic Survey of Canada set in an irregular mass of concrete whose bottom is about $3\frac{1}{2}$ feet below and top about 1 foot below the surface of the ground. A pyramid of bowlders rising a foot or two above the surface of the ground was erected over this mark.

Littleton (Maine, Aroostook County; J. L. Rannie, 1916).—In Littleton Township, on a hill about the middle of lot 3, range 10, of the south division of the township, on land owned by Oscar Crain. It is on a prominent hill, which is cleared north of the station and covered with small growth to the south.

Station mark: Bronze plug cemented in a rock outcrop.

449

Wakefield (New Brunswick, Carleton County; J. L. Rannie, 1916).—In Wakefield Parish, on the farm of Albert Bell, on lot G of the tier of lots on the north side of the Meduxnekeag River. The station is on a hill which is overtopped by higher hills a short distance to the eastward. It is in the middle of a stone pile in nearly the highest part of a cultivated field, about one-fourth mile north of Mr. Bell's buildings.

Station mark: Bronze disk set in cement which holds together a number of rocks in the center of the stone pile.

Monticello (Maine, Aroostook County; J. L. Rannie, 1916).—In Monticello Township, lot 104, on land owned by Ivan Hogan. The station lies on top of a hill about 600 feet east of his house. It is on the highest ground in a cultivated field.

Station mark: Bronze disk cemented in a rock outcrop.

Wilmot (New Brunswick, Carleton County; J. L. Rannie, 1916).—In Wilmot Parish, on lot 5 of the tier of lots on the west side of the road running south from Centreville, New Brunswick, and about 4 miles south of Centreville. The station is on Wm. Page's farm about one-half mile west of the farm buildings on the flat top of a hill in the northeast corner of the intersection of a north-and-south and an east-and-west fence, about 50 feet east of the highest point of the hill.

Station mark: Standard bolt of the Geodetic Survey of Canada set in an irregular mass of concrete whose bottom is about $3\frac{1}{2}$ feet and top about 1 foot below the surface of the ground. A pyramid of bowlders, rising a foot or two above the surface, was erected over this mark.

Blaine (Maine, Aroostook County; J. L. Rannie, 1916).—In "E" plantation, on land known as the Quimby Estate. The station is on the highest point of a hill covered with a heavy growth of hardwood and is about 1 mile north and 2 miles west of the south and east boundaries of the township, respectively. This hill lies about 1 mile northeast of the highest point of a prominent ridge which is somewhat higher than the station. The station is about 1 mile southwest of Mr. Kingsbury's house and is most easily reached from his house.

Station mark: Standard bolt of the Geodetic Survey of Canada cemented in a hole drilled in a depression in bedrock and surrounded by a mass of cement.

Wicklow (New Brunswick, Carleton County; J. L. Rannie, 1916).—In Wicklow Parish, on lot 19 of the tier of lots east of tier 3, between tier 3 and the tier of St. John River lots, on land owned by James Forsyth. The station is about 900 feet northeast of Grenfield post office, on the summit of the highest hill within 4 or 5 miles. In 1916 the top of this hill was partly covered with second-growth spruce and balsam.

Station mark: Standard bolt of the Geodetic Survey of Canada set in an irregular mass of concrete about $1\frac{1}{2}$ feet in diameter and $1\frac{1}{2}$ feet high, resting on bedrock. A pyramid of bowlders about 2 feet high was erected over this mark.

Mars Hill (Maine, Aroostook County; J. L. Rannie, 1916).—In Mars Hill Township, about 4 miles east of Mars Hill village, on a very prominent hill known as Mars Hill, which rises 1,200 feet above the surrounding country, and is in the form of a north-and-south ridge about 4 miles long. The station is on the highest peak, and at the south end of the ridge on open bare bedrock.

Station mark: Standard bolt of the Geodetic Survey of Canada set in bedrock.

Andover (New Brunswick, Victoria County; J. L. Rannie, 1916).—In Andover Parish. It is located near the southwestern corner of the parish, about 2 miles north of where Riviere des Chutes crosses the international boundary and 2,000 feet east of the international boundary. The land is owned by Elmer Kennedy, and the station is on top of the hill across the fields from his house, 25 feet from the corner of a cleared field.

Station mark: Standard bolt of the Geodetic Survey of Canada set in an irregular mass of concrete about $1\frac{1}{2}$ feet in diameter and $1\frac{1}{2}$ feet deep, resting on bedrock. A pyramid of bowlders, rising about 2 feet above the surface, was erected over this mark.

Presque Isle (Maine, Aroostook County; J. L. Rannie, 1916).—In Presque Isle Township, lot 61, on land owned in 1916 by Joseph Ireland. It is 2 miles west of Phair, Me., on the east slope of the hill about one-fourth mile back (east) of Mr. Ireland's house. The station is at the north side of a large rock pile.

Station mark: Standard bolt of the Geodetic Survey of Canada set in an irregular mass of concrete whose bottom is about $3\frac{1}{2}$ feet and whose top is about 1 foot below the surface of the ground. A pyramid of bowlders, rising about 2 feet above the surface of the ground, was erected over the mark.

Caribou (Maine, Aroostook County; J. L. Rannie, 1916).—In Caribou Township, on lot 48, owned by Elmer Chesley. The hill is quite prominent and is locally known as "Old Higgins Hill," and is about 6 miles from Fort Fairfield, Me. The hill is partly cleared on top and partly covered with a heavy growth of maple. The station is about 100 feet south of the north line of Chesley's farm and about 300 feet east of the highest point of the hill, and may be reached by taking the lane back from Chesley's house to the top of the hill.

Station mark: Standard bolt of the Geodetic Survey of Canada set in an irregular mass of concrete whose bottom is $3\frac{1}{2}$ feet and top about 1 foot below the surface of the ground. A pyramid of bowlders, rising a foot or two above the surface, was erected over this mark.

Aroostook (New Brunswick, Victoria County; J. L. Rannie, 1916).—In Andover Parish, on land owned by Simon Ayers. This lot is an irregularly shaped unnumbered piece, described on subdivision plans as the Haskel Sloat property. The hill on which the station is located is the highest in this vicinity, bare on top, with solid rock at the surface. It is about three-fourths mile south of the Aroostook River and one-half mile east of the international boundary. The station is 4 miles east of Fort Fairfield, Me., following the road on the south side of the Aroostook River. At the first house after crossing the international boundary, walk back through the fields and straight up the side of the prominent hill.

Station mark: Bronze disk cemented in a drill hole in solid rock.

Limestone (Maine, Aroostook County; J. L. Rannie, 1916).—In Limestone Township, about 2 miles due west of Limestone village and one-fourth mile south of the schoolhouse, in an open field owned by H. Sloan, of Limestone, Me. The station is on level ground, about 450 feet back of the barn and 42 feet south of the center of a lane which leads back from the barn. The distance from the station to the northwest corner of the barn is 437 feet and to the southwest corner of the potato house is 458 feet.

Station mark: Standard copper bolt of the Geodetic Survey of Canada set in an irregular mass of concrete whose bottom is about $3\frac{1}{2}$ feet and top about 1 foot below the surface of the ground. A pyramid of bowlders, rising a foot or two above the surface, was erected over this mark.

Woodland (Maine, Aroostook County; J. L. Rannie, 1916).—In Woodland Township, lot 34, on land owned by Henry Akerson. The station is on top of a cleared hill, the highest within 2 miles, but lower than the hills 3 miles to the westward. Driving from Caribou, Me., about $5\frac{1}{2}$ miles along the New Sweden Road is a small white church on the north side of the road. Follow the side road north from this point past the church about half a mile to the home of Henry Akerson. From Mr. Akerson's house cross the fields to the right to the top of a knoll about 900 feet from the house.

Station mark: Standard copper bolt of the Geodetic Survey of Canada set in an irregular mass of concrete whose bottom is about $3\frac{1}{2}$ feet and top about 1 foot below the surface of the ground. A pyramid of bowlders, rising a foot or two above the surface, was erected over this mark.

Connor (Maine, Aroostook County; J. L. Rannie, 1916).—In Connor Township, on an isolated, prominent hill near the north side of the township. The hill is about 2 miles east of the halfway house (10 miles from Van Buren) on the road between Van Buren, Me., and Caribou, Me. The land is owned by the John B. Madigan interests of Houlton, Me.

Station mark: Standard copper bolt of the Geodetic Survey of Canada set in an irregular mass of concrete whose bottom is about $3\frac{1}{2}$ feet and top about 1 foot below the surface of the ground. A pyramid of bowlders, rising a foot or two above the surface, was erected over this mark.

Caswell (Maine, Aroostook County; J. L. Rannie, 1916).—In Caswell Township, near the rear of lot 41, on land owned by Eugea Berube. The station is on the top of a hill covered with light brush about one-half mile back of Mr. Berube's house. The hill is the highest in the vicinity, but is not especially prominent. It can be plainly seen from the road passing the house.

Station mark: Standard copper bolt of the Geodetic Survey of Canada set in an irregular mass of concrete whose bottom is about $3\frac{1}{2}$ feet and top about 1 foot below the surface of the ground.

Van Buren (Maine, Aroostook County; J. L. Rannie, 1915).—In Van Buren Township, about 5 miles on the Bangor & Aroostook Railroad from the town of Van Buren, on lot 4 of the tier of lots along the south side of the township, about one-fourth mile south of the north side of the lot and 600 feet east of the west side of the lot.

Station mark: Standard copper bolt of the Geodetic Survey of Canada set in an irregular mass of concrete about $1\frac{1}{2}$ feet in diameter and $1\frac{1}{2}$ feet high, resting on bedrock. A pyramid of bowlders, rising about 2 feet above ground, was erected over the mark.

St. Leonard (New Brunswick, Madawaska County; J. L. Rannie, 1915).—In St. Leonard Parish, on or near lot 5 of the third tier of lots northeast of St. Leonard, New Brunswick, on land owned by Charles Cyr, of St. Leonard. The hill on which the station lies is a small titlike point at the southwestern end of a ridge which runs east and west. This small hill is not the highest point on the ridge, a flat maple-covered hill half a mile to the northwest being slightly higher.

Station mark: Standard copper bolt of the Geodetic Survey of Canada set in an irregular mass of concrete whose bottom is about $3\frac{1}{2}$ feet and top about 1 foot below the surface of the ground. A pyramid of bowlders, rising a foot or two above the surface, was erected over this mark.

Grand Isle (Maine, Aroostook County; J. L. Rannie, 1915).—In Grand Isle Township, on a large flat hill covered in 1915 with a heavy growth of large maple, birch, and beech, about $3\frac{1}{2}$ miles west of the eastern boundary of the township and 2 miles north of the southern boundary.

Station mark: Standard copper bolt of the Geodetic Survey of Canada set in an irregular mass of concrete about $1\frac{1}{2}$ feet in diameter and $1\frac{1}{2}$ feet high, resting on bedrock. A pyramid of bowlders, rising about 2 feet above ground, was erected over the mark.

Ste. Anne (New Brunswick, Madawaska County; J. L. Rannie, 1915).—In Ste. Anne Parish, on a bare hill near the rear of the second tier of lots back from the St. John River at Quisibis, New Brunswick.

Station mark: Standard copper bolt of the Geodetic Survey of Canada set in an irregular mass of concrete about 1½ feet in diameter and 1½ feet high, resting on bedrock. A pyramid of bowlders, about 2 feet high, was erected over the mark.

Van Buren South Base (Maine, Aroostook County; J. L. Rannie, 1915).—In Van Buren Township, lot 269, on land owned by Carice Plourde. The station is about 2,300 feet in a southeasterly direction from Mr. Plourde's house, well up the slope of the hills along the St. John River Valley.

Station mark: Standard copper bolt of the Geodetic Survey of Canada set in an irregular mass of concrete about 1½ feet in diameter and 1½ feet high, resting on bedrock. A pyramid of bowlders, rising about 2 feet above the surface of the ground, was erected over this mark.

Van Buren North Base (Maine, Aroostook County; J. L. Rannie, 1915).—In Van Buren Township, on the southeast half of lot 248. The station is about 350 feet northwest of a road which goes to the back settlements from the St. John River Road near Parent Siding and is about 1,900 feet southwest of Parent Siding.

Station mark: Standard copper bolt of the Geodetic Survey of Canada set in a mass of concrete whose bottom is about 3½ feet and top about 1 foot below the surface of the ground. A pyramid of bowlders, rising a foot or two above the surface, was erected over this mark.

Green River (New Brunswick, Madawaska County; J. L. Rannie, 1915).—In St. Basil Parish, on lot 18 of the tier of lots on the east side of Green River, on land owned by Damas Martin. The station is on the highest point of the mountain and is about one-fourth mile from the back or east end of the lot.

Station mark: Standard copper bolt of the Geodetic Survey of Canada set in an irregular mass of concrete about 1½ feet in diameter and 1½ feet high, resting on bedrock. A pyramid of bowlders, about 2 feet high, was erected over the mark.

Madawaska (Maine, Aroostook County; J. L. Rannie, 1915).—In Madawaska Township, on lot 25, near the western end of the lot. The station is situated on a hill about 4 miles south of the village of Madawaska, at an elevation of approximately 700 feet above the river, or 1,200 feet above sea level. The hill is covered with a heavy growth of maple.

Station mark: Standard copper bolt of the Geodetic Survey of Canada set in an irregular mass of concrete about 1½ feet in diameter and 1½ feet high, resting on bedrock. A pyramid of bowlders, about 2 feet high, was piled over the mark.

Edmund (New Brunswick, Madawaska County; J. L. Rannie, 1915).—In St. Jacques Parish, about 3 miles northwest of Edmundston, New Brunswick, on a conical-shaped hill in the Furline settlement. This hill is about 3 miles north of the St. John River and 2 miles west of the Madawaska River.

Station mark: Standard copper bolt of the Geodetic Survey of Canada set in an irregular mass of concrete about 1½ feet in diameter and 1½ feet high, resting on bedrock. A pyramid of small bowlders, about 2 feet high, was erected over the mark.

St. Hilaire (New Brunswick, Madawaska County; J. L. Rannie, 1915).—In St. Hilaire Parish, about 5 miles southwest of Edmundston, New Brunswick, on lot 71, tier 4, of the Ovelet settlement, on land owned by Josephal Daigle. The station is situated on the highest point of a range of hills 1½ miles back from the St. John River.

Station mark: Standard copper bolt of the Geodetic Survey of Canada set in an irregular mass of concrete about 1½ feet in diameter and about 1½ feet high, resting on bedrock. A pyramid of small bowlders, about 2 feet high, was erected over the mark. The southwest corner of lot 18 of the St. John River tier of lots is distant 835 feet, in azimuth 206° 12′ from the station.

Second (Maine, Aroostook County; J. L. Rannie, 1915).—In Madawaska Township, on lot 136, on land owned in 1915 by Remi Herbert, about 1 mile southeast of Madawaska, Me., railroad station. It is about equidistant from the side lines of the lot and about 1 mile south of the St. John River road. The station is situated on the northern slope of the hill in an open field 300 feet north of the woods.

Station mark: Standard copper bolt of the Geodetic Survey of Canada cemented in a hole drilled in a depression, in bedrock, and surrounded by a mass of cement.

First (New Brunswick, Madawaska County; J. L. Rannie, 1915).—In Madawaska Parish, about 1 mile west of Edmundston, New Brunswick, and about one-half mile north of the St. John River. It is on a hill, which is covered with a heavy growth of spruce, near the back of lot 2 of the tier of lots along the St. John River.

Station mark: Standard copper bolt of the Geodetic Survey of Canada set in an irregular mass of concrete about 1½ feet in diameter and 1½ feet high, resting on bedrock. A pyramid of small bowlders, about 2 feet high, was erected over the mark.

Edmundston Astronomic Station (New Brunswick, Madawaska County; J. L. Rannie, 1915).—In the town of Edmundston, New Brunswick, about 40 feet northeast of the water tank of the Temiscouata Railway, and almost directly across the tracks from the Temiscouata Railway station.

Station mark: No mark was placed at the station. It is 300 feet due north of the center of the astronomic pier of 1908, as found in 1915. The astronomic pier of 1908 is of concrete, 2 feet by 3 feet in cross section and about 2 feet in height. It was set 148.30 feet east and 12.04 feet north of the northeast corner of the Temiscouata Railway station. It has apparently settled about 3 inches to the south and 1 inch to the east since 1908.

Baker (New Brunswick, Madawaska County; J. L. Rannie, 1915).—In St. Hilaire Parish, about 10 miles west of Edmundston, New Brunswick, and about 4 miles north of the village of Baker Brook, New Brunswick, on lot 123, tier 4, on land owned by Vene Baker.

Station mark: Standard copper bolt of the Geodetic Survey of Canada set in an irregular mass of concrete about $1\frac{1}{2}$ feet in diameter and $1\frac{1}{2}$ feet high, resting on bedrock. A pyramid of small bowlders, about 2 feet high, was erected over the mark.

Kent (Maine, Aroostook County; J. L. Rannie, 1915).—In Fort Kent Township, about 4 miles east of Fort Kent, Me., and about $2\frac{1}{2}$ miles almost due south of Baker Brook, New Brunswick. It is on the highest part of a clearly defined conical-shaped mountain covered with scrub and some maple trees. The station is on lot 8.

Station mark: Standard copper bolt of the Geodetic Survey of Canada set in an irregular mass of concrete about $1\frac{1}{2}$ feet in diameter and $1\frac{1}{2}$ feet high, resting on bedrock. A pyramid of small bowlders, about 2 feet high, was erected over the mark.

Ledges (Maine, Aroostook County; J. L. Rannie, 1915).—In St. John Township, about $1\frac{1}{2}$ miles south of the railway station in Ledges, New Brunswick, on the easterly half of lot "F," on land owned by Arthur V. Daigle. It is about 250 feet west of the east side of the lot and 1,600 feet north of the range line on the south side of the lot. The post at the southeasterly corner of lot "F" is 1,600 feet distant from the station, in azimuth 342° 40'. The station is on the highest part of the hill, in the first range of hills on the south side of the valley, almost opposite Ledges. The hill is covered with a heavy growth of maple and small birch.

Station mark: Standard copper bolt of the Geodetic Survey of Canada set in an irregular mass of concrete about $1\frac{1}{2}$ feet in diameter and $1\frac{1}{2}$ feet high, resting on bedrock. A pyramid of small bowlders, about 2 feet high, was erected over the mark.

Long (New Brunswick, Madawaska County; J. L. Rannie, 1915).—In St. Francis Township, about 8 miles northwest of Ledges, New Brunswick, and about $2\frac{1}{4}$ miles from Courchesne station on the Canadian National Railway. It is on the highest point of a range of hills on the west side of a brook running into Long Lake, and is about 2 miles south by east of the head of Long Lake.

Station mark: Standard copper bolt of the Geodetic Survey of Canada set in an irregular mass of concrete about $1\frac{1}{2}$ feet in diameter and $1\frac{1}{2}$ feet high, resting on bedrock. A pyramid of small bowlders, rising about 2 feet above ground, was erected over the mark.

Center (New Brunswick, Madawaska County; J. L. Rannie, 1915).—In St. Francis Parish, about 3 miles north and a little west of Connors, New Brunswick, on the highest point of a range of hills which runs north from the St. John River near Connors. This hill is somewhat flat on top and covered with a heavy growth of maple and birch, with some spruce. It is on the second tract of the New Brunswick Railway Co.

Station mark: Standard copper bolt of the Geodetic Survey of Canada set in an irregular mass of concrete, resting on bedrock. A pyramid of small bowlders, about 2 feet high, was erected over the mark.

St. Francis (Maine, Aroostook County; J. L. Rannie, 1915).—In St. Francis Township, about 2 miles east of the village of St. Francis, Me., and about 1 mile south of the St. John River. It is on the highest point of a ridge which is covered with maple and other small growth, almost opposite the mouth of the St. Francis River.

Station mark: Standard copper bolt of the Geodetic Survey of Canada set in an irregular mass of concrete about $1\frac{1}{2}$ feet in diameter and $1\frac{1}{2}$ feet high, resting on bedrock. A pyramid of small bowlders, about 2 feet high, was erected over the mark.

Canadian Glazier (New Brunswick, Madawaska County; J. L. Rannie, 1915).—In St. Francis Parish on the second tract of the Canadian National Railway, about 4 miles northeast of the head of Glazier Lake, on the highest point in the immediate vicinity, covered with a growth of maple, birch, spruce, and balsam.

Station mark: Standard copper bolt of the Geodetic Survey of Canada set in an irregular mass of concrete about $1\frac{1}{2}$ feet in diameter and $1\frac{1}{2}$ feet high, resting on bedrock. A pyramid of small bowlders, about 2 feet high, was erected over the mark.

U. S. Glazier (Maine, Aroostook County; J. L. Rannie, 1915).—About 1¾ miles west of the head of Glazier Lake, on top of a conical-shaped mountain, the highest point in the vicinity. The mountain is visible from the flat at the mouth of American Touladi Creek, and bears south 85° west, magnetic.

Station mark: Standard copper bolt of the Geodetic Survey of Canada set in an irregular mass of concrete about 1½ feet in diameter and 1½ feet high, resting on bedrock. A pyramid of small bowlders, about 1½ feet high, was erected over the mark.

Canadian Beau (Quebec, Temiscouata County; J. L. Rannie, 1915).—In Botsford Township, on lot 37, Concession I, on the highest point of a ridge roughly parallel to the shore of Beau Lake, about 1 mile from the east shore and about 3 miles south of the head of the lake. The station is 245 feet south and 820 feet west of the north and east sides, respectively, of lot 37. The southeast corner of lot 34, range 1, is distant 2,120 feet in azimuth 202° 55′ from the station.

Station mark: Standard copper bolt of the Geodetic Survey of Canada set in a bowlder.

U. S. Beau (Maine, Aroostook County; J. L. Rannie, 1915).—In township 19, range 11, about 3 miles west of the head of Beau Lake, about 1 mile south of Jones Lake and 2 miles northwest of Mud Lake, on the highest hill in the vicinity. This hill has a conical or sugar-loaf form, with steep sides, and is covered with maple, birch, and spruce. The station is about one-half mile south of the line between townships 19 and 20.

Station mark: Standard copper bolt of the Geodetic Survey of Canada set in a mass of concrete about 1½ feet in diameter and 1½ feet high, resting on bedrock. A pyramid of small bowlders, about 2 feet high, was erected over the mark.

Blue River (Quebec, Temiscouata County; J. L. Rannie, 1915).—In Botsford Township, about 1¼ miles southeast of the town of Blue River, Quebec, almost on the line between lots 1 and 2 of range 1, and about 2,500 feet west of the line between ranges 1 and 2. It is on a projecting rocky shoulder of the ridge which extends southeast from the village of Blue River. It is about 1,400 feet east of the main road south from Blue River to Beau Lake.

Station mark: Standard copper bolt of the Geodetic Survey of Canada set in bedrock.

Estcourt (Quebec, Temiscouata County; J. L. Rannie, 1915).—In Estcourt Township, near the line between ranges 1 and 2, probably on lot 4, range 1. It is on the southwest slope back from the top of the first hill of a range running northeast from Lake Pohenagamook, about one-half mile back of the steep part, in a heavy tangle of burned-over spruce and birch. The church at St. Eleuthere is about 2 miles distant, in azimuth 92° 31′ 35″ from the station.

Station mark: Standard copper bolt of the Geodetic Survey of Canada set in bedrock.

Frontier (Quebec, Kamouraska County; Maine, Aroostook County; Geodetic Survey of Canada, 1912; J. L. Rannie, 1915).—The station is 8 miles along the international boundary southwest from Estcourt, Quebec.

Station mark: Monument No. 189 of the international boundary.

Parke (Quebec, Kamouraska County; Geodetic Survey of Canada, 1912; J. L. Rannie, 1915).—In Parke Township, on lot 31, range 8, about 580 feet northwest of the line between Parke and Pohenagamook Townships and about 400 feet southwest of line between lots 30 and 31. A post on the line between the above townships, marked "VII" on the southwest side and "A" on the northeast side, is situated about 4,800 feet southwest of Pelletier railway station. From this post "Parke" is about 19,380 feet in the direction of the township line (northeast) and about 580 feet northwest of (or at right angles to) this line. The azimuth from the above post to the triangulation station is 222° 50′.

Station mark: Standard copper bolt of the Geodetic Survey of Canada.

Chabot (Quebec, Kamouraska County; J. L. Rannie, 1915).—In Chabot Township, on lot 55, range 4, about 8 miles northeast of St. Eleuthere, on a hill covered with birch and spruce, 75 feet from the northeast and 3,410 feet from the southeast side of lot 55, on land owned by Francois Michaud.

Station mark: Standard copper bolt of the Geodetic Survey of Canada set in bedrock. The post on the line between ranges 4 and 5 and between the townships of Chabot and Pohenagamook is distant 3,540 feet, in azimuth 299° 45′, from the station.

Monument 1 (initial monument; Maine, Aroostook County; New Brunswick, York County; United States Coast and Geodetic Survey, 1889; J. L. Rannie, 1916).—This is international boundary monument No. 1, also known as "initial monument," at the head of the St. Croix River and the southern end of the "North Line." The shaft of the monument is of cast iron, 12 inches square at the base, 6 inches square at the top, and 5.4 feet high above the base. The base is of concrete, 5 feet square and 5 feet high above the ground. The shaft leans 1⅝ inches west and 2 inches south.

The station is the center of the iron shaft where it joins the concrete base.

Westford (Maine, Aroostook County; J. L. Rannie, 1916).—In Hodgdon Township, on lot 8, range 5, on the farm of Murray Esterbrook. It is about 600 feet south of the highest part of a prominent hill known as "Westford Hill." The station occupies the point of a small rock outcrop about 900 feet northwest of the farm buildings.

Station mark: A bronze plug cemeted in the solid rock outcrop.

Porter (Maine, Aroostook County; J. L. Rannie, 1916).—In Monticello Township, on lot 68, on land owned by Mrs. Burleigh Porter. The station lies on the southerly slope of a rise about 300 feet south of and 4 feet lower than the top of the hill, on the north side of a large stone pile in a cultivated field, one-fourth mile north of Mrs. Porter's house.

Station mark: Standard bolt of the Geodetic Survey of Canada set in an irregular mass of concrete whose bottom is about 3½ feet and top about 1 foot below the surface of the ground. A pyramid of bowlders, rising a foot or two above the surface, was erected over this mark.

Lunnon (Maine, Aroostook County; J. L. Rannie, 1916).—In Monticello Township, on land owned by William London. The station is on top of a bare hill, in a cultivated field about 1½ miles south and 2¼ miles east of the village of Monticello, Me., and about 1,000 feet west of the branch of the Meduxnekeag River, which flows through Monticello village.

Station mark: Bronze disk set in solid rock.

Easton (Maine, Aroostook County; J. L. Rannie, 1916).—In Easton Township, near the south side of lot 20, on land owned by H. P. Hoyt. To reach the station from Fairmont, Me., go south about a mile to the first turn to the left (east). Follow this road about 1½ miles to the top of a cleared hill. The station is on the east slope of this hill, about 450 feet from the road, on an outcropping ledge of rock.

Station mark: Bronze disk cemented in the rock.

Watson (Maine, Aroostook County; J. L. Rannie, 1916).—In Fort Fairfield Township, on lot 26 or 28, on land owned by Alvie Spiney. The station may be found by following the Presque Isle road from Fort Fairfield, Me., for one-half mile and taking the first turn to the right (west). After following this road for about 3 miles, one passes over a cleared hill. The station is about 900 feet up the hill, through the fields to the left (south), on a ledge of rock on top of a cleared hill.

Station mark: Bronze disk cemented in an outcropping ledge of rock.

Falls (New Brunswick, Victoria County; J. L. Rannie, 1916).—In Grand Falls Parish, in the California settlement, on one of the lots 38 to 41. It lies in the center of a rock pile on the highest point of a prominent bare hill known as Old Langly Hill, owned by Sandy Hearsy, of Fort Fairfield, Me. The hill is about 1 mile east of the international boundary. The station is 9 miles from Aroostook Junction, New Brunswick, by the road through Four Falls north to the California settlement; or from Limestone, Me., it is 2½ miles south from the village, then about 3 or 4 miles east on the road to Four Falls, New Brunswick.

Station mark: Bronze disk set in cement in a rock pile.

Grand (New Brunswick, Madawaska County; J. L. Rannie, 1916).—In St. Andre Parish, on lot 151 of the tier of St. John River lots, on land owned by Noel B. Gervais. The station is near the top of the ridge in a cleared field about a mile back (northeast) from the St. John River road.

Station mark: Standard copper bolt of the Geodetic Survey of Canada set in an irregular mass of concrete whose bottom is about 3½ feet and top 1 foot below the surface of the ground. A pyramid of bowlders, rising a foot or two above the surface, was erected over this mark.

Hamlin (Maine, Aroostook County; J. L. Rannie, 1916).—In Hamlin Township, on the southeast side of lot 319, owned by Joseph Langlais, on the line between lot 319 and the one to the southeast.

Station mark: Bronze disk set in cement in rocks forming the foundation of the loose rubble wall separating the two lots.

Cyr (New Brunswick, Madawaska County; J. L. Rannie, 1916).—In St. Leonard Parish, on lot 134, of the tier of St. John River lots, on land owned by John Cyr. The station may be reached from St. Leonard, New Brunswick, by driving 5 miles toward Grand Falls, New Brunswick, to the house of John Cyr. The station is on the top of a bare hill (wooded to the north) about half a mile back (northeast) of Mr. Cyr's house.

Station mark: Standard copper bolt of the Geodetic Survey of Canada set in an irregular mass of concrete about 1½ feet in diameter and about 1½ feet deep, resting on bedrock. A pyramid of bowlders, 2 feet high, was erected over the mark.

Edmundston Bench Mark (New Brunswick, Madawaska County; J. L. Rannie, 1915).—At Edmundston, New Brunswick, in the face of the rock cut at the north side of the railway track, 140 feet west of the Canadian Pacific Railway station.

Station mark: Bench mark bolt of the Geodetic Survey of Canada, stamped "B. M. No. 60 B."

Clair (New Brunswick, Madawaska County; J. L. Rannie, 1915).—In St. Francis Parish, about 2½ miles west of Fort Kent, Me., and about 1½ miles north of the St. John River. It is on Clair Mountain, which is the highest of the bordering hills on the north side of the St. John Valley, between Ledges and Clair, New Brunswick. The station is on the highest part of the flat top of the hill, somewhat nearer the south slope.

Station mark: Standard copper bolt of the Geodetic Survey of Canada set in an irregular mass of concrete about 1½ feet in diameter and 1½ feet high, resting on bedrock. A pyramid of small bowlders, about 2 feet high, was erected over the mark.

Fort (Maine, Aroostook County; J. L. Rannie, 1915).—In Fort Kent Township, on lot 27, about $2\frac{1}{2}$ miles southwest of Fort Kent, Me. It is on the northerly slope of some low hills on the south side of the St. John Valley. The station is beside a fence in an open field, 3 feet east of the west side of lot 27 and 3,990 feet south of the northwesterly corner of lot 26.

Station mark: Standard copper bolt of the Geodetic Survey of Canada set in an irregular mass of concrete about $1\frac{1}{2}$ feet in diameter and $1\frac{1}{2}$ feet high, resting on bedrock. A pyramid of small bowlders, about 2 feet high, was erected over the mark.

Baker Brook Bench Mark (New Brunswick, Madawaska County; J. L. Rannie, 1915).—About one-fourth mile west of Baker Brook, New Brunswick. It is in the east face of the concrete retaining wall behind the east abutment of the plate-girder bridge on the Canadian National Railway, and is north of the railway track.

Station mark: Bench-mark bolt of the Geodetic Survey of Canada, stamped "No. 264 B."

Twin (Maine, Aroostook County; J. L. Rannie, 1915).—On the west side of and about $1\frac{1}{2}$ miles from the head of Glazier Lake, on the highest part of the mountain, which is conical in shape and rises sharply out of a valley.

Station mark: Standard copper bolt of the Geodetic Survey of Canada set in a large bowlder and surrounded by a triangle chiseled in the rock.

Dave (Quebec, Temiscouata County; J. L. Rannie, 1915).—In Estcourt Township, about $2\frac{1}{2}$ miles west of Blue River, Quebec, about 750 feet north of the main road from Blue River to Estcourt, on lot 57, range 4, and about 450 feet south of the line between lots 56 and 57. It is on the southwest slope of a round cleared shoulder of a hill about one-fourth mile northwest from the house on lot 57.

Station mark: Standard copper bolt of the Geodetic Survey of Canada set in a large bowlder.

REFERENCE MONUMENTS DETERMINED FROM MINOR SCHEME, ST. JOHN RIVER

Reference Monument C–1 (New Brunswick, Madawaska County; F. H. Brundage, 1917).—About 3 miles southeast of Martins, a post office and station on the Canadian National Railway. It is directly across the St. John River from monument 117, 45 feet back from the top of the Canadian Pacific Railway cut, and 5 feet inside the right-of-way fence.

Station mark: Standard bronze disk set in a 3-foot concrete post whose top surface, 12 inches square, is flush with the surface of the ground.

Reference Monument S–1 (Maine, Aroostook County; F. H. Brundage, 1917).—About 2 miles southeast of Hamlin, Me., post office. It is 410 feet up river from monument 117 and 8 feet from the top of the high bank along the St. John River.

Station mark: Standard bronze disk set in a 3-foot concrete post whose top surface, 12 inches square, is flush with the surface of the ground.

Reference Monument C–2 (New Brunswick, Madawaska County; F. H. Brundage, 1917).—About $2\frac{1}{2}$ miles southeast of Martins, a post office and station on the Canadian National Railway. It is directly across the river from S–2, a large reference monument. It is at the top of the river bank, south of the Canadian Pacific Railway, and about 6 feet inside of the right-of-way fence.

Station mark: Standard bronze disk set in a 3-foot concrete post whose top surface, 12 inches square, is flush with the surface of the ground.

Reference Monument C–4 (New Brunswick, Madawaska County; F. H. Brundage, 1917).—About 2 miles southeast of Martins, a post office and station on the Canadian National Railway. It is directly across the river from S–4, a large reference monument. It is 114 feet down river from the center of a concrete culvert under the Canadian Pacific Railway. It is on the north side of the railway track, 4 feet inside the right-of-way fence.

Station mark: Standard bronze disk set in a 3-foot concrete post whose top surface, 12 inches square, is flush with the surface of the ground.

Reference Monument C–5 (New Brunswick, Madawaska County; F. H. Brundage, 1917).—About $1\frac{1}{2}$ miles southeast of Martins, a post office and station on the Canadian National Railway. It is about 180 feet upstream from the upstream end of a Canadian Pacific Railway trestle. It is on the north side of the railway, 1.5 feet inside the right-of-way fence, and 8 feet upstream from a gate in the fence.

Station mark: Standard bronze disk set in a 3-foot concrete post whose top surface, 12 inches square, is flush with the surface of the ground.

Reference Monument C–6 (New Brunswick, Madawaska County; F. H. Brundage, 1917).—About three-fourths mile southeast of Martins, a post office and station on the Canadian National Railway. It is on the north side of the Canadian Pacific Railway, 2 feet inside the right-of-way fence. It is 29.5 feet upstream from a fence which runs north to a point near the Canadian National Railway crossing of the main highway.

Station mark: Standard bronze disk set in a 3-foot concrete post whose top surface, 12 inches square, is flush with the surface of the ground.

Reference Monument C–8 (New Brunswick, Madawaska County; F. H. Brundage, 1917).—Opposite the middle of Ryan or Six-Mile Island. It is on the north side of the Canadian Pacific Railway, and 2 feet inside the right-of-way fence.

Station mark: Standard bronze disk set in a 3-foot concrete post whose top surface, 12 inches square, is flush with the surface of the ground.

Reference Monument C–9 (New Brunswick, Madawaska County; F. H. Brundage, 1917).—About 1 mile upriver from Martins, a post office and station on the Canadian National Railway. It is on the Canadian National Railway right of way, at the top of a deep cut, and is 2 feet inside the fence on the river side of the track.

Station mark: Standard bronze disk set in a 3-foot concrete post whose top surface, 12 inches square, is flush with the surface of the ground.

Reference Monument C–10 (New Brunswick, Madawaska County; F. H. Brundage, 1917).—About 1¼ miles upriver from Martins, a post office and station on the Canadian National Railway. It is nearly opposite S–11, a large reference monument. It is on a low knoll, 77 feet from the shore of the St. John River and 2 feet upriver from a fence.

Station mark: Standard bronze disk set in a 3-foot concrete post whose top surface, 12 inches square, is flush with the surface of the ground.

Reference Monument C–12 (New Brunswick, Madawaska County; F. H. Brundage, 1917).—About 4½ miles southeast of St. Leonard, New Brunswick. It is directly across the St. John River from S–13, a large reference monument. It is 50 feet from the river and 10 feet lower than the top of the bank.

Station mark: Standard bronze disk set in a 3-foot concrete post whose top surface, 12 inches square, is flush with the surface of the ground.

Reference Monument C–13 (New Brunswick, Madawaska County; F. H. Brundage, 1917).—About 4¼ miles southeast of St. Leonard, New Brunswick. It is directly across the St. John River from S–14, a large reference monument. It is 2 feet upriver from a fence which separates two farms, and 8 feet from the top of the river bank.

Station mark: Standard bronze disk set in a 3-foot concrete post whose top surface, 12 inches square, is flush with the surface of the ground.

Reference Monument C–14 (New Brunswick, Madawaska County; F. H. Brundage, 1917).—About 4 miles southeast of St. Leonard, New Brunswick. It is directly across the St. John River from S–15, a large reference monument. It is 2 feet upriver from an old rail fence and 10 feet from the top of the high river bank.

Station mark: Standard bronze disk set in a 3-foot concrete post whose top surface, 12 inches square, is flush with the surface of the ground.

Reference Monument C–15 (New Brunswick, Madawaska County; F. H. Brundage, 1917).—About 3¾ miles southeast of St. Leonard, New Brunswick. It is about 800 feet down river from the mouth of Nine Brooks Creek and directly across the St. John River from S–16, a large reference monument. It is on the top of the high river bank, 1 foot upriver from a fence.

Station mark: Standard bronze disk set in a 3-foot concrete post whose top surface, 12 inches square, is flush with the surface of the ground.

Reference Monument C–16 (New Brunswick, Madawaska County; F. H. Brundage, 1917).—About 3¼ miles southeast of St. Leonard, New Brunswick. It is about 2,000 feet upriver from the mouth of Nine Brooks Creek and about 800 feet down river from the foot of Kings Island. It is 1 foot inside the Canadian Pacific Railway right-of-way fence on the river side of the track, and about 235 feet down river from an old road leading to an abandoned ferry.

Station mark: Standard bronze disk set in a 3-foot concrete post whose top surface, 12 inches square is flush with the surface of the ground.

Reference Monument C–18 (New Brunswick, Madawaska County; F. H. Brundage, 1917).—About 2 miles southeast of St. Leonard, New Brunswick, and about three-fourths mile down river from the church at L'Eglise. It is on the Canadian National Railway right of way, 1.5 feet inside the fence, and 75 feet upriver from the point where this railway and the Canadian Pacific have a right-of-way fence in common.

Station mark: Standard bronze disk set in a 3-foot concrete post whose top surface, 12 inches square, is flush with the surface of the ground.

Reference Monument C–19 (New Brunswick, Madawaska County; F. H. Brundage, 1917).—About 1½ miles southeast of St. Leonard, New Brunswick, and one-half mile down river from the church at L'Eglise. It is 1.5 feet inside the right-of-way fence of the Canadian National Railway, on the side of the track next to the highway.

Station mark: Standard bronze disk set in a 3-foot concrete post whose top surface, 12 inches square, is flush with the surface of the ground.

Reference Monument C–20 (New Brunswick, Madawaska County; F. H. Brundage, 1917).—About 1 mile southeast of St. Leonard, New Brunswick, and about 1,200 feet upriver from the church at L'Eglise. It is between the highway and the Canadian National Railway, at the top of the steep bank which slopes down to the track, 3 feet outside the railway fence and 3 feet upriver from an old rail fence which separates two farms.

Station mark: Standard bronze disk set in a 3-foot concrete post whose top surface, 12 inches square, is flush with the surface of the ground.

Reference Monument C–21 (New Brunswick, Madawaska County; F. H. Brundage, 1917).—About one-half mile southeast of the Van Buren-St. Leonard highway bridge. It is about 400 feet from the Canadian National Railway and is between it and the river. It is about 400 feet upriver from a small cemetery and 2 feet toward the river from a rail fence which parallels the river.

Station mark: Standard bronze disk set in a 3-foot concrete post whose top surface, 12 inches square, is flush with the surface of the ground.

Van Buren, Me., Highway Bridge Boundary Point.—On the international highway bridge which crosses the St. John River between Van Buren, Me., and St. Leonard, New Brunswick. The middle of the downstream face of a vertical post of the downstream bridge truss at the height of the railing. This vertical member of the truss is 102.3 feet from the center of the pier supporting the United States end of the main span and 222.8 feet from the pier supporting the Canadian end. A white line was painted on the post at the point described.

Reference Monument C–23 (New Brunswick, Madawaska County; F. H. Brundage, 1917).—Directly across the St. John River from St. Bruno's Catholic Church in Van Buren, Me. It is at the edge of a road which leads to an old ferry and which at this point is parallel to the river. It is on the side of the road next to the river and is about 230 feet northwest of the railroad crossing.

Station mark: Standard bronze disk set in a 3-foot concrete post whose top surface, 12 inches square, is flush with the surface of the ground.

Reference Monument S–25 (Maine, Aroostook County; F. H. Brundage, 1917).—About halfway between the highway bridge and the railroad bridge at Van Buren, Me. It is between the Bangor & Aroostook Railroad and the river, about 130 feet from the railroad and about 280 feet from the river. It is 1.5 feet down river from a log fence.

Station mark: Standard bronze disk set in a 3-foot concrete post whose top surface, 12 inches square, is flush with the surface of the ground.

Reference Monument C–24 (New Brunswick, Madawaska County; F. H. Brundage, 1917).—About 1,900 feet down river from the railroad bridge which crosses the St. John River just north of Van Buren, Me. It is 510 feet down river from a road which leads to an old ferry. It is at the edge of a plowed field, 4 feet from the edge of the high bank of the river.

Station mark: Standard bronze disk set in a 3-foot concrete post whose top surface, 12 inches square, is flush with the surface of the ground.

Reference Monument C–25 (New Brunswick, Madawaska County; F. H. Brundage, 1917).—About 600 feet upriver from the railroad bridge which crosses the St. John River just north of Van Buren, Me. It is 10 feet from the top of the high bank of the river.

Station mark: Standard bronze disk set in a 3-foot concrete post whose top surface, 12 inches square, is flush with the surface of the ground.

Keegan, Me., Railroad Bridge Boundary Point.—On the railroad bridge which crosses the St. John River near Keegan, Me. It is the middle of the upstream face of the middle vertical member of the upstream truss of the middle span. The point is marked by a patch of white paint about 7 inches square.

Reference Monument C–27 (New Brunswick, Madawaska County; F. H. Brundage, 1917).—About 900 feet down river from the mouth of Grand River, which flows into the St. John River opposite Keegan, Me. It is directly across the river from S–29, a large reference monument. It is 10 feet back from the top of the river bank.

Station mark: Standard bronze disk set in a 3-foot concrete post whose top surface, 12 inches square, is flush with the surface of the ground.

Reference Monument C–28 (New Brunswick, Madawaska County; F. H. Brundage, 1917).—Directly across the St. John River from Keegan, Me., and about 1,000 feet upriver from the mouth of Grand River. It is about 120 feet from the St. John River on the high ground between the river and a long narrow pond.

Station mark: Standard bronze disk set in a 3-foot concrete post whose top surface, 12 inches square, is flush with the surface of the ground.

Reference Monument C–29 (New Brunswick, Madawaska County; F. H. Brundage, 1917).—Directly opposite the middle of the first island just above Keegan, Me. It is at the top of the river bank about 60 feet from the water's edge.

Station mark: Standard bronze disk set in a 3-foot concrete post whose top surface, 12 inches square, is flush with the surface of the ground.

Reference Monument S–31 (Maine, Aroostook County; F. H. Brundage, 1917).—About one-half mile upriver from Keegan, Me., opposite the foot of the upper island of Les Trois Isles. It is 15 feet back from the top of the high river bank. A reference mark, consisting of an iron pin, whose top is flush with the surface of the ground, is distant 5.76 feet on the line to reference monument C–29.

Station mark: Standard bronze disk set in a 3-foot concrete post whose top surface, 12 inches square, is flush with the surface of the ground.

Reference Monument C–30 (New Brunswick, Madawaska County; F. H. Brundage, 1917).—About one-half mile north of the mill at Keegan, Me. It is about 250 feet upriver from the head of the upper island of the group known as Les Trois Isles. It is at the top of the river bank and about 40 feet from the water's edge.

Station mark: Standard bronze disk set in a 3-foot concrete post whose top surface, 12 inches square, is flush with the surface of the ground.

Reference Monument C–31 (New Brunswick, Madawaska County; F. H. Brundage, 1917).—About one-half mile south of Siegas, New Brunswick. It is on the edge of the high river bank, about 850 feet downstream from the mouth of the Siegas River and just upstream from a small ravine.

Station mark: Standard bronze disk set in a 3-foot concrete post whose top surface, 12 inches square, is flush with the surface of the ground.

Reference Monument S–34 (Maine, Aroostook County; F. H. Brundage, 1917).—About 2 miles northwest of Keegan, Me. It is on the down river edge of the road leading from Violette, a flag station on the Bangor & Aroostook Railroad, to the Van Buren-Fort Kent highway. It is just inside the railroad right-of-way fence and is on the south side of the railway track.

Station mark: Standard bronze disk set in a 3-foot concrete post whose top surface, 12 inches square, is flush with the surface of the ground.

Reference Monument C–33 (New Brunswick, Madawaska County; F. H. Brundage, 1917).—About three-fourths mile west of Siegas, New Brunswick. It is on the edge of the high bank of the St. John River, about 3,000 feet upstream from the mouth of Siegas River and just downstream from a small ravine.

Station mark: Standard bronze disk set in a 3-foot concrete post whose top surface, 12 inches square, is flush with the surface of the ground.

Reference Monument C–34 (New Brunswick, Madawaska County; F. H. Brundage, 1917).—About 1 mile west of Siegas, New Brunswick. It is about 800 feet upstream from the foot of the lower part of La Septieme Isle, about 50 feet down river from a deep ravine, and about 160 feet from the water's edge.

Station mark: Standard bronze disk set in a 3-foot concrete post whose top surface, 12 inches square, is flush with the surface of the ground.

Reference Monument C–35 (New Brunswick, Madawaska County; F. H. Brundage, 1917).—About 1½ miles northwest of Siegas, New Brunswick. It is between the Canadian National Railway and the St. John River, directly opposite the point where the highway crosses the Canadian Pacific Railway. It is close to a fence which runs from the river to the Canadian Pacific Railway, and is about 90 feet from the track of the Canadian National Railway.

Station mark: Standard bronze disk set in a 3-foot concrete post whose top surface, 12 inches square, is flush with the surface of the ground.

Reference Monument C–36 (New Brunswick, Madawaska County; F. H. Brundage, 1917).—About 1 mile downstream from the church at Ste. Anne de Madawaska. It is near the support on the Canadian shore of the ferry near Parent Siding, Me , a station on the Bangor & Aroostook Railroad. It is 2 feet east of a fence on the line between two farms and about 150 feet from the river.

Station mark: Standard bronze disk set in a 3-foot concrete post whose top surface, 12 inches square, is flush with the surface of the ground.

Reference Monument C–38 (New Brunswick, Madawaska County; F. H. Brundage, 1917).—About one-half mile down river from Quisibis, New Brunswick, a station on the Canadian National Railway. It is about 700 feet upstream from the Canadian National Railway bridge across Quisibis River, and is between the river and the railway, 1 foot outside of the right-of-way fence.

Station mark: Standard bronze disk set in a 3-foot concrete post whose top surface, 12 inches square, is flush with the surface of the ground.

Reference Monument C-40 (New Brunswick, Madawaska County; F. H. Brundage, 1917).—About three-fourths mile downstream from Theriault, New Brunswick, a station on the Canadian National Railway. It is on the line between two farms and is about 50 feet back from the top of the steep bank of the St. John River.

Station mark: Standard bronze disk set in a 3-foot concrete post whose top surface, 12 inches square, is flush with the surface of the ground.

Reference Monument C-42 (New Brunswick, Madawaska County; F. H. Brundage, 1917).—About 1 mile northwest of Lille, Me., and about 1,100 feet downstream from the foot of Thibadeau Island. It is on the line between two farms and is near the top of a steep bank about 500 feet back from the St. John River.

Station mark: Standard bronze disk set in a 3-foot concrete post whose top surface, 12 inches square, is flush with the surface of the ground.

Reference Monument C-46 (New Brunswick, Madawaska County; F. H. Brundage, 1917).—About 2 miles northwest of Green River, New Brunswick. It is on the line between two farms and is about 20 feet back from the top of the high bank of the St. John River.

Station mark: Standard bronze disk set in a 3-foot concrete post whose top surface, 12 inches square, is flush with the surface of the ground.

Reference Monument 134-A (New Brunswick, Madawaska County; F. H. Brundage, 1917).—About 1 mile upriver from St. Basil, New Brunswick, near the center of a small island whose flat surface is about 5 feet above the level of the St. John River at its ordinary stage.

Station mark: Standard 8-inch bronze post set in a 3-foot concrete post whose top surface, 12 inches square, is flush with the surface of the ground.

Reference Monument C-51 (New Brunswick, Madawaska County; F. H. Brundage, 1917).—About three-eighths mile upstream from the church at St. Basil, New Brunswick. It is about 300 feet north of the Canadian Pacific Railway and 30 feet southwest of the southwest corner of a large barn. It is in a jog in an east-and-west rail fence.

Station mark: Standard bronze disk set in a 3-foot concrete post whose top surface, 12 inches square, is flush with the surface of the ground.

Reference Monument C-57 (New Brunswick, Madawaska County; F. H. Brundage, 1917).—In the field in which the Edmundston cemetery is located, about three-fourths mile upriver from Edmundston, New Brunswick, and about 600 feet north of the highway. It is at the north edge of the clearing about midway between the north and south boundaries of the field.

Station mark: Standard bronze disk set in a 3-foot concrete post whose top surface, 12 inches square, is flush with the surface of the ground.

Reference Monument C-58 (New Brunswick, Madawaska County; F. H. Brundage, 1917).—About 1 mile upriver from Edmundston, New Brunswick, and about 2,000 feet down river from the mouth of Two Mile Brook. It is between the Temiscouata Railway and the main highway along the St. John River, at the top of the high railroad cut, close to the right-of-way fence.

Station mark: Standard bronze disk set in a 3-foot concrete post whose top surface, 12 inches square, is flush with the surface of the ground.

Reference Monument C-65 (New Brunswick, Madawaska County; F. H. Brundage, 1917).—About 1½ miles north of St. Hilaire, New Brunswick, and about 700 feet west of the highway along the St. John River. It is about 850 feet upriver from C-64, a large reference monument, and is at an elevation of about 15 feet above it.

Station mark: Standard bronze disk set in a 3-foot concrete post whose top surface, 12 inches square, is flush with the surface of the ground.

Reference Monument 151-A (New Brunswick, Madawaska County; F. H. Brundage, 1917).—About one-fourth mile southeast of Baker Brook, New Brunswick, on the highest part of a low island in the St. John River just below Baker Island. The island is entirely under water during the spring floods.

Station mark: Standard 8-inch bronze post set in a 3-foot concrete post whose top surface, 12 inches square, is flush with the surface of the ground.

Reference Monument 159-A (New Brunswick, Madawaska County; F. H. Brundage, 1917).—About 1 mile southwest of Ledges, New Brunswick, and about one-half mile downstream from Savage Island. It is on the farthest rock downstream of a group of three rocks in the St. John River, all on the Canadian side of the boundary.

Station mark: Standard 8-inch bronze post set in a hole drilled in the rock. The mark was set in a depression in the rock as a protection against floating ice and logs.

Reference Monument 159-B (Maine, Aroostook County; F. H. Brundage, 1917).—About 1 mile southwest of Ledges, New Brunswick, and about one-half mile downstream from Savage Island. It is on the rock in the St. John River nearest the United States shore, about 250 feet south of reference monument 159–A.

Station mark: Standard 8-inch bronze post set in a hole drilled in the rock. The mark was set in a pothole about 2 feet deep as a protection against floating ice and logs.

Reference Monument 163-A (New Brunswick, Madawaska County; F. H. Brundage, 1917).—About 1½ miles down river from Wheelock, Me., on the highest part of a long, low island near the Canadian shore.

Station mark: Standard 8-inch bronze post set in a 3-foot concrete post whose top surface, 12 inches square, is flush with the surface of the ground.

Reference Monument S-115 (Maine, Aroostook County; F. H. Brundage, 1917).—About three-fourths mile north of St. Francis, Me., on the southwest bank of the St. Francis River, near its mouth. It is opposite the southwest end of Kendall Island, 38 feet from the water's edge and about 15 feet in elevation above the surface of the river at an ordinary stage. It is at the edge of small second-growth birches and poplars.

Station mark: Standard bronze disk set in a 3-foot concrete post whose top surface, 12 inches square, is flush with the surface of the ground.

LAKE POHENAGAMOOK TO VERMONT-QUEBEC BOUNDARY, MAJOR SCHEME

Leverrier (Quebec, L'Islet County; Geodetic Survey of Canada, 1914; Jesse Hill, 1922).—In Leverrier Township, near the southerly corner, 4 miles northeast of Lac Frontiere, Quebec, on the highest point of a rounded hill known as Sugar Loaf.

Station mark: A three-fourths-inch copper bolt leaded in a drill hole in rock. Three reference bolts are leaded in drill holes in bowlders, as follows: No. 1, azimuth 223° 49′, distance 60.20 feet; No. 2, azimuth 291° 30′, distance 81.08 feet; and No. 3, azimuth 318° 08′, distance 73.80 feet. Monument 269 is 768.33 feet distant in azimuth 320° 09′ 28″, from the station.

Talon (Quebec, Montmagny County; Geodetic Survey of Canada, 1914; Jesse Hill, 1922).—In Talon Township, about 6 miles northwest of Lac Frontiere, Quebec, on the summit of a high detached mountain. The station is about 10 feet east of the highest point, on bare rock.

Station mark: A three-fourths-inch copper bolt leaded in a drill hole in rock.

Standon (Quebec, Dorchester County; Geodetic Survey of Canada, 1914; Jesse Hill, 1922).—On lot 3, range 14, of Standon Township, about 6 miles south of St. Philemon, Quebec, and 15 miles northwest of St. Camille, Quebec, on the summit of a large, high, wooded mountain with steep sides. The station is on the highest part of the mountain, from which three spurs run, one northwest, one east, and one south.

Station mark: A three-fourths-inch copper bolt leaded in rock from which the loam has been removed.

Bonnet (Quebec, Bellechasse County; Jesse Hill, 1922).—In Roux Township, 3½ miles southwest of St. Magloire, Quebec, 7 miles northwest of St. Camille, Quebec, on an isolated peak called Mount Bonnet, which has a large cross erected on its summit. The station is on the highest point of the top on bare rock.

Station mark: The center of the base of the cross which is set in the rock. The reference mark is a bronze disk set in cement in a depression in the rock, distant 6.43 feet, in azimuth 299° 02′, from the center of the station.

Hardwood Mountain (Maine, Somerset County; Jesse Hill, 1922).—In township 9, range 18, on the summit of Hardwood Mountain, about 1¾ miles east of the point where the South Line intersects the Southwest Branch of the St. John River. The station is the center of a fire lookout tower about 80 feet high.

Station mark: A bronze disk set in a concrete base. Distances to the inside corners of the four foundation piers of the tower are as follows: Northwest pier, 7.45 feet; northeast pier, 7.35 feet; southeast pier, 7.20 feet; southwest pier, 7.35 feet.

Maheux (Quebec, Beauce County; Jesse Hill, 1922).—In Metgermette North Township, 4½ miles east of St. Zacharie, Quebec, about one-third mile south from the right-angle turn in the road, about 1 mile west of the Southwest Branch of the St. John River. The station is about 200 feet west of the road on a high ridge in a field about 850 feet south of Leonce Maheux's farmhouse.

Station mark: A bronze disk cemented in a drill hole in bare rock ledge.

Megantic (Quebec, Frontenac County; Geodetic Survey of Canada, 1909; Jesse Hill, 1915).—In Chesham Township, on Megantic Mountain, 10 miles south of Milan, Quebec. The station is located on the south peak on the east side of the range. A small Catholic church is located about 100 feet southeast of the station.

Station mark: A three-fourths inch copper bolt.

Liniere (Quebec, Beauce County; Geodetic Survey of Canada, 1909; Jesse Hill, 1922).—In Liniere Township, about 2 miles east along the international boundary line from Moose River line house on the "Old Canada Road," 15 miles north of Jackman, Me. The station is near the boundary, on the summit of a flat hill.

Station mark: A three-fourths inch copper bolt set in rock 6 inches below the surrounding surface of the ground. Monument 348–23 is 118 feet distant, in azimuth 329° 58′, from the station.

Bald (Maine, Somerset County; Jesse Hill, 1915).—In Bald Mountain Township, on Bald Mountain, about 10 miles north of Jackman, Me. It is centered under the 15-foot lookout tower of Bald fire station, which is on the highest point of the west peak.

Station mark: A bronze disk wedged firmly in a drill hole in rock.

Ste. Cecile (Quebec, Frontenac County; Jesse Hill, 1915).—In Whitton Township, on the southwest end of Little Megantic Mountain, about 1 mile northwest of Ste. Cecile railway station on the Quebec Central Railway, and 10 miles north-northwest of Lake Megantic. The station is on the highest point of the ridge, on a large bowlder 6 feet long and 3 feet wide.

Station mark: A bronze disk cemented in a drill hole in a bowlder.

Kibby (Maine, Franklin County; Jesse Hill, 1915).—In township 7, range 1, on Kibby Mountain, about 10 miles south of Skinner, Me., post office, and about 4 miles east of the international boundary. The station is on the highest point of the mountain and is centered under the fire station lookout tower.

Station mark: A bronze disk cemented in a drill hole in rock.

Snow (Maine, Franklin County; Jesse Hill, 1915).—In township 6, range 2, on Snow Mountain, about 2 miles east of Big Island; on the Megantic fish and game preserve, about 12 miles southeast of Woburn, Quebec. The station is centered under the 30-foot lookout tower of Snow fire station, which is on the highest point of the mountain.

Station mark: A bronze disk cemented in a depression about 8 inches below the surface of the ledge.

Hughey (Maine, Franklin County; Jesse Hill, 1915).—In township 8, range 2, on a high rock ridge, one-third mile east of Boundary Siding, Quebec, railroad station, and about 300 feet south of the international boundary. The station is on the west slope of the ridge, about 125 feet southwest of the top and about 200 feet west of a draw that passes through the ridge.

Station mark: A bronze disk cemented in a drill hole in rock.

Traverse Station 69=H (Maine, Franklin County; J. D. Craig, 1919).—This station is on the highest point of a high spur of a ridge over which the international boundary passes, and is about 1,000 feet southwest of monument 390.

Station mark: A copper bolt set in rock.

Moccasin (Maine, Franklin County; Jesse Hill, 1915).—In township 7, range 1, on the second peak east of monument 411 of the boundary. The station is located on the summit of the ridge about 250 feet south of the north end of the ridge.

Station mark: A bronze disk cemented in a drill hole in solid rock.

Bump (Maine, Franklin County; Jesse Hill, 1915).—In township 7, range 2, on a high peak about three-fourths mile north-northeast of monument 410 and about 1½ miles southeast of Van Dyke's old lumber camps which are located at the forks of Merrill Brook. The station is on the highest part of the hill.

Station mark: A bronze disk cemented in a drill hole in a large bowlder buried in the earth.

Layton (Maine, Franklin County; Jesse Hill, 1915).—In township 7, range 1, on the highest point of a high hill of about 3,200 feet elevation; about 1¾ miles south of Lowelltown, Me., and about 2 miles northeast of monument 410.

Station mark: A bronze disk cemented in a hole drilled in a large rock.

Merrill (Maine, Franklin County; Jesse Hill, 1915).—In township 7, range 2, on the high mountain, about 1¼ miles south-southeast of Van Dyke Mountain and one-half mile east of monument 407, and north of the source of Merrill Brook. The station is on the northeast end of the top of the mountain and about one-fourth mile from the nearest point of the boundary.

Station mark: A bronze disk cemented in a drill hole in an 80-pound rock with loose rocks piled around it.

Van Dyke (Maine, Franklin County; Jesse Hill, 1915).—In township 7, range 2, on the top of Van Dyke Mountain which is the highest cone about 2 miles west of Lowelltown, Me., and between Merrill and Mill Brooks. The station is on the west edge of the top.

Station mark: A bronze disk cemented in a drill hole in rock.

Wait (Maine, Franklin County; Jesse Hill, 1915).—In township 8, range 2, on a high, timbered hill about 1¼ miles south of Boundary Siding, Quebec, railway station, 650 feet southeast of monument 403. The station is on the northeast side of the top of the hill.

Station mark: A bronze disk cemented in a drill hole in a 15-inch square rock.

Lowell (Maine, Franklin County; Jesse Hill, 1915).—In township 8, range 2, on a rocky hill about 1½ miles northwest of Lowelltown, Me., and about one-half mile northeast of the Canadian Pacific Railway. The station is about 20 feet southwest of the highest point of the hill.

Station mark: A bronze disk cemented in a drill hole in rock.

Dome (Maine, Franklin County; Jesse Hill, 1915).—In township 8, range 2, on top of the second rock ridge 1¼ miles southeast of Boundary Siding, Quebec, railway station; about 2½ miles north-northwest of Lowelltown, Me., and about one-third mile east of the railroad track. The station is on the highest point of the ridge.

Station mark: A bronze disk cemented in a drill hole in rock.

Dean (Maine, Franklin County; Jesse Hill, 1915).—In township 8, range 2, on the southwest slope of the first rock ridge one-half mile southeast of Boundary Siding, Quebec, railway station. The station is about 140 feet south-southwest of the top of the ridge, and is just west of a draw that cuts through the ridge.

Station mark: A bronze disk cemented in a drill hole in rock.

Boundary (Maine, Franklin County; Jesse Hill, 1915).—In township 8, range 2, on top of a rocky hill about one-third mile south of Boundary Siding, Quebec, railway station, and about 300 feet east of the international boundary. The station is on the highest point of the hill.

Station mark: A bronze disk cemented in a drill hole in rock.

Lowelltown South Base (Maine, Franklin County; Jesse Hill, 1915).—In township 8, range 2, on the west edge of the fill of the Canadian Pacific Railway about 220 feet south of the north end of the third curve south of Boundary Siding railway station.

Station mark: A stake driven firmly in the ground. The reference mark is a bronze disk cemented in a drill hole in rock, and is 19.46 feet distant, in azimuth 103° 53′, from the station.

Lowelltown North Base (Maine, Franklin County; Jesse Hill, 1915).—In township 8, range 2, on the west side of the fill of the Canadian Pacific Railway about 200 feet north of the south end of the second curve south of Boundary Siding railway station.

Station mark: A stake driven firmly in the ground. The reference mark is a bronze disk cemented in a drill hole in rock, and is 22.95 feet distant, in azimuth 72° 32′, from the station.

Gosford (Quebec, Frontenac County; Jesse Hill, 1916).—In Woburn Township, on the summit of Gosford Mountain, about 6 miles south of Woburn, Quebec. The station is near the east side of the top and about 30 feet from the highest point.

Station mark: A bronze disk cemented in a drill hole in a large rock, that is firmly set among small rocks which form the top of the peak.

Woburn (Quebec, Frontenac County; Jesse Hill, 1916).—In Woburn Township, on the highest point of the high mountain about 2 miles west of Woburn, Quebec, and about one-half mile south of the road to Chesham, Quebec.

Station mark: A bronze disk cemented in a drill hole in rock.

Rump (Maine, Oxford County; Jesse Hill, 1916).—In township 5, range 5, on Rump Mountain (known also as Camels Rump), over which the Maine-New Hampshire line passes, and about 7 miles south of monument 475, which is the Maine-New Hampshire corner. The station is located on the highest point of the highest peak of the mountain.

Station mark: A bronze disk cemented in a drill hole in outcropping rock.

Bon Durban (New Hampshire, Coos County; Jesse Hill, 1916).—In Pittsburg Township, on Bon Durban Mountain, 5 miles east of the village of Chartierville, Quebec, three-fourths mile north of monument 477. The station is on the southeast side of the top and about 30 feet east of the boundary.

Station mark: A bronze disk cemented in a long flat rock that was set in mossy loam. Monument 476–21 is 67.94 feet distant, in azimuth 105° 16′, from station.

Pros (Quebec, Compton County; F. H. Brundage, 1916).—In Emberton Township, 3 miles south-southwest of Chartierville, Quebec, on the eastern hill of the twin peaks known as Prospect Hill, on a rocky hump at the extreme north edge of the summit and the highest point on the hill.

Station mark: Standard bronze disk cemented in a hole drilled in outcropping bedrock. The reference marks are crosses cut in ledge rock at the following distances and azimuths from the station: 18.85 feet, 12° 31′; 5.78 feet, 65° 11′.

Salmon (New Hampshire, Coos County; F. H. Brundage, 1916).—In Pittsburg Township, on the highest point of the boundary peak between monuments 478 and 479, near the boundary line.

Station mark: Standard bronze disk set in a hole drilled in a bowlder.

Northwest Knoll (Quebec, Compton County; F. H. Brundage, 1916).—In Emberton Township, about three-fourths mile northwest of Chartierville, Quebec, and one-half mile north of the road from Chartierville to Sawyerville, Quebec.

Station mark: Standard bronze disk set in a large rock.

Spect (New Hampshire, Coos County; F. H. Brundage, 1916).—In Pittsburg Township, about 3½ miles southwest of Chartierville, Quebec, on the western hill of the twin peaks known as Prospect Hill. It is on the extreme north-northwest edge of the summit and is about 6 feet lower than the highest point.

Station mark: Standard bronze disk cemented in a hole drilled in outcropping bedrock. The reference marks are crosses cut in ledge rock at the following distances and azimuths from the station: 14.20 feet, 2° 10′; 14.20 feet, 349° 46′.

Bien (New Hampshire, Coos County; F. H. Brundage, 1916).—In Pittsburg Township, about 10 feet from the boundary, on the highest ground near monument 489, from which it is distant about 730 feet.

Station mark: Standard bronze disk set in a concrete-filled tile. Reference mark No. 1 is monument 489–6, which bears north 40° east, magnetic, from the station and is distant 65.6 feet. Reference mark No. 2 consists of two nails in a blaze on a small silver birch which bears south 63° west, magnetic, from the station and is distant 54.09 feet. Reference mark No. 3 consists of two nails in a blaze on a large birch which bears north 55° east, magnetic, from the station and is distant 67.54 feet.

Indian (New Hampshire, Coos County; F. H. Brundage, 1916).—In Pittsburg Township, on the northern edge of the top of a high knoll about 2½ miles west of Deer Mountain at the headwaters of Indian Stream.

Station mark: Standard bronze disk set in rock.

Howe (New Hampshire, Coos County; F. H. Brundage, 1916).—In Pittsburg Township, 50 feet from the boundary line on the most northern knoll of the high ridge between monuments 496 and 497.

Station mark: Standard bronze disk. Reference mark No. 1 consists of three nails in a blaze on a birch which bears south 69° west, magnetic, from the station and is 54.46 feet distant. Reference mark No. 2 consists of three nails in a large spruce stump which bears south 40° east, magnetic, from the station and is 20.73 feet distant.

Joe (New Hampshire, Coos County; F. H. Brundage, 1916).—In Pittsburg Township, on the western edge of the first high knoll on the boundary going from monument 501 to monument 502.

Station mark: Standard bronze disk set in concrete. The reference mark is monument 501–1 which is distant 79.04 feet, in azimuth 339° 07′, from the station.

Eck (New Hampshire, Coos County; F. H. Brundage, 1916).—In Pittsburg Township, on the north end of the high ridge three-fourths mile south-southeast of monument 501.

Station mark: Standard bronze disk cemented in a hole drilled in outcropping rock. Reference mark No. 1 consists of three nails in a blaze on a wild cherry tree which bears south 24° east, magnetic, from the station and is 13.03 feet distant. Reference mark No. 2 consists of three nails in a blaze on a spruce tree which bears south 85° west, magnetic, from the station and is 35.38 feet distant.

Hereford (Quebec, Compton County; Geodetic Survey of Canada, 1909; J. D. Craig, 1917).—In Hereford Township, about 5 miles north of the international boundary and about 6½ miles northwest of Beecher Falls, Vt. It is on an outcrop on the highest point of a hill, covered (in June, 1909) with thick burned timber and a thin soil; probably on lot 21, between Concessions V and VI.

Station mark: A three-fourths inch copper bolt surrounded by an 8-inch equilateral triangle. The point is referenced by three three-fourths inch bolts leaded in the rock at the following azimuths and distances from the station: Bolt No. 1, azimuth 172° 01′ 58″, distance 9.7 feet; bolt No. 2, azimuth 255° 45′ 38″, distance 11.35 feet; bolt No. 3, azimuth 11° 25′ 43″, distance 8.71 feet.

Sightly (Quebec, Compton County; J. E. McGrath, 1915).—In Auckland Township, about 3 miles north of Malvina, Quebec, about 500 feet west of the north-and-south road which passes through the village of Malvina, and about 1,400 feet south of the east-and-west road from St. Malo. It is on the more northerly summit about 50 feet southwest of a large bowlder which is on top of the hill.

Station mark: Standard bronze disk set in concrete in a shallow hole in the ledge. The reference mark is a standard bronze disk set in a hole drilled in outcropping bedrock, distant 44.53 feet, in azimuth 248° 24′, from the station.

Ouillette (South Base) (Quebec, Compton County; J. E. McGrath, 1915).—In Auckland Township, about three-fourths mile south of the village of Malvina, Quebec. The station is on a rocky ridge in the pasture on the south side of an east-and-west road and is on the more westerly knoll of two that are very similar in size and shape. It is about 100 feet north of a lane running along a hardwood thicket and it is about 50 feet east of a spruce and fir thicket.

Station mark: Standard bronze disk set in a 2½-foot concrete-filled drain tile.

Metallak (New Hampshire, Coos County; J. E. McGrath, 1915).—In Pittsburg Township, about 2 miles southeast of Malvina, Quebec, railroad station, on the crest of the divide between Halls Stream and Indian Stream.

Station mark: Standard bronze disk set in concrete. The reference mark is a standard bronze disk set in outcropping bedrock, distant 11.50 feet, in azimuth 118° 32′, from the station.

Crete (**North Base**) (Quebec, Compton County; J. E. McGrath, 1915).—In Auckland Township, about 1 mile west of Malvina, Quebec, railroad station. The station is on a flat-topped knoll in the pasture of the Crete farm, about 700 feet west of the barn. It is about 30 feet west of a wire fence which separates the pasture from a cultivated field.

Station mark: Standard bronze disk cemented in a hole in outcropping bedrock.

Corbert (Quebec, Compton County; J. E. McGrath, 1915).—In Auckland Township, about 1 mile north of Malvina, Quebec, railroad station and about 200 feet west of the north-and-south road. It is on a rocky knoll in a cultivated field and is about 40 feet south of an east-and-west fence.

Station mark: A standard bronze disk set in a 2-foot, concrete-filled tile whose top projects 3 inches above the surface of the ground. The subsurface mark is a small bottle on the ledge below the tile.

Laperle (Quebec, Compton County; J. E. McGrath, 1915).—In Auckland Township on a rocky knoll 1 mile south-southwest of Malvina, Quebec, railroad station. It is east of the highway, about 100 feet south of a cultivated field, and about 150 feet north of a heavy growth of hardwood.

Station mark: Standard bronze disk set in a hole drilled in outcropping bedrock.

Hill (New Hampshire, Coos County; J. E. McGrath, 1914).—In Pittsburg Township, 3½ miles north of Beecher Falls, Vt., on the upper edge of the hill pasture of the first farm on the road from the Van Dyke farm across the divide to Indian Stream Valley. It is near the top of the hill, about 1,100 feet southeast of the farm buildings and the road and about 130 feet from the edge of the woods.

Station mark: No mark was set at the station. The reference mark is a standard bronze disk set in a large outcrop of ledge rock, 41.79 feet from the station. The azimuth from the reference mark to station "Fall" is 130° 15' and to station "Hill" is 265° 02'.

Wheeler (Quebec, Compton County; J. E. McGrath, 1914).—In Hereford Township, about one-half mile northeast of the village of East Hereford, Quebec. It is on the second of the large knolls north of the buildings on the Wheeler farm and is about 1,200 feet from the road.

Station mark: Standard bronze disk set in a small outcrop of ledge rock.

Lambert (Quebec, Compton County; Jesse Hill, 1916).—In Hereford Township, on a high hardwood ridge about 3 miles north of Beecher Falls, Vt., about 1 mile west of Halls Stream, and opposite Mr. Lambert's farmhouse. The station is about 75 feet east of the highest point of the peak.

Station mark: A bronze disk cemented in a drill hole in a flat rock, which is buried 1 foot underground on a little knoll rising about 1 foot above the general level.

Beecher Tablet (Vermont, Essex County; Jesse Hill, 1916; J. D. Craig, 1917).—In Canaan Township, on the west shoulder of the high hill about 1¼ miles east-northeast of Beecher Falls, Vt. The station is about 125 feet west of the highest point of the hill.

Station mark: A bronze disk cemented in a drill hole in a buried rock.

Beecher, the first station established in this locality, was not permanently marked. It was 5.13 feet distant, in azimuth 108° 23', from Beecher Tablet.

LAKE POHENAGAMOOK TO VERMONT-QUEBEC BOUNDARY, POINTS SUPPLEMENTARY TO MAJOR SCHEME

Bear (Maine, Franklin County; Jesse Hill, 1915).—In township 8, range 2, 1 mile west of Lowelltown, Me., on the low rocky ridge north of Van Dyke Mountain, about one-fourth mile south of the Canadian Pacific Railway, about 600 feet north of a ridge about 150 feet higher. The station is on the west side of the top of the ridge.

Station mark: A bronze disk cemented in a drill hole in rock.

Saddle (Maine, Franklin County; Jesse Hill, 1915).—In township 6, range 2, on the northeast end of the high ridge of Pisgah Mountain, about 2½ miles northeast of Chain of Ponds; at the head of Spider River Valley. The station is on the highest point on bare rock.

Station mark: A bronze disk cemented in a drill hole in rock. Monument 417 is 63.81 feet distant, in azimuth 222° 29', from the station.

South (Maine, Franklin County; Jesse Hill, 1915).—In township 7, range 2, on a small peak on the south shoulder of Merrill Mountain, about one-third mile southeast of "Merrill" triangulation station and 1¼ miles south of Van Dyke Mountain. The station is on the highest point of the peak.

Station mark: A bronze disk cemented in a drill hole in a 60-pound rock which is buried in small rocks.

Brown (Maine, Franklin County; Jesse Hill, 1915).—In township 7, range 2, on the southerly end of the high boundary ridge, about 1,000 feet south-southwest of monument 414. The station is on the highest point, about 70 feet east of the boundary.

Station mark: A bronze disk cemented in a drill hole in rock. Monument 414–4 is 72.18 feet distant, in azimuth 119° 01', from the station.

Rain (Maine, Franklin County; Jesse Hill, 1915).—In township 6, range 1, about 2 miles west-southwest of Kibby Mountain and $1\frac{3}{4}$ miles east of monument 414, on a long ridge about midway between a saddle and a peak. The station is located on the northerly one of two small peaks.

Station mark: A bronze disk cemented in a drill hole in solid rock ledge.

Back (Quebec, Frontenac County; Jesse Hill, 1915).—In Louise Township, on a small peak on the north shoulder of Pisgah Mountain. The station is on the highest point of the peak.

Station mark: A bronze disk cemented in a drill hole in rock. Monument 418 is 74.3 feet distant, in azimuth $97°$ 26', from the station.

Joseph (Quebec, Frontenac County; Jesse Hill, 1915).—In Louise Township, $1\frac{1}{4}$ miles northeast of Pisgah Mountain. The station is on the summit of the ridge, about 15 feet south of the boundary.

Station mark: A bronze disk cemented in a drill hole in solid rock. Monument 414–28 is about 25 feet in a northwest direction from the station.

Moran (Quebec, Frontenac County; Jesse Hill, 1916).—In Woburn Township, 6 miles south of Woburn, Quebec, on the east peak of Gosford Mountain Range, on which are the sources of Morin Brook and Clearwater Brook. The station is about 1,000 feet west of monument 443, on the top of the flat summit of the peak.

Station mark: A bronze disk cemented in a drill hole in a rock.

Mine (Quebec, Frontenac County; Jesse Hill, 1916).—In Woburn Township, about 3 miles southeast of Woburn, Quebec, $1\frac{1}{2}$ miles east-southeast of the junction of Morin Brook with Arnold River, three-fourths mile west-northwest of monument 435, on the easterly point of a mountain which is separated from the boundary ridge by a low saddle. The station is on a small pointed bowlder, just west of which is a large bowlder.

Station mark: A bronze disk cemented in a drill hole in the bowlder.

Dead (Quebec, Frontenac County; Jesse Hill, 1916).—In Woburn Township, on the west and second highest peak of the hill, about 400 feet southeast of monument 433. The station is on the south end of a flat rock.

Station mark: A bronze disk cemented in a drill hole in rock.

Arnold (Quebec, Frontenac County; Jesse Hill, 1916).—In Woburn Township about $1\frac{1}{2}$ miles southeast of Woburn, Quebec, $1\frac{1}{2}$ miles west of monument 431, and one-half mile south of the road. The station is on the highest point of a bare rocky hill on the highest point of a 20-foot rounded rock.

Station mark: A bronze disk cemented in a drill hole in rock.

Seymour (Quebec, Frontenac County; Jesse Hill, 1916).—In Woburn Township, near the highest point on the south side of a burnt rocky peak which is the second one north from Gosford Mountain, also the second one south from Arnold River, and three-fourths mile west of Morin Brook.

Station mark: A bronze disk cemented in a drill hole in rock.

Steep (Quebec, Frontenac County; Jesse Hill, 1916).—In Woburn Township, on the boundary ridge. The station is west of monument 437, and very close to the boundary.

Station mark: A bronze disk cemented in a drill hole in rock outcropping. Monument 437 is 86.90 feet distant, in azimuth $249°$ 36', from the station.

Boots (Quebec, Frontenac County; Jesse Hill, 1916).—In Woburn Township, on the highest peak on the southerly ridge of Gosford Mountain, distant about 1 mile from its summit and $1\frac{1}{2}$ miles east of Arnold River. The station is near the west edge and about 150 feet north of the south edge of the flat top of the peak.

Station mark: A bronze disk cemented in a drill hole in a rock.

Dutch (Maine, Franklin County; Jesse Hill, 1916).—In township 3, range 5, $2\frac{3}{4}$ miles south-southeast of Gosford Mountain. The station is on the highest point of the peak, on the boundary between monuments 445 and 446, and 600 feet southwest of the former.

Station mark: A bronze disk cemented in a drill hole in rock. Monument 445–3 is 11.48 feet distant, in azimuth $110°$ 44', from the station.

Boggy (Quebec, Frontenac County; Jesse Hill, 1916).—In Woburn Township, on the high boundary hill about three-fourths mile west of Arnold Bog. The station is on the highest point of the southeast peak, about 600 feet north-northwest of monument 455.

Station mark: A bronze disk cemented in a drill hole in a rock. Monument 455–5 is 62.99 feet distant, in azimuth $133°$ 03', from the station.

Suptic (Maine, Oxford County; Jesse Hill, 1916).—In township 4, range 5, on a peak one-half mile east-by-north from Cupsuptic Pond and three-fourths mile southeast of monument 452, which is near the head of Arnold Bog. The station is on the highest point of the hill.

Station mark: A bronze disk cemented in a drill hole in a rock.

Dennison (Maine, Oxford County; Jesse Hill, 1916).—In township 4, range 5, on the boundary ridge, 2 miles east of Arnold Bog, 3½ miles south-southeast of Gosford Mountain. The station is about 750 feet southeast of monument 447, on the highest point of a small peak.

Station mark: A bronze disk cemented in a drill hole in a rock. Monument 447–2 is 20.34 feet distant, in azimuth 149° 09′, from the station.

Smith (Maine, Oxford County; Jesse Hill, 1916).—In township 4, range 6, on the high boundary hill, 2¼ miles northwest of Arnold Bog and one-half mile west of Arnold River and about midway between monuments 460 and 461. The station is on the highest point of the hill about 70 feet northwest of the boundary.

Station mark: A bronze disk cemented in a drill hole in a rock. Monument 460–10 is 150.81 feet distant, in azimuth 21° 57′, from the station.

Boulder (Quebec, Frontenac County; Jesse Hill, 1916).—In Woburn Township, on the more southerly of two hills about three-fourths mile east of Arnold Bog, 1 mile north-northeast of monument 452. The station is on the highest point of the hill.

Station mark: A bronze disk cemented in a drill hole in a rock.

Louis (Quebec, Frontenac County; Jesse Hill, 1916).—In Woburn Township, on the south range of Gosford Mountain, just west of "Boots" triangulation station. The station is at the point where the hill breaks from a gentle slope to a steeper slope toward the Arnold River.

Station mark: A hole cut in the top of a balsam stump into which the signal pole was set.

McLeod (Quebec, Frontenac County; Jesse Hill, 1916).—In Woburn Township, on a small peak on the end of a spur running southwest-by-west from the summit of Gosford Mountain, distant 1¼ miles, and three-fourths mile east of Arnold River. The station is on the highest point of the east peak.

Station mark: A bronze disk cemented in a drill hole in a rock.

Jule (Quebec, Frontenac County; Jesse Hill, 1916).—In Woburn Township, about one-fourth mile west of the summit of Gosford Mountain. The station is located near the highest point of a small peak.

Station mark: No permanent mark. Signal was a flag on a trimmed fir tree.

Nicollet (Maine, Oxford County; Jesse Hill, 1916).—In township 4, range 6, on the more easterly of the two peaks of Mount Nicollet, a mountain that is very steep on its east side, 1¾ miles southeast of Marble Mountain, and 1¼ miles east of monument 472. The station is on the highest point of the peak near the center of the top.

Station mark: A bronze disk cemented in a bowlder which was set in the earth.

Bowman (Maine, Oxford County; Jesse Hill, 1916).—In township 4, range 6, on a low peak about 2 miles south of monument 474 and west of the Magalloway road. The station is on the highest point of the peak.

Station mark: A bronze disk cemented in a drill hole in a rock.

Barker (Maine, Oxford County; Jesse Hill, 1916).—In township 4, range 6, about one-fourth mile south of the boundary, one-half mile east of the Magalloway Road, 1 mile west of Barker Pond, and about 1 mile east-southeast of monument 474. The station is on the highest point of the hill.

Station mark: A bronze disk cemented in a drill hole in outcropping rock.

Lake (Maine, Oxford County; Jesse Hill, 1916).—In township 4, range 6, on a low ridge three-fourths mile south of Barker Pond and north of the Magalloway Road. The station is on the highest point of the ridge.

Station mark: A bronze disk cemented in a drill hole in a rock.

Marble (Quebec, Frontenac County; Jesse Hill, 1916).—In Chesham Township, on Marble Mountain, about 5 miles southeast of Chesham, Quebec, and 1 mile south of monument 470, which is on Saddle Hill. The station is on the highest point of the peak, about 20 feet north of its south edge on outcropping rock and about 250 feet southwest of the boundary.

Station mark: A bronze disk cemented in a drill hole in rock.

Landon (Quebec, Frontenac County; Jesse Hill, 1916).—In Woburn Township about one-fourth mile southeast-by-east of monument 465, on the north slope of the ridge. The station is about 40 feet east of the boundary.

Station mark: A block of wood nailed to the exposed roots of a tree with a signal at its top.

Fish (Maine, Oxford County; Jesse Hill, 1916).—In township 4, range 6, on the southeast peak of Saddle Hill, about 4 miles southeast of Chesham, Quebec, one-half mile southeast of monument 470. The station is near the southeast edge of the flat top of the peak.

Station mark: A bronze disk cemented in a drill hole in the rock. Monument 469–12 is 8.68 feet distant, in azimuth 276° 39′, from the station.

Hugh (Maine, Oxford County; Jesse Hill, 1916).—In township 4, range 6, one-fourth mile southwest-by-west of Mount Nicollet, 1 mile east-by-south of monument 472. The station is on the highest point of a small peak.

Station mark: A short hub driven in the ground.

Campbell (Quebec, Frontenac County; Jesse Hill, 1916).—In Chesham Township, on the northeast slope of Bon Durban Mountain, about three-fourths mile from its top, about 1,400 feet west of monument 476. The station is on the east side of the ridge.

Station mark: Cross cut on small soapstone ledge.

Trumbull (Quebec, Frontenac County; Jesse Hill, 1916).—In Chesham Township, on the high mountain peak on the boundary between monuments 477 and 478, $5\frac{1}{4}$ miles east-southeast of Chartierville, Quebec. The station is on the highest part of the peak.

Station mark: A bronze disk cemented in a drill hole in a flat rock placed for the purpose. Monument 477–33 is 23.90 feet distant, in azimuth 188° 43', from the station.

Peterie (Quebec, Compton County; F. H. Brundage, 1916).—In Emberton Township, about 300 feet north of the east-and-west road which runs parallel to and 3 miles south of the east-and-west road through Chartierville, Quebec. It is on the ridge which forms the divide between the two branches of Salmon Creek.

Station mark: Standard bronze disk set in a large rock.

Southeast Knoll (Quebec, Compton County; F. H. Brundage, 1916).—In Emberton Township, about about 1 mile south of Chartierville, Quebec, one-half mile east of the road leading south from Chartierville to Lake Sophy (Third Lake). It is on a high rock in the pasture belonging to Fred Boudreau, about 60 feet from his east-and-west fence.

Station mark: Standard bronze disk set in the rock.

Birches (Quebec, Compton County; F. H. Brundage, 1916).—In Emberton Township, about 3 miles south and $3\frac{1}{2}$ miles east of Chartierville, Quebec, on the same ridge on which triangulation station "Peterie" and monument 481 are located. It is about 900 feet north of the boundary, on the eastern edge of the ridge.

Station mark: Standard bronze disk set in solid rock.

Nash (Quebec, Frontenac County; Jesse Hill, 1916).—In Chesham Township, on the southwest slope of Trumbull Mountain, about 600 feet north of monument 478. The station is about 200 feet northwest of monument 477–48.

Station mark: A wooden hub, with a hole bored in its center, driven flush with the ground.

Deer (New Hampshire, Coos County; F. H. Brundage, 1916).—In Pittsburg Township, about 6 miles south of Chartierville, Quebec. The observation tower used by the fire warden, whose cabin is located near by on Deer Mountain, was used as an observing tower.

Station mark: Standard bronze disk set in rock.

Fourth (Quebec, Compton County; F. H. Brundage, 1916).—In Auckland Township, on the summit of of the boundary ridge, on the Quebec side of the boundary.

Station mark: Standard bronze disk set in concrete-filled tile. The reference mark is monument 492–7, which is north 10° east (magnetic) of the station and distant 29.8 feet.

Nob (New Hampshire, Coos County; F. H. Brundage, 1916).—In Pittsburg Township, about 1 mile south of monument 488. The station is on the extreme north edge of the summit of a knoll which rises abruptly from the lowland extending to the northeast, north, and southeast of the station.

Station mark: Standard bronze disk set in a concrete-filled tile. The reference mark is a spike in a birch stump which bears south 57° west (magnetic) from the station and is 10.4 feet distant.

Hollis (New Hampshire, Coos County; F. H. Brundage, 1916).—In Pittsburg Township, about 255 feet south of monument 498, on the highest ground on the low ridge.

Station mark: Standard bronze disk. The reference mark consists of three nails in a blaze 3 feet above ground on a silver birch whose true bearing from the station is north 27° east and distance 20.17 feet.

Ridge (New Hampshire, Coos County; F. H. Brundage, 1916)—In Pittsburg Township, on the summit of a ridge about one-half mile west of Indian Stream and parallel to it, and 1 mile southeast of monument 499. The station is on the southwest end of a knoll 200 feet long and 50 feet wide.

Station mark: Standard bronze disk set in a 4-inch tile filled with concrete. The tile projects 6 inches above ground and is surrounded by a small cairn.

Near (New Hampshire, Coos County; F. H. Brundage, 1916).—In Pittsburg Township, on a ridge parallel to that part of the boundary which runs west from monument 500. It is about 200 feet south of the tote road to monument 500 and about 250 feet in elevation above the valley at monument 500.

Station mark: Standard bronze disk set in rock.

Alec (New Hampshire, Coos County; F. H. Brundage, 1916).—In Pittsburg Township, 200 feet south of the line between monuments 498 and 499, and about halfway between these monuments.

Station mark: A nail in a notch on the root of the tree in which the flag was raised.

King (Quebec, Compton County; J. E. McGrath, 1915).—In Auckland Township, about 1½ miles south of Malvina, Quebec, railroad station. It is about 175 feet west of the west side of the Maine Central Railroad right of way and about 600 feet south of where the Maine Central Railroad crosses King Brook.

Station mark: Standard bronze disk cemented in a flat bare rock.

HALLS STREAM, MINOR SCHEME

Reference Monument 512–6 (Quebec, Compton County; J. E. McGrath, 1914–15).—In Hereford Township, about five-eighths mile north of Beecher Falls, Vt. It is about 180 feet north of the Canadian customs office, about 50 feet east of the middle of the highway, and about 75 feet west of the Maine Central Railroad.

Station mark: Standard bronze disk set in a 2½-foot concrete post. The subsurface mark is a beer bottle filled with sand, buried beneath the concrete post.

Tank (Quebec, Compton County; J. E. McGrath, 1914).—In Hereford Township, in Sylvester Hibbard's open pasture west of the main road on the Quebec side of the stream. It is about 175 feet north of the boundary and about 210 feet from the reservoir which supplies Beecher Falls with water.

Station mark: The surface mark is a standard bronze disk set in a 3-foot concrete post whose top is flush with the surface of the ground. The subsurface mark is a small glass bottle set about 3¼ feet below the surface of the ground.

Lot (Vermont, Essex County; J. E. McGrath, 1914).—In Canaan Township, on the east side of Halls Stream, on a small knoll about 120 feet from Halls Stream and about 175 feet south of the international boundary produced across the stream.

Station mark: A standard bronze disk set flush with the surface of the ground in the top of a 3-foot concrete post. The subsurface mark is a gin bottle buried 3¼ feet below the surface of the ground.

Chaloux (New Hampshire, Coos County; J. E. McGrath, 1914–15).—In Pittsburg Township, on the land belonging to George Chaloux and about 300 feet south of his house. It is a narrow point of rock which shows a precipitous face (about 25 feet high) toward the public road.

Station mark: The point occupied with theodolite and at which the signal was set was not marked. The reference mark is a standard bronze disk set in a hole drilled in the rock about 3 feet north of the center of the bare rocky surface of the point and about 15 feet east of where the precipitous descent of the west face of the point begins. From the reference mark to station "Chaloux" the azimuth is 213° 45′ and the distance is 2.77 feet. The azimuth from the reference mark to station "Rock" is 153° 23′.

Rock (Quebec, Compton County; J. E. McGrath, 1914).—In Hereford Township, about 1 mile north of Beecher Falls, Vt. It is between the main highway and the railroad, on top of a prominent ledge which rises 20 feet above the road.

Station mark: A standard bronze disk set in a hole drilled in the ledge.

Beecher Falls South Base (New Hampshire, Coos County; J. E. McGrath, 1914).—In Pittsburg Township, about 1 mile north of Beecher Falls, Vt. It is on the hillside at the top of the steep slope about 350 feet east of the highway. It is directly opposite a small knoll which is about 500 feet west of the highway.

Station mark: The surface mark is a standard bronze disk set in a 2½-foot concrete post whose top is flush with the surface of the ground. The subsurface mark is a cross chiseled in ledge rock. Two inches of earth separate the ledge from the concrete.

Beecher Falls North Base (New Hampshire, Coos County; J. E. McGrath, 1914).—In Pittsburg Township, about one-half mile southeast of the first highway bridge, north of Beecher Falls, which crosses Halls Stream. It is on the hillside about 600 feet east of the highway and about 50 feet south of the southern boundary of the Van Dyke farm.

Station mark: The surface mark is a standard bronze disk set in a 3-foot concrete post whose top is flush with the surface of the ground. The subsurface mark is a small bottle buried below the concrete.

Van (Quebec, Compton County; J. E. McGrath, 1914).—In Hereford Township, 1 mile north of Beecher Falls, Vt. It is on the railroad right of way, 2 feet west of the fence separating the Van Dyke farm from the railroad, and is opposite the sixth rail joint (of west line of rails) counting northward from milepost P–156.

Station mark: No mark was set at the station. The reference mark, 7.95 feet distant, is a standard bronze disk set in a 2-foot concrete post whose top is flush with the surface of the ground. A glass bottle was buried 3 feet below the bronze disk, as a subsurface mark. The azimuth from the reference mark to station "Van" is 10° 05′. The azimuth from the reference mark to station "Pasture" is 243° 50′.

Pasture (New Hampshire, Coos County; J. E. McGrath, 1914).—In Pittsburg Township, on the hillside east of Halls Stream about one-fourth mile northeast of the first bridge above Beecher Falls. It is due east of the old cemetery on the Canadian side and is about 300 feet above the foot of the slope.

Station mark: The surface mark is a standard bronze disk set in a 3-foot concrete post whose top is flush with the surface of the ground. The subsurface mark is a railroad spike driven in the shattered ledge.

Reference Monument 512–4 (Quebec, Compton County; J. E. McGrath, 1914).—In Hereford Township, about 2 miles north of Beecher Falls, Vt. It is on the west side of the Maine Central right of way, about 3 feet inside of the railway fence, about 100 feet south of a farm road crossing the railroad, and about 900 feet south of the Van Dyke farm buildings.

Station mark: A bronze disk set in a 3-foot concrete post whose top is flush with the surface of the ground. The subsurface mark is a pint flask filled with sand, buried beneath the concrete post.

Advent (Quebec, Compton County; J. E. McGrath, 1914).—In Hereford Township, about 2½ miles north of Beecher Falls, Vt., and about 600 feet west of the main highway. It is opposite a small chapel and cemetery, and is about 100 feet in elevation above the road. A farm road leads to the station from the field below.

Station mark: The surface mark is a standard bronze disk set in a 3-foot concrete post whose top surface is flush with the surface of the ground. The subsurface mark is a catsup bottle buried below the concrete.

Shift (Quebec, Compton County; J. E. McGrath, 1914).—In Hereford Township, about 1 mile south of East Hereford railway station. It is about 850 feet west of the Maine Central Railroad and about 900 feet south of the road leading from Halls Stream Valley to Hereford Hill. It is on the summit of the first small ridge west of the flat land of Halls Stream Valley and is about 300 feet west of a small brook.

Station mark: The surface mark is a standard bronze disk set in a 3-foot concrete post whose top surface is flush with the ground. The subsurface mark is a railroad spike driven in a crack in the ledge.

Cherry (New Hampshire, Coos County; J. E. McGrath, 1914).—In Pittsburg Township, on the Bryan farm, directly across the river and due east from Thos. Lambart's farmhouse. It is on the top of the knoll nearest the middle of the big bend in Halls Stream.

Station mark: A standard bronze disk set in a large outcrop of rock.

Fall (Quebec, Compton County; J. E. McGrath, 1914).—In Hereford Township, about 1,200 feet southwest of East Hereford railway station. It is on the eastern side of a knoll, a little below the top, about 350 feet west of the highway, and about 100 feet south of a fence.

Station mark: The surface mark is a standard bronze disk set in a 2-foot concrete post whose top is flush with the surface of the ground. The subsurface mark is a cross cut in ledge rock.

Gendreau (Quebec, Compton County; J. E. McGrath, 1914).—In Hereford Township, between the Maine Central Railroad and the road nearest Halls Stream of the two roads between East Hereford and Paquetteville. It is on the point of the easternmost of two large ledges in the pasture of Gendreau's farm, about 500 feet east of his farm buildings and 1,100 feet east of the road.

Station mark: No mark was set at the station. The reference mark is a standard bronze disk set in outcropping bedrock at a distance of 8.39 feet from the station. The azimuth from the reference mark to station "Caron" is 318° 59', and from the reference mark to station "Gendreau" is 148° 30'.

Cone (New Hampshire, Coos County; J. E. McGrath, 1914).—In Pittsburg Township, 1 mile due east of the village of East Hereford, Quebec. It is on a smooth conical-shaped hill about 600 feet northeast of the farm buildings on the Beloir farm.

Station mark: Standard bronze disk set in a 2½-foot concrete post whose top is flush with the surface of the ground. The subsurface mark is a bottle filled with gravel and buried below the concrete.

Caron (New Hampshire, Coos County; J. E. McGrath, 1914).—In Pittsburg Township, on a flat ridge or bench in the pasture of the old Caron farm and about 700 feet northeast of the farm buildings.

Station mark: The surface mark is a standard bronze disk set in a 2½-foot concrete post whose surface is flush with the ground. The subsurface mark is a glass bottle filled with sand.

Cedar (Quebec, Compton County; J. E. McGrath, 1914).—In Hereford Township, about 1 mile south of Paquetteville, Quebec, railroad station and about 700 feet west of the Maine Central Railroad. It is on the west edge of the top of a steep, wooded knoll.

Station mark: No mark was set at the station. The reference mark is a standard bronze disk set in outcropping bedrock, 7.90 feet distant. The azimuth from the reference mark to station "Caron" is 354° 27' and to station "Cedar" is 1° 06'.

Ledge (Quebec, Compton County; J. E. McGrath, 1914).—In Hereford Township, three-fourths mile south of the Paquetteville, Quebec, railroad station and 900 feet west of the railroad. It is on a high exposed ledge of the group of outcrops in the pasture north of the Gendreau farm. Map No. 10, prepared by the International Boundary Commission, showing part of Halls Stream, should be used in recovering this station.

Station mark: Standard bronze disk set in the ledge.

Poplar (Quebec, Compton County; J. E. McGrath, 1914).—In Hereford Township, about five-eighths mile south of Paquetteville, Quebec, railroad station and one-fourth mile west of the railroad. It is about 50 feet north of the line fence along the north side of the first farm north of the Gendreau farm. The ridge on which this outcrop occurs is covered with a thicket of small poplar and raspberry bushes. A farm road leads from the railroad north and then west of this ridge, thence on to the highway to Paquetteville village. Map No. 10, prepared by the International Boundary Commission, showing part of Halls Stream, should be used in recovering this station.

Station mark: A standard bronze disk set in the top of the highest outcrop of the ledge.

Paquette (Quebec, Compton County; J. E. McGrath, 1914).—In Hereford Township, on an open piece of ground, 530 feet from the northwest corner of Paquetteville railroad station, 210 feet south of an old fence which continues along the east side of the road that runs from the railroad station to the village, 215 feet from the center of the highway, and 160 feet from the railroad.

Station mark: The surface mark is a standard bronze disk set in an 18-inch concrete post whose top is flush with the surface of the ground. The subsurface mark is a marmalade jar buried 3 feet below the surface of the ground.

Stump (Quebec, Compton County; J. E. McGrath, 1914).—In Hereford Township, on the highest point of a bare ledge at the north end of a knoll about 200 feet south of the Paquetteville, Quebec, railroad station and about 240 feet west of the railroad.

Station mark: Standard bronze disk set in a hole drilled in the ledge.

N (Quebec, Compton County; J. E. McGrath, 1914).—In Hereford Township, about one-half mile northeast of Paquetteville, Quebec, railroad station, on land belonging to Joseph Brule, about 135 feet west of the railroad and almost abreast of the northern end of the second long railroad curve north of Paquetteville. It is near the edge of a high, steep, wooded bank.

Station mark: The surface mark is a standard bronze disk set in a 3-foot concrete post whose top is flush with the surface of the ground. The subsurface mark is a beer bottle filled with sand and buried below the concrete post.

Brush (Quebec, Compton County; J. E. McGrath, 1914).—In Hereford Township, about three-fourths mile northeast of Paquetteville, Quebec, railroad station in a thicket on the property of Jos. Brule. It is about 800 feet northwest of the Maine Central Railroad and 150 feet south of an old farm road. Map No. 11, prepared by the International Boundary Commission, showing part of Halls Stream, should be used in recovering this station.

Station mark: The surface mark is a standard bronze disk set in an 18-inch concrete post whose top is flush with the surface of the ground. The subsurface mark is a liniment bottle filled with sand and buried $2\frac{1}{2}$ feet below the surface of the ground.

Thicket (Quebec, Compton County; J. E. McGrath, 1914).—In Hereford Township, about 1 mile north of Paquetteville, Quebec, railroad station and one-fourth mile west of the railroad, on a high knoll in a pasture that belongs to Mme. Paquette. Map No. 11, prepared by the International Boundary Commission, showing part of Halls Stream, should be used in recovering this station.

Station mark: The surface mark is a standard bronze disk set in a $2\frac{1}{2}$-foot concrete post whose top is flush with the surface of the ground. The subsurface mark is a Paschall fruit-tablet bottle filled with sand and buried 3 feet below the surface of the ground.

Duran (Quebec, Compton County; J. E. McGrath, 1914–15).—In Hereford Township, about $2\frac{1}{2}$ miles north of Paquetteville, Quebec, railroad station. It is about 1,100 feet southeast of the more northerly of the Maine Central Railroad bridges and about 800 feet west of the railroad. It is on the southern slope of a hill, about 100 feet above Halls Stream and 45 feet north of a line fence between farms. The station is on the easternmost line of rock outcrops, the second one north of the point of the hill.

Station mark: Standard bronze disk set in a hole drilled in the ledge.

Bird (New Hampshire, Coos County; J. E. McGrath, 1914–15).—In Pittsburg Township, about $2\frac{1}{2}$ miles north of Paquetteville, Quebec, railroad station, and about 380 feet east of the more northerly of the two Maine Central Railroad bridges. It is on the north edge of a small cleared area, and about 200 feet east of Halls Stream.

Station mark: Standard bronze disk set in a concrete-filled tile.

Reference Monument 511–4 (New Hampshire, Coos County; J. E. McGrath, 1914–15).—In Pittsburg Township, about 3 miles northeast of the Paquetteville, Quebec, railroad station, and about 1,000 feet north of the steel railroad bridge. It is on the edge of a 10-foot bank running, from near the river, back in a northeasterly direction away from the river. About 40 feet from the monument and at the foot of the bank is a large rock about 10 feet high and 20 feet on a side, triangular in shape. The monument is 138 feet due east of the water's edge.

Station mark: A manganese bronze post, 8 inches high, set in a concrete base.

104709—25†——32

Cut (New Hampshire, Coos County; J. E. McGrath, 1914–15).—In Pittsburg Township, about 2¼ miles north of Paquetteville, Quebec, railroad station. It is about 900 feet south of the more northerly of the two railroad bridges and about 55 feet east of the railroad.

Station mark: Standard bronze disk set in a 2-foot concrete-filled drain tile. The subsurface mark is a cross cut in the ledge under the tile.

Reference Monument 511–3 (Quebec, Compton County; J. E. McGrath, 1915).—In Hereford Township, about 2 miles south of Malvina, Quebec, railroad station. The monument is on high ground, about 190 feet east of the railroad and about 800 feet upstream from an old dam and trestle. Map No. 11, prepared by the International Boundary Commission, showing part of Halls Stream, will be of assistance in recovering this monument.

Station mark: A manganese bronze post, 8 inches high, set in a concrete base.

Reference Monument 511–2 (Quebec, Compton County; J. E. McGrath, 1915).—In Hereford Township, about 2 miles south of Malvina, Quebec, railroad station. The monument is about 280 feet east of the railroad, on the river side of a knoll which is surrounded by water during the flood season. Upstream from the monument is a sharp bend in the stream and then a comparatively straight channel for 800 feet. Map No. 11, prepared by the International Boundary Commission, showing part of Halls Stream, will be of assistance in recovering this monument.

Station mark: A manganese bronze post, 8 inches high, set in a concrete base.

Reference Monument 511–1 (Quebec, Compton County; J. E. McGrath, 1915).—In Hereford Township, about 1¾ miles south of the Malvina, Quebec, railroad station. The monument is about 420 feet east of the railroad and about 130 feet west of the first bend in the stream extending toward the railroad near the upstream end of a long, comparatively straight stretch of river. Map No. 12, prepared by the International Boundary Commission, showing part of Halls Stream, will be of assistance in recovering this monument.

Station mark: A manganese bronze post, 8 inches high, set in a concrete base.

Culvert (Quebec, Compton County; J. E. McGrath, 1915).—In Auckland Township, about 1½ miles south of Malvina, Quebec, railroad station and 12 feet east of the east fence of the right of way of the Maine Central Railroad. A small shallow ravine, about 4 feet deep and 20 feet wide, is about 10 feet north of the station and runs from the railroad to Halls Stream.

Station mark: Standard bronze disk set in a 3-foot concrete-filled drain tile. The subsurface mark is a bottle filled with gravel buried 3 inches below the tile.

Reference Monument 510–26 (Quebec, Compton County; J. E. McGrath, 1915).—In Auckland Township, about 1¼ miles southeast of Malvina, Quebec, railroad station, about 1,500 feet east of the railroad, about 1,900 feet southeast of the farm buildings which are at the end of the road from Malvina, and about 160 feet from the west bank of Halls Stream.

Station mark: A manganese bronze post, 8 inches high, set in a concrete base.

Robert's West Base (Quebec, Compton County; J. E. McGrath, 1915).—In Auckland Township, about 1 mile south-southeast of Malvina, Quebec, railroad station and about 800 feet east of the Maine Central Railroad. It is in a stumpy pasture about 1,100 feet southeast of the farm buildings which are at the end of the road from Malvina.

Station mark: Standard bronze disk set in a 3-foot concrete-filled drain tile. The subsurface mark is a bottle filled with gravel and buried 2 inches below the tile.

Reference Monument 510–27 (New Hampshire, Coos County; J. E. McGrath, 1915).—In Pittsburg Township, about 1⅜ miles southeast of Malvina, Quebec, railroad station. The monument is in an alder swamp about 40 feet east of Halls Stream, about 1,000 feet upstream from the mouth of King Brook, and about 1,000 feet east of the railroad. It is about 50 feet south of a swampy tributary from the New Hampshire side. Map No. 12, prepared by the International Boundary Commission, showing part of Halls Stream, will be of assistance in recovering this monument.

Station mark: A manganese bronze post, 8 inches high, set in concrete.

Reference Monument 510–25 (New Hampshire, Coos County; J. E. McGrath, 1915).—In Pittsburg Township, about 1⅛ miles southeast of Malvina, Quebec, railroad station, across the stream from the upstream end of the big flat on the Canadian side, and about 550 feet from the east bank of Halls Stream. It is in the southwest corner of an abandoned pasture, 150 feet east of the right of way of the abandoned Mink Valley Railroad, and about 100 feet from an old road leading from a bridge across Halls Stream.

Station mark: A manganese bronze post, 8 inches high, set in a concrete base.

Reference Monument 510–24 (Quebec, Compton County; J. E. McGrath, 1915).—In Auckland Township, about 1 mile southeast of Malvina, Quebec, railroad station. The monument is about 300 feet west of Halls Stream on a hillside which is covered with raspberry bushes, with a few small spruce, cherry, and maple, and several large birch.   The station is about 150 feet east of the logging road from the farm on the flat south of the monument.

Station mark: A manganese bronze post, 8 inches high, set in a concrete base.

Reference Monument 510–23 (Quebec, Compton County; J. E. McGrath, 1915).—In Auckland Township, about 1 mile east-southeast of Malvina, Quebec, railroad station.   The monument is about 300 feet west of Halls Stream, in a thicket of small spruce and fir with a few large birch, and about 50 feet west of the woods road leading from the farm on the flat up the river to the old field back of Mose King's farm.   Map No. 12, prepared by the International Boundary Commission, showing part of Halls Stream, will be of assistance in recovering this monument.

Station mark: A manganese bronze post, 8 inches high, set in a concrete base.

Reference Monument 510–22 (Quebec, Compton County; J. E. McGrath, 1915).—In Auckland Township, about 1 mile east of Malvina, Quebec, railroad station.   The monument is on a hillside sloping east, covered with raspberry bushes and a few large birch and small fir.   It is about 75 feet west of the logging road which parallels the stream from the farm on the flat north to Mose King's field.   It is about 300 feet west of Halls Stream.

Station mark: A manganese bronze post, 8 inches high, set in a concrete base.

Reference Monument 510–21 (Quebec, Compton County; J. E. McGrath, 1915).—In Auckland Township, about 1 mile east of Malvina, Quebec, railroad station.   It is about 700 feet south of the road over the hill from Mose King's farm to Halls Stream, measured from where the road enters a small field.   It is about 280 feet west of the mouth of the large brook which flows into Halls Stream from the Canadian side.   It is about 75 feet east of the logging road leading from the farm on the flat upriver to Mose King's field.

Station mark: A manganese bronze post, 8 inches high, set in a concrete base.

Reference Monument 510–20 (Quebec, Compton County; J. E. McGrath, 1915).—In Auckland Township, about 1 mile east of Malvina, Quebec, railroad station, in the northwest corner of an old field on the side of the hill west of a large brook flowing into Halls Stream from the northwest.   The monument is about 500 feet west of this brook and about 150 feet north of the road from Mose King's farm which crosses the south side of this small field.

Station mark: A manganese bronze post, 8 inches high, set in a concrete base.

Reference Monument 510–19 (Quebec, Compton County; J. E. McGrath, 1915).—In Auckland Township, about 1¼ miles east-northeast of Malvina, Quebec, railroad station.   The monument is on the top of a knoll which slopes abruptly to the stream and gently to the westward.   It is about 210 feet west of Halls Stream and about 360 feet northwest of the bridge across Halls Stream on the road from Mose King's farm.

Station mark: A manganese bronze post, 8 inches high, set in a concrete base.

Reference Monument 510–18 (New Hampshire, Coos County; J. E. McGrath, 1915).—In Pittsburg Township, about 1½ miles northeast of Malvina, Quebec, railroad station, and about one-fourth mile northeast of the bridge across Halls Stream on the road from Mose King's farm.   It is about 145 feet east of Halls Stream.

Station mark: A manganese bronze post, 8 inches high, set in a concrete base.

Reference Monument 510–17 (New Hampshire, Coos County; J. E. McGrath, 1915).—In Pittsburg Township, about 1⅝ miles northeast of Malvina, Quebec, railroad station.   The monument is on the east edge of an old logging road, and is about 160 feet north of a brook at the point where it crosses the road.   It is about 600 feet east of Halls Stream.

Station mark: A manganese bronze post, 8 inches high, set in a concrete base.

Reference Monument 510–16 (New Hampshire, Coos County; J. E. McGrath, 1915).—In Pittsburg Township, about 1¾ miles northeast of Malvina, Quebec, railroad station.   The monument is about 290 feet southeast of Halls Stream measured parallel with the brook which passes 60 feet north of the monument.   It is about 100 feet west of an old logging road and 5 feet southeast of a large yellow birch.

Station mark: A manganese bronze post, 8 inches high, set in a concrete base.

Reference Monument 510–15 (New Hampshire, Coos County; J. E. McGrath, 1915).—In Pittsburg Township, about 2 miles northeast of Malvina, Quebec, railroad station.   The monument is about 20 feet west of the logging road which follows the stream on the United States side and about 45 feet from the bank of Halls Stream.   It is about 130 feet downstream from the mouth of a small brook on the United States side.   Map No. 13, prepared by the International Boundary Commission, showing part of Halls Stream, will be of assistance in recovering this monument.

Station mark: A manganese bronze post, 8 inches high, set in a concrete base.

Reference Monument 510–14 (New Hampshire, Coos County; J. E. McGrath, 1915).—In Pittsburg Township, about 2⅛ miles northeast of Malvina, Quebec, railroad station.   The monument is about 50 feet east of the old logging road which runs close under the high point of land on which the monument is located.

This point of land extends into the alder swamp and is covered with large white birch and spruce. The monument is about 60 feet south of a small brook and about 65 feet southwest of the mouth of this brook.

Station mark: A manganese bronze post, 8 inches high, set in a concrete base.

Reference Monument 510-13 (New Hampshire, Coos County; J. E. McGrath, 1915).—In Pittsburg Township, about 2¼ miles northeast of Malvina, Quebec, railroad station, about 30 feet east of the top of the high bank along the east side of Halls Stream. An old logging road runs along the foot of this bank and a strip of alders lies between the road and the river. It is about 90 feet east of Halls Stream.

Station mark: A manganese bronze post, 8 inches high, set in a concrete base.

Reference Monument 510-12 (New Hampshire, Coos County; J. E. McGrath, 1915).—In Pittsburg Township, about 2¼ miles northeast of Malvina, Quebec, railroad station, about 60 feet east of Halls Stream and about 20 feet east of western edge of a spruce and fir thicket. Map No. 13, prepared by the International Boundary Commission, showing part of Halls Stream, will be of assistance in recovering this station.

Station mark: A manganese bronze post, 8 inches high, set in a concrete base.

Reference Monument 510-11 (New Hampshire, Coos County; J. E. McGrath, 1915).—In Pittsburg Township, about 2½ miles northeast of Malvina, Quebec, railroad station and about 200 feet east of Halls Stream, in a mixed birch and spruce woods. Map No. 13, prepared by the International Boundary Commission, showing part of Halls Stream, will be of assistance in recovering this monument.

Station mark: A manganese bronze post, 8 inches high, set in a concrete base.

Reference Monument 510-10 (New Hampshire, Coos County; J. E. McGrath, 1915).—In Pittsburg Township, about 2½ miles northeast of Malvina, Quebec, railroad station, about 50 feet east of the old logging road, and about 75 feet east of Halls Stream. It is about 20 feet inside of the western edge of the timberland. Map No. 13, prepared by the International Boundary Commission, showing part of Halls Stream, will be of assistance in recovering this station.

Station mark: A manganese bronze post, 8 inches high, set in a concrete base.

Reference Monument 510-9 (New Hampshire, Coos County; J. E. McGrath, 1915).—In Pittsburg Township, about 2½ miles northeast of Malvina, Quebec, railroad station, about 100 feet east of the confluence of Halls Stream and the North Fork. It is on the eastern side of the clearing around the old lumber camp at the forks of the stream, and is about 40 feet from the North Fork. Map No. 13, prepared by the International Boundary Commission, showing part of Halls Stream, will be of assistance in recovering this monument.

Station mark: A manganese bronze post, 8 inches high, set in a concrete base.

Reference Monument 510-8 (Quebec, Compton County; J. E. McGrath, 1915).—In Auckland Township, about 3 miles northeast of Malvina, Quebec, railroad station. The monument is on the west side of Halls Stream near the edge of the low swampy ground and about 30 feet from the bank of the stream. It is about 1,000 feet northwest of the junction of the North Fork with Halls Stream and is about 650 feet north of a well-defined woods road leading from the settlement on the Canadian side to the forks of the stream.

Station mark: A manganese bronze post, 8 inches high, set in a concrete base.

Reference Monument 510-7 (Quebec, Compton County; J. E. McGrath, 1915).—In Auckland Township, about 3 miles north-northeast of Malvina, Quebec, railroad station, on the high bank south of Halls Stream. A woods road runs about 12 feet south of the monument, and about 18 feet southeast of the monument a small spring brook crosses the woods road and runs in a northeast direction. The monument is about 90 feet from Halls Stream.

Station mark: A manganese bronze post, 8 inches high, set in a concrete base.

Reference Monument 510-6 (Quebec, Compton County; J. E. McGrath, 1915).—In Auckland Township, about 3 miles north-northeast of Malvina, Quebec, railroad station, on top of the high bank on the south side of Halls Stream. A woods road runs about 100 feet south of the monument—the same road which runs past reference monument 510-7. The monument is about 75 feet from Halls Stream. Map No. 13, prepared by the International Boundary Commission, showing part of Halls Stream, will be of assistance in recovering this monument.

Station mark: A manganese bronze post, 8 inches high, set in a concrete base.

Reference Monument 510-5 (Quebec, Compton County; J. E. McGrath, 1915).—In Auckland Township, in a heavy growth of hardwood near the top of the gradually sloping bank of the south side of Halls Stream. A shallow ravine runs just east of the monument and then in a northeast direction to the stream. The monument is about 250 feet from Halls Stream. Map No. 13, prepared by the International Boundary Commission, showing part of Halls Stream, will be of assistance in recovering this monument.

Station mark: A manganese bronze post, 8 inches high, set in a concrete base.

Reference Monument 510-4 (Quebec, Compton County; J. E. McGrath, 1915).—In Auckland Township, about 2½ miles north-northeast of Malvina, Quebec, railroad station. It is about 10 feet south of the top of the steep bank on the south side of Halls Stream. About 150 feet southeast of the monument there is a broad, shallow ravine and about 300 feet to the northwest is a deep gorge running down to the stream. A rough woods road runs about 100 feet south of the station. The monument is about 140 feet from Halls Stream. Map No. 13, prepared by the International Boundary Commission, showing part of Halls Stream, will be of assistance in recovering this monument.

Station mark: A manganese bronze post, 8 inches high, set in a concrete base.

Shade (Quebec, Compton County; J. E. McGrath, 1915).—In Auckland Township, about 2½ miles north of Malvina, Quebec, railroad station, and about 1½ miles downstream from the head of Halls Stream. It is about midway between monuments 510-3 and 510-4 and is about 160 feet southwest of the stream. About 300 feet south of the station a deep gorge runs down to the stream.

Station mark: Standard bronze disk set in a 3-foot concrete-filled drain tile. The subsurface mark is a bottle filled with gravel, buried 4 inches below the tile.

Reference Monument 510-3 (Quebec, Compton County; J. E. McGrath, 1915).—In Auckland Township, about 2½ miles north of Malvina, Quebec, railroad station, on a flat ridge sloping gently to Halls Stream. It is in a heavy growth of hardwood, with a few spruce. It is about 170 feet from Halls Stream at its nearest point and about 65 feet north of a small brook which flows into Halls Stream. Map No. 13, prepared by the International Boundary Commission, showing part of Halls Stream, will be of assistance in recovering this monument.

Station mark: A manganese bronze post, 8 inches high, set in a concrete base.

Reference Monument 510-2 (Quebec, Compton County; J. E. McGrath, 1915).—In Auckland Township, about 2¾ miles north of Malvina, Quebec, railroad station, in a heavy hardwood growth on land sloping gently toward Halls Stream. It is about 200 feet from the west bank of Halls Stream. Map No. 13, prepared by the International Boundary Commission, showing part of Halls Stream, will be of assistance in recovering this monument.

Station mark: A manganese bronze post, 8 inches high, set in a concrete base.

Reference Monument 510-1 (Quebec, Compton County; J. E. McGrath, 1915).—In Auckland Township, about 2¾ miles north of Malvina, Quebec, railroad station, on slightly rolling land. To the north of the monument is heavy hardwood timber. To the south is burnt land covered with a dense spruce and fir thicket with a few dead birch stubs. The monument is about 100 feet from Halls Stream. Map No. 13, prepared by the International Boundary Commssion, showing part of Halls Stream, will be of assistance in recovering this monument.

Station mark: A manganese bronze post, 8 inches high, set in a concrete base.

Shine (Quebec, Compton County; J. E. McGrath, 1915).—In Auckland Township, about 3 miles north of Malvina, Quebec, railroad station, about 500 feet southwest of Halls Stream, and about 900 feet east of the north-and-south road that begins at Malvina railroad station. Map No. 13, prepared by the International Boundary Commission, showing part of Halls Stream, should be used in recovering this station.

Station mark: A bronze disk set in a 3-foot concrete-filled drain tile. The subsurface mark is a bottle filled with gravel and buried 4 inches below the tile.

Labor (Quebec, Compton County; J. E. McGrath, 1915).—In Auckland Township, about 3 miles north of Malvina, Quebec, railroad station, about 600 feet southwest of Halls Stream, and about 400 feet east of the north-and-south road that begins at Malvina railroad station. Map No. 13, prepared by the International Boundary Commission, showing part of Halls Stream, should be used in recovering this station.

Station mark: Standard bronze disk set in a 3-foot concrete-filled drain tile. The subsurface mark is a bottle filled with gravel and buried 4 inches below the tile.

Berry (Quebec, Compton County; J. E. McGrath, 1915).—In Auckland Township, about 1 mile downstream from the head of Halls Stream and about 400 feet from the stream; about 700 feet downstream from the first brook on the south side of the stream. An old tote road crosses the stream at the mouth of the brook.

Station mark: Standard bronze disk set in a 3-foot concrete-filled drain tile. The subsurface mark is a bottle filled with gravel and buried 4 inches below the bottom of the tile.

Run (New Hampshire, Coos County; J. E. McGrath, 1915).—In Pittsburg Township, about one-half mile downstream from the head of Halls Stream. It is in the alder swamp on the east side of Halls Stream and about 15 feet from the middle of the stream. It is 275 feet northwest of monument 509.

Station mark: Standard bronze disk set in a 3-foot concrete-filled drain tile. The subsurface mark is a bottle filled with gravel and buried 4 inches below the bottom of the tile.

Bog (New Hampshire, Coos County; J. E. McGrath, 1915).—In Pittsburg Township, about 3 miles north of Malvina, Quebec, railroad station, about 1,800 feet downstream from the head of Halls Stream, and about 275 feet from the stream.

Station mark: Standard bronze disk set in a 3-foot concrete-filled drain tile. The subsurface mark is a bottle filled with gravel buried 4 inches below the tile.

Solid (New Hampshire, Coos County; J. E. McGrath, 1915).—In Pittsburg Township, about 3 miles north of Malvina, Quebec, railroad station, about 1,100 feet downstream from the head of Halls Stream, and about 100 feet east of its east bank. It is on the southern end of a small flat ridge extending out into the alder swamp, about 10 feet above the swamp, and about 3 feet from where the ridge drops off to the level of the swamp.

Station mark: Standard bronze disk set in a 3-foot concrete-filled drain tile. The subsurface mark is a bottle filled with gravel and buried 3 inches below the tile.

Hub (Quebec, Compton County; J. E. McGrath, 1915).—In Auckland Township, about 3 miles north of Malvina, Quebec, railroad station and about 600 feet downstream from the head of Halls Stream. It is on a high spruce knoll about 80 feet south of Halls Stream, on the southeastern side of the knoll, just at the edge of the rather flat top.

Station mark: Standard bronze disk set in a 2-foot concrete-filled drain tile. The subsurface mark is a bottle filled with gravel and buried in a hole in the ledge, 3 inches below the bottom of the tile.

Still (Quebec, Compton County; J. E. McGrath, 1915).—In Auckland Township, about 3 miles north of Malvina, Quebec, railroad station, in very swampy ground at the head of Halls Stream, and 52 feet west of monument 507.

Station mark: Standard bronze disk set in a 3-foot concrete-filled drain tile. The subsurface mark is a bottle filled with gravel and buried 4 inches below the tile.

Big (Quebec, Compton County; J. E. McGrath, 1915).—In Auckland Township, about 3 miles north of Malvina, Quebec, railroad station, on the high land north of the head of Halls Stream and about 65 feet northwest of monument 505.

Station mark: Standard bronze disk set in a 3-foot concrete-filled drain tile. The subsurface mark is a bottle filled with gravel and buried 4 inches below the tile.

HALLS STREAM, POINTS SUPPLEMENTARY TO MINOR SCHEME

Reference Monument 512-5 (Quebec, Compton County; J. E. McGrath, 1914).—In Hereford Township, about 1 mile north of Beecher Falls, Vt., on the west bank of Halls Stream, in Frank Rowell's meadow, about 900 feet south of his house. It is about 100 feet south of the south end of a small pond, about 170 feet east of the Maine Central Railroad, and about 15 feet from the bank of the stream. It is distant 272 feet, in azimuth 229° 48′, from station "Rock."

Station mark: Standard bronze disk set in a 3-foot concrete post. The subsurface mark is a beer bottle filled with sand buried beneath the concrete post.

Reference Monument 512-3 (New Hampshire, Coos County; J. E. McGrath, 1914).—In Pittsburg Township, about 3 miles north of Beecher Falls, Vt. It is on the east bank of Halls Stream, about 15 feet above the northeast side of the bridge over Halls Stream, on the road leading from the Van Dyke farm to the Bryan farm. Directly south of the monument the water is but 1 foot distant. This ledge is about 7 feet above ordinary water level.

Station mark: A bronze disk set in a hole drilled in ledge rock.

Reference Monument 512-2 (New Hampshire, Coos County; J. E. McGrath, 1914).—In Pittsburg Township, about 3 miles north of Beecher Falls, Vt. It is on the east bank of Halls Stream, in Thomas Lambart's pasture, about 10 feet west of the line fence between the Lambart and Bryan farms and about 110 feet north of the river bank, measured along this line fence.

Station mark: A bronze disk set in a 3-foot concrete post whose top is flush with the surface of the ground. The subsurface mark is a small bottle filled with sand buried beneath the concrete post.

Reference Monument 512-1 (New Hampshire, Coos County; J. E. McGrath, 1914).—In Pittsburg Township, about 3½ miles north of Beecher Falls, Vt. It is on the east bank of Halls Stream, about 450 feet southwest of Jubal Wheeler's farm buildings on his lower farm. It is on the edge of a hayfield about 45 feet southwest of a small ravine that extends from the river bank back to the woods. It is about 6 feet from the edge of the high, steep bank.

Station mark: A bronze disk set in a 3-foot concrete post whose top is flush with the surface of the ground. The subsurface mark is a small bottle filled with sand buried beneath the concrete post.

Reference Monument 512 (New Hampshire, Coos County; J. E. McGrath, 1914).—In Pittsburgh Township, about 4 miles north of Beecher Falls, Vt. It is on the east side of Halls Stream, 3 feet south of the southeast wing wall of the east abutment of the highway bridge on the road leading from Fred Owen's farm, in Quebec, to Jubal Wheeler's farm.

Station mark: Cast-iron obelisk extending 3 feet above its concrete base.

Reference Monument 511–16 (New Hampshire, Coos County; J. E. McGrath, 1914).—In Pittsburg Township, on the east side of Halls Stream, one-half mile southeast of East Hereford, Quebec, about one-fourth mile north of Jubal Wheeler's farm buildings. It is about 300 feet upstream from the mouth of the West Branch of Halls Stream, which flows through East Hereford village, and about 75 feet from the bank of Halls Stream.

Station mark: A bronze disk set in a 3-foot concrete post whose top is flush with the surface of the ground. The subsurface mark is a beer bottle filled with sand buried beneath the concrete.

Reference Monument 511–15 (Quebec, Compton County; J. E. McGrath, 1914).—In Hereford Township, about three-fourths mile east of East Hereford, Quebec. It is on the west bank of Halls Stream in the southeast corner of the wooded pasture of Chouinard's farm and about 85 feet upstream from the fence between the pasture and the hay and grain field. It is about 450 feet above the farm road leading from Chouinard's farm across the stream to Beloir's farm, and about 138 feet downstream from the mouth of the Middle Branch of Halls Stream.

Station mark: A bronze disk set in a hole drilled in ledge rock.

Reference Monument 511–14 (New Hampshire, Coos County; J. E. McGrath, 1914).—In Pittsburg Township, about 1½ miles northeast of East Hereford, Quebec. It is on the east bank of Halls Stream, on the upper end of Beloir's meadow at the edge of a piece of swampy wooded land. It is about 180 feet north of the road from Beloir's to the Caron farm, and 30 feet from the bank of Halls Stream.

Station mark: A bronze disk set in a 3-foot concrete post whose top is flush with the surface of the ground. The subsurface mark is a small bottle filled with sand buried beneath the concrete post.

Reference Monument 511–13 (Quebec, Compton County; J. E. McGrath, 1914).—In Hereford Township, about 2 miles northeast of East Hereford, Quebec. It is on the highest ground on the west bank of Halls Stream, directly opposite the buildings on the Caron farm, which are at the end of the road on the New Hampshire side. Mile post L. R. 47 of the Maine Central Railroad bears northwest from the monument. The monument is on the middle one of three ledges and is about 50 feet from the stream.

Station mark: A bronze disk set in a hole drilled in ledge rock.

Reference Monument 511–12 (New Hampshire, Coos County; J. E. McGrath, 1914).—In Pittsburg Township, about 2½ miles northeast of East Hereford, Quebec. It is on the east side of Halls Stream. It is near the northeast corner of the level part of the old Caron farm. It is about 35 feet south of the top of a high, steep bank into which the stream is cutting.

Station mark: A bronze disk set in a 3-foot concrete post. The subsurface mark is a small bottle filled with sand, buried beneath the concrete post.

Reference Monument 511–11 (Quebec, Compton County; J. E. McGrath, 1914).—In Hereford Township, about seven-eighths mile south of Paquetteville, Quebec, railroad station. It is on a bowlder which is 15 feet long, 8 feet wide, and 4 feet high. The monument is about 55 feet from the railroad track and about 180 feet from Halls Stream.

Station mark: A bronze disk set in a hole drilled in the bowlder.

Reference Monument 511–10 (New Hampshire, Coos County; J. E. McGrath, 1914).—In Pittsburg Township, about one-half mile south of Paquetteville, Quebec, railroad station. It is on a large, nearly flat rock at the water's edge, on the east bank of Halls Stream. The surface of the rock is roughly 5½ feet long and 2½ feet wide. Map No. 10, prepared by the International Boundary Commission, showing part of Halls Stream, will be of assistance in recovering this monument.

Station mark: A bronze disk set in a hole drilled in the rock at its highest point.

Reference Monument 511–9 (New Hampshire, Coos County; J. E. McGrath, 1914).—In Pittsburg Township, about 1,700 feet east of Paquetteville, Quebec, railroad station. At this point the level bank (on the New Hampshire shore) shows a flat stretch, about 15 feet above water level and about 20 feet wide; and at a point about 125 feet downstream this level area disappears in a high bank nearly 20 feet high which is washing away. The monument is on a bowlder at the water's edge, whose dimensions are roughly 3 feet by 4 feet by 2½ feet.

Station mark: A bronze disk set in a hole drilled in the bowlder.

Reference Monument 511-8 (New Hampshire, Coos County; J. E. McGrath 1914).—In Pittsburg Township, 1¼ miles northeast of Paquetteville, Quebec, railroad station. It is at the top of the only steep, high, river bank (50 feet high) in this vicinity on the New Hampshire side of Halls Stream. The monument may be reached by crossing Halls Stream from the Paquetteville railroad station and following the road which leads to Moses St. Cyr's, on the New Hampshire side. The monument is about 600 feet southwest of St. Cyr's house and about 40 feet west of the road.

Station mark: A bronze disk set in a 3-foot concrete post whose top is flush with the surface of the ground.

Reference Monument 511-7 (Quebec, Compton County; J. E. McGrath, 1914).—In Hereford Township, 1¾ miles northeast of Paquetteville, Quebec, railroad station, in a black bowlder on the river bank, the only one of its kind in this vicinity. It is about 2,300 feet south of the more southerly of the two railroad bridges crossing Halls Stream. The stream follows the railroad for about 800 feet, in this vicinity, keeping at an average distance of about 25 feet, and the monument is near the point where the stream turns away from the railroad. The monument is about 6 feet from the edge of the stream and about 18 feet from the center of the railroad.

Station mark: A bronze disk set in a hole drilled in the bowlder.

Reference Monument 511-6 (New Hampshire, Coos County; J. E. McGrath, 1914).—In Pittsburg Township, about 2 miles northeast of the Paquetteville, Quebec, railroad station. It is set in the coping stone of the northeast wing wall of the north abutment of the wooden railroad bridge crossing Halls Stream.

Station mark: A bronze disk set in a hole drilled in the top of the bridge abutment.

Reference Monument 511-5 (New Hampshire, Coos County; J. E. McGrath, 1914).—In Pittsburg Township, about 2½ miles northeast of the Paquetteville, Quebec, railroad station. It is set in a granite block which forms the top of the southwest corner of the abutment of the steel bridge over Halls Stream. The distance from the monument to the southwest corner of the steel bridge is 9.28 feet; to the southeast corner of the bridge is 19.14 feet; and to the center line of the railroad is 8.76 feet.

Station mark: Standard bronze disk cemented in a hole drilled in the top of the bridge abutment.

VERMONT-QUEBEC AND NEW YORK-QUEBEC BOUNDARIES TO THE ST. LAWRENCE RIVER

Stewart (New Hampshire, Coos County; J. D. Craig, 1917).—In Stewartstown Township, on top of a rock bluff, an outcrop on the south end of the ridge on the east side of the Connecticut River, overlooking West Stewartstown, N. H.

Station mark: Bronze disk of the Geodetic Survey of Canada set in a crevice in the rock.

Fino (Quebec, Compton County; J. D. Craig, 1917).—In Hereford Township, on the bald southwest shoulder of a hill on the property of Mose Leandon, at a point where the hill breaks off abruptly to the south and west. To reach the station from Hereford, Quebec, post office, take the first turn at the church to the right across the creek, and go up the hill; turn to the left at a red barn and follow the road to the foot of the hill.

Station mark: Bronze disk of the Geodetic Survey of Canada set in rock flush with the surface of the ground.

Searchme (Vermont, Essex County; J. D. Craig, 1917).—In Canaan Township, on the highest point of Harrimans Hill, immediately southeast of Wallace Pond. To reach the station, take the road to the south at the east end of Wallace Pond. It is 20 minutes' walk from the end of the road to the summit of the hill, which is heavily timbered with hardwood.

Station mark: Copper bolt of the Geodetic Survey of Canada, set in rock flush with the surface of the ground.

Brown (Quebec, Stanstead County; J. D. Craig, 1917).—In Barford Township, on a bald shoulder on the southwest end of Spring Hill, on property of Mr. Chamberlain, of Dixville, Quebec. To reach the station, take the road east from Dixville, Quebec, to the foot of the hill, at which point the road turns abruptly north.

Station mark: Copper bolt set in solid rock.

Averill (Vermont, Essex County; J. D. Craig, 1917).—In Norton Township, on a partly cleared hill just west of Averill Lakes. The station is on a small rock outcrop on the highest point of the hill, in a clump of spruce and birch. To reach the station, go east from Norton Mills, Vt., take the second turn to the right, and climb from the end of the road. The hill is the property of the Connecticut Valley Lumber Co.

Station mark: Copper bolt set in solid rock.

Pinnacle (Quebec, Stanstead County; J. D. Craig, 1917).—In Barnston Township, on Barnston Pinnacle. To reach the station, follow the road south along the lake shore from Baldwins Mills. A trail leads up from the end of the road. The station is on the highest point of the hill overlooking the country to the south and west.

Station mark: Bronze disk of the Geodetic Survey of Canada set in solid rock.

Duck (Vermont, Orleans County; J. D. Craig, 1917).—In Holland Township, on the northerly slope of John Mountain, about 2 miles east of Holland Center. The station is at the lower edge of the timber which covers the summit of the hill.

Station mark: Bronze disk of the Geodetic Survey of Canada set in solid rock.

Fairfax (Quebec, Stanstead County; J. D. Craig, 1917).—In Stanstead Township, on the summit of a bald hill about 3 miles southwest of Ways Mills, Quebec. The hill is locally known as Fairfax Heights. The station is just west of H. Gould's farmhouse and north of the farmhouse of Wilfrid Senecal. A 30-foot tripod and scaffold were erected here.

Station mark: Bronze disk of the Geodetic Survey of Canada set in solid rock.

Dufferin (Quebec, Stanstead County; J. D. Craig, 1917).—In Stanstead Township, in an open field about 600 feet west of the flagpole on Dufferin Heights, which is approximately 5 miles north of Rock Island, Quebec.

Station mark: Bronze disk of the Geodetic Survey of Canada set in solid rock.

Oats (Quebec, Stanstead County; J. D. Craig, 1917).—In Stanstead Township, 1 mile west of Smiths Mills, Quebec. It is on a rock outcrop in the open field 750 feet northeast of J. S. Derick's barn.

Station mark: Bronze disk of the Geodetic Survey of Canada set in solid rock.

Derrick (Quebec, Stanstead County; J. D. Craig, 1917).—In Stanstead Township, in a hayfield about 1 mile west of Smiths Mills, Quebec, and 450 feet north of the barn on the farm of J. S. Derick.

Station mark: Nail in hub.

East Lake (Vermont, Orleans County; J. D. Craig, 1917).—In Derby Township, on the bald summit of Dowlings Hill, about 2 miles south of Beebe Plain, Vt.

Station mark: Bronze disk of the Geodetic Survey of Canada set in solid rock. An old drill hole near-by marks a station of unknown origin.

Newport (Vermont, Orleans County; J. D. Craig, 1917).—In Troy Township, on the northerly slope of a hill about 3 miles due east of Newport Center, Vt. It is in thick spruce timber and near its southerly limit. A 35-foot tripod and scaffold were erected at the station.

Station mark: No mark could be set at the station. Two reference bolts were set as follows: East bolt is 115.4 feet distant, in azimuth 214° 31', from the station; west bolt is 134.5 feet distant, in azimuth 77° 13', from the station.

Owls Head (Quebec, Brome County; Geodetic Survey of Canada, J. D. Craig, 1917).—In Potton Township, about 6 miles from the village of Mansonville, Quebec, on the highest point of the most northerly knob of the mountain known as Owls Head. Information and livery can be had from Wright Magoun, who lives at the base of the mountain. A path to the summit runs up the north side of the mountain from the Magoun farm.

Station mark: Copper bolt set in rock and stamped with the die of the Geodetic Survey of Canada, around which an equilateral triangle is cut in the rock. The reference marks are three copper bolts, each of which is set in the rock at the point of an arrow carved in the rock. They are located at the following azimuths and distances from the station: No. 1, azimuth 8° 21', distance 20.8 feet; No. 2, azimuth 199° 06', distance 17.1 feet; No. 3, azimuth 267° 08', distance 49.65 feet.

Jay (Vermont, Franklin County; J. D. Craig, 1917).—In Jay Township, on the highest point of Jay Peak.

Station mark: Bronze disk of the Geodetic Survey of Canada set in solid rock.

Round Top (Quebec, Brome County; J. D. Craig, 1917).—In Sutton Township, on "Round Top"—a mountain about 3 miles north and east of Glen Sutton (Glenton), Quebec. The station is on the southeasterly side of the top of the hill. To reach the station, take the Fourth Concession road, which leaves the main road between Sutton and Glen Sutton, go east about 2 miles, pass Alex. Westover's house, turn north at the orchard, and follow the creek to the watershed; then go northeast to the station.

Station mark: Bronze disk of the Geodetic Survey of Canada set in solid rock.

Doctor (Vermont, Franklin County; J. D. Craig, 1917).—In Enosburg Township, on the summit of a bald hill about 4 miles south of East Berkshire, Vt. To reach the station, cross the river at East Berkshire, take the first turn to the right, then a sharp turn to the left 2½ miles from the village. Continue over the hill, down across the creek, and take the first turn to the right, then climb to the top of the hill.

Station mark: Bronze disk of the Geodetic Survey of Canada set in solid rock.

St. Armand (Quebec, Missisquoi County; Geodetic Survey of Canada, 1910; J. D. Craig, 1917).—In St. Armand Seigneury, on the top of a mountain called The Pinnacle. The station is most easily reached from the town of Richford, Vt., on the Newport and Boston branch of the Canadian Pacific Railway, by a drive of 4 miles to the farm of F. S. Clark, and thence by way of a path leading from the back of his farm to the top of the mountain. The top of the mountain is almost bare rock, with scattered small scrub. An unobstructed view can be had in all directions. To the north of the summit is a triangulation station used by the Militia Department, marked by a copper bolt with a cross on it. The summit of the hill is a flat rock, which was selected as the best location for the station.

Station mark: A copper bolt leaded in the rock. An equilateral triangle is cut around it; the bolt is stamped with the Canadian Geodetic Survey die; it is referenced by the triangulation mark of the Canadian Militia Department and by three arrows cut in the rock, with copper bolts at their points, situated as follows:

	Azimuth (from the south)		Distance
	°	′	Feet
Reference bolt	131	08	43.5
Station of Militia Department	165	50	133.23
Reference bolt	266	34	24.3
Reference bolt	350	30	49.6

Three concrete foot blocks for the tripod of the large observing instrument were built, also a lamp stand for the lightman; the directions of the principal points were marked on the top of the stand.

Franklin (Vermont, Grand Isle County; J. D. Craig, 1917).—In Franklin Township, on a bare hill on the property of ex-Governor Gates, of Vermont, about 1½ miles west of Franklin Pond.

Station mark: Bronze disk of the Geodetic Survey of Canada set in solid rock.

McDermott (Quebec, Missisquoi County; J. D. Craig, 1917).—In St. Armand Seigneury, about 1½ miles west of Frelighsburg, Quebec. It is on the southerly slope of the hill behind W. Pelletier's farmhouse.

Station mark: Bronze disk of the Geodetic Survey of Canada set in rock outcrop.

Sheldon (Vermont, Franklin County; J. D. Craig, 1917).—In Sheldon Township, about 1 mile south of Sheldon Springs, Vt., on the northerly shoulder of the hill immediately west of the county poorhouse. The station is on a rock outcrop just north of the most northerly trees on the summit of the ridge.

Station mark: Bronze disk of the Geodetic Survey of Canada set in solid rock.

Saint (Vermont, Grand Isle County; J. D. Craig, 1917).—In Alburg Township, on the bare hill east of Lamoreux Bros.' farm buildings, about 2 miles south of St. Armand, Quebec.

Station mark: Bronze disk of the Geodetic Survey of Canada set in solid rock.

Blair (Vermont, Grand Isle County; J. D. Craig, 1917).—In Alburg Township, about 1 mile north and west of East Alburg, Vt., on the summit of the ridge where it is crossed by the road. The station is about 5 feet south of the fence on the north side of the road and about 20 feet east of the gate in the fence.

Station mark: Bronze disk of the Geodetic Survey of Canada set in rock flush with the surface of the ground.

Alburg (Vermont, Grand Isle County; J. D. Craig, 1917).—In Alburg Township, on a bare ridge about 2½ miles south and west of Alburg Center, Vt. To reach the station, go south from Alburg Center about 2 miles, west across the railway, and south one-fourth mile. The station is on a bare ridge west of the road, on the property of Edson L. Mitchell. A 30-foot tripod and scaffold were erected here.

Station mark: Bronze disk of the Geodetic Survey of Canada set in rock flush with the ground.

Champlain (New York, Clinton County; J. D. Craig, 1917).—In Champlain Township, about 2 miles south of Champlain, N. Y. To reach the station, take the road turning south at the bridge in the village. The station is in the northeast corner of a thick clump of cedars, and about 450 feet east of the road. It is on the property of P. Catelli, Champlain, N. Y.

Station mark: Bronze disk of the Geodetic Survey of Canada.

Covey Hill (Quebec, Huntingdon County; Geodetic Survey of Canada, 1908; J. D. Craig, 1917).—In Havelock Township, on Covey Hill, on lots 34C and 35C of range 1, the property of John Waddell, Franklin Center, Quebec.

Station mark: Iron bolt in solid rock. Two copper reference bolts are set in rock along the south fence of the main road about 350 feet from the station. These reference bolts and the northeast corner of lot 34C, range 1, are located as follows with reference to the station:

	Azimuth (from the south)			Distance
	°	′	″	Feet
Bolt No. 1	157	27	56	338.5
Bolt No. 2	208	14	12	357.93
Northeast corner of lot 34C	249	28	14	922.9

Bolt No. 1 was not found in 1917, being covered with rock thrown in against the fence.

The distance, measured along the road fence from the above-mentioned northeast corner of the lot to bolt No. 2 is 694.98 feet, and from bolt No. 2 to bolt No. 1 is 298.45 feet.

Huntingdon (Quebec, Huntingdon County; Geodetic Survey of Canada, 1908; J. D. Craig, 1917).—In Godmanchester Township, on lot 77, range 4, on land owned by Angus Stark, who lives a short distance east of the station. The station may be reached from the railway station of Huntingdon, on the Grand Trunk and St. Lawrence & Adirondack Railways, by a drive of about 5½ miles.

Station mark: Underground and surface marks consisting of small spikes in the centers of concrete-filled vitrified-clay sewer tiles placed on end, the lower one 4.6 feet and the upper one 0.8 foot below the surface of the ground. The reference marks are as follows: Concrete monument, distant 131.51 feet, in azimuth 68° 52′ 10″, from the station; northwest corner of lot 77, distant 3,166.80 feet, in azimuth 138° 16′ 55″ from the station. A 70-foot tripod and a scaffold were erected over the station.

Bonville (Ontario, Stormont County; Geodetic Survey of Canada, 1908; J. A. Pounder, 1923).—In Cornwall Township, on the east half of lot 15, Concession VIII, on the property of Arthur Beaudette.

Station mark: The subsurface mark is the point of a 6-inch spike placed head down in cement in a 4 by 24 inch tile set in cement. Immediately above this mark is a flat stone, and above this, a near-surface mark similar in construction to the subsurface mark placed 18 inches below the surface of the ground. The southwest corner of the east half of lot 15 is distant 1,080.4 feet, in azimuth 358° 20′ 15″, from the station. A reference monument was placed close to the same lot corner at a distance of 1,070.8 feet in the same direction. A 70-foot tower was built at the station.

Sup (Quebec, Stanstead County; J. D. Craig, 1917).—In Barford Township, on the southerly slope of a sparsely timbered hill about 1 mile northwest of Stanhope, Quebec. The station is about three-fourths of the distance up the hill, near the cliffs on the east face.

Station mark: Bronze disk of the Geodetic Survey of Canada set in solid rock.

Craig's Knoll (Vermont, Essex County; J. D. Craig, 1917).—In Norton Township, on a grassy knoll about 1,400 feet south of the international boundary and about 350 feet east of the Grand Trunk Railroad.

Station mark: Copper bolt set in solid rock.

Pond (Quebec, Stanstead County; J. D. Craig, 1917).—In Barnston Township, on a rock outcrop on the southern isolated shoulder of the mountain immediately west of Lyster or Barnston Lake. The station is near the southeastern edge of the summit of the isolated shoulder, which is considerably lower than the main mountain. To reach the station, go south from Baldwins Mills along the west shore of the lake and climb the gulch between the mountain and the shoulder.

Station mark: Bronze disk of the Geodetic Survey of Canada set in solid rock.

Stanstead Bench Mark (Quebec, Stanstead County; J. D. Craig, 1917).—In Stanstead Township, in the east end of the north face of the capstone on the north end of the old stone culvert under the Boston & Maine Railroad, 45 feet east of the water tank at Stanstead, Quebec, railway station.

Station mark: Bench mark bolt of the Geodetic Survey of Canada, stamped "B. M. No. 34."

Broo (Quebec, Brome County; J. D. Craig, 1917).—In Potton Township, in a small opening in the timber on the southerly slope of the hill northwest of the farm of Fritz Broo, of Mansonville, Quebec, about three-fourths mile from his house.

Station mark: Bronze disk of the Geodetic Survey of Canada set in solid rock.

Sicard (Vermont, Orleans County; J. D. Craig, 1917).—In Troy Township, in a field, about 8 feet south of the fence along the south side of the lake. It is south of Mr. Sicard's house, which is about 3 miles due southeast of North Troy, Vt.

Station mark: Nail in hub. No permanent mark could be set.

Bickford (Vermont, Orleans County; J. D. Craig, 1917).—In Troy Township, in the second field south of Newell Bickford's farmhouse. The station is just south of a small clump of trees in the northwest corner of the field.

Station mark: Bronze disk of the Geodetic Survey of Canada set in rock outcrop mostly covered with moss.

Abercorn Bench Mark (Quebec, Brome County; J. D. Craig, 1917).—In Sutton Township, in the east face of a concrete culvert under the Canadian Pacific Railway, 250 feet north of a diagonal highway crossing, at mileage 25.8 from Enlaugra, Quebec, 1 mile south of Abercorn, Quebec.

Station mark: Bench mark bolt of the Geodetic Survey of Canada, stamped "B. M. No. 55."

Fort (New York, Clinton County; J. D. Craig, 1917).—In Champlain Township, on the site of the old astronomical station of 1845, about one-half mile north of Rouses Point, N. Y., in the open field west of old Fort Montgomery.

Station mark: The more westerly of the two holes in an 18-inch square cut stone lying just east of the two vertical cut stones forming the piers for the old prime vertical instrument.

Havelock (Quebec, Huntingdon County; J. D. Craig, 1917).—In Havelock Township, lot 37A, range 1, about three-fourths mile west of "Covey Hill" triangulation station, on the property of Jos. Charlois, in the third field south of the east-and-west road over Covey Hill. It is on a pile of rocks cleared from the field. A 35-foot tripod and scaffold were erected here.

Station mark: Bronze disk of the Geodetic Survey of Canada set in rock flush with the surface of the ground.

Clinton (New York, Clinton County; J. D. Craig, 1917).—In Clinton Township, on a slight rise in second growth about one-half mile southwest of the northeast corner of Clinton Township. A 30-foot scaffold was erected around a tree.

Station mark: Nail driven in the roots of the tree forming the center of the tripod.

Mooers (New York, Clinton County; J. D. Craig, 1917).—In Mooers Township, about 1½ miles southeast of the northwest corner of the township, on a slight rise in an open field with woods to the southeast and a burnt-over tract to the northwest. To reach the station, go west from Cannons Corners, N. Y., to the next road north. The station is about one-fourth mile west of the end of the traveled road.

Station mark: Bronze disk of the Geodetic Survey of Canada set in solid rock.

Bolt Near Line (New York, Clinton County; J. D. Craig, 1917).—In Mooers Township, about 2,000 feet west of monument 688 and just south of the Quebec-New York boundary. It is about three-fourths mile west of the "Gulf."

Station mark: Bronze disk of the Geodetic Survey of Canada set in solid rock.

Dalgliesh (Quebec, Huntingdon County; J. D. Craig, 1917).—In Godmanchester Township, about 1 mile north of Clyde Corners, Quebec, on a bare ridge with a scrub cedar to the north of the station and an old orchard to the south of it. It is on the property of Chas. T. Dalgliesh, and about 450 feet east of the road.

Station mark: Bronze disk of the Geodetic Survey of Canada set in rock flush with the surface of the ground.

Fee (Quebec, Huntingdon County; J. D. Craig, 1917).—In Elgin Township, one-half mile north of monument 722–A, on the Quebec-New York boundary and about 5 feet east of a fence.

Station mark: Nail in hub.

Leblanc (Quebec, Huntingdon County; J. D. Craig, 1917).—In Godmanchester Township, about 10 miles west of Huntingdon, Quebec. It is on the southeastern slope, near the edge of the timber, on a timbered knoll on the farm of Alphonse Leblanc.

Station mark: Nail driven in a root of the tree, which forms the center of the 30-foot tripod.

Boulder (New York, Franklin County; J. D. Craig, 1917).—In Constable Township, about three-fourths mile west of Trout River, N. Y., on a rock outcrop about 200 feet north of the road and north of an orchard. To reach the station take the road leading southwest from the village on the New York side of the line. The station is near the old foundation of a burned house. The rock has a flat top and rises 3 feet above the surface of the ground.

Station mark: Bronze disk of the Geodetic Survey of Canada set in solid rock.

Langevin (Quebec, Huntingdon County; J. D. Craig, 1917).—In Godmanchester Township, about 1½ miles northwest of Trout River, N. Y., on a slight rise just west of the barn of Mr. Langevin.

Station mark: Bronze disk of the Geodetic Survey of Canada set in solid rock.

Brady (Quebec, Huntingdon County; J. D. Craig, 1917).—In Godmanchester Township, in the flat open field between the house of Mr. Brady and the Grand Trunk Railway. The Brady house is about 1 mile north and west of Trout River, N. Y.

Station mark: Nail in hub.

U. S. L. S. No. 13 (New York, Franklin County; United States Lake Survey; J. A. Pounder, 1923).—On the Indian reservation, 1,800 feet south of the St. Lawrence River, 2,500 feet east of the Raquette River, and about 50 feet above the water surface.

Station mark: Surface and subsurface stones marked with triangles and holes; the lower stone, buried 1 foot below the surface, is 0.8 by 0.5 by 1.8 feet. The reference marks are as follows:

	Azimuth (from the south)	Distance
	° ′	*Feet*
Cross on bowlder 5 by 8 by 3½ feet above ground	170 48	136
Cross on bowlder 5 by 8 by 3½ feet	130 00	80
Cross on bowlder 6 by 6 by 2 feet	90 33	122
Southeast corner of barn	7 18	521

U. S. L. S. No. 8 (New York, Franklin County; United States Lake Survey; J. A. Pounder, 1923).—On the St. Regis Indian Reservation, 1¼ miles east of the international bridge and 1,300 feet back from the river bank.

Station mark: Surface and subsurface stones marked with triangles and center holes. Lower stone buried 3 feet below the surface of the ground. Reference marks as follows:

	Azimuth (from the south)	Distance
	° ′	*Feet*
North end stone fence	8 48	18. 5
Cross cut in rock 4 by 2 feet	121 10	17. 5
Southwest corner of house	323 52	373. 0
Northwest corner of schoolhouse	340 00	509. 0

INDEX TO TRIANGULATION AND TRAVERSE STATIONS

Station	Position	Description	Sketch	Station	Position	Description	Sketch
	Page	Page	Number		Page	Page	Number
C–260	378		8	Connor, N. B., protestant church, spire, 1910	394		6
C–261	379		8	Convent cupola, St. Basil, N. B	392		5
C–262	379		8	Convent school dome, Van Buren, Me	391		4
C–263	379		8				
C–264	379		8	Cookee	408		12
C–265	379		8	Corbert	398	465	2, 13
C–267	379		8	Corner	433		14
C–268	380		8	Cornwall, east church (Catholic)	448		3
C–269	380		8				
C–270	380		8	Cornwall, west church (Catholic)	448		3
C–271	380		8				
C–272	380		8	Covey Hill (Geodetic Survey of Canada)	444	480	3
C–273	380		8				
C–274	380		8	Craig's Knoll	444	481	3
C–275	380		8	Crete (north base)	398	465	2, 13
C–276	380		8	Cross Lake north base (S–148)	366		7
C–277	380		8				
C–278	381		8	Cross Lake south base (S–147)	366		7
C–279	381		8				
C–280	381		8	Cross on nun's building, Van Buren, Me	391		4
C–281	381		8				
C–282	381		8	Culvert	436	472	13
C–283	381		8	Customhouse flagpole, Madawaska, Me	393		5
C–284	381		8				
C–285	381		8	Customhouse flagpole, Van Buren, Me	390		4
C–286	381		8				
C–288	382		8	Cut	435	472	13
C–289	382		8	Cyr (Halls Stream)	434		14
C–291	382		8	Cyr (St. John River)	349	455	1
C–292	382		8				
C–293	382		8	Dalgliesh	447	482	3
C–294	382		8	Dave	350	456	1
C–295	382		8	Day	439		13
C–296	383		8	Dead	402	466	11
C–297	383		8	Dean	396	463	2, 11
C–299	383		8	Deer	410	468	12
C–300	383		8	Dennison	404	467	11
Camp	435		13	Derrick	443	479	3
Campbell	408	468	12	Doctor	443	479	3
Canadian Beau	348	454	1	Dome	396	463	2, 11
Canadian Glazier	347	453	1	Dry	439		13
Car	442		13	Duck	443	478	3
Caribou	346	450	1	Dufferin	443	479	3
Caron	433	470	14	Duke	438		13
Caswell	346	451	1	Duran	435	471	13
Cedar	433	470	14	Dutch	404	466	11
Cedar reference mark	433						
Center (Halls Stream)	432		14	East base, St. Regis	448		3
Center (St. John River)	347	453	1	East Hereford, Catholic Church cross	441		14
Chabot	348	454	1				
Chaloux	432	469	14	East Lake	443	479	3
Champlain	444	480	3	Easton	349	455	1
Chapel of St. Joseph and St. Anthelm (Anselme), spire, near Hamlin, Me., 1909	390		4	Eck	397	464	2, 12
				Edmund	347	452	1
Charlie	407		12	Edmundston astronomic	347	453	1
Chartierville, church spire	413		12	Edmundston bench mark	350	337, 455	1
Cherry	432	470	14	Edmundston, N. B., Catholic Church, spire, 1909	393		5
Chesham, church spire	413		12				
Clair	350	455	1	Edmundston, N. B., flagpole on cupola of brick building, 1909	393		5
Clair, N. B., church spire, 1910	394		6				
Clair east base	360		6	Edmundston, N. B., flagpole on cupola with round windows, 1909	393		5
Clair west base	360		6				
Clay	436		13	Edmundston, N. B., flagpole on pointed green cupola, 1909	393		5
Cliff	434		13, 14				
Clinton	447	482	3				
Coat	437		13	Edmundston, N. B., flagpole on sheet-iron-covered cupola, 1909	393		5
Company	436		13				
Cone	433	470	14				
Connor	346	451	1				
Connor, N. B., Catholic church, spire, 1910	394		6				

Station	Position	Description	Sketch	Station	Position	Description	Sketch
	Page	*Page*	*Number*		*Page*	*Page*	*Number*
Mon. 457 ecc	406		11	Mon. 496	411		12
Mon. 458	406		11	Mon. 496 ecc	411		12
Mon. 458 ecc	406		11	Mon. 497	412		12
Mon. 459	406		11	Mon. 497 ecc	412		12
Mon. 459 ecc	406		11	Mon. 498	412		12
Mon. 460	406		11	Mon. 499	412		12
Mon. 460 ecc	406		11	Mon. 500	412		12
Mon. 461	407		11	Mon. 500 ecc	412		12
Mon. 461 ecc	406		11	Mon. 501	412		12
Mon. 462	407		11	Mon. 501 ecc	412		12
Mon. 462 ecc	407		11	Mon. 502	412		12
Mon. 463	407		11	Mon. 502 ecc	412		12
Mon. 463 ecc	407		11	Mon. 503	412		12
Mon. 464	407		11, 12	Mon. 503 ecc	412		12
Mon. 464 ecc	407		11, 12	Mon. 504	412		12
Mon. 465	407		11, 12	Mon. 505	412		12, 13
Mon. 465 ecc	407		11, 12	Mon. 505 ecc	412		12
Mon. 466	407		12	Mon. 506	442		13
Mon. 466 ecc	407		12	Mon. 507	442		13
Mon. 467	407		12	Mon. 518	440		14
Mon. 467 ecc	407		12	Mon. 519	440, 444		3, 14
Mon. 468	407		12	Mon. 520	440		14
Mon. 468 ecc	407		12	Mon. 523–A	444		3
Mon. 469	408		12	Mon. 534–A	445		3
Mon. 469 ecc	408		12	Mon. 538–B	445		3
Mon. 470	397		2, 12	Mon. 539	445		3
Mon. 471	408		12	Mon. 545	445		3
Mon. 471 ecc	408		12	Mon. 545 ecc	445		3
Mon. 472	408		12	Mon. 550	445		3
Mon. 472 ecc	408		12	Mon. 550 ecc	445		3
Mon. 473	408		12	Mon. 551–A	445		3
Mon. 473 ecc	408		12	Mon. 566	445		3
Mon. 474	408		12	Mon. 567	445		3
Mon. 474 ecc	408		12	Mon. 574	445		3
Mon. 475 (Maine-New Hampshire boundary)	408		12	Mon. 581	445		3
				Mon. 581–A	445		3
Mon. 475 ecc	408		12	Mon. 584	445		3
Mon. 476	409		12	Mon. 588–B	446		3
Mon. 476 ecc	409		12	Mon. 590	446		3
Mon. 477	409		12	Mon. 602	446		3
Mon. 477 ecc	409		12	Mon. 606	446		3
Mon. 478	409		12	Mon. 606 ecc	446		3
Mon. 478 ecc	409		12	Mon. 621–B	446		3
Mon. 479	410		12	Mon. 621–B ecc	446		3
Mon. 479 ecc	410		12	Mon. 625	446		3
Mon. 480	409		12	Mon. 629	446		3
Mon. 481	409		12	Mon. 632 and 633	446		3
Mon. 482	409		12	Mon. 634	446		3
Mon. 483	410		12	Mon. 641–A	446		3
Mon. 483 ecc	410		12	Mon. 641–A ecc	446		3
Mon. 484	410		12	Mon. 644	447		3
Mon. 484 ecc	410		12	Mon. 644 ecc	447		3
Mon. 485	410		12	Mon. 646	446		3
Mon. 485 ecc	410		12	Mon. 647	447		3
Mon. 486	410		12	Mon. 650–A	444		3
Mon. 486 ecc	410		12	Mon. 682	447		3
Mon. 487	410		12	Mon. 688	447		3
Mon. 487 ecc	410		12	Mon. 722–A	447		3
Mon. 488	410		12	Mon. 739	448		3
Mon. 488 ecc	410		12	Mon. 739 ecc	448		3
Mon. 489	411		12	Mon. 774	448		3
Mon. 489 ecc	411		12	Mon. 1 (I. W. C.)	448		3
Mon. 490	411		12	Mon. 3 (I. W. C.)	448		3
Mon. 490 ecc	411		12	Mon. 4 (I. W. C.)	448		3
Mon. 491	411		12	Mon., 45th Parallel	446		3
Mon. 491 ecc	411		12	Mon., 45th Parallel ecc	446		3
Mon. 492	411		12	Mooers	447	482	3
Mon. 492 ecc	411		12	Moran	401	466	11
Mon. 493	411		12				
Mon. 493 ecc	411		12	N	434	471	14
Mon. 494	411		12	Nail	440		12, 13
Mon. 494 ecc	411		12	Nash	409	468	12
Mon. 495	411		12	Near	412	468	12
Mon. 495 ecc	411		12	Neil	407		12

Station	Position	Description	Sketch	Station	Position	Description	Sketch
	Page	*Page*	*Number*		*Page*	*Page*	*Number*
Ref. Mon. C-171	390		8	Ref. Mon. S-38	354		4
Ref. Mon. C-172	390		8	Ref. Mon. S-39	355		4
Ref. Mon. C-173	382		8	Ref. Mon. S-39 (Southwest Branch)	417		9
Ref. Mon. C-174	382		8				
Ref. Mon. C-175	383		8	Ref. Mon. S-40	355		4
Ref. Mon. C-176	350		1, 8	Ref. Mon. S-41	355		4
Ref. Mon. S-1	384	456	4	Ref. Mon. S-41 (Southwest Branch)	417		9
Ref. Mon. S-2	349, 351		1, 4				
Ref. Mon. S-3	351		4	Ref. Mon. S-42	349, 355		1, 4, 5
Ref. Mon. S-4	351		4	Ref. Mon. S-43	355		5
Ref. Mon. S-5	351		4	Ref. Mon. S-43 (Southwest Branch)	417		9
Ref. Mon. S-6	349, 351		1, 4				
Ref. Mon. S-7	351		4	Ref. Mon. S-44	355		5
Ref. Mon. S-8	351		4	Ref. Mon. S-45	355		5
Ref. Mon. S-8 (West base—Southwest Branch)	414		9	Ref. Mon. S-45 (Southwest Branch)	417		9
Ref. Mon. S-9	351		4	Ref. Mon. S-46	355		5
Ref. Mon. S-10	351		4	Ref. Mon. S-47	355		5
Ref. Mon. S-11	352		4	Ref. Mon. S-48	355		5
Ref. Mon. S-12	352		4	Ref. Mon. S-49	356		5
Ref. Mon. S-13	352		4	Ref. Mon. S-49 (Southwest Branch)	418		9
Ref. Mon. S-14	352		4				
Ref. Mon. S-14 (Southwest Branch)	414		9	Ref. Mon. S-50	356		5
Ref. Mon. S-15	352		4	Ref. Mon. S-50 (Southwest Branch)	418		9
Ref. Mon. S-16	352		4	Ref. Mon. S-51	356		5
Ref. Mon. S-16 (Southwest Branch)	415		9	Ref. Mon. S-52	356		5
Ref. Mon. S-17	349, 352		1, 4	Ref. Mon. S-53	356		5
Ref. Mon. S-18	352		4	Ref. Mon. S-53 (Southwest Branch)	418		9
Ref. Mon. S-18 (Southwest Branch)	415		9	Ref. Mon. S-54	356		5
Ref. Mon. S-19	352		4	Ref. Mon. S-55	356		5
Ref. Mon. S-20	352		4	Ref. Mon. S-56	356		5
Ref. Mon. S-20 (Southwest Branch)	415		9	Ref. Mon. S-56 (Southwest Branch)	419		9
Ref. Mon. S-21	353		4	Ref. Mon. S-57	356		5
Ref. Mon. S-22	353		4	Ref. Mon. S-58	357		5
Ref. Mon. S-22 (North base—Southwest Branch)	415		9	Ref. Mon. S-58 (Southwest Branch)	419		9, 10
Ref. Mon. S-23	353		4	Ref. Mon. S-59	357		5
Ref. Mon. S-24	353		4	Ref. Mon. S-59 (Southwest Branch)	419		10
Ref. Mon. S-25	385	458	4	Ref. Mon. S-60	357		5
Ref. Mon. S-25 (Southwest Branch)	416		9	Ref. Mon. S-60 (Southwest Branch)	419		10
Ref. Mon. S-26	353		4	Ref. Mon. S-61	357		5
Ref. Mon. S-26 (Southwest Branch)	416		9	Ref. Mon. S-61 (Southwest Branch)	419		10
Ref. Mon. S-27	353		4	Ref. Mon. S-62	357		5
Ref. Mon. S-28	353		4	Ref. Mon. S-62 (Southwest branch)	419		10
Ref. Mon. S-29	353		4	Ref. Mon. S-63	357		5
Ref. Mon. S-29 (Southwest Branch)	416		9	Ref. Mon. S-63 (Southwest Branch)	419		10
Ref. Mon. S-30	353		4	Ref. Mon. S-64	357		5
Ref. Mon. S-31	385	459	4	Ref. Mon. S-64 (Southwest Branch)	420		10
Ref. Mon. S-31 ecc	385			Ref. Mon. S-65	357		5
Ref. Mon. S-31 (Southwest Branch)	416		9	Ref. Mon. S-65 (Southwest Branch)	420		10
Ref. Mon. S-32	349, 354		1, 4	Ref. Mon. S-66	357		5
Ref. Mon. S-32 (Southwest Branch)	416		9	Ref. Mon. S-66 (Southwest Branch)	420		10
Ref. Mon. S-33	354		4	Ref. Mon. S-67	357		5
Ref. Mon. S-34	385	459	4	Ref. Mon. S-67 (Southwest Branch)	420		10
Ref. Mon. S-34 (Southwest Branch)	416		9	Ref. Mon. S-68	358		5
Ref. Mon. S-35	354		4	Ref. Mon. S-68 (Southwest Branch)	420		10
Ref. Mon. S-35 (Southwest Branch)	416		9	Ref. Mon. S-69	350, 358		1, 5
Ref. Mon. S-36	354		4	Ref. Mon. S-69 (Southwest Branch)	420		10
Ref. Mon. S-37	354		4	Ref. Mon. S-70	358		5
Ref. Mon. S-37 (Southwest Branch)	417		9				

Station	Position	Description	Sketch	Station	Position	Description	Sketch
	Page	*Page*	*Number*		*Page*	*Page*	*Number*
Ref. Mon. S-70 (Southwest Branch)	420		10	Ref. Mon. S-125	364		7
Ref. Mon. S-71	358		5	Ref. Mon. S-126	389		7
Ref. Mon. S-71 (Southwest Branch)	421		10	Ref. Mon. S-127	365		7
Ref. Mon. S-72	358		5	Ref. Mon. S-128	366		7
Ref. Mon. S-72 (Southwest Branch)	421		10	Ref. Mon. S-129	366		7
Ref. Mon. S-73	358, 398		5	Ref. Mon. S-130	367		7
Ref. Mon. S-73 (Southwest Branch)	421		1, 10	Ref. Mon. S-131	367		7
Ref. Mon. S-74	358, 398		5	Ref. Mon. S-132	367		7
Ref. Mon. S-74 (Southwest Branch)	421		1, 10	Ref. Mon. S-133	367		7
Ref. Mon. S-75	358		5, 6	Ref. Mon. S-134	389		7
Ref. Mon. S-75 (Southwest Branch)	421		10	Ref. Mon. S-135	350, 389		1, 7
Ref. Mon. S-76	358		5, 6	Ref. Mon. S-136	389		7
Ref. Mon. S-76 (Southwest Branch)	421		10	Ref. Mon. S-137	389		7
Ref. Mon. S-77	358		6	Ref. Mon. S-137-A	368		7
Ref. Mon. S-77 (Southwest Branch)	421		10	Ref. Mon. S-138	369		8
Ref. Mon. S-78	350, 358		1, 6	Ref. Mon. S-139	369		8
Ref. Mon. S-78 (Southwest Branch)	421		10	Ref. Mon. S-140	369		8
Ref. Mon. S-79	359		6	Ref. Mon. S-141	370		8
Ref. Mon. S-79 (Southwest Branch)	421		10	Ref. Mon. S-142	370		8
Ref. Mon. S-80	359		6	Ref. Mon. S-143	389		8
Ref. Mon. S-81	359		6	Ref. Mon. S-144	370		8
Ref. Mon. S-82	359		6	Ref. Mon. S-145	370		8
Ref. Mon. S-83	359		6	Ref. Mon. S-146	372		8
Ref. Mon. S-84	359		6	Ref. Mon. S-147	372		8
Ref. Mon. S-85	359		6	Ref. Mon. S-148	389		8
Ref. Mon. S-86	359		6	Ref. Mon. S-149	372		8
Ref. Mon. S-87	350, 359		1, 6	Ref. Mon. S-150	373		8
Ref. Mon. S-88	360		6	Ref. Mon. S-151	373		8
Ref. Mon. S-89	359		6	Ref. Mon. S-152	373		8
Ref. Mon. S-90	387		6	Ref. Mon. S-153	374		8
Ref. Mon. S-91	360		6	Ref. Mon. S-154	390		8
Ref. Mon. S-92	360		6	Eef. Mon. S-155	374		8
Ref. Mon. S-93	360		6	Ref. Mon. S-156	375		8
Ref. Mon. S-94	360		6	Ref. Mon. S-157	375		8
Ref. Mon. S-95	360		6	Ref. Mon. S-158	376		8
Ref. Mon. S-96	350, 360		1, 6	Ref. Mon. S-159	377		8
Ref. Mon. S-97	360		6	Ref. Mon. S-160	378		8
Ref. Mon. S-98	361		6	Ref. Mon. S-161	379		8
Ref. Mon. S-99	361		6	Ref. Mon. S-162	379		8
Ref. Mon. S-100	361		6	Ref. Mon. S-163	379		8
Ref. Mon. S-101	361		6	Ref. Mon. S-164	390		8
Ref. Mon. S-102	361		6	Ref. Mon. S-165	390		8
Ref. Mon. S-103	361		6	Ref. Mon. S-166	382		8
Ref. Mon. S-104	361		6	Ref. Mon. S-167	383		8
Ref. Mon. S-105	361		6	Richmond	346	449	1
Ref. Mon. S-106	361		6	Ridge (Halls Stream)	439		13
Ref. Mon. S-107	362		6	Ridge (Highlands)	411	468	12
Ref. Mon. S-108	362		6	River	402		11
Ref. Mon. S-109	362		6	Road	434		14
Ref. Mon. S-110	362		6	Roberts east base (Ref. Mon. 510-26)	436	472	13
Ref. Mon. S-111	362		6	Roberts west base	436	472	13
Ref. Mon. S-112	362		6	Rock	432	469	14
Ref. Mon. S-113	362		6	Rotten	434		13
Ref. Mon. S-114	362		6	Round Top (Highlands)	409		12
Ref. Mon. S-115	388	461	6	Round Top (West Line)	443	479	3
Ref. Mon. S-116	388		6	Rowell's house chimney	440		14
Ref. Mon. S-117	388		6	Rump	397	463	2, 12
Ref. Mon. S-118	388		6	Run	439	475	13
Ref. Mon. S-119	388		6	S-1	351		4
Ref. Mon. S-120	389		6	S-1 (Southwest Branch)	413		9
Ref. Mon. S-121	389		6	S-2 (Southwest Branch)	413		9
Ref. Mon. S-122	350, 363		1, 6, 7	S-3 (Southwest Branch)	413		9
Ref. Mon. S-123	363		6, 7	S-4 (Southwest Branch)	413		9
Ref. Mon. S-124	389		7	S-5 (Southwest Branch)	413		9
				S-6 (Southwest Branch)	413		9
				S-7 (East base — Southwest Branch)	413		9
				S-9 (Southwest Branch)	414		9
				S-10 (Southwest Branch)	414		9
				S-11 (Southwest Branch)	414		9
				S-12 (Southwest Branch)	414		9
				S-13 (Southwest Branch)	414		9

Station	Position	Description	Sketch	Station	Position	Description	Sketch
	Page	Page	Number		Page	Page	Number
S–15 (Southwest Branch)	414	_____	9	S–169	368	_____	7
S–17 (Southwest Branch)	415	_____	9	S–173	368	_____	8
S–19 (Southwest Branch)	415	_____	9	S–178	369	_____	8
S–21 (Southwest Branch)	415	_____	9	S–180	369	_____	8
S–23 (South base—Southwest Branch)	415	_____	9	S–186	370	_____	8
S–24 (Southwest Branch)	415	_____	9	S–190	370	_____	8
S–25	353	_____	4	S–192	370	_____	8
S–27 (Southwest Branch)	416	_____	9	S–195	370	_____	8
S–28 (Southwest Branch)	416	_____	9	S–197	371	_____	8
S–30 (Southwest Branch)	416	_____	9	S–198	371	_____	8
S–31	354	_____	4	S–199	371	_____	8
S–33 (Southwest Branch)	416	_____	9	S–201	371	_____	8
S–34	354	_____	4	S–202	371	_____	8
S–36 (Southwest Branch)	416	_____	9	S–203 (Blue River east base)	371	_____	8
S–38 (Southwest Branch)	417	_____	9	S–205	372	_____	8
S–40 (Southwest Branch)	417	_____	9	S–206	372	_____	8
S–42 (Southwest Branch)	417	_____	9	S–208	372	_____	8
S–44 (Southwest Branch)	417	_____	9	S–210	372	_____	8
S–46 (Southwest Branch)	418	_____	9	S–211	372	_____	8
S–47 (Southwest Branch)	418	_____	9	S–212	372	_____	8
S–48 (Southwest Branch)	418	_____	9	S–214	372	_____	8
S–51 (Southwest Branch)	418	_____	9	S–215	372	_____	8
S–52 (Southwest Branch)	418	_____	9	S–216	372	_____	8
S–54 (Southwest Branch)	418	_____	9	S–217	373	_____	8
S–55 (Southwest Branch)	419	_____	9	S–218	373	_____	8
S–57 (Southwest Branch)	419	_____	9, 10	S–219	373	_____	8
S–90	360	_____	____	S–220	373	_____	8
S–115	362	_____	6	S–221	373	_____	8
S–116	362	_____	6	S–223	373	_____	8
S–117	363	_____	6	S–226	374	_____	8
S–118	363	_____	6	S–227	374	_____	8
S–119	363	_____	6	S–228	374	_____	8
S–120	363	_____	6	S–229	374	_____	8
S–123	363	_____	7	S–230	374	_____	8
S–124	363	_____	7	S–232	374	_____	8
S–125	363	_____	7	S–233	374	_____	8
S–126	364	_____	7	S–234	374	_____	8
S–127	364	_____	7	S–235	375	_____	8
S–129	364	_____	7	S–237	375	_____	8
S–130	364	_____	7	S–238	375	_____	8
S–131	364	_____	7	S–240	375	_____	8
S–132	364	_____	7	S–241	375	_____	8
S–133	364	_____	7	S–242	375	_____	8
S–134	364	_____	7	S–243	375	_____	8
S–135 (Rapids south base)	365	_____	7	S–245	376	_____	8
S–136 (Rapids north base)	365	_____	7	S–246	376	_____	8
S–137	365	_____	7	S–247	376	_____	8
S–138	365	_____	7	S–248	376	_____	8
S–139	365	_____	7	S–249	376	_____	8
S–141	365	_____	7	S–250	376	_____	8
S–142	365	_____	7	S–251	376	_____	8
S–143	365	_____	7	S–252	376	_____	8
S–144	365	_____	7	S–253	377	_____	8
S–145	366	_____	7	S–254	377	_____	8
S–147 (Cross Lake south base)	366	_____	7	S–255	377	_____	8
S–148 (Cross Lake north base)	366	_____	7	S–256	377	_____	8
				S–258	377	_____	8
S–149	366	_____	7	S–259	377	_____	8
S–151	366	_____	7	S–260	377	_____	8
S–152	366	_____	7	S–261	377	_____	8
S–153	366	_____	7	S–262	377	_____	8
S–154	366	_____	7	S–264	378	_____	8
S–155	367	_____	7	S–265	378	_____	8
S–156	367	_____	7	S–266	378	_____	8
S–157	367	_____	7	S–267	378	_____	8
S–158	367	_____	7	S–268	378	_____	8
S–161	367	_____	7	S–269	378	_____	8
S–164	367	_____	7	S–270	378	_____	8
S–165	368	_____	7	S–271	378	_____	8
S–166	368	_____	7	S–273	379	_____	8
S–167	368	_____	7	S–274	379	_____	8
S–168	368	_____	7	S–276	379	_____	8
				S–277	379	_____	8

Station	Position	Description	Sketch	Station	Position	Description	Sketch
	Page	Page	Number		Page	Page	Number
S–278	379	------	8	St. Francis east base	362	------	6
S–280	379	------	8	St. Francis west base	362	------	6
S–281	379	------	8	St. Francis, Me., Catholic			
S–282	380	------	8	Church spire, 1910	394	------	6
S–283	380	------	8	St. Francis, Me., protes-			
S–284	380	------	8	tant church, spire, 1910	394	------	6
S–285	380	------	8	St. Francis, Me., upper			
S–286	380	------	8	schoolhouse, west of			
S–287	380	------	8	village, 1910	394	------	6
S–288	380	------	8	St. Hilaire	347	452	1
S–289	380	------	8	St. Hilaire, N. B., church			
S–290	380	------	8	spire, 1910	393	------	5
S–291	381	------	8	St. John Lumber Co.'s			
S–292	381	------	8	stack, Keegan, Me	391	------	4
S–293	381	------	8	St. Joseph and St. An-			
S–294	381	------	8	thelm (Anselme) Chapel	390	------	4
S–295	381	------	8	Ste. Justine Church, north-			
S–296	381	------	8	east spire	395	------	1
S–297	381	------	8	St. Leonard	346	451	1
S–298	381	------	8	St. Leonard, N. B., build-			
S–299	381	------	8	ing north of village, flag-			
S–300	381	------	8	pole on cupola, 1909	391	------	4
S–301	382	------	8	St. Leonard, N. B., large			
S–302	382	------	8	red barn northeast of			
S–303	382	------	8	village, south peak, 1909	391	------	4
S–304	382	------	8	St. Leonard, N. B., L'Eg-			
S–305	382	------	8	lise Church, southeast			
S–306	382	------	8	of village, spire, 1909	390	------	4
S–307	382	------	8	St. Mary's College, flag-			
S–309	382	------	8	pole, Van Buren, Me	390	------	4
S–310	382	------	8	St. Raphael Church, spire			
S–311	383	------	8	(Geodetic Survey of			
S–312	383	------	8	Canada)	444	------	3
S–313	383	------	8	St. Regis Church	448	------	3
S–315 (Boundary Lake				St. Regis east base	448	------	3
east base)	383	------	8	St. Regis west base	448	------	3
S–316 (Boundary Lake				Salmon	397	463	2, 12
west base)	383	------	8	Sawmill stack, Edmund-			
Saddle	399	465	2, 11	ston, N. B	393	------	5
Saint (Halls Stream)	434	------	14	Sawmill stack, Grand Isle,			
Saint (West Line)	444	480	3	Me	392	------	5
Ste. Anne	347	452	1	Sawmill stack, Lille, Me	392	------	5
Ste. Anne, N. B., butter				Sawmill stack, Mada-			
factory stack, 1909	391	------	4	waska, Me	393	------	5
Ste. Anne, N. B., church				School flagpole, Lille, Me	392	------	5
spire, 1909	391	------	4	School flagpole, Mada-			
Ste. Anne east base (C–35)	354	------	4	waska, Me	393	------	5
Ste. Anne west base (C–36)	354	------	4	Schoolhouse belfry, St.			
St. Armand (Geodetic Sur-				David, Me	392	------	5
vey of Canada)	444	479	3	Searchme	443	478	3
St. Basil, N. B., church				Second	347	452	1
spire, 1909	392	------	5	Seymour	402	466	11
St. Basil, N. B., convent				Shack	434	------	13, 14
cupola, gilded cross,				Shade (south base)	438	475	13
1909	392	------	5	Shea	447	------	3
St. Basil, N. B., flagpole				Sheet-iron cupola, flag-			
on brown house with				pole, Edmundston, N.			
red roof, 1909	392	------	5	B	393	------	5
St. Basil, N. B., flagpole				Sheldon	444	480	3
on white house with				Shift	432	470	14
black roof, west of vil-				Shine	439	475	13
lage, 1909	392	------	5	Shot	437	------	13
St. Basil, N. B., flagpole				Sicard	445	481	3
on white house with				Sightly	397	464	2, 12, 13
red roof, west of village,				Slim	438	------	13
1909	392	------	5	Smith	404	467	11
St. Bruno's Church, Van				Snag	439	------	13
Buren, Me	391	------	4	Snow	395	462	2, 11
Ste. Cecile	395	462	2	Solid	439	476	13
St. David, Me., church,				South	399	465	11
cross on cupola, 1909	392	------	5	South base, Lowelltown	396	463	2, 11
St. David, Me., school-				Southeast Knoll	409	468	12
house belfry, 1909	392	------	5	South peak, red barn, St.			
St. Francis	347	453	1	Leonard, N. B	391	------	4

Station	Position	Description	Sketch	Station	Position	Description	Sketch
	Page	*Page*	*Number*		*Page*	*Page*	*Number*
				Substation 387	430	--------	10
Southwest base, Hunting-				Substation 388	430	--------	10
don	447	--------	3	Substation 389	430	--------	10
Spect	397	464	2, 12	Substation 390	430	--------	10
Spring Hill (U. S. C. &				Substation 391	430	--------	10
G. S.)	345	449	1	Substation 392	430	--------	10
Spruce	434	--------	13	Substation 393	430	--------	10
Standon (Geodetic Survey				Substation 394	430	--------	10
of Canada)	395	461	1	Substation 395	430	--------	10
Stanstead bench mark	445	481	3	Substation 396	431	--------	10
Station. (*See* Traverse				Substation 397	431	--------	10
station; Substation.)				Substation 398	431	--------	10
Steep (Halls Stream)	437	--------	13	Substation 399	431	--------	10
Steep (Highlands)	403	466	11	Substation 400	431	--------	10
Stewart	443	478	3	Substation 401	431	--------	10
Still	440	476	12, 13	Substation C-58	419	--------	9, 10
Stone	402	--------	11	Substation "M"	431	--------	10
Stop	439	--------	13	Substation "N"	431	--------	10
Stream	435	--------	13	Substation "P"	431	--------	10
Stub	434	--------	13, 14	Sun	439	--------	13
Stump (south base)	433	471	14	Sup	444	481	3
Substation 315	421	--------	10	Suptic	404	466	11
Substation 316	421	--------	10	Swamp	435	--------	13
Substation 317	422	--------	10	Switch	435	--------	13
Substation 319	422	--------	10				
Substation 320	422	--------	10	Tall (Halls Stream)		--------	13
Substation 321	422	--------	10	Tall (Highlands)	438	--------	12
Substation 325	423	--------	10	Tallman	412	--------	12
Substation 327	423	--------	10	Talon (Geodetic Survey	409		
Substation 328	423	--------	10	of Canada)		461	1
Substation 330	423	--------	10	Tank	395	469	14
Substation 333	424	--------	10	Thicket	432	471	13, 14
Substation 334	424	--------	10	Township corner (God-	434		
Substation 335	424	--------	10	manchester Tp.)		--------	3
Substation 337	424	--------	10	Traverse station 5	448	--------	10
Substation 338	424	--------	10	Traverse station 7	420	--------	10
Substation 339	424	--------	10	Traverse station 18	420	--------	10
Substation 340	424	--------	10	Traverse station 21	422	--------	10
Substation 341	425	--------	10	Traverse station 22	422	--------	10
Substation 342	425	--------	10	Traverse station 23	422	--------	10
Substation 343	425	--------	10	Traverse station 24	422	--------	10
Substation 345	425	--------	10	Traverse station 25	422	--------	10
Substation 347	425	--------	10	Traverse station 26	422	--------	10
Substation 348	426	--------	10	Traverse station 27	422	--------	10
Substation 349	426	--------	10	Traverse station 28	422	--------	10
Substation 351	426	--------	10	Traverse station 29	422	--------	10
Substation 353	426	--------	10	Traverse station 30	423	--------	10
Substation 354	426	--------	10	Traverse station 31	423	--------	10
Substation 355	426	--------	10	Traverse station 32	423	--------	10
Substation 356	426	--------	10	Traverse station 33	423	--------	10
Substation 357	427	--------	10	Traverse station 34	423	--------	10
Substation 358	427	--------	10	Traverse station 35	423	--------	10
Substation 359	427	--------	10	Traverse station 36	423	--------	10
Substation 360	427	--------	10	Traverse station 37	423	--------	10
Substation 362	427	--------	10	Traverse station 38	424	--------	10
Substation 363	427	--------	10	Traverse station 39	424	--------	10
Substation 364	427	--------	10	Traverse station 40	424	--------	10
Substation 365	427	--------	10	Traverse station 41	424	--------	10
Substation 366	427	--------	10	Traverse station 42	424	--------	10
Substation 368	428	--------	10	Traverse station 43	424	--------	10
Substation 369	428	--------	10	Traverse station 44	425	--------	10
Substation 370	428	--------	10	Traverse station 45	425	--------	10
Substation 371	428	--------	10	Traverse station 46	425	--------	10
Substation 373	428	--------	10	Traverse station 47	425	--------	10
Substation 372 and 374	428	--------	10	Traverse station 48	425	--------	10
Substation 375	428	--------	10	Traverse station 49	425	--------	10
Substation 376	428	--------	10	Traverse station 50	425	--------	10
Substation 377	429	--------	10	Traverse station 51	425	--------	10
Substation 378	429	--------	10	Traverse station 52	425	--------	10
Substation 379	429	--------	10	Traverse station 53	425	--------	10
Substation 380	429	--------	10	Traverse station 54	426	--------	10
Substation 382	429	--------	10	Traverse station 55	426		
Substation 383	429	--------	10	(Liniere)	395, 426	461	1, 2, 10
Substation 385	429	--------	10	Traverse station 56	426	--------	10
Substation 386	429	--------	10				

Station	Position	Description	Sketch	Station	Position	Description	Sketch
	Page	*Page*	*Number*		*Page*	*Page*	*Number*
Traverse station 57	426		10	Van Buren, Me., Episcopal Church, cross on spire, 1909	390		4
Traverse station 58	426		10				
Traverse station 59	427		10				
Traverse station 60	427		10	Van Buren, Me., firehouse bell clapper, 1909	391		4
Traverse station 61	428		10				
Traverse station 62	428		10	Van Buren, Me., iron cross on bowlder, 1909	391		4
Traverse station 63	428		10				
Traverse station 64	429		10	Van Buren, Me., judges' stand, race track, 1909	391		4
Traverse station 65	429		10				
Traverse station 66	429		10	Van Buren, Me., nuns' building, cross on red roof, 1909	391		4
Traverse station 67	429		10				
Traverse station 68	430		10				
Traverse station 69=H	395, 430	462	2, 10	Van Buren, Me., St. Bruno's Catholic Church, spire, 1909	391		4
Traverse station A	399, 431		11				
Traverse station B	399, 431		10, 11				
Traverse station C	431		10	Van Buren, Me., St. Mary's Catholic College, cupola, flagpole, 1909	390		4
Traverse station D	431		10				
Traverse station E	431		10				
Traverse station F	431		10				
Traverse station G	430		10	Van Dyke	396	462	2, 11
Traverse station H=69	395, 430	462	2, 10	Van Dyke's house chimney	440		14
Tripod	354		4	Van Dyke's tenant's house chimney	440		14
Trumbull	409	468	12				
Twin	350	456	1	Van reference mark	432	469	14
Union	345	449	1	Wait	396	462	2, 11
Upper Frenchville, Me., church spire, 1910	393		5	Wakefield	346	450	1
				Water tower, Keegan, Me	354		4
U. S. Beau	348	454	1	Watson	349	455	1
U. S. Glazier	347	454	1	West base, St. Regis	448		3
U. S. L. S. No. 8 (Int. Bdy. Comm., 1923)	448	483	3	Westford	348	454	1
				Wheeler	398	465	2, 14
U. S. L. S. No. 8 ecc	448		3	White (Halls Stream)	434		13
U. S. L. S. No. 13 (Int. Bdy. Comm., 1923)	448	482	3	White (Highlands)	402		11
				White cupola flagpole, Edmundston, N. B	393		5
Valley	435		13	Wicklow	346	450	1
Van	432	469	14	Willow	436		13
Van Buren	346	451	1	Wilmot	346	450	1
Van Buren highway bridge boundary point	385	458	4	Windmill, Grand Isle, Me	392		5
				Woburn	397	463	2, 11, 12
Van Buren Lumber Co.'s mill, largest stack (Me.), 1909	391		4	Woodland	346	451	1
				Woods	435		13
Van Buren north base	347	452	1				
Van Buren south base	347	452	1	Yard	437		13
Van Buren, Me., convent school, base of gilded figure, 1909	391		4	Yellow house chimney, Madawaska, Me	393		5
Van Buren, Me., customhouse flagpole, 1909	390		4	Yellow store flagpole, Madawaska, Me	393		5

GENERAL INDEX